MICROELECTRONIC CIRCUIT DESIGN

SOLUTIONS MANUAL

by

Richard C. Jaeger

and

Arthur T. Bradley

McGraw-Hill
   A Division of The McGraw-Hill Companies

Solutions Manual to accompany
Microelectronic Circuit Design

1 2 3 4 5 6 7 8 9 0 QPD QPD 9 0 0 9 8 7

ISBN 0-07-032483-2

Publisher: Tom Casson
Sponsoring editor: Lynn B. Cox
Marketing manager: John Wannemacher
Production supervisor: Rich Devitto
Supplement coordinator: Louis Swaim
Printer: Quebecor Press Dubuque

http://www.mhhe.com

Table of Contents

CHAPTER 1

1.1

Answering machine
Alarm clock
Automatic door
Automatic lights
ATM
Automobile:
  Engine controller
  Temp. control
  ABS
  Electronic dash
Automotive tune-up equip.
Bar code scanner
Battery charger
Calculator
Camcorder
Carbon monoxide detector
Cash register
Cellular phone
Copy machine
Cordless phone
Depth finder
Digital watch
Digital scale
Digital thermometer
Electric guitar
Electronic door bell
Electronic gas pump
Exercise machine
Fax machine
Fish finder
Garage door opener
GPS
Hearing aid
Light dimmer
Musical greeting cards
Keyboard synthesizer
Keyless entry system
Laboratory instruments
Model airplanes
Microwave oven
Musical tuner
Pagers
Personal computer
Personal planner/organizer

Radar detector
Radio
Razor
Satellite receiver/decoder
Security systems
Smoke detector
Stereo system
  Amplifier
  CD player
  Receiver
  Tape player
Stud sensor
Telephone
Traffic light controller
TV & remote control
Variable speed appliances
  Blender
  Drill
  Mixer
  Food processor
  Fan
Vending machines
Video games
Workstations

Electromechanical Appliances*
  Air conditioning
  Clothes washer
  Clothes dryer
  Dish washer
  Electrical timer
  Heating system
  Iron
  Oven
  Refrigerator
  Stove
  Toaster
  Vacuum cleaner

*These appliances are historically based only upon on-off (bang-bang) control. However, many of the high end versions of these appliances have now added sophisticated electronic control.

1.2 $B = 45.8 \times 10^{0.239(2020-1965)} = 6.40 \times 10^{14}$ bits / chip

---

1.3 (a)

$$\frac{B_2}{B_1} = \frac{45.8 \times 10^{0.239(Y_2 - 1965)}}{45.8 \times 10^{0.239(Y_1 - 1965)}} = 10^{0.239(Y_2 - Y_1)} \quad \text{so} \quad 2 = 10^{0.239(Y_2 - Y_1)}$$

$$Y_2 - Y_1 = \frac{\log 2}{0.239} = 1.26 \text{ years}$$

(b)

$$Y_2 - Y_1 = \frac{\log 10}{0.239} = 4.18 \text{ years}$$

1.4 $N = 1300 \times 10^{0.15(2020 - 1970)} = 4.11 \times 10^{10}$ circuits / chip

---

1.5

$$\frac{N_2}{N_1} = \frac{1300 \times 10^{0.15(Y_2 - 1970)}}{1300 \times 10^{0.15(Y_1 - 1970)}} = 10^{0.15(Y_2 - Y_1)}$$

$$\text{(a)} \quad Y_2 - Y_1 = \frac{\log 2}{0.15} = 2.01 \text{ years}$$

$$\text{(b)} \quad Y_2 - Y_1 = \frac{\log 10}{0.15} = 6.67 \text{ years}$$

1.6 $F = 8.9 \times 10^{-0.063(2020 - 1970)} \mu m = 6.3$ nm. No, this distance corresponds to the diameter of only 10 atoms. Also, the wavelength of the radiation needed to expose such patterns during fabrication is also a problem.

1.7 $P = (75 \times 10^6 \text{ tubes})(1.5 \text{ W/tube}) = 1.13 \times 10^8 \text{ W} = 113$ MW

$$I = \frac{1.13 \times 10^8 \text{ W}}{220 \text{V}} = 511 \text{ kA!}$$

1.8 D, D, A, A, D, A, A, D, A, D, A

1.9

$$\frac{10V}{2^{12} \text{bits}} = \frac{10V}{4096 \text{bits}} = 2.44 \text{ mV}$$

$$100100100100_2 = 2^{11} + 2^8 + 2^5 + 2^2 = 2340_{10} \qquad V_O = 10V \frac{2340}{4096} = 5.71 \text{ V}$$

1.10

$$\frac{2.5V}{2^{10} \text{bits}} = \frac{2.5V}{1024 \text{bits}} = 2.44 \frac{mV}{\text{bit}}$$

$$0101100101_2 = \left(2^8 + 2^6 + 2^5 + 2^2 + 2\right)_{10} = 357_{10} \qquad V_O = 2.5V \frac{357}{1024} = 0.872 \text{ V}$$

1.11

$$\frac{5V}{2^8 \text{bits}} = \frac{5V}{256 \text{bits}} = 19.53 \frac{mV}{\text{bit}} \qquad \frac{2.77V}{19.53 \frac{mV}{\text{bit}}} = 142 \text{ bits}$$

$$142_{10} = \left(128 + 8 + 4 + 2\right)_{10} = 10001110_2$$

1.12

$$\frac{10V}{2^{15} \text{bits}} = 0.3052 \frac{mV}{bit} \qquad \frac{6.83V}{10V}\left(2^{15} \text{bits}\right) = 22381 \text{ bits}$$

$$22381_{10} = (16384 + 4096 + 1024 + 512 + 256 + 64 + 32 + 8 + 4 + 1)_{10}$$

$$22381_{10} = 101011101101101_2$$

1.13 I_B = dc component = 0.002 A, i_b = ac component = 0.002 cos (1000t) A

1.14 v_{CE} = [5 + 2 cos (5000t)] V

1.15 v_{DS} = [5 + 2 sin (2500t) + 4 sin (1000t)] V

1.16 V = 10 V, R_1 = 4.7 kΩ, R_2= 2.2 kΩ and R_3 = 18 kΩ.

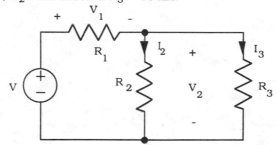

$$V_1 = 10V \frac{4.7k\Omega}{4.7k\Omega + 2.2k\Omega \| 18k\Omega} = 10V \frac{4.7k\Omega}{4.7k\Omega + 1.96k\Omega} = 7.06 \text{ V}$$

$$V_2 = 10V \frac{1.96k\Omega}{4.7k\Omega + 1.96k\Omega} = 2.94 \text{ V}$$

$$I_2 = I_1 \frac{18k\Omega}{2.2k\Omega + 18k\Omega} = \left(\frac{10V}{4.7k\Omega + 1.96k\Omega}\right)\frac{18k\Omega}{2.2k\Omega + 18k\Omega} = 1.34 \text{ mA}$$

$$I_3 = I_1 \frac{2.2k\Omega}{2.2k\Omega + 18k\Omega} = \left(\frac{10V}{4.7k\Omega + 1.96k\Omega}\right)\frac{2.2k\Omega}{2.2k\Omega + 18k\Omega} = 0.164 \text{ mA}$$

1.17 V = 18 V, R_1 = 39 kΩ, R_2= 43 kΩ and R_3 = 11 kΩ.

$$V_1 = 18V \frac{39k\Omega}{39k\Omega + 43k\Omega \| 11k\Omega} = 14.7 \text{ V}$$

$$V_2 = 18V \frac{43k\Omega \| 11k\Omega}{39k\Omega + 43k\Omega \| 11k\Omega} = 3.30 \text{ V}$$

$$I_2 = I_1 \frac{11k\Omega}{43k\Omega + 11k\Omega} = \left(\frac{18V}{39k\Omega + 43k\Omega \| 11k\Omega}\right)\frac{11k\Omega}{43k\Omega + 11k\Omega} = 76.7 \text{ μA}$$

$$I_3 = I_1 \frac{43k\Omega}{43k\Omega + 11k\Omega} = \left(\frac{18V}{39k\Omega + 43k\Omega \| 11k\Omega}\right)\frac{43k\Omega}{43k\Omega + 11k\Omega} = 0.300 \text{ mA}$$

1.18

$$I_2 = 5mA \frac{(2.2k\Omega + 3.6k\Omega)}{(2.2k\Omega + 3.6k\Omega) + 4.7k\Omega} = 2.76 \text{ mA}$$

$$I_3 = 5mA \frac{4.7k\Omega}{5.8k\Omega + 4.7k\Omega} = 2.24 \text{ mA}$$

$$V_3 = 5mA(4.7k\Omega\|5.8k\Omega)\frac{3.6k\Omega}{2.2k\Omega + 3.6k\Omega} = 8.06V$$

1.19

$$I_2 = 250\mu A \frac{150k\Omega}{150k\Omega + 100k\Omega} = 150 \text{ μA}$$

$$I_3 = 250\mu A \frac{100k\Omega}{150k\Omega + 100k\Omega} = 100 \text{ μA}$$

$$V_3 = 250\mu A(100k\Omega\|150k\Omega)\frac{82k\Omega}{68k\Omega + 82k\Omega} = 8.20V$$

1.20

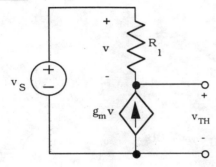

Summing currents at the output node yields:

$$\frac{v}{10^5} + .002v = 0 \text{ so } v = 0 \text{ and } v_{TH} = v_S - v = v_S$$

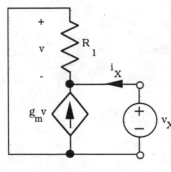

Summing currents at the output node:

$$i_X = -\frac{v}{10^5} - 0.002v = 0 \text{ but } v = -v_X$$

$$i_X = \frac{v_X}{10^5} + 0.002v_X = 0 \quad R_{TH} = \frac{v_X}{i_X} = 498\Omega$$

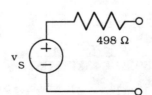

Thévenin equivalent circuit:

1.21 The Norton equivalent resistance is found using the same approach as Problem 1.20,

and $R_{TH} = \left(\frac{1}{40k\Omega} + .025\right)^{-1} = 40 \ \Omega$

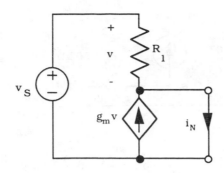

The short circuit current is:

$$i_N = \frac{v}{40k\Omega} + 0.025v \quad \text{and} \quad v = v_S$$

$$i_N = \frac{v_S}{40k\Omega} + 0.025v_S = 0.025v_S$$

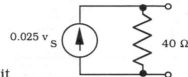

Norton equivalent circuit

1.22

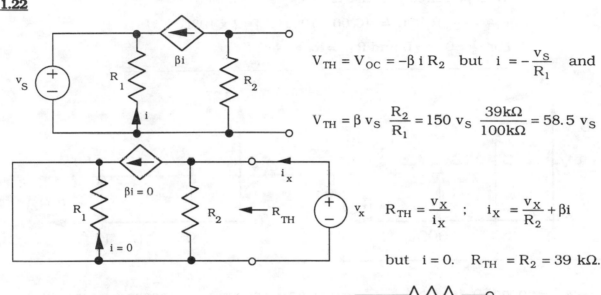

$$V_{TH} = V_{OC} = -\beta i R_2 \quad \text{but} \quad i = -\frac{v_S}{R_1} \quad \text{and}$$

$$V_{TH} = \beta v_S \frac{R_2}{R_1} = 150 \, v_S \frac{39k\Omega}{100k\Omega} = 58.5 \, v_S$$

$$R_{TH} = \frac{v_X}{i_X} \quad ; \quad i_X = \frac{v_X}{R_2} + \beta i$$

but $i = 0$. $R_{TH} = R_2 = 39$ kΩ.

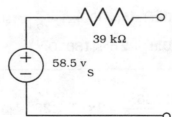

Thévenin equivalent circuit:

1.23

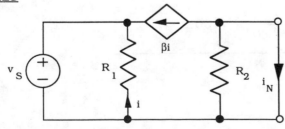

$$i_N = -\beta i \quad \text{but} \quad i = -\frac{v_S}{R_1} \quad \text{and}$$

$$i_N = \frac{\beta}{R_1} v_S = \frac{\beta}{R_1} v_S \frac{80}{75k\Omega} = 1.07 \times 10^{-3} \, v_S$$

From problem 1.22, $R_{TH} = R_2 = 56$ kΩ.

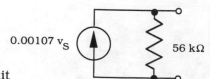

Norton equivalent circuit

1.24

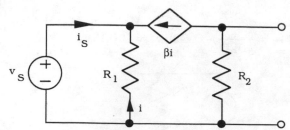

$$i_S = \frac{v_S}{R_1} - \beta i = \frac{v_S}{R_1} + \beta \frac{v_S}{R_1} = v_S \frac{\beta+1}{R_1}$$

$$R = \frac{v_S}{i_S} = \frac{R_1}{\beta+1} = \frac{100k\Omega}{151} = 662 \ \Omega$$

1.25

The open circuit voltage is $v_{TH} = -g_m v R_2$ and $v = +i_S R_1$.

$v_{TH} = -g_m R_1 R_2 i_S = -(0.002)(10^5)(10^6) = 2 \times 10^8 i_S$

For $i_S = 0$, $v = 0$ and $R_{TH} = R_2 = 1 \ M\Omega$

1.26

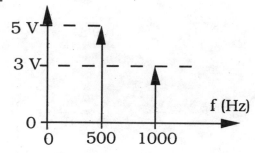

1.27

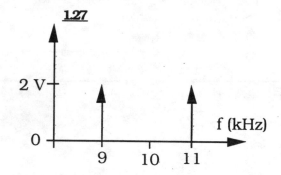

$$v = 4\sin(20000\pi t)\sin(2000\pi t) = \frac{4}{2}\left[\cos(20000\pi t + 2000\pi t) + \cos(20000\pi t - 2000\pi t)\right]$$

$$v = 2\cos(22000\pi t) + 2\cos(18000\pi t)$$

1.28 $\qquad A = \dfrac{2\angle 36^\circ}{10^{-5}\angle 0^0} = 2\times10^5 \angle 36^\circ \quad |A| = 2\times10^5 \quad \angle A = 36^\circ$

1.29 (a) $A = \dfrac{10^{-2}\angle -45^\circ}{2\times10^{-3}\angle 0^0} = 5\angle -45^\circ$ (b) $A = \dfrac{10^{-1}\angle -12^\circ}{10^{-3}\angle 0^0} = 100\angle -12^\circ$

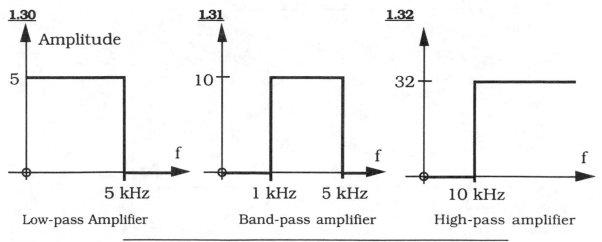

1.30 Low-pass Amplifier

1.31 Band-pass amplifier

1.32 High-pass amplifier

1.33

$$v_O(t) = 5 \text{x} 5 \sin(2000\pi t) + 5 \text{x} 3 \cos(8000\pi t) + 0 \text{x} 3 \cos(15000\pi t)$$

$$v_O(t) = 25.0 \sin(2000\pi t) + 15.0 \cos(8000\pi t) \quad \text{volts}$$

1.34

$$v_O(t) = 10 \text{x} 0.5 \sin(2500\pi t) + 10 \text{x} 0.75 \cos(8000\pi t) + 0 \text{x} 0.6 \cos(12000\pi t)$$

$$v_O(t) = 5.00 \sin(2500\pi t) + 7.50 \cos(8000\pi t) \quad \text{volts}$$

1.35 The gain is zero at each frequency: $v_O(t) = 0$.

1.36
```
»t=linspace(0,.005,1000);
»w=2*pi*1000;
»v=(4/pi)*(sin(w*t)+sin(3*w*t)/3+sin(5*w*t)/5);
»v1=5*v;
»v2=5*(4/pi)*sin(w*t);
»v3=(4/pi)*(5*sin(w*t)+3*sin(3*w*t)/3+sin(5*w*t)/5);
»plot(t,v)
»plot(t,v1)
»plot(t,v2)
»plot(t,v3)
```

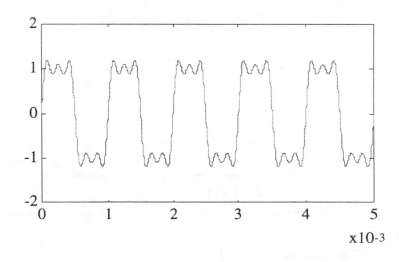

(a)

x10-3

7

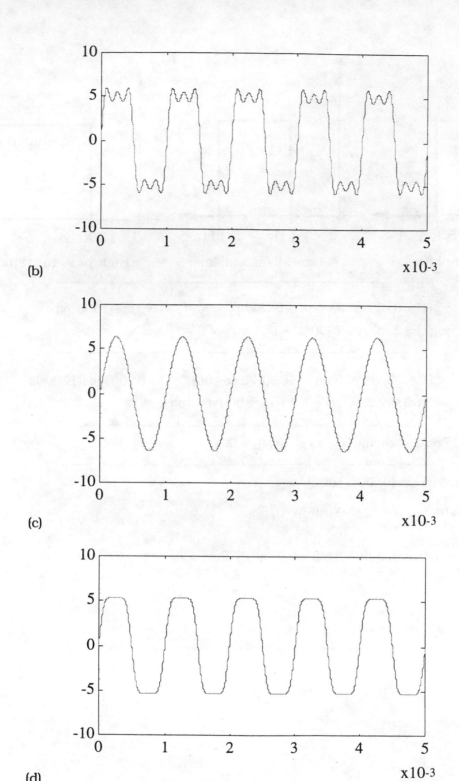

(b)

    x10-3

(c)

    x10-3

(d)

    x10-3

1.37 3.29, 0.995, -6.16; 3.295, 0.9952, -6.155

1.38 (a) (1.763 mA)(20.70 kΩ) = 36.5 V (b) 36 V

    (c) (0.1021 μA)(97.80 kΩ) = 9.99 V; 10 V

CHAPTER 2

2.1 Based upon Table 2.1, a resistivity of 2.6 $\mu\Omega$-cm < 1 mΩ-cm so aluminum is a conductor.

2.2

$$n_i^2 = BT^3 \exp\left(-\frac{E_G}{kT}\right) \qquad B = 1.08\text{x}10^{31}$$

$$\left(10^{10}\right)^2 = 1.08\text{x}10^{31}\,T^3 \exp\left(-\frac{1.12}{8.62\text{x}10^{-5}\,T}\right)$$

Using a spreadsheet, solver, or MATLAB yields T = 305.22K

Define an M-File:
```
function f=temp(T)
f=1e20-1.08e31*T^3*exp(-1.12/(8.62e-5*T));
```

Then: fzero('temp',300) | ans = 305.2262

2.3

$$j = Qv = \left(0.5\,\frac{C}{cm^3}\right)\left(10^7\,\frac{cm}{sec}\right) = 5\text{x}10^6\,\frac{A}{cm^2} = 5\,\frac{MA}{cm^2}$$

2.4

$$v - \frac{j}{Q} = \frac{-1000A\,/\,cm^2}{0.02C\,/\,cm^2} = -5\text{ x }10^4\,\frac{cm}{s}$$

2.5

$$n_i = \sqrt{BT^3 \exp\left(-\frac{E_G}{8.62\text{x}10^{-5}\,T}\right)}$$

For silicon, B = 1.08 x 10^{31} and E_G = 1.12 eV:

n_i = 2.01 x10^{-10}/cm^3 6.73 x10^9/cm^3 8.36 x 10^{13}/cm^3.

For germanium, B = 2.31 x 10^{30} and E_G = 0.66 eV:

n_i = 35.9/cm^3 2.27 x10^{13}/cm^3 8.04 x 10^{15}/cm^3.

2.6 Using an M-file similar to that in Problem 2.2 yields

n_i = 10^{15}/cm^3 for T = 602.07K n_i = 10^{18}/cm^3 for T = 1292.1K

2.7

$$v_n = -\mu_n E = -710\,\frac{cm^2}{V-s}\,3000\,\frac{V}{cm} = -2.13\text{x}10^6\,\frac{cm}{s}$$

$$v_p = +\mu_p E = +260\,\frac{cm^2}{V-s}\,3000\,\frac{V}{cm} = +7.80\text{x}10^5\,\frac{cm}{s}$$

$$j_n = -qnv_n = -1.60\text{x}10^{-19}\,C\left(10^{17}\,\frac{1}{cm^3}\right)\left(-2.13\text{x}10^6\,\frac{cm}{s}\right) = 3.41\text{x}10^4\,\frac{A}{cm^2}$$

$$jp_n = qnv_p = 1.60\text{x}10^{-19}\,C\left(10^3\,\frac{1}{cm^3}\right)\left(7.80\text{x}10^5\,\frac{cm}{s}\right) = 1.25\text{x}10^{-10}\,\frac{A}{cm^2}$$

2.8

For intrinsic silicon, $\sigma = q(\mu_n n_i + \mu_p n_i) = q n_i(\mu_n + \mu_p)$

$\sigma \geq 1000(\Omega - cm)^{-1}$ for a conductor

$$n_i \geq \frac{\sigma}{q(\mu_n + \mu_p)} = \frac{1000(\Omega - cm)^{-1}}{1.602 \times 10^{-19} C(100 + 50)\dfrac{cm^2}{v - sec}} = \frac{4.16 \times 10^{19}}{cm^3}$$

$$n_i^2 = \frac{1.73 \times 10^{39}}{cm^6} = BT^3 \exp\left(-\frac{E_G}{kT}\right) \text{ with}$$

$$B = 1.08 \times 10^{31} K^{-3} cm^{-6}, \quad k = 8.62 \times 10^{-5} eV / K \text{ and } E_G = 1.12 eV$$

This is a transcendental equation and must be solved numerically by iteration. Using the HP solver routine or a spread sheet yields T = 2701 K. Note that this temperature is far above the melting temperature of silicon.

2.9

For intrinsic silicon, $\sigma = q(\mu_n n_i + \mu_p n_i) = q n_i(\mu_n + \mu_p)$

$\sigma \leq 10^{-5}(\Omega - cm)^{-1}$ for a conductor

$$n_i \geq \frac{\sigma}{q(\mu_n + \mu_p)} = \frac{10^{-5}(\Omega - cm)^{-1}}{1.602 \times 10^{-19} C(2000 + 750)\dfrac{cm^2}{v - sec}} = \frac{2.270 \times 10^{10}}{cm^3}$$

$$n_i^2 = \frac{5.152 \times 10^{20}}{cm^6} = BT^3 \exp\left(-\frac{E_G}{kT}\right) \text{ with}$$

$$B = 1.08 \times 10^{31} K^{-3} cm^{-6}, \quad k = 8.62 \times 10^{-5} eV / K \text{ and } E_G = 1.12 eV$$

Using MATLAB as in Problem 2.2 yields T = 316.6 K.

2.10

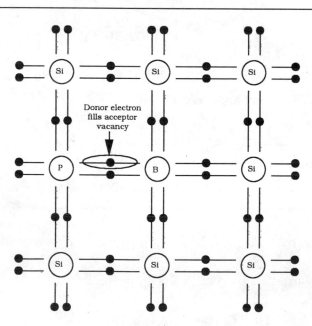

No free electrons or holes (except those corresponding to n_i).

2.11 (a) Gallium is from column 3 and silicon is from column 4. Thus silicon has an extra electron and will act as a donor impurity.
(b) Arsenic is from column 5 and silicon is from column 4. Thus silicon is deficient in one electron and will act as an acceptor impurity.

2.12

$$E = \frac{j}{\sigma} = j\rho = 10000 \frac{A}{cm^2} \, 0.01\Omega - cm = 100 \frac{V}{cm}, \text{ a small electric field.}$$

2.13

$$\left|j_n^{drift}\right| = \left|qn\mu_n E\right| = \left|qnv_n\right| = 1.602 \times 10^{-19}\left(10^{16}\right)\frac{C}{cm^3} 10^6 \frac{cm}{s} = 1600 \frac{A}{cm^2}$$

2.14

$$N_A > N_D: \ N_A - N_D = 10^{15} - 10^{14} = 9 \times 10^{14} \, / \, cm^3$$

If we assume $N_A - N_D >> 2n_i = 10^{14} \, / \, cm^3$:

$$p = N_A - N_D = 9 \times 10^{14} \, / \, cm^3 \quad | \quad n = \frac{n_i^2}{p} = \frac{2510^{26}}{9 \times 10^{14}} = 2.78 \times 10^{12} \, / \, cm^3$$

If we use Eq. 2.12: $p = \dfrac{9 \times 10^{14} \pm \sqrt{\left(9 \times 10^{14}\right)^2 + 4\left(5 \times 10^{13}\right)^2}}{2} = 9.03 \times 10^{14}$

and $n = 2.77 \times 10^{12} \, / \, cm^3$. The answers are essentially the same.

2.15

$$N_A > N_D: \ N_A - N_D = 4 \times 10^{16} - 10^{16} = 3 \times 10^{16} \, / \, cm^3 >> 2n_i = 2 \times 10^{11} \, / \, cm^3$$

$$p = N_A - N_D = 3 \times 10^{14} \, / \, cm^3 \quad | \quad n = \frac{n_i^2}{p} = \frac{10^{22}}{3 \times 10^{16}} = 3.33 \times 10^5 \, / \, cm^3$$

2.16

$$N_D > N_A: \ N_D - N_A = 2 \times 10^{17} - 10^{17} = 1 \times 10^{17} \, / \, cm^3$$

$$2n_i = 2 \times 10^{17} \, / \, cm^3; \quad \text{Need to use Eq. (2.11)}$$

$$n = \frac{10^{17} \pm \sqrt{\left(10^{17}\right)^2 + 4\left(10^{17}\right)^2}}{2} = 1.62 \times 10^{17} \, / \, cm^3$$

$$p = \frac{n_i^2}{n} = \frac{10^{34}}{1.62 \times 10^{17}} = 6.18 \times 10^{16} \, / \, cm^3$$

2.17

$$N_D - N_A = -2.5 \times 10^{18} \, / \, cm^3$$

Using Eq. 2.11: $n = \dfrac{-2.5 \times 10^{18} \pm \sqrt{\left(-2.5 \times 10^{18}\right)^2 + 4\left(10^{10}\right)^2}}{2}$

Evaluating this with a calculator yields n = 0, and $n = \dfrac{n_i^2}{p} = \infty$.

No, the result is incorrect because of loss of significant digits within the calculator. It does not have enough digits.

2.18 $N_A = 2N_D$

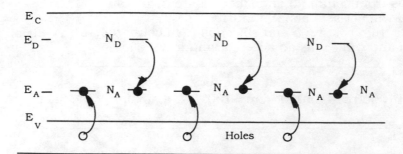

2.19

$$\lambda = \frac{hc}{E} = \frac{\left(6.626x10^{-34} J-s\right)\left(3x10^{10} cm/s\right)}{1.12eV\left(1.602x10^{-19} J/eV\right)} = 1.11x10^{-4} cm = 1.11 \ \mu m$$

2.20

$N_D > N_A$: material is n-type $\ | \ N_D - N_A = 5x10^{16}/cm^3 >> 2n_i = 2x10^{10}/cm^3$

$n = 5x10^{16}/cm^3 \ | \ p = \dfrac{n_i^2}{n} = \dfrac{10^{20}}{5x10^{16}} = 2x10^3/cm^3$

$N_D + N_A = 5x10^{16}/cm^3 \ | \$ Using Fig. 2.13, $\mu_n = 870 \dfrac{cm^2}{V-s}$ and $\mu_p = 310 \dfrac{cm^2}{V-s}$

$\rho = \dfrac{1}{q\mu_n n} = \dfrac{1}{1.602x10^{-19} C \left(870 \dfrac{cm^2}{V-s}\right)\left(\dfrac{5x10^{16}}{cm^3}\right)} = 0.144 \ \Omega-cm$

2.21

$N_A > N_D$: material is p-type $\ | \ N_A - N_D = 10^{18}/cm^3 >> 2n_i = 2x10^{10}/cm^3$

$p = 10^{18}/cm^3 \ | \ n = \dfrac{n_i^2}{p} = \dfrac{10^{20}}{10^{18}} = 100/cm^3$

$N_D + N_A = 10^{18}/cm^3 \ | \$ Using Fig. 2.13, $\mu_n = 350 \dfrac{cm^2}{V-s}$ and $\mu_p = 150 \dfrac{cm^2}{V-s}$

$\rho = \dfrac{1}{q\mu_p p} = \dfrac{1}{1.602x10^{-19} C \left(150 \dfrac{cm^2}{V-s}\right)\left(\dfrac{10^{18}}{cm^3}\right)} = 0.0417 \ \Omega-cm$

2.22 Indium is from column 3 and is an acceptor.

$N_A > N_D$: material is p-type $\ | \ N_A - N_D = 7x10^{19}/cm^3 >> 2n_i = 2x10^{10}/cm^3$

$p = 7x10^{19}/cm^3 \ | \ n = \dfrac{n_i^2}{p} = \dfrac{10^{20}}{7x10^{19}} = 1.43/cm^3$

$N_D + N_A = 7x10^{19}/cm^3 \ | \$ Using Fig. 2.13, $\mu_n = 105 \dfrac{cm^2}{V-s}$ and $\mu_p = 80 \dfrac{cm^2}{V-s}$

$\rho = \dfrac{1}{q\mu_p p} = \dfrac{1}{1.602x10^{-19} C \left(80 \dfrac{cm^2}{V-s}\right)\left(\dfrac{7x10^{19}}{cm^3}\right)} = 1.12 \ m\Omega-cm$

2.23

Phosphorus is a donor: $N_D = 4.5 \times 10^{16} / cm^3$ | Boron is an acceptor: $N_A = 5.5 \times 10^{16} / cm^3$

$N_A > N_D$: material is p-type | $N_A - N_D = 10^{16} / cm^3 \gg 2n_i = 2 \times 10^{10} / cm^3$

$p = 10^{16} / cm^3$ | $n = \dfrac{n_i^2}{p} = \dfrac{10^{20}}{10^{16}} = 10^4 / cm^3$

$N_D + N_A = 10^{17} / cm^3$ | Using Fig. 2.13, $\mu_n = 710 \dfrac{cm^2}{V-s}$ and $\mu_p = 260 \dfrac{cm^2}{V-s}$

$\rho = \dfrac{1}{q\mu_p p} = \dfrac{1}{1.602 \times 10^{-19} C \left(260 \dfrac{cm^2}{V-s} \right) \left(\dfrac{10^{16}}{cm^3} \right)} = 2.40 \ \Omega-cm$

2.24

$$\rho = \dfrac{1}{q\mu_p p} \quad | \quad \mu_p p = \dfrac{1}{1.602 \times 10^{-19} C (.054 \Omega - cm)} = \dfrac{1.16 \times 10^{20}}{V - cm - s}$$

An iterative solution is required:

N_A	μ_p	$\mu_p p$
10^{18}	150	1.5×10^{20}
10^{17}	260	2.6×10^{19}
8×10^{17}	160	1.28×10^{20}
7×10^{17}	**170**	**1.19×10^{20}**

2.25

$$\rho = \dfrac{1}{q\mu_p p} \quad | \quad \mu_p p = \dfrac{1}{1.602 \times 10^{-19} C (0.75 \Omega - cm)} = \dfrac{8.32 \times 10^{19}}{V - cm - s}$$

An iterative solution is required, and the solution does not appear to be unique:

N_A	μ_p	$\mu_p p$	N_A	μ_p	$\mu_p p$
10^{16}	400	4.0×10^{18}	4×10^{17}	185	7.4×10^{19}
2×10^{16}	370	7.4×10^{18}	5×10^{17}	175	8.8×10^{19}
3×10^{16}	340	1.0×10^{19}	**4.5×10^{17}**	**180**	**8.1×10^{19}**
2.4×10^{16}	**350**	**8.4×10^{19}**			

2.26

$N_A = N_D$ so $n = p = n_i$ but $N_D + N_A = 10^{20} / cm^3$

Using Fig. 2.13, $\mu_n = 100 \dfrac{cm^2}{V-s}$ and $\mu_p = 80 \dfrac{cm^2}{V-s}$

$\rho = \dfrac{1}{q n_i (\mu_n + \mu_p)} = \dfrac{1}{1.602 \times 10^{-19} C \left(\dfrac{10^{10}}{cm^3} \right) \left(180 \dfrac{cm^2}{V-s} \right)} = 3.47 \times 10^6 \ \Omega - cm$

Based upon the value of its resistivity, the material is an insulator. However, it is not intrinsic because it contains impurities. Addition of the impurities has increased the resistivity.

2.27

$$\rho = \frac{1}{q\mu_n n} \quad | \quad \mu_n n \approx \mu_n N_D = \frac{1}{1.602 \times 10^{-19} C(2\Omega - cm)} = \frac{3.12 \times 10^{18}}{V - cm - s}$$

An iterative solution is required:

N_D	μ_n	$\mu_n n$
10^{15}	1300	1.3×10^{18}
2×10^{15}	1260	2.5×10^{18}
3×10^{15}	1230	3.7×10^{18}
2.5 x 10^{15}	**1240**	**3.1 x 10^{18}**

2.28 (a)

$$\rho = \frac{1}{q\mu_n n} \quad | \quad \mu_n n \approx \mu_n N_D = \frac{1}{1.602 \times 10^{-19} C(0.001\Omega - cm)} = \frac{6.24 \times 10^{21}}{V - cm - s}$$

An iterative solution is required:

N_D	μ_n	$\mu_n n$
10^{19}	160	1.6×10^{21}
7×10^{19}	100	7.0×10^{21}
6 x 10^{19}	**100**	**6 x 10^{21}**

(b)
$$\rho = \frac{1}{q\mu_p p} \quad | \quad \mu_p p \approx \mu_p N_A = \frac{1}{1.602 \times 10^{-19} C(0.001\Omega - cm)} = \frac{6.24 \times 10^{21}}{V - cm - s}$$

An iterative solution is required:

N_A	μ_p	$\mu_p p$
8 x 10^{19}	**80**	**6.4 x 10^{21}**

2.29 Yes, by adding equal amounts of donor and acceptor impurities the mobilities are reduced, but the hole and electron concentrations remain unchanged. See Problem 2.26 for example. However, it is physically impossible to add exactly equal amounts of the two impurities.

2.30 (a) For the 1 ohm-cm starting material:

$$\rho = \frac{1}{q\mu_p p} \quad | \quad \mu_p p \approx \mu_p N_A = \frac{1}{1.602 \times 10^{-19} C(1\Omega - cm)} = \frac{6.25 \times 10^{18}}{V - cm - s}$$

An iterative solution is required:

N_A	μ_p	$\mu_p p$
10^{16}	400	4.0×10^{18}
1.5×10^{16}	380	5.7×10^{18}
1.7 x 10^{16}	**370**	**6.3 x 10^{19}**

To change the resistivity to 0.25 ohm-cm:

$$\rho = \frac{1}{q\mu_p p} \quad | \quad \mu_p p \approx \mu_p N_A = \frac{1}{1.602 \times 10^{-19} C(0.25\Omega - cm)} = \frac{2.5 \times 10^{19}}{V - cm - s}$$

N_A	μ_p	$\mu_p p$
6×10^{16}	300	1.8×10^{19}
8×10^{16}	280	2.2×10^{19}
1×10^{17}	**260**	**2.6×10^{19}**

Additional acceptor concentration = $1 \times 10^{17} - 1.7 \times 10^{16} = 8.3 \times 10^{16}/cm^3$

(b) If donors are added:

N_D	$N_D + N_A$	μ_n	$N_D - N_A$	$\mu_n n$
2×10^{16}	3.7×10^{16}	930	3×10^{15}	2.8×10^{18}
1×10^{17}	1.2×10^{17}	670	8.3×10^{16}	5.6×10^{19}
8×10^{16}	9.7×10^{16}	700	6.3×10^{16}	4.4×10^{19}
5×10^{16}	**6.7×10^{16}**	**790**	**3.3×10^{16}**	**2.6×10^{19}**

So $N_D = 5 \times 10^{16}/cm^3$ must be added to change achieve a resistivity of 0.25 ohm-cm. The silicon is converted to n-type material.

2.31 Phosphorus is a donor: $N_D = 10^{16}/cm^3$ and $\mu_n = 1110$ cm^2/V-s from Fig. 2.13.

$$\sigma = q\mu_n n \approx q\mu_n N_D = 1.602 \times 10^{-19} C(1110)(10^{16}) = \frac{1.78}{\Omega - cm}$$

Now we add acceptors until $\sigma = 5.0$ (Ω-cm)$^{-1}$:

$$\sigma = q\mu_p p \quad | \quad \mu_p p \approx \mu_p(N_A - N_D) = \frac{5(\Omega - cm)^{-1}}{1.602 \times 10^{-19} C} = \frac{3.12 \times 10^{19}}{V - cm - s}$$

N_A	$N_D + N_A$	μ_p	$N_A - N_D$	$\mu_p p$
1×10^{17}	1.1×10^{17}	250	9×10^{16}	2.3×10^{19}
1.5×10^{17}	1.6×10^{17}	230	1.4×10^{17}	3.2×10^{19}
1.4×10^{17}	**1.5×10^{17}**	**240**	**1.3×10^{16}**	**3.1×10^{19}**

2.32 Boron is an acceptor: $N_A = 10^{16}/cm^3$ and $\mu_p = 400 \ cm^2/V\text{-}s$ from Fig. 2.13.

$$\sigma = q\mu_p p \approx q\mu_p N_A = 1.602 \times 10^{-19} C(400)(10^{16}) = \frac{0.64}{\Omega - cm}$$

Now we add donors until $\sigma = 5.0 \ (\Omega\text{-}cm)^{-1}$:

$$\sigma = q\mu_n n \ | \ \mu_n n \approx \mu_n(N_d - N_A) = \frac{5.5(\Omega - cm)^{-1}}{1.602 \times 10^{-19} C} = \frac{3.43 \times 10^{19}}{V - cm - s}$$

N_D	$N_D + N_A$	μ_p	$N_A - N_D$	$\mu_p p$
8×10^{16}	9×10^{16}	730	7×10^{16}	5.1×10^{19}
6×10^{16}	7×10^{16}	790	5×10^{16}	3.9×10^{19}
$\mathbf{5 \times 10^{16}}$	$\mathbf{6 \times 10^{16}}$	$\mathbf{820}$	$\mathbf{4 \times 10^{16}}$	$\mathbf{3.3 \times 10^{19}}$

2.33

$$V_T = \frac{kT}{q} = \frac{1.38 \times 10^{-23} T}{1.602 \times 10^{-19}} = 8.62 \times 10^{-5} T \rightarrow 6.64 \ mV, \ 12.9 \ mV, \ 25.9 \ mV$$

2.34

$$j = -qD_n\left(-\frac{dn}{dx}\right) = qV_T\mu_n\frac{dn}{dx}$$

$$j = 1.602 \times 10^{-19} C(0.025V)\left(350\frac{cm^2}{V-s}\right)\frac{10^{18} - 0}{10^{-4} cm}\frac{1}{cm^3} = 14.0 \ \frac{kA}{cm^2}$$

2.35

$$j = -qD_p\frac{dp}{dx} = -1.602 \times 10^{-19} C\left(15\frac{cm^2}{s}\right)\left(-\frac{10^{18} \ / cm^3}{2 \times 10^{-4} cm}\right)\exp\left(-\frac{x}{2 \times 10^{-4} cm}\right)$$

$$j = 12000 \exp\left(-5000\frac{x}{cm}\right)\frac{A}{cm^2}$$

$$I(0) = j(0)A = 12000\frac{A}{cm^2}\left(10\mu m^2\right)\frac{10^{-8} cm^2}{\mu m^2} = 1.20 \ mA$$

2.36

$$j_p = q\mu_p pE - qD_p\frac{dp}{dx} = q\mu_p p\left(E - V_T\frac{1}{p}\frac{dp}{dx}\right) = 0 \rightarrow E = V_T\frac{1}{p}\frac{dp}{dx}$$

$$E \approx V_T\frac{1}{N_A}\frac{dN_A}{dx} = 0.025\frac{-10^{22}\exp(-10^4 x)}{10^{14} + 10^{18}\exp(-10^4 x)}$$

$$E(0) = -0.025\frac{10^{22}}{10^{14} + 10^{18}} = -250\frac{V}{cm}$$

$$E(5 \times 10^{-4} cm) = -0.025\frac{10^{22}\exp(-5)}{10^{14} + 10^{18}\exp(-5)} = -246\frac{V}{cm}$$

2.37 (a)

$$j_n^{drift} = q\mu_n nE = 1.602\text{x}10^{-19}C\left(350\,\frac{cm^2}{V-s}\right)\left(\frac{10^{16}}{cm^3}\right)\left(-25\,\frac{V}{cm}\right) = -14.0\,\frac{A}{cm^2}$$

$$j_p^{drift} = q\mu_p pE = 1.602\text{x}10^{-19}C\left(150\,\frac{cm^2}{V-s}\right)\left(\frac{1.01\text{x}10^{18}}{cm^3}\right)\left(-25\,\frac{V}{cm}\right) = -607\,\frac{A}{cm^2}$$

$$j_n^{diff} = qD_n\frac{dn}{dx} = 1.602\text{x}10^{-19}C\left(350\cdot0.025\,\frac{cm^2}{s}\right)\left(\frac{10^4-10^{16}}{3\text{x}10^{-4}cm^4}\right) = -46.7\,\frac{A}{cm^2}$$

$$j_p^{diff} = -qD_p\frac{dp}{dx} = -1.602\text{x}10^{-19}C\left(150\cdot0.025\,\frac{cm^2}{s}\right)\left(\frac{10^{18}-1.01\text{x}10^{18}}{3\text{x}10^{-4}cm^4}\right) = 20.0\,\frac{A}{cm^2}$$

$$j_T = -14.0 - 607 - 46.7 + 20.0 = -648\,\frac{A}{cm^2}$$

2.37 (b)

$$j_n^{drift} = 1.602\text{x}10^{-19}C\left(\frac{0.5\text{x}10^{16}}{cm^3}\right)\left(350\,\frac{cm^2}{V-s}\right)\left(-25\,\frac{V}{cm}\right) = -7.01\,\frac{A}{cm^2}$$

$$j_p^{drift} = 1.602\text{x}10^{-19}C\left(\frac{1.005\text{x}10^{18}}{cm^3}\right)\left(150\,\frac{cm^2}{V-s}\right)\left(-25\,\frac{V}{cm}\right) = -604\,\frac{A}{cm^2}$$

$$j_n^{diff} = qD_n\frac{dn}{dx} = 1.602\text{x}10^{-19}C\left(350\cdot0.025\,\frac{cm^2}{s}\right)\left(\frac{10^4-10^{16}}{3\text{x}10^{-4}cm^4}\right) = -46.7\,\frac{A}{cm^2}$$

$$j_p^{diff} = -qD_p\frac{dp}{dx} = -1.602\text{x}10^{-19}C\left(150\cdot0.025\,\frac{cm^2}{s}\right)\left(\frac{10^{18}-1.01\text{x}10^{18}}{3\text{x}10^{-4}cm^4}\right) = 20.0\,\frac{A}{cm^2}$$

$$j_T = -7.01 - 604 - 46.7 + 20.0 = -638\,\frac{A}{cm^2}$$

2.38

(a) $N = 8\left(\frac{1}{8}\right) + 6\left(\frac{1}{2}\right) + 4(1) = 8$ atoms

(b) $V = 1^3 = \left(0.543\text{x}10^{-9}\,m\right)^3 = \left(0.543\text{x}10^{-7}\,cm\right)^3 = 1.60\text{x}10^{-22}\,cm^3$

(c) $D = \dfrac{8\text{ atoms}}{1.60\text{x}10^{22}\,cm^3} = 5.00\text{x}10^{22}\,\dfrac{atoms}{cm^3}$

(d) $m = \left(2.33\,\dfrac{g}{cm^3}\right)1.60\text{x}10^{22}\,cm^3 = 3.73\text{x}10^{-22}\,g$

(e) From Table 2.2, silicon has a mass of 28.086 protons.

$$m_p = \frac{3.73\text{x}10^{-22}\,g}{28.082(8)\text{protons}} = 1.66\text{x}10^{-24}\,\frac{g}{proton}$$

Yes, near the actual proton rest mass.

CHAPTER 3

3.1

$$p_{po} = N_A = \frac{10^{18}}{cm^3} \quad | \quad n_{po} = \frac{n_i^2}{p_{po}} = \frac{10^{20}}{10^{18}} = \frac{10^2}{cm^3}$$

$$n_{no} = N_D = \frac{10^{15}}{cm^3} \quad | \quad p_{no} = \frac{n_i^2}{n_{no}} = \frac{10^{20}}{10^{15}} = \frac{10^5}{cm^3}$$

$$\phi_j = V_T \ln \frac{N_A N_D}{n_i^2} = (0.025V) \ln \frac{\left(10^{18} cm^{-3}\right)\left(10^{15} cm^{-3}\right)}{10^{20} cm^{-6}} = 0.748 \text{ V}$$

$$w_{do} = \sqrt{\frac{2\varepsilon_s}{q}\left(\frac{1}{N_A} + \frac{1}{N_D}\right)\phi_j} = \sqrt{\frac{2\left(11.7 \cdot 8.854 \times 10^{-14} F \cdot cm^{-1}\right)}{1.602 \times 10^{-19} C}\left(\frac{1}{10^{18} cm^{-3}} + \frac{1}{10^{15} cm^{-3}}\right)(0.748V)}$$

$$w_{do} = 98.4 \times 10^{-6} cm = 0.984 \ \mu m$$

3.2

$$\phi_j = V_T \ln \frac{N_A N_D}{n_i^2} = (0.025V) \ln \frac{\left(10^{19} \cdot cm^{-3}\right)\left(10^{18} \cdot cm^{-3}\right)}{10^{20} \cdot cm^{-6}} = 0.979V$$

$$w_{do} = \sqrt{\frac{2\varepsilon_s}{q}\left(\frac{1}{N_A} + \frac{1}{N_D}\right)\phi_j} = \sqrt{\frac{2\left(11.7 \cdot 8.854 \times 10^{-14} F \cdot cm^{-1}\right)}{1.602 \times 10^{-19} C}\left(\frac{1}{10^{19} cm^{-3}} + \frac{1}{10^{18} cm^{-3}}\right)(0.979V)}$$

$$w_{do} = 3.73 \times 10^{-6} cm = 0.0373 \mu m$$

$$x_n = \frac{w_{do}}{1 + \frac{N_D}{N_A}} = \frac{0.0373 \mu m}{1 + \frac{10^{18} cm^{-3}}{10^{19} cm^{-3}}} = 0.0339 \ \mu m \quad | \quad x_p = \frac{w_{do}}{1 + \frac{N_A}{N_D}} = \frac{0.0373 \mu m}{1 + \frac{10^{19} cm^{-3}}{10^{18} cm^{-3}}} = 3.39 \times 10^{-3} \ \mu m$$

$$E_{MAX} = \frac{q N_A x_p}{\varepsilon_s} = \frac{\left(1.60 \times 10^{-19} C\right)\left(10^{19} cm^{-3}\right)\left(3.39 \times 10^{-7} cm\right)}{11.7 \cdot 8.854 \times 10^{-14} F / cm} = 5.24 \times 10^5 \ \frac{V}{cm}$$

3.3

$$\phi_j = V_T \ln \frac{N_A N_D}{n_i^2} = (0.025V) \ln \frac{\left(10^{19} \cdot cm^{-3}\right)\left(10^{15} \cdot cm^{-3}\right)}{10^{20} \cdot cm^{-6}} = 0.806V$$

$$w_{do} = \sqrt{\frac{2\varepsilon_s}{q}\left(\frac{1}{N_A} + \frac{1}{N_D}\right)\phi_j} = \sqrt{\frac{2\left(11.7 \cdot 8.854 \times 10^{-14} F \cdot cm^{-1}\right)}{1.602 \times 10^{-19} C}\left(\frac{1}{10^{19} cm^{-3}} + \frac{1}{10^{15} cm^{-3}}\right)(0.806V)}$$

$$w_{do} = 1.02 \ \mu m$$

$$x_n = \frac{w_{do}}{1 + \frac{N_D}{N_A}} = \frac{1.02 \mu m}{1 + \frac{10^{15} cm^{-3}}{10^{19} cm^{-3}}} = 1.02 \ \mu m \quad | \quad x_p = \frac{w_{do}}{1 + \frac{N_A}{N_D}} = \frac{1.02 \mu m}{1 + \frac{10^{19} cm^{-3}}{10^{15} cm^{-3}}} = 1.02 \times 10^{-4} \ \mu m$$

$$E_{MAX} = \frac{2\phi_j}{w_{do}} = \frac{2(0.806)}{1.02 \times 10^{-4}} = 15.8 \ \frac{kV}{cm}$$

3.4

$$\phi_j = V_T \ln \frac{N_A N_D}{n_i^2} = (0.025V) \ln \frac{(10^{18} \cdot cm^{-3})(10^{18} \cdot cm^{-3})}{10^{20} \cdot cm^{-6}} = 0.921V$$

$$w_{do} = \sqrt{\frac{2\varepsilon_s}{q}\left(\frac{1}{N_A} + \frac{1}{N_D}\right)\phi_j} = \sqrt{\frac{2(11.7 \cdot 8.854 \times 10^{-14} F \cdot cm^{-1})}{1.602 \times 10^{-19} C}\left(\frac{1}{10^{18} cm^{-3}} + \frac{1}{10^{18} cm^{-3}}\right)(0.921V)}$$

$$w_{do} = 4.881 \times 10^{-6} cm = 0.0488 \ \mu m$$

$$x_n = \frac{w_{do}}{1 + \frac{N_D}{N_A}} = \frac{0.0488 \mu m}{1 + \frac{10^{18} cm^{-3}}{10^{18} cm^{-3}}} = 0.0244 \ \mu m \quad | \quad x_p = \frac{w_{do}}{1 + \frac{N_A}{N_D}} = \frac{0.0488 \mu m}{1 + \frac{10^{18} cm^{-3}}{10^{18} cm^{-3}}} = 0.0244 \ \mu m$$

$$E_{MAX} = \frac{2\phi_j}{w_{do}} = \frac{2(0.921)}{0.0488 \times 10^{-4}} = 378 \ \frac{kV}{cm}$$

3.5

$$w_d = w_{do}\sqrt{1 + \frac{V_R}{\phi_j}} \quad | \quad (a) \ V_R = 3\phi_j = 1.8 \ V \quad | \quad w_d = 1\mu m \sqrt{1 + \frac{5}{0.6}} = 3.06 \ \mu m$$

3.6

$$j = \sigma E, \quad \sigma = \frac{1}{\rho} = \frac{1}{0.5 \ \Omega \cdot cm} = \frac{2}{\Omega \cdot cm} \quad | \quad E = \frac{j}{\sigma} = \frac{1000 A \cdot cm^{-2}}{2(\Omega \cdot cm)^{-1}} = 500 \ \frac{V}{cm}$$

3.7

$$j = Q''v = \left(\frac{10^{15}}{cm^3}\right)(1.60 \times 10^{-19} C)\left(\frac{10^6 cm}{s}\right) = 160 \ \frac{A}{cm^2}$$

3.8

$$j_p = q\mu_p pE - qD_p \frac{dp}{dx} = 0 \rightarrow E = -\left(\frac{D_p}{\mu_p}\right)\frac{1}{p}\frac{dp}{dx} = -\left(\frac{kT}{q}\right)\frac{1}{p}\frac{dp}{dx}$$

$$p(x) = N_o \exp\left(-\frac{x}{L}\right) \quad | \quad \frac{1}{p}\frac{dp}{dx} = \frac{1}{L} \quad | \quad E = -\frac{V_T}{L} = -\frac{0.025V}{10^{-4} cm} = -250 \ \frac{V}{cm}$$

The exponential doping results in a constant electic field.

3.9

$$j_p = qD_n \frac{dn}{dx} = q\mu_n V_T \frac{dn}{dx} \quad | \quad \frac{dn}{dx} = \frac{1000 A / cm^2}{(500 cm^2 / V - s)(0.025V)(1.60 \times 10^{-19} C)} = \frac{5 \times 10^{20}}{cm^4}$$

3.10

$$f = 10 - 10^4 I_D - 0.025 \ln \frac{I_D + I_S}{I_S} \quad | \quad f' = -10^4 - \frac{0.025}{I_D + I_S} \quad | \quad I_D' = I_D - \frac{f}{f'}$$

Starting the iteration process with $I_D = 100 \ \mu A$ and $I_S = 10^{-13}A$:

I_D	f	f'
1.000E-04	8.482E+00	-1.025E+04
9.275E-04	1.512E-01	-1.003E+04
9.426E-04	3.268E-06	-1.003E+04
9.426E-04	9.992E-16	-1.003E+04

3.11 (a) Create the following m-file:

```
function fd=current(id)
fd=10-1e4*id-0.025*log(1+id/1e-13);
```

Then: fzero('current',1)   yields   ans = 9.4258e-04

(b) Changing I_S to 10^{-15}A:

```
function fd=current(id)
fd=10-1e4*id-0.025*log(1+id/1e-15);
```

Then: fzero('current',1)   yields   ans = 9.3110e-04

3.12

$$T = \frac{qV_T}{k} = \frac{1.60 \times 10^{-19} C(0.025V)}{1.38 \times 10^{-23} J/K} = 290 \text{ K}$$

3.13   Graphing $I_D = I_S \left[\exp\left(\frac{40V_D}{n}\right) - 1 \right]$ yields:

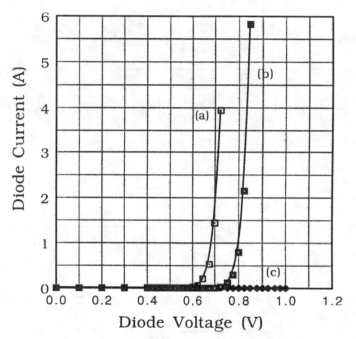

3.14

$$i_D = I_S \left[\exp\left(\frac{v_D}{nV_T}\right) - 1 \right] \quad \text{or} \quad \frac{v_D}{nV_T} = \ln\left(1 + \frac{i_D}{I_S}\right)$$

$$\text{For } i_D \gg I_S, \quad \frac{v_D}{nV_T} \cong \ln\left(\frac{i_D}{I_S}\right) \quad \text{or} \quad \ln(I_D) = \left(\frac{1}{nV_T}\right) v_D + \ln(I_S)$$

which is the equation of a straight line with slope $1/nV_T$ and x-axis intercept at $-\ln(I_S)$. The values of n and I_S can be found from any two points on the line in the figure: e. g. $i_D = 10^{-4}$ A for $v_D = 0.60$ V and $i_D = 10^{-9}$ A for $v_D = 0.20$ V. Then there are two equations in two unknowns:

$$\ln(10^{-9}) = \left(\frac{40}{n}\right).20 + \ln(I_S) \quad \text{or} \quad 9.21 = \left(\frac{8}{n}\right) + \ln(I_S)$$

$$\ln(10^{-4}) = \left(\frac{40}{n}\right).60 + \ln(I_S) \quad \text{or} \quad 20.72 = \left(\frac{24}{n}\right) + \ln(I_S)$$

Solving for n and I_S yields n = 1.39 and I_S = 3.17 x 10^{-12} A = 3.17 pA.

3.15

$$V_D = nV_T \ln\left(1 + \frac{I_D}{I_S}\right) \quad | \quad I_D = I_S\left[\exp\left(\frac{V_D}{nV_T}\right) - 1\right]$$

(a) $V_D = 0.025V \ln\left(1 + \frac{10^{-4}A}{10^{-17}A}\right) = 0.748V$ | (b) $V_D = 0.025V \ln\left(1 + \frac{10^{-5}A}{10^{-17}A}\right) = 0.691V$

(c) $I_D = 10^{-17}A\left[\exp\left(\frac{0}{0.025V}\right) - 1\right] = 0$ A

(d) $I_D = 10^{-17}A\left[\exp\left(\frac{-0.06V}{0.025V}\right) - 1\right] = -0.909 \times 10^{-17}$ A

(e) $I_D = 10^{-17}A\left[\exp\left(\frac{-4V}{0.025V}\right) - 1\right] = -1.00 \times 10^{-17}$ A

3.16

$$I_D = I_S\left[\exp\left(\frac{V_D}{V_T}\right) - 1\right] = 10^{-17}\left[\exp\left(\frac{0.675}{0.025}\right) - 1\right]A = 5.32 \times 10^{-6}A = 5.32 \ \mu A$$

$$V_D = V_T \ln\left(\frac{I_D}{I_S} + 1\right) = (0.025V) \ln\left(\frac{15.9 \times 10^{-6}A}{10^{-17}A} + 1\right) = 0.703 \text{ V}$$

3.17

$$V_D = nV_T \ln\left(1 + \frac{I_D}{I_S}\right) = 2(0.025V) \ln\left(1 + \frac{50A}{10^{-10}A}\right) = 1.35 \text{ V}$$

$$V_D = 2(0.025V) \ln\left(1 + \frac{100A}{10^{-10}A}\right) = 1.38 \text{ V}$$

3.18

(a) $I_S = \dfrac{I_D}{\left[\exp\left(\dfrac{V_D}{nV_T}\right) - 1\right]} = \dfrac{250\mu A}{\left[\exp\left(\dfrac{0.75}{0.025}\right) - 1\right]} = 2.34 \times 10^{-17}$ A

(b) $I_D = 2.34 \times 10^{-17}A\left[\exp\left(\frac{-3}{0.025}\right) - 1\right]A = -2.34 \times 10^{-17}$ A

3.19

$$V_D = nV_T \ln\left(1 + \frac{I_D}{I_S}\right) \quad | \quad 10^{-14} \le I_S \le 10^{-12} \quad | \quad 1 \le n \le 2$$

$$V_D = (0.025V) \ln\left(1 + \frac{10^{-3}A}{10^{-12}A}\right) = 0.518 \text{ V} \ | \ V_D = (0.025V) \ln\left(1 + \frac{10^{-3}A}{10^{-14}A}\right) = 0.633 \text{ V}$$

$$V_D = 2(0.025V)\ln\left(1 + \frac{10^{-3}A}{10^{-12}A}\right) = 1.04 \text{ V} \mid V_D = 2(0.025V)\ln\left(1 + \frac{10^{-3}A}{10^{-14}A}\right) = 1.26 \text{ V}$$

Including just I_S variations, $0.518V \le V_D \le 0.633V$ – the most realistic case
Including both I_S and n, $0.518V \le V_D \le 1.26V$

3.20

$$V_T = \frac{1.38\text{x}10^{-23}(307)}{1.60\text{x}10^{-19}} = 0.264V \mid I_D = I_S\left[\exp\left(\frac{V_D}{0.0264n}\right) - 1\right]$$

Varying n and I_S by trial-and-error with a spreadsheet:

n	I_S		
1.039	7.606E-15		
V_D	I_D-Measured	I_D-Calculated	Error Squared
0.500	6.591E-07	6.276E-07	9.9198E-16
0.550	3.647E-06	3.885E-06	5.6422E-14
0.600	2.158E-05	2.404E-05	6.0672E-12
0.650	1.780E-04	1.488E-04	8.518E-10
0.675	3.601E-04	3.702E-04	1.0261E-10
0.700	8.963E-04	9.211E-04	6.1409E-10
0.725	2.335E-03	2.292E-03	1.8902E-09
0.750	6.035E-03	5.701E-03	1.1156E-07
0.775	1.316E-02	1.418E-02	1.0471E-06
	Total Squared Error		1.1622E-06

3.21

$$\frac{kT}{q} = \frac{1.38\text{x}10^{-23}(303)}{1.60\text{x}10^{-19}} = 26.1 \text{ mV} \mid V_D = 0.0261\ln\left(1 + \frac{10^{-3}}{2.5\text{x}10^{-16}}\right) = 0.757 \text{ V}$$

$$\Delta V = (-1.8\text{mV} / \text{K})(20\text{K}) = -36.0 \text{ mV} \mid V_D = 0.757 - 0.036 = 0.721 \text{ V}$$

3.22

$$\frac{kT}{q} = \frac{1.38\text{x}10^{-23}(298)}{1.602\text{x}10^{-19}} = 25.67 \text{ mV} \mid \text{(a) } V_D = (0.02567)\ln\left(1 + \frac{10^{-4}}{2.5\text{x}10^{-15}}\right) = 0.650 \text{ V}$$

$$\Delta V = (-2.0\text{mV} / \text{K})(25\text{K}) = -50.0 \text{ mV}$$

(b) $V_D = 0.650 - 0.050 = 0.600 \text{ V} \mid$ (c) $V_D = 0.650 + 0.050 = 0.700 \text{ V}$

3.23

$$\frac{dv_D}{dT} = \frac{v_D - V_G - 3V_T}{T} = \frac{0.7 - 1.21 - 3(0.0259)}{300} = -1.96 \frac{\text{mV}}{\text{K}}$$

3.24

$$\frac{I_{S2}}{I_{S1}} = \left(\frac{T_2}{T_1}\right)^3 \exp\left[-\left(\frac{E_G}{k}\right)\left(\frac{1}{T_2} - \frac{1}{T_1}\right)\right] = \left(\frac{T_2}{T_1}\right)^3 \exp\left[\left(\frac{E_G}{kT_1}\right)\left(1 - \frac{T_1}{T_2}\right)\right]$$

$$f(x) = (x)^3 \exp\left[\left(\frac{E_G}{kT_1}\right)\left(1 - \frac{1}{x}\right)\right] \qquad x = \frac{T_2}{T_1}$$

x	f(x)	Delta T
1.00000	1.00000	0.00000
1.00500	1.27888	1.50000
1.01000	1.63167	3.00000
1.01500	2.07694	4.50000
1.01400	1.97945	4.20000
1.01422	2.00051	4.26600
1.01922	2.54151	5.76600
1.02422	3.22151	7.26600
1.02922	4.07433	8.76600
1.03422	5.14160	10.26600
1.03922	6.47438	11.76600
1.04422	8.13522	13.26600
1.04922	10.20058	14.76600
1.04880	10.00936	14.64000
1.10000	90.67434	30.00000
1.10239	100.00120	30.71610

3.25

$$E_{max} = \frac{2\left(\phi_j + V_R\right)}{w_d} = \frac{2\left(\phi_j + V_R\right)}{w_{do}\sqrt{1 + \frac{V_R}{\phi_j}}} = \frac{2\phi_j}{w_{do}}\sqrt{1 + \frac{V_R}{\phi_j}}$$

$$3 \times 10^5 \frac{V}{cm} = \frac{2(0.6V)}{10^{-4}cm}\sqrt{1 + \frac{V_R}{0.6}} \rightarrow V_R = 374 \text{ V}$$

3.26

$$E = \frac{2\phi_j}{w_{do}} = \frac{2(0.748V)}{0.984 \times 10^{-4} cm} = 15.2 \frac{kV}{cm} \mid \sqrt{\phi_j + V_R} = \frac{E_{max}}{2}\frac{w_{do}}{\sqrt{\phi_j}} = \frac{3 \times 10^5 \frac{V}{cm}\left(0.984 \times 10^{-4} cm\right)}{2\sqrt{0.748V}}$$

$$V_R = 291.3 - 0.748 = 291 \text{ V}$$

3.27 $V_Z = 4$ V; $R_Z = 0 \, \Omega$ since the reverse breakdown slope is infinite

3.28 Since $N_A \gg N_D$, the depletion layer is all on the lightly-doped side of the junction.

Also, $V_R \gg \phi_j$, so ϕ_j can be neglected.

$$E_{max} = \frac{qN_A x_p}{\varepsilon_S} = \frac{qN_A w_d}{\varepsilon_S} = \frac{qN_A}{\varepsilon_S}\sqrt{\frac{2\varepsilon_S}{q}\frac{V_R}{N_A}}$$

$$N_A = \frac{E_{max}^2 \varepsilon_S}{2qV_R} = \frac{(3x10^5)^2(11.7)(8.854x10^{-14})}{2(1.602x10^{-19})1000} = 2.91 \times 10^{14}/cm^3$$

3.29

$$\phi_j = V_T \ln\frac{N_A N_D}{n_i^2} = 0.025\ln\frac{10^{15}10^{20}}{10^{20}} = 0.864V$$

$$w_{do} = \sqrt{\frac{2\varepsilon_S}{q}\left(\frac{1}{N_A}+\frac{1}{N_D}\right)\phi_j} = \sqrt{\frac{2(11.7)(8.854x10^{-14})}{1.602x10^{-19}}\left(\frac{1}{10^{15}}+\frac{1}{10^{20}}\right)0.864} = 1.057x10^{-4}\,cm$$

$$C_{jo}'' = \frac{\varepsilon_S}{w_{do}} = \frac{11.7(8.854x10^{-14})}{1.057x10^{-4}} = 9.80x10^{-9}\,F/cm^2$$

$$C_j = \frac{C_{jo}''A}{\sqrt{1+\dfrac{V_R}{\phi_j}}} = \frac{9.80x10^{-9}(0.01)}{\sqrt{1+\dfrac{5}{0.864}}} = 37.6\ pF$$

3.30

(a) $C_D = \dfrac{I_D \tau_T}{V_T} = \dfrac{10^{-4}A(10^{-10}s)}{0.025V} = 400\ fF$ (b) $Q = I_D\tau_T = 10^{-4}A(10^{-10}s) = 10\ fC$

(c) $C_D = \dfrac{25x10^{-3}A(10^{-10}s)}{0.025V} = 100\ pF$ | $Q = I_D\tau_T = 25x10^{-3}A(10^{-10}s) = 2.5\ pC$

3.31

$$\phi_j = V_T \ln\frac{N_A N_D}{n_i^2} = 0.025\ln\frac{10^{19}10^{16}}{10^{20}} = 0.864V$$

$$w_{do} = \sqrt{\frac{2\varepsilon_S}{q}\left(\frac{1}{N_A}+\frac{1}{N_D}\right)\phi_j} = \sqrt{\frac{2(11.7)(8.854x10^{-14})}{1.602x10^{-19}}\left(\frac{1}{10^{19}}+\frac{1}{10^{16}}\right)0.864} = 0.3344\mu m$$

$$C_{jo} = \frac{\varepsilon_S A}{w_{do}} = \frac{11.7(8.854x10^{-14})(10^{-4})}{0.3344x10^{-4}} = 3.098pF/cm^2$$

$$C_j = \frac{C_{jo}}{\sqrt{1+\dfrac{V_R}{\phi_j}}} = \frac{3.098pF}{\sqrt{1+\dfrac{2}{0.864}}} = 1.702\ pF$$

3.32

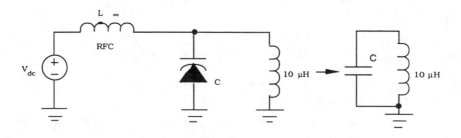

$$C = \frac{C_{jo}}{\sqrt{1 + \dfrac{V_R}{\phi_j}}} \quad \text{(a) } C = \frac{20pF}{\sqrt{1 + \dfrac{1V}{0.75V}}} = 13.1pF \mid f_o = \frac{1}{2\pi\sqrt{LC}} = \frac{1}{2\pi\sqrt{(10^{-5}H)13.1pF}} = 13.9MHz$$

$$\text{(b) } C = \frac{20pF}{\sqrt{1 + \dfrac{10V}{0.75V}}} = 5.28pF \mid f_o = \frac{1}{2\pi\sqrt{LC}} = \frac{1}{2\pi\sqrt{(10^{-5}H)5.28pF}} = 21.9MHz$$

3.33

(a) $V_D = (0.025V)\ln\left(1 + \dfrac{50A}{10^{-7}A}\right) = 0.501\ V$ | (b) $V_D = (0.025V)\ln\left(1 + \dfrac{50A}{10^{-14}A}\right) = 0.904\ V$

3.34

$$5 = 10^4 I_D + V_D \mid V_D = 0 \;\; I_D = 0.500mA \mid I_D = 0 \;\; V_D = 5V$$

$$\text{Forward biased - } V_D = 0.5V \;\; I_D = \frac{4.5V}{10^4\Omega} = 0.450\ mA$$

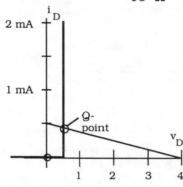

3.35

*Problem 3.35 - Diode Circuit   SPICE Results
V 1 0 DC 5
R 1 2 10K $V_D = 0.693\ V$
D1 2 0 DIODE1 $I_D = 0.431\ mA$
.OP
.MODEL DIODE1 D IS=1E-15
.END

3.36

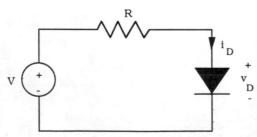

Load line equation: $V = i_D R + v_D$ We need two points to plot the load line.

(a)   V = 6 V and R = 4 kΩ: For $v_D = 0$, $i_D = 6V/4\ k\Omega = 1.5\ mA$ and for $i_D = 0$, $v_D = 6V$.
    Plotting this line on the graph yields the Q-pt: (0.5 V, 1.4 mA).

(b)   V = -6 V and R = 3 kΩ: For $v_D = 0$, $i_D = -6V/3\ k\Omega = -2\ mA$ and for $i_D = 0$, $v_D = -6V$.
    Plotting this line on the graph yields the Q-pt: (-4 V, -0.67 mA).

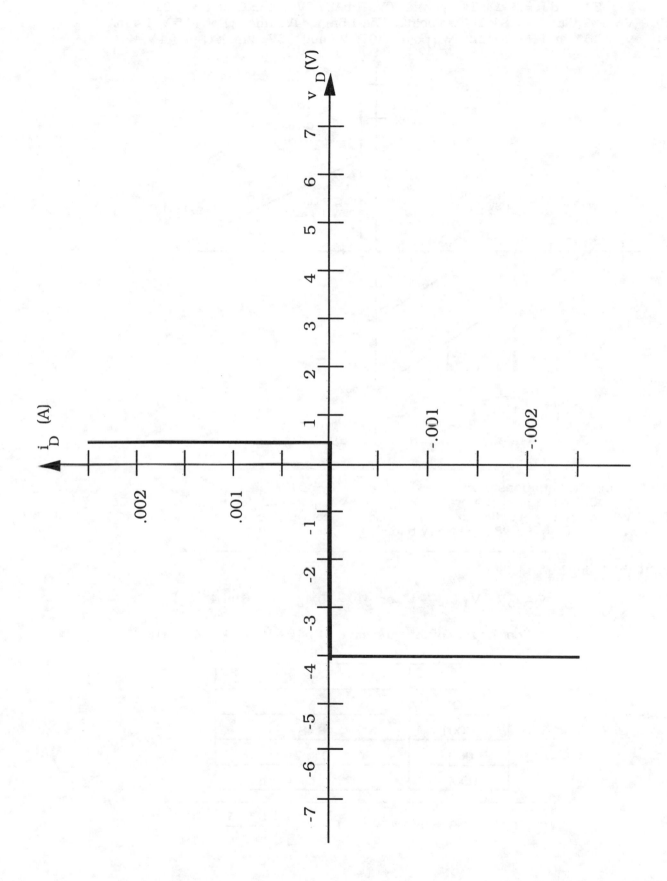

(c) V = -3 V and R = 3 kΩ: Two points: (0V, -1mA), (-3V, 0mA); Q-pt: (-3 V, 0 mA)

(d) V = +12 V and R = 8 kΩ: Two points: (0V, 1.5mA), (4V, 1mA); Q-pt: (0.5 V, 1.4 mA)

(e) V = -25 V and R = 10 kΩ: Two points: (0V, -2.5mA), (-5V, -2mA); Q-pt: (-4 V, -2.1 mA)

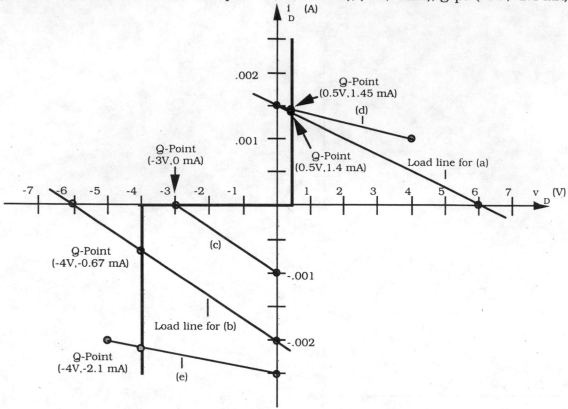

3.37 Using the equations from Table 3.1, (f = 10-10^{-9} exp..., etc.)
$V_D = 0.7$ V requires 12 iterations, $V_D = 0.5$ V requires 22 iterations,
$V_D = 0.2$ V requires 384 iterations - very poor convergence because the second
iteration ($V_D = 9.9988$ V) is very bad.

3.38 (b) Using Eqn. (3.28),

$$V = i_D R + V_T \ln\left(\frac{i_D}{I_S}\right) \quad \text{or} \quad 10 = 10^4 i_D + 0.025 \ln\left(10^{13} i_D\right).$$

We want to find the zero of the function f: $f = 10 - 10^4 i_D - 0.025 \ln\left(10^{13} i_D\right)$

i_D	f
.001	-0.576
.0001	8.48
.0009	0.427
.00094	0.0259 - converged

3.39 $f = 10 - 10^4 I_D - 0.025 \ln\left(1 + \frac{I_D}{I_S}\right) \quad | \quad f' = -10^4 - \frac{0.025}{I_D + I_S}$

x	f(x)	f'(x)
1.0000E+00	-9.991E+03	-1.000E+04
9.2766E-04	1.496E-01	-1.003E+04
9.4258E-04	3.199E-06	-1.003E+04
9.4258E-04	9.992E-16	-1.003E+04
9.4258E-04	9.992E-16	-1.003E+04

3.40 Create the following m-file:

```
function fd=current(id)
fd=10-1e4*id-0.025*log(1+id/1e-13);
```

Then: fzero('current',1) yields ans = 9.4258e-04 + 1.0216e-21i

---

3.41 The one-volt source will forward bias the diode. Load line:

$1 = 10^4 I_D + V_D \mid I_D = 0 \quad V_D = 1V \mid V_D = 0 \quad I_D = 0.1mA \rightarrow (50\mu A, 0.5V)$

Mathematical model: $f = 1 - 10^{-9}\left[\exp(40V_D) - 1\right] + V_D \rightarrow (49.9\mu A, 0.501V)$

Ideal diode model: $I_D = 1V/10k\Omega = 100\ \mu A$; $(100\ \mu A, 0V)$

Constant voltage drop model: $I_D = (1-0.6)V/10k\Omega = 40.0\ \mu A$; $(40.0\ \mu A, 0V)$

3.42 Using Thévenin equivalent circuits yields and then combining the sources

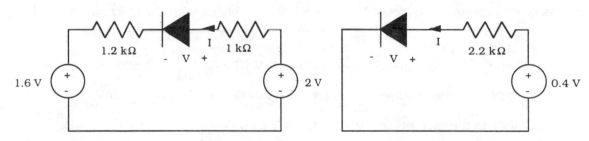

(a) Ideal diode model: The 0.4 V source appears to be forward biasing the diode so we will assume it is "on". Substituting the ideal diode model for the forward region yields $I = \dfrac{0.4V}{2.2k\Omega} = 0.182$ mA. This current is greater than zero, which is consistent with the diode being "on". Thus the Q-pt is (0 V, +0.182 mA).

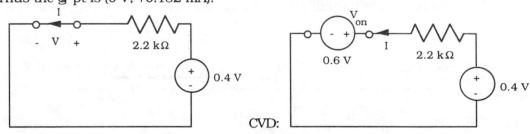

Ideal Diode: CVD:

(b) CVD model: The 0.4 V source appears to be forward biasing the diode so we will assume it is "on". Substituting the CVD model with $V_{on} = 0.6$ V yields $I = \dfrac{0.4V - 0.6V}{2.2k\Omega} = -90.9\ \mu A$. This current is negative which is not consistent with the assumption that the diode is "on". Thus the diode must be off. The resulting Q-pt is: (0.4 V, 0 mA).

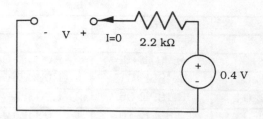

(c) The second estimate is more realistic. 0.4 V is not sufficient to forward bias the diode into significant conduction. For example, let us assume that $I_S = 10^{-15}$ A and assume that the full 0.4 V appears across the diode. Then

$$i_D = 10^{-15} A \left[\exp\left(\frac{0.4V}{0.025V} \right) - 1 \right] = 8.89 \text{ nA}, \text{ a very small current.}$$

3.43

SPICE Input		Results	
*Problem 3.43		NAME	D1
V1 1 0 DC 4		MODEL	DIODE
R1 1 2 2K		ID	5.20E-09
R2 2 0 2K		VD	4.00E-01
R3 1 3 3K			
R4 3 0 2K			
D1 2 3 DIODE			
.MODEL DIODE D IS=1E-15 RS=0			
.OP			
.END			

The diode is essentially off - V_D = 0.4 V and I_D = 5.2 nA. Agrees with the CVD model results.

3.44 (a)

(a) Diode is forward biased: $V = -5 + 0 = -5$ V | $I = \dfrac{5-(-5)}{20k\Omega} = 0.500$ mA

(b) Diode is reverse biased: $I = 0$ | $V = 7 - 20k\Omega(I) = 7$ V | $V_D = -10$ V

(c) Diode is forward biased: $V = 3 - 0 = 3$ V | $I = \dfrac{3-(-7)}{20k\Omega} = 0.500$ mA

(d) Diode is reverse biased: $I = 0$ | $V = -5 + 20k\Omega(I) = -5$ V | $V_D = -10$ V

(b)

(a) Diode is forward biased: $V = -5 + 0.7 = -4.3$ V | $I = \dfrac{5-(-4.3)}{20k\Omega} = 0.465$ mA

(b) Diode is reverse biased: $I = 0$ | $V = 7 - 20k\Omega(I) = 7$ V | $V_D = -10$ V

(c) Diode is forward biased: $V = 3 - 0.7 = 2.3$ V | $I = \dfrac{2.3-(-7)}{20k\Omega} = 0.465$ mA

(d) Diode is reverse biased: $I = 0$ | $V = -5 + 20k\Omega(I) = -5$ V | $V_D = -10$ V

3.45 (a)

(a) D_1 off, D_2 on: $I_{D1} = 0$ | $I_{D2} = \dfrac{10-(-15)}{15k\Omega} = +1.67$ mA | $V_{D1} = 10 - 10^4 I_{D2} = -6.67V$

$D_1: (0A, -6.67V)$ $D_2: (1.67mA, 0V)$

(b) D_1 on, D_2 on: $I_{D2} = \dfrac{0-(-10)}{10k\Omega} = 1.00$ mA | $I_{D1} = \dfrac{15-0}{5k\Omega} - 1.00$ mA $= 2.00$ mA

$D_1: (2.00mA, 0V)$ $D_2: (1.00mA, 0V)$

(c) D_1 on, D_2 on: $I_{D2} = \dfrac{0-(-15)}{5k\Omega} = 3.00mA \mid I_{D1} = 3.00mA - \dfrac{10-0}{10k\Omega} = 2.00mA$

$\qquad$ $D_1:(2.00mA, 0V)$ $\quad$ $D_2:(3.00mA, 0V)$

(d) D_1 on, D_2 off: $I_{D2} = 0 \mid I_{D1} = \dfrac{10-0}{10k\Omega} = +1.00mA \mid V_{D2} = -15 - 0 = -15V$

$\qquad$ $D_1:(1.00mA, 0V)$ $\quad$ $D_2:(0A, -15V)$

(b)

$\qquad$ (a) D_1 off, D_2 on:

$\qquad$ $I_{D1} = 0 \mid I_{D2} = \dfrac{10 - 0.75 - (-15)}{15k\Omega} = +1.62mA \mid V_{D1} = 10 - 10^4 I_{D2} = -6.17V$

$\qquad$ $D_1:(0A, -6.17V)$ $\quad$ $D_2:(1.62mA, 0.75V)$

$\qquad$ (b) D_1 on, D_2 on:

$\qquad$ $I_{D2} = \dfrac{+0.75 - 0.75 - (-10)}{10k\Omega} = 1.00mA \mid I_{D1} = \dfrac{15 - 0.75}{5k\Omega} - 1.00mA = 1.85mA$

$\qquad$ $D_1:(1.85mA, 0.75V)$ $\quad$ $D_2:(1.00mA, 0.75V)$

$\qquad$ (c) D_1 on, D_2 on:

$\qquad$ $I_{D2} = \dfrac{-0.75 - 0.75 - (-15)}{5k\Omega} = 2.70mA \mid I_{D1} = 2.70mA - \dfrac{10 - (-0.75)}{10k\Omega} = 1.63mA$

$\qquad$ $D_1:(1.63mA, 0.75V)$ $\quad$ $D_2:(2.70mA, 0.75V)$

$\qquad$ (d) D_1 on, D_2 off:

$\qquad$ $I_{D2} = 0 \mid I_{D1} = \dfrac{10 - 0.75}{10k\Omega} = 0.925mA \mid V_{D2} = -15 - 0.75 = -15.75V$

$\qquad$ $D_1:(0.925mA, 0.75V)$ $\quad$ $D_2:(0A, -15.75V)$

3.46 (a)

$\qquad$ (a) D_1 on, D_2 off, D_3 on: $I_{D2} = 0 \mid I_{D1} = \dfrac{10 - 0}{3k\Omega + 7k\Omega} = 1mA$

$\qquad$ $I_{D3} + 1.00mA = \dfrac{0 - (-5)}{2.5k\Omega} \rightarrow I_{D3} = 1.00mA \mid V_{D2} = 5 - (10 - 3000 I_{D1}) = -2V$

$\qquad$ $D_1:(1.00mA, 0V)$ $\quad$ $D_2:(0mA, -2V)$ $\quad$ $D_3:(1.00mA, 0V)$

$\qquad$ (b) D_1 on, D_2 off, D_3 off: $I_{D2} = 0 \mid I_{D3} = 0$

$\qquad$ $I_{D1} = \dfrac{10 - (-5)}{8k\Omega + 10k\Omega + 12k\Omega} = 0.500mA \mid V_{D2} = 5 - (10 - 8000 I_{D1}) = -1.00V$

$\qquad$ $V_{D3} = -(-5 + 12000 I_{D1}) = -1.00V$

$\qquad$ $D_1:(0.500mA, 0V)$ $\quad$ $D_2:(0A, -1.00V)$ $\quad$ $D_3:(0A, -1.00V)$

(b)

$\qquad$ (a) D_1 on, D_2 off, D_3 on: $I_{D2} = 0 \mid I_{D1} = \dfrac{10 - 0.6 - (-0.6)}{3k\Omega + 7k\Omega} = 1.00mA$

$\qquad$ $I_{D3} + 1.00mA = \dfrac{-0.6 - (-5)}{2.5k\Omega} \rightarrow I_{D3} = 0.760mA \mid V_{D2} = 5 - (10 - 0.6 - 3000 I_{D1}) = -1.40V$

$\qquad$ $D_1:(1.00mA, 0.6V)$ $\quad$ $D_2:(0mA, -1.40V)$ $\quad$ $D_3:(0.760mA, 0.6V)$

(b) D_1 on, D_2 off, D_3 off: $I_{D2} = 0 \mid I_{D3} = 0$

$$I_{D1} = \frac{10 - 0.6 - (-5)}{8k\Omega + 10k\Omega + 12k\Omega} = 0.480\text{mA} \mid V_{D2} = 5 - (10 - 0.6 - 8000I_{D1}) = -0.560\text{V}$$

$$V_{D3} = -(-5 + 12000I_{D1}) = -0.760\text{V}$$

$$D_1:(0.480\text{mA}, 0.6\text{V}) \quad D_2:(0\text{A}, -0.560\text{V}) \quad D_3:(0\text{A}, -0.760\text{V})$$

3.47

```
*Problem 3.47(a)
V1 1 0 DC 10
V2 4 0 DC 5
V3 6 0 DC -5
R1 2 3 3K
R2 3 5 7K
R3 5 6 2.5K
D1 1 2 DIODE
D2 4 3 DIODE
D3 0 5 DIODE
.MODEL DIODE D IS=1E-14 RS=0
.OP
.END
```

NAME	D1	D2	D3
MODEL	DIODE	DIODE	DIODE
ID	9.99E-04	-1.36E-12	7.42E-04
VD	6.55E-01	-1.35E+00	6.47E-01

```
*Problem 3.47(b)
V1 1 0 DC 10
V2 4 0 DC 5
V3 6 0 DC -5
R1 2 3 8K
R2 3 5 10K
R3 5 6 12K
D1 1 2 DIODE
D2 4 3 DIODE
D3 0 5 DIODE
.MODEL DIODE D IS=1E-14 RS=0
.OP
.END
```

NAME	D1	D2	D3
MODEL	DIODE	DIODE	DIODE
ID	4.79E-04	-5.44E-13	-7.56E-13
VD	6.36E-01	-5.34E-01	-7.46E-01

For both cases, the results are very similar to the hand analysis.

3.48

$$I_{D1} = \frac{10 - (-20)}{10k\Omega + 10k\Omega} = 1.50\text{mA} \mid I_{D2} = 0$$

$$I_{D3} = \frac{0 - (-10)}{10k\Omega} = 1.00\text{mA} \mid V_{D2} = 10 - 10^4 I_{D1} - 0 = -5.00\text{V}$$

$$D_1:(1.50\text{mA}, 0\text{V}) \quad D_2:(0\text{mA}, -5.00\text{V}) \quad D_3:(1.00\text{mA}, 0\text{V})$$

3.49

```
*Problem 3.49
V1 1 0 DC -20
V2 4 0 DC 10
V3 6 0 DC -10
R1 1 2 10K
R2 4 3 10K
R3 5 6 10K
D1 3 2 DIODE
D2 3 5 DIODE
D3 0 5 DIODE
.MODEL DIODE D IS=1E-14 RS=0
.OP
.END
```

NAME	D1	D2	D3
MODEL	DIODE	DIODE	DIODE
ID	1.47E-03	-4.02E-12	9.35E-04
VD	6.65E-01	-4.01E+00	6.53E-01

The simulation results are very close to those of Eq. (3.43).

3.50

$$V_{TH} = 20V \frac{3.6k\Omega}{3.6k\Omega + 11k\Omega} = 4.93V \mid R_{TH} = 11k\Omega \| 3.6k\Omega = 2.71k\Omega$$

$$I_Z = \frac{4.93 - 4}{2.71k\Omega} = 0.343mA > 0 \mid (I_Z, V_Z) = (0.343 \text{ mA}, 4 \text{ V})$$

3.51 $-4.93 = 2710 I_D + V_D \mid I_D = 0, V_D = -4.93V \mid V_D = 0, I_D = \dfrac{-4.93}{2710} = -1.82mA$

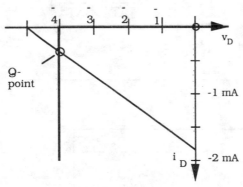

Q-Point: (0.3 mA, -4 V)

3.52

$$I_S = \frac{30 - 9}{15k\Omega} = 1.40mA \rightarrow I_L < 1.40 \text{ mA} \mid R_L > \frac{9V}{1.4mA} = 6.43 \text{ k}\Omega$$

3.53

$$I_S = \frac{30 - 9}{15k\Omega} = 1.40mA \mid P = (9V)(1.40mA) = 12.6 \text{ mW}$$

3.54

(a) $V_{TH} = 50V \dfrac{75\Omega}{150\Omega + 75\Omega} = 16.67V \mid R_{TH} = 150\Omega \| 75\Omega = 50\Omega \mid I_Z = \dfrac{16.67 - 15}{150} = 33.4 \text{ mA}$

$P = 15I_Z = 0.501 \text{ W} \quad \mid \quad$ (b) $I_Z = \dfrac{50 - 15}{150} = 233 \text{ mA} \mid P = 15I_Z = 3.50 \text{ W}$

3.55 Using MATLAB: Create the following m-file with f = 60 Hz:

```
function f=ctime(t)
f=5*exp(-10*t)-6*cos(2*pi*60*t)+1;
```

Then: fzero('ctime',1/60)   yields   ans = 0.01536129698461
and $\Delta T = (1/60)-0.0153613 = 1.305$ ms.

$$\Delta T = \frac{1}{120\pi}\sqrt{\frac{2V_r}{V_P}} \quad | \quad V_r = \frac{IT}{C} = \frac{5}{0.1(60)} = 0.8333 \text{V}$$

$$\Delta T = \frac{1}{120\pi}\sqrt{\frac{2(0.8333)}{6}} = 1.40 \text{ ms}$$

3.56

$$V_D = 2(0.025)\ln\left(1+\frac{48.6}{10^{-9}}\right) = 1.230 \text{ V}$$

3.57

$$V_{DC} = \frac{1}{T}\int_0^T v(t)dt = \frac{1}{T}\left[(V_P - V_{on})T - \frac{TV_r}{2}\right] = \left[(V_P - V_{on}) - \frac{0.05(V_P - V_{on})}{2}\right] = 0.975(V_P - V_{on})$$

$$V_{DC} = 0.975(15V) = 14.6 \text{ V}$$

3.58

$$P_D = \frac{1}{T}\int_0^T i_D^2(t)R_S dt = \frac{1}{T}\int_0^{\Delta T} I_P^2\left(1-\frac{t}{\Delta T}\right)^2 R_S dt$$

$$P_D = \frac{I_P^2 R_S}{T}\int_0^{\Delta T}\left(1-\frac{2t}{\Delta T}+\frac{t^2}{\Delta T^2}\right)^2 dt = \frac{I_P^2 R_S}{T}\left(t-\frac{t^2}{\Delta T}+\frac{t^3}{3\Delta T^2}\right)\Bigg|_0^{\Delta T}$$

$$P_D = \frac{I_P^2 R_S}{T}\left(\Delta T - \Delta T + \frac{\Delta T}{3}\right) = \frac{1}{3}I_P^2 R_S\left(\frac{\Delta T}{T}\right)$$

3.59

Using SPICE with V_P = 10 V.

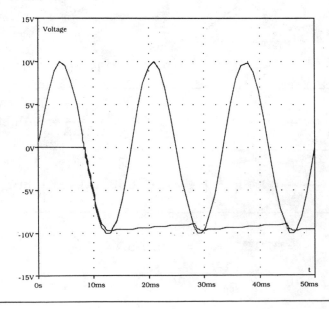

3.60

(a) $V_{dc} = -(V_P - V_{on}) = -(6.3\sqrt{2} - 1) = -7.91V$　　(b) $C = \dfrac{I\,T}{V_r} = \dfrac{7.91}{0.55}\dfrac{1}{0.5}\dfrac{1}{60} = 1.05F$

(c) $PIV \geq 2V_P = 2 \cdot 6.3\sqrt{2} = 17.8V$　　(d) $I_{surge} = \omega C V_P = 2\pi(60)(1.05)(6.3\sqrt{2}) = 3530A$

(e) $\Delta T = \dfrac{1}{\omega}\sqrt{\dfrac{2V_r}{V_P}} = \dfrac{1}{2\pi(60)}\sqrt{\dfrac{2(.25)}{6.3\sqrt{2}}} = 0.628ms$　$|$　$I_P = I_{dc}\dfrac{2T}{\Delta T} = \dfrac{7.91}{.5}\dfrac{2}{60}\dfrac{1}{.628ms} = 841A$

3.61

```
*Problem 3.61
VS 1 0 DC 0 AC 0 SIN(0 8.910 60)
D1 2 1 DIODE
R 2 0 0.25
C 2 0 0.5
.MODEL DIODE D IS=1E-10 RS=0
.OPTIONS RELTOL=1E-6
.TRAN 1US 80MS
.PRINT TRAN V(1) V(2) I(VS)
.PROBE V(1) V(2) I(VS)
.END
```

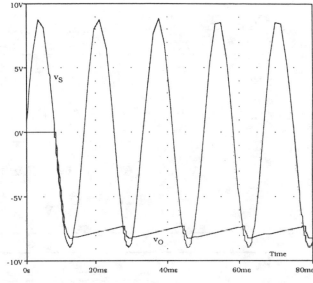

PROBE Graph Results: $V_{DC} = 8.2\,V$, $V_r = 0.9\,V$, $I_P = 720\,A$, $I_{SC} = 1680\,A$
SPICE PRINT Results: $V_{DC} = 8.2\,V$, $V_r = 0.93\,V$, $I_P = 717\,A$, $I_{SC} = 1670\,A$

$V_{dc} = -(V_P - V_{on}) = -(6.3\sqrt{2} - 1) = -7.91V$　$|$　$V_r = \dfrac{I\,T}{C} = \dfrac{7.91C}{0.25\Omega}\dfrac{1}{60s}\dfrac{1}{0.5F} = 1.06V$

$I_{SC} = \omega C V_P = 2\pi(60)(1.06)(6.3\sqrt{2}) = 1680A$　$|$　$\Delta T = \dfrac{1}{\omega}\sqrt{\dfrac{2V_r}{V_P}} = \dfrac{1}{2\pi(60)}\sqrt{\dfrac{2(1.06)}{6.3\sqrt{2}}} = 1.294ms$

$I_P = I_{dc}\dfrac{2T}{\Delta T} = \dfrac{7.91}{0.25}\dfrac{2}{60}\dfrac{1}{1.294ms} = 815A$

3.62

(a) $V_{dc} = -(V_P - V_{on}) = -(6.3\sqrt{2} - 1) = -7.91V$　　(b) $C = \dfrac{I\,T}{V_r} = \dfrac{7.91}{0.25}\dfrac{1}{0.5}\dfrac{1}{400} = 0.158F$

(c) $PIV \geq 2V_P = 2 \cdot 6.3\sqrt{2} = 17.8V$　　(d) $I_{surge} = \omega C V_P = 2\pi(400)(0.158)(6.3\sqrt{2}) = 3540A$

(e) $\Delta T = \dfrac{1}{\omega}\sqrt{\dfrac{2V_r}{V_P}} = \dfrac{1}{2\pi(400)}\sqrt{\dfrac{2(.25)}{6.3\sqrt{2}}} = 94.3\mu s$　$|$　$I_P = I_{dc}\dfrac{2T}{\Delta T} = \dfrac{7.91}{.5}\dfrac{2}{400}\dfrac{1}{94.3\mu s} = 839A$

3.63

(a) $V_{dc} = -(V_P - V_{on}) = -(6.3\sqrt{2} - 1) = -7.91V$　　(b) $C = \dfrac{I\,T}{V_r} = \dfrac{7.91}{0.25}\dfrac{1}{0.5}\dfrac{1}{10^5} = 633\mu F$

(c) $PIV \geq 2V_P = 2 \cdot 6.3\sqrt{2} = 17.8V$　　(d) $I_{surge} = \omega C V_P = 2\pi(10^5)(633\mu F)(6.3\sqrt{2}) = 3540A$

(e) $\Delta T = \dfrac{1}{\omega}\sqrt{\dfrac{2V_r}{V_P}} = \dfrac{1}{2\pi(10^5)}\sqrt{\dfrac{2(.25)}{6.3\sqrt{2}}} = 0.377\mu s$　$|$　$I_P = I_{dc}\dfrac{2T}{\Delta T} = \dfrac{7.91}{.5}\dfrac{2}{10^5}\dfrac{1}{0.377\mu s} = 839A$

3.64

(a) $C = \dfrac{I\,T}{V_r} = \dfrac{1}{2000(0.01)}\dfrac{1}{60} = 833\mu F$ (b) $PIV \geq 2V_P = 2 \cdot 2000 = 4000V$

(c) $V_S = \dfrac{2000}{\sqrt{2}} = 1414V$ (d) $\Delta T = \dfrac{1}{\omega}\sqrt{\dfrac{2V_r}{V_P}} = \dfrac{1}{2\pi(60)}\sqrt{\dfrac{2(20)}{2000}} = 0.375ms$

$I_P = I_{dc}\dfrac{2T}{\Delta T} = 1\dfrac{2}{60}\dfrac{1}{0.375ms} = 88.9A$ (e) $I_{surge} = \omega C V_P = 2\pi(60)(833\mu F)(2000) = 628A$

3.65

$C = \dfrac{V_P - V_{on}}{V_r}T\dfrac{1}{R} = \dfrac{1}{.025}\dfrac{1}{60}\dfrac{25}{5} = 3.33F$ | $PIV = 2V_P = 2(6) = 12V$ | $V_{RMS} = \dfrac{6}{\sqrt{2}} = 4.24V$

$\Delta T = \dfrac{1}{\omega}\sqrt{\dfrac{2T}{RC}\dfrac{V_P - V_{on}}{V_P}} = \dfrac{1}{2\pi(60)}\sqrt{\dfrac{2}{0.2(3.33)}\dfrac{1}{60}\dfrac{5}{6}} = 0.542ms$

$I_P = I_{dc}\dfrac{2T}{\Delta T} = 25\dfrac{2}{60}\dfrac{1}{0.542ms} = 1540A$ | $I_{surge} = \omega C V_P = 2\pi(60)(3.33)(6) = 7530A$

3.66

$$V_{DC} = 12.6\sqrt{2} - 0.8 = 17.0V \mid V_r^{max} = 17.0 - 14 = 3V$$

$$I = \dfrac{12}{10} = 1.20A \mid C = \dfrac{I}{V_r}T = \dfrac{1.20}{3}\dfrac{1}{60} = 6.67mF$$

3.67

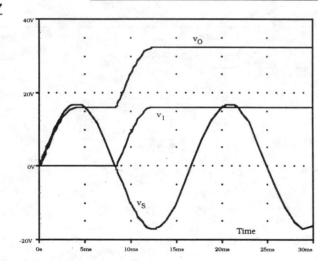

$V_{DC} = 2(V_P - V_{on}) = 2(17 - 1) = 32\ V.$

3.68

```
*Problem 3.68
VS 2 1 DC 0 AC 0 SIN(0 1500 60)
D1 2 3 DIODE
D2 0 2 DIODE
C1 1 0 500U
C2 3 1 500U
RL 3 0 3K
.MODEL DIODE D IS=1E-15 RS=0
.OPTIONS RELTOL=1E-6
.TRAN 0.1MS 100MS
.PRINT TRAN V(2,1) V(3) I(VS)
.PROBE V(3) V(2,1) I(VS)
.END
```

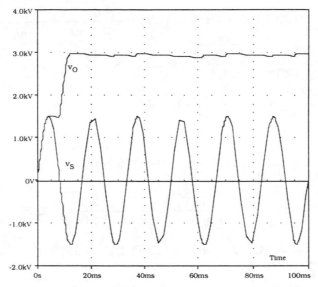

Simulation Results: $V_{DC} = 2981$ V, $V_r = 63$ V

The doubler circuit is effectively two half wave rectifiers connected in serier. Each capacitor is discharged by I = 3000V/3000Ω = 1 A for 1/60 second. The ripple voltage on each capacitor is 33.3 V. With two capacitors in series, the output ripple should be 66.6 V which is close to the simulation result.

3.69

(a) $V_{dc} = V_P - V_{on} = 6.3\sqrt{2} - 1 = 7.91V$ (b) $C = \frac{I\,T}{V_r} = \frac{7.91}{0.5}\frac{1}{0.25}\frac{1}{120} = 0.527F = 527,000\mu F$

(c) $PIV \geq 2V_P = 2 \cdot 6.3\sqrt{2} = 17.8V$ (d) $I_{surge} = \omega C V_P = 2\pi(60)(0.527)(6.3\sqrt{2}) = 1770A$

(e) $\Delta T = \frac{1}{\omega}\sqrt{\frac{2V_r}{V_P}} = \frac{1}{2\pi(60)}\sqrt{\frac{2(.25)}{6.3\sqrt{2}}} = 0.628ms$ | $I_P = I_{dc}\frac{T}{\Delta T} = \frac{7.91}{.5}\frac{1}{600}\frac{1}{0.628ms} = 420A$

3.70

```
*Problem 3.70
VS1 1 0 DC 0 AC 0 SIN(0 14.14 400)
VS2 0 2 DC 0 AC 0 SIN(0 14.14 400)
D1 3 1 DIODE
D2 3 2 DIODE
C 3 0 22000U
R 3 0 3
.MODEL DIODE D IS=1E-10 RS=0
.OPTIONS RELTOL=1E-6
.TRAN 1US 5MS
.PRINT TRAN V(1) V(2) V(3) I(VS1)
.PROBE V(1) V(2) V(3) I(VS1)
.END
```

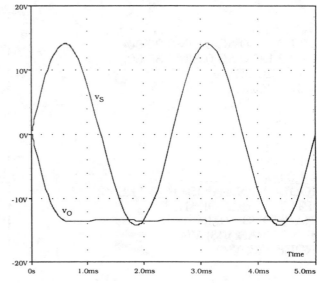

Simulation Results: $V_{DC} = -13.4$ V, $V_r = 0.23$ V, $I_P = 108$ A

$$V_{DC} = V_P - V_{on} = 10\sqrt{2} - 0.7 = 13.4 \text{ V} \quad | \quad V_r = \frac{13.4}{3} \frac{1}{800} \frac{1}{22000\mu F} = 0.254 \text{ V}$$

$$\Delta T = \frac{1}{120\pi} \sqrt{\frac{2V_r}{V_P}} = \frac{1}{120\pi} \sqrt{\frac{2(0.254)}{14.1}} = 0.504 \text{ ms}$$

$$I_P = I_{dc} \frac{T}{\Delta T} = \frac{13.4V}{3\Omega} \frac{1}{60} s \frac{1}{0.504 \text{ ms}} = 150 \text{ A}$$

3.71

(a) $C = \frac{I}{V_r} \frac{T}{2} = \frac{1}{2000(0.01)} \frac{1}{2 \cdot 60} = 417 \text{ } \mu F$ (b) $PIV \geq V_P = 2000 \text{ V}$

(c) $V_S = \frac{2000}{\sqrt{2}} = 1414 \text{ V}$ (d) $\Delta T = \frac{1}{\omega} \sqrt{\frac{2V_r}{V_P}} = \frac{1}{2\pi(60)} \sqrt{\frac{2(20)}{2000}} = 0.375 \text{ms}$

$I_P = I_{dc} \frac{T}{\Delta T} = 1 \frac{1}{60} \frac{1}{0.375 \text{ms}} = 44.4 \text{ A}$ (e) $I_{surge} = \omega C V_P = 2\pi(60)(417\mu F)(2000) = 314 \text{ A}$

3.72
The circuit is behaving like a half-wave rectifier. The capacitor should charge during the first 1/2 cycle, but it is not. Therefore, diode D_1 is not functioning properly. It acts as an open circuit.

3.73

(a) $C = \frac{I}{V_r} \frac{T}{} = \frac{1}{2000(0.01)} \frac{1}{120} = 417\mu F$ (b) $PIV \geq 2V_P = 2 \cdot 2000 = 4000V$

(c) $V_S = \frac{2000}{\sqrt{2}} = 1410V$ (d) $\Delta T = \frac{1}{\omega} \sqrt{\frac{2V_r}{V_P}} = \frac{1}{2\pi(60)} \sqrt{2(0.01)} = 0.375 \text{ms}$

$I_P = I_{dc} \frac{T}{\Delta T} = 1 \frac{1}{60} \frac{1}{0.375 \text{ms}} = 44.4 \text{A}$ (e) $I_{surge} = \omega C V_P = 2\pi(60)(417\mu F)(2000) = 314A$

3.74
$$V_1 = V_P - V_{on} = 49.3 \text{ V}, \quad V_2 = -(V_P - V_{on}) = -49.3V.$$

3.75

```
*Problem 3.75
VS1 1 0 DC 0 AC 0 SIN(0 35 60)
VS2 0 2 DC 0 AC 0 SIN(0 35 60)
D1 1 3 DIODE
D4 2 3 DIODE
D2 4 1 DIODE
D3 4 2 DIODE
C1 3 0 0.1
C2 4 0 0.1
R1 3 0 500
R2 4 0 500
.MODEL DIODE D IS=1E-10 RS=0
.OPTIONS RELTOL=1E-6
.TRAN 10US 50MS
.PRINT TRAN V(3) V(4)
.PROBE V(3) V(4)
.END
```

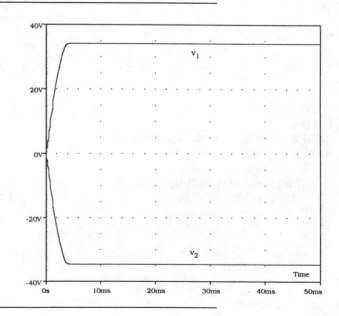

3.76

(a) $V_{dc} = V_P - 2V_{on} = 6.3\sqrt{2} - 2 = 6.91$ V   (b) $C = \dfrac{I\,T}{V_r} = \dfrac{6.91}{0.5}\dfrac{1}{0.25}\dfrac{1}{120} = 0.461$ F

(c) $PIV \geq V_P = 6.3\sqrt{2} = 8.91$ V   (d) $I_{surge} = \omega C V_P = 2\pi(60)(0.461)\left(6.3\sqrt{2}\right) = 1550$ A

(e) $\Delta T = \dfrac{1}{\omega}\sqrt{\dfrac{2V_r}{V_P}} = \dfrac{1}{2\pi(60)}\sqrt{\dfrac{2(.25)}{6.3\sqrt{2}}} = 0.628$ ms $\mid$ $I_P = I_{dc}\dfrac{T}{\Delta T} = \dfrac{6.91}{0.5}\dfrac{1}{60}\dfrac{1}{0.628ms} = 367$ A

3.77

$\delta = 1 - \dfrac{V_S}{V_O} = 1 - \dfrac{5}{15} = \dfrac{2}{3}$ $\mid$ $R = \dfrac{15V}{0.5A} = 30\Omega$ $\mid$ $C = \dfrac{V_O}{V_r}\dfrac{T}{R}\delta = \dfrac{15}{0.1}\dfrac{\frac{1}{45x10^3}}{30}\dfrac{2}{3} = 74.1\ \mu F$

$L = \dfrac{V_S}{I_r}T\delta = \dfrac{5V}{0.05A}\dfrac{1}{45x10^3}\dfrac{2}{3} = 1.48$ mH

3.78

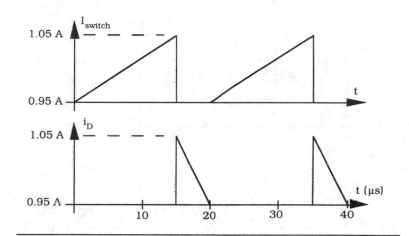

3.79

$i_L(T_{ON}) = i_L(0^+) + \dfrac{V_S}{L}T_{ON}$ $\mid$ $i_L(T) = i_L(T_{ON}) + \dfrac{V_S - V_{ON} - V_O}{L}T_{OFF}$

$i_L(T) = i_L(0^+) + \dfrac{V_S}{L}T_{ON} + \dfrac{V_S - V_{ON} - V_O}{L}T_{OFF}$ but $i_L(T) = i_L(0^+)$

$\dfrac{V_S}{L}T_{ON} + \dfrac{V_S - V_{ON} - V_O}{L}T_{OFF} = 0 \rightarrow \dfrac{V_S}{L}\left(T_{ON} + T_{OFF}\right) = \dfrac{V_{ON} + V_O}{L}T_{OFF}$

$\dfrac{V_O}{L}T_{OFF} = \dfrac{V_S}{L}T - \dfrac{V_{ON}}{L}T_{OFF} \rightarrow V_O = V_S\dfrac{T}{T_{OFF}} - V_{ON} = V_S\dfrac{1}{1-\delta} - V_{ON}$

$V_O = \dfrac{5}{1 - \dfrac{3}{4}} - 0.75 = 19.25$ V $\mid$ $I_r = \dfrac{V_S}{L}T\delta = \dfrac{5}{0.75mH}\dfrac{1}{50kHz}\dfrac{3}{4} = 100$ mA

$V_r = \dfrac{V_O}{R}\dfrac{1}{C}T\delta = \dfrac{19.25}{20}\dfrac{1}{60\mu F}\dfrac{1}{50kHz}\dfrac{3}{4} = 0.241$ V

3.80 (a)

$$P_O = I_O V_O \quad | \quad P_S = I_S V_S + I_S V_{ON} \frac{T_{OFF}}{T}$$

$$\eta = \frac{I_O V_O}{I_S V_S + I_S V_{ON} \dfrac{T_{OFF}}{T}} = \frac{I_O \dfrac{V_S}{1-\delta}}{I_S V_S + I_S V_{ON}(1-\delta)} = \frac{I_O \dfrac{V_S}{1-\delta}}{\dfrac{I_O}{1-\delta} V_S \left[1 + \dfrac{V_{ON}}{V_S}(1-\delta)\right]}$$

$$\eta = \frac{100\%}{1 + \dfrac{V_{ON}}{V_S}(1-\delta)} = \frac{100\%}{1 + \dfrac{0.75}{5}(1-0.75)} = 96.4\%$$

(b)

$$P_O = I_O V_O \quad | \quad P_S = I_S V_S + I_S V_{ONS}\delta + I_S V_{OND}(1-\delta)$$

$$\eta = \frac{100\%}{1 + \dfrac{V_{ONS}}{V_S}\delta + \dfrac{V_{OND}}{V_S}(1-\delta)} = \frac{100\%}{1 + \dfrac{0.75}{5}(1-0.75)} = 96.4\%$$

3.81

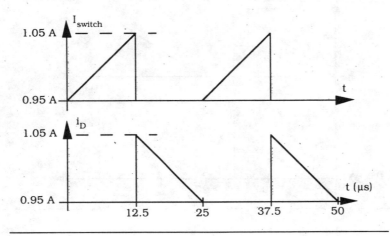

3.82

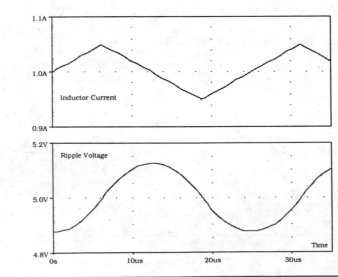

40

3.83

$$\delta = \frac{V_O}{V_S} = \frac{15}{50} = 0.30 \quad | \quad L = \frac{V_O}{I_r} T(1-\delta) = \frac{15V}{0.1 \cdot 0.5A} \frac{1}{30kHz}(1-0.3) = 7.00 \text{ mH}$$

$$C = \frac{I_r}{8V_r} T = \frac{0.05A}{8 \cdot 0.1V} \frac{1}{30kHz} = 2.08 \text{ μF}$$

3.84

$$\delta = \frac{V_O}{V_S} = \frac{15}{170} = 0.08824 \quad | \quad C = \frac{I_r}{8V_r} T = \frac{0.375A}{8 \cdot 0.5V} \frac{1}{50kHz} = 1.88 \text{ μF} \rightarrow 2.2 \text{ μF}$$

$$L = \frac{V_O}{I_r} T(1-\delta) = \frac{15V}{0.15 \cdot 2.5A} \frac{1}{50kHz}(1-0.08824) = 0.729 \text{ mH} \rightarrow 1 \text{ mH}$$

3.85

$$\frac{V_S - V_O}{L} T_{ON} = \frac{V_O + V_{ON}}{L} T_{OFF} \rightarrow \frac{V_S}{L} T_{ON} - \frac{V_{ON}}{L} T_{OFF} = \frac{V_O}{L} T \quad | \quad V_O = V_S \delta - V_{ON}(1-\delta)$$

The output voltage is reduced slightly by the on-voltage of the diode. The ripple voltage and current are reduced by a factor of 2 due to the increase in inductor size.

3.86 (a)

$$I_O V_S \delta = I_O V_O + I_O V_{ON}(1-\delta) \quad | \quad P_O = I_O V_O = I_O V_S \delta - I_O V_{ON}(1-\delta) \quad | \quad P_S = I_O V_S \delta$$

$$\eta = 100\% \frac{I_O V_S \delta - I_O V_{ON}(1-\delta)}{I_O V_S \delta} = 100\% \left[1 - \frac{V_{ON}(1-\delta)}{V_S \delta}\right] = 100\% \left[1 - \frac{V_{ON}}{V_O}(1-\delta)\right]$$

(b)

$$\eta = 100\% \left(1 - \frac{0.75}{5}\left(1 - \frac{1}{2}\right)\right) = 92.5\%$$

(c)

$$I_O V_S \delta = I_O V_O + I_O V_{ONS} \delta + I_O V_{OND}(1-\delta) \quad | \quad P_S = I_O V_S \delta$$

$$\eta = 100\% \left[1 - \frac{V_{ONS} \delta + V_{OND}(1-\delta)}{V_O}\right]$$

3.87 (a) 15 V. The output voltage cannot exceed the positive power supply voltage. (b) -9 V. The output voltage cannot be lower than the negative power supply voltage.

3.88

(a)

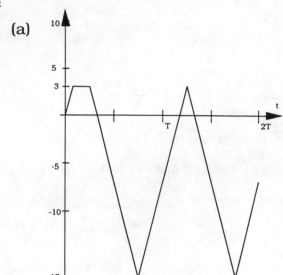

(b)

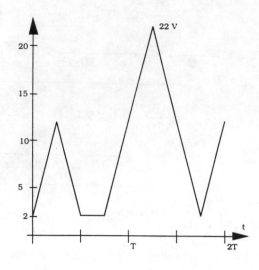

Note in Part (b) that the capacitor is charged to 2 V at t = 0.

3.89

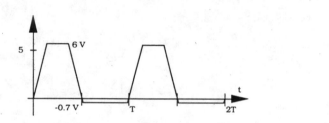

3.90

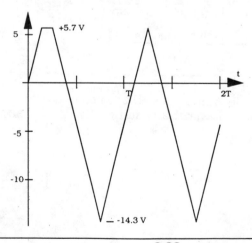

3.91

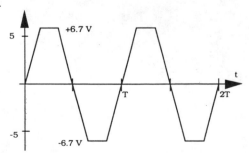

3.92

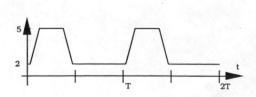

3.93 Using PSPICE:

```
*Problem 3.93
VS 1 0 PWL(0 0 0.00025 10 .00075
+ -10 .00125 10 .00175 -10 .002
0)
R1 1 2 22K
D1 2 3 DIODE
V1 3 0 DC 5
V2 2 4 DC 2
D2 0 4 DIODE
.MODEL DIODE D IS=1E-12 RS=0
.TRAN 10US 2MS
.PRINT TRAN V(1) V(2)
.PROBE V(1) V(2)
.END
```

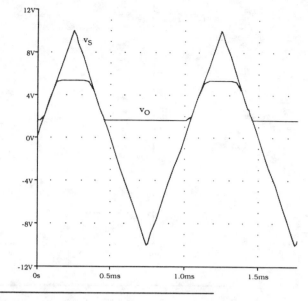

3.94   **3.95**

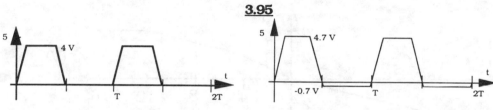

3.96 The 6 V source is backwards in the first printing.   For the circuit as drawn, the output is indeterminate.   The two diodes are forward biased and at least one would be destroyed in a real circuit.   Reversing the 6 V source yields:

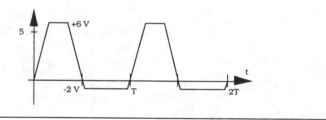

3.97 Using PSPICE:

```
*Problem 3.97
VS 1 0 DC -10
R1 1 2 4.7K
D1 2 3 DIODE
V1 3 0 DC 6
V2 4 2 DC 2
D2 0 4 DIODE
.MODEL DIODE D IS=1E-12 RS=0
.DC VS -10 10 .025
.PRINT DC V(1) V(2)
.PROBE V(1) V(2)
.END
```

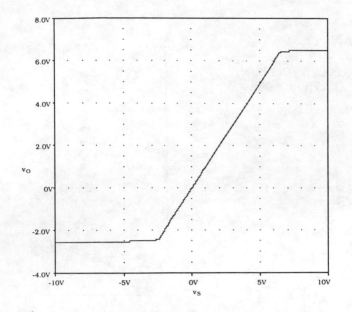

3.98

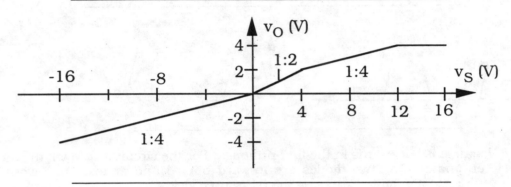

3.99 Using PSPICE:

```
*Problem 3.99
VS 1 0 DC 0
RS 1 2 10K
D1 2 3 DIODE
R1 3 4 5K
V1 4 0 DC 2
D2 5 2 DIODE
R2 5 0 5K
D3 2 6 DIODE
V2 6 0 DC 4
RL 2 0 10K
.MODEL DIODE D IS=1E-12 RS=0
.DC VS -15 15 .025
.PRINT DC V(1) V(2)
.PROBE V(1) V(2)
.END
```

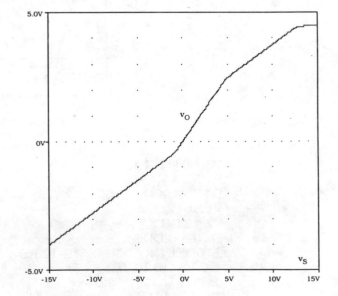

3.100 Using PSPICE:

```
*Problem 3.100
VS 1 0 DC 0 AC 0 SIN(0 10 1000)
C1 1 2 1U
D1 2 3 DIODE
V1 3 0 DC 3
C2 1 4 1U
D2 5 4 DIODE
V2 5 0 DC 2
.MODEL DIODE D IS=1E-10 RS=0
.TRAN 5US 5MS
.PRINT TRAN V(1) V(2) V(4)
.PROBE V(1) V(2) V(4)
.END
```

3.101

3.102 Using PSPICE:

```
*Problem 3.102
VS 1 0 DC 0
RS 1 2 100K
D1 3 2 DIODE
R1 3 0 200K
D2 4 2 DIODE
V2 0 4 DC 2
RL 2 0 200K
.MODEL DIODE D IS=1E-12 RS=0
.DC VS -6 6 .025
.PRINT DC V(1) V(2)
.PROBE V(1) V(2)
.END
```

The results are similar to the drawing above except for the shifts due to the diode turn-on voltage.

$$i_D(0^+) = \frac{5V}{1k\Omega} = 5 \text{ mA} \quad | \quad I_F = \frac{5 - V_D}{1k\Omega} = \frac{5 - 0.6}{1k\Omega} = 4.4 \text{ mA}$$

$$I_r = \frac{-3 - 0.6}{1k\Omega} = -3.6 \text{ mA} \quad | \quad \tau_S = (7ns) \ln\left(1 - \frac{4.4mA}{-3.6mA}\right) = 5.59 \text{ ns}$$

```
*Problem 3.104 - Diode Switching
Delay
V1 1 0 PWL(0 0 0.01N 5 10N 5 10.02N -3
20N -3)
R1 1 2 1K
D1 2 0 DIODE
.TRAN .01NS 20NS
.MODEL DIODE D TT=7NS IS=1E-15
.PROBE V(1) V(2) I(V1)
.OPTIONS RELTOL=1E-6
.OP
.END
```

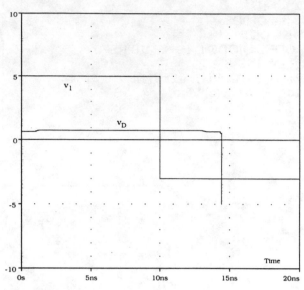

Simulation results give $\tau_S = 4.4$ ns.

```
*Problem 3.105(a) - Diode Switching
Delay
V1 1 0 DC 1.5 PWL(0 0 .01N 1.5 7.5N 1.5
7.52N -1.5 15N -1.5)
R1 1 2 0.75K
D1 2 0 DIODE
.TRAN .02NS 100NS
.MODEL DIODE D TT=50NS IS=1E-15
CJO=0.5PF
.PROBE V(1) V(2) I(V1)
.OPTIONS RELTOL=1E-6
.OP
.END
```

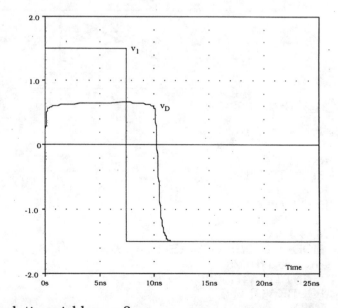

For this case, simulation yields $\tau_S = 3$ ns.

```
*Problem 3.105(b) - Diode Switching Delay
V1 1 0 DC 1.5 PWL(0 1.5 7.5N 1.5 7.52N -1.5 15N -1.5)
R1 1 2 0.75K
D1 2 0 DIODE
.TRAN .02NS 100NS
```

```
.MODEL DIODE D TT=50NS IS=1E-15 CJO=0.5PF
.PROBE V(1) V(2) I(V1)
.OPTIONS RELTOL=1E-6
.OP
.END
```

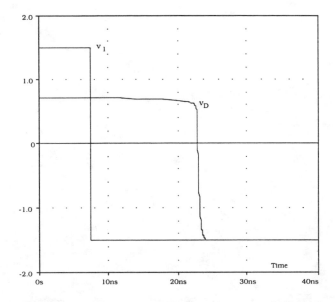

For this case, simulation yields τ_S = 15.5 ns.

In case (a), the charge in the diode does not have time to reach the steady-state value given by Q = (1mA)(50ns) = 50 pC. At most, only 1mA(7.5ns) = 7.5 pC can be stored in the diode. Thus is turns off more rapidly than predicted by the storage time formula. It should turn off in approximately t = 7.5pC/3mA = 2.5 ns which agrees with the simulation results. In (b), the diode charge has had time to reach its steady-state value. Eq. (3.103) gives: (50 ns) ln (1-1mA/(-3mA)) = 14.4 ns which is close to the simulation result.

3.106

$$I_C = 1 - 10^{-15}\left[\exp(40V_C) - 1\right] \text{ A} \mid \text{For } V_C = 0, \ I_{SC} = 1A$$

$$V_{OC} = \frac{1}{40}\ln\left(1 + \frac{1}{10^{-15}}\right) = 0.864 \text{ V}$$

$$P = V_C I_C = V_C\left[1 - 10^{-15}\left[\exp(40V_C) - 1\right]\right]$$

$$\frac{dP}{dV_C} = 1 - 10^{-15}\left[\exp(40V_C) - 1\right] - 40x10^{-15}V_C\exp(40V_C) = 0$$

Using the computer to find V_C yields V_C = 0.7768 V, I_C = 0.9688 A, and P_{max} = 7.53 Watts

---

3.107

$$\lambda = \frac{hc}{E}$$

(a) $\lambda = \dfrac{6.625x10^{-34}J-s\left(3x10^8 m/s\right)}{1.12eV\left(1.602x10^{-19}j/eV\right)} = 1.11 \ \mu m$ - far infrared

(b) $\lambda = \dfrac{6.625x10^{-34}J-s\left(3x10^8 m/s\right)}{1.42eV\left(1.602x10^{-19}j/eV\right)} = 0.875 \ \mu m$ - near infrared

CHAPTER 4

4.1 (a)

$$K_n' = \mu_n C_{ox}'' = \mu_n \frac{\varepsilon_{ox}}{T_{ox}} = \mu_n \frac{3.9\varepsilon_0}{T_{ox}} = \left(500 \frac{cm^2}{V-sec}\right) \frac{3.9\left(8.854 \times 10^{-14}\,F/cm\right)}{50 \times 10^{-9}\,m(100cm/m)}$$

$$K_n' = 34.5 \times 10^{-6} \frac{F}{V-sec} = 34.5 \times 10^{-6} \frac{A}{V^2} = 34.5 \frac{\mu A}{V^2}$$

(b) & (c) Scaling the result from part (a) yields

$$K_n' = 34.5 \frac{\mu A}{V^2} \frac{50nm}{20nm} = 86.3 \frac{\mu A}{V^2} \quad \text{and} \quad K_n' = 34.5 \frac{\mu A}{V^2} \frac{50nm}{10nm} = 173 \frac{\mu A}{V^2}$$

4.2 The carrier velocities must increase as the carriers travel down the channel.

4.3 Identify the source, drain, gate and bulk terminals and find the current I in the transistors in Fig. P-4.3.

(a)

$$V_{GS} = V_G - V_S = 5V \quad V_{DS} = V_D - V_S = 0.2V$$

$$I = I_{DS} = K_n' \frac{W}{L}\left(V_{GS} - V_{TN} - \frac{V_{DS}}{2}\right)V_{DS}$$

$$I = I_{DS} = \left(25 \frac{\mu A}{V^2}\right)\frac{10}{1}\left(5 - 0.75 - \frac{0.2}{2}\right)0.2 = +208 \ \mu A$$

(b)

$$V_{GS} = V_G - V_S = 5 - (-0.2) = 5.2V \quad V_{DS} = V_D - V_S = 0 - (-0.2) = 0.2V$$

$$I = -I_{DS} = -\left(25 \frac{\mu A}{V^2}\right)\frac{10}{1}\left(5.2 - 0.75 - \frac{0.2}{2}\right)0.2 = -218 \ \mu A$$

4.4

$$\text{(a)} \quad I = \left(25 \frac{\mu A}{V^2}\right)\frac{10}{1}\left(5 - 0.75 - \frac{0.5}{2}\right)0.5 = 500 \ \mu A$$

$$\text{(b)} \quad I = \left(25 \frac{\mu A}{V^2}\right)\frac{10}{1}\left(3 - 0.75 - \frac{0.2}{2}\right)0.2 = 108 \ \mu A$$

4.5

$$R_{on} = \frac{1}{K_n' \frac{W}{L}(V_{GS} - V_{TN})} = \frac{1}{25 \times 10^{-6}\frac{100}{1}(5 - 0.75)} = 94.1 \ \Omega$$

4.6

$$R_{on} = \frac{1}{K_n' \frac{W}{L}(V_{GS} - V_{TN})} \quad \text{or} \quad \frac{W}{L} = \frac{1}{K_n'(V_{GS} - V_{TN})R_{on}}$$

(a) $\dfrac{W}{L} = \dfrac{1}{25 \times 10^{-6}(5 - 0.75)(1000)} = \dfrac{9.41}{1}$

(b) $\dfrac{W}{L} = \dfrac{1}{10 \times 10^{-6}(5 - 0.75)(1000)} = \dfrac{23.5}{1}$

4.7

(a) $R_{on} = \dfrac{1}{K_n' \frac{W}{L}(V_{GS} - V_{TN})} = \dfrac{1}{25 \times 10^{-6} \frac{100}{1}(5 - 0.75)} = 94.1 \ \Omega$

(b) $R_{on} = \dfrac{1}{K_p' \frac{W}{L}(V_{SG} + V_{TP})} = \dfrac{1}{10 \times 10^{-6} \frac{100}{1}(5 - 0.75)} = 235 \ \Omega$

(c) $\dfrac{W}{L} = \dfrac{1}{K_p'(V_{SG} + V_{TP})R_{on}} = \dfrac{1}{10 \times 10^{-6}(5 - 0.75)94.1} = \dfrac{250}{1}$

4.8

$$R_{on} \le \frac{0.1V}{4A} = 0.025\Omega = 25m\Omega$$

$$K_n = \frac{I_{DS}}{(V_{GS} - V_{TN} - 0.5V_{Ds})V_{DS}} = \frac{4}{(5 - 2 - 0.5(0.1))(0.1)} = 13.6 \frac{A}{V^2}$$

4.9

```
*DC-DC Boost Converter
VS 1 0 5
L 1 2 0.75MH
MS 2 4 0 0 SWITCH
D1 2 3 DIODE
R 3 0 20
C 3 5 50UF
VC 5 0 0
VG 4 0 DC 0 PULSE(0 5 0 1N 1N 15U
20U)
.MODEL DIODE D TT=5NS IS=1E-15
CJO=25PF
.MODEL SWITCH NMOS KP=15 VTO = 2
.OP
.TRAN 10US 2MS
.PROBE V(4) V(2) V(3) I(VS) I(VC)
.END
```

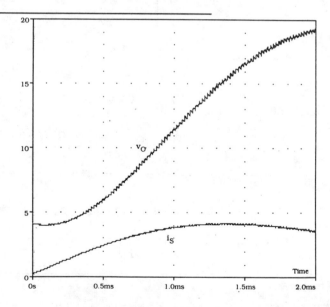

4.10

$$R_{on} \le \frac{0.1V}{0.5A} = 0.2\Omega$$

$$K_p = \frac{I_{SD}}{(V_{SG} + V_{TP} - 0.5V_{SD})V_{SD}} = \frac{0.5A}{(10V - 2V - 0.5(0.1V))(0.1V)} = 0.629 \frac{A}{V^2}$$

4.11

*DC-DC Buck Converter
VS 1 0 10
L 2 3 0.625MH
MS 2 4 1 1 SWITCH
D1 0 2 DIODE
R 3 0 5
C 3 5 2UF
VC 5 0 0
VG 4 0 DC 10 PULSE(10 0 0 1N 1N 12.5U 25U)
.MODEL DIODE D TT=5NS IS=1E-15 CJO=25PF
.MODEL SWITCH PMOS KP=15 VTO=-2
.OP
.TRAN 10US 2MS
.PROBE V(4) V(2) V(3) I(VS) I(VC) I(L)
.END

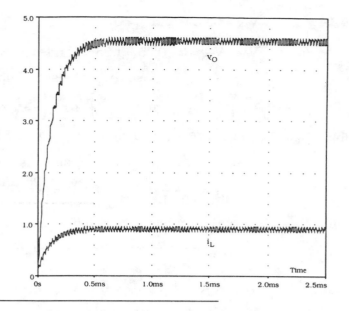

4.12

Picking two values in saturation:

$$395\mu A = \frac{K_n}{2}\left(4 - V_{TN}\right)^2 \quad \text{and} \quad 140\mu A = \frac{K_n}{2}\left(3 - V_{TN}\right)^2$$

Taking the ratio of these two equations:

$$\frac{395}{140} = \frac{\left(4 - V_{TN}\right)^2}{\left(3 - V_{TN}\right)^2} \rightarrow V_{TN} = 1.5 \text{ V} \rightarrow \overline{K_n} = 125\frac{\mu A}{V^2}$$

$$\frac{W}{L} = \frac{125\frac{\mu A}{V^2}}{25\frac{\mu A}{V^2}} = \frac{5}{1} \quad | \quad V_{TN} > 0 \rightarrow \text{enhancement - mode transistor}$$

4.13 Using the parameter values from problem 4.12:

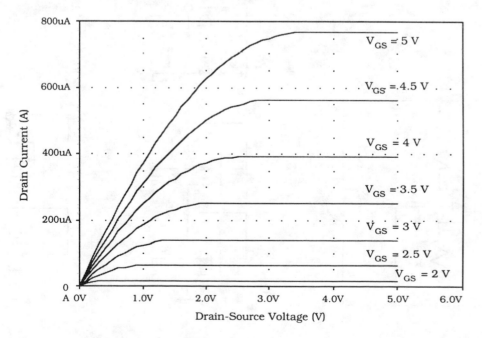

51

4.14 $V_{TN} = 0.75$ V and $\lambda = 0$.

(a) $V_{GS} - V_{TN} = 2 - 0.75 = 1.25$ V   and $V_{DS} = 0.2$ V.

$V_{DS} < V_{GS} - V_{TN}$ so the transistor is operating in the <u>linear region</u>.

$$I_{DS} = K_n' \frac{W}{L}\left(V_{GS} - V_{TN} - \frac{V_{DS}}{2}\right)V_{DS} = \left(25\,\frac{\mu A}{V^2}\right)\frac{10}{1}\left(2 - 0.75 - \frac{0.2}{2}\right)0.2 = 57.5\ \mu A$$

(b) $V_{GS} - V_{TN} = 2 - 0.75 = 1.25$ V   and $V_{DS} = 2.5$ V.

$V_{DS} > V_{GS} - V_{TN}$ so the transistor is operating in the <u>saturation region</u>.

$$I_{DS} = \frac{K_n'}{2}\frac{W}{L}(V_{GS} - V_{TN})^2 = \left(\frac{25\,\mu A}{2\ V^2}\right)\frac{10}{1}(2 - 0.75)^2 = 195\ \mu A$$

(c) $V_{GS} < V_{TN}$ so the transistor is <u>cutoff</u> with $I_{DS} = 0$.

4.15

(a) $V_{GS} - V_{TN} = 4$ V, $V_{DS} = 6$ V. $V_{DS} > V_{GS} - V_{TN}$ --> Saturation region

(b) $V_{GS} < V_{TN}$ --> Cutoff region

(c) $V_{GS} - V_{TN} = 1$ V, $V_{DS} = 2$ V. $V_{DS} > V_{GS} - V_{TN}$ --> Saturation region

(d) $V_{GS} - V_{TN} = 0.5$ V, $V_{DS} = 0.5$ V. $V_{DS} = V_{GS} - V_{TN}$ --> Boundary between linear and saturation regions

(e) The source and drain of the transistor are now reversed because of the sign change in V_{DS}. Assuming the voltages are defined relative to the original S and D terminals as in Problem 4.3(b), $V_{GS} - V_{TN} = 2.5-(-0.5) = 2.0$ V and $V_{DS} = 0.5$ V --> linear region

(f) The source and drain of the transistor are again reversed because of the sign change in V_{DS}. Assuming the voltages are defined relative to the original S and D terminals as in Problem 4.3(b), $V_{GS} - V_{TN} = 3-(-6) = 9$ V and $V_{DS} = 6$ V --> linear region

---

4.16

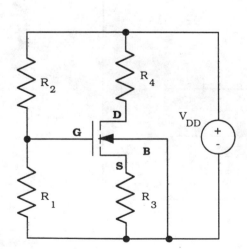

4.17

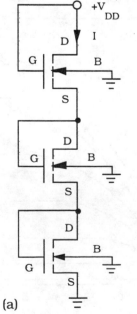

(a)

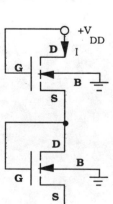

(b)

4.18 $V_{DS} > V_{GS} - V_{TN}$ so the transistor is saturated.

(a) $I_{DS} = \dfrac{K_n}{2}\left(V_{GS} - V_{TN}\right)^2\left(1 + \lambda V_{DS}\right) = \dfrac{250}{2}\dfrac{\mu A}{V^2}\left(5 - 1\right)^2\left(1 + 0.025(6)\right) = 2.30 \text{ mA}$

(b) $I_{DS} = \dfrac{K_n}{2}\left(V_{GS} - V_{TN}\right)^2 = \dfrac{250}{2}\dfrac{\mu A}{V^2}\left(5 - 1\right)^2 = 2.00 \text{ mA}$

4.19 $V_{DS} > V_{GS} - V_{TN}$ so the transistor is saturated.

(a) $I_{DS} = \dfrac{K_n}{2}\left(V_{GS} - V_{TN}\right)^2\left(1 - \lambda V_{DS}\right) = \dfrac{500}{2}\dfrac{\mu A}{V^2}\left(4 - 1.5\right)^2\left(1 + 0.02(5)\right) = 1.72 \text{ mA}$

(b) $I_{DS} = \dfrac{K_n}{2}\left(V_{GS} - V_{TN}\right)^2 = \dfrac{500}{2}\dfrac{\mu A}{V^2}\left(4 - 1.5\right)^2 = 1.56 \text{ mA}$

4.20 (a) The transistor is saturated by connection.

$$I_{DS} = \frac{12V - V_{GS}}{10^5 \Omega} = \frac{250 \times 10^{-6}}{2}\frac{A}{V^2}\left(V_{GS} - 0.75V\right)^2$$

$$12.5V_{GS}^2 - 17.8V_{GS} - 4.97 = 0$$

$$V_{GS} = -0.24V, \ 1.66V \Rightarrow V_{GS} = 1.66 \text{ V since it can't be negative.}$$

$$I_{DS} = \frac{12 - 1.66}{10^5} = 103 \ \mu A$$

(b) $\quad I_{DS} = \dfrac{12V - V_{GS}}{10^5 \Omega} = \dfrac{250 \times 10^{-6}}{2}\dfrac{A}{V^2}\left(V_{GS} - 0.75V\right)^2\left(1 + 0.025V_{GS}\right)$

Starting with the solution from part (a) and solving iteratively yields $V_{GS} = 1.64$ V and $I_{DS} = 104 \ \mu A$.

4.21 (a) Since $V_{DS} = V_{GS}$ and $V_{TN} > 0$ for both transistors, both devices are saturated.

Therefore $\quad I_{DS1} = \dfrac{K_n'}{2}\dfrac{W}{L}\left(V_{GS1} - V_{TN}\right)^2 \quad$ and $\quad I_{DS2} = \dfrac{K_n'}{2}\dfrac{W}{L}\left(V_{GS2} - V_{TN}\right)^2$.

From the circuit, however, I_{DS2} must equal I_{DS1} since $I_G = 0$ for the MOSFET:

$$I = I_{DS1} = I_{DS2} \quad \text{or} \quad \frac{K_n'}{2}\frac{W}{L}\left(V_{GS1} - V_{TN}\right)^2 = \frac{K_n'}{2}\frac{W}{L}\left(V_{GS2} - V_{TN}\right)^2$$

which requires $V_{GS1} = V_{GS2}$. Using KVL:

$$V_{DD} = V_{DS1} + V_{DS2} = V_{GS1} + V_{GS2} = 2V_{GS2}$$

$$V_{GS1} = V_{GS2} = \frac{V_{DD}}{2} = 5V$$

$$I = \frac{K_n'}{2}\frac{W}{L}\left(V_{GS1} - V_{TN}\right)^2 = \frac{25}{2}\frac{\mu A}{V^2}\frac{10}{1}\left(5 - 0.75\right)^2 V^2 = 2.26 \text{ mA}$$

(Checking saturation: $V_{GS} - V_{TN} = 5 - 0.75 = 4.25$ V and $V_{DS} = 5$ V for both transistors, so the assumed region of operation is correct.)

(b) For this case,

$$I_{DS1} = \frac{K_n'}{2}\frac{W}{L}\left(V_{GS1} - V_{TN}\right)^2\left(1 + \lambda V_{DS1}\right) \text{ and } I_{DS2} = \frac{K_n'}{2}\frac{W}{L}\left(V_{GS2} - V_{TN}\right)^2\left(1 + \lambda V_{DS2}\right).$$

Since $V_{GS} = V_{DS}$ for both transistors

$$I_{DS1} = \frac{K_n'}{2}\frac{W}{L}\left(V_{GS1} - V_{TH}\right)^2\left(1 + \lambda V_{GS1}\right) \text{ and } I_{DS2} = \frac{K_n'}{2}\frac{W}{L}\left(V_{GS2} - V_{TH}\right)^2\left(1 + \lambda V_{GS2}\right)$$

and $I_{DS1} = I_{DS2} = I$

$$\frac{K_n'}{2}\frac{W}{L}(V_{GS1} - V_{TN})^2(1 + \lambda V_{GS1}) = \frac{K_n'}{2}\frac{W}{L}(V_{GS2} - V_{TN})^2(1 + \lambda V_{GS2})$$

which again requires $V_{GS1} = V_{GS2} = V_{DD}/2 = 5V$.

$$I = \frac{K_n'}{2}\frac{W}{L}(V_{GS1} - V_{TN})^2(1 + \lambda V_{DS}) = \frac{25}{2}\frac{\mu A}{V^2}\frac{10}{1}(5 - 0.75)^2 V^2(1 + (.02)5) = 2.48 \text{ mA}$$

4.22 Since $V_{DS} = V_{GS}$, and $V_{TN} < 0$ for an NMOS depletion mode device, $V_{GS} - V_{TN}$ will be greater than V_{DS} and the transistor will be operating in the linear region.

4.23 $V_{GS} - V_{TN} = 5 - (-2) = 7 \text{ V} > V_{DS} = 6 \text{ V}$ so the transistor is operating in the linear region.

(a) $I_{DS} = 250 \times 10^{-6}\left(5 - (-2) - \frac{6}{2}\right)6 = 6.00 \text{ mA}$

(b) Our linear region model is independent of λ, so $I_{DS} = 6.00 \text{ mA}$.

4.24

(a) $V_{DS} = 6V$ | $V_{GS} - V_{TN} = 0 - (-3) = 3V$ so the transistor is saturated

$$I_{DS} = \frac{K_n'}{2}\frac{W}{L}(V_{GS1} - V_{TN})^2 = \frac{200}{2}\frac{\mu A}{V^2}[0 - (-3V)]^2 = 0.900 \text{ mA}$$

(b) $I_{DS} = \frac{200}{2}\frac{\mu A}{V^2}[0 - (-3V)]^2(1 + 0.025(6)) = 1.035 \text{ mA}$

4.25

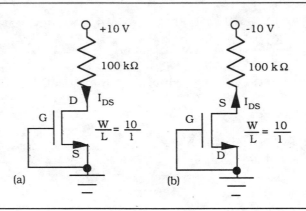

(a)

(b)

(a)   If the transistor were saturated, then $I_{DS} = \frac{250 \times 10^{-6}}{2}(-2)^2 = 500\mu A$ but this would require a power supply of greater than 50 V. Thus the transistor must be operating in the linear region.

$$\frac{10V - V_{DS}}{10^5 \Omega} = 250 \times 10^{-6}\left(0 - (-2) - \frac{V_{DS}}{2}\right)V_{DS}$$

$$10 - V_{DS} = 12.5 V_{DS}(4 - V_{DS})$$

and $V_{DS} = 0.2065V$ using the quadratic equation.

$$I_{DS} = 250 \times 10^{-6}\left(2 - \frac{0.2065}{2}\right)0.2065 = 97.9 \text{ } \mu A$$

(b)   In this circuit, the drain and source terminals of the transistor are reversed because of the power supply voltage, and the current direction is also reversed. However, now $V_{DS} =$

V_{GS} and since the transistor is a depletion-mode device, it is still operating in the linear region.

$$\frac{10V - V_{DS}}{10^5 \Omega} = 250 \times 10^{-6} \left(V_{DS} - (-2) - \frac{V_{DS}}{2} \right) V_{DS}$$

$$10 - V_{DS} = 12.5 V_{DS} \left(4 + V_{DS} \right)$$

and $V_{DS} = 0.1876V$ using the quadratic equation.

$$I_{DS} = 250 \times 10^{-6} \left(0.1876 - (-2) - \frac{0.1876}{2} \right) 0.1876 = 98.1 \ \mu A$$

4.26 (a)

$$V_{TN} = 0.75 + 0.75 \left(\sqrt{1.5 + 0.6} - \sqrt{0.6} \right) = 1.26V$$

$$V_{GS} - V_{TN} = 2 - 1.26 = 0.74V \ > \ V_{DS} = 0.2V \Rightarrow \text{Linear region}$$

$$I_{DS} = 250 \times 10^{-6} \left(2 - 1.26 - \frac{0.2}{2} \right) 0.2 = 32.0 \ \mu A \ \text{(compared to } 57.5 \mu A)$$

(b)

$$V_{GS} - V_{TN} = 2 - 1.26 = 0.74V \ < \ V_{DS} = 2.5V \Rightarrow \text{Saturation region}$$

$$I_{DS} = \frac{250 \times 10^{-6}}{2} (2 - 1.26)^2 = 68.5 \ \mu A \ \text{(compared to } 195 \ \mu A!)$$

(c) $V_{GS} < V_{TN}$ so transistor is cutoff - $I_{DS} = 0$.

4.27 (a)

$$V_{TN} = 1 + 0.7 \left(\sqrt{3 + 0.6} - \sqrt{0.6} \right) = 1.79V$$

$$V_{GS} - V_{TN} = 2.5 - 1.79 = 0.71V \ < \ V_{DS} = 5V \Rightarrow \text{Saturation region}$$

$$I_{DS} = \frac{25 \times 10^{-6}}{2} \frac{5}{1} (0.71)^2 = 31.5 \ \mu A$$

(b)

$$0.5 < 0.71 \Rightarrow \text{Linear region}$$

$$I_{DS} = 25 \times 10^{-6} \frac{5}{1} \left(0.71 - \frac{0.5}{2} \right) 0.5 = 28.8 \ \mu A$$

4.28

$$V_{TN} = 1.5 + 0.5 \left(\sqrt{5 + 0.75} - \sqrt{0.75} \right) = 2.27V$$

$$V_{GS} \ < \ V_{TN} \Rightarrow \text{Cutoff \& } I_{DS} = 0$$

4.29

$$0.75 = -1.5 + 1.5 \left(\sqrt{V_{SB} + 0.75} - \sqrt{0.75} \right)$$

Solving for V_{SB} yields $V_{SB} = 4.85V$

4.30 Using trial and error with a spreadsheet yielded

$$V_{TO} = 0.74V \quad \gamma = 0.84 \sqrt{V} \quad 2\phi_F = 0.87V \quad \text{RMS Error} = 51.9 \ mV$$

4.31 (a)

$$K_p' = \mu_p C_{ox}'' = \mu_p \frac{\varepsilon_{ox}}{T_{ox}} = \mu_p \frac{3.9 \varepsilon_o}{T_{ox}} = \left(200 \frac{cm^2}{V - sec} \right) \frac{3.9 \left(8.854 \times 10^{-14} F / cm \right)}{50 \times 10^{-9} m (100 cm / m)}$$

$$K_p' = 13.8 \times 10^{-6} \frac{F}{V - sec} = 13.8 \frac{\mu A}{V^2}$$

(b) & (c) Scaling the result from part (a) yields

$$K'_n = 13.8 \frac{\mu A}{V^2} \frac{50nm}{20nm} = 34.5 \frac{\mu A}{V^2} \quad \text{and} \quad K'_n = 13.8 \frac{\mu A}{V^2} \frac{50nm}{10nm} = 69.0 \frac{\mu A}{V^2}$$

4.32 The pinchoff points and threshold voltage can be estimated directly from the graph: e. g. $V_{SG} = 3$ V curve gives $V_{TP} = 2.5 - 3 = -0.5$ V or from the $V_{SG} = 5$ V curve gives $V_{TP} = 4.5 - 5 = -0.5$ V. Choosing two points in saturation, say $I_{SD} = 1.25$ mA for $V_{SG} = 3$ V and $I_{SD} = 4.05$ mA for $V_{SG} = 5$ V,

$$\sqrt{\frac{I_{SD1}}{I_{SD2}}} = \frac{(V_{SG1} + V_{TP})}{(V_{SG2} + V_{TP})} \quad \text{or} \quad \sqrt{\frac{1.25}{4.05}} = \frac{(3 + V_{TP})}{(5 + V_{TP})}$$

Solving for V_{TP} yields: $0.444 V_{TP} = -0.222V$ and $V_{TP} = -0.500V$.

Solving for K_p: $K_p = \frac{2I_{SD}}{(V_{SG} + V_{TP})^2} = \frac{2(1.25mA)}{(3 - 0.5)^2} = 0.400 \frac{mA}{V^2}$

$$\frac{W}{L} = \frac{K_p}{K'_p} = \frac{400 \frac{\mu A}{V^2}}{10 \frac{\mu A}{V^2}} = \frac{40}{1}$$

4.33

(a) $V_{SG} + V_{TP} = 1.1 - 0.75 = 0.35V > V_{SD} = 0.2V \rightarrow$ Linear region

$I_{SD} = \frac{10\mu A}{V^2} \frac{10}{1} \left(1.1 - 0.75 - \frac{0.2}{2} \right) 0.2 = 5.00 \ \mu A$

(b) $V_{SG} + V_{TP} = 1.3 - 0.75 = 0.55V > V_{SD} = 0.2V \rightarrow$ Linear region

$I_{SD} = \frac{10\mu A}{V^2} \frac{10}{1} \left(1.3 - 0.75 - \frac{0.2}{2} \right) 0.2 = 9.00 \ \mu A$

(c) $V_{TP} = -\left[0.75 + .5 \left(\sqrt{1 + .6} - \sqrt{-6} \right) \right] = -0.995V$

$V_{SG} + V_{TP} = 1.1 - 0.995 = 0.105V < V_{SD} = 0.2V \rightarrow$ saturation region

$I_{SD} = \frac{1}{2} \frac{10\mu A}{V^2} \frac{10}{1} (1.1 - 0.995)^2 = 0.551 \ \mu A$

(d) $V_{SG} + V_{TP} = 1.3 - 0.995 = 0.305V < V_{SD} = 0.2V \rightarrow$ linear region

$I_{SD} = \frac{10\mu A}{V^2} \frac{10}{1} \left(1.3 - 0.995 - \frac{0.2}{2} \right) 0.2 = 4.10 \ \mu A$

4.34

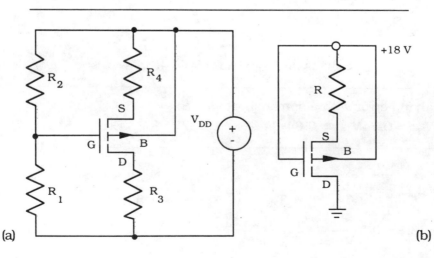

(a)   (b)

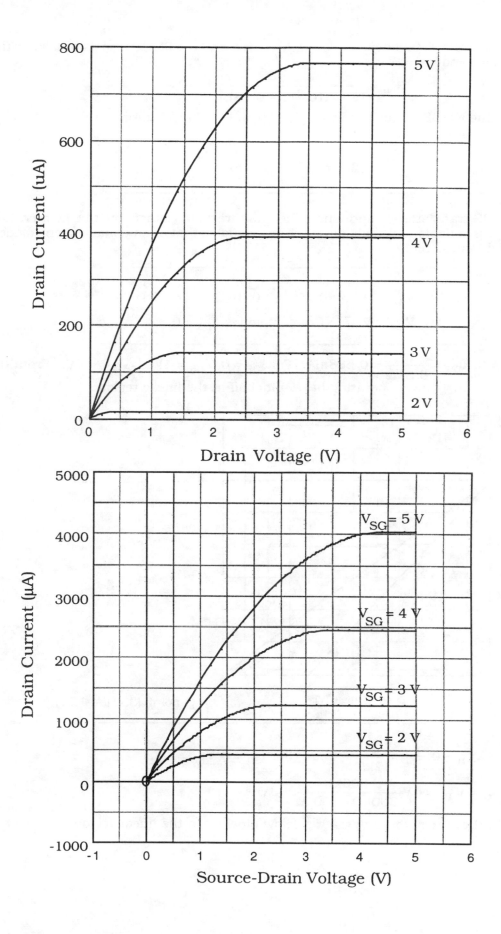

4.35 (a) For $V_{IN} = 0$, the NMOS device is on with $V_{GS} = 5$ and the PMOS transistor is off with $V_{SG} = 0$. $V_O = 0$ and $V_{SB} = 0$.

$$R_{on} = \frac{1}{(250 \times 10^{-6})(5 - 0.75)} = 941\Omega$$

(b) For $V_{IN} = 5V$, the NMOS device is off with $V_{GS} = 0$ and the PMOS transistor is on with $V_{SG} = 5V$. $V_O = 5V$ and $V_{SB} = 0$.

$$R_{on} = \frac{1}{(250 \times 10^{-6})(5 - 0.75)} = 941\Omega$$

4.36 If this PMOS transistor is conducting, then its threshold voltage must be greater than zero and it is a depletion-mode device. The symbol is that of an enhancement-mode device and is incorrect.

4.37

$$V_{TN} = 0.75 + 0.75\left(\sqrt{4 + 0.6} - \sqrt{0.6}\right) = 1.78V$$

$$V_{GS} < V_{TN} \Rightarrow \text{Cutoff region} \ \& \ I_{DS} = 0$$

4.38 For $V_{DS} = 0$, $I_{DS} = \frac{4V}{6.8k\Omega} = 0.588mA$. For $I_{DS} = 0, V_{DS} = 4V$. | $V_{GS} = 4V$. From the graph, the transistor is operating below pinchoff in the linear region.

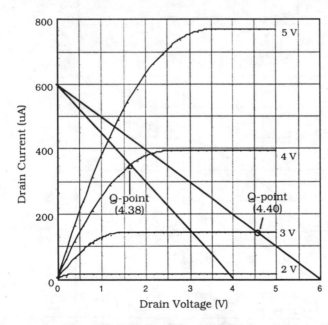

Q-point: (350 µA, 1.7V)

4.39

$$\text{For } V_{SD} = 0, \ I_{SD} = \frac{4V}{2k\Omega} = 2mA. \quad \text{For } I_{SD} = 0, V_{SD} = 4V.$$

$$V_{SG} = V_{TH} = 4V \frac{300k\Omega}{300k\Omega + 100k\Omega} = 3V$$

From the graph, the transistor is operating below pinchoff in the linear region.

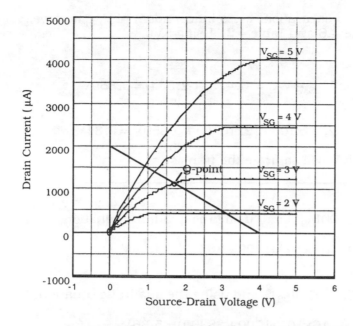

Q-point: (1.15 mA, 1.7V)

4.40 $V_{GS} = \dfrac{V_{DD}}{2} = 3V \mid 6 = 10^4 I_{DS} + V_{DS} \mid V_{DS} = 0, I_{DS} = 0.6mA \mid I_{DS} = 0, V_{DS} = 6V$

See graph for Problem 4.37 -- Q-pt: (150 μA, 4.6V) in saturation region.

4.41 (a) See solution to Problem 4.20(a).

(b) Using KVL, $V_{DS} = 10^7 I_G + V_{GS}$. But, since $I_G = 0$, $V_{GS} = V_{DS}$. Also $V_{IN} = 0.75$ V > 0, so the transistor is saturated by connection.

$$I_{DS} = \frac{K_n'}{2}\frac{W}{L}(V_{GS} - V_{TN})^2 = \left(\frac{25}{2}\frac{\mu A}{V^2}\right)\frac{10}{1}(V_{GS} - 0.75)^2$$

$$V_{GS} = 12 - 330k\Omega(I_{DS} + I_G) - 10M\Omega(I_G) \quad \text{but} \quad I_G = 0$$

$$V_{GS} = 12 - 330k\Omega(I_{DS})$$

$$V_{GS} = 12 - \left(3.30 \times 10^5\right)\left(\frac{2.50 \times 10^{-4}}{2}\frac{A}{V^2}\right)(V_{GS} - 0.75)^2$$

$$41.25 V_{GS}^2 - 60.88 V_{GS} + 11.2 = 0 \quad \text{yields} \quad V_{GS} = 1.26V, \ 0.215V$$

V_{GS} must be 1.26 V since 0.215 V is below threshold.

$$I_{DS} = \left(\frac{25}{2}\frac{\mu A}{V^2}\right)\frac{10}{1}(1.26 - 0.75)^2 = 32.5 \ \mu A \text{ and } V_{DS} = V_{GS}$$

Q-Point: (32.5 μA, 1.26 V)

In the circuit diagram:

$\dfrac{W}{L} = \dfrac{10}{1}$

10 MΩ

+12 V

330 kΩ

I_{DS}

I_G

V_{GS}

V_{DS}

4.42 (a) Since the transistor will remain in saturation, I_{DS} is independent of V_{DS}, and we can use the results already found in Example 4.5. Using KVL,

$$V_{DS} = V_{DD} - I_{DS}R_S \text{ where } V_{DD} \text{ is the supply voltage}$$

For saturation: $V_{DS} \geq V_{GS} - V_{TN} = -2 - (-3) = 1V$

$$V_{DD} - I_{DS}R_S \geq 1V \text{ or } V_{DD} \geq I_{DS}R_S + 1 = 10^{-4}A\left(2 \times 10^4 \Omega\right) + 1V = 3V$$

$V_{DD} \geq 3$ V will saturate the transistor.

(b) Since the transistor will remain in saturation, I_{DS} is independent of V_{DS}, and we can use the results already found in Example 4.6 and Table 4.2. Using KVL,

$$V_{DS} = V_{DD} - I_{DS}R_S$$

For saturation: $V_{DS} \geq V_{GS} - V_{TN} = -1.475 - (-2.334) = 0.859V$

$$V_{DD} - I_{DS}R_S \geq 0.859V$$

$$V_{DD} \geq I_{DS}R_S + 0.859 = 7.38 \times 10^{-5} A(2 \times 10^4 \Omega) + 0.859V = 2.34V$$

$$V_{DD} \geq 2.34 \text{ V will saturate the transistor.}$$

4.43 (a)

$$I_{DS} = \frac{35 \times 10^{-6}}{2}(4 - 1 - 1700I_{DS})^2 \text{ and using the quadratic equation,}$$

$$I_{DS} = 134\mu A. \quad V_{DS} = 10 - 134 \times 10^{-6}(1700 + 38300) = 4.64V$$

(b)

$$I_{DS} = \frac{25 \times 10^{-6}}{2}(4 - 0.75 - 1700I_{DS})^2 \text{ and using the quadratic equation,}$$

$$I_{DS} = 116\mu A. \quad V_{DS} = 10 - 116 \times 10^{-6}(1700 + 38300) = 5.36V$$

4.44

```
*Problem 4.44(a) - Example 4.4
VDD 1 0 10
RD 1 2 75K
RS 4 0 39K
R1 3 0 100K
R2 1 3 150K
M1 2 3 4 4 NMOSFET
.MODEL NMOSFET NMOS KP=25U VTO=1
.OP
.END
```

Q-point: (34.4 µA, 6.08 V) with V_{GS} = 2.66 V - Identical to hand calculations

```
*Problem 4.44(b) - Example 4.5
VDD 1 0 10
RD 1 2 18K
RS 4 0 22K
R1 3 0 150K
R2 1 3 100K
M1 2 3 4 4 NMOSFET
.MODEL NMOSFET NMOS KP=25U VTO=1
.OP
.END
```

Q-point: (99.2 µA, 6.03 V) with V_{GS} = 3.82 V - Almost identical to hand calculations

---

4.45 (a) To start the design we must assume some value for V_{EQ} or for the voltage drop across R_D. One choice of a very large set of possibilities is to set $V_{EQ} = V_{DD}/3 = 4V$.

$$\frac{R_1}{R_1 + R_2}12V = 4V \text{ and } R_1\|R_2 = 250k\Omega \Rightarrow R_2 = 750k\Omega \text{ and } R_1 = 375k\Omega$$

From the table of 5% resistor values in Appendix C, R_2 = 750 kΩ and R_1 = 390 kΩ which yield V_{EQ} = 4.10 V and R_{EQ} = 257 kΩ. For a saturated transistor with I_{DS} = 50 µA,

$$V_{GS} = V_{TN} + \sqrt{\frac{2I_{DS}}{K_n}} = 0.75V + \sqrt{\frac{2(50\mu A)}{25\frac{\mu A}{V^2}}} = 2.75V$$

Checking saturation: $V_{DS} = 4V > V_{GS} - V_{TN} = 2V$ which is OK.

$$R_S = \frac{V_{EQ} - V_{GS}}{I_{DS}} = \frac{4.10 - 2.75}{50x10^{-6}}\frac{V}{A} = 27k\Omega.$$

$R_S = 27$ kΩ is available as a 5% value (sometimes we get lucky).

$$R_D = \frac{V_{R_D}}{I_{DS}} = \frac{V_{DD} - V_{DS} - V_S}{I_{DS}} = \frac{12 - 4.1 - (4 - 2.75)}{50x10^{-6}}\frac{V}{A} = 133 \text{ k}\Omega$$

$R_D = 130$ kΩ is the nearest 5% value. The final design is

$$R_1 = 360 \text{ k}\Omega, R_2 = 750 \text{ k}\Omega, R_D = 130 \text{ k}\Omega, R_S = 27 \text{ k}\Omega$$

for which the Q-point will be (50 μA, 4.15 V).

(b) For the PMOS design, a larger value of V_{SG} will be required since $K_P = 10^{-5}$A:

$$V_{SG} = -V_{TP} + \sqrt{\frac{2I_{SD}}{K_p}} = 0.75V + \sqrt{\frac{2(50\mu A)}{10\frac{\mu A}{V^2}}} = 3.91V$$

If the same value of V_{EQ} were used, only 0.09 V would appear across R_S. A much larger value is desired to achieve a stable bias point.

Assuming a -12V supply, let us increase V_{EQ} to $V_{DD}/2 = $ -6V. Then

$$\frac{R_1}{R_1 + R_2}(-12V) = -6V \text{ and } R_1 \| R_2 = 250k\Omega \Rightarrow R_2 = 500k\Omega \text{ and } R_1 = 500k\Omega.$$

From the table of 5% resistor values, $R_2 = 510$ kΩ and $R_1 = 510$ kΩ which yield $V_{EQ} = $ -6.00 V and $R_{EQ} = 255$ kΩ. R_S is found from

$$R_S = \frac{-V_{EQ} - V_{SG}}{I_{SD}} = \frac{6.00 - 3.91}{50x10^{-6}}\frac{V}{A} = 41.8k\Omega.$$

$R_S = 43$ kΩ is the nearest 5% value, and the actual drain current will be

$$\frac{6 - V_{SG}}{43k\Omega} = \frac{10^{-5}}{2}(V_{SG} - 0.75)^2 \Rightarrow V_{SG} = 3.87 \text{ and } I_{SD} = 49\mu A$$

(The transistor is in saturation: 4V > 3.91 - 0.75 = 3.16 V.)
$R_D = $ is given by

$$R_D = \frac{V_{R_D}}{I_{SD}} = \frac{12 - V_{SD} + V_S}{I_{SD}} = \frac{12 - 4 - (6 - 3.87)}{49x10^{-6}}\frac{V}{A} = 120k\Omega$$

The final design is

$$R_1 = 510 \text{ k}\Omega, R_2 = 510 \text{ k}\Omega, R_D = 120 \text{ k}\Omega, R_S = 43 \text{ k}\Omega$$

for which the Q-point will be (49 μA, 4.01 V).

4.46 (a) Note: A 1 mA drain current is quite large for a device with $K_p = 10$ μA/V^2. This problem may be modified in the second printing.

Assuming saturation and finding $V_{SG} = -V_{TP} + \sqrt{\frac{2I_{DS}}{K_p}} = 0.75 + \sqrt{\frac{2(10^{-3})}{10^{-5}}} = 14.89V$

Device will be in linear region: $V_{SG} + V_{TP} = 14.14V$ and $V_{SD} = 5V$.

Recalculating: $10^{-3} = 10^{-5}\left(V_{SG} - 0.75 - \dfrac{5}{2}\right)5 \rightarrow V_{SG} = 23.25V$

There is not enough voltage available. Design is not possible.

b) The NMOS will also be in the linear region.

$10^{-3} = 2.5 \times 10^{-5}\left(V_{GS} - 0.75 - \dfrac{5}{2}\right)5 \rightarrow V_{GS} = 11.25V$ and the transistor

is indeed in the linear region for $V_{DS} = 5V$. One possible design is given in the figure. R_1 is set to infinity so that $V_G = 15V$. Then

$V_S = 15 - 11.25 = 3.75V$ and $R_S = \dfrac{3.75V}{1mA} = 3.75k\Omega \rightarrow 3.6\ k\Omega$ using

standard resistor values. $R_D = \dfrac{15 - 5 - 3.75}{1mA}V = 6.25k\Omega \rightarrow 6.2\ k\Omega$.

The gate resistor can be almost any value $\geq 100k\Omega$. For example 470 $k\Omega$.

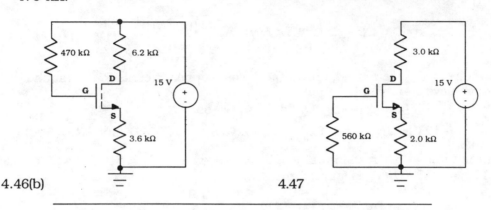

4.46(b)   4.47

4.47 For the depletion-mode device with $V_{GS} < 0$, we only need the 3 resistor bias network with $R_2 = \infty$.

$V_{GS} = -5 + \sqrt{\dfrac{2(0.25mA)}{1mA/V^2}} = -4.293V \mid R_S = -\dfrac{V_{GS}}{I_{DS}} = \dfrac{4.293V}{0.25mA} = 17.2k\Omega \rightarrow 18k\Omega$

$R_D = \dfrac{(15 - 5 - 4.29)V}{0.25mA} = 22.84k\Omega \rightarrow 22k\Omega$

R_1 is arbitrary but would usually be reasonably large - say 560 $k\Omega$.

4.48 Here we may want the four-resistor bias network because $V_{GS} > 0$:

$V_{GS} = -2 + \sqrt{\dfrac{2(2mA)}{0.25mA/V^2}} = +2V \mid$ Setting $V_S = 4V$ yields convenient resistor values:

$R_S = \dfrac{4V}{2mA} = 2k\Omega \quad R_D = \dfrac{(15 - 5 - 4.)V}{2mA} = 3k\Omega$

$V_G = 4 + 2 = 6V \rightarrow \dfrac{R_1}{R_1 + R_2} = \dfrac{6V}{15V} = 0.40 \rightarrow R_1 = 200k\Omega \ R_2 = 300k\Omega$ is convenient.

4.49 (a) Create an M-file:
```
function f=bias(ids)
f=ids-1e-4*((-2e4*ids)-(-3+1*(sqrt(2e4*ids+0.6)-sqrt(0.6))))^2;
```

fzero('bias',1e-4)   yields   ans = 7.3760e-05

(b) Modify the M-file:
    function f=bias(ids)
    f=ids-1e-4*((-2e4*ids)-(-3+**0.75***(sqrt(2e4*ids+0.6)-sqrt(0.6))))^2;

fzero('bias',1e-4)   yields   ans = 7.9155e-05

4.50 Using a spreadsheet similar to Table 4.2 yields: (a) 79.16 µA, (b) 68.96 µA.

4.51 (a)

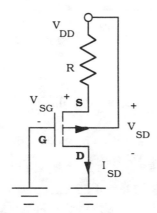

The arrow identifies the transistor as a PMOS device. Since $\gamma = 0$, we do not need to worry about body effect: $V_{TP} = V_{TO}$. Since $V_{SD} = V_{SG}$, and $V_{TP} < 0$, the transistor is saturated.

$$I_{SD} = \frac{K_p'}{2}\frac{W}{L}(V_{SG} + V_{TP})^2 \quad \text{and} \quad V_{SG} = 12 - 10^5 I_{SD}$$

$$V_{SG} = 12 - 10^5 \frac{10^{-5}}{2}\frac{10}{1}(V_{SG} + (-0.75))^2$$

$$5V_{SG}^2 - 6.5V_{SG} - 9.188 = 0 \quad \text{yields} \quad V_{SG} = 2.153V, -0.853V$$

We require $V_{SG} \geq -V_{TP} = +0.75$ V for the transistor to be conducting so
$$V_{SG} = 2.153V$$

$$I_{SD} = \frac{10^{-5}}{2}\frac{10}{1}\frac{A}{V^2}(2.153 + (-0.75))^2 = 98.42 \ \mu A$$

Since $V_{SD} = V_{SG}$, the Q-point is given by: Q-Point = (98.4 µA, 2.15 V) .

(b) Using MATLAB for the second part (Set gamma = 0 for part (a)):

```
function f=bias2(ids)
gamma=1.0;
vsg=12-1e5*ids;
vsb=vsg;
vtp=-0.75-gamma*(sqrt(vsb+0.6)-sqrt(0.6));
f=ids-5e-5*(vsg+vtp)^2;
```

fzero('bias2',1e-4) --> ans = 8.7373e-05 and Q-Point = (87.4 µA, 3.26 V).

4.52

$$V_{GG} = \frac{100k\Omega}{100k\Omega + 220k\Omega} 12V = 3.75V$$

$$3.75 = V_{GS} + 24x10^3 I_{DS} = V_{GS} + 24x10^3 \frac{5}{1} \frac{25x10^{-6}}{2} (V_{GS} - 1)^2$$

$$1.5V_{GS}^2 - 2V_{GS} - 2.25 = 0 \rightarrow V_{GS} = 2.061V \text{ and } I_{DS} = 70.36\mu A$$

$$V_{DS} = 12 - 36x10^3 I_{DS} = 9.467V$$

$$Q - point: \ (70.4\mu A, 9.47V)$$

4.53 (a) Using MATLAB:

```
function f=bias3(ids)
gamma=0.75;
vbs=24e3*ids;
vgs=3.75-vbs;
vtn=1+gamma*(sqrt(vbs+0.6)-sqrt(0.6));
f=ids-62.5e-6*(vgs-vtn)^2;
```

$$fzero('bias3', 1e-5) \rightarrow ans = 5.5863e-05 - 1.1743e-20i$$

$$V_{DS} = 12 - (12k\Omega + 24k\Omega) I_{DS} = 9.989 \ V \ \rightarrow \ Q\text{-Point} = (55.9 \ \mu A, 9.99 \ V).$$

(b) The solution is the same as Problem 4.52 except

$$V_{DS} = 12 - (48k\Omega + 24k\Omega) I_{DS} = 6.934 \ V \ \rightarrow \ Q\text{-Point} = (70.4 \ \mu A, 6.93 \ V).$$

4.54

```
*Problem 4.54(a) - Problem 4.52 Simulation
VDD 1 0 12
R4 1 2 12K
R3 4 0 24K
R1 3 0 100K
R2 1 3 220K
M1 2 3 4 0 NMOSFET W=5U L=1U
.MODEL NMOSFET NMOS KP=25U VTO=1 GAMMA=0
.OP
.END
*Problem 4.54(b) - Problem 4.53(a) Simulation
VDD 1 0 12
R4 1 2 12K
R3 4 0 24K
R1 3 0 100K
R2 1 3 220K
M1 2 3 4 0 NMOSFET W=5U L=1U
.MODEL NMOSFET NMOS KP=25U VTO=1 GAMMA=0.75
.OP
.END
*Problem 4.5c(b) - Problem 4.53(b) Simulation
VDD 1 0 12
R4 1 2 48K
R3 4 0 24K
R1 3 0 100K
R2 1 3 220K
M1 2 3 4 0 NMOSFET W=5U L=1U
.MODEL NMOSFET NMOS KP=25U VTO=1 GAMMA=0
.OP
.END
```

4.55 (a) The transistor is saturated by connection. For this circuit,

$$V_{SG} = -V_{DD} - I_{SD}R = 15 - 75000 I_{SD}$$

$$I_{SD} = \frac{10^{-5}}{2}(15 - 75000 I_{SD} - 0.75)^2 \Rightarrow 124 \ \mu A$$

$$V_{SD} = V_{SG} = 5.70V \ | \ Q\text{-point: } (124\mu A, 5.70V)$$

(b) Here the transistor has $V_{SG} = 15$ V, a large value, so the transistor is most likely operating in the linear region.

$$\frac{15 - V_{SD}}{75000} = 10^{-5}\left(15 - 0.75 - \frac{V_{SD}}{2}\right)V_{SD} \Rightarrow V_{SD} = 1.34V \text{ and } I_{SD} = 182 \ \mu A.$$

Q-point: $(182\mu A, 1.34)$

Checking the region of operation:

$$V_{SD} = 1.34V < V_{SG} + V_{TP} = 15 - 0.75 = 14.25V$$

4.56 (a) Both transistors are saturated by connection and the two drain currents must be equal.

$$I_{DS1} = \frac{K_{n1}}{2}(V_{GS1} - V_{TN1})^2 \quad \text{and} \quad I_{DS2} = \frac{K_{n2}}{2}(V_{GS2} - V_{TN2})^2$$

But since the transistors are identical, $I_{DS1} = I_{DS2}$ requires $V_{GS1} = V_{GS2} = V_{DD}/2 = 2.5V$.

$$I_{DS1} = I_{DS2} = \frac{25 \times 10^{-6}}{2}\frac{10}{1}(2.5 - 1)^2 = 281 \ \mu A$$

(b) For this case, the same arguments hold, and $V_{GS1} = V_{GS2} = V_{DD}/2 = 5V$.

$$I_{DS1} = I_{DS2} = \frac{25 \times 10^{-6}}{2}\frac{10}{1}(5 - 1)^2 = 2.00 \ mA$$

(c) For this case, the the threshold voltages will be different due to the body-effect in the upper transistor. The drain currents must be the same, but the gate-source voltages will be different:

$$V_{GS1} = V_{TN1} + \sqrt{\frac{2I_{DS}}{K_n}} \ ; \ V_{GS2} = V_{TN2} + \sqrt{\frac{2I_{DS}}{K_n}} \ ; \ V_{GS1} + V_{GS2} = 5V.$$

$$V_{TN1} = 1V \quad V_{TN2} = 1 + 0.5\left(\sqrt{V_{GS1} + 0.6} - \sqrt{0.6}\right)$$

Combining these equations yields

$$5 - 2V_{GS1} - 0.5\left(\sqrt{V_{GS1} + 0.6} - \sqrt{0.6}\right) = 0 \Rightarrow V_{GS1} = 2.27V \ ; \ V_{GS2} = 5 - V_{GS1} = 2.73V$$

$$I_{DS2} = I_{DS1} = \frac{25 \times 10^{-6}}{2}\frac{10}{1}(2.27 - 1)^2 = 202 \ \mu A.$$

Checking: $V_{TN2} = 1 + 0.5\left(\sqrt{2.27 + 0.6} - \sqrt{0.6}\right) = 1.46V$

$$I_{DS2} = \frac{25 \times 10^{-6}}{2}\frac{10}{1}(2.73 - 1.46)^2 = 202 \ \mu A.$$

4.57

(a) $I_{SDP} = I_{DSN}$, and both transistors are saturated by connection. $V_{SGP} = 10 - V_{GSN}$

$$\frac{1}{2}\frac{10\mu A}{V^2}\frac{20}{1}(10 - V_{GSN} - 0.75)^2 = \frac{1}{2}\frac{25\mu A}{V^2}\frac{20}{1}(V_{GSN} - 0.75)^2$$

$$(9.25 - V_{GSN}) = \sqrt{2.5}(V_{GSN} - 0.75) \rightarrow V_{GSN} = 4.04V \mid V_{SGP} = 5.96V$$

$$I_{SDP} = I_{DSN} = 2.71 \text{ mA} \mid V_O = V_{GSN} = 4.04V$$

(b) Everything is the same except the currents scale by 80 / 20:

$$I_{SDP} = I_{DSN} = 10.8 \text{ mA}$$

4.58

```
*Problem 4.58(a) - Problem 4.55(a) Simulation
VDD 1 0 -15
R 1 2 75K
M1 2 2 0 0 PMOSFET W=1U L=1U
.MODEL PMOSFET PMOS LEVEL=1 KP=10U VTO=-0.75 GAMMA=0
.OP
.END
*Problem 4.58(b) - Problem 4.55(b) Simulation
VDD 1 0 -15
R 1 2 75K
M1 2 1 0 0 PMOSFET W=1U L=1U
.MODEL PMOSFET PMOS LEVEL=1 KP=10U VTO=-0.75 GAMMA=0
.OP
.END
*Problem 4.58(c-1) - Problem 4.56(a) Simulation
VDD 1 0 5
M1 1 1 2 0 NMOSFET W=10U L=1U
M2 2 2 0 0 NMOSFET W=10U L=1U
.MODEL NMOSFET NMOS LEVEL=1 KP=25U VTO=0.75 GAMMA=0
.OP
.END
*Problem 4.58(c-2) - Problem 4.56(b) Simulation
VDD 1 0 5
M1 1 1 2 0 NMOSFET W=10U L=1U
M2 2 2 0 0 NMOSFET W=10U L=1U
.MODEL NMOSFET NMOS LEVEL=1 KP=25U VTO=0.75 GAMMA=0.5
.OP
.END
*Problem 4.58(d) - Problem 4.57 Simulation
VDD 1 0 10
M1 2 2 1 1 PMOSFET W=20U L=1U
M2 2 2 0 0 NMOSFET W=20U L=1U
.MODEL NMOSFET NMOS LEVEL=1 KP=25U VTO=0.75
.MODEL PMOSFET PMOS LEVEL=1 KP=10U VTO=-0.75
.OP
.END
```

4.59 For (a) and (b), $\gamma = 0$. The transistor parameters are identical so $3V_{GS} = 15V$ or $V_{GS} = 5V$.

$$\text{(a) } I_{DS} = \frac{1}{2}(25\text{x}10^{-6})\frac{20}{1}(5 - 0.75)^2 = 4.52 \text{ mA}$$

$$\text{(b) } I_{DS} = \frac{1}{2}(25\text{x}10^{-6})\frac{50}{1}(5 - 0.75)^2 = 11.3 \text{ mA}$$

(c) Now we have three different threshold voltages and need an iterative solution. Using MATLAB:

```
function f=Prob59(ids)
gamma=0.5;
vgs1=.75+sqrt(2*ids/5e-4);
```

```
vtn2=0.75+gamma*(sqrt(vgs1+0.6)-sqrt(0.6));
vgs2=vtn2+sqrt(2*ids/5e-4);
vtn3=0.75+gamma*(sqrt(vgs1+vgs2+0.6)-sqrt(0.6));
vgs3=vtn3+sqrt(2*ids/5e-4);
f=15-vgs1-vgs2-vgs3;
```

fzero('Prob59',1e-4) --> ans = 0.00325596231933 - 0.00000000000000i

$$I = 3.26 \text{ mA}.$$

4.60

```
*Problem 4.60(a)
VDD 3 0 15
M1 1 1 0 0 NMOSFET W=20U L=1U
M2 2 2 1 0 NMOSFET W=20U L=1U
M3 3 3 2 0 NMOSFET W=20U L=1U
.MODEL NMOSFET NMOS  LEVEL=1 KP=25U VTO=0.75 GAMMA=0
.OP
.END
*Problem 4.60(b)
VDD 3 0 15
M1 1 1 0 0 NMOSFET W=50U L=1U
M2 2 2 1 0 NMOSFET W=50U L=1U
M3 3 3 2 0 NMOSFET W=50U L=1U
.MODEL NMOSFET NMOS  LEVEL=1 KP=25U VTO=0.75 GAMMA=0
.OP
.END
*Problem 4.60(c)
VDD 3 0 15
M1 1 1 0 0 NMOSFET W=20U L=1U
M2 2 2 1 0 NMOSFET W=20U L=1U
M3 3 3 2 0 NMOSFET W=20U L=1U
.MODEL NMOSFET NMOS  LEVEL=1 KP=25U VTO=0.75 GAMMA=0.5
.OP
.END
```

4.61 For (a) and (b), $\gamma = 0$. The transistor parameters are identical so $3V_{SG} = 15V$ or $V_{SG} = 5V$.

$$\text{(a) } I_{SD} = \frac{1}{2}\left(10\text{x}10^{-6}\right)\frac{40}{1}\left(5 - 0.75\right)^2 = 3.61 \text{ mA}$$

$$\text{(b) } I_{SD} = \frac{1}{2}\left(10\text{x}10^{-6}\right)\frac{75}{1}\left(5 - 0.75\right)^2 = 6.77 \text{ mA}$$

(c)   Now we have three different threshold voltages and need an iterative solution. Using MATLAB:

```
function f=Prob61(isd)
gamma=0.5;
vsg1=.75+sqrt(2*isd/4e-4);
vtp2=-0.75-gamma*(sqrt(vsg1+0.6)-sqrt(0.6));
vsg2=-vtp2+sqrt(2*isd/4e-4);
vtp3=-0.75-gamma*(sqrt(vsg1+vsg2+0.6)-sqrt(0.6));
vsg3=-vtp3+sqrt(2*isd/4e-4);
f=15-vsg1-vsg2-vsg3;
```

fzero('Prob61',1e-4) --> ans = 0.00260476985546 + 0.00000000000000i

$$I = 2.60 \text{ mA}.$$

4.62
```
*Problem 4.62(a)
VDD 3 0 15
M1 0 0 1 3 PMOSFET W=40U L=1U
M2 1 1 2 3 PMOSFET W=40U L=1U
M3 2 2 3 3 PMOSFET W=40U L=1U
.MODEL PMOSFET PMOS  LEVEL=1 KP=10U VTO=-0.75 GAMMA=0
.OP
.END
*Problem 4.62(b)
VDD 3 0 15
M1 0 0 1 3 PMOSFET W=75U L=1U
M2 1 1 2 3 PMOSFET W=75U L=1U
M3 2 2 3 3 PMOSFET W=75U L=1U
.MODEL PMOSFET PMOS  LEVEL=1 KP=10U VTO=-0.75 GAMMA=0
.OP
.END
*Problem 4.62(c)
VDD 3 0 15
M1 0 0 1 3 PMOSFET W=40U L=1U
M2 1 1 2 3 PMOSFET W=40U L=1U
M3 2 2 3 3 PMOSFET W=40U L=1U
.MODEL PMOSFET PMOS  LEVEL=1 KP=10U VTO=-0.75 GAMMA=0.5
.OP
.END
```

4.63

(a) $V_{GG} = \dfrac{15V}{2} = 7.5V \mid 7.5 = V_{SG} + 10^5 I_{SD} \mid 7.5 = V_{SG} + 10^5 \left(\dfrac{10^{-5}}{2}\right)\dfrac{20}{1}\left(V_{SG} - 0.75\right)^2$

$10V_{SG}^2 - 14V_{SG} - 1.875 = 0 \rightarrow V_{SG} = 1.523V$ and $I_{SD} = 59.77\mu A$

$V_{SD} = 15 - (100k\Omega + 50k\Omega)I_{SD} = 6.04V \mid Q\text{-point: } (59.78\mu A, 6.04V)$

(b) For saturation, $V_{SD} \geq V_{SG} + V_{TP}$

$15 - (100k\Omega + R)I_{SD} \geq 7.5 - 100k\Omega I_{SD} - 0.75 \rightarrow R \leq 138 \text{ k}\Omega$

4.64

(a) Using MATLAB:
```
function f=bias64(isd)
gamma=0.5;
vbs=1e5*isd;
vsg=7.5-vbs;
vtp=-0.75-gamma*(sqrt(vbs+0.6)-sqrt(0.6));
f=isd-(2e-4/2)*(vsg+vtp)^2;
```

fzero('bias64',4e-5) --> ans = 5.2103e-05 --> I_{SD} = 52.1 µA

$$V_{SD} = 15 - (100k\Omega + R)I_{SD}$$

Note: fzero('bias64',1e-4) converges to the wrong solution

(b) $\quad V_{SD} = 15 - (100k\Omega + R)I_{SD} \geq V_{GS} + V_{TP} = 2.290 - 1.568 = 0.722$ V

$$R \leq 174 \text{ k}\Omega$$

4.65
```
*Problem 4.65
VDD 1 0 15
R1 3 0 510K
R2 1 3 510K
R3 1 4 100K
```

```
R4 2 0 100K
M1 2 3 4 1 PMOSFET W=20U L=1U
.MODEL PMOSFET PMOS LEVEL=1 KP=10U VTO=-0.75 GAMMA=0.5
.OP
.END
```
Answers agree with the previous problem.

4.66 (a) Using MATLAB:
```
function f=bias66(R)
gamma=0.5;
vsb=1e-4*R;
vgs=-vsb;
vtn=-5+gamma*(sqrt(vsb+0.6)-sqrt(0.6));
f=1e-4-(6.25e-4/2)*(vgs-vtn)^2;
```

fzero('bias66',1e4) --> ans = 3.7757e+04- 4.6380e-15i --> R = 37.8 kΩ.

$$V_{DS} = V - V_S \geq V_{GS} - V_{TN}$$

$$V_{GS} = -I_{DS} R = -3.776$$

$$V_{GS} = -I_{DS}R = -3.776V \mid V_{TN} - 5 + 0.5\left(\sqrt{3.766 + 0.6} - \sqrt{0.6}\right) = -4.343V$$

$$V - 3.766 \geq -3.766 - (-4.343) = 4.34 \text{ V.}$$

4.67 (300 kΩ, 700 kΩ) or (1.2 MΩ, 2.8 MΩ). We normally desire the current in the gate bias network to be much less than I_{DS}. We also usually like the parallel combination of R_1 and R_2 to be as large as possible.

4.68 If we assume saturation, we find I_{DS} = 234 µA and V_{DS} = 0.65 V, and the transistor is not saturated. Assuming linear region operation,

$$V_{GS} = 10 - 2 \times 10^4 I_{DS} \mid V_{DS} = 10 - 4 \times 10^4 I_{DS}$$

$$I_{DS} = 25 \frac{\mu A}{V^2} \left(10 - 2 \times 10^4 I_{DS} - 1 - \frac{10 - 4 \times 10^4 I_{DS}}{2} \right) \left(10 - 4 \times 10^4 I_{DS} \right)$$

Collecting terms: $5 \times 10^4 I_{DS} = 10 \rightarrow I_{DS} = 200$ µA

$$V_{DS} = 10 - 4 \times 10^4 \left(2.00 \times 10^{-4} \right) = 2.00V \mid Q\text{-Pt: } (200\mu A, 2.00V)$$

Checking the operating region: $V_{GS} - V_{TN} = 5.00V > V_{DS}$

and the linear region assumption is correct.

4.69 If we assume saturation, we find an inconsistent answer. Assuming linear region operation,

$$V_{GS} = 10 - 2 \times 10^4 I_{DS} \mid V_{DS} = 10 - 3 \times 10^4 I_{DS}$$

$$I_{DS} = 25 \frac{\mu A}{V^2} \frac{1}{1} \left(10 - 2 \times 10^4 I_{DS} - 1 - \frac{10 - 3 \times 10^4 I_{DS}}{2} \right) \left(10 - 3 \times 10^4 I_{DS} \right)$$

Collecting terms: $1.5 \times 10^8 I_{DS}^2 - 2.1 \times 10^5 I_{DS} + 40 = 0 \rightarrow I_{DS} = 227.4 \mu A$

$$V_{DS} = 10 - 3 \times 10^4 \left(2.274 \times 10^{-4} \right) = 3.178V \mid Q\text{-Pt: } (227\mu A, 3.18V)$$

Checking the operating region: $V_{GS} - V_{TN} = 4.452V > V_{DS}$

and the linear region assumption is correct.

4.70

$$V_{SG} = 15 - 10^4 I_{SD} - 15 = -10^4 I_{SD} \mid \text{Assume saturation:}$$

$$I_{SD} = \frac{10 \ \mu A}{2 \ V^2} \frac{10}{1} \left(-10^4 I_{SD} + 4 \right)^2$$

Collecting terms: $10^8 I_{SD}^2 - 10^5 I_{SD} + 16 = 0 \rightarrow I_{DS} = 200.0 \mu A$

$$V_{DS} = 15 - 10^4 I_{SD} = 13.0V \mid Q\text{-Pt:} \ (200\mu A, 13.0V)$$

Checking: $V_{SG} + V_{TP} = -2V + 4 = 2 \mid V_{SD} = 13 \mid$ Saturation is correct.

4.71

$$V_{SG} = -10^4 I_{SD}$$

$$V_{TP} = 4 - 0.25 \left(\sqrt{-V_{SG} + 0.6} - \sqrt{0.6} \right)$$

$$I_{SD} = \frac{10^{-4}}{2} \left(V_{SG} + V_{TP} \right)^2$$

Solving these equations iteratively yields $I_{SD} = 186.8 \ \mu A$

$$V_{DS} = 15 - 10^4 I_{SD} = 13.13V \mid Q\text{-Pt:} \ (187\mu A, 13.1V)$$

4.72

Saturated by connection with $V_{TP} = -1$

$$I_{SD} = \frac{10^{-4}}{2} \left(12 - 3.3 \times 10^5 I_{SD} - 1 \right)^2 \rightarrow 121 - 7.280 \times 10^6 I_{SD} + 1.089 \times 10^{11} I_{SD}^2 = 0$$

$$I_{SD} = 35.9\mu A \mid V_{SD} = 12 - 3.3 \times 10^5 I_{SD} = 0.153V \mid Q\text{-point:} (35.9\mu A, 0.153V)$$

4.73

$$I_{DS} = \frac{(5 - 0.5)V}{100k\Omega} = 45.0\mu A \mid 45.0 \times 10^{-6} = 25 \times 10^{-6} \frac{W}{L} \left(5 - 0.75 - \frac{0.5}{2} \right) 0.5 \mid \frac{W}{L} = \frac{0.900}{1} = \frac{1}{1.11}$$

4.74

$$I_{DS} = \frac{(3.3 - 0.25)V}{150k\Omega} = 20.33\mu A \mid 20.33 \times 10^{-6} = 25 \times 10^{-6} \frac{W}{L} \left(3.3 - 0.75 - \frac{0.25}{2} \right) 0.25 \mid \frac{W}{L} = \frac{1.34}{1}$$

4.75 Note: The following problems are very sensitive to round-off error and are best solved iteratively using MATLAB, a spreadsheet, HP solver, etc. Hand calculations using the quadratic equation will generally yield poor results.

(a) $V_{DS} = 12 - 3.3 \times 10^5 I_{DS} \mid I_{DS} = 25 \times 10^{-6} \frac{10}{1} \left(12 - 0.75 - \frac{V_{DS}}{2} \right) V_{DS}$

$\quad Q\text{-point:} \ (36.32\mu A, 12.92mV)$

(b) $I_{SD} = \frac{10 \times 10^{-6}}{2} \left(\frac{10}{1} \right) \left(12 - 3.3 \times 10^5 I_{SD} - 0.75 \right)^2$

$\quad Q\text{-point:} \ (31.68\mu A, 1.54V)$

(c) $V_{TP} = -0.75 - 0.5 \left(\sqrt{3.3 \times 10^5 I_{SD} + 0.6} - \sqrt{0.6} \right)$

$\quad I_{SD} = \frac{10 \times 10^{-6}}{2} \left(\frac{10}{1} \right) \left(12 - 3.3 \times 10^5 I_{SD} + V_{TP} \right)^2$

$\quad Q\text{-point:} \ (28.22\mu A, 2.69V)$

4.76　(a)

$$C_{ox}^{"} = \frac{\varepsilon_{ox}}{T_{ox}} = \frac{(3.9)\left(8.854\text{x}10^{-14}\,\dfrac{F}{cm}\right)}{5\text{x}10^{-6}\,cm} = 6.906\text{x}10^{-8}\,\frac{F}{cm^2}$$

$$C_{GC} = C_{ox}^{"}WL = \left(6.906\text{x}10^{-8}\,\frac{F}{cm^2}\right)(20\text{x}10^{-4}\,cm)(2\text{x}10^{-4}\,cm) = 27.6\text{ fF}$$

(b)　$C_{ox}^{"} = 1.73\text{ x }10^{-7}\,\dfrac{F}{cm^2}$　|　$C_{GC} = 69.1\text{ fF}$

(c)　$C_{ox}^{"} = 3.45\text{ x }10^{-7}\,\dfrac{F}{cm^2}$　|　$C_{GC} = 138\text{ fF}$

4.77

$$C_{ox}^{"} = \frac{\varepsilon_{ox}}{T_{ox}} = \frac{(3.9)\left(8.854\text{x}10^{-14}\,\dfrac{F}{cm}\right)}{2\text{x}10^{-6}\,cm} = 1.73\text{x}10^{-7}\,\frac{F}{cm^2}$$

$$C_{GC} = C_{ox}^{"}WL = \left(1.73\text{x}10^{-7}\,\frac{F}{cm^2}\right)(5\text{x}10^{-4}\,cm)(5\text{x}10^{-5}\,cm) = 4.32\text{ fF}$$

4.78

$$C_{OL}^{'} = \frac{\varepsilon_{ox}}{T_{ox}}L = \frac{(3.9)\left(8.854\text{x}10^{-14}\,\dfrac{F}{cm}\right)}{20\text{x}10^{-9}\,m\left(10^2\,\dfrac{cm}{m}\right)}10^{-4}\,cm = 17.3\,\frac{pF}{cm}$$

4.79　(a)

$$C_{GS} = C_{GD} = \frac{C_{ox}^{"}WL}{2} + C_{OL}^{'}W = \frac{\left(1.4\text{x}10^{-15}\,\dfrac{F}{\mu m^2}\right)(10\mu m)(1\mu m)}{2} + \left(4\text{x}10^{-15}\,\frac{F}{\mu m}\right)(10\mu m) = 47\text{ fF}$$

(b)
$$C_{GS} = \frac{2}{3}C_{ox}^{"}WL + C_{OL}^{'}W = \frac{2}{3}14\text{fF} + 40\text{fF} = 49\text{ fF}$$

$$C_{GD} = C_{OL}^{'}W = \left(4\text{x}10^{-15}\,\frac{F}{\mu m}\right)(10\mu m) = 40\text{ fF}$$

4.80

$$C_{ox}^{"} = \frac{\varepsilon_{ox}}{T_{ox}} = \frac{(3.9)\left(8.854\text{x}10^{-14}\,\dfrac{F}{cm}\right)}{100\text{x}10^{-9}\,m\left(10^2\,\dfrac{cm}{m}\right)} = 3.453\text{x}10^{-8}\,\frac{F}{cm^2}$$

$$C_{GC} = C_{ox}^{"}WL = \left(3.453\text{x}10^{-8}\,\frac{F}{cm^2}\right)(25\text{x}10^6\,\mu m^2)\left(10^{-4}\,\frac{cm}{\mu m}\right)^2 = 8.63\text{ nF}$$

4.81　(a)
R = 0, $V_{GS} = 0$, $V_{DS} = 5V$, $V_{GS} - V_P = 3 \rightarrow$ Saturation: $I_{DS} = I_{DSS} = 500\mu A$, $V_{DS} = 5V$
Q - point: (500 μA, 5.00 V)

(b) $R = 0$, $V_{GS} = 0$, $V_{DS} = 0.25V$, $V_{GS} - V_P = 3 \rightarrow$ Linear region

$$I_{DS} = \frac{2I_{DSS}}{V_P^2}\left(V_{GS} - V_P - \frac{V_{DS}}{2}\right)V_{DS} = \frac{2(5 \times 10^{-4})}{(-3)^2}\left(0 - (-3) - \frac{0.25}{2}\right)0.25 = 79.86\mu A$$

Q - point: $(79.9\ \mu A, 0.25\ V)$

(c) $I_{DS} = I_{DSS}\left(1 - \frac{V_{GS}}{V_P}\right)^2 = 5 \times 10^{-4}\left(1 - \frac{-8200 I_{DS}}{-3}\right)^2$ | $7.471 \times 10^6 I_{DS}^2 - 7.467 \times 10^3 I_{DS} + 1 = 0$

Using the quadratic equation: $I_{DS} = 159.3\ \mu A$, $840.3\ \mu A \rightarrow I_{DS} = 159\ \mu A$ since $V_P = -3V$.

$V_{DS} = 5 - 8200 I_{DS} = 3.696V$ | Q - point: $(159\ \mu A,\ 3.70\ V)$

Checking saturation: $V_{GS} - V_P = -8200 I_{DS} - (-3) = 1.70V$ | $V_{DS} = 3.70V$ - Ok.

4.82

$$I_{DS} = I_{DSS}\left(1 - \frac{V_{GS}}{V_P}\right)^2 = 5 \times 10^{-3}\left(1 - \frac{-8200 I_{DS}}{-5}\right)^2$$ | $2.689 \times 10^6 I_{DS}^2 - 3.48 \times 10^3 I_{DS} + 1 = 0$

Using the quadratic equation: $I_{DS} = 431\ \mu A$, $863\ \mu A \rightarrow I_{DS} = 431\ \mu A$ since $V_P = -5V$.

$V_{DS} = 10 - 8200 I_{DS} = 6.466V$ | Q - point: $(431\ \mu A,\ 6.47\ V)$

Checking saturation: $V_{GS} - V_P = -8200 I_{DS} - (-5) = 1.47V$ | $V_{DS} = 6.47V$ - Ok.

4.83

$$I_{DS} = \frac{2I_{DSS}}{V_P^2}\left(V_{GS} - V_{TN} - \frac{V_{DS}}{2}\right)V_{DS}$$ | $R_{on} = \dfrac{1}{\dfrac{2I_{DSS}}{V_P^2}(V_{GS} - V_{TN})}$

(a) $R_{on} = \dfrac{1}{2\dfrac{10^{-3}}{(-5)^2}[0 - (-5)]} = 2.50\ k\Omega$ | (b) $R_{on} = \dfrac{1}{2\dfrac{10^{-4}}{(-2)^2}[0 - (-2)]} = 10.0\ k\Omega$

4.84 (a)

$I \le I_{DSS}$ so $I_{DS} = I = 0.500mA$ | $I_G = 0$ | $V_{GS} = V_P\left(1 - \sqrt{\dfrac{I_{DS}}{I_{DSS}}}\right) = -4\left(1 - \sqrt{\dfrac{0.5mA}{1mA}}\right) = -1.17V$

$V_S = -V_{GS} = +1.17\ V$ $I_{DS} = 0.500mA$ $I_G = 0$

(b) Now, $I_{DS} > I_{DSS}$ and the gate diode must become forward biased.

$V_{GS} = V_P\left(1 - \sqrt{\dfrac{I_{DS}}{I_{DSS}}}\right) = -4\left(1 - \sqrt{\dfrac{2mA}{1mA}}\right) = 1.66V$ but the diode will limit this to $0.7V$.

$I_{DS} = 1mA\left(1 - \dfrac{0.7}{-4}\right)^2 = 1.38mA$. The rest of the current will flow in the gate.

$I_{DS} = 1.38\ mA$ $I_G = 0.62\ mA$ $V_S = -0.7\ V$

4.85

(a) $I_{DS1} = \dfrac{2I_{DSS}}{V_P^2}\left(V_{GS1} - V_P - \dfrac{V_{DS1}}{2}\right)V_{DS1} = \dfrac{2(0.2mA)}{(-2)^2}\left(0 - (-2) - \dfrac{V_{DS1}}{2}\right)V_{DS1} = 10^{-4}\left(2 - \dfrac{V_{DS1}}{2}\right)V_{DS1}$

$I_{DS2} = I_{DSS}\left(1 - \dfrac{V_{GS2}}{V_P}\right)^2 = 0.5mA\left(1 - \dfrac{V_{GS2}}{-4}\right)^2 = 0.5mA\left(1 - \dfrac{V_{DS1}}{4}\right)^2$ | $I_{DS1} = I_{DS2}$

$$10^{-4}\left(2 - \frac{V_{DS1}}{2}\right)V_{DS1} = 0.5mA\left(1 - \frac{V_{DS1}}{4}\right)^2 \rightarrow 13V_{DS1}^2 - 72V_{DS1} + 80 = 0$$

$V_{DS1} = 4V, 1.538V \rightarrow V_{DS1} = 1.538V \mid I_{DS1} = 189.3\mu A$

$J_1: (189\mu A, 1.54V) \quad J_2: (189\mu A, 7.46V)$

(b) Require $V_{DS1} \geq V_{GS1} - V_{P1} = 0 - (-2) = 2V$ but $V_{DS1} = 1.54V$ independent of
V for V large enough to pinch off J_2. Thus J_1 cannot be pinched off.

___

4.86

(a) Assume J_1 and J_2 are both saturated:

$$I_{SD1} = I_{DSS}\left(1 + \frac{V_{SG1}}{V_P}\right)^2 = 200\mu A\left(1 - \frac{10^4 I_{SD1}}{2}\right)^2 \rightarrow I_{SD1} = 76.39\mu A \mid V_{SG1} = -0.7639V$$

$$V_{S2} = V_{G2} + V_{SG2} \mid V_{SG2} = V_{SG1} = -0.7639V \mid V_{G2} = \frac{390k\Omega}{390k\Omega + 620k\Omega}15V = 5.79V$$

$V_{S2} = 5.79 - .764 = 5.03V \mid V_{SD1} = (15 - 0.764) - 5.03 = 9.21V \rightarrow J_1$ is saturated

$V_{SD2} = 5.03V$ and $V_{SG2} + V_P = -0.764 + 2 = 1.24V$ so J_2 is also saturated.

$J_1: (76.4\mu A, 9.21V) \quad J_2: (76.4\mu A, 5.03V)$

(b) For saturation of J_2: $V_{G2} \geq V_{SD2} - V_{SG2} = 2V \mid \dfrac{390k\Omega}{390k\Omega + 620k\Omega}V \geq 2V \mid V \geq 5.18V$

___

4.87

(a) Assume saturation: $I_{DS} = I_{DSS}\left(1 - \dfrac{V_{GS}}{V_P}\right)^2 = 250\mu A\left(1 - \dfrac{6 - 10^5 I_{DS}}{-2}\right)^2 \rightarrow I_{DS} = 69.5\mu A$

$$V_{DS} = 6 - 2.2x10^4 I_{DS} - 10^5 I_{DS} - (-6) = 3.52V \mid V_{GS} = -2\left(1 - \sqrt{\frac{69.5\mu A}{250\mu A}}\right) = -0.946V$$

$V_{GS} - V_P = -0.946V + 2 = 1.05V$ and saturation is correct: Q-point $= (69.5\mu A, 3.52V)$

(b) Assume saturation: $I_{SD} = I_{DSS}\left(1 + \dfrac{V_{SG}}{V_P}\right)^2 = 250\mu A\left(1 + \dfrac{6 - 5x10^4 I_{SD}}{2}\right)^2 \rightarrow I_{SD} = 131\mu A$

$$V_{SG} = 2\left(\sqrt{\frac{131\mu A}{250\mu A}} - 1\right) = -0.552V \mid V_{SD} = 6 - 5x10^4 I_{SD} - 1.2x10^4 I_{SD} - (-6) = 3.88V$$

$V_{SG} + V_P = -0.552V + 2 = 1.49V$ and saturation is correct: Q-point $= (131\mu A, 3.88V)$

___

4.88

```
*Problem 4.88
VDD 1 0 6
R1 1 2 22K
J1 2 0 3 JFET1
R2 3 4 100K
VSS 4 0 -6
R3 4 5 12K
J2 5 0 6 JFET2
R4 6 1 50K
.MODEL JFET1 NJF IS=1E-15 BETA=62.5U VTO=-2
*Remember the VTO parameter sign error in the JFET Model
.MODEL JFET2 PJF IS=1E-15 BETA=62.5U VTO=-2
.OP
.END
```

___

4.89

(a) Assume saturation: $I_{DS} = I_{DSS}\left(1 - \dfrac{V_{GS}}{V_P}\right)^2 = 250\mu A\left(1 - \dfrac{6 - 10^5 I_{DS}}{-2}\right)^2 \rightarrow I_{DS} = 69.5\mu A$

$V_{DS} = 6 - 10^5 I_{DS} - (-6) = 5.05V \mid V_{GS} = -2\left(1 - \sqrt{\dfrac{69.5\mu A}{250\mu A}}\right) = -0.946V$

$V_{GS} - V_P = -0.946V + 2 = 1.05V \rightarrow$ Saturation is correct: Q-point $= (69.5\mu A, 5.05V)$

(b) Assume saturation: $I_{DS} = I_{DSS}\left(1 - \dfrac{V_{GS}}{V_P}\right)^2 = 250\mu A\left(1 - \dfrac{6 - 10^4 I_{DS}}{-2}\right)^2$

which yields $I_{DS} = 513.4\mu A, 1.247mA$ Both are greater than I_{DSS}

$V_{GS} = -2\left(1 - \sqrt{\dfrac{513.4\mu A}{250\mu A}}\right) = +0.866V \rightarrow$ Gate diode will turn on

Assume $V_{GS} = 0.7V$: $I_{DS} = 250\mu A\left(1 - \dfrac{0.7}{-2}\right)^2 = 456\mu A \mid I_G = \dfrac{6 - 0.7}{10^4} - 456\mu A = 74.0\mu A$

$V_{DS} = 6 - (-0.7)2 = 6.2V \rightarrow$ Saturation is correct: Q-point $= (456\mu A, 6.2V)$ with gate diode forward biased by $0.7V$.

4.90

(a) For $V_{SG} = 0$, $I_{SD} = I_{DSS} = 500\mu A \mid Q$-point: $(500\mu A, 6.00V)$

(b) Assume saturation: $I_{SD} = I_{DSS}\left(1 + \dfrac{V_{SG}}{V_P}\right)^2 = 500\mu A\left(1 + \dfrac{-10^4 I_{DS}}{3}\right)^2 \rightarrow I_{SD} = 140.8\mu A$

$V_{SG} = 3\left(\sqrt{\dfrac{140.8\mu A}{500\mu A}} - 1\right) = -1.408V \mid V_{SD} = 6 - 10^4 I_{SD} = 4.59V$

$V_{SG} + V_P = -1.408V + 3 = 1.59V$ and saturation is correct: Q-point $= (141\mu A, 4.59V)$

(c) Assume saturation: $I_{SD} = I_{DSS}\left(1 + \dfrac{V_{SG}}{V_P}\right)^2 = 500\mu A\left(1 + \dfrac{-10^5 I_{DS}}{3}\right)^2 \rightarrow I_{SD} = 23.49\mu A$

$V_{SG} = 3\left(\sqrt{\dfrac{23.49\mu A}{500\mu A}} - 1\right) = -2.350V \mid V_{SD} = 6 - 10^5 I_{SD} = 3.65V$

$V_{SG} + V_P = -2.35V + 3 = 0.650V$ and saturation is correct: Q-point $= (23.5\mu A, 3.65V)$

4.91

```
*Problem 4.91
VDD 1 0 DC 9
J2 1 0 2 JFET2
J1 2 0 0 JFET1
.MODEL JFET1 NJF IS=1E-15 BETA=50U VTO=-2
.MODEL JFET2 NJF IS=1E-15 BETA=31.25U VTO=-4
.OP
.END
```
                    Results agree with hand calculations.

---

*Problem 4.92
VDD 1 0 DC 15
R1 1 2 10K
J1 3 1 2 JFET1
J2 0 4 3 JFET1
R2 1 4 620K
R3 4 0 390K
*Remember the VTO parameter sign error in the JFET Model
.MODEL JFET1 PJF IS=1E-15 BETA=50U VTO=-2
.OP
.END

Results agree with hand calculations.

4.93   *Problem 4.93
VDD 1 0 DC 9
J2 1 0 2 JFET2
J1 2 0 0 JFET1
.MODEL JFET1 NJF IS=1E-15 BETA=50U VTO=-2
.MODEL JFET2 NJF IS=1E-15 BETA=31.25U VTO=-4
.DC VDD 0 15 0.1
.PROBE I(VDD)
.END

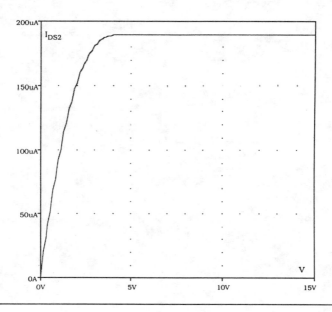

CHAPTER 5

5.1 Base contact = G   collector contact = F emitter contact = D
n-type emitter = E   n-type collector = B   active region = A

5.2

For $V_{BE} > 0$ and $V_{BC} = 0$, $I_C = \beta_F I_B$ or $\beta_F = \dfrac{I_C}{I_B} = \dfrac{275\mu A}{5\mu A} = 55$.

$\beta_R = \dfrac{\alpha_R}{1-\alpha_R} = \dfrac{0.5}{1-0.5} = 1$

$I_C = I_S \exp\left(\dfrac{V_{BE}}{V_T}\right)$ or $I_S = \dfrac{I_C}{\exp\left(\dfrac{V_{BE}}{V_T}\right)} = \dfrac{275\mu A}{\exp\left(\dfrac{0.63}{0.025}\right)} = 3.13$ fA

5.3 Using $\beta = \dfrac{\alpha}{1-\alpha}$ and $\alpha = \dfrac{\beta}{\beta+1}$:

Table P-5.3	
α	β
0.167	**0.200**
0.400	0.667
0.750	3.00
0.909	**10.0**
0.980	49.0
0.995	**200**
0.999	**1000**
0.9998	5000

5.4 (a) For this circuit, $V_{BE} = 0$ V, $V_{BC} = -5$ V and $I = I_C$. Substituting these values into the collector current expression in Eq. (5.13):

$$I_C = I_S\left[\exp(0) - \exp\left(\dfrac{-5}{.025}\right)\right] - \dfrac{I_S}{\beta_R}\left[\exp\left(\dfrac{-5}{.025}\right) - 1\right]$$

$$I = I_C = I_S\left(1 + \dfrac{1}{\beta_R}\right) = 10^{-15}\,A\left(1 + \dfrac{1}{1}\right) = 2 \text{ fA}.$$

(b) For this circuit, the constraints are $V_{BC} = -5$ V and $I_E = 0$. Substituting these values into the emitter current expression in Eq. (5.13):

$$I_E = I_S\left[\exp\left(\frac{V_{BE}}{V_T}\right) - \exp\left(\frac{V_{BC}}{V_T}\right)\right] + \frac{I_S}{\beta_F}\left[\exp\left(\frac{V_{BE}}{V_T}\right) - 1\right] = 0 \quad \text{which gives}$$

$$\exp\left(\frac{V_{BE}}{V_T}\right) = \frac{1}{1+\beta_F} + \frac{\beta_F}{1+\beta_F}\exp\left(\frac{V_{BC}}{V_T}\right). \quad \text{Substituing this result into } I_C:$$

$$I_C = \frac{I_S}{1+\beta_F}\left[1 - \exp\left(\frac{V_{BC}}{V_T}\right)\right] - \frac{I_S}{\beta_R}\left[\exp\left(\frac{V_{BC}}{V_T}\right) - 1\right].$$

For $V_{BC} = -5V$, $I_C = I_S\left[\frac{1}{1+\beta_F} + \frac{1}{\beta_R}\right] = 10^{-15}\,A\left[\frac{1}{101} + \frac{1}{1}\right] = 1.01\ fA$, and

$$V_{BE} = V_T\ln\left(\frac{1}{1+\beta_F}\right) = 0.025V\ln\left(\frac{1}{101}\right) = -0.115\ V \neq 0!$$

5.5

(a) - (c)   (b) npn transistor   (d) $V_{BE} = V_{BC}$

(e) $I_C = -\dfrac{I_S}{\beta_R}\left[\exp\left(\dfrac{V_{BE}}{V_T}\right) - 1\right]$

$$I_E = +\frac{I_S}{\beta_F}\left[\exp\left(\frac{V_{BE}}{V_T}\right) - 1\right] \qquad \frac{I_E}{I_B} = \frac{1}{1+\dfrac{\beta_F}{\beta_R}} \quad \text{and} \quad \frac{I_E}{I_C} = -\frac{\beta_R}{\beta_F}$$

$$I_B = I_S\left(\frac{1}{\beta_F} + \frac{1}{\beta_R}\right)\left[\exp\left(\frac{V_{BE}}{V_T}\right) - 1\right]$$

(f) Using $I_C = -\dfrac{\beta_F}{\beta_R}I_E = -400 I_E$ and $I_B = I_E - I_C = 401\ I_E$

For the circuit $I_B = 150\mu A$

Therefore $I_E = \dfrac{150\mu A}{401} = 0.374\ \mu A$, and $I_C = -149.6\ \mu A$.

$$V_{BC} = V_{BE} = V_T\ln\left(\frac{I_B}{I_S\left(\dfrac{1}{\beta_F} + \dfrac{1}{\beta_R}\right)}\right) = (0.025V)\ln\left(\frac{150\mu A}{2fA\left(\dfrac{1}{100} + \dfrac{1}{0.25}\right)}\right) = 0.591\ V$$

5.6

Using $V_{BC} = 0$ in Eq. 5.13 and recognizing that $i = i_C + i_B = i_E$:

$$i = i_E = I_S\left(1 + \frac{1}{\beta_F}\right)\left[\exp\left(\frac{v_{BE}}{V_T}\right) - 1\right], \text{ and the reverse saturation current}$$

of the diode connected transistor is $I_S' = I_S\left(1 + \dfrac{1}{\beta_F}\right) = (2fA)\left(1 + \dfrac{1}{100}\right) = 2.02\ fA$

5.7

$$i_T = I_S\left[\exp\left(\frac{v_{BE}}{V_T}\right) - \exp\left(\frac{v_{BC}}{V_T}\right)\right] = 10^{-16}A\left[\exp\left(\frac{0.75}{0.025}\right) - \exp\left(\frac{-3}{0.025}\right)\right] = 1.07 \text{ mA}$$

The current is symmetric: For $V_{BC} = 0.75$ V and $V_{BE} = -3$ V, $i_T = -1.07$ mA.

5.8   base contact = A   collector contact = D   emitter contact = B
         p-type emitter = E   p-type collector = F   active region = G

5.9   (a) pnp   (d) Using Eq. (5.17) with $v_{EB} = 0$ and droping the "-1" terms:

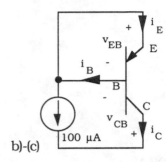

b)-(c)

$$i_C = -I_S\left(1 + \frac{1}{\beta_R}\right)\exp\left(\frac{v_{CB}}{V_T}\right)$$

$$i_E = -I_S \exp\left(\frac{v_{CB}}{V_T}\right)$$

$$i_B = \frac{I_S}{\beta_R}\exp\left(\frac{v_{CB}}{V_T}\right)$$

$$\frac{I_E}{I_C} = \frac{1}{1 + \frac{1}{\beta_R}} = \frac{\beta_R}{\beta_R + 1} = \alpha_R \qquad \frac{I_E}{I_B} = -\beta_R$$

$$I_C = -100\mu A, \quad I_E = \alpha_R I_C = 0.25 I_C = -25.0\mu A$$

$$I_B = -\frac{I_E}{\beta_R} \qquad \beta_R = \frac{\alpha_R}{1 - \alpha_R} = \frac{0.25}{1 - 0.25} = \frac{1}{3} \qquad I_B = +75\mu A$$

$$\beta_F = \frac{\alpha_F}{1 - \alpha_F} = \frac{0.985}{1 - 0.985} = 65.7$$

$$V_{EB} = 0 \quad \text{and} \quad I_E = -I_S \exp\left(\frac{V_{CB}}{V_T}\right)$$

$$V_{CB} = V_T \ln\left(-\frac{I_E}{I_s}\right)$$

$$V_{CB} = 0.025V \ln\left(-\frac{-25\times 10^{-6} A}{10^{-15} A}\right) = 0.599 \text{ V}$$

5.10

Using $V_{CB} = 0$ in Eq. 5.17 and recognizing that $i = i_E$:

$$i = i_E = I_S\left(1 + \frac{1}{\beta_F}\right)\left[\exp\left(\frac{v_{EB}}{V_T}\right) - 1\right],$$ and the reverse saturation current

of the diode connected transistor is $I_S' = I_S\left(1 + \frac{1}{\beta_F}\right) = (2fA)\left(1 + \frac{1}{100}\right) = 2.02$ fA

5.11 (b) pnp transistor

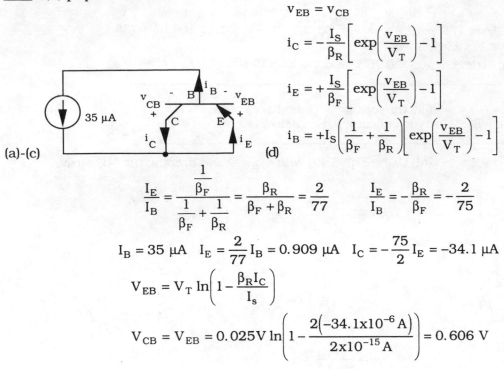

$$v_{EB} = v_{CB}$$

$$i_C = -\frac{I_S}{\beta_R}\left[\exp\left(\frac{v_{EB}}{V_T}\right) - 1\right]$$

$$i_E = +\frac{I_S}{\beta_F}\left[\exp\left(\frac{v_{EB}}{V_T}\right) - 1\right]$$

(d)

$$i_B = +I_S\left(\frac{1}{\beta_F} + \frac{1}{\beta_R}\right)\left[\exp\left(\frac{v_{EB}}{V_T}\right) - 1\right]$$

$$\frac{I_E}{I_B} = \frac{\dfrac{1}{\beta_F}}{\dfrac{1}{\beta_F} + \dfrac{1}{\beta_R}} = \frac{\beta_R}{\beta_F + \beta_R} = \frac{2}{77} \qquad \frac{I_E}{I_B} = -\frac{\beta_R}{\beta_F} = -\frac{2}{75}$$

$$I_B = 35\ \mu A \quad I_E = \frac{2}{77}I_B = 0.909\ \mu A \quad I_C = -\frac{75}{2}I_E = -34.1\ \mu A$$

$$V_{EB} = V_T \ln\left(1 - \frac{\beta_R I_C}{I_s}\right)$$

$$V_{CB} = V_{EB} = 0.025V \ln\left(1 - \frac{2(-34.1\times10^{-6}\,A)}{2\times10^{-15}\,A}\right) = 0.606\ V$$

5.12

Base-Emitter Voltage	Base-Collector Voltage	
	0.7 V	-5.0 V
-5.0 V	Reverse Active	Cutoff
0.7 V	Saturation	Forward Active

5.13

Emitter-Base Voltage	Collector-Base Voltage	
	0.7 V	-0.65 V
0.7 V	Saturation	Forward Active
-0.65 V	Reverse Active	Cutoff

5.14

At $I_C = 5$ mA and $V_{CE} = 5$ V, $I_B = 60\mu A$: $\beta_F = \dfrac{I_C}{I_B} = \dfrac{5mA}{60\mu A} = 83.3$

At $I_C = 7$ mA and $V_{CE} = 7.5$ V, $I_B = 80\mu A$: $\beta_F = \dfrac{I_C}{I_B} = \dfrac{7mA}{80\mu A} = 87.5$

At $I_C = 10$ mA and $V_{CE} = 14$ V, $I_B = 100\mu A$: $\beta_F = \dfrac{I_C}{I_B} = \dfrac{10mA}{100\mu A} = 100$

5.15 (a) The base-emitter junction breaks down with $V_{EB} = 6.3$ V.
$$I_R = \dfrac{5 - 6.3 - (-5)}{1600} \dfrac{V}{\Omega} = 2.31 \text{ mA}$$

(b) The base-emitter junction is forward biased; $V_{BE} = 0.7$ V
$$I_R = \dfrac{5 - 0.7 - (-5)}{24000} \dfrac{V}{\Omega} = 388 \text{ }\mu A$$

(c) $V_{BE} = 0$, and the collector-base junction is reversed biased with $V_{BC} \approx -10V$. The transistor is operating in cutoff.

Using Eq. (5.13), $I_R = I_C = I_S(1-0) - \dfrac{I_S}{\beta_R}(0-1) = I_S\left(1 + \dfrac{1}{\beta_R}\right) \approx 0$

5.16 $V_{CE} = V_{CB} + V_{BE} = V_{CB} + 0.7 \le 60.7$ V

5.17 (a) I_B is forced to be negative by the current source, and the largest negative base current according to the Transport model is

$$I_B = -I_S\left(\dfrac{1}{\beta_F} + \dfrac{1}{\beta_R}\right) = -10^{-15}A\left(\dfrac{1}{50} + \dfrac{1}{0.5}\right) = -2.02 \text{ fA}$$

(b) I_B is forced to be -1 mA by the current source. One or both of the junctions must enter the breakdown region in order to supply this current. For the case of a normal BJT, the base-emitter junction will break down and supply the current since it has the lower reverse breakdown voltage.

5.18

Using Fig. 2.13 with $N = \dfrac{10^{18}}{cm^3}$, $\mu_n = 360 \dfrac{cm^2}{v\text{-}s}$ and $\mu_p = 150 \dfrac{cm^2}{v\text{-}s}$

(a) npn: $\tau_F = \dfrac{W_B^2}{2D_n} = \dfrac{W_B^2}{2V_T\mu_n} = \dfrac{\left(2x10^{-4}cm\right)^2}{2(0.025V)360\dfrac{cm^2}{v\text{-}s}} = 2.22 \text{ ns}$

(b) pnp: $\tau_F = \dfrac{W_B^2}{2D_p} = \dfrac{W_B^2}{2V_T\mu_p} = \dfrac{\left(2x10^{-4}cm\right)^2}{2(0.025V)150\dfrac{cm^2}{v\text{-}s}} = 5.33 \text{ ns}$

5.19

$$C_D = \dfrac{I_C}{V_T}\tau_F = \dfrac{150x10^{-12}}{0.025}I_C = 6x10^{-9}I_C \text{ (F)} \quad \text{(a) } 12 \text{ fF} \quad \text{(b) } 1.2 \text{ pF} \quad \text{(c) } 120 \text{ pF}$$

5.20

$$N_A = \frac{5 \times 10^{18}}{cm^3} \rightarrow \mu_n = 200 \frac{cm^2}{v-s} \text{ using Fig. 2.13.} \quad D_n = \mu_n V_T = 200 \frac{cm^2}{v-s}(0.025V) = 5.00 \frac{cm^2}{s}$$

$$I_S = \frac{qAD_n n_i^2}{N_A W_B} = \frac{1.60 \times 10^{-19} C \left(25 \times 10^{-8} cm^2\right)\left(5.00 \frac{cm^2}{s}\right)\left(\frac{10^{20}}{cm^6}\right)}{\frac{5 \times 10^{18}}{cm^3}\left(0.5 \times 10^{-4} cm\right)} = 8.00 \times 10^{-20} A$$

5.21

$$W_B = \sqrt{2 D_n \tau_F} \quad | \quad \tau_F \le \frac{1}{2\pi f} = \frac{1}{2\pi \left(2 \times 10^9\right)} = 79.6 ps$$

$$N_A = \frac{5 \times 10^{18}}{cm^3} \rightarrow \mu_n = 200 \frac{cm^2}{v-s} \text{ using Fig. 2.13.}$$

$$D_n = \mu_n V_T = 200 \frac{cm^2}{v-s}(0.025V) = 5.00 \frac{cm^2}{s}$$

$$W_B \le \sqrt{2\left(5.00 \frac{cm^2}{s}\right) 79.6 \times 10^{-12} s} = 0.282 \ \mu m$$

5.22

pnp transistor with $V_{EB} = -3V$ and $V_{CB} = -3V \rightarrow$ Cutoff | Using Eq. (5.17):

$$I_C = +\frac{I_S}{\beta_R} = \frac{10^{-15} A}{2} = 0.5 \times 10^{-15} = 0.5 \ fA \quad | \quad I_E = -\frac{I_S}{\beta_F} = \frac{10^{-15} A}{75} = 13.3 \times 10^{-18} = 13.3 \ aA$$

$$I_B = -I_S\left(\frac{1}{\beta_F} + \frac{1}{\beta_R}\right) = 10^{-15} A\left(\frac{1}{75} + \frac{1}{2}\right) = 0.513 \times 10^{-15} = 0.513 \ fA$$

5.23

$$i_C = 10^{-16}\left[\exp\left(\frac{0.3}{0.025}\right) - \exp\left(\frac{-5}{0.025}\right)\right] - \frac{10^{-16}}{1}\left[\exp\left(\frac{-5}{0.025}\right) - 1\right] = 16.3 \ pA$$

$$i_E = 10^{-16}\left[\exp\left(\frac{0.3}{0.025}\right) - \exp\left(\frac{-5}{0.025}\right)\right] + \frac{10^{-16}}{19}\left[\exp\left(\frac{0.3}{0.025}\right) - 1\right] = 17.1 \ pA$$

$$i_B = \frac{10^{-16}}{19}\left[\exp\left(\frac{0.3}{0.025}\right) - 1\right] + \frac{10^{-16}}{1}\left[\exp\left(\frac{-5}{0.025}\right) - 1\right] = 0.857 \ pA$$

These currents are all very small - for most practical purposes it still appears to be cutoff. Since $V_{BE} > 0$ and $V_{BC} < 0$, the transistor is actually operating in the forward-active region. Note that $I_C = \beta_F I_B$.

5.24

npn transistor with $V_{BE} = 0.7V$ and $V_{BC} = -0.7V \rightarrow$ Forward active region

Using Eq. (5.35): $I_E = (\beta_F + 1)I_B \quad | \quad \beta_F = \frac{I_E}{I_B} - 1 = \frac{10mA}{0.2mA} - 1 = 49$

$$I_E = I_S\left(1 + \frac{1}{\beta_F}\right)\exp\left(\frac{V_{BE}}{V_T}\right) \quad | \quad I_S = \frac{0.01A}{\left(1 + \frac{1}{49}\right)\exp\left(\frac{0.7}{0.025}\right)} = 6.78 \times 10^{-15} A = 6.78 \ fA$$

5.25

pnp transistor with $V_{EB} = 0.7V$ and $V_{CB} = -0.7V \Rightarrow$ Forward - active region

Using Eq. (5.17): $\beta_F = \dfrac{I_C}{I_B} = \dfrac{2.5mA}{0.05mA} = 50 \ | \ I_C = I_S \exp\left(\dfrac{V_{EB}}{V_T}\right) \ | \ I_S = \dfrac{2.5mA}{\exp\left(\dfrac{0.7V}{0.025V}\right)} = 1.73 \ fA$

5.26

$$I_E = \frac{-0.7V - (-3.3V)}{47k\Omega} = 55.3\mu A \ | \ I_B = \frac{I_E}{\beta_F + 1} = \frac{55.3\mu A}{91} = 0.608\mu A$$

$$I_C = \beta_F I_B = 90(0.608\mu A) = 54.7\mu A \ | \ \text{Check: } I_B + I_C = I_E \text{ is ok}$$

5.27

(a) $f_\beta = \dfrac{f_T}{\beta_F} = \dfrac{500MHz}{80} = 6.25 \ MHz$

(b) The graph represents the Bode magnitude plot. Thus $\beta(s) = \dfrac{\beta_F}{1 + \dfrac{s}{\omega_\beta}} = \dfrac{\beta_F \omega_\beta}{s + \omega_\beta} = \dfrac{\omega_T}{s + \omega_\beta}$

$$\alpha(s) = \frac{\beta(s)}{\beta(s) + 1} = \frac{\dfrac{\omega_T}{s + \omega_\beta}}{\dfrac{\omega_T}{s + \omega_\beta} + 1} = \frac{\omega_T}{s + \omega_T + \omega_\beta} = \frac{\beta_F \omega_\beta}{s + (\beta_F + 1)\omega_\beta} = \frac{\dfrac{\beta_F}{\beta_F + 1}}{1 + \dfrac{s}{(\beta_F + 1)\omega_\beta}} \approx \frac{\alpha_F}{1 + \dfrac{s}{\omega_T}}$$

$$|\alpha(j\omega)| = \frac{\alpha_F}{\sqrt{1 + \left(\dfrac{\omega}{\omega_T}\right)^2}}$$

5.28

$v_{EB} > 0 \quad v_{CB} < -4V_T$

$$i_C = I_S \exp\left(\frac{V_{EB}}{V_T}\right) + \frac{I_S}{\beta_R} \approx I_S \exp\left(\frac{V_{EB}}{V_T}\right)$$

$$i_E = I_S \exp\left(\frac{V_{EB}}{V_T}\right) + \frac{I_S}{\beta_F} \exp\left(\frac{V_{EB}}{V_T}\right) = \frac{I_S}{\alpha_F} \exp\left(\frac{V_{EB}}{V_T}\right)$$

$$i_B = \frac{I_S}{\beta_F} \exp\left(\frac{V_{EB}}{V_T}\right) - \frac{I_S}{\beta_R} \approx \frac{I_S}{\beta_F} \exp\left(\frac{V_{EB}}{V_T}\right)$$

$$i_C = \beta_F i_B \ | \ i_C = \alpha_F i_E$$

5.29

npn transistor with $V_{BE} = -0.7V$ and $V_{BC} = +0.7V \rightarrow$ Reverse - active region

Using Eq. (5.43): $I_C = -(\beta_R + 1)I_B \ | \ \beta_R = -\dfrac{I_C}{I_B} - 1 = -\dfrac{-75\mu A}{50\mu A} - 1 = 0.5$

$$I_E = -I_S \exp\left(\frac{V_{BC}}{V_T}\right) \ | \ I_S = \frac{25\mu A}{\exp\left(\dfrac{0.7}{0.025}\right)} = 1.73 \times 10^{-17} A = 0.0173 \ fA = 17.3 \ aA$$

5.30

$$i_C = -I_S \exp\left(\frac{V_{CB}}{V_T}\right) - \frac{I_S}{\beta_R} \exp\left(\frac{V_{CB}}{V_T}\right) = -\frac{I_S}{\alpha_R} \exp\left(\frac{V_{CB}}{V_T}\right)$$

$$i_E = -I_S \exp\left(\frac{V_{CB}}{V_T}\right) - \frac{I_S}{\beta_F} \approx -I_S \exp\left(\frac{V_{CB}}{V_T}\right)$$

$$i_B = -\frac{I_S}{\beta_F} + \frac{I_S}{\beta_R} \exp\left(\frac{V_{CB}}{V_T}\right) \approx \frac{I_S}{\beta_R} \exp\left(\frac{V_{CB}}{V_T}\right)$$

$$\beta_R = -\frac{i_E}{i_B} = -\frac{(-0.1\text{mA})}{0.2\text{mA}} = \frac{1}{2} \mid I_S = -\frac{i_E}{\exp\left(\frac{V_{CB}}{V_T}\right)} = -\frac{-10^{-4}\,\text{A}}{\exp\left(\frac{0.7}{0.025}\right)} = 6.91 \times 10^{-17}\,\text{A}$$

5.31

$$I_C = -\frac{-0.7\text{V} - (-3.3\text{V})}{47\text{k}\Omega} = -55.3\ \mu\text{A} \mid I_B = -\frac{I_C}{\beta_R + 1} = -\frac{-55.3\mu\text{A}}{1.75} = 31.6\ \mu\text{A}$$

$$I_E = I_C + I_B = -55.3\mu\text{A} + 31.6\mu\text{A} = -23.7\ \mu\text{A}$$

5.32

$$\beta_{FOR} = \frac{I_C}{I_B} = \frac{1\text{mA}}{1\text{mA}} = 1 \mid V_{CESAT} = V_T \ln\left[\left(\frac{1}{\alpha_R}\right)\frac{1 + \frac{\beta_{FOR}}{(\beta_R+1)}}{1 - \left(\frac{\beta_{FOR}}{\beta_F}\right)}\right] \mid \alpha_R = \frac{\beta_R}{\beta_R+1} = \frac{1}{2}$$

$$V_{CESAT} = 0.025 \ln\left[(2)\frac{1 + \frac{1}{(1+1)}}{1 - \left(\frac{1}{50}\right)}\right] = 28.0\ \text{mV}$$

$$V_{BE} = V_T \ln\left[\frac{I_B + (1-\alpha_R)I_C}{I_S\left(\frac{1}{\beta_F} + 1 - \alpha_R\right)}\right] = (0.025\text{V})\ln\left[\frac{1\text{mA} + (1-0.5)1\text{mA}}{10^{-15}\text{A}(0.02 + 1 - .5)}\right] = 0.717\ \text{V}$$

5.33

$$i_C = I_S \exp\left(\frac{v_{EB}}{V_T}\right) - \frac{I_S}{\alpha_R} \exp\left(\frac{v_{CB}}{V_T}\right) \mid i_B = \frac{I_S}{\beta_F} \exp\left(\frac{v_{EB}}{V_T}\right) + \frac{I_S}{\beta_R} \exp\left(\frac{v_{CB}}{V_T}\right) \mid \text{Simultaneous}$$

solution yields: $v_{EB} = V_T \ln\dfrac{i_B + (1-\alpha_R)i_C}{I_S\left[\dfrac{1}{\beta_F} + (1-\alpha_R)\right]}$ $\bigg|$ $v_{CB} = V_T \ln\dfrac{i_B - \dfrac{i_C}{\beta_F}}{I_S\left[\dfrac{1}{\alpha_R}\right]\left[\dfrac{1}{\beta_F} + (1-\alpha_R)\right]}$

$$v_{ECSAT} = v_{EB} - v_{CB} = V_T \ln\left[\left(\frac{1}{\alpha_R}\right)\frac{1 + \frac{i_C}{(\beta_R+1)i_B}}{1 - \frac{i_C}{\beta_F i_B}}\right] \quad \text{for } i_B > \frac{i_C}{\beta_F}$$

5.34 (a) Substituting $I_C = 0$ in Eq. 5.46 gives

$$V_{CESAT} = V_T \ln\left(\frac{1}{\alpha_R}\right) = (0.025V)\ln\left(\frac{1}{0.5}\right) = 0.0173 \text{ V} = 17.3 \text{ mV}$$

(b) By symmetry

$$V_{ECSAT} = V_T \ln\left(\frac{1}{\alpha_F}\right)$$

or by using $I_E = 0$ and $I_C = -I_B$,

$$V_{CESAT} = V_T \ln\left(\frac{1}{\alpha_R}\right)\frac{1-\dfrac{1}{\beta_R+1}}{1+\dfrac{1}{\beta_F}} = V_T \ln\left(\frac{1}{\alpha_R}\right)\frac{\dfrac{\beta_R}{\beta_R+1}}{\dfrac{\beta_F+1}{\beta_F}} = V_T \ln\left(\frac{1}{\alpha_R}\right)\frac{\alpha_R}{\dfrac{1}{\alpha_F}}$$

$$V_{CESAT} = V_T \ln(\alpha_F) \text{ and } V_{ECSAT} = V_T \ln\left(\frac{1}{\alpha_F}\right)$$

$$V_{ECSAT} = V_T \ln\left(\frac{1}{\alpha_F}\right) = (0.025V)\ln\left(\frac{1}{0.99}\right) = 0.000251 \text{ V} = 0.251 \text{ mV}$$

5.35

(a) $$V_{CESAT} = V_T \ln\left[\left(\frac{1}{\alpha_R}\right)\frac{1+\dfrac{\beta_{FOR}}{(\beta_R+1)}}{1-\left(\dfrac{\beta_{FOR}}{\beta_F}\right)}\right] \mid \alpha_R = \frac{\beta_R}{\beta_R+1} = \frac{0.9}{0.9+1} = 0.4737$$

$$0.1 = 0.025\ln\left[\left(\frac{1}{0.4737}\right)\frac{1+\dfrac{\beta_{FOR}}{(0.9+1)}}{1-\left(\dfrac{\beta_{FOR}}{15}\right)}\right] \rightarrow \beta_{FOR} = 11.05$$

$$0.4737\exp(4) = \frac{1+\dfrac{\beta_{FOR}}{(0.9+1)}}{1-\left(\dfrac{\beta_{FOR}}{15}\right)} \rightarrow \beta_{FOR} = 11.05 \mid I_B = \frac{I_C}{\beta_{FOR}} = \frac{20A}{11.05} = 1.81A$$

(b) $$0.04 = 0.025\ln\left[\left(\frac{1}{0.4737}\right)\frac{1+\dfrac{\beta_{FOR}}{(0.9+1)}}{1-\left(\dfrac{\beta_{FOR}}{15}\right)}\right] \rightarrow \beta_{FOR} = 1.97 \mid I_B = \frac{I_C}{\beta_{FOR}} = \frac{20A}{1.97} = 10.1A$$

5.36 With $V_{BE} = 0.7$ and $V_{BC} = 0.5$, the transistor is technically in the saturation region, but calculating the currents using the transport model in Eq. (5.13) yields

$$i_C = 10^{-16}\left[\exp\left(\frac{0.7}{0.025}\right) - \exp\left(\frac{0.5}{0.025}\right)\right] - \frac{10^{-16}}{1}\left[\exp\left(\frac{0.5}{0.025}\right) - 1\right] = 144.5 \text{ μA}$$

$$i_E = 10^{-16}\left[\exp\left(\frac{0.7}{0.025}\right) - \exp\left(\frac{0.5}{0.025}\right)\right] + \frac{10^{-16}}{39}\left[\exp\left(\frac{0.7}{0.025}\right) - 1\right] = 148.3 \text{ μA}$$

$$i_B = \frac{10^{-16}}{39}\left[\exp\left(\frac{0.7}{0.025}\right) - 1\right] + \frac{10^{-16}}{1}\left[\exp\left(\frac{0.5}{0.025}\right) - 1\right] = 3.757 \text{ μA}$$

At 0.5 V, the collector-base junction is not heavily forward biased compared to the base-emitter junction, and $I_C = 38.5I_B \approx \beta_F I_B$. The transistor still acts as if it is operating in the forward-active region.

(a) The current source will forward bias the base-emitter junction ($V_{BE} = 0.7V$) and the collector base juntion will then be reverse biased ($V_{BC} = -2.3V$). Therefore the npn transistor is in the forward-active region.

$$I_C = \beta_F I_B = I_S \exp\left(\frac{V_{BE}}{V_T}\right) \mid V_{BE} = 0.025 \ln\left(\frac{50\left(250\text{x}10^{-6}\,A\right)}{10^{-16}\,A}\right) = 0.812\ V$$

(b) Since $I_B = 250\mu A$ and $I_C = 0$, $I_C < \beta_F I_B$, and the transistor is saturated.

Using Eq. (5.45): $V_{BE} = 0.025 \ln\dfrac{250\text{x}10^{-6} + 0}{10^{-16}\left[\dfrac{1}{50} + \left(1 - \dfrac{.5}{1.5}\right)\right]} = 0.723\ V$

5.38

(a) $I_C = I_S\left[\exp\left(\dfrac{V_{BE}}{V_T}\right) - 1\right]\left(1 + \dfrac{V_{CE}}{V_A}\right) = 10^{-16}\,A\left[\exp\left(\dfrac{0.72V}{0.025V}\right) - 1\right]\left(1 + \dfrac{10V}{65V}\right) = 371\ \mu A$

(b) $I_C = I_S\left[\exp\left(\dfrac{V_{BE}}{V_T}\right) - 1\right] = 10^{-16}\,A\left[\exp\left(\dfrac{0.72V}{0.025V}\right) - 1\right] = 322\ \mu A$

(c) 1.15:1 (a) is 15% larger than (b) due to the Early effect.

5.39

$$I_C = \beta_F I_B = \beta_{FO}\left(1 + \frac{V_{CE}}{V_A}\right)I_B \mid \beta_{FO}\left(1 + \frac{5}{V_A}\right) = \frac{240\mu A}{3\mu A} \quad \text{and} \quad \beta_{FO}\left(1 + \frac{10}{V_A}\right) = \frac{265\mu A}{3\mu A}$$

$$\frac{\left(1 + \dfrac{10}{V_A}\right)}{\left(1 + \dfrac{5}{V_A}\right)} = \frac{265\mu A}{240\mu A} \Rightarrow V_A = 43.1\ V \mid \beta_{FO} = \frac{80}{\left(1 + \dfrac{5}{43.1}\right)} = 71.7$$

5.40

$$I_C = \beta_F I_B = \beta_{FO}\left(1 + \frac{V_{CE}}{V_A}\right)I_B \quad \text{Need two Q-points from the output characteristics.}$$

For example: (10 mA, 14 V) and (5 mA, 5 V)

$10\text{mA} = \beta_{FO}\left(1 + \dfrac{14}{V_A}\right)0.1\text{mA}$ and $5\text{mA} = \beta_{FO}\left(1 + \dfrac{5}{V_A}\right)0.06\text{mA}$ yields

$100 = \beta_{FO}\left(1 + \dfrac{14}{V_A}\right)$ and $83.3 = \beta_{FO}\left(1 + \dfrac{5}{V_A}\right)$. Solving these two Eqs. yields

$\beta_{FO} = 72.9$ and $V_A = 37.6\ V$.

5.41

Fig. 5.19(a): $I_E = I_C + I_B = \left[\beta_{FO}\left(1 + \dfrac{V_{CE}}{V_A}\right) + 1\right]I_B \approx \left[\beta_{FO}\left(1 + \dfrac{V_{CB} + V_{BE}}{V_A}\right) + 1\right]\dfrac{I_s}{\beta_{FO}}\exp\left(\dfrac{V_{BE}}{V_T}\right)$

$\left[1 + \dfrac{5 + V_{BE}}{50} + \dfrac{1}{19}\right]\left(5\text{x}10^{-15}\right)\exp\left(\dfrac{V_{BE}}{0.025}\right) = 100\mu A \rightarrow V_{BE} = 0.5892V$ by iteration

$$I_B = \frac{100\mu A}{\left[19\left(1 + \frac{5.589}{50}\right) + 1\right]} = 4.52 \ \mu A \ | \ I_C = 19\left(1 + \frac{5.589}{50}\right)I_B = 95.48 \ \mu A$$

For $V_A = \infty$, $I_E = I_s \exp\left(\frac{V_{BE}}{V_T}\right)$ | $V_{BE} = 0.025 \ln \frac{100\mu A}{5fA} = 0.593$ V

Fig. 5.19(b): $I_B = \frac{I_s}{\beta_{FO}} \exp\left(\frac{V_{BE}}{V_T}\right) \rightarrow V_{BE} = 0.025 \ln \frac{19(100\mu A)}{5fA} = 0.667$ V

$$I_C = \beta_{FO}\left(1 + \frac{V_{CE}}{V_A}\right)I_B = 19\left(1 + \frac{5}{50}\right)100\mu A = 2.09 \text{ mA} \ | \ I_E = I_C + I_B = 2.19 \text{ mA}$$

V_{BE} is independent of V_A in the equation above.

5.42

$$I_C = \beta_F I_B \ | \ I_E = (\beta_F + 1)I_B \ | \ \beta_F = \beta_{FO}\left(1 + \frac{V_{CE}}{V_A}\right) = 50\left(1 + \frac{9+0.7}{50}\right) = 59.7$$

$$I_E = \frac{(9-0.7)V}{8200\Omega} = 1.01 \text{ mA} \ | \ I_B = \frac{I_E}{\beta_F + 1} = \frac{1.01mA}{60.7} = 16.7 \ \mu A \ | \ I_C = 59.7I_B = 0.996 \text{ mA}$$

5.43

(a) $V_{TH} = \frac{36k\Omega}{36k\Omega + 68k\Omega}10V = 3.462V$ | $R_{TH} = 36k\Omega\|68k\Omega = 23.54k\Omega$

$I_B = \frac{3.462 - 0.7}{23.54 + (50+1)33} \frac{V}{k\Omega} = 1.618\mu A$ | $I_C = 50I_B = 80.92 \ \mu A$ | $I_E = 51I_B = 82.54 \ \mu A$

$V_{CE} = 10 - 43000I_C - 33000I_E = 3.797V$ | Q-point: $(80.9 \ \mu A, 3.80 \text{ V})$

(b) The pnp circuit is the same. | Q-point: $(80.9 \ \mu A, 3.80 \text{ V})$

(a) $V_{TH} = \frac{7.2k\Omega}{7.2k\Omega + 13.6k\Omega}10V = 3.462V$ | $R_{TH} = 7.2k\Omega\|13.6k\Omega = 4.708k\Omega$

$I_B = \frac{3.462 - 0.7}{4.708 + (50+1)6.6} \frac{V}{k\Omega} = 8.092\mu A$ | $I_C = 50I_B = 404.6\mu A$ | $I_E = 51I_B = 412.7 \ \mu A$

$V_{CE} = 10 - 8600I_C - 6600I_E = 3.7976V$ | Q-point: $(405 \ \mu A, 3.80 \text{ V})$

(b) The pnp circuit is the same. | Q-point: $(405 \ \mu A, 3.80 \text{ V})$

5.44

(a) $V_{TH} = \frac{36k\Omega}{36k\Omega + 68k\Omega}10V = 3.462V$ | $R_{TH} = 36k\Omega\|68k\Omega = 23.54k\Omega$

$I_B = \frac{3.462 - 0.7}{23.54 + (75+1)22} \frac{V}{k\Omega} = 1.629\mu A$ | $I_C = 75I_B = 122.2\mu A$ | $I_E = 76I_B = 123.8\mu A$

$V_{CE} = 10 - 43000I_C - 22000I_E = 2.022V$ | Q-point: $(122\mu A, 2.02V)$

(b) The pnp circuit is the same. | Q-point: $(122\mu A, 2.02V)$

5.45

*Problem 5.45(a)
VCC 1 0 10
R1 3 0 36K
R2 1 3 68K
RC 1 2 43K
RE 4 0 33K

Q1 2 3 4 NPN
.MODEL NPN NPN IS=1E-16 BF=50 BR=0.25
.OP
.END
*Problem 5.45(b)
VCC 1 0 10
R1 3 0 36K
R2 1 3 68K
RC 1 2 43K
RE 4 0 33K
Q1 2 3 4 NPN
.MODEL NPN NPN IS=1E-16 BF=50 BR=0.25 VA=60
.OP
.END
*Problem 5.45(c)
VCC 1 0 10
R1 1 3 36K
R2 3 0 68K
RC 4 0 43K
RE 1 2 33K
Q1 4 3 2 PNP
.MODEL PNP PNP IS=1E-16 BF=50 BR=0.25
.OP
.END
*Problem 5.45(d)
VCC 1 0 10
R1 1 3 36K
R2 3 0 68K
RC 4 0 43K
RE 1 2 33K
Q1 4 3 2 PNP
.MODEL PNP PNP IS=1E-16 BF=50 BR=0.25 VA=60
.OP
.END

5.46

$$V_{BB} = 10\frac{6.2}{6.2+12} = 3.41V \text{ and } R_{BB} = 6.2k\Omega\|12k\Omega = 4.09k\Omega$$

$$I_C = 100\frac{3.41-0.7}{4090+101(7500)} = 0.356mA.$$

$$V_{CE} = 10 - 0.356(5.1) - \frac{101}{100}0.356(7.5) = 5.49V$$

$$Q - po\,int: (0.356 \text{ mA, } 5.49 \text{ V}))$$

5.47

$$V_{BB} = 15\frac{120}{120+240} = 5.00V \text{ and } R_{BB} = 120k\Omega\|240k\Omega = 80k\Omega$$

$$I_C = 100\frac{5.00-0.700}{80000+101(100000)} = 42.2\mu A.$$

$$V_{CE} = 15 - 42.2x10^{-6}(10^5) - \frac{101}{100}42.2x10^{-6}(1.5x10^5) = 4.39V$$

$$Q - po\,int: (42.2 \text{ }\mu A, \text{ } 4.39 \text{ V}))$$

5.48

$$I_E = \frac{I_C}{\alpha_F} = \left(\frac{76}{75}\right)10\mu A = 10.13\mu A \quad | \quad \text{Let } V_{R_C} = V_{R_E} = V_{CE} = 6V$$

$$R_E = \frac{6V}{10.13\mu A} = 592k\Omega \rightarrow 620 \text{ k}\Omega$$

$$R_C = \frac{6V}{10\mu A} = 600k\Omega \rightarrow 620 \text{ k}\Omega \quad | \quad V_B = 6 + 0.7 = 6.7V$$

$$\text{Set } R_1 = \frac{V_B}{10I_B} = \frac{6.7V}{10\left(\frac{10\mu A}{75}\right)} = 5.03M\Omega \rightarrow 5.1 \text{ M}\Omega$$

$$R_2 = \frac{(18 - 6.7)V}{11I_B} = \frac{11.3V}{11\left(\frac{10\mu A}{75}\right)} = 7.71M\Omega \rightarrow 7.5 \text{ M}\Omega$$

(b) $V_{TH} = \dfrac{5.1M\Omega}{5.1M\Omega + 7.5M\Omega}18V = 7.286V \quad | \quad R_{TH} = 5.1M\Omega\|7.5M\Omega = 3.036M\Omega$

$$I_B = \frac{7.286 - 0.7}{3036 + (75+1)620}\frac{V}{k\Omega} = 0.1313\mu A \mid I_C = 75I_B = 9.848\mu A \mid I_E = 76I_B = 9.980\mu A$$

$$V_{CE} = 18 - 620000I_C - 620000I_E = 5.707V \mid Q\text{-point: } (9.85 \text{ }\mu A, 5.71 \text{ V})$$

5.49 (a)

$$I_E = \frac{I_C}{\alpha_F} = \left(\frac{101}{100}\right)1mA = 1.01mA \quad | \quad R_E = \frac{2V}{1.01mA} = 1.98k\Omega \rightarrow 2.0 \text{ k}\Omega$$

$$R_C = \frac{(12 - 5 - 2)V}{1.00mA} = 5k\Omega \rightarrow 5.1 \text{ k}\Omega \quad | \quad V_B = 2 + 0.7 = 2.7V$$

$$\text{Set } R_1 = \frac{V_B}{10I_B} = \frac{2.7V}{10(0.01mA)} = 27k\Omega \rightarrow 27 \text{ k}\Omega$$

$$R_2 = \frac{(12 - 2.7)V}{11I_B} = \frac{9.3V}{11(0.01mA)} = 84.55k\Omega \rightarrow 82 \text{ k}\Omega$$

(b) $V_{TH} = \dfrac{27k\Omega}{27k\Omega + 82k\Omega}12V = 2.972V \quad | \quad R_{TH} = 27k\Omega\|82k\Omega = 20.31k\Omega$

$$I_B = \frac{2.972 - 0.7}{20.31 + (100+1)2}\frac{V}{k\Omega} = 10.22\mu A \mid I_C = 100I_B = 1.022mA \mid I_E = 101I_B = 1.033mA$$

$$V_{CE} = 12 - 5100I_C - 2000I_E = 4.723V \mid Q\text{-point: } (1.02mA, 4.72V)$$

5.50 (a)

$$\text{Choosing } V_{R_4} = V_{R_3} = \frac{V_{CC}}{3} = 5V \quad | \quad I_B = \frac{13mA}{50} = 0.260mA$$

$$I_E = \frac{I_C}{\alpha_F} = \left(\frac{51}{50}\right)13mA = 13.26mA \quad | \quad R_E = \frac{5V}{13.26mA} = 385\Omega \rightarrow 390 \text{ }\Omega$$

$$R_C = \frac{5V}{13.0mA} = 377\Omega \rightarrow 390 \text{ }\Omega \quad | \quad V_{R_1} = 5 + 0.7 = 5.7V$$

$$\text{Set } R_1 = \frac{V_{R_1}}{10I_B} = \frac{5.7V}{10(0.260mA)} = 2.19k\Omega \rightarrow 2.2 \text{ k}\Omega$$

$$R_2 = \frac{(15 - 5.7)V}{11I_B} = \frac{9.3V}{11(0.260mA)} = 3.25k\Omega \rightarrow 3.3 \text{ k}\Omega$$

(b) $V_{TH} = \dfrac{3.3k\Omega}{3.3k\Omega + 2.2k\Omega} 15V = 9.00V$ | $R_{TH} = 2.2k\Omega \| 3.3k\Omega = 1.32k\Omega$

$I_B = \dfrac{15 - 0.7 - 9}{1.32 + (50+1)0.39} \dfrac{V}{k\Omega} = 0.250mA$ | $I_C = 50I_B = 12.5mA$ | $I_E = 51I_B = 12.75mA$

$V_{CE} = 15 - 390I_C - 390I_E = 5.15V$ | Q-point: $(12.5mA, 5.15V)$

5.51 (a)

$I_E = \dfrac{I_C}{\alpha_F} = \left(\dfrac{61}{60}\right)85\mu A = 86.42\mu A$ | $R_E = \dfrac{1V}{86.42\mu A} = 11.57k\Omega \rightarrow 12\ k\Omega$

$R_C = \dfrac{2V}{85\mu A} = 23.53k\Omega \rightarrow 24\ k\Omega$ | $V_{R_1} = 1 + 0.7 = 1.7V$

Set $R_1 = \dfrac{V_{R_1}}{10I_B} = \dfrac{1.7V}{10\left(\dfrac{85\mu A}{60}\right)} = 120k\Omega \rightarrow 120\ k\Omega$

$R_2 = \dfrac{(5 - 1.7)V}{11I_B} = \dfrac{3.3V}{11\left(\dfrac{85\mu A}{60}\right)} = 211.8k\Omega \rightarrow 220\ k\Omega$

(b) $V_{TH} = \dfrac{120k\Omega}{120k\Omega + 220k\Omega} 5V = 1.765V$ | $R_{TH} = 120k\Omega \| 220k\Omega = 77.65k\Omega$

$I_B = \dfrac{1.765 - 0.7}{77.65 + (60+1)12} \dfrac{V}{k\Omega} = 1.315\mu A$ | $I_C = 60I_B = 78.92\mu A$ | $I_E = 61I_B = 80.24\mu A$

$V_{CE} = 5 - 24000I_C - 12000I_E = 2.143V$ | Q-point: $(78.9\ \mu A, 2.14\ V)$

5.52 Modifying Eq. 5.63 for the pnp current mirror:

$I_{C2} = I_{REF} \dfrac{\left[1 + \dfrac{V_{EC2}}{V_A}\right]}{\left[1 + \dfrac{V_{EB}}{V_A} + \dfrac{2}{\beta_{FO}}\right]}$ 　(a) $I = I_{REF} \dfrac{\left[1 + \dfrac{V_{EC2}}{V_A}\right]}{\left[1 + \dfrac{V_{EB}}{V_A} + \dfrac{2}{\beta_{FO}}\right]} = \dfrac{18V - 0.7V}{470k\Omega} \dfrac{1}{\left[1 + \dfrac{2}{20}\right]} = 33.5\ \mu A$

(b) $I = I_{REF} \dfrac{\left[1 + \dfrac{V_{EC2}}{V_A}\right]}{\left[1 + \dfrac{V_{EB}}{V_A} + \dfrac{2}{\beta_{FO}}\right]} = \dfrac{18V - 0.7V}{470k\Omega} \dfrac{\left[1 + \dfrac{18}{35}\right]}{\left[1 + \dfrac{0.7}{35} + \dfrac{2}{20}\right]} = 49.8\ \mu A$

5.53

(a) $I_{E1} = \dfrac{10 - 0.65}{4.7 + 43} \dfrac{V}{k\Omega} = 196\mu A$ | $4700I_{E1} + 0.65 = 9100I_{E2} + 0.65$

$I_{E2} = \dfrac{4700}{9100} I_{E1} = 101\mu A$ | $\beta_{FO} = \infty \rightarrow I = I_{E2} = 101\mu A$

(b) $10 = 4700I_{E1} + 0.65 + 43000(I_{C1} + I_{B1} + I_{B2}) = 4700(51I_{B1}) + 0.65 + 43000\left(51 + \dfrac{I_{B2}}{I_{B1}}\right)I_{B1}$

$4700I_{E1} - 0.65 = 9100I_{E2} - 0.65 \rightarrow \dfrac{I_{E2}}{I_{E1}} = \dfrac{4700}{9100} \rightarrow \dfrac{I_{B2}}{I_{B1}} = \dfrac{4700}{9100}$

$$I_{E1} = 51I_{B1} = 51\frac{10-0.65}{4700(51)+43000(51+0.5165)} = 194.2\mu A \quad | \quad I_{E2} = \frac{4.7}{9.1}I_{E1} = 100.3\mu A$$

$$I = \alpha_F I_{E2} = \frac{50}{51}100.3\mu A = 98.4 \ \mu A$$

5.54 Since the transistor parameters and voltages are the same in magnitude, I_1 and I_2 will be the same

(a) $$I_1 = I_2 = I_{REF}\frac{[1]}{\left[1+\dfrac{2}{\beta_{FO}}\right]} = \frac{12-0.7-0.7}{220k\Omega}\frac{[1]}{\left[1+\dfrac{2}{50}\right]} = 46.3 \ \mu A$$

(b) $$I_1 = I_2 = I_{REF}\frac{\left[1+\dfrac{V_{CE}}{V_A}\right]}{\left[1+\dfrac{V_{BE}}{V_A}+\dfrac{2}{\beta_{FO}}\right]} = \frac{12-1.4}{220k\Omega}\frac{\left[1+\dfrac{12}{50}\right]}{\left[1+\dfrac{0.7}{50}+\dfrac{2}{50}\right]} = 56.7 \ \mu A$$

$$I_{C2} = I_S\left[\exp\left(\frac{V_{BE}}{V_T}\right)\right]\left[1+\frac{V_{CE2}}{V_A}\right] = I_{REF}\frac{\left[1+\dfrac{V_{CE2}}{V_A}\right]}{\left[1+\dfrac{V_{BE}}{V_A}+\dfrac{2}{\beta_{FO}}\right]}$$

5.55

*Problem 5.55   SPICE: I = 45.6 μA
VCC 1 0 18
RREF 2 0 470K
Q1 2 2 1 PNP
Q2 0 2 1 PNP
.MODEL PNP PNP IS=1E-16 BF=50 BR=0.25 VA=60
.OP
.END

$$I = I_{C2} = I_{REF}\frac{\left[1+\dfrac{V_{CE2}}{V_A}\right]}{\left[1+\dfrac{V_{BE1}}{V_A}+\dfrac{2}{\beta_{FO}}\right]} = \frac{18-0.7}{470k\Omega}\frac{\left[1+\dfrac{18}{60}\right]}{\left[1+\dfrac{0.7}{60}+\dfrac{2}{60}\right]} = 45.5 \ \mu A$$

5.56

*Problem 5.56   SPICE: I = 101 μA
VCC 1 0 10
RE1 1 2 4.7K
RREF 3 0 43K
Q1 3 3 2 PNP
RE2 1 4 9.1K
Q2 0 3 4 PNP
.MODEL PNP PNP IS=1E-16 BF=50 BR=0.25 VA=60
.OP
.END

5.57

*Problem 5.57   SPICE: I₁ = 55.1 μA, I₂ = 55.1 μA
VCC 1 0 12
RREF 2 3 220K
Q1 2 2 1 PNP
Q2 0 2 1 PNP
Q3 3 3 0 NPN

```
Q4 1 3 0 NPN
.MODEL NPN NPN IS=1E-16 BF=50 BR=0.25 VA=60
.MODEL PNP PNP IS=1E-16 BF=50 BR=0.25 VA=60
.OP
.END
```

$$I_1 = I_{C2} = I_{REF} \frac{\left[1 + \dfrac{V_{CE2}}{V_A}\right]}{\left[1 + \dfrac{V_{BE1}}{V_A} + \dfrac{2}{\beta_{FO}}\right]} = \frac{12 - 0.7 - 0.7}{220k\Omega} \frac{\left[1 + \dfrac{12}{60}\right]}{\left[1 + \dfrac{0.7}{60} + \dfrac{2}{50}\right]} = 55.0 \ \mu A$$

$I_{C4} = I_{C2}$ - exactly the same equation applies to both the npn and pnp current mirrors.

5.58

$$V_{TH} = \frac{3.3k\Omega}{3.3k\Omega + 7.5k\Omega} 10V = 3.056V \quad | \quad R_{TH} = 7.5k\Omega \| 3.3k\Omega = 2.292k\Omega$$

$$V_{CE} = 10 - 820I_C - 1200I_E \quad | \quad \text{From characteristics at } V_{CE} = 5V: \ \beta_F \approx \frac{5mA}{60\mu A} = 83$$

$$V_{CE} = 10 - 820I_C - 1200\frac{84}{83}I_C = 10 - 2034I_C$$

Load line points: $I_C = 0$, $V_{CE} = 10V$ and $V_{CE} = 0$, $I_C = 4.9mA$

$$I_B = \frac{3.056 - 0.7}{2292 + (83 + 1)1200} = 23\mu A$$

From Graph: Q-point: $(1.9 \ mA, 6.0 \ V)$

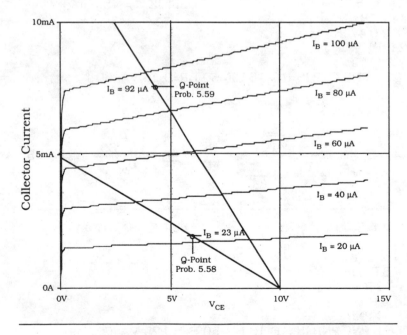

5.59

$$V_{TH} = \frac{6.8k\Omega}{6.8k\Omega + 3.6k\Omega}(10) = 6.538V \quad | \quad R_{TH} = 6.8k\Omega \| 3.6k\Omega = 2.354k\Omega$$

$$V_{EC} = 10 - 420I_C - 330I_E \quad | \quad \text{From characteristics at } V_{EC} = 5V: \ \beta_F \approx \frac{5mA}{60\mu A} = 83$$

$$V_{EC} = 10 - 420I_C - 3300\frac{84}{83}I_C = 10 - 754I_C$$

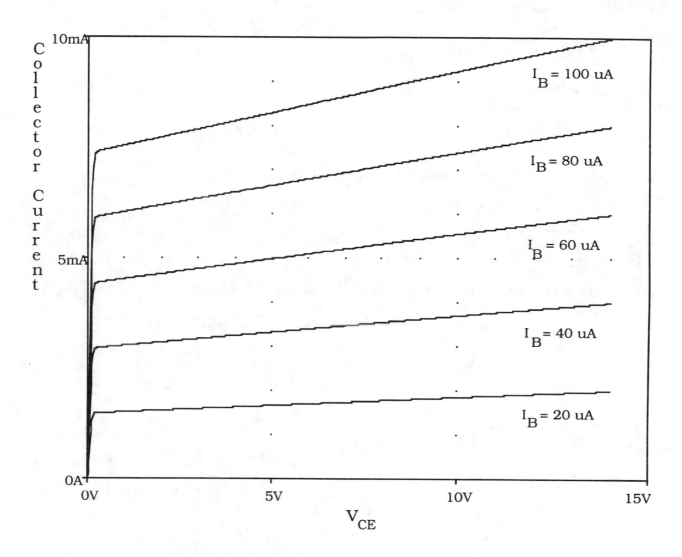

V_{CE} (or V_{EC} for a pnp transistor)

Load line points: $I_C = 0$, $V_{EC} = 10V$ and $V_{EC} = 0$, $I_C = 13.3mA$ – off the graph

$V_{EC} = 5V$, $I_C = 6.63mA$ | $I_B = \dfrac{10 - 0.7 - 6.538}{2354 + (83 + 1)330} = 92\mu A$

From Graph: Q-point: $(7.5\ mA, 4.3\ V)$

5.60 Writing a loop equation starting at the 9 V supply gives:

$$9 = 1500(I_C + I_B) + 10000 I_B + V_{BE}$$

Assuming forward-active region operation, $V_{BE} = 0.7$ V and $I_C = \beta_F I_B$.

$$9 = 1500(\beta_F I_B + I_B) + 10000 I_B + 0.7$$

$$I_B = \frac{9 - 0.7}{1500(\beta_F + 1) + 1000} \quad \text{and} \quad I_C = \beta_F I_B = \frac{\beta_F(9 - 0.7)}{1500(\beta_F + 1) + 1000}$$

(a) $I_C = \dfrac{30(9 - 0.7)V}{1.5k\Omega(30 + 1) + 10k\Omega} = 4.41\ mA$ | $V_{CE} = 9 - 1500 I_E = 2.17V$ | Q-pt: $(4.41mA, 2.17V)$

(b) $I_C = \dfrac{100(9 - 0.7)V}{1.5k\Omega(100 + 1) + 10k\Omega} = 5.14\ mA$ | $V_{CE} = 9 - 1500 I_E = 1.21V$ | Q-pt: $(5.14mA, 1.21V)$

(c) $I_C = \dfrac{250(9 - 0.7)V}{1.5k\Omega(250 + 1) + 10k\Omega} = 5.37\ mA$

$V_{CE} = 9 - 1500 I_E = 0.913V$ | Q-pt: $(5.37mA, 0.913V)$

(d) $I_C = \dfrac{(9 - 0.7)V}{1500\Omega} = 5.53\ mA$ | $V_{CE} = 9 - 1500 I_E = 0.705V$ | Q-pt: $(5.53mA, 0.705V)$

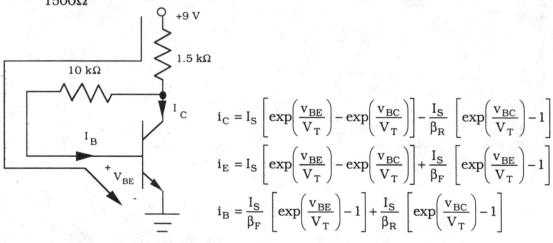

$$i_C = I_S\left[\exp\left(\frac{v_{BE}}{V_T}\right) - \exp\left(\frac{v_{BC}}{V_T}\right)\right] - \frac{I_S}{\beta_R}\left[\exp\left(\frac{v_{BC}}{V_T}\right) - 1\right]$$

$$i_E = I_S\left[\exp\left(\frac{v_{BE}}{V_T}\right) - \exp\left(\frac{v_{BC}}{V_T}\right)\right] + \frac{I_S}{\beta_F}\left[\exp\left(\frac{v_{BE}}{V_T}\right) - 1\right]$$

$$i_B = \frac{I_S}{\beta_F}\left[\exp\left(\frac{v_{BE}}{V_T}\right) - 1\right] + \frac{I_S}{\beta_R}\left[\exp\left(\frac{v_{BC}}{V_T}\right) - 1\right]$$

5.61

$V_{CE} = 9 - (I_C + I_B)1500$ | $V_{CE} = 9 - \left(I_C + \dfrac{I_C}{\beta_F}\right)1500$ | $I_B = \dfrac{V_{CE} - 0.7}{10^4}$

From Fig. P5.14 at 5V: $\beta_F = \dfrac{5mA}{60\mu A} = 83.3$ | $V_{CE} = 9 - 1518 I_C$

$I_C = 0$, $V_{CE} = 9V$ | $V_{CE} = 0$, $I_C = 5.93mA$

$V_{CE} = 0.9V$, $I_B = 20\mu A$ | $V_{CE} = 1.3V$, $I_B = 60\mu A$ | $V_{CE} = 1.7V$, $I_B = 100\mu A$

From graph: Q-point $= (5.0\ mA,\ 1.3\ V)$

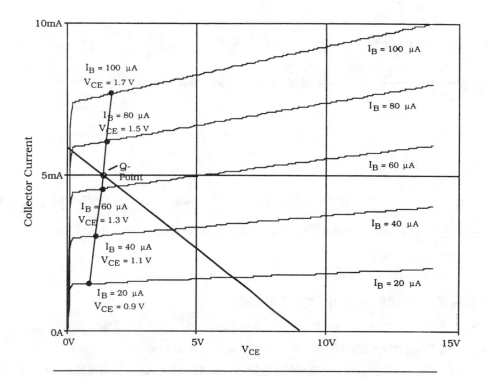

5.62

(a) $V_{EC} = 10 - (I_C + I_B)R_C = 10 - I_E R_C \mid I_E = \dfrac{I_C}{\alpha_F} = \dfrac{\beta_F + 1}{\beta_F}I_C = \dfrac{76}{75}10\text{mA} = 10.13\text{mA}$

$R_C = \dfrac{(10-3)V}{10.13\text{mA}} = 691\Omega \rightarrow 680\ \Omega \mid R_B = \dfrac{V_{EC} - V_{ED}}{I_B} = \dfrac{(3-0.7)V}{0.1333\text{mA}} = 17.3\text{k}\Omega \rightarrow 18\ \text{k}\Omega$

(b) $5 - 0.7 - 18000 I_B - 680(I_C + I_B) - (-5) = 0$

$I_B = \dfrac{10 - 0.7}{18000 + 41(680)}\dfrac{V}{\Omega} = 202.7\mu\text{A} \mid I_C = \beta_F I_B = 8.108\text{mA}$

$V_{EC} = 10V - (8.311\text{mA})680\Omega = 4.35\ V \mid Q\text{-point}:(8.11\ \text{mA},\ 4.35\ V)$

5.63

$V_{CE} = 1.5 - (I_C + I_B)R_C \rightarrow R_C = \dfrac{1.5 - 0.9}{10\mu\text{A} + \dfrac{10\mu\text{A}}{60}} = 59.0\text{k}\Omega \rightarrow 62\ \text{k}\Omega\ \text{or}\ 56\text{k}\Omega$

$R_B = \dfrac{V_{CE} - V_{BE}}{I_B} = \dfrac{0.9 - 0.65}{\dfrac{10\mu\text{A}}{60}} = 1.50\text{M}\Omega \rightarrow 1.5\ \text{M}\Omega$

For $R_C = 56\text{k}\Omega$: $V_{CE} = 1.5 - 56000(I_C + I_B)R_C = 1.5 - 56000(126)I_B \mid I_B = \dfrac{V_{CE} - 0.65}{1.5\text{M}\Omega}$

$V_{CE} = 1.5 - 56000(126)\dfrac{V_{CE} - 0.65}{1.5\text{M}\Omega} \rightarrow V_{CE} = 0.799V$

$I_C = 125 I_B = 125\dfrac{0.799 - 0.65}{1.5\text{M}\Omega} = 12.42\mu\text{A} \mid Q\text{-point}:(12.4\ \mu\text{A},\ 0.799\ V)$

5.64

$$12 = R_C(I_C + I_B) + V_Z + V_{BE} = 500(I_E) + 5.7 \quad | \quad I_E = \frac{12 - 5.7}{500} = 12.6mA$$

$$I_B = \frac{I_E}{\beta_F + 1} = \frac{12.6mA}{101} = 124.8\mu A \quad | \quad I_C = \beta_F I_B = 12.48mA \quad | \quad V_{CE} = 5.70V$$

$$Q\text{-point} = (12.5 \text{ mA}, \ 5.70 \text{ V})$$

5.65

$$I_C = \beta_F I_B = \beta_F \frac{V_{TH} - V_{BE}}{R_{TH} + (\beta_F + 1)R_E} \quad | \quad \text{For } I_C^{min}: V_{CC} = 0.95(15) = 14.25 \text{ V}$$

$$R_1 = 0.95(56k\Omega) = 53.20k\Omega \mid R_2 = 1.05(91k\Omega) = 95.55k\Omega \mid R_E = 1.05(6.8k\Omega) = 7.140k\Omega$$

$$V_{TH} = \frac{53.20}{53.20 + 95.55}14.25V = 5.10V \mid R_{TH} = 53.20k\Omega\|95.55k\Omega = 34.17k\Omega$$

$$I_C^{min} = 100\frac{5.10V - 0.7V}{34.17k\Omega + (101)7.14k\Omega} = 582.5\mu A$$

$$V_{CE}^{max} = 14.25 - I_C^{min}[0.95(6.8k\Omega)] - I_E^{min}7.140k\Omega$$

$$V_{CE}^{max} = 14.25 - 3.760 - 4.201 = 6.286V \quad | \quad Q\text{-point}: (583 \ \mu A, \ 6.29 \text{ V})$$

For I_C^{max}: $V_{CC} = 1.055(15) = 15.75$ V

$$R_1 = 1.05(56k\Omega) = 58.80k\Omega \mid R_2 = 0.95(91k\Omega) = 86.45k\Omega \mid R_E = 0.95(6.8k\Omega) = 6.460k\Omega$$

$$V_{TH} = \frac{58.80}{58.80 + 86.45}15.75V = 6.376V \mid R_{TH} = 58.80k\Omega\|86.45k\Omega = 35.00k\Omega$$

$$I_C^{max} = 100\frac{6.376V - 0.7V}{35.00k\Omega + (101)6.460k\Omega} = 825.6\mu A$$

$$V_{CE}^{min} = 15.75 - I_C^{max}[1.05(6.8k\Omega)] - I_E^{max}6.460k\Omega$$

$$V_{CE}^{min} = 15.75 - 5.895 - 5.387V = 4.469V \quad | \quad Q\text{-point}: (826 \ \mu A, \ 4.47 \text{ V})$$

5.66 Using the Spreadsheet approach in Fig. 5.43 for Fig. 5.36, Eq. set (5.75) becomes:

1. $\quad V_{CC} = 15 \ (1 + 0.1 \ (RAND() - 0.5))$ $\quad | \quad$ 2. $\quad R_1 = 56000 \ (1 + 0.1 \ (RAND() - 0.5))$

3. $\quad R_2 = 91000 \ (1 + 0.1 \ (RAND() - 0.5))$ $\quad | \quad$ 4. $\quad R_E = 6800 \ (1 + 0.1 \ (RAND() - 0.5))$

5. $\quad R_C = 6800 \ (1 + 0.1 \ (RAND() - 0.5))$ $\quad | \quad$ 6. $\quad \beta_F = 100 \ (1 + 0.0(RAND() - 0.5))$

A 100-case Monte Carlo analysis yielded: (Min, Mean, Max, Standard Deviation)

I_C: $(643\mu A, 708\mu A, 787\mu A, 33.1\mu A)$ $\quad V_{CE}$: $(4.44V, 5.36V, 6.07V, 0.348V)$

5.67

$$9 = V_{EC} + (I_C + I_B)(1k\Omega) = V_{EC} + (\beta_F + 1)I_B(1k\Omega) \quad | \quad I_B = \frac{V_{EC} - V_{EB}}{18k\Omega} = \frac{V_{EC} - 0.7}{18k\Omega}$$

Solving for I_C yields:

$$9 = 18k\Omega I_B + 0.7 + (\beta_F + 1)I_B(1k\Omega) \rightarrow I_C = \frac{\beta_F}{\beta_F + 1 + \dfrac{18k\Omega}{1k\Omega}}\frac{9 - 0.7}{1k\Omega}$$

$$I_C^{MAX} = \frac{150}{150 + 1 + \dfrac{18k\Omega(0.95)}{1k\Omega(0.95)}} \frac{9 - 0.7}{1k\Omega(0.95)} = 7.755mA$$

$$V_{EC} = 9 - (151)\frac{7.755mA}{150}(1k\Omega)(0.95) = 1.584V$$

$$I_C^{MIN} = \frac{50}{50 + 1 + \dfrac{18k\Omega(1.05)}{1k\Omega(1.05)}} \frac{9 - 0.7}{1k\Omega(1.05)} = 5.728mA$$

$$V_{EC} = 9 - (51)\frac{5.728mA}{50}(1k\Omega)(1.05) = 2.865V$$

$$9 = V_{EC} + (I_C + I_B)(1k\Omega) = V_{EC} + (\beta_F + 1)I_B(1k\Omega) \quad | \quad I_B = \frac{V_{EC} - V_{EB}}{18k\Omega} = \frac{V_{EC} - 0.7}{18k\Omega}$$

Solving for V_{EC} yields:

$$9 = V_{EC} + (\beta_F + 1)(V_{EC} - 0.7)\frac{1k\Omega}{18k\Omega} \rightarrow V_{EC} = \frac{\dfrac{18k\Omega}{1k\Omega}\left(\dfrac{9}{\beta_F + 1}\right) + 0.7}{1 + \dfrac{18k\Omega}{1k\Omega}\left(\dfrac{1}{\beta_F + 1}\right)}$$

$$V_{EC}^{MAX} = \frac{\dfrac{18k\Omega(1.05)}{1k\Omega(0.95)}\left(\dfrac{9}{51}\right) + 0.7}{1 + \dfrac{18k\Omega(1.05)}{1k\Omega(0.95)}\left(\dfrac{1}{51}\right)} = 3.029V \mid I_C = 50\frac{9 - 3.029}{51(0.95)(1k\Omega)} = 6.162mA$$

$$V_{EC}^{MIN} = \frac{\dfrac{18k\Omega(0.95)}{1k\Omega(1.05)}\left(\dfrac{9}{151}\right) + 0.7}{1 + \dfrac{18k\Omega(0.95)}{1k\Omega(1.05)}\left(\dfrac{1}{151}\right)} = 1.576V \mid I_C = 150\frac{9 - 1.576}{151(1.05)(1k\Omega)} = 7.024mA$$

(b) Using the Spreadsheet approach in Fig. 5.43, the equations become:

1. $V_{CC} = 9\left(1 + 0.0\left(RAND() - 0.5\right)\right)$ | 2. $R_B = 18000\left(1 + 0.1\left(RAND() - 0.5\right)\right)$
3. $R_C = 1000\left(1 + 0.1\left(RAND() - 0.5\right)\right)$ | 4. $\beta_F = 100\left(1 + 1.0(RAND() - 0.5)\right)$

A 100 - case Monte Carlo analysis yielded: (Min, Mean, Max, Standard Deviation)
I_C: $(6.03mA, 6.84mA, 7.55mA, 397\mu A)$ V_{EC}: $(1.53V, 2.08V, 2.94V, 0.346V)$

I_C falls within the worst case limits, but some V_{EC} values actually exceed the worst case limts.

5.68 Repeating the Spreadsheet approach in Fig. 5.43, Eq. set (5.75) becomes:

1. $V_{CC} = 12\left(1 + 0.0\left(RAND() - 0.5\right)\right)$ | 2. $R_1 = 18000\left(1 + 0.1\left(RAND() - 0.5\right)\right)$
3. $R_2 = 36000\left(1 + 0.1\left(RAND() - 0.5\right)\right)$ | 4. $R_E = 16000\left(1 + 0.1\left(RAND() - 0.5\right)\right)$
5. $R_C = 22000\left(1 + 0.1\left(RAND() - 0.5\right)\right)$ | 6. $\beta_F = 100\left(1 + 0.0(RAND() - 0.5)\right)$

A 100 - case Monte Carlo analysis yielded: (Min, Mean, Max, Standard Deviation)
I_C: $(189\mu A, 207\mu A, 228\mu A, 8.24\mu A)$ V_{CE}: $(3.38V, 4.11V, 4.29V, 0.281V)$

5.69

(a) Approximately 22 cases fall outside the interval $[170\mu A, 250\mu A]$: $100\%\dfrac{22}{500} = 4.4\%$ fail

(b) Approximately 151 cases fall inside the interval $[3.2V, 4.8V]$: $100\%\dfrac{500 - 151}{500} = 69.8\%$ fail

---

5.70 Repeating the Spreadsheet approach in Fig. 5.43, Eq. set (5.75) becomes:

1. $V_{CC} = 12\left(1 + 2\,TP\,(RAND() - 0.5)\right)$ | 2. $R_1 = 18000\left(1 + 2\,TR\,(RAND() - 0.5)\right)$

3. $R_2 = 36000\left(1 + 2\,TR\,(RAND() - 0.5)\right)$ | 4. $R_E = 16000\left(1 + 2\,TR\,(RAND() - 0.5)\right)$

5. $R_C = 22000\left(1 + 2\,TR\,(RAND() - 0.5)\right)$ | 6. $\beta_F = 100\left(1 + (RAND() - 0.5)\right)$

10,000 case Monte Carlo runs indicate that the specifications cannot be achieved even with ideal resistors. For TP = 5% and TR = 0%, 18 % of the circuits fail. With TP = 2% and TR = 0%, 1.5% percent fail. The specifications can be met with TP = 1% and TR = 1%.

5.71

$$9 = V_{EC} + (I_C + I_B)(1k\Omega) = V_{EC} + (\beta_F + 1)I_B(1k\Omega) \quad | \quad I_B = \frac{V_{EC} - V_{EB}}{18k\Omega} = \frac{V_{EC} - 0.7}{18k\Omega}$$

Solving for I_C yields:

$$9 = 18k\Omega I_B + 0.7 + (\beta_F + 1)I_B(1k\Omega) \rightarrow I_C = \frac{\beta_F}{\beta_F + 1 + \dfrac{18k\Omega}{1k\Omega}}\frac{9 - 0.7}{1k\Omega}$$

$$I_C^{MAX} = \frac{150}{150 + 1 + \dfrac{18k\Omega(0.8)}{1k\Omega(0.8)}}\frac{9(1.05) - 0.7}{1k\Omega(0.8)} = 9.708mA$$

$$V_{EC} = 9(1.05) - (151)\frac{9.708mA}{150}(1k\Omega)(0.8) = 1.632V$$

$$I_C^{MIN} = \frac{50}{50 + 1 + \dfrac{18k\Omega(1.2)}{1k\Omega(1.2)}}\frac{9(0.95) - 0.7}{1k\Omega(1.2)} = 4.740mA$$

$$V_{EC} = 9(0.95) - (51)\frac{4.740mA}{50}(1k\Omega)(1.2) = 2.748V$$

$$9 = V_{EC} + (I_C + I_B)(1k\Omega) = V_{EC} + (\beta_F + 1)I_B(1k\Omega) \quad | \quad I_B = \frac{V_{EC} - V_{EB}}{18k\Omega} = \frac{V_{EC} - 0.7}{18k\Omega}$$

Solving for V_{EC} yields:

$$9 = V_{EC} + (\beta_F + 1)(V_{EC} - 0.7)\frac{1k\Omega}{18k\Omega} \rightarrow V_{EC} = \frac{\dfrac{18k\Omega}{1k\Omega}\left(\dfrac{9}{\beta_F + 1}\right) + 0.7}{1 + \dfrac{18k\Omega}{1k\Omega}\left(\dfrac{1}{\beta_F + 1}\right)}$$

$$V_{EC}^{MAX} = \frac{\dfrac{18k\Omega(1.2)}{1k\Omega(0.8)}\left(\dfrac{9(1.05)}{51}\right) + 0.7}{1 + \dfrac{18k\Omega(1.2)}{1k\Omega(0.8)}\left(\dfrac{1}{51}\right)} = 3.729V \mid I_C = 50\frac{9(1.05) - 3.729}{51(0.8)(1k\Omega)} = 7.011mA$$

$$V_{EC}^{MIN} = \frac{\dfrac{18k\Omega(0.8)}{1k\Omega(1.2)}\left(\dfrac{9(0.95)}{151}\right)+0.7}{1+\dfrac{18k\Omega(0.8)}{1k\Omega(1.2)}\left(\dfrac{1}{151}\right)} = 1.278V \mid I_C = 150\,\frac{9(0.95)-1.278}{151(1.2)(1k\Omega)} = 6.020mA$$

5.72

$$9 = V_{EC} + (I_C + I_B)(1k\Omega) = V_{EC} + (\beta_F + 1)I_B(1k\Omega) = V_{EC} + \left[\beta_{FO}\left(1+\frac{V_{EC}}{V_A}\right)+1\right]I_B(1k\Omega)$$

$$I_B = \frac{V_{EC} - V_{EB}}{18k\Omega} = \frac{V_{EC}-0.7}{18k\Omega}\qquad \text{Solving for } V_{EC} \text{ yields:}$$

$$V_{EC}^2\,\frac{1}{V_A}\frac{R_C}{R_B} + V_{EC}\left(1+\beta_{FO}\frac{R_C}{R_B}+0.7\frac{R_C}{R_B}\right) - \left[9-0.7(\beta_{FO}+1)\frac{R_C}{R_B}\right] = 0 \quad \text{which can be solved}$$

using the quadratic equation. Then, $I_C = \beta_{FO}\left(1+\dfrac{V_{EC}}{V_A}\right)\dfrac{V_{EC}-0.7}{R_B}$

A 100 - case Monte Carlo analysis yielded: (Min, Mean, Max, Standard Deviation)

V_{EC}: $(1.44V, 2.03V, 3.05V, 0.405V)$ I_C: $(5.61mA, 7.02mA, 8.97mA, 841\mu A)$

5.73

$$V_{TH} = 7 + 100\,\frac{15-7}{7800+100} = 7.101V \mid R_{TH} = 100\Omega\|7800\Omega = 98.73\Omega$$

$$I_B = \frac{20mA}{51} + \frac{V_E}{51(4700\Omega)} = \frac{20mA}{51} + \frac{7.101 - 98.7I_B - V_{BE}}{51(4700\Omega)} \rightarrow I_C = 50I_B = 50\,\frac{101.1 - V_{BE}}{2.398x10^5}$$

$$V_{BE} = 0.025\ln\frac{I_C}{10^{-16}}$$

Using MATLAB: fzero('IC73',.02) ---> ans =0.0209

```
function f=IC73(ic)
vbe=0.025*log(ic/1e-16);
f=ic-50*(101.1-vbe)/2.398e5;
```

$$V_O = 7.101 - 98.7\,\frac{20.9mA}{51} - .025\ln\frac{0.0209}{10^{-16}} = 6.236V$$

5.74

```
*Problem 5.74
VCC 1 0 DC 15
R1 1 2 7.8K
RZ 2 4 100
VZ 4 0 DC 7
Q1 1 2 3 NPN
RE 3 0 4.7K
IL 3 0 20MA
.MODEL NPN NPN IS=1E-16 BF=50 BR=0.25
.OP
.END
```

Output voltage will differ slightly due to different value of V_T.

5.75

$$v_O = 7 - 100i_B - v_{BE} = 7 - 100i_B - V_T \ln \frac{i_C}{I_S} = 7 - 100i_B - V_T \ln \frac{\alpha_F i_L}{I_S}$$

$$v_O = 7 - 100i_B - V_T \ln i_L - V_T \ln \frac{\alpha_F}{I_S}$$

$$R_O = -\frac{dv_O}{di_L} = -\left(-100\Omega \frac{di_B}{di_L} - \frac{V_T}{i_L}\right) = \frac{100\Omega}{51} + \frac{0.025V}{0.02A} = 3.21\Omega$$

5.76

$$i_C = I_S \left[\exp\left(\frac{v_{BE}}{V_T}\right) - 1 - \exp\left(\frac{v_{BC}}{V_T}\right) - (-1) \right] - \frac{I_S}{\beta_R} \left[\exp\left(\frac{v_{BC}}{V_T}\right) - 1 \right]$$

$$i_C = I_S \left[\exp\left(\frac{v_{BE}}{V_T}\right) - 1 \right] - \left(I_S + \frac{I_S}{\beta_R}\right) \left[\exp\left(\frac{v_{BC}}{V_T}\right) - 1 \right] = I_S \left[\exp\left(\frac{v_{BE}}{V_T}\right) - 1 \right] - \frac{I_S}{\alpha_R} \left[\exp\left(\frac{v_{BC}}{V_T}\right) - 1 \right]$$

$$i_C = \alpha_R I_{CS} \left[\exp\left(\frac{v_{BE}}{V_T}\right) - 1 \right] - I_{CS} \left[\exp\left(\frac{v_{BC}}{V_T}\right) - 1 \right] = \alpha_F I_{ES} \left[\exp\left(\frac{v_{BE}}{V_T}\right) - 1 \right] - I_{CS} \left[\exp\left(\frac{v_{BC}}{V_T}\right) - 1 \right]$$

$$i_E = I_S \left[\exp\left(\frac{v_{BE}}{V_T}\right) - 1 - \exp\left(\frac{v_{BC}}{V_T}\right) - (-1) \right] + \frac{I_S}{\beta_F} \left[\exp\left(\frac{v_{BE}}{V_T}\right) - 1 \right]$$

$$i_E = \left(I_S + \frac{I_S}{\beta_F}\right) \left[\exp\left(\frac{v_{BE}}{V_T}\right) - 1 \right] - I_S \left[\exp\left(\frac{v_{BC}}{V_T}\right) - 1 \right] = \frac{I_S}{\alpha_F} \left[\exp\left(\frac{v_{BE}}{V_T}\right) - 1 \right] - I_S \left[\exp\left(\frac{v_{BC}}{V_T}\right) - 1 \right]$$

$$i_E = I_{ES} \left[\exp\left(\frac{v_{BE}}{V_T}\right) - 1 \right] - \alpha_F I_{ES} \left[\exp\left(\frac{v_{BC}}{V_T}\right) - 1 \right] = I_{ES} \left[\exp\left(\frac{v_{BE}}{V_T}\right) - 1 \right] - \alpha_R I_{CS} \left[\exp\left(\frac{v_{BC}}{V_T}\right) - 1 \right]$$

$$i_C = \alpha_F I_{ES} \left[\exp\left(\frac{v_{BE}}{V_T}\right) - 1 \right] - I_{CS} \left[\exp\left(\frac{v_{BC}}{V_T}\right) - 1 \right]$$

$$i_E = I_{ES} \left[\exp\left(\frac{v_{BE}}{V_T}\right) - 1 \right] - \alpha_R I_{CS} \left[\exp\left(\frac{v_{BC}}{V_T}\right) - 1 \right]$$

CHAPTER 6

6.1 (a) $P_{avg} = \dfrac{1W}{10^5 \, gates} = 10 \, \mu W \,/\, gate$ (b) $I = \dfrac{10^{-5} W \,/\, gate}{5V} = 2 \, \mu A \,/\, gate$

6.2

(a) $P_{avg} = \dfrac{40W}{10^7 \, gates} = 4 \, \mu W \,/\, gate$ (b) $I = \dfrac{4 \times 10^{-6} W \,/\, gate}{3.3V} = 1.21 \, \mu A \,/\, gate$

(c) $I_{total} = 1.21 \dfrac{\mu A}{gate} \left(10^7 \, gates\right) = 12.1 \, A$

6.3

(a) $V_{OH} = 5 \, V$ $V_{OL} = 0 \, V$ $P_{V_{OH}} = I^2 R = 0 \, mW$ $P_{V_{OL}} = \left(\dfrac{5-0}{10^5}\right)^2 10^5 = 0.25 \, mW$

(b) $V_{OH} = 3.3 \, V$ $V_{OL} = 0 \, V$ $P_{V_{OH}} = I^2 R = 0 \, mW$ $P_{V_{OL}} = \left(\dfrac{3.3-0}{10^5}\right)^2 10^5 = 0.109 \, mW$

6.4

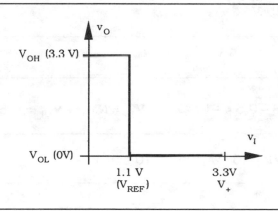

6.5

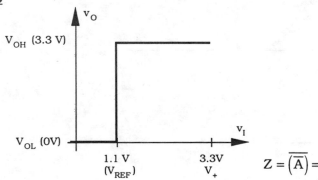

$Z = \left(\overline{\overline{A}}\right) = A$

6.6

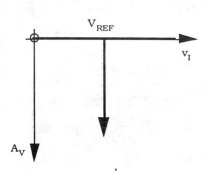

6.7 $V_{OH} = 3 \, V$ $V_{OL} = 0 \, V$ $V_{IH} = 2 \, V$ $V_{IL} = 1 \, V$ $A_V = \dfrac{dv_O}{dv_I} = \dfrac{-3V}{1V} = -3$

6.8

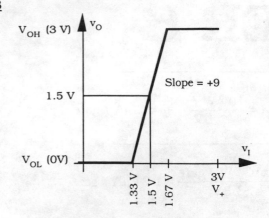

6.9

$$V_{OH} = 5\ V \quad V_{IH} = V_{REF} = 2\ V$$
$$NM_H = 5 - 2 = 3\ V$$
$$V_{IL} = 0\ V \quad V_{IL} = V_{REF} = 2\ V$$
$$NM_L = 2 - 0 = 2\ V$$

6.10 We would like to achieve the highest possible noise margins for both states and have them be symmetrical. Therefore $V_{REF} = 3.3/2 = 1.65\ V$.

6.11

$$V_{OH} = 3.3\ V \quad V_{OL} = 0\ V \quad V_{IH} = 1.8\ V \quad V_{IL} = 1.5\ V$$
$$NM_H = 3.3 - 1.8 = 1.5\ V \quad NM_L = 1.5 - 0 = 1.5\ V$$

6.12 $V_{OH} = 5\ V \quad V_{OL} = 0.25\ V$

6.13 $V_{OH} = -0.80\ V \quad V_{OL} = -1.35\ V$

6.14

$$V_{IH} = V_{OH} - NM_H = -0.8 - 0.5 = -1.3\ V \quad | \quad V_{IL} = NM_L + V_{OL} = 0.5 + (-2) = -1.5\ V$$

6.15 $\tau_P = PDP/P = 10^{-13}J / 10^{-4}W = 10^{-9}\ s = 1\ ns$

6.16

(a) $P_{avg} = \dfrac{1W}{2.5 \times 10^5\ \text{gates}} = 4\ \mu W\ /\ \text{gate}$ (b) $I = \dfrac{4 \times 10^{-6}\ W\ /\ \text{gate}}{5V} = 0.80\ \mu A\ /\ \text{gate}$

(c) $PDP = 2ns(4\ \mu W) = 8\ fJ$

6.17

(a) $P_{avg} = \dfrac{40W}{8 \times 10^6\ \text{gates}} = 5\ \mu W\ /\ \text{gate}$ (b) $I = \dfrac{5\mu W\ /\ \text{gate}}{3.3V} = 1.5\ \mu A\ /\ \text{gate}$

(c) $PDP = 1ns\ (5\mu W) = 5\ fJ$

6.18

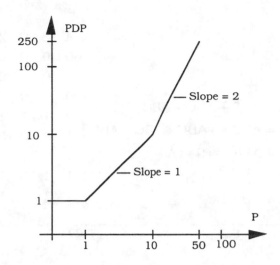

6.19

(a) $v(t) = i(t)R + v_C(t)$ | $i(t) = C\dfrac{dv_c(t)}{dt}$ | $v(t) = RC\dfrac{dv_c(t)}{dt} + v_C(t)$ | $v(t) = 1$ for $t \geq 0$

$v(t) = 1 - \exp\left(-\dfrac{t}{RC}\right)$ | $0.9 = 1 - \exp\left(-\dfrac{t_{90\%}}{RC}\right) \rightarrow t_{90\%} = -RC\ln(0.1)$

$0.1 = 1 - \exp\left(-\dfrac{t_{10\%}}{RC}\right) \rightarrow t_{10\%} = -RC\ln(0.9)$ | $t_r = t_{90\%} - t_{10\%} = RC\ln(9) = 2.20RC$

(b) $v(t) = 0$ $v_C(0) = 1$ $v(t) = \exp\left(-\dfrac{t}{RC}\right)$ | $0.9 = \exp\left(-\dfrac{t_{90\%}}{RC}\right) \rightarrow t_{90\%} = -RC\ln(0.9)$

$0.1 = \exp\left(-\dfrac{t_{10\%}}{RC}\right) \rightarrow t_{10\%} = -RC\ln(0.1)$ | $t_f = t_{10\%} - t_{90\%} = RC\ln(9) = 2.20RC$

6.20

(a) $V_{OH} = 5V$ $V_{OL} = 0.25V$

(b) $V_{10\%} = V_{OL} + 0.1\Delta V = 0.25 + 0.475 = 0.725V \rightarrow t_{10\%} \approx 22$ ns for v_O

$V_{90\%} = V_{OL} + 0.9\Delta V = 0.25 + 4.275 = 4.525V \rightarrow t_{90\%} \approx 33$ ns for $v_O \rightarrow t_r = 33 - 22 = 11$ ns

For fall time: $t_{10\%} \approx 2.5$ ns for v_O $t_{90\%} \approx 0.8$ ns for $v_O \rightarrow t_f = 1.7$ ns

For v_I, $t_{10\%} \approx 0$ ns $t_{90\%} \approx 1$ ns $t_r = 1$ ns | $t_f \approx 1$ ns

(c) $\tau_{PHL} \approx 1.5ns - 0.5ns = 1$ ns | $\tau_{PLH} \approx 26ns - 21ns = 5$ ns   (d) $\tau_P = \dfrac{1+5}{2}$ ns $= 3$ ns

---

6.21

(a) $V_{OH} = -0.78V$ $V_{OL} = -1.36V$

(b) $V_{10\%} = V_{OL} + 0.1\Delta V = -1.36 + 0.1(0.58) = -1.30V \rightarrow t_{10\%} \approx 32.5$ ns for v_O

$V_{90\%} = V_{OL} + 0.9\Delta V = -1.36 + 0.9(0.58) = -0.84V \rightarrow t_{90\%} \approx 42$ ns for v_O

$t_r = 42 - 32.5 = 9.5$ ns

For fall time: $t_{10\%} \approx 11.5$ ns for v_O $t_{90\%} \approx 2$ ns for $v_O \rightarrow t_f = 9.5$ ns

For v_I, $t_{10\%} \approx 0$ ns $t_{90\%} \approx 1$ ns $t_r = 1$ ns | $t_f \approx 1$ ns

(c) $V_{50\%} = \dfrac{-0.78 - 1.36}{2} = -1.07V$ | $\tau_{PHL} \approx 4$ ns | $\tau_{PLH} \approx 4$ ns   (d) $\tau_P = \dfrac{4+4}{2}$ ns $= 4$ ns

6.22

$(A + B)(A + C)$

$AA + AC + BA + BC$

$A + AC + BA + BC$

$A(1 + C) + AB + BC$

$A + AB + BC$

$A(1 + B) + BC$

$A + BC$

6.23

$Z = AB\overline{C} + ABC + \overline{A}BC$

$Z = AB\overline{C} + + ABC + ABC + \overline{A}BC$

$Z = AB(\overline{C} + C) + (A + \overline{A})BC$

$Z = AB(1) + (1)BC$

$Z = AB + BC$

6.24

A	B	C	Z
0	0	0	0
0	0	1	0
0	1	0	0
0	1	1	1
1	0	0	0
1	0	1	0
1	1	0	1
1	1	1	1

$Z=AB+BC$

6.25

$Z = \overline{A}\overline{B}C + ABC + \overline{A}BC + A\overline{B}C$

$Z = C(\overline{A}\overline{B} + AB + \overline{A}B + A\overline{B})$

$Z = C(\overline{A}\overline{B} + \overline{A}B + AB + A\overline{B})$

$Z = C(\overline{A}(\overline{B} + B) + A(B + \overline{B}))$

$Z = C(\overline{A}(1) + A(1))$

$Z = C(\overline{A} + A)$

$Z = C(1)$

$Z = C$

6.26

A	B	C	Z
0	0	0	0
0	0	1	1
0	1	0	0
0	1	1	1
1	0	0	0
1	0	1	1
1	1	0	0
1	1	1	1

$Z = C$

6.27

A	B	C	D	Z
0	0	0	0	0
0	0	0	1	0
0	0	1	0	0
0	0	1	1	0
0	1	0	0	0
0	1	0	1	0
0	1	1	0	0
0	1	1	1	0
1	0	0	0	0
1	0	0	1	0
1	0	1	0	0
1	0	1	1	0
1	1	0	0	0
1	1	0	1	0
1	1	1	0	0
1	1	1	1	1

$Z = \overline{\overline{AB} + \overline{CD}}$

$Z = (\overline{\overline{AB}})(\overline{\overline{CD}})$

$Z = ABCD$

6.28

A	B	C	Z_1	Z_2
0	0	0	0	1
0	0	1	0	1
0	1	0	0	0
0	1	1	0	1
1	0	0	0	0
1	0	1	0	1
1	1	0	1	1
1	1	1	1	1

$Z_1 = \overline{\overline{AB}} = AB$

$Z_2 = \overline{AB} + C$

6.29   (a) Fanout = 2   (b) Fanout = 1

6.30   (a) Diode AND; Z=ABC   (b) Diode OR; Z=A+B+C

6.31   (a) Diode AND; Z=AB   (b) Diode OR; Z=A+B

6.32

(a) $I_B = \dfrac{3.3 - 0.6 - 0.7}{10000} = 200$ μA $\mid$ $I_C = \dfrac{3.3 - 0.05}{3000} = 1.083$ mA

The transistor is saturated since $I_B > \dfrac{I_C}{\beta_F} = 54.2$ μA (b) $I = \dfrac{3.3 - 0.6}{10000} = 270$ μA

(c) $P = VI = 3.3V(0.200mA + 1.083mA) = 4.23$ mW

(d) $P = VI = 3.3V(0.270mA) = 0.891$ mW

6.33

$I_B = \dfrac{3.3 - 0.6 - 0.7}{30000} = 66.67$ μA $\mid$ $I_C = \dfrac{3.3 - 0.05}{3000} = 1.083$ mA

The transistor is saturated for $\beta_F > \dfrac{I_C}{I_B} = \dfrac{1.083 \text{ mA}}{0.06667 \text{mA}} = 16.2$

6.34

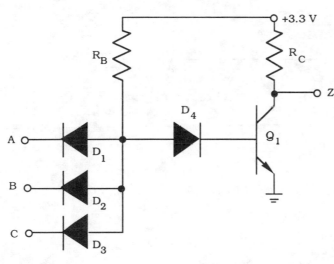

6.35

$$Z = \overline{(AB)C} = \overline{ABC}$$

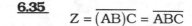

6.36 Each diode causes a voltage level loss of 0.75V. Therefore, $0.75n \le 2.5$ V and $n \le 3$.

6.37 $V_{REF} > 4(0.7V) = 2.8$ V

6.38

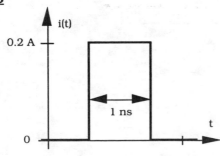

For each line: $i = C\dfrac{dv}{dt}$

$i = 40 \times 10^{-12} F \dfrac{5V}{10^{-9} s} = 200mA = 0.2A$

For all 64 lines, $I = 64(0.2A) = 12.8$ A !

6.39

$$C = 3\left(\frac{\varepsilon_{ox}A}{t_{ox}}\right) = 3\frac{3.9\varepsilon_o LW}{t_{ox}} = 3\frac{3.9\left(8.854\times10^{-14}\frac{F}{cm}\right)\left(\frac{7.5mm}{2}\frac{0.1cm}{mm}\right)(1.5\mu m)}{1\mu m} = 0.583 \text{ pF}$$

6.40

$$\Delta T = \frac{C\Delta V}{I} = \frac{KC_{ox}''WL\Delta V}{\frac{1}{2}\mu_n C_{ox}''\left(\frac{W}{L}\right)(V_{GS}-V_{TN})^2} \quad | \quad \text{Let } W' = \alpha W \text{ and } L' = \alpha L$$

$$\Delta T' = \frac{C'\Delta V'}{I'} = \frac{K(\alpha W)(\alpha L)(\alpha\Delta V)}{\frac{1}{2}\mu_n\left(\frac{\alpha W}{\alpha L}\right)(\alpha V_{GS}-\alpha V_{TN})^2} = \alpha\Delta T$$

$$P = VI = \frac{V}{2}\mu_n C_{ox}''\left(\frac{W}{L}\right)(V_{GS}-V_{TN})^2 = \frac{V}{2}\mu_n\frac{\varepsilon_{ox}}{T_{ox}}\left(\frac{W}{L}\right)(V_{GS}-V_{TN})^2$$

$$P' = \frac{\alpha V}{2}\mu_n\frac{\varepsilon_{ox}}{\alpha T_{ox}}\left(\frac{\alpha W}{\alpha L}\right)(\alpha V_{GS}-\alpha V_{TN})^2 = \alpha^2 P$$

$$PDP' = P'\Delta T' = (\alpha\Delta T)\alpha^2 P = \alpha^3 P\Delta T = \alpha^3 \text{ PDP}$$

$$\text{Power density} = \frac{P}{A} = \frac{P}{WL} \quad | \quad \frac{P'}{A'} = \frac{\alpha^2 P}{\alpha W(\alpha L)} = \frac{P}{A}$$

6.41

(a) $I_{DS} = \frac{1}{2}\mu_n C_{ox}''\left(\frac{W}{L}\right)(V_{GS}-V_{TN})^2 = \frac{1}{2}\mu_n\frac{\varepsilon_{ox}}{T_{ox}}\left(\frac{W}{L}\right)(V_{GS}-V_{TN})^2$

$$I'_{DS} = \frac{1}{2}\mu_n\frac{\varepsilon_{ox}}{T_{ox}}\left(\frac{\frac{W}{2}}{\frac{L}{2}}\right)(V_{GS}-V_{TN})^2 = 2I_{DS}$$

(b) $P' = V(2I) = 2VI = 2P$ - The power has increased by a factor of two.

(c) $C_G = C_{ox}''WL = \frac{\varepsilon_{ox}}{T_{ox}}WL \quad | \quad C'_G = \frac{\varepsilon_{ox}}{\frac{T_{ox}}{2}}\frac{W}{2}\frac{L}{2} = \frac{C_G}{2}$

The capacitance has decreased by a factor of two.

(d) $\Delta T' = \frac{C'\Delta V'}{I'} = \frac{K\left(\frac{W}{2}\right)\left(\frac{L}{2}\right)(\Delta V)}{\frac{1}{2}\mu_n\left(\frac{\frac{W}{2}}{\frac{L}{2}}\right)(V_{GS}-V_{TN})^2} = \frac{\Delta T}{4}$

CHAPTER 7

7.1

(a) $P_{avg} = \dfrac{1W}{0.5(10^5 \text{gates})} = 20\ \mu W\ /\ \text{gate}$ (b) $I = \dfrac{20\mu W\ /\ \text{gate}}{5V} = 4\ \mu A\ /\ \text{gate}$

7.2

(a) $P_{avg} = \dfrac{20W}{\left(\dfrac{2}{3}\right)5 \times 10^6\ \text{gates}} = 6\ \mu W\ /\ \text{gate}$ (b) $I = \dfrac{6\mu W\ /\ \text{gate}}{3.3V} = 1.82\ \mu A\ /\ \text{gate}$

7.3

$$K_n' = \mu_n C_{ox}'' = \mu_n \frac{\varepsilon_{ox}}{T_{ox}} = \mu_n \frac{3.9\varepsilon_o}{T_{ox}} = \left(500\frac{cm^2}{V-sec}\right)\frac{3.9(8.854 \times 10^{-14} F\ /\ cm)}{20 \times 10^{-9} m(100cm\ /\ m)} = 86.3\frac{\mu A}{V^2}$$

$$K_p' = \mu_p C_{ox}'' = \mu_p \frac{\varepsilon_{ox}}{T_{ox}} = \mu_p \frac{3.9\varepsilon_o}{T_{ox}} = \left(200\frac{cm^2}{V-sec}\right)\frac{3.9(8.854 \times 10^{-14} F\ /\ cm)}{20 \times 10^{-9} m(100cm\ /\ m)} = 34.5\frac{\mu A}{V^2}$$

7.4

For M_S off, $I_{DS} = 0$ and $V_{OH} = 5V$.

For V_{OL}, $I_{DS} = \dfrac{5 - V_{OL}}{200k\Omega} = K_n\left(V_{OH} - V_{TN} - \dfrac{V_{OL}}{2}\right)V_{OL}$ | $K_n = \left(\dfrac{3}{1}\right)\left(25\dfrac{\mu A}{V^2}\right) = 75\dfrac{\mu A}{V^2}$

$5 - V_{OL} = (2 \times 10^5)\left(75\dfrac{\mu A}{V^2}\right)\left(5 - 1 - \dfrac{V_{OL}}{2}\right)V_{OL} \rightarrow 7.5V_{OL}^2 - 61V_{OL} + 5 = 0$

$V_{OL} = 0.0828\ V$ | Checking: $I_{DS} = \dfrac{5 - 0.0828}{200k\Omega} = 24.6\ \mu A$ and

$I_{DS} = 75\dfrac{\mu A}{V^2}\left(5 - 1 - \dfrac{0.0828}{2}\right)0.0828 = 24.6\ \mu A$ | $P = 5V(24.6\ \mu A) = 123\ \mu W$

7.5

From Problem 7.4, $V_{OH} = 5V$ and $V_{OL} = 0.0828V$

$V_{IL} = V_{TN} + \dfrac{1}{K_n R} = 1V + \dfrac{1}{\left(3 \times 25\dfrac{\mu A}{V^2}\right)(200k\Omega)} = 1 + \dfrac{1}{15} = 1.067\ V$

$V_{IH} = V_{TN} - \dfrac{1}{K_n R} + 1.63\sqrt{\dfrac{V_{DD}}{K_n R}} = 1 - \dfrac{1}{15} + 1.63\sqrt{\dfrac{5}{15}} = 1.874V$

$NM_L = 1.067 - 0.0828 = 0.984\ V$ | $NM_H = 5 - 1.874 = 3.13\ V$

7.6

$I_{DS} = \dfrac{P}{V_{DD}} = \dfrac{0.25mW}{5V} = 50\mu A$ | $R = \dfrac{V_{DD} - V_{OL}}{I_{DS}} = \dfrac{5 - 0.5}{5 \times 10^{-5}} = 90.0\ k\Omega$

$50\mu A = (25 \times 10^{-6})\left(\dfrac{W}{L}\right)_S\left(5 - 1 - \dfrac{0.5}{2}\right)0.5 \rightarrow \left(\dfrac{W}{L}\right)_S = \dfrac{1.067}{1}$

$$V_{OH} = 5V \mid V_{OL} = 0.5V$$

$$V_{IL} = V_{TN} + \frac{1}{K_n R} = 1V + \frac{1}{\left(1.067 \times 25 \frac{\mu A}{V^2}\right)(90 k\Omega)} = 1 + \frac{1}{2.401} = 1.417 \text{ V}$$

$$V_{IH} = V_{TN} - \frac{1}{K_n R} + 1.63\sqrt{\frac{V_{DD}}{K_n R}} = 1 - \frac{1}{2.401} + 1.63\sqrt{\frac{5}{2.401}} = 2.936V$$

$$NM_L = 1.417 - 0.5 = 0.917 \text{ V} \mid NM_H = 5 - 2.936 = 2.064 \text{ V}$$

7.7

(a) $I_{DS} = \dfrac{P}{V_{DD}} = \dfrac{0.25mW}{3.3V} = 75.76\mu A \mid R = \dfrac{V_{DD} - V_{OL}}{I_{DS}} = \dfrac{3.3 - 0.25}{75.76 \times 10^{-6}} = 40.3 \text{ k}\Omega$

$$75.76 \times 10^{-6} = \left(25 \times 10^{-6}\right)\left(\frac{W}{L}\right)_S\left(3.3 - 0.7 - \frac{0.25}{2}\right)0.25 \rightarrow \left(\frac{W}{L}\right)_S = \frac{4.90}{1}$$

(b) $V_{OH} = 3.3V \mid V_{OL} = 0.25V$

$$V_{IL} = V_{TN} + \frac{1}{K_n R} = 0.7V + \frac{1}{(4.90)\left(25 \frac{\mu A}{V^2}\right)(40.3 k\Omega)} = 0.7 + \frac{1}{4.937} = 0.903 \text{ V}$$

$$V_{IH} = V_{TN} - \frac{1}{K_n R} + 1.63\sqrt{\frac{V_{DD}}{K_n R}} = 0.7 - \frac{1}{4.937} + 1.63\sqrt{\frac{3.3}{4.937}} = 1.83V$$

$$NM_L = 0.903 - 0.25 = 0.653 \text{ V} \mid NM_H = 3.3 - 1.83 = 1.47 \text{ V}$$

7.8

$$R = \frac{V_{DD} - V_{OL}}{I_{DS}} = \frac{3.3 - 0.2}{33 \times 10^{-6}} = 93.94 \text{ k}\Omega$$

$$33\mu A = \left(60 \times 10^{-6}\right)\left(\frac{W}{L}\right)_S\left(3.3 - 0.75 - \frac{0.2}{2}\right)0.2 \rightarrow \left(\frac{W}{L}\right)_S = \frac{1.122}{1}$$

7.9

(a) $R_{on} = \dfrac{1}{K_n' \dfrac{W}{L}(V_{GS} - V_{TN})} = \dfrac{1}{25 \times 10^{-6} \dfrac{10}{1}(5 - 1)} = 1000 \ \Omega$

(b) $R_{on} = \dfrac{1}{K_p' \dfrac{W}{L}(V_{SG} + V_{TP})} = \dfrac{1}{10 \times 10^{-6} \dfrac{10}{1}(5 - 1)} = 2500 \ \Omega$

(c) A resistive connection exists between the source and drain.

(d) $\dfrac{W}{L} = \dfrac{1}{K_n'(V_{GS} - V_{TN})R_{on}} = \dfrac{1}{25 \times 10^{-6}(3 - 1)1000} = \dfrac{20}{1}$

$\dfrac{W}{L} = \dfrac{1}{K_p'(V_{SG} + V_{TP})R_{on}} = \dfrac{1}{10 \times 10^{-6}(3 - 1)2500} = \dfrac{20}{1}$

7.10

$$V_{OH} = V_{DD} - \left(V_{TO} + \gamma\left(\sqrt{V_{SB} + 2\phi_F} - \sqrt{2\phi_F}\right)\right) \rightarrow V_{OH} = 5 - \left(0.75 + 0.75\left(\sqrt{V_{OH} + 0.7} - \sqrt{0.7}\right)\right)$$

$$\left(V_{OH} - 4.88\right)^2 = 0.5625(V_{OH} + 0.7) \rightarrow V_{OH}^2 - 10.3V_{OH} + 23.4 = 0$$

$$V_{OH} = 6.92V, \quad 3.38V \rightarrow V_{OH} = 3.38 \text{ V}$$

Checking: $V_{TH} = 0.75 + 0.75\left(\sqrt{3.38 + 0.75} - \sqrt{0.75}\right) = 1.63V \mid 5 - 1.63 = 3.37V$

7.11

$$V_{OH} = V_{DD} - \left(V_{TO} + \gamma\left(\sqrt{V_{SB} + 2\phi_F} - \sqrt{2\phi_F}\right)\right) \rightarrow V_{OH} = 3 - \left(0.5 + 0.85\left(\sqrt{V_{OH} + 0.6} - \sqrt{0.6}\right)\right)$$

$$(V_{OH} - 3.158)^2 = 0.7225(V_{OH} + 0.6) \rightarrow V_{OH}^2 - 7.038V_{OH} + 9.539 = 0$$

$$V_{OH} = 1.832V, \quad 5.206V \rightarrow V_{OH} = 1.832 \text{ V}$$

Checking: $V_{TH} = 0.5 + 0.85\left(\sqrt{1.832 + 0.6} - \sqrt{0.6}\right) = 1.167V \quad | \quad 3 - 1.167 = 1.833V$

7.12

For $\gamma = 0$, $V_{OH} = V_{DD} - V_{TN} = 3.3 - 1 = 2.3V \quad | \quad$ For V_{OL}: $I_{DSL} = I_{DSS}$

$$\frac{K_n'}{2}\frac{1}{2}(3.3 - V_{OL} - 1)^2 = K_n'\left(\frac{4}{1}\right)\left(2.3 - 1 - \frac{V_{OL}}{2}\right)V_{OL} \rightarrow 9V_{OL}^2 - 25V_{OL} + 5.29 = 0$$

$$V_{OL} = 0.2264V \quad | \quad I_{DD} = \frac{25 \times 10^{-6}}{2}\frac{1}{2}(3.3 - 0.2264 - 1)^2 = 26.87\mu A$$

$$P = (3.3V)(26.87\mu A) = 88.68 \text{ }\mu W$$

Checking: $I_{DD} = 25 \times 10^{-6}\left(\frac{4}{1}\right)\left(2.3 - 1 - \frac{0.2264}{2}\right)0.2264 = 26.87\mu A$

7.13

$$V_{IL} = V_{TNS} = 1V \quad | \quad \text{At } V_{IH} \text{ (Eq. 7.25) } V_O = \frac{3.3 - 1}{\sqrt{1 + 3\frac{4}{0.5}}} = 0.46V$$

$$V_{IH} = 1 + \frac{0.46}{2} + \frac{0.5}{2(4)}\frac{1}{0.46}(3.3 - 0.46 - 1)^2 = 1.69V$$

$$NM_H = 2.3 - 1.69 = 0.610 \text{ V} \quad | \quad NM_L = 1 - 0.226 = 0.774 \text{ V}$$

7.14

(a) $V_{OH} = V_{DD} - \left(V_{TO} + \gamma\left(\sqrt{V_{SB} + 2\phi_F} - \sqrt{2\phi_F}\right)\right) \rightarrow V_{OH} = 3.3 - \left(0.7 + 0.5\left(\sqrt{V_{OH} + 0.6} - \sqrt{0.6}\right)\right)$

$$(V_{OH} - 2.987)^2 = 0.25(V_{OH} + 0.6) \rightarrow V_{OH}^2 - 6.225V_{OH} + 8.772 = 0 \rightarrow V_{OH} = 2.156 \text{ V}$$

$$V_{OL} = 0.25V \quad | \quad I_{DS} = \frac{0.25mW}{3.3V} = 75.76\mu A \quad | \quad 75.76 = 25\left(\frac{W}{L}\right)_S\left(2.156 - 0.7 - \frac{0.25}{2}\right)0.25$$

$$\left(\frac{W}{L}\right)_S = \frac{9.107}{1} \quad | \quad V_{TNL} = 0.7 + 0.5\left(\sqrt{0.25 + 0.6} - \sqrt{0.6}\right) = 0.7737V$$

$$75.76 = \frac{25}{2}\left(\frac{W}{L}\right)_L(3.3 - 0.25 - 0.7737)^2 \rightarrow \left(\frac{W}{L}\right)_L = \frac{1.170}{1}$$

(b) $V_{IL} = V_{TNS} = 0.70V \quad | \quad$ Finding V_{IH}: $v_O = \frac{V_{DD} - V_{TNL}}{\sqrt{1 + 3\frac{(W/L)_S}{(W/L)_L}}} = \frac{3.3 - V_{TNL}}{\sqrt{1 + 3\frac{9.107}{1.170}}} = \frac{3.3 - V_{TNL}}{4.935}$

$$V_{TNL} = 0.7 + 0.5\left(\sqrt{v_O + 0.6} - \sqrt{0.6}\right) \quad | \quad 4.395v_O = 3.3 - \left(0.7 + 0.5\left(\sqrt{v_O + 0.6} - \sqrt{0.6}\right)\right)$$

Using the quadratic equation: $v_O = 0.4990V \rightarrow V_{TNL} = 0.8369V$

$$V_{IH} = V_{TNS} + \frac{v_O}{2} + \frac{(W/L)_L}{(W/L)_S}\frac{1}{v_O}(V_{DD} - v_O - V_{TNL})^2 = 0.7 + \frac{0.499}{2} + \frac{1.170}{9.107}\frac{1}{0.499}(3.3 - 0.499 - 0.837)^2$$

$$V_{IH} = 1.943V \quad | \quad NM_H = 2.156 - 1.943 = 0.213 \text{ V} \quad | \quad NM_L = 0.7 - 0.25 = 0.45 \text{ V}$$

7.15

$$I_{DD} = \frac{0.5\text{mW}}{5\text{V}} = 100\mu\text{A} \quad | \quad V_{TNL} = 1 + 0.5\left(\sqrt{0.5 + 0.6} - \sqrt{0.6}\right) = 1.137\text{V}$$

$$100\text{x}10^{-6} = \frac{25\text{x}10^{-6}}{2}\left(\frac{W}{L}\right)_L (5 - 0.5 - 1.137)^2 \rightarrow \left(\frac{W}{L}\right)_L = \frac{1}{1.41}$$

$$100\text{x}10^{-6} = 25\text{x}10^{-6}\left(\frac{W}{L}\right)_S\left(3.39 - 1 - \frac{0.5}{2}\right)0.5 \rightarrow \left(\frac{W}{L}\right)_S = \frac{3.74}{1}$$

7.16 (a) $V_{DD} = 3.3$ V $V_{TN} = 1$ V $I_{DS} = 33$ mA $V_{OL} = 0.2$ V $V_{OH} = V_{DD} - V_{TN} = 3.3$ V - 1V = 2.3 V

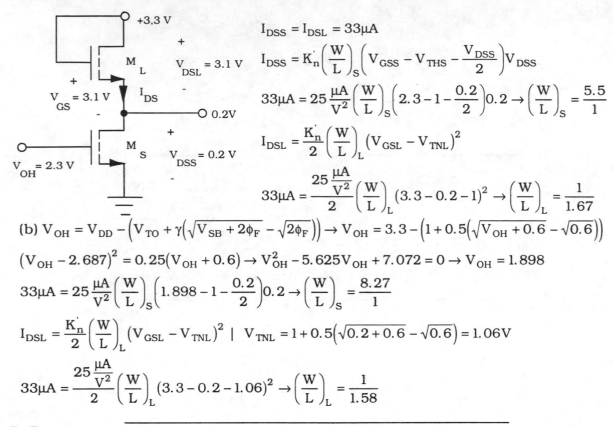

$$I_{DSS} = I_{DSL} = 33\mu\text{A}$$

$$I_{DSS} = K_n'\left(\frac{W}{L}\right)_S\left(V_{GSS} - V_{THS} - \frac{V_{DSS}}{2}\right)V_{DSS}$$

$$33\mu\text{A} = 25\frac{\mu\text{A}}{V^2}\left(\frac{W}{L}\right)_S\left(2.3 - 1 - \frac{0.2}{2}\right)0.2 \rightarrow \left(\frac{W}{L}\right)_S = \frac{5.5}{1}$$

$$I_{DSL} = \frac{K_n'}{2}\left(\frac{W}{L}\right)_L\left(V_{GSL} - V_{TNL}\right)^2$$

$$33\mu\text{A} = \frac{25\frac{\mu\text{A}}{V^2}}{2}\left(\frac{W}{L}\right)_L(3.3 - 0.2 - 1)^2 \rightarrow \left(\frac{W}{L}\right)_L = \frac{1}{1.67}$$

(b) $V_{OH} = V_{DD} - \left(V_{TO} + \gamma\left(\sqrt{V_{SB} + 2\phi_F} - \sqrt{2\phi_F}\right)\right) \rightarrow V_{OH} = 3.3 - \left(1 + 0.5\left(\sqrt{V_{OH} + 0.6} - \sqrt{0.6}\right)\right)$

$\left(V_{OH} - 2.687\right)^2 = 0.25\left(V_{OH} + 0.6\right) \rightarrow V_{OH}^2 - 5.625V_{OH} + 7.072 = 0 \rightarrow V_{OH} = 1.898$

$$33\mu\text{A} = 25\frac{\mu\text{A}}{V^2}\left(\frac{W}{L}\right)_S\left(1.898 - 1 - \frac{0.2}{2}\right)0.2 \rightarrow \left(\frac{W}{L}\right)_S = \frac{8.27}{1}$$

$I_{DSL} = \frac{K_n'}{2}\left(\frac{W}{L}\right)_L\left(V_{GSL} - V_{TNL}\right)^2 \quad | \quad V_{TNL} = 1 + 0.5\left(\sqrt{0.2 + 0.6} - \sqrt{0.6}\right) = 1.06\text{V}$

$$33\mu\text{A} = \frac{25\frac{\mu\text{A}}{V^2}}{2}\left(\frac{W}{L}\right)_L(3.3 - 0.2 - 1.06)^2 \rightarrow \left(\frac{W}{L}\right)_L = \frac{1}{1.58}$$

7.17

$$I_{DSS} = I_{DSL} \quad | \quad K_n'\left(\frac{W}{L}\right)_S\left(V_{GSS} - V_{TNS} - \frac{V_{DSL}}{2}\right)V_{DSL} = \frac{K_n'}{2}\left(\frac{W}{L}\right)_L\left(V_{GSL} - V_{TNL}\right)^2$$

$$K_n'\left(\frac{2.78}{1}\right)\left(5 - 1 - \frac{V_O}{2}\right)V_O = \frac{K_n'}{2}\left(\frac{1}{3.52}\right)(5 - V_O - 1)^2$$

$$19.6V_O\left(4 - \frac{V_O}{2}\right) = (4 - V_O)^2 \rightarrow V_O^2 - 8V_O + 1.483 = 0 \rightarrow V_O = 0.190\text{V}$$

7.18

The problem is similar to Prob. 17.17 except now $V_{TNL} = 1 + 0.5\left(\sqrt{V_O + 0.6} - \sqrt{0.6}\right)$

and $K_n'\left(\frac{3.53}{1}\right)\left(5 - 1 - \frac{V_O}{2}\right)V_O = \frac{K_n'}{2}\left(\frac{1}{3.39}\right)(5 - V_O - V_{TNL})^2$

Using MATLAB or other solver $\rightarrow V_O = 0.154$ V

7.19

$$I_{DSS} = I_{DSL} \mid K_n'\left(\frac{W}{L}\right)_S\left(V_{OH} - V_{TNS} - \frac{V_{OL}}{2}\right)V_{OL} = \frac{K_n'}{2}\left(\frac{W}{L}\right)_L\left(5 - V_{OL} - V_{TNL}\right)^2$$

which is independent of K_n'. Ratioed logic maintains V_{OL} and V_{OH} independent of K_n'. So $V_{OH} = 3.39V$ and $V_{OL} = 0.25V$. However, $I_{DSS} = I_{DSL} \propto K_n'$:

$$I_{DSS} = 18\frac{\mu A}{V^2}\left(\frac{3.53}{1}\right)\left(3.39 - 1 - \frac{0.25}{2}\right)0.25 = 36.0\mu A \mid P = 5(36.0\mu A) = 0.180 \text{ mW}$$

7.20

$$V_{TNL} = 1 + 0.5\left(\sqrt{0.25 + 0.6} - \sqrt{0.6}\right) = 1.074V$$

$$V_{GSL} - V_{TNL} = 7.5 - 0.25 - 1.074 = 6.18V \mid V_{DSL} = 5 - 0.25 = 4.75V \rightarrow \text{Linear region}$$

$$50\mu A = 25\frac{\mu A}{V^2}\left(\frac{W}{L}\right)_L\left(7.5 - 0.25 - 1.074 - \frac{4.75}{2}\right)4.75 \rightarrow \left(\frac{W}{L}\right)_L = \frac{1}{9.03}$$

The value is incorrect in the First Printing in Figs. 7.16 and 7.20(c).

7.21

For linear operation at $v_o = V_{OL}$: $V_{TNL} = 1 + 0.5\left(\sqrt{0.25 + 0.6} - \sqrt{0.6}\right) = 1.074V$

$V_{GSL} - V_{TNL} \geq V_{DSL}$: $V_{GG} - 0.25 - 1.074 \geq 5 - 0.25 \rightarrow V_{GG} \geq 6.07V$

Also require: $V_{GG} \geq 5 + V_{TNL} = 5 + 1 + 0.5\left(\sqrt{5 + 0.6} - \sqrt{0.6}\right) = 6.80V$ so $V_{GG} \geq 6.80V$

7.22

$$V_{TN} = 1V \mid V_{OH} = 6 - 1 = 5.00V \mid I_{DSS} = I_{DSL} \mid K_n'\left(\frac{5}{1}\right)\left(5 - 1 - \frac{V_{OL}}{2}\right)V_{OL} = \frac{K_n'}{2}\left(\frac{1}{2}\right)\left(6 - V_{OL} - 1\right)^2$$

$$11V_{OL}^2 - 90V_{OL} + 25 = 0 \rightarrow V_{OL} = 0.2879V = 0.288 \text{ V}$$

$$I_{DSS} = \frac{25\mu A}{2}\left(\frac{1}{2}\right)\left(6 - 0.2879 - 1\right)^2 = 138.8\mu A \mid P = 5V(138.8\mu A) = 0.694 \text{ mW}$$

7.23

We require $V_{TNL} \leq 0$: $-3 + \gamma\left(\sqrt{5 + 0.6} - \sqrt{0.6}\right) \leq 0 \rightarrow \gamma \leq 1.89$

7.24

$$V_{OH} = V_{DD} \mid I_{DSS} = I_{DSL} \mid K_n'\left(\frac{W}{L}\right)_S\left(V_{DD} - V_{TNS} - \frac{V_{OL}}{2}\right)V_{OL} = \frac{K_n'}{2}\left(\frac{W}{L}\right)_L\left(V_{TNL}\right)^2$$

For ratioed logic, both V_{OH} and V_{OL} are independent of K_n'. $V_{OH} = 5$ V $\mid V_{OL} = 0.25V$

However, $I_{DS} \propto K_n' \mid I_{DS} = 50\mu A\left(\frac{40}{25}\right) = 80\mu A \mid P = 5V(80\mu A) = 0.400 \text{ mW}$

7.25

(a) $I_{DD} = \frac{0.25mW}{3.3V} = 75.76\mu A$

$$V_{TNL} = -3 + 0.5\left(\sqrt{3.3 + 0.6} - \sqrt{0.6}\right) = -2.40V \rightarrow V_{OH} = 3.3V$$

$$75.76\mu A = 25\mu A\left(\frac{W}{L}\right)_S\left(3.3 - 0.7 - \frac{0.25}{2}\right)0.25 \rightarrow \left(\frac{W}{L}\right)_S = \frac{4.90}{1}$$

$V_{TNL} = -3 + 0.5\left(\sqrt{0.25 + 0.6} - \sqrt{0.6}\right) = -2.926V$ | $75.8\mu A = \dfrac{25\mu A}{2}\left(\dfrac{W}{L}\right)_L (-2.926)^2$ | $\left(\dfrac{W}{L}\right)_L = \dfrac{1}{1.41}$

(b) $V_{TNL} = -3 + 0.5\left(\sqrt{V_O + 0.6} - \sqrt{0.6}\right)$ | $V_{IL} = 0.7 - \dfrac{V_{TNL}}{\sqrt{K_R^2 + K_R}}$ | $K_R = 4.90(1.41) = 6.91$

$V_O = V_{DD} + V_{TNL} + \sqrt{V_{TNL}^2 - K_R(V_{IL} - V_{TNS})^2} = 3.3 + V_{TNL} + \sqrt{V_{TNL}^2 - 6.91(V_{IL} - 0.7)^2}$

By MATLAB: $V_O = 3.142V$ | $V_{TNL} = -2.420V$ | $V_{IL} = 1.027V$ | $NM_L = 1.027 - 0.25 = 0.777$ V

$V_O = -\dfrac{V_{TNL}}{\sqrt{3K_R}} = -\dfrac{-3 + 0.5\left(\sqrt{V_O + 0.6} - \sqrt{0.6}\right)}{4.553} \rightarrow V_O = 0.6225V \rightarrow V_{TNL} = -2.834V$

$V_{IH} = V_{TNS} - \dfrac{2V_{TNL}}{\sqrt{3K_R}} = 0.7 - \dfrac{2(-2.834)}{4.553} = 1.945V$ | $NM_H = 3.3 - 1.945 = 1.36$ V

7.26
With $A = 1 = B$, the circuit is equivalent to a single 4.12 / 1 switching device.

$25\mu A\left(\dfrac{4.12}{1}\right)\left(5 - 1 - \dfrac{V_{OL}}{2}\right)V_{OL} = \dfrac{25\mu A}{2}\left(\dfrac{1}{2.15}\right)(V_{TNL})^2$ | $V_{TNL} = -3 + 0.5\left(\sqrt{V_{OL} + 0.6} - \sqrt{0.6}\right)$

Solving iteratively $\rightarrow V_{OL} = 0.1257V$ | $V_{TNL} = -2.961V$ (b) $\dfrac{25\mu A}{2}\left(\dfrac{1}{2.15}\right)(2.961)^2 = 50.1$ μA

7.27

$50\mu A = 25\mu A\left(\dfrac{W}{L}\right)_A\left(5 - 1 - \dfrac{0.125}{2}\right)0.125 \rightarrow \left(\dfrac{W}{L}\right)_A = \dfrac{4.06}{1}$

$50\mu A = 25\mu A\left(\dfrac{W}{L}\right)_B\left(5 - 0.125 - 1.04 - \dfrac{0.125}{2}\right)0.125 \rightarrow \left(\dfrac{W}{L}\right)_A = \dfrac{4.24}{1}$

7.28
We require $\dfrac{R_{on}}{\left(\dfrac{W}{L}\right)_A} + \dfrac{R_{on}}{\left(\dfrac{W}{L}\right)_B} = \dfrac{R_{on}}{K}$ and the total area $A_T \propto (WL)_A + (WL)_B$

Setting $L = 1$, $\dfrac{1}{W_A} + \dfrac{1}{W_B} = \dfrac{1}{K} \rightarrow W_A = \dfrac{KW_B}{W_B - K} \rightarrow A_T \propto \dfrac{KW_B}{W_B - K} + W_B = \dfrac{W_B^2}{W_B - K}$

Finding the minimum: $\dfrac{d}{dW_B}\left(\dfrac{W_B^2}{W_B - K}\right) = \dfrac{W_B^2 - 2KW_B}{(W_B - K)^2} = 0 \rightarrow W_B = 2K$ & $W_A = 2K$.

7.29

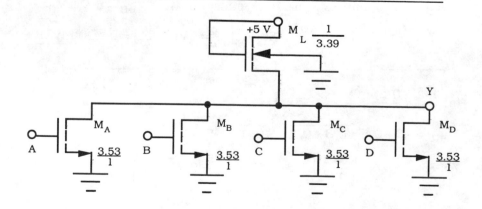

7.30

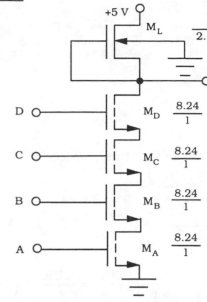

M_L $\dfrac{1}{2.15}$

M_D $\dfrac{8.24}{1}$

M_C $\dfrac{8.24}{1}$

M_B $\dfrac{8.24}{1}$

M_A $\dfrac{8.24}{1}$

7.31

For M_N off, $I_{SDP} = 0$, $V_{SDP} = 0$, $V_{OH} = V_{DD} = 5V$

$$\frac{K_P}{2}(5 + V_{TP})^2 = K_n\left(V_{OH} - V_{TN} - \frac{V_{OL}}{2}\right)V_{OL}$$

$$\frac{10^{-5}}{2}\left(\frac{1}{1}\right)(5-1)^2 = 25\times10^{-6}\left(\frac{5}{1}\right)\left(5 - 1 - \frac{V_{OL}}{2}\right)V_{OL}$$

$$V_{OL} = 0.163 \text{ V}$$

7.32

	A	B	Y
	0	0	1
(a)	0	1	0
	1	0	0
	1	1	1

(b) $Y = \overline{A}\overline{B} + AB = \overline{A \oplus B}$

(c) Assuming equal voltage drops (0.125V) across M_P and M_S:

M_P must carry one unit of load current with $V_{DS} = 0.125V \rightarrow \left(\dfrac{W}{L}\right)_P = \dfrac{4.12}{1}$

M_S must carry two units of load current with $V_{DS} = 0.125V \rightarrow \left(\dfrac{W}{L}\right)_S = \dfrac{8.24}{1}$

(d) M_S will not change. M_P will need to be somewhat larger.

(e) Coincidence gate (Exclusive NOR)

7.33

$$Y = \overline{(A + B)(C + D)(E + F)} \quad | \quad \left(\frac{W}{L}\right)_L = \frac{1}{2.15} \quad | \quad \left(\frac{W}{L}\right)_{A-F} = 3\left(\frac{2.06}{1}\right) = \frac{6.18}{1}$$

7.34

$$Y = \overline{(A + B)(C + D)E} \quad | \quad \left(\frac{W}{L}\right)_L = \frac{1}{2.15} \quad | \quad \left(\frac{W}{L}\right)_{A-E} = 3\left(\frac{2.06}{1}\right) = \frac{6.18}{1}$$

7.35

$$Y = \overline{ACE + ACDF + BF + BDE} \quad | \quad \left(\frac{W}{L}\right)_L = 3\frac{1}{2.15} = \frac{1.40}{1} \quad | \quad \text{ACDF path contains 4 devices}$$

$$\left(\frac{W}{L}\right)_{A,C,D,F} = 3\left[4\left(\frac{2.06}{1}\right)\right] = \frac{24.7}{1} \quad | \quad \frac{1}{\left(\dfrac{W}{L}\right)_B} + \frac{1}{\left(\dfrac{24.7}{1}\right)} + \frac{1}{\left(\dfrac{W}{L}\right)_E} = \frac{1}{3\dfrac{2.06}{1}} \rightarrow \left(\frac{W}{L}\right)_{B,E} = \frac{16.5}{1}$$

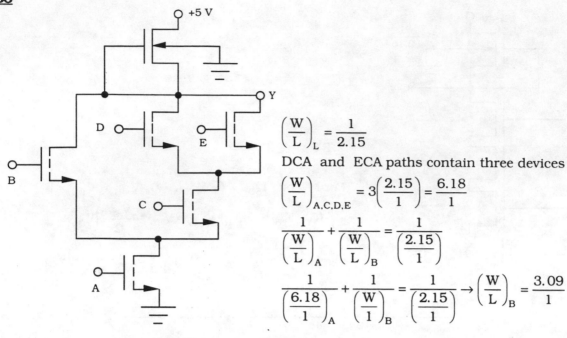

$$\left(\frac{W}{L}\right)_L = \frac{1}{2.15}$$

DCA and ECA paths contain three devices

$$\left(\frac{W}{L}\right)_{A,C,D,E} = 3\left(\frac{2.15}{1}\right) = \frac{6.18}{1}$$

$$\frac{1}{\left(\frac{W}{L}\right)_A} + \frac{1}{\left(\frac{W}{L}\right)_B} = \frac{1}{\left(\frac{2.15}{1}\right)}$$

$$\frac{1}{\left(\frac{6.18}{1}\right)_A} + \frac{1}{\left(\frac{W}{1}\right)_B} = \frac{1}{\left(\frac{2.15}{1}\right)} \rightarrow \left(\frac{W}{L}\right)_B = \frac{3.09}{1}$$

7.37

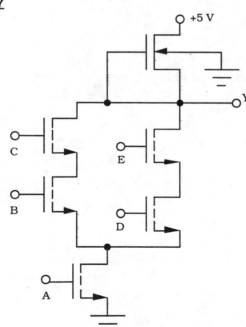

$$\left(\frac{W}{L}\right)_L = \frac{1}{2}\left(\frac{1}{2.15}\right) = \frac{1}{4.30}$$

CBA and EDA paths contain three devices

$$\left(\frac{W}{L}\right)_{A-E} = \frac{1}{2}(3)\left(\frac{2.15}{1}\right) = \frac{3.09}{1}$$

7.38

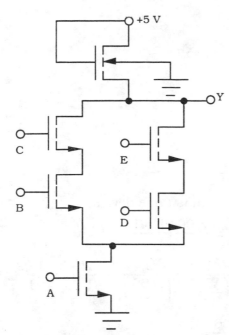

$$\left(\frac{W}{L}\right)_L = \frac{1}{3.39}$$

CBA and EDA paths contain three devices

$$\left(\frac{W}{L}\right)_{A-E} = 3\left(\frac{3.53}{1}\right) = \frac{10.6}{1}$$

7.39

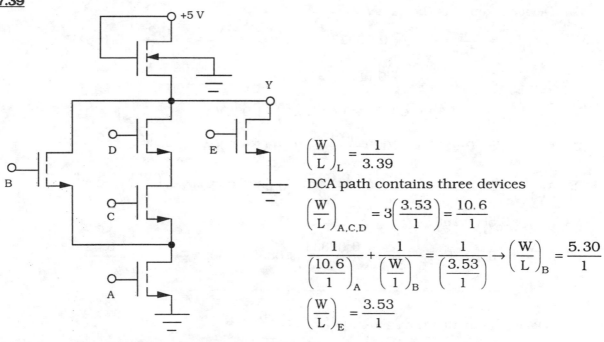

$$\left(\frac{W}{L}\right)_L = \frac{1}{3.39}$$

DCA path contains three devices

$$\left(\frac{W}{L}\right)_{A,C,D} = 3\left(\frac{3.53}{1}\right) = \frac{10.6}{1}$$

$$\frac{1}{\left(\frac{10.6}{1}\right)_A} + \frac{1}{\left(\frac{W}{1}\right)_B} = \frac{1}{\left(\frac{3.53}{1}\right)} \rightarrow \left(\frac{W}{L}\right)_B = \frac{5.30}{1}$$

$$\left(\frac{W}{L}\right)_E = \frac{3.53}{1}$$

7.40

$$Y = \overline{A(B+D)(C+E)+(C+E)G+F} = \overline{(C+E)\left[A(B+D)+G\right]+F}$$

$$\left(\frac{W}{L}\right)_L = 2\frac{1}{2.15} = \frac{1}{1.08} \quad | \quad \left(\frac{W}{L}\right)_{A-E} = 2\left[3\left(\frac{2.06}{1}\right)\right] = \frac{12.4}{1}$$

$$\left(\frac{W}{L}\right)_F = 2\left(\frac{2.06}{1}\right) = \frac{4.12}{1} \quad | \quad \frac{1}{\left(\frac{W}{L}\right)_G} + \frac{1}{\left(\frac{12.36}{1}\right)} = \frac{1}{2\frac{2.06}{1}} \rightarrow \left(\frac{W}{L}\right)_G = \frac{6.18}{1}$$

7.41 (a)

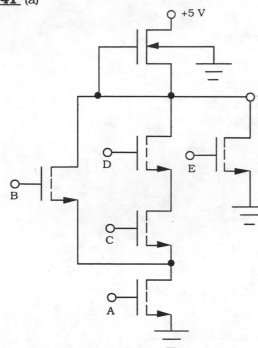

$$\left(\frac{W}{L}\right)_L = \frac{1}{2.15}$$

DCA path contains three devices

$$\left(\frac{W}{L}\right)_{A,C,D} = 3\left(\frac{2.06}{1}\right) = \frac{6.18}{1}$$

$$\frac{1}{\left(\frac{6.18}{1}\right)_A} + \frac{1}{\left(\frac{W}{1}\right)_B} = \frac{1}{\left(\frac{2.06}{1}\right)} \rightarrow \left(\frac{W}{L}\right)_B = \frac{3.09}{1}$$

$$\left(\frac{W}{L}\right)_E = \frac{2.06}{1}$$

(b) Device E remains the same.

A, C, D: $V_{DS} = \dfrac{V_{OL}}{3} = \dfrac{0.25}{3} = 0.08333V$ | B: $V_{DS} = 2\dfrac{V_{OL}}{3} = 2\dfrac{0.25}{3} = 0.1667V$

$$25\mu A\left(\frac{W}{L}\right)_A\left(5 - 1 - \frac{0.08333}{2}\right)0.08333 = 50\mu A \rightarrow \left(\frac{W}{L}\right)_A = \frac{6.06}{1}$$

$$V_{TNB} = V_{TNC} = 1 + 0.5\left(\sqrt{0.08333 + 0.6} - \sqrt{0.6}\right) = 1.026V$$

$$25\mu A\left(\frac{W}{L}\right)_B\left(5 - 0.08333 - 1.026 - \frac{0.1667}{2}\right)0.1667 = 50\mu A \rightarrow \left(\frac{W}{L}\right)_B = \frac{3.15}{1}$$

$$25\mu A\left(\frac{W}{L}\right)_C\left(5 - 0.08333 - 1.026 - \frac{0.08333}{2}\right)0.08333 = 50\mu A \rightarrow \left(\frac{W}{L}\right)_C = \frac{6.24}{1}$$

$$V_{TND} = 1 + 0.5\left(\sqrt{0.1667 + 0.6} - \sqrt{0.6}\right) = 1.051V$$

$$25\mu A\left(\frac{W}{L}\right)_D\left(5 - 0.1667 - 1.051 - \frac{0.08333}{2}\right)0.08333 = 50\mu A \rightarrow \left(\frac{W}{L}\right)_D = \frac{6.42}{1}$$

7.42

Device A remains the same. $\left(\dfrac{W}{L}\right)_A = \dfrac{2.06}{1}$

B, C, D: $V_{DS} = \dfrac{V_{OL}}{2} = \dfrac{0.25}{2} = 0.125V$

$$25\mu A\left(\frac{W}{L}\right)_{C,D}\left(5 - 1 - \frac{0.125}{2}\right)0.125 = 50\mu A \rightarrow \left(\frac{W}{L}\right)_{C,D} = \frac{4.06}{1}$$

$$V_{TNB} = 1 + 0.5\left(\sqrt{0.125 + 0.6} - \sqrt{0.6}\right) = 1.038V$$

$$25\mu A\left(\frac{W}{L}\right)_B\left(5 - 0.125 - 1.038 - \frac{0.125}{2}\right)0.125 = 50\mu A \rightarrow \left(\frac{W}{L}\right)_B = \frac{4.24}{1}$$

7.43

$$\text{BCD: } V_{DS} = \frac{V_{OL}}{3} = \frac{0.25}{3} = 0.08333V \quad | \quad \text{A: } V_{DS} = 2\frac{V_{OL}}{3} = 2\frac{0.25}{3} = 0.1667V$$

$$25\mu A\left(\frac{W}{L}\right)_B\left(5 - 1 - \frac{0.08333}{2}\right)0.08333 = 50\mu A \rightarrow \left(\frac{W}{L}\right)_B = \frac{6.06}{1}$$

$$V_{TNA} = 1 + 0.5\left(\sqrt{0.08333 + 0.6} - \sqrt{0.6}\right) = 1.026V$$

$$25\mu A\left(\frac{W}{L}\right)_A\left(5 - 0.08333 - 1.026 - \frac{0.1667}{2}\right)0.1667 = 50\mu A \rightarrow \left(\frac{W}{L}\right)_A = \frac{3.15}{1}$$

$$25\mu A\left(\frac{W}{L}\right)_D\left(5 - 0.08333 - 1.026 - \frac{0.08333}{2}\right)0.08333 = 50\mu A \rightarrow \left(\frac{W}{L}\right)_D = \frac{6.24}{1}$$

$$V_{TNC} = 1 + 0.5\left(\sqrt{0.1667 + 0.6} - \sqrt{0.6}\right) = 1.051V$$

$$25\mu A\left(\frac{W}{L}\right)_C\left(5 - 0.1667 - 1.051 - \frac{0.08333}{2}\right)0.08333 = 50\mu A \rightarrow \left(\frac{W}{L}\right)_C = \frac{6.42}{1}$$

7.44

$$25\mu A\left(\frac{W}{L}\right)_B\left(5 - 1 - \frac{0.125}{2}\right)0.125 = 50\mu A \rightarrow \left(\frac{W}{L}\right)_B = \frac{4.06}{1}$$

$$V_{TNA} = V_{TND} = 1 + 0.5\left(\sqrt{0.125 + 0.6} - \sqrt{0.6}\right) = 1.038V$$

$$25\mu A\left(\frac{W}{L}\right)_A\left(5 - 0.125 - 1.038 - \frac{0.125}{2}\right)0.125 = 50\mu A \rightarrow \left(\frac{W}{L}\right)_A = 4.24$$

$$25\mu A\left(\frac{W}{L}\right)_D\left(5 - 0.125 - 1.038 - \frac{0.0625}{2}\right)0.0625 = 50\mu A \rightarrow \left(\frac{W}{L}\right)_D = 8.41$$

$$V_{TNC} = 1 + 0.5\left(\sqrt{0.1875 + 0.6} - \sqrt{0.6}\right) = 1.056V$$

$$25\mu A\left(\frac{W}{L}\right)_C\left(5 - 0.1875 - 1.056 - \frac{0.0625}{2}\right)0.0625 = 50\mu A \rightarrow \left(\frac{W}{L}\right)_B = \frac{8.59}{1}$$

7.45

$$\text{Worst case situation A - E: } V_{DS} = \frac{V_{OL}}{3} = \frac{0.25}{3} = 0.08333V$$

$$25\mu A\left(\frac{W}{L}\right)_{B,E}\left(5 - 1 - \frac{0.08333}{2}\right)0.08333 = 50\mu A \rightarrow \left(\frac{W}{L}\right)_{B,E} = \frac{6.06}{1}$$

$$V_{TND} = 1 + 0.5\left(\sqrt{0.08333 + 0.6} - \sqrt{0.6}\right) = 1.026V$$

$$25\mu A\left(\frac{W}{L}\right)_D\left(5 - 0.08333 - 1.026 - \frac{0.08333}{2}\right)0.08333 = 50\mu A \rightarrow \left(\frac{W}{L}\right)_A = \frac{6.24}{1}$$

$$V_{TNA} = V_{TNC} = 1 + 0.5\left(\sqrt{0.1667 + 0.6} - \sqrt{0.6}\right) = 1.051V$$

$$25\mu A\left(\frac{W}{L}\right)_{A,C}\left(5 - 0.1667 - 1.051 - \frac{0.08333}{2}\right)0.08333 = 50\mu A \rightarrow \left(\frac{W}{L}\right)_{A,C} = \frac{6.42}{1}$$

7.46

Original design 0.25 mW - 1 mW requires 4 times larger current.

(a) $R = \dfrac{95k\Omega}{4} = 23.8k\Omega$ $\left(\dfrac{W}{L}\right)_S = 4\dfrac{2.06}{1} = \dfrac{8.24}{1}$

(b) $\left(\dfrac{W}{L}\right)_L = 4\dfrac{1}{3.39} = \dfrac{1.18}{1}$ $\left(\dfrac{W}{L}\right)_S = 4\dfrac{3.53}{1} = \dfrac{14.1}{1}$

(c) $\left(\dfrac{W}{L}\right)_L = 4\dfrac{1}{9.03} = \dfrac{1}{2.26}$ $\left(\dfrac{W}{L}\right)_S = 4\dfrac{2.06}{1} = \dfrac{8.24}{1}$

(d) $\left(\dfrac{W}{L}\right)_L = 4\dfrac{1}{2.15} = \dfrac{1.86}{1}$ $\left(\dfrac{W}{L}\right)_S = 4\dfrac{2.06}{1} = \dfrac{8.24}{1}$

7.47

$\left(\dfrac{W}{L}\right)_L = 4\dfrac{1}{2.15} = \dfrac{1.86}{1}$ | $\left(\dfrac{W}{L}\right)_{A-E} = 4\left[3\left(\dfrac{2.06}{1}\right)\right] = \dfrac{24.7}{1}$

$\left(\dfrac{W}{L}\right)_F = 4\left(\dfrac{2.06}{1}\right) = \dfrac{8.24}{1}$ | $\dfrac{1}{\left(\dfrac{W}{L}\right)_G} + \dfrac{1}{\left(\dfrac{24.72}{1}\right)} = \dfrac{1}{4\dfrac{2.06}{1}} \rightarrow \left(\dfrac{W}{L}\right)_G = \dfrac{12.4}{1}$

7.48

$\left(\dfrac{W}{L}\right)_L = \dfrac{1}{4}\dfrac{1}{2.15} = \dfrac{1}{8.60}$ | $\left(\dfrac{W}{L}\right)_{A-F} = \dfrac{1}{4}\left[3\left(\dfrac{2.06}{1}\right)\right] = \dfrac{1.55}{1}$

7.49

(a) $I_{DS} = \dfrac{1}{2}\mu_n C''_{ox}\left(\dfrac{W}{L}\right)(V_{GS} - V_{TN})^2 = \dfrac{1}{2}\mu_n \dfrac{\varepsilon_{ox}}{T_{ox}}\left(\dfrac{W}{L}\right)(V_{GS} - V_{TN})^2$

$I'_{DS} = \dfrac{1}{2}\mu_n \dfrac{\varepsilon_{ox}}{\dfrac{T_{ox}}{2}}\left(\dfrac{\dfrac{W}{2}}{\dfrac{L}{2}}\right)(V_{GS} - V_{TN})^2 = 2I_{DS}$ | $\dfrac{I'_{DS}}{I_{DS}} = 2$

(b) $P'_D = V(2I) = 2VI = 2P_D$ - Power dissipation has increased by a factor of two.

7.50

For each line: $i = C\dfrac{dv}{dt}$ | Assume the transition occurs in DT seconds generating

a current pulse with constant amplitidue $I = 10\times10^{-12}\,F\dfrac{5V}{\Delta T}$.

Then $I_{avg} = \dfrac{5\times10^{-11}}{\Delta T}\dfrac{\Delta T}{50ns} = 1.00mA$ and $P = 64(5V)I_{avg} = 64(5)(1.00mA) = 0.320$ W

(b) $P \propto V^2$ so $P = 0.320W\left(\dfrac{3.3}{5}\right)^2 = 0.139$ W

7.51

$\tau_{PHL} \propto \dfrac{C}{K_S}$ and $\tau_{PLH} \propto \dfrac{C}{K_L}$ | For either case,

$\tau_{PHL} \propto \dfrac{C}{K_S} = \dfrac{C''_{ox}WL}{\mu_n C''_{ox}\dfrac{W}{L}} = \dfrac{L^2}{\mu_n}$

7.52

$$\tau_P = \frac{PDP}{P_D} = \frac{100fJ}{100\mu W} = \frac{10^{-13}J}{10^{-4}W} = 1 \text{ ns}$$

7.53

$$V_{OH} = 5V \mid V_{OL} = 0.25V \mid V_{50\%} = \frac{5+0.25}{2} = 2.63V$$

$$V_{90\%} = 5 - 0.475 = 4.53V \mid V_{10\%} = 0.25 + 0.475 = 0.725V$$

(a) v_I: $t_r = 22.5 - 1.5 = 21$ ns $\mid$ v_O: $t_r = 81 - 58 = 23$ ns

v_I: $t_f = 62 - 55 = 7$ ns $\mid$ v_O: $t_r = 12.5 - 6 = 6.5$ ns

(b) $\tau_{PHL} = 2.5$ ns $\mid$ $\tau_{PLH} = 7$ ns   (c) $\tau_P = \frac{2.5+7}{2} = 4.8$ ns

---

7.54

(a) $T = 301(\tau_{PHL} + \tau_{PLH}) = 602 \frac{(\tau_{PHL} + \tau_{PLH})}{2} = 602\tau_P = 602(0.1\text{ns}) = 60.2$ ns

(b) An even number of inverters has a potential steady state and may not oscillate.

7.55

$$t_r = 2.2RC = 2.2(95k\Omega)(0.5pF) = 105 \text{ ns}$$

$$t_f = \frac{1}{2.06(25 \times 10^{-6})(5-1)}(0.5pF)\left[\ln\left(2\frac{5-1}{5-0.9(4.75)}-1\right)+2\frac{1-0.1(4.75)}{5-1}\right] = 6.23 \text{ ns}$$

$$\tau_{PLH} = 0.69RC = 0.69(95k\Omega)(0.5pF) = 32.8 \text{ ns}$$

$$\tau_{PHL} = \frac{0.3C}{K_S} = \frac{0.3(0.5pF)}{2.06\left(25\frac{\mu A}{V^2}\right)} = 2.91 \text{ ns}$$

$$\tau_P = \frac{32.8+2.91}{2} = 17.9 \text{ ns}$$

7.56

For M_S off, $I_{DS} = 0$ and $V_{OH} = 3.3V$.

For V_{OL}, $I_{DS} = \frac{3.3-V_{OL}}{95k\Omega} = \left(\frac{2.06}{1}\right)\left(25\frac{\mu A}{V^2}\right)\left(3.3-1-\frac{V_{OL}}{2}\right)V_{OL}$

$$2.446V_{OL}^2 - 12.25V_{OL} + 3.3 = 0 \rightarrow V_{OL} = 0.2856V$$

$$t_r = 2.2RC = 2.2(95k\Omega)(0.5pF) = 105 \text{ ns}$$

$$t_f = \frac{1}{2.06(25 \times 10^{-6})(3.3-1)}(0.5pF)\left[\ln\left(2\frac{3.3-1}{3.3-0.9(3.01)}-1\right)+2\frac{1-0.1(3.01)}{3.3-1}\right] = 10.7\text{ns}$$

$$\tau_{PLH} = 0.69RC = 0.69(95k\Omega)(0.5pF) = 32.8 \text{ ns}$$

$$\tau_{PHL} = \frac{1}{2.06(25 \times 10^{-6})(3.3-1)}(0.5pF)\left[\ln\left(4\frac{3.3-1}{3.3+0.286}-1\right)+\frac{1}{2}\right] = 4.00\text{ns}$$

$$\tau_P = \frac{32.8+4.00}{2} = 18.4 \text{ ns}$$

7.57

$$V_{TN} = 1 \rightarrow V_{OH} = 5 - 1 = 4V$$

$$\frac{4}{1}\left(25 \times 10^{-6}\right)\left(4 - 1 - \frac{V_{OL}}{2}\right)V_{OL} = \frac{1}{2}\frac{\left(25 \times 10^{-6}\right)}{2}\left(5 - V_{OL} - 1\right)^2$$

$$9V_{OL}^2 - 56V_{OL} + 16 = 0 \rightarrow V_{OL} = 0.300V \quad | \quad \Delta V = 4 - 0.3 = 3.7V$$

$$t_r = \frac{160}{9}\frac{(0.5pF)}{\left(25 \times 10^{-6}\right)(0.5)(5 - 1 - 0.3)} = 192 \text{ ns}$$

$$t_f = \frac{(0.5pF)}{\left(25 \times 10^{-6}\right)(4)(5 - 1 - 1)}\left[\ln\frac{5 - 1 - 1 + 0.9(3.7)}{5 - 1 - 0.9(3.7)} + 2\frac{1 - 0.1(3.7)}{5 - 1 - 1}\right] = 4.44 \text{ ns}$$

$$\tau_{PLH} = 2R_{ONL}C = \frac{2}{\left(25 \times 10^{-6}\right)(0.5)(5 - 1 - 0.3)}(0.5pF) = 21.6 \text{ ns}$$

$$\tau_{PHL} = \frac{(0.5pF)}{4\left(25 \times 10^{-6}\right)(5 - 1 - 1)}\left[\ln\left(4\frac{5 - 1 - 1}{5 - 1 + 0.3} - 1\right) + \frac{2}{3}\right] = 2.08 \text{ ns}$$

$$\tau_P = \frac{21.6 + 2.08}{2} = 11.8 \text{ ns}$$

7.58

$$V_{TN} = 1 \rightarrow V_{OH} = 3.3 - 1 = 2.3V$$

$$\frac{4}{1}\left(25 \times 10^{-6}\right)\left(3.3 - 1 - \frac{V_{OL}}{2}\right)V_{OL} = \frac{1}{2}\frac{\left(25 \times 10^{-6}\right)}{2}\left(3.3 - V_{OL} - 1\right)^2$$

$$9V_{OL}^2 - 41.40V_{OL} + 5.29 = 0 \rightarrow V_{OL} = 0.132V \quad | \quad \Delta V = 2.3 - 0.132 = 2.17V$$

$$t_r = \frac{160}{9}\frac{(0.3pF)}{\left(25 \times 10^{-6}\right)(0.5)(3.3 - 1 - 0.132)} = 197 \text{ ns}$$

$$t_f = \frac{(0.3pF)}{\left(25 \times 10^{-6}\right)(4)(3.3 - 1 - 1)}\left[\ln\frac{3.3 - 1 - 1 + 0.9(2.17)}{3.3 - 1 - 0.9(2.17)} + 2\frac{1 - 0.1(2.17)}{3.3 - 1 - 1}\right] = 7.94 \text{ ns}$$

$$\tau_{PLH} = 2R_{ONL}C = \frac{2}{\left(25 \times 10^{-6}\right)(0.5)(3.3 - 1 - 0.132)}(0.3pF) = 22.1 \text{ ns}$$

$$\tau_{PHL} = \frac{(0.3pF)}{4\left(25 \times 10^{-6}\right)(3.3 - 1 - 1)}\left[\ln\left(4\frac{3.3 - 1 - 1}{3.3 - 1 + 0.132} - 1\right) + \frac{2}{3}\right] = 1.84 \text{ ns}$$

$$\tau_P = \frac{22.1 + 1.84}{2} = 12.0 \text{ ns}$$

7.59

```
*Problem 7.59
VDD 3 0 DC 5
VI 1 0 DC 0 PWL (0 0.25 1N 3.39 25N 3.39 26N 0.25 300N 0.25)
CL 2 0 0.25PF
ML 3 3 2 0 NMOSFET W=1U L=3.39U
MS 2 1 0 0 NMOSFET W=3.53U L=1U
.MODEL NMOSFET NMOS LEVEL=1 KP=25U VTO=1 GAMMA=0.5 PHI=0.6
.OP
.TRAN 0.25N 300N
.DC VI 0 5 .01
.PROBE V(1) V(2)
```

```
.PRINT TRAN V(1) V(2)
.END
```

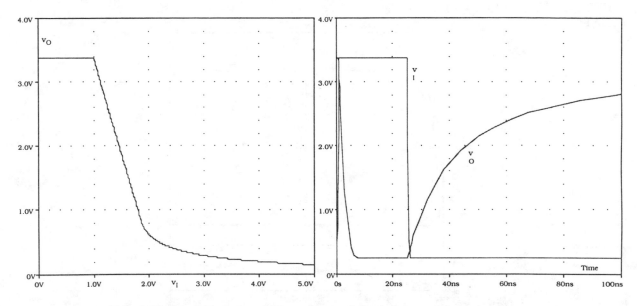

Results: t_f = 3.7 ns, t_r = 152 ns, t_{PHL} = 1.9 ns, t_{PLH} = 16 ns, t_P = 9 ns

$$t_r = \frac{160}{9}\frac{(0.25pF)}{(25\times10^{-6})\left(\dfrac{1}{3.39}\right)(5-1.61-0.25)} = 192 \text{ ns}$$

$$t_f = \frac{(0.25pF)}{(25\times10^{-6})(3.53)(5-1.61-1)}\left[\ln\frac{5-1.61-1+0.9(3.14)}{5-1.61-0.9(3.14)} + 2\frac{1-0.1(3.14)}{5-1.61-1}\right] = 3.32 \text{ ns}$$

$$\tau_{PLH} = 2R_{ONL}C = 2\frac{(0.25pF)}{(25\times10^{-6})\left(\dfrac{1}{3.39}\right)(5-1.61-0.25)} = 21.6 \text{ ns}$$

$$\tau_{PHL} = \frac{(0.25pF)}{(25\times10^{-6})(3.53)(5-1.61-1)}\left[\ln\left(4\frac{5-1.61-1}{5-1.61+0.25}-1\right)+\frac{2}{3}\right] = 1.37 \text{ ns}$$

$$\tau_P = \frac{21.6+1.37}{2} \text{ ns} = 11.5 \text{ ns}$$

7.60

```
*Problem 7.60 - Saturated load cascade inverter delay
VDD 1 0 DC 5
VI 2 0 PWL (0 3.39 0.1N .25 100N .25 100.1N 3.39 200N 3.39)
ML1 1 1 3 0 NMOSFET W=2U L=6.78U AS=8P AD=8P
MS1 3 2 0 0 NMOSFET W=7.06U L=2U AS=28P AD=28P
ML2 1 1 4 0 NMOSFET W=2U L=6.78U AS=8P AD=8P
MS2 4 3 0 0 NMOSFET W=7.06U L=2U AS=28P AD=28P
ML3 1 1 5 0 NMOSFET W=2U L=6.78U AS=8P AD=8P
MS3 5 4 0 0 NMOSFET W=7.06U L=2U AS=28P AD=28P
ML4 1 1 6 0 NMOSFET W=2U L=6.78U AS=8P AD=8P
MS4 6 5 0 0 NMOSFET W=7.06U L=2U AS=28P AD=28P
ML5 1 1 7 0 NMOSFET W=2U L=6.78U AS=8P AD=8P
MS5 7 6 0 0 NMOSFET W=7.06U L=2U AS=28P AD=28P
.MODEL NMOSFET NMOS LEVEL=1 KP=25U VTO=1 GAMMA=0.5 PHI=0.6
+TOX=40N CJ=390U CJSW=500P CGDO=330P CGSO=330P CGBO=395P
```

```
.OP
.TRAN 0.2N 200N
.PROBE V(2) V(3) V(5) V(6)
.END
```

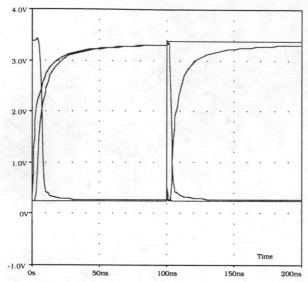

The results of this problem are highly dependent upon the models used. The model must include capacitances. Thus, at a minimum, the TOX parameter must be specified. For the models above:

First inverter: $t_r = 25\text{ns}$ $t_f = 0.5\text{ns}$ $\tau_{PLH} = 2.5\text{ns}$ $\tau_{PHL} = 0.4\text{ns}$

$$C = \frac{9}{160}\frac{t_r}{R_{onL}} = \frac{9}{160}\left(25\text{x}10^{-9}\right)\left(\frac{25\text{x}10^{-6}}{3.39}\right)(5-1-0.25) = 39\text{ fF}$$

Fourth inverter: $t_r = 25\text{ns}$ $t_f = 4\text{ns}$ $\tau_{PLH} = 2.5\text{ns}$ $\tau_{PHL} = 1.3\text{ns}$

Rise time and τ_{PLH} are controlled by the slow transition of the load device and are essentially the same. Fall time and τ_{PHL} are faster for the first inverter because of the much faster input signal transistion.

7.61

```
*Problem 7.61
VDD 3 0 DC 5
VGG 4 0 DC 7.5
VI 1 0 DC 0 PWL (0 0.25 1N 5 25N 5 26N 0.25 300N 0.25)
CL 2 0 0.15PF
ML 3 4 2 0 NMOSFET W=1U L=9.03U
MS 2 1 0 0 NMOSFET W=2.06U L=1U
.MODEL NMOSFET NMOS LEVEL=1 KP=25U VTO=1 GAMMA=0.5 PHI=0.6
.OP
.DC VI 0 5 .01
.TRAN 0.25N 300N
.PROBE V(1) V(2)
.PRINT TRAN V(1) V(2)
.END
```

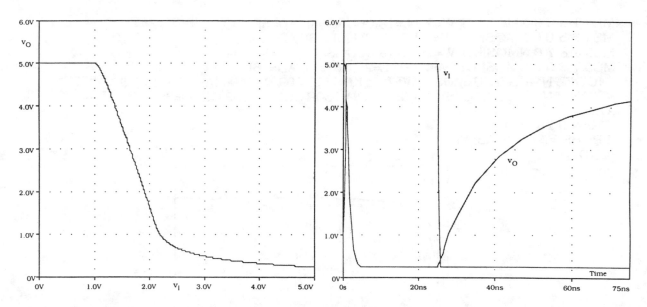

Results: $t_f = 2.1$ ns, $t_r = 76$ ns, $t_{PHL} = 1.1$ ns, $t_{PLH} = 14$ ns, $t_P = 7.5$ ns

t_f and τ_{PHL} are the same as for the resistor load:

$$t_f = \frac{(0.15\text{pF})}{(2.06)(25\text{x}10^{-6})(5-1)}\left[\ln\left(2\frac{5-1}{5-0.9(4.75)}\right)+2\frac{1-0.1(4.75)}{5-1}\right] = 1.87 \text{ ns}$$

$$\tau_{PHL} = \frac{(0.15\text{pF})}{(2.06)(25\text{x}10^{-6})(5-1)}\left[\ln\left(4\frac{5-1}{5+0.25}-1\right)+\frac{1}{2}\right] = 0.886 \text{ ns}$$

Estimates for t_r and τ_{PLH} were not developed in the text, but we see from Fig. 7.40 that they will be less than those for the saturated load resistor and greater than those of the resistor load.

$$2.2RC \leq t_r \leq \frac{160}{9}R_{ONL}C$$

$$2.2(95\text{k}\Omega)(0.15\text{pF}) \leq t_r \leq \frac{17.78(0.15\text{pF})}{(25\text{x}10^{-6})\left(\dfrac{1}{3.53}\right)(5-1-0.25)} \rightarrow 31.4\text{ns} \leq t_r \leq 100\text{ns}$$

$$0.69RC \leq \tau_{PLH} \leq 2R_{ONL}C$$

$$0.69(95\text{k}\Omega)(0.15\text{pF}) \leq t_{PLH} \leq \frac{2(0.15\text{pF})}{(25\text{x}10^{-6})\left(\dfrac{1}{3.53}\right)(5-1-0.25)} \rightarrow 8.80\text{ns} \leq \tau_{PLH} \leq 11.3\text{ns}$$

7.62

```
*Problem 7.62 - Linear load cascade inverter delay
VDD 1 0 DC 5
VGG 8 0 DC 7.5
VI 2 0 PWL (0 5 0.1N .25 100N .25 100.1N 5 200N 5)
ML1 1 8 3 0 NMOSFET W=2U L=18.06U AS=8P AD=8P
MS1 3 2 0 0 NMOSFET W=4.12U L=2U AS=16P AD=16P
ML2 1 8 4 0 NMOSFET W=2U L=18.06U AS=8P AD=8P
MS2 4 3 0 0 NMOSFET W=4.12U L=2U AS=16P AD=16P
ML3 1 8 5 0 NMOSFET W=2U L=18.06U AS=8P AD=8P
MS3 5 4 0 0 NMOSFET W=4.12U L=2U AS=16P AD=16P
```

ML4 1 8 6 0 NMOSFET W=2U L=18.06U AS=8P AD=8P
MS4 6 5 0 0 NMOSFET W=4.12U L=2U AS=16P AD=16P
ML5 1 8 7 0 NMOSFET W=2U L=18.06U AS=8P AD=8P
MS5 7 6 0 0 NMOSFET W=4.12U L=2U AS=16P AD=16P
.MODEL NMOSFET NMOS LEVEL=1 KP=25U VTO=1 GAMMA=0.5 PHI=0.6
+TOX=40N CJ=390U CJSW=500P CGDO=330P CGSO=330P CGBO=395P
.OP
.TRAN 0.2N 200N
.PROBE V(2) V(3) V(5) V(6)
.END

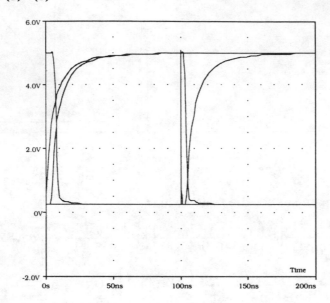

The results of this problem are highly dependent upon the models used. The model must include capacitances. Thus, at a minimum, the TOX parameter must be specified. For the models above:

First inverter: $t_r = 19\text{ns}$ $t_f = 0.5\text{ns}$ $\tau_{PLH} = 3.8\text{ns}$ $\tau_{PHL} = 0.2\text{ns}$

$$C = \frac{\tau_{PHL}}{R_{ons}} \frac{1}{\left[\ln\left(4\dfrac{V_{DD} - V_{TNS}}{V_{DD} + V_{OL}} - 1\right) + \dfrac{1}{2}\right]} = 0.4\text{x}10^{-9} \frac{(2.06)(25\text{x}10^{-6})(5-1)}{\left[\ln\left(4\dfrac{5-1}{5+0.25} - 1\right) + \dfrac{1}{2}\right]} = 68 \text{ fF}$$

Fourth inverter: $t_r = 19\text{ns}$ $t_f = 3.5\text{ns}$ $\tau_{PLH} = 3.8\text{ns}$ $\tau_{PHL} = 0.4\text{ns}$

Rise time and τ_{PLH} are controlled by the slow transition of the load device and are essentially the same. Fall time and τ_{PHL} are faster for the first inverter because of the much faster input signal transistion.

7.63

We will start by assuming $\tau_P \approx \dfrac{\tau_{PLH}}{2}$ since we expect $\tau_{PLH} \gg \tau_{PHL}$

$$\tau_{PLH} = R_{onL}C\left[\ln\left(4\frac{-(-3)}{3-0.25} - 1\right) + 2\frac{3-3-0.25}{-(-3)}\right] = 1.046 R_{onL}C$$

$$R_{onL} = \frac{2(3\text{ns})}{1.046(1\text{pF})} = 5.736\text{k}\Omega \quad | \quad \left(\frac{W}{L}\right)_L = \frac{1}{5736(25\text{x}10^{-6})(3)} = \frac{2.324}{1}$$

$\left(\dfrac{W}{L}\right)_S$ must be chosen to set the design value of V_{OL}

$$25\text{x}10^{-6}\left(\frac{W}{L}\right)_S\left(3-1-\frac{0.25}{2}\right)0.25 = \frac{25\text{x}10^{-6}}{2}\left(\frac{2.324}{1}\right)(-3)^2 \rightarrow \left(\frac{W}{L}\right)_S = \frac{22.3}{1}$$

Now find the actual value of τ_P

$$\tau_{PHL} = \frac{(1pF)}{22.3\left(25\text{x}10^{-6}\right)(3-1)}\left[\ln\left(4\frac{3-1}{3+0.25}-1\right)+\frac{1}{2}\right] = 0.789ns \rightarrow \tau_P = \frac{6+.789}{2} = 3.40ns$$

To compensate for this error, we simply rescale the device sizes which changes the currents but not the value of V_{OL}.

$$\left(\frac{W}{L}\right)_S = \frac{22.3}{1}\frac{3.40ns}{3ns} = \frac{25.3}{1} \quad | \quad \left(\frac{W}{L}\right)_L = \frac{2.324}{1}\frac{3.40ns}{3ns} = \frac{2.63}{1}$$

$$t_f = \frac{(1pF)}{25.3\left(25\text{x}10^{-6}\right)(3-1)}\left[\ln\left(2\frac{3-1}{3-0.9(2.75)}-1\right)+2\frac{1-0.1(2.75)}{3-1}\right] = 2.07\ ns$$

$$t_r = \frac{(1pF)}{2.63\left(25\text{x}10^{-6}\right)(3)}\left[\ln\left(-\frac{20(-3)}{2.75}-1\right)+2\frac{3-3-0.25-0.1(2.75)}{-(-3)}\right] = 13.6\ ns$$

7.64

```
*Problem 7.64
VDD 3 0 DC 5
VI 1 0 DC 0 PWL (0 0.25 1N 5 25N 5 26N 0.25 300N 0.25)
CL 2 0 0.20PF
ML 3 2 2 0 DMOSFET W=1U L=2.15U
MS 2 1 0 0 NMOSFET W=2.06U L=1U
.MODEL DMOSFET NMOS LEVEL=1 KP=25U VTO=-3 GAMMA=0.5 PHI=0.6
.MODEL NMOSFET NMOS LEVEL=1 KP=25U VTO=1 GAMMA=0.5 PHI=0.6
.OP
.DC VI 0 5 0.01
.TRAN 0.25N 300N
.PROBE V(1) V(2)
.PRINT TRAN V(1) V(2)
.END
```

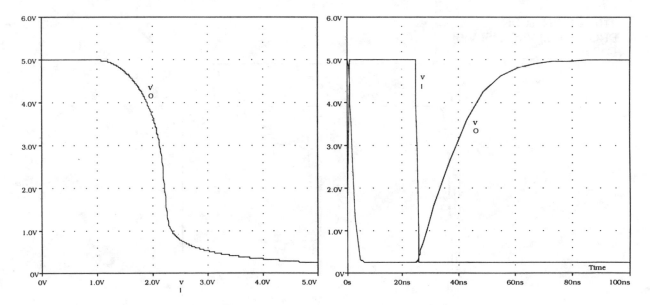

Results: $t_f = 3.3$ ns, $t_r = 26$ ns, $t_{PHL} = 1.4$ ns, $t_{PLH} = 11$ ns, $t_P = 6.2$ ns

$$t_f = \frac{(0.2pF)}{2.06\left(25x10^{-6}\right)(5-1)}\left[\ln\left(2\frac{5-1}{5-0.9(4.75)}-1\right)+2\frac{1-0.1(4.75)}{5-1}\right]=2.49 \text{ ns}$$

$$\tau_{PHL} = \frac{(0.2pF)}{2.06\left(25x10^{-6}\right)(5-1)}\left[\ln\left(4\frac{5-1}{5+0.25}-1\right)+\frac{1}{2}\right]=1.18 \text{ns}$$

$$t_r = \frac{(0.2pF)}{\frac{1}{2.15}\left(25x10^{-6}\right)(2.93)}\left[\ln\left(-\frac{20(-2.93)}{4.75}-1\right)+2\frac{5-2.93-0.25-0.1(4.75)}{-(-2.93)}\right]=19.6 \text{ ns}$$

$$\tau_{PLH} = \frac{(0.2pF)}{\frac{1}{2.15}\left(25x10^{-6}\right)(2.93)}\left[\ln\left(4\frac{-(-2.93)}{5-0.25}-1\right)+2\frac{5-2.93-0.25}{-(-2.93)}\right]=9.54 \text{ ns}$$

$$\tau_P = \frac{1.18+9.54}{2}=5.36 \text{ ns}$$

7.65

```
*Problem 7.65 - Depletion load cascade inverter delay
VDD 1 0 DC 5
VI 2 0 PWL (0 5 0.1N .25 50N .25 50.1N 5 100N 5)
ML1 1 3 3 0 DMOSFET W=2U L=4.30U AS=8P AD=8P
MS1 3 2 0 0 NMOSFET W=4.12U L=2U AS=16P AD=16P
ML2 1 4 4 0 DMOSFET W=2U L=4.30U AS=8P AD=8P
MS2 4 3 0 0 NMOSFET W=4.12U L=2U AS=16P AD=16P
ML3 1 5 5 0 DMOSFET W=2U L=4.30U AS=8P AD=8P
MS3 5 4 0 0 NMOSFET W=4.12U L=2U AS=16P AD=16P
ML4 1 6 6 0 DMOSFET W=2U L=4.30U AS=8P AD=8P
MS4 6 5 0 0 NMOSFET W=4.12U L=2U AS=16P AD=16P
ML5 1 7 7 0 DMOSFET W=2U L=4.30U AS=8P AD=8P
MS5 7 6 0 0 NMOSFET W=4.12U L=2U AS=16P AD=16P
.MODEL NMOSFET NMOS LEVEL=1 KP=25U VTO=1 GAMMA=0.5 PHI=0.6
+TOX=40N CJ=390U CJSW=500P CGDO=330P CGSO=330P CGBO=395P
.MODEL DMOSFET NMOS LEVEL=1 KP=25U VTO=-3 GAMMA=0.5 PHI=0.6
+TOX=40N CJ=390U CJSW=500P CGDO=330P CGSO=330P CGBO=395P
.OP
.TRAN 0.2N 100N
.PROBE V(2) V(3) V(5) V(6)
.END
```

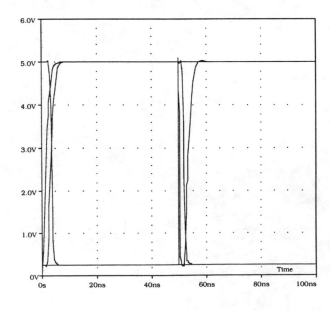

The results of this problem are highly dependent upon the models used. The model must include capacitances. Thus, at a minimum, the TOX parameter must be specified. For the models above:

First inverter: $t_r = 2.6$ns $\quad t_f = 0.3$ns $\quad \tau_{PLH} = 1.3$ns $\quad \tau_{PHL} = 0.15$ns

$$C = \frac{\tau_{PHL}}{R_{ons}} \frac{1}{\left[\ln\left(4\dfrac{V_{DD} - V_{TNS}}{V_{DD} + V_{OL}} - 1\right) + \dfrac{1}{2}\right]} = 0.15 \times 10^{-9} \frac{(2.06)(25 \times 10^{-6})(5-1)}{\left[\ln\left(4\dfrac{5-1}{5+0.25} - 1\right) + \dfrac{1}{2}\right]} = 25 \text{ fF}$$

Fourth inverter: $t_r = 2.6$ns $\quad t_f = 1$ns $\quad \tau_{PLH} = 1.3$ns $\quad \tau_{PHL} = 0.4$ns

Rise time and τ_{PLH} are controlled by the slow transition of the laod device and are essentially the same. Fall time and τ_{PHL} are faster for the first inverter because of the much faster input signal transistion.

_____

7.66

```
*Problem 7.66 - 2-Input Depletion load NAND Gate
VDD 5 0 DC 5
VB 3 0 DC 5
VA 1 0 DC 5 PWL (0 5 0.1N .25 100N .25 100.1N 5 200N 5)
*NAND1 - A Input Switching
ML1 5 4 4 0 DMOSFET W=2U L=4.30U AS=8P AD=8P
MSB1 4 3 2 0 NMOSFET W=8.48U L=2U AS=16P AD=16P
MSA1 2 1 0 0 NMOSFET W=8.12U L=2U AS=16P AD=16P
*NAND2 - B Input Switching
ML2 5 6 6 0 DMOSFET W=2U L=4.30U AS=8P AD=8P
MSB2 6 1 7 0 NMOSFET W=8.48U L=2U AS=16P AD=16P
MSA2 7 3 0 0 NMOSFET W=8.12U L=2U AS=16P AD=16P
*NAND3 - Both Inputs Switching
ML3 5 9 9 0 DMOSFET W=2U L=4.30U AS=8P AD=8P
MSB3 9 1 8 0 NMOSFET W=8.48U L=2U AS=16P AD=16P
MSA3 8 1 0 0 NMOSFET W=8.12U L=2U AS=16P AD=16P
.MODEL NMOSFET NMOS LEVEL=1 KP=25U VTO=1 GAMMA=0.5 PHI=0.6
+TOX=40N CJ=390U CJSW=500P CGDO=330P CGSO=330P CGBO=395P
.MODEL DMOSFET NMOS LEVEL=1 KP=25U VTO=-3 GAMMA=0.5 PHI=0.6
+TOX=40N CJ=390U CJSW=500P CGDO=330P CGSO=330P CGBO=395P
.OP
.DC VA 5 0 .01
.TRAN 0.2N 200N
.PROBE V(4) V(6) V(9)
.END
```

The VTC for the case of B is shifted by approximately 0.1 V relative to the case for A switching, and the case of both switching is shifted by an additional 0.3 V. The delay results for this problem are highly dependent upon the models used. The model must include capacitances. Thus, at a minimum, the TOX parameter must be specified. For the models above:

A switching: $t_r = 3.5$ns $\quad t_f = 0.3$ns $\quad \tau_{PLH} = 2.6$ns $\quad \tau_{PHL} = 80$ps

B switching: $t_r = 1.5$ns $\quad t_f = 0.25$ns $\quad \tau_{PLH} = 0.8$ns $\quad \tau_{PHL} = 130$ps

For both inputs switching, the results are identical to the B switching case.

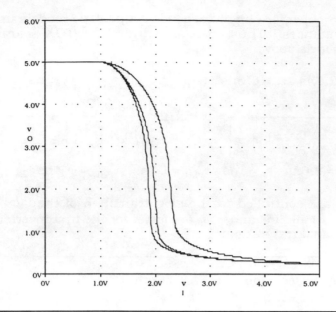

(a) $V_{TN} = 1 + 0.5\left(\sqrt{0.25 + 0.6} - \sqrt{0.6}\right) = 1.07V$

$50 \times 10^{-6} = \dfrac{25 \times 10^{-6}}{2}\left(\dfrac{W}{L}\right)_L (5 - 0.25 - 1.07)^2 \rightarrow \left(\dfrac{W}{L}\right)_L = \dfrac{1}{3.39}$

(b) $50 \times 10^{-6} = \dfrac{25 \times 10^{-6}}{2}\left(\dfrac{W}{L}\right)_L (5 - 0.25 - 1)^2 \rightarrow \left(\dfrac{W}{L}\right)_L = \dfrac{1}{3.52}$

(c) $50 \times 10^{-6} = 25 \times 10^{-6}\left(\dfrac{W}{L}\right)_L \left(7.5 - 0.25 - 1.07 - \dfrac{4.75}{2}\right)4.75 \rightarrow \left(\dfrac{W}{L}\right)_L = \dfrac{1}{9.03}$

(d) $50 \times 10^{-6} = 25 \times 10^{-6}\left(\dfrac{W}{L}\right)_L \left(7.5 - 0.25 - 1 - \dfrac{4.75}{2}\right)4.75 \rightarrow \left(\dfrac{W}{L}\right)_L = \dfrac{1}{9.20}$

(e) $V_{TN} = -3 + 0.5\left(\sqrt{0.25 + 0.6} - \sqrt{0.6}\right) = -2.93V$

$50 \times 10^{-6} = \dfrac{25 \times 10^{-6}}{2}\left(\dfrac{W}{L}\right)_L (-2.93)^2 \rightarrow \left(\dfrac{W}{L}\right)_L = \dfrac{1}{2.15}$

(f) $50 \times 10^{-6} = \dfrac{25 \times 10^{-6}}{2}\left(\dfrac{W}{L}\right)_L (-3)^2 \rightarrow \left(\dfrac{W}{L}\right)_L = \dfrac{1}{2.25}$

7.68 For $V_{DD} = -5$ V, we have $V_{OH} = -0.25$ V with a power dissipation of 0.25 mW. Since these gates are all ratioed logic design, the ratio of the W/L ratios of the load and switching transistors does not change. We only need to scale both equally to achieve the power level.

(a) $R_L = 95k\Omega \quad \left(\dfrac{W}{L}\right)_S = \dfrac{25}{10}\dfrac{2.06}{1} = \dfrac{5.15}{1}$

(b) $\left(\dfrac{W}{L}\right)_L = \dfrac{25}{10}\dfrac{1}{3.39} = \dfrac{1}{1.36} \quad | \quad \left(\dfrac{W}{L}\right)_S = \dfrac{25}{10}\dfrac{3.53}{1} = \dfrac{8.83}{1}$

(c) $\left(\dfrac{W}{L}\right)_L = \dfrac{25}{10}\dfrac{1}{9.03} = \dfrac{1}{3.61} \quad | \quad \left(\dfrac{W}{L}\right)_S = \dfrac{25}{10}2.06 = \dfrac{5.15}{1}$

(d) $\left(\dfrac{W}{L}\right)_L = \dfrac{25}{10}\dfrac{1}{2.15} = \dfrac{1.16}{1} \quad | \quad \left(\dfrac{W}{L}\right)_S = \dfrac{25}{10}\dfrac{2.06}{1} = \dfrac{5.15}{1}$

7.69

$$V_{OL} = -5 + 1 = -4 \text{ V} \quad | \quad \left(\frac{2}{1}\right)10^{-5}\left(4 - 1 - \frac{-V_{OH}}{2}\right)(-V_{OH}) = \frac{1}{4}\frac{10^{-5}}{2}(5 + V_{OH} - 1)^2$$

$$9V_{OH}^2 + 56V_{OH} + 16 = 0 \rightarrow V_{OH} = -0.300 \text{ V}$$

7.70

Pretending this is an NMOS gate and using symmetry of the equations:

$$V_{DD} = +5 \quad | \quad V_{OH} = +4V \quad | \quad V_{OL} = 0.300V \quad | \quad V_{TN} = 1V \quad | \quad V_{IL} = V_{TN} = 1V$$

$$V_{IH}: V_O = \frac{5-1}{\sqrt{1 + 3\frac{(2/1)}{(1/4)}}} = 0.800V \quad | \quad V_{IH} = 1 + \frac{0.800}{2} + \frac{(1/4)}{2(2/1)}\frac{1}{0.800}(5 - 0.8 - 1)^2 = 2.20V$$

Then for the PMOS gate, $V_{IH} = -1V$ and $V_{IL} = -2.20V$

$$NM_L = V_{IL} - V_{OL} = -2.20 - (-4) = 1.80 \text{ V} \quad | \quad NM_H = V_{OH} - V_{IH} = -0.3 - (-1) = 0.700 \text{ V}$$

7.71 Note that V_{TO} is incorrect in the first printing and K'_p should be 10 µA/V².

Pretend this is an NMOS gate with $V_{DD} = 3.3V$ and $V_{OL} = 0.33V$

$$V_{OH} = 3.3 - \left[0.7 + 0.5\left(\sqrt{V_{OH} + 0.6} - \sqrt{0.6}\right)\right] \rightarrow V_{OH} = 2.16V$$

$$V_{TNL} = 0.7 + 0.5\left(\sqrt{0.33 + 0.6} - \sqrt{0.6}\right) = 0.795 \quad | \quad I_{DS} = \frac{0.1mW}{3.3V} = 30.3\mu A$$

$$30.3\mu A = \frac{10\mu A}{2}\left(\frac{W}{L}\right)_L(3.3 - 0.33 - 0.795)^2 \rightarrow \left(\frac{W}{L}\right)_L = \frac{1.28}{1}$$

$$30.3\mu A = 10\mu A\left(\frac{W}{L}\right)_S\left(2.16 - 0.70 - \frac{0.33}{2}\right)0.33 \rightarrow \left(\frac{W}{L}\right)_S = \frac{7.09}{1}$$

7.72

Using the results from Problem 7.71 and pretending this is an NMOS gate:

$$V_{DD} = +3.3V \quad | \quad V_{OH} = +2.16V \quad | \quad V_{OL} 0.33V \quad | \quad V_{TN} = 0.7V \quad | \quad V_{IL} = V_{TN} = 0.7V$$

$$V_{IH}: V_O = \frac{3.3 - V_{TNL}}{\sqrt{1 + 3\frac{(7.09)}{(1.28)}}} \quad | \quad V_{TNL} = 0.7 + 0.5\left(\sqrt{V_O + 0.6} - \sqrt{0.6}\right)$$

Solving these two equations yields $V_O = 0.582V \quad | \quad V_{TNL} = 0.856V$

$$V_{IH} = 1 + \frac{0.582}{2} + \frac{1.28}{2(7.09)}\frac{1}{0.582}(3.3 - 0.581 - 0.856)^2 = 1.83V$$

For the PMOS gate, these become $V_{IH} = -0.70V$ and $V_{IL} = -1.83V$

$$NM_L = V_{IL} - V_{OL} = -1.83 - (-2.16) = 0.33 \text{ V} \quad | \quad NM_H = V_{OH} - V_{IH} = -0.33 - (-0.7) = 0.37 \text{ V}$$

7.73

$$V_{OL} = -V_{TP} \quad | \quad V_{OL} = -\left[-1 - 0.5\left(\sqrt{5 - V_{OL} + 0.6} - \sqrt{0.6}\right)\right] \rightarrow V_{OL} = 1.611V$$

$$K'_p\left(\frac{W}{L}\right)_S\left(V_{SGS} + V_{TP} - \frac{V_{SDS}}{2}\right)V_{SDS} = \frac{K'_p}{2}\left(\frac{W}{L}\right)_L(V_{SGL} + V_{TL})^2$$

$$\frac{3}{1}\left(5 - 1.61 + (-1) - \frac{5 - V_{OH}}{2}\right)(5 - V_{OH}) = \frac{1}{2}\left(\frac{1}{3}\right)(V_{OH} + V_{TPL})^2$$

$$V_{TPL} = -1 - 0.5\left(\sqrt{5 - V_{OH} + 0.6} - \sqrt{0.6}\right)$$

Solving the last two equations iteratively: $V_{OH} = 4.677$ V

7.74

Y is low only when both A and B are high: $\overline{Y} = AB$ or $Y = \overline{AB}$.

Alternatively, Y is high when either A or B is low: $Y = \overline{A} + \overline{B} = \overline{AB}$

7.75   Y is high only when both A and B are low: $Y = \overline{A}\,\overline{B}$ or $Y = \overline{A + B}$

7.76   The Using the SPICE lisiting below, $V_{OH} = 4.0$ V, $V_{OL} = -0.300$ V.

```
*Problem 7.76 Simulation of Fig.P7.69
VDD 3 0 DC -5
VI 1 0 DC 0
ML 3 3 2 2 PMOSFET W=1U L=4U
MS 2 1 0 0 PMOSFET W=2U L=1U
.MODEL PMOSFET PMOS LEVEL=1 KP=10U VTO=-1 GAMMA=0 PHI=0.6
.DC VI 0 -5 0.05
.PRINT DC V(1) V(2)
.END
```

7.77   Using the SPICE lisiting below, $V_{OL} = -2.16$ V, $V_{OH} = -0.33$ V and $I_{DS} = 30.3$ µA.

```
*Problem 7.76 - Simulation of the design of Fig. P7.71
VDD 3 0 DC -3.3
VI 1 0 DC 0
ML 3 3 2 0 PMOSFET W=1.28U L=1U
MS 2 1 0 0 PMOSFET W=7.09U L=1U
.MODEL PMOSFET PMOS LEVEL=1 KP=10U VTO=-0.7 GAMMA=0.5 PHI=0.6
.DC VI 0 -3.3 0.05
.PRINT DC V(1) V(2) I(VDD)
.END
```

7.78   Using the SPICE lisiting below, $V_{OL} = 1.61$ V, $V_{OH} = -4.68$ V.

```
*Problem 7.78 Simulation of Fig. P7.73
VDD 3 0 DC 5
VI 2 0 DC 0
ML 0 0 1 3 PMOSFET W=1U L=3U
MS 1 2 3 3 PMOSFET W=3U L=1U
.MODEL PMOSFET PMOS LEVEL=1 KP=10U VTO=-1 GAMMA=0.5 PHI=0.6
.DC VI 0 5 0.05
.PRINT DC V(1) V(2) I(VDD)
.END
```

7.79   Using the SPICE lisiting below:

```
*Problem 7.79 - Simulation of Fig. P7.69
VDD 3 0 DC -5
VI 1 0 PWL (0 -0.3 1N -4 250N -4 251N -0.3 3000N -0.3)
CL 2 0 1PF
ML 3 3 2 2 PMOSFET W=1U L=4U
MS 2 1 0 0 PMOSFET W=2U L=1U
```

```
.MODEL PMOSFET PMOS LEVEL=1 KP=10U VTO=-1
*.TRAN 1N 250N
.TRAN 5N 2U
.PROBE V(1) V(2)
.PRINT TRAN V(1) V(2)
.END
```

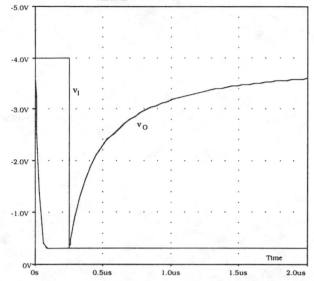

$t_r = 1.92 \ \mu s, \quad t_f = 48 \ ns,$

$\tau_{PLH} = 215 \ ns, \quad \tau_{PHL} = 22 \ ns, \quad \tau_P = 119 \ ns$

7.80   Using the SPICE lisiting below:

```
*Problem 7.80 - Simulation of Fig. P7.73
VDD 3 0 DC 5
VI 2 0 PWL (0 4.68 1N 1.61 250N 1.61 251N 4.68 3U 4.68)
CL 1 0 1PF
ML 0 0 1 3 PMOSFET W=1U L=3U
MS 1 2 3 3 PMOSFET W=3U L=1U
.MODEL PMOSFET PMOS LEVEL=1 KP=10U VTO=-1 GAMMA=0.5 PHI=0.6
.TRAN 1N 300N
*.TRAN 5N 2U
.PRINT TRAN V(1) V(2)
.END
```

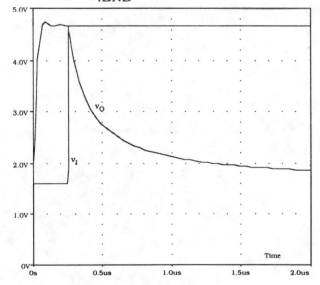

$t_r = 41 \ ns, \quad t_f = 1.34 \ \mu s,$

$\tau_{PLH} = 19 \ ns, \quad \tau_{PHL} = 145 \ ns, \quad \tau_P = 82 \ ns$

CHAPTER 8

8.1

$$K_n' = \mu_n C_{ox}'' = \mu_n \frac{\varepsilon_{ox}}{T_{ox}} = \mu_n \frac{3.9\varepsilon_0}{T_{ox}} = \left(500 \frac{cm^2}{V-sec}\right) \frac{(3.9)(8.854x10^{-14} F/cm)}{16x10^{-9} m(100cm/m)}$$

$$K_n' = 108x10^{-6} \frac{F}{V-sec} = 108 \times 10^{-6} \frac{A}{V^2} = 108 \frac{\mu A}{V^2}$$

$$K_p' = \mu_p C_{ox}'' = \frac{\mu_p}{\mu_n} K_n' = \left(\frac{200}{500}\right) 108 \frac{\mu A}{V^2} = 43.2 \frac{\mu A}{V^2}$$

8.2

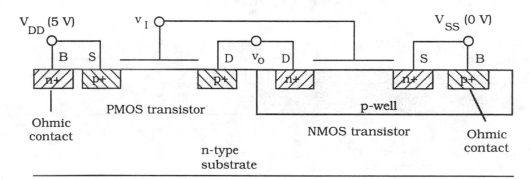

8.3

(a) $I = I_S A = \left(500 \frac{pA}{cm^2}\right)(1cm \times 0.5cm) = 250pA$

(b) $I = I_S A + (5x10^6)\left(100 \frac{pA}{cm^2}\right)(4x10^{-4} cm)(10x10^{-4} cm) = 250 + 200 = 450pA$

(c) Same as (b)

8.4

$$C = 3\left(\frac{\varepsilon_{ox} A}{t_{ox}}\right) = 3\frac{3.9\varepsilon_0 LW}{t_{ox}} = 3\frac{3.9\left(8.854x10^{-14} \frac{F}{cm}\right)\left(\frac{5mm}{2} \frac{0.1cm}{mm}\right)(2\mu m)}{1\mu m} = 0.518 \text{ pF}$$

8.5 For $v_I = v_O$, both transistors will be saturated since $v_{GS} = v_{DS}$ for each device. Equating the drain currents with $K_n = K_p$ yields:

(a) $\frac{K_n}{2}(v_I - V_{TN})^2 = \frac{K_p}{2}(V_{DD} - v_I + V_{TP})^2$ and $v_I - V_{TN} = V_{DD} - v_I + V_{TP}$

$$v_O = v_I = \frac{V_{DD} + V_{TN} + V_{TP}}{2} = \frac{5+1-1}{2} = 2.5V$$

(b) For $K_n = 2.5 K_p$,

$$\frac{2.5K_p}{2}(v_I - V_{TN})^2 = \frac{K_p}{2}(V_{DD} - v_I + V_{TP})^2 \text{ and } 1.58(v_I - V_{TN}) = V_{DD} - v_I + V_{TP}$$

$$v_O = v_I = \frac{V_{DD} + 1.58V_{TN} + V_{TP}}{2.58} = \frac{5+1.58(1)+(-1)}{2.58} = 2.16V$$

8.6   (a) $V_{OH} = 0$ V, $V_{OL} = -5.2$ V   (b) Same as (a). V_{OH} and V_{OL} don't depend upon W/L in a CMOS gate.

8.7
___

```
*PROBLEM 8.7 - CMOS INVERTER TRANSFER CHARACTERISTICS
VIN 1 0 DC 0
VDD 3 0 DC 5
M1 2 1 0 0 MOSN W=2U L=2U
M2 2 1 3 3 MOSP W=2U L=2U
.DC VIN 0 5 .01
*.DC VIN 2.16 2.17 .0001
.MODEL MOSN NMOS KP=2.5E-5 VTO=1.0 GAMMA=0
.MODEL MOSP  PMOS  KP=1.0E-5 VTO=-1.0 GAMMA=0
.PRINT DC V(2)
.END
```

Result: $v_I = 2.1628$ V

$$\frac{2.5K_p}{2}(v_I - V_{TN})^2 = \frac{K_p}{2}(V_{DD} - v_I + V_{TP})^2 \quad \text{and} \quad 1.58(v_I - V_{TN}) = V_{DD} - v_I + V_{TP}$$

$$v_O = v_I = \frac{V_{DD} + 1.58V_{TN} + V_{TP}}{2.58} = \frac{5 + 1.58(1) + (-1)}{2.58} = 2.16V$$

8.8
___

$$V_{OH} = 5 \text{ V} \quad | \quad \frac{K_p'}{2}\left(\frac{1}{1}\right)(5-1)^2 = K_n'\left(\frac{4}{1}\right)\left(5 - 1 + \frac{V_{OL}}{2}\right)V_{OL}$$

$$\frac{10^{-5}}{2(2.5\times10^{-5})}\left(\frac{16}{4}\right) = \left(4 + \frac{V_{OL}}{2}\right)V_{OL} \quad \text{and rearranging: } V_{OL}^2 - 8V_{OL} + 1.6 = 0$$

$$V_{OL} = 0.205V$$

___

8.9   For the NMOS device

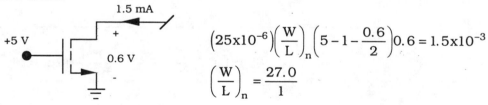

$$\left(25\times10^{-6}\right)\left(\frac{W}{L}\right)_n\left(5 - 1 - \frac{0.6}{2}\right)0.6 = 1.5\times10^{-3}$$

$$\left(\frac{W}{L}\right)_n = \frac{27.0}{1}$$

and for the PMOS device

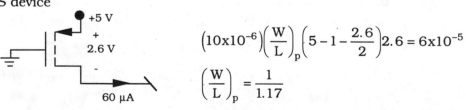

$$\left(10\times10^{-6}\right)\left(\frac{W}{L}\right)_p\left(5 - 1 - \frac{2.6}{2}\right)2.6 = 6\times10^{-5}$$

$$\left(\frac{W}{L}\right)_p = \frac{1}{1.17}$$

___

8.10

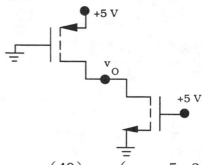

$K_n = 500 \frac{\mu A}{V^2} \approx K_p = 400 \frac{\mu A}{V^2}.$

Therefore the output will be forced below $V_{DD} / 2$.

Assume that both devices are in the linear region.

$\left(\frac{40}{1}\right)(10^{-5})\left(5 - 1 - \frac{5 - V_O}{2}\right)V_O = \left(\frac{20}{1}\right)(2.5 \times 10^{-5})\left(5 - 1 - \frac{V_O}{2}\right)V_O$

Rearranging: $V_O^2 - 32V_O + 60 = 0 \Rightarrow V_O = 2.00$ V

and the assumed operating regions are correct.

$I = \left(\frac{40}{1}\right)(10^{-5})\left(5 - 1 - \frac{5-2}{2}\right)2 = 3.00$ mA or $I = \left(\frac{20}{1}\right)(2.5 \times 10^{-5})\left(5 - 1 - \frac{2}{2}\right)2 = 3.00$ mA

8.11

$K_R = \frac{K_n}{K_p} = 2.5 \quad | \quad V_{IH} = \frac{2(2.5)(5 - 1 - 1)}{(2.5 - 1)\left(\sqrt{1 + 3(2.5)}\right)} - \frac{5 - 2.5(1) - 1}{2.5 - 1} = 2.43V$ (Eq. 8.7)

$NM_H = V_{DD} - V_{IH} = 5 - 2.43 = 2.57V$

$V_{IL} = \frac{2\left(\sqrt{2.5}\right)(5 - 1 - 1)}{(2.5 - 1)\left(\sqrt{2.5 + 3}\right)} - \frac{5 - 2.5(1) - 1}{2.5 - 1} = 1.70V$ (Eq. 8.11) $\quad | \quad NM_L = V_{IL} = 1.70V$

8.12

$K_R = 1 \quad | \quad NM_H = \frac{3(3.3) - 3(0.75) - 5(-0.75)}{8} = 1.43V$ (Eq. 8.9)

$NM_L = \frac{3(3.3) + 5(0.75) + 3(-0.75)}{8} = 1.43V$ (Eq. 8.13)

8.13

$K_R = \frac{K_n}{K_p} = 2.5 \quad | \quad V_{IH} = \frac{2(2.5)(3.3 - 0.75 - 0.75)}{(2.5 - 1)\left(\sqrt{1 + 3(2.5)}\right)} - \frac{3.3 - 2.5(0.75) - 0.75}{2.5 - 1} = 1.61V$ (Eq. 8.7)

$NM_H = V_{DD} - V_{IH} = 3.3 - 1.61 = 1.69V$

$V_{IL} = \frac{2\left(\sqrt{2.5}\right)(3.3 - 0.75 - 0.75)}{(2.5 - 1)\left(\sqrt{2.5 + 3}\right)} - \frac{3.3 - 2.5(0.75) - 0.75}{2.5 - 1} = 1.17V$ (Eq. 8.11)

$NM_L = V_{IL} = 1.17V$

8.14

$\tau_{PHL} = R_{onn}C\left\{\ln\left[4\left(\frac{V_{DD} - V_{TN}}{V_{DD} + V_{OL}}\right) - 1\right] + \frac{1}{2}\right\} = R_{onn}C\left\{\ln\left[4\left(\frac{3.3 - 1}{3.3 + 0}\right) - 1\right] + \frac{1}{2}\right\} = 1.08R_{onn}C$

$\tau_{PHL} = \frac{1.08(0.5 \times 10^{-12})}{\frac{2}{1}(25 \times 10^{-6})(3.3 - 1)} = 4.70ns \quad | \quad \tau_{PLH} = 1.08R_{onp}C = \frac{1.08(0.5 \times 10^{-12})}{\frac{2}{1}(10 \times 10^{-6})(3.3 - 1)} = 11.7$ ns

$\tau_P = \frac{\tau_{PHL} + \tau_{PLH}}{2} = 8.20$ ns $\quad | \quad \tau_f = 2\tau_{PHL} = 9.40$ ns $\quad \tau_r = 2\tau_{PLH} = 23.4$ ns

---

8.15

For the symmetrical inverter, $\tau_P = \dfrac{0.322C}{K_n} = 3$ ns

$$\left(\frac{W}{L}\right)_n = \frac{0.322(10^{-12})}{(3\times10^{-9})(25\times10^{-6})} = \frac{4.29}{1} \quad \text{and} \quad \left(\frac{W}{L}\right)_p = 2.5\left(\frac{W}{L}\right)_n = \frac{10.7}{1}$$

8.16

(a) For the symmetrical inverter, $\tau_P = \dfrac{0.322C}{K_n} = 1$ ns $\quad \left(\dfrac{W}{L}\right)_n = \dfrac{0.322(10^{-11})}{(10^{-9})(25\times10^{-6})} = \dfrac{129}{1}$

and $\left(\dfrac{W}{L}\right)_p = 2.5\left(\dfrac{W}{L}\right)_n = \dfrac{322}{1}$ (These are fairly large.)

(b) For the symmetrical inverter, $\tau_{PHL} = \tau_{PLH} = \tau_P = 1$ ns;

$$\tau_{PHL} = R_{onn}C\left\{\ln\left[4\left(\frac{V_{DD}-V_{TN}}{V_{DD}+V_{OL}}\right)-1\right]+\frac{1}{2}\right\} = R_{onn}C\left\{\ln\left[4\left(\frac{3.3-0.7}{3.3+0}\right)-1\right]+\frac{1}{2}\right\} = 1.27R_{onn}C$$

$$\left(\frac{W}{L}\right)_n = \frac{1.27(10^{-11})}{(10^{-9})(25\times10^{-6})(3.3-0.70)} = \frac{195}{1} \quad \text{and} \quad \left(\frac{W}{L}\right)_p = 2.5\left(\frac{W}{L}\right)_n = \frac{488}{1}$$

8.17

```
*PROBLEM 8.17 - CMOS INVERTER
DELAY
VIN 1 0 PULSE (0 5 0 0.1N 0.1N 10N
20N)
VDD 3 0 DC 5
M1 2 1 0 0 MOSN W=4U L=2U
AS=16P AD=16P
M2 2 1 3 3 MOSP W=10U L=2U
AS=40P AD=40P
CL 2 0 100FF
.OP
.TRAN 0.1N 20N
.MODEL MOSN NMOS KP=5E-5
VTO=0.91 GAMMA=0.99
+LAMBDA=.02 TOX=41.5N
+CGSO=330P CGDO=330P CJ=3.9E-4
CJSW=510P
.MODEL MOSP PMOS KP=2E-5
VTO=-0.77 GAMMA=0.5
+LAMBDA=.05 TOX=41.5N
+CGSO=315P CGDO=315P CJ=2.0E-4
CJSW=180P
.PRINT TRAN V(2)
.PROBE V(1) V(2)
.END
```

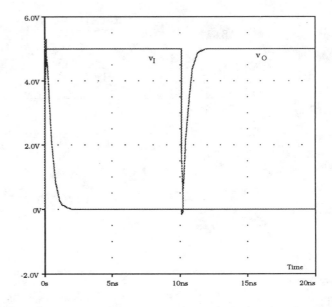

Results: $t_r = 0.75$ ns, $t_f = 0.90$ ns, $\tau_{PHL} = 0.40$ ns, $\tau_{PLH} = 0.35$ ns

$$C_1 = \frac{\tau_{PHL}}{1.29R_{onn}} = \frac{4\times10^{-10}}{1.29}\left(\frac{2}{1}\right)(50\times10^{-6})(5-0.91) = 127 \text{ fF}$$

$$C_1 = \frac{\tau_{PLH}}{1.29R_{onp}} = \frac{3.5\times10^{-10}}{1.29}\left(\frac{5}{1}\right)(20\times10^{-6})(5-0.77) = 115 \text{ fF} \mid \overline{C} = \frac{127+115}{2} \text{ fF} = 121 \text{ fF}$$

8.18

```
*PROBLEM 8.18 - FIVE CASCADED INVERTERS
VDD 1 0 DC 5
VIN 2 0 PULSE (0 5 0 0.1N 0.1N 10N 20N)
*
MN1 3 2 0 0 MOSN W=16U L=2U AS=64P AD=64P
MP1 3 2 1 1 MOSP W=40U L=2U AS=160P AD=160P
*AS=4UM*W  - AD=4UM*W
*
MN2 4 3 0 0 MOSN W=16U L=2U AS=64P AD=64P
MP2 4 3 1 1 MOSP W=40U L=2U AS=160P AD=160P
*
MN3 5 4 0 0 MOSN W=16U L=2U AS=64P AD=64P
MP3 5 4 1 1 MOSP W=40U L=2U AS=160P AD=160P
*
MN4 6 5 0 0 MOSN W=16U L=2U AS=64P AD=64P
MP4 6 5 1 1 MOSP W=40U L=2U AS=160P AD=160P
*
MN5 7 6 0 0 MOSN W=16U L=2U AS=64P AD=64P
MP5 7 6 1 1 MOSP W=40U L=2U AS=160P AD=160P
.OP
.TRAN 0.025N 20N
.MODEL MOSN NMOS KP=5E-5 VTO=0.91 GAMMA=0.99
+LAMBDA=.02 TOX=41.5N
+CGSO=330P CGDO=330P CJ=3.9E-4 CJSW=510P
.MODEL MOSP  PMOS  KP=2E-5 VTO=-0.77 GAMMA=0.5
+LAMBDA=.05 TOX=41.5N
+CGSO=315P CGDO=315P CJ=2.0E-4 CJSW=180P
.PROBE V(2) V(3) V(5) V(6)
.END
```

First inverter: $t_r = 0.35$ ns, $t_f = 0.35$ ns, $\tau_{PLH} = 0.15$ ns, $\tau_{PHL} = 0.20$ ns

Fourth inverter: $t_r = 0.50$ ns, $t_f = 0.45$ ns, $\tau_{PLH} = 0.25$ ns, $\tau_{PHL} = 0.30$ ns

$$C = \frac{\tau_{PHL}}{1.29R_{onn}} = \frac{2x10^{-10}}{1.29}\left(\frac{8}{1}\right)\left(50x10^{-6}\right)(5-0.91) = 254 \text{ fF}$$

$$C = \frac{\tau_{PLH}}{1.29R_{onp}} = \frac{1.5x10^{-10}}{1.29}\left(\frac{20}{1}\right)\left(20x10^{-6}\right)(5-0.77) = 197 \text{ fF} \mid \overline{C} = \frac{254+197}{2} \text{ fF} = 226 \text{ fF}$$

The average capacitance of 224 fF that is required to fit the results is consistent with the device capacitances calculated by SPICE in the .OP statement. The approximate 2:1 relationship holds between rise/fall times and the propagation delay times. The first inverter response is faster than that of the fourth inverter because of the rapid rise and fall times on the input signal. The first inverter response is closest to our model used for hand calculations. However, the response of inverter four is more representative of the actual logic situation.

8.19

(a) $\dfrac{2W}{10^6 \text{gates}} = 2\mu W / \text{gate}$; $P = CV_{DD}^2 f$; $C = \dfrac{2x10^{-6}}{5^2\left(5x10^6\right)} = 16.0 \text{ fF}$

(b) $C = \dfrac{2x10^{-6}}{3.3^2\left(5x10^6\right)} = 36.7 \text{ fF}$

8.20

(a) $\dfrac{20W}{5x10^6 \text{gates}} = 4\mu W / \text{gate}$ (b) $I = \dfrac{20W}{3.3V} = 6.06 \text{ A}$

8.21

(a) $P = 64CV_{DD}^2 f = 64(25 \times 10^{-12})(5^2)\dfrac{1}{10^{-8}} = 4$ W | (b) $P = 64(25 \times 10^{-12})(3.3^2)\dfrac{1}{10^{-8}} = 1.74$ W

8.22

$$\frac{20}{1}\frac{25 \times 10^{-6}}{2}(v_I - V_{TN})^2 = \frac{20}{1}\frac{10 \times 10^{-6}}{2}(V_{DD} - v_I + V_{TP})^2 \rightarrow 1.58(v_I - V_{TN}) = V_{DD} - v_I + V_{TP}$$

(a) $v_O = v_I = \dfrac{V_{DD} + 1.58V_{TN} + V_{TP}}{2.58}\quad \dfrac{5 + 1.58(1) + (-1)}{2.58} = 2.16$ V

Peak current occurs for $v_O = v_I$: $\quad i_{DS} = \dfrac{20}{1}\dfrac{25 \times 10^{-6}}{2}(2.16 - 1)^2 = 336\ \mu A$

(b) $v_O = v_I = \dfrac{3.3 + 1.58(1) + (-1)}{2.58} = 1.50$ V $\quad | \quad i_{DS} = \dfrac{20}{1}\dfrac{10 \times 10^{-6}}{2}(1.50 - 1)^2 = 25.0\ \mu A$

8.23

For a symmetrical inverter, the peak current occurs for $v_O = v_I = \dfrac{V_{DD}}{2}$:

$$\frac{2}{1}\frac{25 \times 10^{-6}}{2}(v_I - V_{TN})^2 = \frac{25}{1}\frac{10 \times 10^{-6}}{2}(V_{DD} - v_I + V_{TP})^2 \rightarrow (v_I - V_{TN}) = V_{DD} - v_I + V_{TP}$$

(a) $v_O = v_I = \dfrac{V_{DD} + V_{TN} + V_{TP}}{2} = \dfrac{3.3 + (0.7) + (-0.7)}{2} = 1.65$ V

$\qquad i_{DS} = \dfrac{2}{1}\dfrac{25 \times 10^{-6}}{2}(1.65 - 0.7)^2 = 22.6\ \mu A$

(b) $v_O = v_I = \dfrac{V_{DD} + V_{TN} + V_{TP}}{2} = \dfrac{2 + (0.7) + (-0.7)}{2} = 1.00$ V

$\qquad i_{DS} = \dfrac{2}{1}\dfrac{25 \times 10^{-6}}{2}(1.00 - 0.7)^2 = 2.25\ \mu A$

8.24

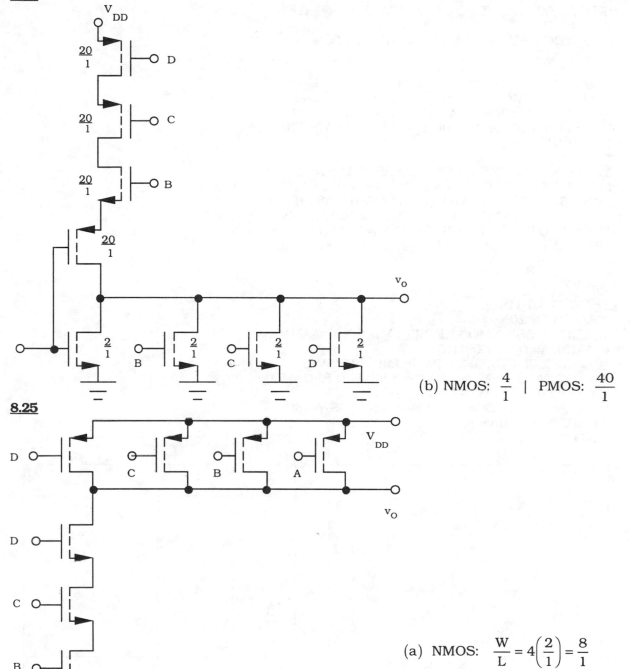

(b) NMOS: $\dfrac{4}{1}$ | PMOS: $\dfrac{40}{1}$

8.25

(a) NMOS: $\dfrac{W}{L} = 4\left(\dfrac{2}{1}\right) = \dfrac{8}{1}$

PMOS: $\dfrac{W}{L} = \dfrac{5}{1}$

(b) NMOS: $\dfrac{W}{L} = 3(4)\left(\dfrac{2}{1}\right) = \dfrac{24}{1}$

PMOS: $\dfrac{W}{L} = 3\left(\dfrac{5}{1}\right) = \dfrac{15}{1}$

8.26

```
*PROBLEM 8.26 - TWO-INPUT CMOS NOR GATE
VDD 1 0 DC 5
VA 2 0 DC 0 PULSE (0 5 0 0.1N 0.1N 10N 20N)
VB 5 0 DC 5
*
MNA 4 2 0 0 MOSN W=4U L=2U AS=16P AD=16P
MPA 4 2 3 1 MOSP W=20U L=2U AS=80P AD=80P
MNB 4 5 0 0 MOSN W=4U L=2U AS=16P AD=16P
MPB 3 5 1 1 MOSP W=20U L=2U AS=80P AD=80P
CL 4 0 1PF
*
MNC 6 5 0 0 MOSN W=4U L=2U AS=16P AD=16P
MPC 6 5 7 1 MOSP W=20U L=2U AS=80P AD=80P
*MNC 6 2 0 0 MOSN W=4U L=2U AS=16P AD=16P
*MPC 6 2 7 1 MOSP W=20U L=2U AS=80P AD=80P
MND 6 2 0 0 MOSN W=4U L=2U AS=16P AD=16P
MPD 7 2 1 1 MOSP W=20U L=2U AS=80P AD=80P
CL 6 0 1PF
*
.OP
.DC VDD 0 5 0.01
.TRAN 0.1N 20N
.MODEL MOSN NMOS KP=5E-5 VTO=0.91 GAMMA=0
+LAMBDA=.02 TOX=41.5N
+CGSO=330P CGDO=330P CJ=3.9E-4 CJSW=510P
.MODEL MOSP  PMOS  KP=2E-5 VTO=-0.77 GAMMA=0
+LAMBDA=.05 TOX=41.5N
+CGSO=315P CGDO=315P CJ=2.0E-4 CJSW=180P
.PROBE V(2) V(4) V(6)
.END
```

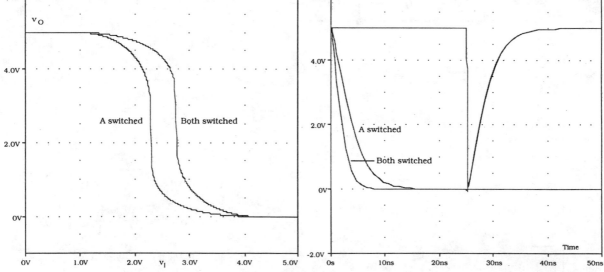

The transitions of the two VTCs are separated by approximately 0.1 V. The dynamic characteristics for switching one input with the other constant are essentially identical. If both inputs are swtiched together, t_r and t_{PLH} are the same as the single input case, but t_f and t_{PHL} are faster by a factor of two because the two pull-down transistors are operating in parallel.

8.27 The simulation results show little or no change from those of Problem 8.28.

8.28

```
*PROBLEM 8.28 - TWO-INPUT CMOS NAND GATE
VDD 1 0 DC 5
VA 2 0 DC 0 PULSE (0 5 0 0.1N 0.1N 25N 50N)
VB 4 0 DC 5
*
MNA 3 4 0 0 MOSN W=4U L=2U AS=16P AD=16P
MPA 5 4 1 1 MOSP W=20U L=2U AS=80P AD=80P
MNB 5 2 3 0 MOSN W=4U L=2U AS=16P AD=16P
MPB 5 2 1 1 MOSP W=20U L=2U AS=80P AD=80P
CL1 5 0 1PF
*
MNC 6 2 0 0 MOSN W=4U L=2U AS=16P AD=16P
MPC 7 2 1 1 MOSP W=20U L=2U AS=80P AD=80P
MND 7 4 6 0 MOSN W=4U L=2U AS=16P AD=16P
MPD 7 4 1 1 MOSP W=20U L=2U AS=80P AD=80P
CL2 7 0 1PF
*
.OP
.DC VA 0 5 0.01
.TRAN 0.05N 50N
.MODEL MOSN NMOS KP=5E-5 VTO=0.91 GAMMA=0
+LAMBDA=.02 TOX=41.5N
+CGSO=330P CGDO=330P CJ=3.9E-4 CJSW=510P
.MODEL MOSP PMOS KP=2E-5 VTO=-0.77 GAMMA=0
+LAMBDA=.05 TOX=41.5N CGSO=315P CGDO=315P CJ=2.0E-4 CJSW=180P
.PROBE V(2) V(5) V(7)
.END
```

The transitions of the two VTCs are separated by approximately 0.1 V. The dynamic characteristics for switching one input with the other constant are essentially identical. If both inputs are swtiched together, t_f and t_{PHL} are the same as the single input case, but t_r and t_{PLH} are faster by a factor of two because the two pull-up transistors are operating in parallel. The results are similar to Problem 10.26.

8.29 The simulation results show a slight increase in t_f and t_{PHL} due to the large value of γ in the MOS devices.

8.30 Worst case paths are the same as the symmetrical reference inverter:

PMOS tree: $\left(\dfrac{1}{3}\right)\left(\dfrac{15}{1}\right)=\left(\dfrac{5}{1}\right)$ | NMOS tree: $\left(\dfrac{1}{2}\right)\left(\dfrac{4}{1}\right)=\left(\dfrac{2}{1}\right)$ | Assuming $V_{DD}=5V$,

$$\tau_P = \frac{0.322C}{K_n} = \frac{0.322\left(1.25\text{x}10^{-12}\right)}{\left(\dfrac{2}{1}\right)\left(25\text{x}10^{-6}\right)} = 8.05 \text{ ns} \ | \ t_r = t_f = 2\tau_{PHL} = 2\tau_P = 16.1 \text{ ns}$$

8.31 (a) Depletion-mode design requires the same number of NMOS transistors in the switching network, but only one load transistor.

Depletion-mode design requires 5 transistors total

CMOS design requires 8 transistors.

(b) For the CMOS design, first find the delay of the circuit in Fig. 8.26 and then scale the result to achieve the desired delay.

$$\tau_{PHL} = \frac{0.322C}{K_n} = \frac{0.322(10^{-12})}{\frac{1}{2}\left(\frac{2}{1}\right)(25\times10^{-6})} = 12.9 \text{ns} \mid \tau_{PLH} = \frac{0.322C}{K_p} = \frac{0.322(10^{-12})}{\frac{1}{3}\left(\frac{2}{1}\right)(10\times10^{-6})} = 48.3 \text{ ns}$$

$$\tau_P = \frac{12.9 + 48.3}{2} \text{ns} = 30.6\text{ns} \rightarrow \left(\frac{W}{L}\right)_{all} = \frac{30.6\text{ns}}{10\text{ns}}\left(\frac{2}{1}\right) = \left(\frac{6.12}{1}\right)$$

Relative Area = $8(6.12)(1) = 49.0$

- - - - -

For the Depletion-mode design, first assume that τ_P is dominated by τ_{PLH}.

$$\tau_{PLH} \approx 2\tau_P \mid \tau_{PLH} = R_{onL}C\left[\ln\left(4\frac{3}{5-.25} - 1\right) + 2\frac{5-3-.25}{3}\right] = 1.59R_{onL}C$$

$$\left(\frac{W}{L}\right)_L = \frac{1.59(10^{-12})}{2(10^{-8})(25\times10^{-6})(3)} = \frac{1.06}{1} \mid \text{ Since NMOS is ratioed logic, the } \frac{W}{L} \text{ ratios}$$

must maintain the ratio in Fig. 7.20(d): $\left(\frac{W}{L}\right)_S = \frac{(1.06/1)}{(1/2.15)}\frac{2.06}{1} = \frac{4.70}{1}$

Using this value, $\tau_{PHL} = \dfrac{10^{-12}}{4.70(25\times10^{-6})(5-1)}\left[\ln\left(4\frac{5-1}{5+.25} - 1\right) + \frac{1}{2}\right] = 2.59\text{ns}$ and

$$\tau_P = \frac{20 + 2.59}{2}\text{ns} = 11.3\text{ns}$$

Rescaling to achieve $\tau_P = 10$ns:

$$\left(\frac{W}{L}\right)_L = \frac{11.3}{10}\left(\frac{1.06}{1}\right) = \frac{1.20}{1} \mid \left(\frac{W}{L}\right)_A = \frac{11.3}{10}\left(\frac{4.70}{1}\right) = \frac{5.31}{1} \mid \left(\frac{W}{L}\right)_{B-D} = 2\left(\frac{W}{L}\right)_A = \frac{10.6}{1}$$

Relative area = $(5.31)(1) + 3(10.6)(1) + (1.20)(1) = 38.3$

The CMOS design uses 29% more area, but consumes no static power.

8.32

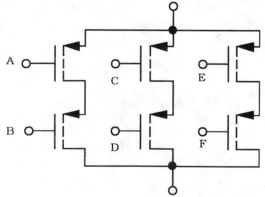

8.33

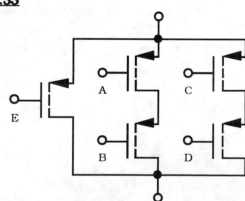

(a) $Y = \overline{(A+B)(C+D)(E+F)}$

(b) NMOS: $\dfrac{W}{L} = 3\left(\dfrac{2}{1}\right) = \dfrac{6}{1}$

PMOS: $\dfrac{W}{L} = 2\left(\dfrac{5}{1}\right) = \dfrac{10}{1}$

(a) $Y = \overline{(A+B)(C+D)E}$

(b) NMOS: $\dfrac{W}{L} = 3(3)\left(\dfrac{2}{1}\right) = \dfrac{18}{1}$

PMOS: $\left(\dfrac{W}{L}\right)_{A-D} = 2(3)\left(\dfrac{5}{1}\right) = \dfrac{30}{1}$

$\left(\dfrac{W}{L}\right)_{E} = (3)\left(\dfrac{5}{1}\right) = \dfrac{15}{1}$

8.34

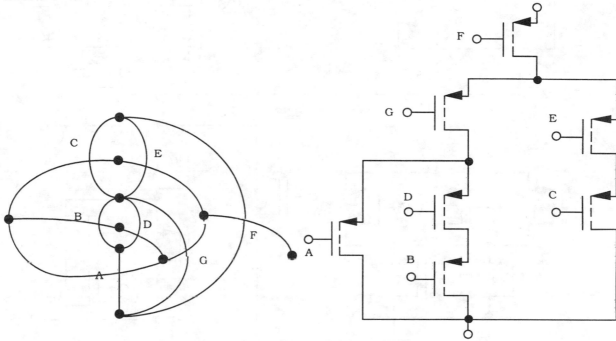

(a) $Y = \overline{F + G(C+E) + A(B+D)(C+E)} = \overline{F + (C+E)(G + A(B+D))}$

(b) NMOS: $\left(\dfrac{W}{L}\right)_{A-E} = 3(2)\left(\dfrac{2}{1}\right) = \dfrac{12}{1}$ | $\left(\dfrac{W}{L}\right)_{F} = (2)\left(\dfrac{2}{1}\right) = \dfrac{4}{1}$ | $\left(\dfrac{W}{L}\right)_{G} = \dfrac{1}{\dfrac{1}{4} - \dfrac{1}{12}} = \dfrac{6}{1}$

PMOS: $\left(\dfrac{W}{L}\right)_{F,G,B,D} = 4(2)\left(\dfrac{5}{1}\right) = \dfrac{40}{1}$ | $\left(\dfrac{W}{L}\right)_{A} = \dfrac{1}{\dfrac{1}{10} - \dfrac{2}{40}} = \dfrac{20}{1}$ | $\left(\dfrac{W}{L}\right)_{C,E} = 2\dfrac{1}{\dfrac{1}{10} - \dfrac{1}{40}} = \dfrac{26.7}{1}$

8.35

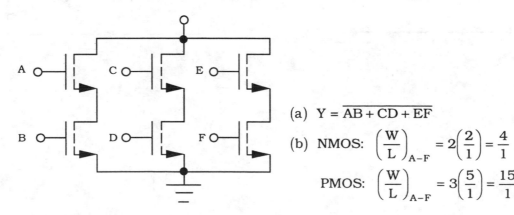

(a) $Y = \overline{AB + CD + EF}$

(b) NMOS: $\left(\dfrac{W}{L}\right)_{A-F} = 2\left(\dfrac{2}{1}\right) = \dfrac{4}{1}$

PMOS: $\left(\dfrac{W}{L}\right)_{A-F} = 3\left(\dfrac{5}{1}\right) = \dfrac{15}{1}$

8.36

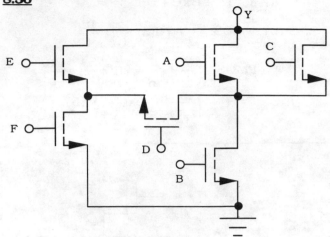

(a) $Y = \overline{(A+C)(B+DF) + E(F+DB)}$

(b) NMOS: $\left(\dfrac{W}{L}\right)_{A-F} = 3(3)\left(\dfrac{2}{1}\right) = \dfrac{18}{1}$

PMOS: $\left(\dfrac{W}{L}\right)_{A,C,D,F} = 4(3)\left(\dfrac{5}{1}\right) = \dfrac{60}{1}$

$\left(\dfrac{W}{L}\right)_{B,E} = 2\,\dfrac{1}{\dfrac{1}{15} - \dfrac{1}{60}} = \dfrac{40}{1}$

8.37   **8.38**

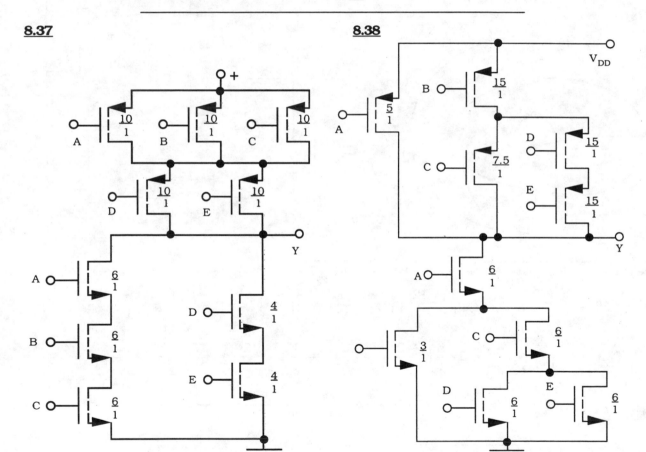

8.39

8.40

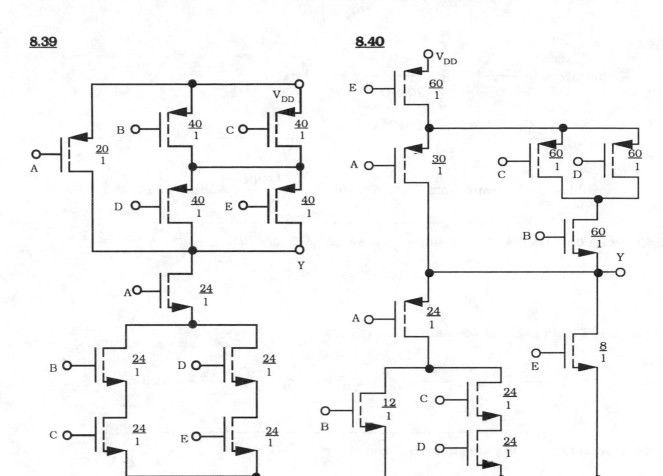

8.41

(a) $\tau_{PHL} = \dfrac{0.322C}{K_n} = \dfrac{0.322\left(4\text{x}10^{-13}\right)}{\left(\dfrac{2}{1}\right)\left(25\text{x}10^{-6}\right)} = 2.58$ ns

$\tau_{PLH} = \dfrac{0.322C}{K_p} = \dfrac{0.322\left(4\text{x}10^{-13}\right)}{\left(\dfrac{2}{3}\right)\left(10\text{x}10^{-6}\right)} = 19.3$ ns $\quad|\quad \tau_P = \dfrac{\tau_{PLH} + \tau_{PLH}}{2} = 10.9$ ns

(b) $\tau_{PHL} = \dfrac{0.322C}{K_n} = \dfrac{0.322\left(4\text{x}10^{-13}\right)}{\left(\dfrac{2}{1}\right)\left(25\text{x}10^{-6}\right)} = 2.58$ ns

$\tau_{PLH} = \dfrac{0.322C}{K_p} = \dfrac{0.322\left(4\text{x}10^{-13}\right)}{\left(\dfrac{5}{1}\right)\left(10\text{x}10^{-6}\right)} = 2.58$ ns $\quad|\quad \tau_P = \dfrac{\tau_{PLH} + \tau_{PLH}}{2} = 2.58$ ns

8.42

(a) $\tau_{PHL} = \dfrac{0.322C}{K_n} = \dfrac{0.322(1.8 \times 10^{-13})}{\left(\dfrac{2}{5}\right)(25 \times 10^{-6})} = 5.80$ ns

$\tau_{PLH} = \dfrac{0.322C}{K_p} = \dfrac{0.322(1.8 \times 10^{-13})}{\left(\dfrac{2}{1}\right)(10 \times 10^{-6})} = 2.90$ ns $\quad | \quad \tau_P = \dfrac{\tau_{PLH} + \tau_{PLH}}{2} = 4.35$ ns

(b) Using the result from Prob. 8.41(b), $\tau_P = \left(\dfrac{180\text{fF}}{400\text{fF}}\right)(2.58\text{ns}) = 1.16$ ns

---

8.43 Worst case NMOS path contains 3 transistors (ABE or CBD).

$$\tau_{PHL} = \dfrac{0.322C}{K_n} = \dfrac{0.322(10^{-12})}{\left(\dfrac{2}{3}\right)(25 \times 10^{-6})} = 19.3 \text{ ns}$$

Worst case PMOS path also contains 3 transistors

$$\tau_{PLH} = \dfrac{0.322C}{K_p} = \dfrac{0.322(10^{-12})}{\left(\dfrac{2}{3}\right)(10 \times 10^{-6})} = 48.3 \text{ ns} \quad | \quad \tau_P = \dfrac{19.3 + 48.3}{2} = 33.8 \text{ ns}$$

8.44 Worst case NMOS path contains 3 transistors

$$\tau_{PHL} = \dfrac{0.322C}{K_n} = \dfrac{0.322(10^{-12})}{\left(\dfrac{1}{3}\right)\left(\dfrac{2}{1}\right)(25 \times 10^{-6})} = 19.3 \text{ ns}$$

8.45 Student PSPICE will only accept 9 inverters.

```
*PROBLEM 8.45(a) - NINE CASCADED INVERTERS
VDD 1 0 DC 5
VIN 2 0 PULSE (0 5 0 0.1N 0.1N 20N 40N)
*
MN1 3 2 0 0 MOSN W=4U L=2U AS=16P AD=16P
MP1 3 2 1 1 MOSP W=4U L=2U AS=16P AD=16P
C1 3 0 200fF
*AS=4UM*W  - AD=4UM*W
*
MN2 4 3 0 0 MOSN W=4U L=2U AS=16P AD=16P
MP2 4 3 1 1 MOSP W=4U L=2U AS=16P AD=16P
C2 4 0 200fF
*
MN3 5 4 0 0 MOSN W=4U L=2U AS=16P AD=16P
MP3 5 4 1 1 MOSP W=4U L=2U AS=16P AD=16P
C3 5 0 200fF
*
MN4 6 5 0 0 MOSN W=4U L=2U AS=16P AD=16P
MP4 6 5 1 1 MOSP W=4U L=2U AS=16P AD=16P
C4 6 0 200fF
*
```

```
MN5 7 6 0 0 MOSN W=4U L=2U AS=16P AD=16P
MP5 7 6 1 1 MOSP W=4U L=2U AS=16P AD=16P
C5 7 0 200fF
*
MN6 8 7 0 0 MOSN W=4U L=2U AS=16P AD=16P
MP6 8 7 1 1 MOSP W=4U L=2U AS=16P AD=16P
C6 8 0 200fF
*
MN7 9 8 0 0 MOSN W=4U L=2U AS=16P AD=16P
MP7 9 8 1 1 MOSP W=4U L=2U AS=16P AD=16P
C7 9 0 200fF
*
MN8 10 9 0 0 MOSN W=4U L=2U AS=16P AD=16P
MP8 10 9 1 1 MOSP W=4U L=2U AS=16P AD=16P
C8 10 0 200fF
*
MN9 11 10 0 0 MOSN W=4U L=2U AS=16P AD=16P
MP9 11 10 1 1 MOSP W=4U L=2U AS=16P AD=16P
C9 11 0 200fF
*
.OP
.TRAN 0.025N 40N
.MODEL MOSN NMOS KP=5E-5 VTO=0.91 GAMMA=0.99
+LAMBDA=.02 TOX=41.5N
+CGSO=330P CGDO=330P CJ=3.9E-4 CJSW=510P
.MODEL MOSP  PMOS  KP=2E-5 VTO=-0.77 GAMMA=0.5
+LAMBDA=.05 TOX=41.5N
+CGSO=315P CGDO=315P CJ=2.0E-4 CJSW=180P
.PROBE V(2) V(3) V(4) V(10) V(11)
.END
```

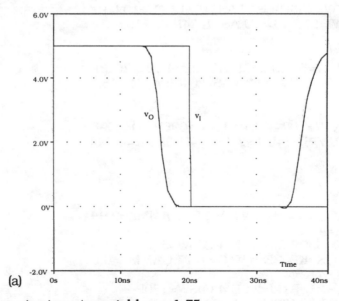

(a)

(a) The minimum size inverters yield τ_P = 1.75 ns.

(b) The symmetrical inverters yield τ_P = 1.25 ns.

Note that these results are approximtely two times the estimate in Eq. 8.15 because of the slope of the waveforms.

8.46

```
*PROBLEM 8.46 - INVERTER PDP
VDD 1 0 DC 5
VIN 2 0 PULSE (0 5 0 0.1N 0.1N 25N 50N)
*
MN1 3 2 0 0 MOSN W=4U L=2U AS=16P AD=16P
MP1 3 2 1 1 MOSP W=4U L=2U AS=16P AD=16P
C1 3 0 200fF
*AS=4UM*W  - AD=4UM*W
*
MN2 4 2 0 0 MOSN W=8U L=2U AS=32P AD=32P
MP2 4 2 1 1 MOSP W=8U L=2U AS=32P AD=32P
C2 4 0 200fF
*
MN3 5 2 0 0 MOSN W=16U L=2U AS=64P AD=64P
MP3 5 2 1 1 MOSP W=16U L=2U AS=64P AD=64P
C3 5 0 200fF
*
MN4 6 2 0 0 MOSN W=32U L=2U AS=128P AD=128P
MP4 6 2 1 1 MOSP W=32U L=2U AS=128P AD=128P
C4 6 0 200fF
*
MN5 7 2 0 0 MOSN W=64U L=2U AS=256P AD=256P
MP5 7 2 1 1 MOSP W=64U L=2U AS=256P AD=256P
C5 7 0 200fF
*
MN6 8 2 0 0 MOSN W=128U L=2U AS=512P AD=512P
MP6 8 2 1 1 MOSP W=128U L=2U AS=512P AD=512P
C6 8 0 200fF
*
MN7 9 2 0 0 MOSN W=256U L=2U AS=1024P AD=1024P
MP7 9 2 1 1 MOSP W=256U L=2U AS=1024P AD=1024P
C7 9 0 200fF
*
MN8 10 2 0 0 MOSN W=512U L=2U AS=2048P AD=2048P
MP8 10 2 1 1 MOSP W=512U L=2U AS=2048P AD=2048P
C8 10 0 200fF
*
MN9 11 2 0 0 MOSN W=1024U L=2U AS=4096P AD=4096P
MP9 11 2 1 1 MOSP W=1024U L=2U AS=4096P AD=4096P
C9 11 0 200fF
*
.OP
.TRAN 0.025N 50N
.MODEL MOSN NMOS KP=5E-5 VTO=0.91 GAMMA=0.99
+LAMBDA=.02 TOX=41.5N
+CGSO=330P CGDO=330P CJ=3.9E-4 CJSW=510P
.MODEL MOSP  PMOS  KP=2E-5 VTO=-0.77 GAMMA=0.5
+LAMBDA=.05 TOX=41.5N
+CGSO=315P CGDO=315P CJ=2.0E-4 CJSW=180P
.PROBE V(2) V(3) V(4) V(5) V(6) V(7) V(8) V(9) V(10) V(11)
.END
```

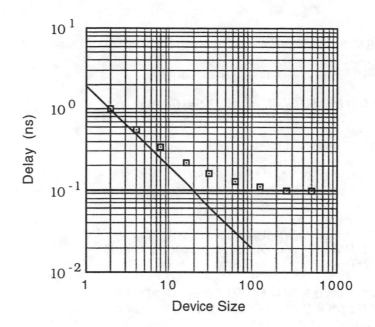

8.47

$$\Delta T = \frac{C\Delta V}{I} = \frac{KC_{ox}^{"}WL\Delta V}{\frac{1}{2}\mu_n C_{ox}^{"}\left(\frac{W}{L}\right)(V_{GS} - V_{TN})^2} \quad | \quad \text{Let } W^{'} = \alpha W, \ L^{'} = \alpha L, \ T_{ox}^{'} = \alpha T_{ox}, \ V^{'} = \alpha V$$

$$\Delta T' = \frac{C^{'}\Delta V^{'}}{I^{'}} = \frac{K(\alpha W)(\alpha L)(\alpha\Delta V)}{\frac{1}{2}\mu_n\left(\frac{\alpha W}{\alpha L}\right)(\alpha V_{GS} - \alpha V_{TN})^2} = \alpha\Delta T$$

$$P = VI = \frac{V}{2}\mu_n C_{ox}^{"}\left(\frac{W}{L}\right)(V_{GS} - V_{TN})^2 = \frac{V}{2}\mu_n \frac{\varepsilon_{ox}}{T_{ox}}\left(\frac{W}{L}\right)(V_{GS} - V_{TN})^2$$

$$P' = \frac{\alpha V}{2}\mu_n \frac{\varepsilon_{ox}}{\alpha T_{ox}}\left(\frac{\alpha W}{\alpha L}\right)(\alpha V_{GS} - \alpha V_{TN})^2 = \alpha^2 P$$

$$PDP' = P'\Delta T' = (\alpha\Delta T)\alpha^2 P = \alpha^3 P\Delta T = \alpha^3 \ PDP$$

8.48

$$\Delta T = \frac{C\Delta V}{I} = \frac{KC_{ox}^{"}WL\Delta V}{\frac{1}{2}\mu_n C_{ox}^{"}\left(\frac{W}{L}\right)(V_{GS} - V_{TN})^2} \quad | \quad \text{Let } W^{'} = \alpha W, \ L^{'} = \alpha L, \ T_{ox}^{'} = \alpha T_{ox}$$

$$\Delta T' = \frac{C^{'}\Delta V^{'}}{I^{'}} = \frac{K(\alpha W)(\alpha L)(\Delta V)}{\frac{1}{2}\mu_n\left(\frac{\alpha W}{\alpha L}\right)(V_{GS} - V_{TN})^2} = \alpha^2\Delta T$$

$$P = VI = \frac{V}{2}\mu_n C_{ox}^{"}\left(\frac{W}{L}\right)(V_{GS} - V_{TN})^2 = \frac{V}{2}\mu_n \frac{\varepsilon_{ox}}{T_{ox}}\left(\frac{W}{L}\right)(V_{GS} - V_{TN})^2$$

$$P' = \frac{V}{2}\mu_n \frac{\varepsilon_{ox}}{\alpha T_{ox}}\left(\frac{\alpha W}{\alpha L}\right)(V_{GS} - V_{TN})^2 = \frac{P}{\alpha}$$

$$PDP' = P'\Delta T' = \left(\alpha^2\Delta T\right)\frac{P}{\alpha} = \alpha P\Delta T = \alpha \ PDP$$

```
*PROBLEM 8.49 - FIVE CASCADED INVERTERS
VDD 1 0 DC 5
VIN 2 0 PULSE (0 5 0 0.1N 0.1N 14N 30N)
*

MN1 3 2 0 0 MOSN W=4U L=2U AS=16P AD=16P
MP1 3 2 1 1 MOSP W=10U L=2U AS=40P AD=40P
C1 3 0 0.25P
*AS=4UM*W  - AD=4UM*W
*

MN2 4 3 0 0 MOSN W=4U L=2U AS=16P AD=16P
MP2 4 3 1 1 MOSP W=10U L=2U AS=40P AD=40P
C2 4 0 0.25P
*

MN3 5 4 0 0 MOSN W=4U L=2U AS=16P AD=16P
MP3 5 4 1 1 MOSP W=10U L=2U AS=40P AD=40P
C3 5 0 0.25P
*

MN4 6 5 0 0 MOSN W=4U L=2U AS=16P AD=16P
MP4 6 5 1 1 MOSP W=10U L=2U AS=40P AD=40P
C4 6 0 0.25P
*

MN5 7 6 0 0 MOSN W=4U L=2U AS=16P AD=16P
MP5 7 6 1 1 MOSP W=10U L=2U AS=40P AD=40P
C5 7 0 0.25P
.OP
.TRAN 0.025N 30N
.MODEL MOSN NMOS KP=5E-5 VTO=0.91 GAMMA=0.99
+LAMBDA=.02 TOX=41.5N
+CGSO=330P CGDO=330P CJ=3.9E-4 CJSW=510P
.MODEL MOSP  PMOS  KP=2E-5 VTO=-0.77 GAMMA=0.5
+LAMBDA=.05 TOX=41.5N
+CGSO=315P CGDO=315P CJ=2.0E-4 CJSW=180P
.PROBE V(2) V(3) V(5) V(6)
.END
```

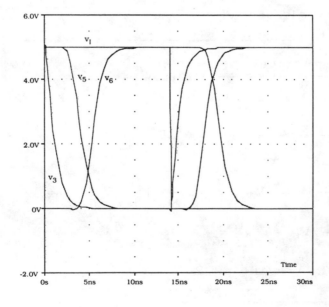

First inverter: $t_r = 1.8$ ns, $t_f = 2.1$ ns, $\tau_{PLH} = 0.80$ ns, $\tau_{PHL} = 0.90$ ns

Fourth inverter: $t_r = 2.6$ ns, $t_f = 2.5$ ns, $\tau_{PLH} = 1.4$ ns, $\tau_{PHL} = 1.6$ ns

$$\tau_{PHL} = R_{onn}C\left[\ln\left(4\frac{V_{DD} - V_{TN}}{V_{DD}} - 1\right) + \frac{1}{2}\right] = \frac{0.25\text{x}10^{-12}}{\left(\frac{2}{1}\right)\left(50\text{x}10^{-6}\right)(5 - 0.91)}\left[\ln\left(4\frac{5 - 0.91}{5} - 1\right) + \frac{1}{2}\right] = 0.81\text{ns}$$

$$\tau_{PLH} = R_{onp}C\left[\ln\left(4\frac{V_{DD} - V_{TN}}{V_{DD}} - 1\right) + \frac{1}{2}\right] = \frac{0.25\text{x}10^{-12}}{\left(\frac{5}{1}\right)\left(20\text{x}10^{-6}\right)(5 - 0.77)}\left[\ln\left(4\frac{5 - 0.77}{5} - 1\right) + \frac{1}{2}\right] = 0.81\text{ns}$$

The first inverter matches the equations well. The 2:1 relation between rise/fall time and propagation delay holds as well. The delay of the interior inverts is a factor of 2 slower than predicted by the formula because of the slow rise and fall times of the signals.

8.50

```
*PROBLEM 8.50(a)  - FIVE CASCADED SYMMETRICAL INVERTERS
VDD 1 0 DC 5
VIN 2 0 PULSE (0 5 0 0.1N 0.1N 19N 40N)
*
MN1 3 2 0 0 MOSN W=4U L=2U AS=16P AD=16P
MP1 3 2 1 1 MOSP W=10U L=2U AS=40P AD=40P
C1 3 0 1P
*AS=4UM*W  - AD=4UM*W
*
MN2 4 3 0 0 MOSN W=4U L=2U AS=16P AD=16P
MP2 4 3 1 1 MOSP W=10U L=2U AS=40P AD=40P
C2 4 0 1P
*
MN3 5 4 0 0 MOSN W=4U L=2U AS=16P AD=16P
MP3 5 4 1 1 MOSP W=10U L=2U AS=40P AD=40P
C3 5 0 1P
*
MN4 6 5 0 0 MOSN W=4U L=2U AS=16P AD=16P
MP4 6 5 1 1 MOSP W=10U L=2U AS=40P AD=40P
C4 6 0 1P
*
MN5 7 6 0 0 MOSN W=4U L=2U AS=16P AD=16P
MP5 7 6 1 1 MOSP W=10U L=2U AS=40P AD=40P
C5 7 0 1P
.OP
.TRAN 0.025N 40N
.MODEL MOSN NMOS KP=5E-5 VTO=0.91 GAMMA=0.99
+LAMBDA=.02 TOX=41.5N
+CGSO=330P CGDO=330P CJ=3.9E-4 CJSW=510P
.MODEL MOSP PMOS  KP=2E-5 VTO=-0.77 GAMMA=0.5
+LAMBDA=.05 TOX=41.5N
+CGSO=315P CGDO=315P CJ=2.0E-4 CJSW=180P
.PROBE V(2) V(3) V(5) V(6)
.END
```

First inverter: $t_r = 6.5$ ns, $t_f = 7$ ns, $\tau_{PLH} = 2.6$ ns, $\tau_{PHL} = 3.2$ ns

Fourth inverter: $t_r = 8.2$ ns, $t_f = 9.3$ ns, $\tau_{PLH} = 4.7$ ns, $\tau_{PHL} = 5.5$ ns

$$\tau_{PHL} = R_{onn}C\left[\ln\left(4\frac{V_{DD}-V_{TN}}{V_{DD}}-1\right)+\frac{1}{2}\right] = \frac{10^{-12}}{\left(\frac{2}{1}\right)(50\text{x}10^{-6})(5-0.91)}\left[\ln\left(4\frac{5-0.91}{5}-1\right)+\frac{1}{2}\right] = 3.2\text{ns}$$

$$\tau_{PLH} = R_{onp}C\left[\ln\left(4\frac{V_{DD}-V_{TN}}{V_{DD}}-1\right)+\frac{1}{2}\right] = \frac{10^{-12}}{\left(\frac{5}{1}\right)(20\text{x}10^{-6})(5-0.77)}\left[\ln\left(4\frac{5-0.77}{5}-1\right)+\frac{1}{2}\right] = 3.2\text{ns}$$

The first inverter matches the equations well. The 2:1 relation between rise/fall time and propagation delay holds as well. The propagation delay of the interior inverters is a factor of 2 slower than predicted by the formula because of the slow rise and fall times of the signals.

```
*PROBLEM 8.50(b) - FIVE CASCADED MINIMUM SIZE INVERTERS
VDD 1 0 DC 5
VIN 2 0 PULSE (0 5 0 0.1N 0.1N 30N 70N)
*
MN1 3 2 0 0 MOSN W=4U L=2U AS=16P AD=16P
MP1 3 2 1 1 MOSP W=4U L=2U AS=16P AD=16P
C1 3 0 1P
*AS=4UM*W  - AD=4UM*W
*
MN2 4 3 0 0 MOSN W=4U L=2U AS=16P AD=16P
MP2 4 3 1 1 MOSP W=4U L=2U AS=16P AD=16P
C2 4 0 1P
*
MN3 5 4 0 0 MOSN W=4U L=2U AS=16P AD=16P
MP3 5 4 1 1 MOSP W=4U L=2U AS=16P AD=16P
C3 5 0 1P
*
MN4 6 5 0 0 MOSN W=4U L=2U AS=16P AD=16P
MP4 6 5 1 1 MOSP W=4U L=2U AS=16P AD=16P
C4 6 0 1P
*
MN5 7 6 0 0 MOSN W=4U L=2U AS=16P AD=16P
MP5 7 6 1 1 MOSP W=4U L=2U AS=16P AD=16P
C5 7 0 1P
.OP
.TRAN 0.025N 70N
.MODEL MOSN NMOS KP=5E-5 VTO=0.91 GAMMA=0.99
+LAMBDA=.02 TOX=41.5N
+CGSO=330P CGDO=330P CJ=3.9E-4 CJSW=510P
.MODEL MOSP  PMOS  KP=2E-5 VTO=-0.77 GAMMA=0.5
+LAMBDA=.05 TOX=41.5N
+CGSO=315P CGDO=315P CJ=2.0E-4 CJSW=180P
.PROBE V(2) V(3) V(5) V(6)
.END
```

First inverter: $t_r = 16$ ns, $t_f = 7$ ns, $\tau_{PLH} = 6.5$ ns, $\tau_{PHL} = 3.0$ ns

Fourth inverter: $t_r = 17.5$ ns, $t_f = 11$ ns, $\tau_{PLH} = 10$ ns, $\tau_{PHL} = 7.5$ ns

$$\tau_{PHL} = R_{onn}C\left[\ln\left(4\frac{V_{DD}-V_{TN}}{V_{DD}}-1\right)+\frac{1}{2}\right] = \frac{10^{-12}}{\left(\frac{2}{1}\right)(50\times10^{-6})(5-0.91)}\left[\ln\left(4\frac{5-0.91}{5}-1\right)+\frac{1}{2}\right] = 3.2\text{ns}$$

$$\tau_{PLH} = R_{onp}C\left[\ln\left(4\frac{V_{DD}-V_{TN}}{V_{DD}}-1\right)+\frac{1}{2}\right] = \frac{10^{-12}}{\left(\frac{2}{1}\right)(20\times10^{-6})(5-0.77)}\left[\ln\left(4\frac{5-0.77}{5}-1\right)+\frac{1}{2}\right] = 8.0\text{ns}$$

The first inverter matches the equations well. The 2:1 relation between rise/fall time and propagation delay holds as well. The propagation delay of the interior inverter is a factor of 2 slower than predicted by the formula because of the slow rise and fall times of the signals.

8.51

$$\text{(a) } R_{onn} = \frac{1}{K_n(V_{GS}-V_{TN})} = \left[\left(\frac{20}{1}\right)(25\times10^{-6})(5-1)\right]^{-1} = 500\Omega$$

$$\text{(b) } R_{onp} = \frac{1}{K_p(V_{SG}+V_{TP})} = \left[\left(\frac{20}{1}\right)(10\times10^{-6})(5-1)\right]^{-1} = 1250\Omega$$

(c) A resistive channel exists connecting the source and drain.

8.52

$$G_{on} = G_{onn}+G_{onp} = K_n(V_{GS}-V_{TN})+K_p(V_{SG}+V_{TP}) = K_n(V_{GS}-V_{TN}+V_{SG}+V_{TP})$$

$$G_{on} = K_n(V_{DD}-V_I-V_{TN}+V_I+V_{TP}) = K_n(V_{DD}-V_{TN}+V_{TP}) =$$

$$R_{on} = \frac{1}{K_n(V_{DD}-V_{TN}+V_{TP})} \text{ which is constant if we ignore body effect.}$$

If not, $V_{TN}-V_{TP} = \left[0.75+0.5\left(\sqrt{V_I+0.6}-\sqrt{0.6}\right)\right]-\left[-0.75-0.5\left(\sqrt{5-V_I+0.6}-\sqrt{0.6}\right)\right]$

$V_{TN}-V_{TP} = 1.5+0.5\left(\sqrt{V_I+0.6}-\sqrt{5.6-V_I}\right)$ which is not constant.

8.53

From Fig. 8.29, we see that the worst case occurs at the point where the NMOS device just cuts off. From Fig. 8.29, $R_{max} = 20\text{k}\Omega$ for a (2/1) device. (Note that the figure caption should read $K_p = 20\frac{\mu A}{V^2}$ and $K_n = 50\frac{\mu A}{V^2}$.)

$R_{max} = 250\Omega$ would require $\frac{W}{L} = \frac{20\text{k}\Omega}{250\Omega}\frac{2}{1} = \frac{160}{1}$. Using direct calculation:

$$R_{onp} = \frac{1}{K_p'\frac{W}{L}(V_{SG}+V_{TP})} \quad | \quad V_{TP} = -0.75-0.5\left(\sqrt{5-3.64+0.6}-\sqrt{0.6}\right) = -1.063\text{V}$$

$$\frac{W}{L} = \frac{1}{250(10\times10^{-6})(3.64-1.063)} = \frac{155}{1}$$

8.54

```
*Figure 8.31 - CMOS Latchup
VDD 1 0
R1 1 2 25
RL 3 4 2000
RN 2 3 2000
RP 4 0 500
Q1 3 4 0 NBJT
Q2 4 3 2 PBJT
.DC VDD 0 5 .01
.MODEL NBJT NPN BF=25 BR=.25 IS=1E-15
.MODEL PBJT PNP  BF=60 BR=.25 IS=1E-15
.PROBE I(VDD) V(1) V(2) V(3) V(4)
.OPTIONS ABSTOL=1E-12 RELTOL=1E-6 VNTOL=1E-6
.END
```

8.55

(a) $\quad V_{IH} = \dfrac{2K_R(V_{DD} - V_{TN} + V_{TP})}{(K_R - 1)\sqrt{1 + 3K_R}} - \dfrac{(V_{DD} - K_R V_{TN} + V_{TP})}{(K_R - 1)}$

$$V_{IH} = \frac{2K_R(V_{DD} - V_{TN} + V_{TP}) - (V_{DD} - K_R V_{TN} + V_{TP})\sqrt{1 + 3K_R}}{(K_R - 1)\sqrt{1 + 3K_R}} = \frac{0}{0}$$

$$\lim_{K_R \to 1} V_{IH} = \lim_{K_R \to 1} \frac{2(V_{DD} - V_{TN} + V_{TP}) - (V_{DD} - K_R V_{TN} + V_{TP})\dfrac{3}{2\sqrt{1 + 3K_R}} + V_{TN}\sqrt{1 + 3K_R}}{\sqrt{1 + 3K_R} + \dfrac{3}{2}\dfrac{(K_R - 1)}{\sqrt{1 + 3K_R}}}$$

$$\lim_{K_R \to 1} V_{IH} = \frac{2(V_{DD} - V_{TN} + V_{TP}) - (V_{DD} - V_{TN} + V_{TP})\dfrac{3}{4} + 2V_{TN}}{2} = \frac{5V_{DD} + 3V_{TN} + 5V_{TP}}{8}$$

$$NM_H = V_{DD} - \frac{5V_{DD} + 3V_{TN} + 5V_{TP}}{8} = \frac{3V_{DD} - 3V_{TN} - 5V_{TP}}{8}$$

(b) $\quad V_{IL} = \dfrac{2\sqrt{K_R}(V_{DD} - V_{TN} + V_{TP})}{(K_R - 1)\sqrt{K_R + 3}} - \dfrac{(V_{DD} - K_R V_{TN} + V_{TP})}{(K_R - 1)}$

$$\lim_{K_R \to 1} V_{IL} = \frac{2\sqrt{K_R}(V_{DD} - V_{TN} + V_{TP}) - (V_{DD} - K_R V_{TN} + V_{TP})\sqrt{K_R + 3}}{(K_R - 1)\sqrt{K_R + 3}} = \frac{0}{0}$$

$$\lim_{K_R \to 1} V_{IL} = \lim_{K_R \to 1} \frac{\dfrac{2}{2\sqrt{K_R}}(V_{DD} - V_{TN} + V_{TP}) - (V_{DD} - K_R V_{TN} + V_{TP})\dfrac{1}{2\sqrt{K_R + 3}} + V_{TN}\sqrt{K_R + 3}}{\sqrt{K_R + 3} + \dfrac{1}{2}\dfrac{(K_R - 1)}{\sqrt{K_R + 3}}}$$

$$\lim_{K_R \to 1} V_{IL} = \frac{(V_{DD} - V_{TN} + V_{TP}) - (V_{DD} - V_{TN} + V_{TP})\dfrac{1}{4} + 2V_{TN}}{2} = \frac{3V_{DD} + 5V_{TN} + 3V_{TP}}{8}$$

$$NM_L = \frac{3V_{DD} + 5V_{TN} + 3V_{TP}}{8} - 0 = \frac{3V_{DD} + 5V_{TN} + 3V_{TP}}{8}$$

8.56

(a) $\tau_P = \dfrac{0.325C}{K_n}$ | $\dfrac{d\tau_P}{dK_n} = -\dfrac{0.325C}{K_n^2} = -\dfrac{\tau_P}{K_n}$ | $S_{K_n}^{\tau_P} = \dfrac{K_n}{\tau_P}\dfrac{d\tau_P}{dK_n} = -1$

$\dfrac{\Delta\tau_P}{\tau_P} \approx S_{K_n}^{\tau_P}\dfrac{\Delta K_n}{K_n} = -\dfrac{\Delta K_n}{K_n} = -(-0.25) = +0.25$ | A 25% decrease in K_n will cause

a 25% increase in propagation delay.

(b) Assuming a symmetrical inverter with $V_{DD} = 5V$ and $V_{TN} = 0.75V$,

$\tau_P = \dfrac{C}{K_n(5-V_{TN})}\left[\ln\left(4\dfrac{5-V_{TN}}{5}-1\right)+\dfrac{1}{2}\right] = \dfrac{C}{K_n(5-V_{TN})}\left[\ln(3-0.8V_{TN})+\dfrac{1}{2}\right] = \dfrac{0.324C}{K_n}$

$\dfrac{d\tau_P}{dV_{TN}} = \dfrac{-0.8C}{K_n(5-V_{TN})(3-0.8V_{TN})} + \dfrac{C}{K_n(5-V_{TN})^2}\left[\ln(3-0.8V_{TN})+\dfrac{1}{2}\right] = -\dfrac{2.25\times10^{-3}C}{K_n}$

$\tau_P = \dfrac{0.324C}{K_n}$ | $S_{V_{TN}}^{\tau_P} = \dfrac{V_{TN}}{\tau_P}\dfrac{d\tau_P}{dV_{TN}} = \dfrac{0.75K_n}{0.324C}\left(-\dfrac{2.25\times10^{-3}C}{K_n}\right) = -5.21\times10^{-3}$

$\dfrac{\Delta\tau_P}{\tau_P} \approx S_{K_n}^{\tau_P}\dfrac{\Delta V_{TN}}{V_{TN}} = -5.21\times10^{-3}\dfrac{0.1}{0.75} = -6.94\times10^{-4} = -0.0694\%$. A 13% increase in

V_{TN} causes only a 0.07% decrease in τ_P.

8.57

```
*PROBLEM 8.57 - INVERTER DELAY VS RISETIME
VDD 1 0 DC 5
V1 2 0 PULSE (0 5 0 0.1N 0.1N 25N 50N)
MN1 3 2 0 0 MOSN W=4U L=2U AS=16P AD=16P
MP1 3 2 1 1 MOSP W=4U L=2U AS=16P AD=16P
C1 3 0 1PF
*
V2 4 0 PULSE (0 5 0 0.2N 0.2N 25N 50N)
MN3 5 4 0 0 MOSN W=4U L=2U AS=16P AD=16P
MP3 5 4 1 1 MOSP W=4U L=2U AS=16P AD=16P
C3 5 0 1PF
*
V3 6 0 PULSE (0 5 0 0.5N 0.5N 25N 50N)
MN5 7 6 0 0 MOSN W=4U L=2U AS=16P AD=16P
MP5 7 6 1 1 MOSP W=4U L=2U AS=16P AD=16P
C5 7 0 1PF
*
V4 8 0 PULSE (0 5 0 1N 1N 25N 50N)
MN7 9 8 0 0 MOSN W=4U L=2U AS=16P AD=16P
MP7 9 8 1 1 MOSP W=4U L=2U AS=16P AD=16P
C7 9 0 1PF
*
V5 10 0 PULSE (0 5 0 2N 2N 25N 50N)
MN9 11 10 0 0 MOSN W=4U L=2U AS=16P AD=16P
MP9 11 10 1 1 MOSP W=4U L=2U AS=16P AD=16P
C9 11 0 1PF
*
.OP
.TRAN 0.025N 50N
.MODEL MOSN NMOS KP=5E-5 VTO=0.91 GAMMA=0.99
+LAMBDA=.02 TOX=41.5N
+CGSO=330P CGDO=330P CJ=3.9E-4 CJSW=510P
.MODEL MOSP PMOS KP=2E-5 VTO=-0.77 GAMMA=0.5
+LAMBDA=.05 TOX=41.5N
```

+CGSO=315P CGDO=315P CJ=2.0E-4 CJSW=180P
.PROBE V(2) V(3) V(4) V(5) V(6) V(7) V(8) V(9) V(10) V(11)
.END

t_r	t_P
0.1 ns	4.6 ns
0.2 ns	4.6 ns
0.5 ns	4.7 ns
1 ns	4.9 ns
2 ns	5.1 ns

CHAPTER 9

9.1

(a) $256\text{Mb} = 2^8\left(2^{10}\right)\left(2^{10}\right) = 268,435,456$ bits (b) $1\text{Gb} = \left(2^{10}\right)^3 = 1,073,741,824$ bits

9.2

$256\text{Mb} = 2^8\left(2^{10}\right)\left(2^{10}\right) = 2^{28}$ | $128\text{kb} = 2^7\left(2^{10}\right) = 2^{17}$ | $\dfrac{2^{28}}{2^{17}} = 2^{11} = 2048$ blocks

9.3

$$I \leq \frac{1\text{mA}}{2^{28}\text{bits}} = 3.73\,\frac{\text{pA}}{\text{bit}}$$

9.4

$"1" = V_{DD} = 3$ V | $"0":\ \dfrac{3-V_O}{10^{10}} = \dfrac{2}{1}\left(25\text{x}10^{-6}\right)\left(3-1-\dfrac{V_O}{2}\right)V_O \rightarrow V_O = 3.00\mu\text{V}$ | $"0" = 3.00\ \mu$V

9.5

```
*PROBLEM 9.5 - 6-T Cell
VDD 1 0 DC 3
MN1 3 2 0 0 MOSN W=4U L=2U AS=16P AD=16P
MP1 3 2 1 1 MOSP W=10U L=2U AS=40P AD=40P
MN2 2 3 0 0 MOSN W=4U L=2U AS=16P AD=16P
MP2 2 3 1 1 MOSP W=10U L=2U AS=40P AD=40P
MN3 3 0 0 0 MOSN W=4U L=2U AS=16P AD=16P
MN4 2 0 0 0 MOSN W=4U L=2U AS=16P AD=16P
.IC V(3)=1.55V V(2)=1.45V V(1)=3
.OP
.TRAN 0.025N 10N UIC
.MODEL MOSN NMOS KP=5E-5 VTO=0.91 GAMMA=0.99
+LAMBDA=.02 TOX=41.5N
+CGSO=330P CGDO=330P CJ=3.9E-4 CJSW=510P
.MODEL MOSP PMOS  KP=2E-5 VTO=-0.77 GAMMA=0.5
+LAMBDA=.05 TOX=41.5N
+CGSO=315P CGDO=315P CJ=2.0E-4 CJSW=180P
.PRINT TRAN V(2) V(3)
.PROBE V(2) V(3)
.END
```

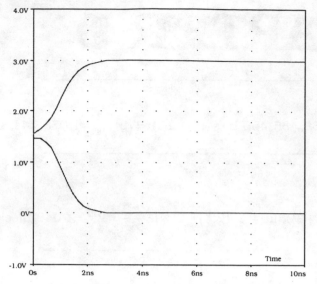

Result: $t = 1.5 \text{ ns}$

9.6

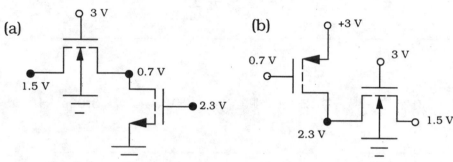

(a)   (b)

First Case: Both transistors are in the linear region

$$I_{DS} = 25 \times 10^{-6} \left(\frac{1}{1} \right) \left(2.3 - 0.7 - \frac{0.7}{2} \right) 0.7 = 21.88 \mu A$$

$$21.88 \mu A = 25 \times 10^{-6} \left(\frac{W}{L} \right) \left(3 - 0.7 - 0.7 - \frac{0.8}{2} \right) 0.8 \rightarrow \left(\frac{W}{L} \right) \leq 0.911 = \frac{1}{1.10}$$

Second Case: Both transistors are also in the linear region

$$10 \times 10^{-6} \left(\frac{1}{1} \right) \left(3 - 0.7 - 0.7 - \frac{0.7}{2} \right) 0.7 = 25 \times 10^{-6} \left(\frac{W}{L} \right) \left(3 - 1.5 - 0.7 - \frac{0.8}{2} \right) 0.8 \rightarrow \left(\frac{W}{L} \right) \leq \frac{1.09}{1}$$

So $\left(\frac{W}{L} \right) \leq \frac{1}{1.10}$

9.7

```
*Problem 9.7 - WRITING THE CMOS SRAM
VWL 6 0 DC 0 PULSE(0 3 1NS 1NS 1NS 100NS)
VDD 3 0 DC 3
VBL1 4 0 DC 0
VBL2 5 0 DC 3
CBL1 4 0 500FF
CBL2 5 0 500FF
*Storage Cell
MCN1 2 1 0 0 MOSN W=1U L=1U AS=4P AD=4P
MCP1 2 1 3 3 MOSP W=1U L=1U AS=4P AD=4P
MCN2 1 2 0 0 MOSN W=1U L=1U AS=4P AD=4P
```

```
MCP2 1 2 3 3 MOSP  W=1U L=1U  AS=4P AD=4P
MA1 4 6 2 0 MOSN W=1U L=1U AS=4P AD=4P
MA2 5 6 1 0 MOSN W=1U L=1U AS=4P AD=4P
*
.OP
.TRAN 0.01NS 20NS
.NODESET V(1)=3 V(2)=0
.MODEL MOSN NMOS KP=2.5E-5 VTO=.70 GAMMA=0.5
+LAMBDA=.05 TOX=20N
+CGSO=4E-9 CGDO=4E-9 CJ=2.0E-4 CJSW=5.0E-10
.MODEL MOSP  PMOS  KP=1.0E-5 VTO=-.70 GAMMA=0.75
+LAMBDA=.05 TOX=20N
+CGSO=4E-9 CGDO=4E-9 CJ=2.0E-4 CJSW=5.0E-10
.PROBE V(1) V(2) V(3) V(4) V(5) V(6)
.END
```

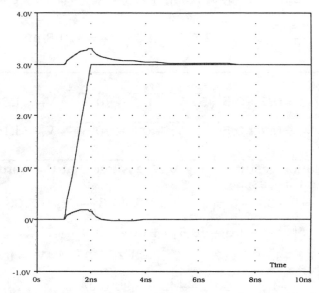

Small voltage transients occur on both cell storage nodes which die out in 5 - 7 ns.

9.8

The transistor will fully discharge C_C: "0" = 0 V

$$V_{C1} = 5 - V_{TN} = 5 - 1 - 0.5\left(\sqrt{V_{C1} + 0.6} - \sqrt{0.6}\right) \rightarrow V_{C1} = 3.39V \mid \text{"1"} = 3.39 \text{ V}$$

$$\text{For } V_{C1} = 5V, V_{TN} = 1 + 0.5\left(\sqrt{5 + 0.6} - \sqrt{0.6}\right) = 1.80V \mid V_{W/L} \geq 5 + V_{TN} = 6.80 \text{ V}$$

9.9 For "0" = 0V, the bias across the source-substrate junction is 0 V, so the leakage current would be 0 and the "0" state is undisturbed. For a "1" corresponding to a positive voltage, a reverse bias across the source-substrate junction, and the diode leakage current will tend to destroy the "1" state.

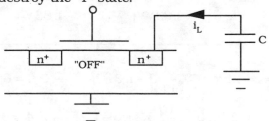

9.10

$$V_C = 3 - V_{TN} = 3 - 0.8 - 0.5\left(\sqrt{V_C + 0.6} - \sqrt{0.6}\right) \rightarrow V_C = 1.81V$$

$$\Delta V_C = \frac{\dfrac{1}{sC_C}}{\dfrac{1}{sC_C} + \dfrac{1}{sC_{GS}}} \Delta V_{W/L} = \frac{\Delta V_{W/L}}{1 + \dfrac{C_C}{C_{GS}}} = \frac{3}{1 + \dfrac{75fF}{100fF}} = 1.71 \text{ V}$$

9.11

$$Q_I = 60fF(0V) + 7.5pF(2.5V) \mid Q_F = 7.56pF(V_F) \mid Q_F = Q_I \rightarrow V_F = \frac{7.5pF}{7.56pF}2.5V$$

$$V_F = 2.48 \text{ V} \mid \Delta V = \frac{7.5pF}{7.56pF}2.5V - 2.5V = -2.5\frac{0.06}{1.56} = -19.8 \text{ mV}$$

9.12

(a) "1" = +5 V $\mid V_C = -V_{TP} = 0.7 + 0.5\left(\sqrt{5 - V_C + 0.6} - \sqrt{0.6}\right) \rightarrow V_C = 1.34V \mid$ "0" = 1.34 V

(b) "1" = +3 V $\mid V_C = -V_{TP} = 0.7 + 0.5\left(\sqrt{3 - V_C + 0.6} - \sqrt{0.6}\right) \rightarrow V_C = 1.10V \mid$ "0" = 1.10 V

9.13 Note that the simulation results in Fig. 9.28 assume that the word line is also driven higher than 3 V. For this case:

(a) $V_C = 5 - V_{TN} = 5 - 0.7 - 0.5\left(\sqrt{V_C + 0.6} - \sqrt{0.6}\right) \rightarrow V_C = 3.66 \text{ V}$

(b) $V_{TN} = 0.7 - 0.5\left(\sqrt{1.3 + 0.6} - \sqrt{0.6}\right) = 1.00V$

$V_{GS} - V_{TN} = 5 - 1.3 - 1.00 = 2.7V \mid V_{DS} = 3.7 - 1.3 = 2.4V \rightarrow$ linear region

$$i_{DS} = 25 \times 10^{-6}\left(\frac{1}{1}\right)\left(5 - 1.3 - 1.00 - \frac{2.4}{2}\right)2.4 = 90.0 \text{ μA}$$

9.14

(a) "0" = +0 V $\mid V_C = 3 - V_{TN} = 3 - 0.7 - 0.5\left(\sqrt{V_C + 0.6} - \sqrt{0.6}\right) \rightarrow V_C = 1.90V \mid$ "1" = 1.90 V

(b) A "0" will have 0 V across the drain - substrate junction, so no leakage occurs.

A "1" will have a reverse bias of 1.9 V across the junction, so the junction leakage will tend to destroy the "1" level. (Note that this discussion ignores subthreshold leakage through the FET which has not been discussed in the text.)

9.15

(a) "1" = +5 V $\mid V_C = -V_{TP} = 0.8 + 0.65\left(\sqrt{5 - V_C + 0.6} - \sqrt{0.6}\right) \rightarrow V_C = 1.60V \mid$ "0" = +1.60 V

(b) $V_{TP} = -0.8 - 0.65\left(\sqrt{5 + 0.6} - \sqrt{0.6}\right) = -1.83V \mid V_{W/L} \leq -1.83V$

9.16

$$\text{Original: } i_{DS} = 25 \times 10^{-6}\left(\frac{1}{1}\right)\left(3 - 1.3 - 1 - \frac{0.6}{2}\right)0.6 = 6\mu A$$

$$\text{New: } \quad i_{DS} = 25 \times 10^{-6}\left(\frac{1}{1}\right)\left(5 - 1.3 - 1 - \frac{2.4}{2}\right)2.4 = 90\mu A.$$

Gate drive terms: $\dfrac{5-1.3-1-1.2}{3-1.3-1-0.3} = \dfrac{1.5}{0.4} = 3.75$ | V_{DS} ratio: $\dfrac{2.4}{0.6} = 4$

Improved gate drive yields a 3.75 times improvement, although it is reduced by the larger V_{DS} term. Improved drain - source voltage yields a 4 times improvement. 4 x 3.75 = 15.

9.17

```
*Problem 9.17 - 4-T Refresh SRAM
VWL 3 0 DC 0 PULSE(0 3 1NS 1NS 1NS 6NS)
VBL 4 0 DC 3
VBLB 5 0 DC 3
CC1 1 0 50FF
CC2 2 0 50FF
*Storage Cell
MCN1 2 1 0 0 MOSN W=4U L=2U AS=16P AD=16P
MCN2 1 2 0 0 MOSN W=4U L=2U AS=16P AD=16P
MA1 4 3 2 0 MOSN W=4U L=2U AS=16P AD=16P
MA2 5 3 1 0 MOSN W=4U L=2U AS=16P AD=16P
.IC V(1)=0 V(2)=1 V(3)=0 V(4)=3 V(5)=3
.OP
.TRAN 0.01NS 20NS UIC
.MODEL MOSN NMOS KP=5E-5 VTO=0.91 GAMMA=0.99
+LAMBDA=.02 TOX=41.5N
+CGSO=330P CGDO=330P CJ=3.9E-4 CJSW=510P
.PROBE V(1) V(2) V(3) V(4) V(5)
.END
```

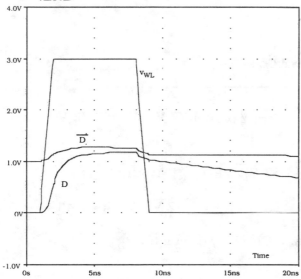

Note the very slow recovery due to relatively high threshold and gamma values relative to the power supply voltage.

9.18

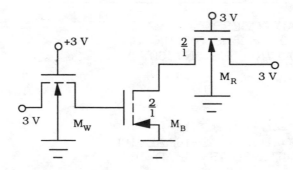

If both transistors were saturated, then their gate-source voltages would be the same, and $V_{DSB} = 3-1.9 = 1.1V$. But $V_{GS}-V_{TN} = 1.9-0.7 = 1.2V$ which is not a consistent result. However, M_R is saturated since $V_{DS} = V_{GS}$. Equating drain curents:

(a) $i_{DSB} = i_{DSR}$ | M_B linear - M_R saturated

$$25 \times 10^{-6}\left(\frac{2}{1}\right)\left(1.9 - 0.7 - \frac{V_{DSB}}{2}\right)V_{DSB} = \frac{25 \times 10^{-6}}{2}\left(\frac{2}{1}\right)(3 - V_{DSB} - V_{TNR})^2 \text{ with}$$

$$V_{TNR} = 0.7 + 0.5\left(\sqrt{V_{DSB} + 0.6} - \sqrt{0.6}\right) \text{ | Using MATLAB: } V_{DSB} = 0.9089 \text{ V}$$

$$V_{TNR} = 0.9269V \text{ | } i_{DSB} = 25 \times 10^{-6}\left(\frac{2}{1}\right)\left(1.9 - 0.7 - \frac{.9089}{2}\right).9089 = 33.9 \text{ } \mu A$$

Checking: $i_{DSR} = \dfrac{25 \times 10^{-6}}{2}\left(\dfrac{2}{1}\right)(3 - 0.9089 - 0.9269)^2 = 33.9 \text{ } \mu A$

(b) This is not a trival problem. An iterative solution is needed.

Pick $\gamma \rightarrow V_{TNW} \rightarrow V_{GSB}$. Then find V_{GSR} and see if M_B is saturated.

$$V_{GSB} = 3 - V_{TNW} = 3 - \left(0.7 + \gamma\left(\sqrt{V_{GSB} + 0.6} - \sqrt{0.6}\right)\right) \rightarrow V_{GSB}$$

$i_{DSB} = i_{DSR}$ | Assume both transistors are saturated.

$$25 \times 10^{-6}\left(\frac{2}{1}\right)(V_{GSB} - 0.7)^2 = \frac{25 \times 10^{-6}}{2}\left(\frac{2}{1}\right)(V_{GSR} - V_{TNR})^2 \text{ or } V_{GSB} - 0.7 = V_{GSR} - V_{TNR}$$

with $V_{TNR} = 0.7 + 0.5\left(\sqrt{3 - V_{GSR} + 0.6} - \sqrt{0.6}\right)$

For saturation we require $V_{DSB} = 3 - V_{GSR} \geq V_{GSB} - 0.7$

Using MATLAB: $\gamma \geq 0.922$ insures saturation of M_B

with $V_{GSB} = 1.636V$, $V_{DSR} = 0.936V$ and $V_{GSR} = 2.064V$.

___

9.19

$$V_C = 5 - V_{TNW} = 5 - 1 - 0.65\left(\sqrt{5 - V_{TNW} + 0.6} - \sqrt{0.6}\right) \rightarrow V_{TNW} = 1.77 \text{ V | } V_C = 3.23 \text{ V}$$

$i_{DSB} = i_{DSR}$ | M_B linear - M_R saturated

$$25 \times 10^{-6}\left(\frac{2}{1}\right)\left(3.23 - 1 - \frac{V_{DSB}}{2}\right)V_{DSB} = \frac{25 \times 10^{-6}}{2}\left(\frac{2}{1}\right)(5 - V_{DSB} - V_{TNR})^2 \text{ with}$$

$$V_{TNR} = 1 + 0.65\left(\sqrt{V_{DSB} + 0.6} - \sqrt{0.6}\right) \text{ | Using MATLAB: } V_{DSB} = 1.47 \text{ V | } V_{TNR} = 1.43 \text{ V}$$

$$i_{DSB} = 25 \times 10^{-6}\left(\frac{2}{1}\right)\left(3.23 - 1 - \frac{1.47}{2}\right)1.47 = 110 \text{ } \mu A \text{ | Check by calculating } i_{DSR}:$$

$$i_{DSR} = \frac{25 \times 10^{-6}}{2}\left(\frac{2}{1}\right)(5 - 1.47 - 1.43)^2 = 110 \text{ } \mu A$$

___

9.20

```
*Problem 9.20 4-T READ ACCESS
VPC 7 0 DC 3 PULSE(3 0 1NS .5NS .5NS 100NS)
VWL 6 0 DC 0 PULSE(0 3 2NS .5NS .5NS 100NS)
VDD 3 0 DC 3
CBL1 4 0 1PF
CBL2 5 0 1PF
*Storage Cell
MCN1 2 1 0 0 MOSN W=4U L=2U AS=16P AD=16P
MCN2 1 2 0 0 MOSN W=4U L=2U AS=16P AD=16P
MA1 4 6 2 0 MOSN W=4U L=2U AS=16P AD=16P
```

```
MA2 5 6 1 0 MOSN W=4U L=2U AS=16P AD=16P
CC1 1 0 50FF
CC2 2 0 50FF
*
*Sense Amplifier
MSN1 4 5 0 0 MOSN W=4U L=2U AS=16P AD=16P
MSP1 4 5 3 3 MOSP W=4U L=2U AS=16P AD=16P
MSN2 5 4 0 0 MOSN W=4U L=2U AS=16P AD=16P
MSP2 5 4 3 3 MOSP W=4U L=2U AS=16P AD=16P
MRS 5 7 4 0 MOSN W=4U L=2U AS=16P AD=16P
*
.OP
.TRAN 0.01NS 40NS UIC
.IC V(1)=1.5 V(2)=0 V(3)=3 V(4)=1.7 V(5)=1.7 V(6)=0 V(7)=3
.MODEL MOSN NMOS KP=5E-5 VTO=0.91 GAMMA=0.99
+LAMBDA=.02 TOX=41.5N
+CGSO=330P CGDO=330P CJ=3.9E-4 CJSW=510P
.MODEL MOSP PMOS KP=2E-5 VTO=-0.77 GAMMA=0.5
+LAMBDA=.05 TOX=41.5N
+CGSO=315P CGDO=315P CJ=2.0E-4 CJSW=180P
.PROBE V(1) V(2) V(3) V(4) V(5) V(6) V(7)
.END
```

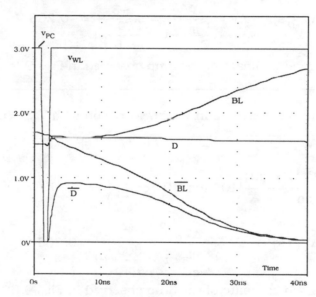

9.21

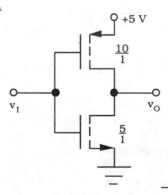

Each inverter will have $v_I = v_O$.

Equating inverter drain currents:

$$\left(\frac{25 \times 10^{-6}}{2}\right)\left(\frac{5}{1}\right)(v_I - 0.7)^2 = \left(\frac{10 \times 10^{-6}}{2}\right)\left(\frac{10}{1}\right)(5 - v_I - 0.7)^2$$

$\rightarrow v_O = v_I = 2.4 V$

Sense amp current $= 2i_{DS} = 361 \ \mu A$

$P = 1024(5V)(361 \ \mu A) = 1.85 \ W$

163

9.22

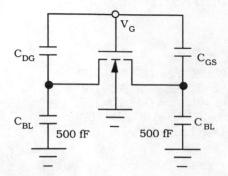

The precharge transistor is operating in the linear region with $V_{DS} = 0$

$$C_{GS} = \frac{1}{2} C_{ox}^{"} WL + C_{GSO}W$$

$$C_{GS} = \frac{1}{2} \frac{3.9\left(8.854\text{x}10^{-14}\,\text{F / cm}\right)}{2\text{x}10^{-6}\,\text{cm}}\left(10^{-3}\,\text{cm}\right)\left(10^{-4}\,\text{cm}\right) + \left(4\text{x}10^{-11}\,\text{F / cm}\right)\left(10^{-3}\,\text{cm}\right) = 48.6\text{fF}$$

$$\Delta V(s) = \frac{\dfrac{1}{sC_{BL}}}{\dfrac{1}{sC_{GS}} + \dfrac{1}{sC_{BL}}}\Delta V_G(s) \rightarrow \Delta V = \frac{\Delta V_G}{\dfrac{C_{BL}}{C_{GS}} + 1} = \frac{-3}{\dfrac{500}{48.6} + 1} = -0.266\text{ V}$$

This value provides a good estimate of the drop observed in Fig. 9.26.

9.23

The precharge transistor is operating in the linear region with $V_{DS} = 0$

$$C_{GS} = \frac{1}{2} C_{ox}^{"} WL + C_{GSO}W$$

$$C_{GS} = \frac{1}{2} \frac{3.9\left(8.854\text{x}10^{-14}\,\text{F / cm}\right)}{2\text{x}10^{-6}\,\text{cm}}\left(10^{-3}\,\text{cm}\right)\left(10^{-4}\,\text{cm}\right) + \left(4\text{x}10^{-11}\,\text{F / cm}\right)\left(10^{-3}\,\text{cm}\right) = 48.6\text{fF}$$

$$\Delta V(s) = \frac{\dfrac{1}{sC_{BL}}}{\dfrac{1}{sC_{GS}} + \dfrac{1}{sC_{BL}}}\Delta V_G(s) \rightarrow \Delta V = \frac{\Delta V_G}{\dfrac{C_{BL}}{C_{GS}} + 1} = \frac{3}{\dfrac{500}{48.6} + 1} = 0.266\text{ V}$$

This value provides a good estimate of the drop observed in Fig. 9.30.

The source - substrate diode will clamp the voltage to $\Delta V \leq 0.7$ V.

9.24

The bitline will charge to an initial volatge of $V_{BL} = 3 - V_{TN}$

$$V_{TN} = 0.7 + 0.5\left(\sqrt{3 - V_{TN} + 0.6} - \sqrt{0.6}\right) \rightarrow V_{TN} = 1.10\text{V} \mid V_{BL} = 1.90\text{V}$$

The initial charge Q_I on C_{BL}: $Q_I = 10^{-12}\,\text{F}(1.9\text{V}) = 1.9\text{pC}$

After charge sharing: $V_{BL} = \dfrac{1.9\text{pC}}{1.05\text{pF}} = 1.81\text{V}$. The voltage will be restored to 1.90V

by the transistor. The total charge delivered through the transistor is

$$\Delta Q = 0.09\text{V}(1.05\text{pF}) = 0.0945\text{pC} \mid \Delta v_O = \frac{9.45\text{x}10^{-14}\,\text{C}}{10^{-13}\,\text{F}} = 0.945\text{ V}$$

This sense amplifier provides a voltage gain of $A_V = \dfrac{0.945}{0.09} = 10.5$

9.25

```
*PROBLEM 9.25 Charge Transfer Sense Amplifier
VSW 5 0 DC 0 PULSE(0 3 2NS .5NS .5NS 100NS)
VGG 3 0 DC 3
CL 2 0 100FF
CBL 4 0 1PF
CC 6 0 50FF
M1 2 3 4 0 MOSN W=100U L=2U
M2 4 5 6 0 MOSN W=8U L=2U
.IC V(2)=3 V(4)=1.9
.TRAN 0.02NS 100NS UIC
.MODEL MOSN NMOS KP=25U VTO=0.7 GAMMA=0.5 PHI=0.6
.PROBE V(2) V(3) V(4) V(5) V(6)
.END
```

9.26

```
*PROBLEM 9.26 - Cross-Coupled Latch
VDD 1 0 DC 5
MN1 3 2 0 0 MOSN W=4U L=2U AS=16P AD=16P
MP1 3 2 1 1 MOSP W=4U L=2U AS=16P AD=16P
MN2 2 3 0 0 MOSN W=4U L=2U AS=16P AD=16P
MP2 2 3 1 1 MOSP W=4U L=2U AS=16P AD=16P
CBL1 3 0 1PF
CBL2 2 0 1PF
.IC V(3)=1V V(2)=1.25V V(1)=5
.OP
.TRAN 0.05N 50N UIC
.MODEL MOSN NMOS KP=5E-5 VTO=0.91 GAMMA=0.99
+LAMBDA=.02 TOX=41.5N
+CGSO=330P CGDO=330P CJ=3.9E-4 CJSW=510P
.MODEL MOSP PMOS KP=2E-5 VTO=-0.77 GAMMA=0.5
+LAMBDA=.05 TOX=41.5N
+CGSO=315P CGDO=315P CJ=2.0E-4 CJSW=180P
.PRINT TRAN V(2) V(3)
.PROBE V(2) V(3)
.END
```

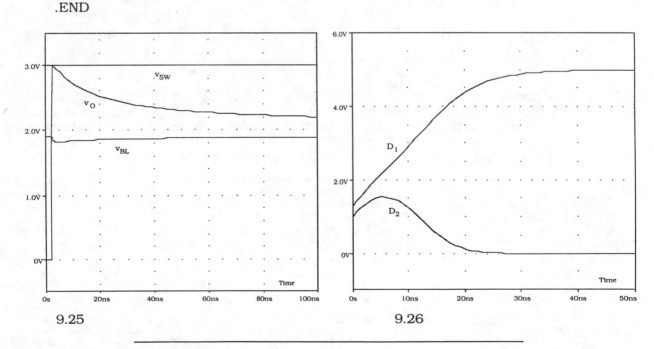

9.25   9.26

9.27

```
*PROBLEM 9.27 - Cross-Coupled Latch
VDD 1 0 DC 3
VSW 4 0 DC 0 PULSE(3 0 5NS 1NS 1NS 100NS)
MPC 3 4 2 0 MOSN W=20U L=2U AS=80P AD=80P
MN1 3 2 0 0 MOSN W=4U L=2U AS=16P AD=16P
MP1 3 2 1 1 MOSP W=8U L=2U AS=32P AD=32P
MN2 2 3 0 0 MOSN W=4U L=2U AS=16P AD=16P
*MN2 2 3 0 0 MOSN W=4.4U L=2U AS=17.6P AD=17.6P
MP2 2 3 1 1 MOSP W=8U L=2U AS=32P AD=32P
CBL1 3 0 400FF
CBL2 2 0 400FF
.OP
.TRAN 0.05N 50N
.MODEL MOSN NMOS KP=5E-5 VTO=0.91 GAMMA=0.99
+LAMBDA=.02 TOX=41.5N
+CGSO=330P CGDO=330P CJ=3.9E-4 CJSW=510P
.MODEL MOSP  PMOS  KP=2E-5 VTO=-0.77 GAMMA=0.5
+LAMBDA=.05 TOX=41.5N
+CGSO=315P CGDO=315P CJ=2.0E-4 CJSW=180P
.PROBE V(2) V(3) V(4)
.END
```

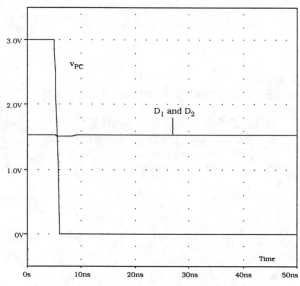

The latch is perfectly balanced in Part (a) and the voltage levels remain symmetrical even after the PC transistor turns off. This would not happen in the real case because of small asymmetries and noise in the latch. Even a small capacitive imbalance will cause the latch to assume a preferred state. Try setting CBL2 = 425 FF in Part (a) for example. The asymmetry in the latch in Part (b) causes it to switch to a preferred state.

9.28

```
*PROBLEM 9.28 - Clocked NMOS Sense Amplifier
VPC 2 0 DC 0 PULSE(3 0 1NS .5NS .5NS 250NS)
VWL 6 0 DC 0 PULSE(0 3 2NS .5NS .5NS 250NS)
VLC 9 0 DC 0 PULSE(0 3 3NS .5NS .5NS 250NS)
VDD 3 0 DC 3
CBL1 5 0 2PF
CBL2 4 0 2PF
*Storage Cell
MA1 5 6 1 0 MOSN W=2U L=2U AS=8P AD=8P
CC 1 0 100FF
```

```
*Dummy Cell
MA2 4 6 7 0 MOSN W=2U L=2U AS=8P AD=8P
CD 7 0 50FF
*Sense Amplifier
MPC 5 2 4 0 MOSN W=10U L=2U AS=40P AD=40P
ML1 3 2 4 0 MOSN W=10U L=2U AS=40P AD=40P
ML2 3 2 5 0 MOSN W=10U L=2U AS=40P AD=40P
MS1 5 4 8 0 MOSN W=50U L=2U AS=200P AD=200P
MS2 4 5 8 0 MOSN W=50U L=2U AS=200P AD=200P
MLC 8 9 0 0 MOSN W=50U L=2U AS=200P AD=200P
*
.OP
.TRAN 0.01NS 250NS
.MODEL MOSN NMOS KP=5E-5 VTO=0.91 GAMMA=0.99
+LAMBDA=.02 TOX=41.5N
+CGSO=330P CGDO=330P CJ=3.9E-4 CJSW=510P
.PROBE V(1) V(2) V(3) V(4) V(5) V(6) V(7) V(8) V(9)
.END
```

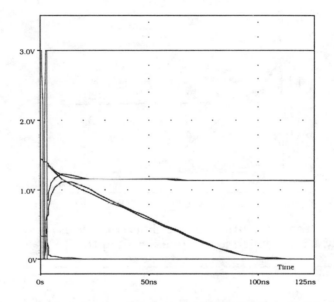

With only a 3 V power supply, the maximum bit-line differential is only 1.14 V which is achieved in 120 ns. (Relatively slow due to discharge of large bitline capacitance and relatively large threshold voltage of the NMOS transistors.)

9.29

```
*PROBLEM 9.29 - Clocked NMOS Sense Amplifier
VPC 2 0 DC 0 PULSE(5 0 1NS .5NS .5NS 250NS)
VWL 6 0 DC 0 PULSE(0 5 2NS .5NS .5NS 250NS)
VLC 9 0 DC 0 PULSE(0 5 3NS .5NS .5NS 250NS)
VDD 3 0 DC 5
CBL1 5 0 2PF
CBL2 4 0 2PF
*Storage Cell
MA1 5 6 1 0 MOSN W=2U L=2U AS=8P AD=8P
CC 1 0 100FF
*Dummy Cell
MA2 4 6 7 0 MOSN W=2U L=2U AS=8P AD=8P
CD 7 0 50FF
*Sense Amplifier
MPC 5 2 4 0 MOSN W=10U L=2U AS=40P AD=40P
```

```
ML1 3 2 4 0 MOSN W=10U L=2U AS=40P AD=40P
ML2 3 2 5 0 MOSN W=10U L=2U AS=40P AD=40P
MS1 5 4 8 0 MOSN W=50U L=2U AS=200P AD=200P
MS2 4 5 8 0 MOSN W=50U L=2U AS=200P AD=200P
MLC 8 9 0 0 MOSN W=50U L=2U AS=200P AD=200P
*
.OP
.TRAN 0.01NS 250NS
.MODEL MOSN NMOS KP=5E-5 VTO=0.91 GAMMA=0.99
+LAMBDA=.02 TOX=41.5N
+CGSO=330P CGDO=330P CJ=3.9E-4 CJSW=510P
.PROBE V(1) V(2) V(3) V(4) V(5) V(6) V(7) V(8) V(9)
.END
```

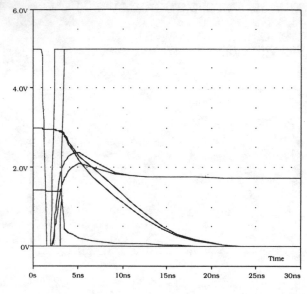

With the 5 V power supply, the maximum bit-line differential is 1.75 V. A 1.5 V differential is achieved in approximately 15 ns, which is much faster than the 3 V case.

9.30

```
*PROBLEM 9.30 - Cascaded Inverter Pair
VDD 1 0 DC 3
VI 2 0 DC 0
MN1 3 2 0 0 MOSN W=4U L=2U AS=16P AD=16P
MP1 3 2 1 1 MOSP W=4U L=2U AS=16P AD=16P
MN2 4 3 0 0 MOSN W=4U L=2U AS=16P AD=16P
MP2 4 3 1 1 MOSP W=4U L=2U AS=16P AD=16P
.OP
.DC VI 0 3 0.001
.MODEL MOSN NMOS KP=5E-5 VTO=0.91 GAMMA=0.99
+LAMBDA=.02 TOX=41.5N
+CGSO=330P CGDO=330P CJ=3.9E-4 CJSW=510P
.MODEL MOSP  PMOS  KP=2E-5 VTO=-0.77 GAMMA=0.5
+LAMBDA=.05 TOX=41.5N
+CGSO=315P CGDO=315P CJ=2.0E-4 CJSW=180P
.PROBE V(2) V(3) V(4)
.END
```

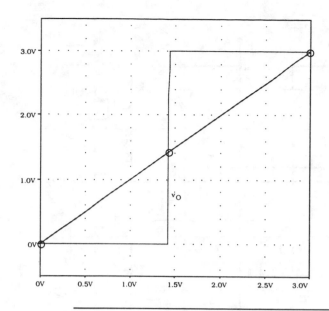

Results: $0\,\text{V},\ 1.429\,\text{V},\ 3\,\text{V}$

9.31

(a) The array requires: $(10\ \text{transistors}\,/\,\text{row})\left(2^{10}\,\text{rows}\right) + (1\ \text{load transistor}\,/\,\text{row})\left(2^{10}\,\text{rows}\right)$

$= 11\left(2^{10}\right) = 11{,}264$ transistors. The 20 inverters require an additional 40 transistors.

$N = 11304$ transistors | (b) The number is the same.

9.32

(a) NMOS Pass Transistor Tree: $2 \times \left(2^{0} + 2^{1} + 2^{2} + 2^{3} + 2^{4} + 2^{5} + 2^{6}\right) = 254$ Transistors

2 logic inverters per level = 14 inverters = 28 transistors.

Total = 282 Transistors

(b) An estimate: 128 data bits requires 128 7 - input gates for data selectors;

1 - 128 input NOR gate; 14 address bit inverters

Total $= 128(8) + 1(129) + 14(2) = 1181$ transistors without looking closely at the logic detail.

A number of additional inverters may be needed, and the 128 input gate can likely be replaced with a smaller NOR tree.

9.33 See next page

9.34

(a) The output of the first NMOS transistor will be

$V_1 = 5 - V_{TN} = 5 - \left[0.75 + 0.55\left(\sqrt{V_1 + 0.6} - \sqrt{0.6}\right)\right] \rightarrow V_1 = 3.56\text{V} \mid V_{TN} = 1.44\text{V}$

The output of the other gates reaches this same value. All three nodes = 3.56V.

(b) It first printing, the substrates of the PMOS transistors should be connected to $+5$V. Then the node voltages will all be $+5$ V.

9.33

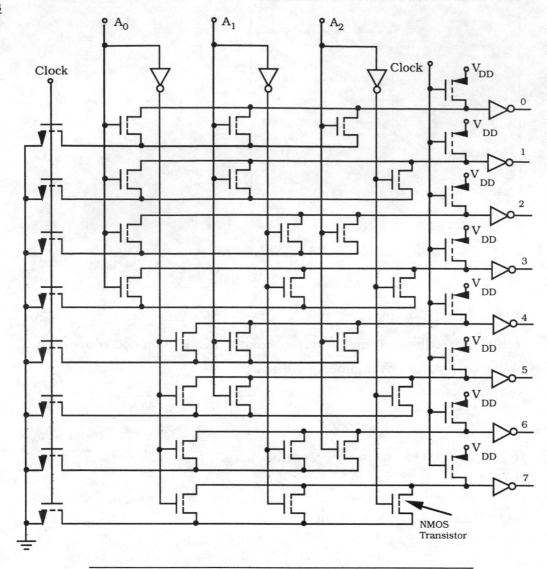

9.34 See previous page

9.35

Charge sharing occurs. Assuming C_2 and C_3 are discharged (the worst case)

(a) $V_B = \dfrac{C_1 V_{DD} + C_2(0)}{C_1 + C_2} = \dfrac{2C_2 V_{DD}}{2C_2 + C_2} = \dfrac{2}{3} V_{DD}$ | Node B drops to $\dfrac{2}{3} V_{DD}$.

(b) $V_B = \dfrac{(C_1 + C_2)\dfrac{2}{3} V_{DD} + C_3(0)}{C_1 + C_2 + C_3} = \dfrac{3C_2\left(\dfrac{2}{3} V_{DD}\right)}{2C_2 + C_2 + C_2} = \dfrac{V_{DD}}{2}$ | Node B drops to $\dfrac{1}{2} V_{DD}$.

(c) $V_B = \dfrac{C_1 V_{DD}}{C_1 + C_2 + C_3} = \dfrac{RC_2 V_{DD}}{RC_2 + C_2 + C_2} = \dfrac{R}{R+2} V_{DD} \geq V_{IH} \rightarrow R(V_{DD} - V_{IH}) \geq 2V_{IH}$

$R \geq \dfrac{2V_{IH}}{V_{DD} - V_{IH}} = \dfrac{2V_{IH}}{NM_H}$

Using $V_{DD} = 5V$, $V_{TN} = 0.7V$, $V_{TP} = -0.7V$ in Eq. (8.9):

$$V_{IH} = \frac{5(5) + 3(0.7) + 5(-0.7)}{8} = 2.95V \quad | \quad NM_H = \frac{3(5) - 3(0.7) - 5(-0.7)}{8} = 2.05V$$

$$R \geq \frac{2V_{IH}}{NM_H} = \frac{2(2.95)}{2.05} = 2.88 \quad | \quad C_1 \geq 2.88C_2$$

9.36 $Z = A_0 + A_1 + A_2$

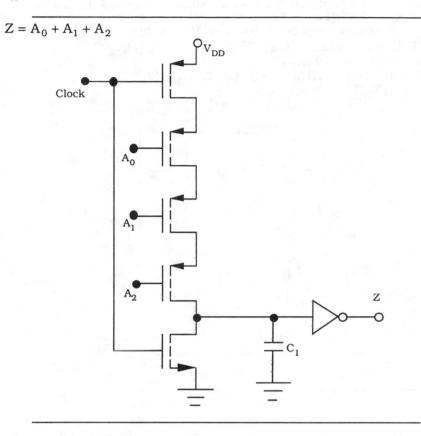

9.37

	B_7	B_6	B_5	B_4	B_3	B_2	B_1	B_0
W_0	1	0	1	1	0	0	0	0
W_1	0	1	0	0	0	1	1	0
W_2	1	1	0	0	0	1	0	0
W_3	0	0	1	0	1	0	1	1
W_4	0	0	0	0	1	1	1	0
W_5	0	1	0	0	0	0	0	0

9.38

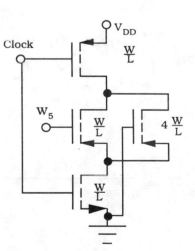

*PROBLEM 9.38 - Simplified ROM Cross-Section
VCLK 1 0 DC 0 PULSE(0 5 2.5NS 1NS 1NS 25NS)
VW5 3 0 DC 0 PULSE(0 5 4.5NS 1NS 1NS 25NS)
VDD 5 0 DC 5

171

```
MPC 4 1 5 5 MOSP W=4U L=2U AS=16P AD=16P
MNC 2 1 0 0 MOSN W=4U L=2U AS=16P AD=16P
MW5 4 3 2 0 MOSN W=4U L=2U AS=16P AD=16P
MWW 4 0 2 0 MOSN W=16U L=2U AS=64P AD=64P
.OP
.TRAN 0.01NS 15NS
.MODEL MOSN NMOS KP=5E-5 VTO=0.91 GAMMA=0.99
+LAMBDA=.02 TOX=41.5N
+CGSO=330P CGDO=330P CJ=3.9E-4 CJSW=510P
.MODEL MOSP  PMOS  KP=2E-5 VTO=-0.77 GAMMA=0.5
+LAMBDA=.05 TOX=41.5N
+CGSO=315P CGDO=315P CJ=2.0E-4 CJSW=180P
.PROBE V(1) V(2) V(3) V(4) V(5)
.END
```

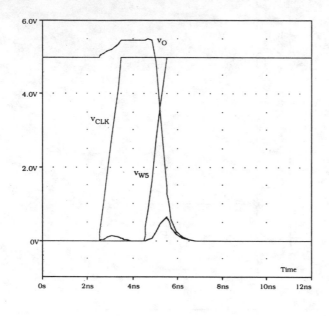

9.39

	B_5	B_4	B_3	B_2	B_1	B_0
W_1	0	0	1	0	1	0
W_2	1	0	0	1	0	1
W_3	0	1	1	1	0	1

9.40

	B_2	B_1	B_0
$\overline{W_0}$	1	0	1
$\overline{W_1}$	1	1	0
$\overline{W_2}$	1	0	1
$\overline{W_3}$	0	1	0

Note that the input lines are active low.

9.41

The four inputs should be labeled $(A + B)$, $(\overline{A} + B)$, $(A + \overline{B})$, $(\overline{A} + \overline{B})$

Then the four intermediate outputs become

$I_0 = (A + B)(A + \overline{B}) = AA + B\overline{B} + AB + A\overline{B} = A(A + B + \overline{B}) = A$

$I_1 = (\overline{A} + B)(A + \overline{B}) = \overline{A}A + \overline{A}B + \overline{A}\overline{B} + B\overline{B} = \overline{A}B + A\overline{B}$

$I_2 = (A + B)(\overline{A} + \overline{B}) = \overline{A}A + A\overline{B} + B\overline{A} + B\overline{B} = A\overline{B} + \overline{A}B$

$I_3 = (A + B)(\overline{A} + B) = A\overline{A} + AB + B\overline{A} + BB = B(B + A + \overline{A}) = B$

$O_0 = I_1 + I_2 = AB + \overline{A}\overline{B} + A\overline{B} + \overline{A}B = 1$

$O_1 = I_1 = AB + \overline{A}\overline{B}$

$O_2 = I_0 + I_3 = A + B$

9.42

$O_0 = \overline{A + B + C} = \overline{A}\overline{B}\overline{C}$

$O_1 = \overline{\overline{A} + B + \overline{C}} = A\overline{B}C$

$O_2 = \overline{A + \overline{B} + C} = \overline{A}B\overline{C}$

$O_3 = \overline{\overline{A} + \overline{B} + \overline{C}} = ABC$

$O_4 = \overline{\overline{B} + C} = B\overline{C}$

$O_5 = \overline{A + C} = \overline{A}\overline{C}$

$O_6 = \overline{\overline{A} + \overline{B} + \overline{C}} = ABC$

$O_7 = \overline{A + B + \overline{C}} = \overline{A}\overline{B}C$

9.43 Note that rows 3 and 6 are redundant in the array below.

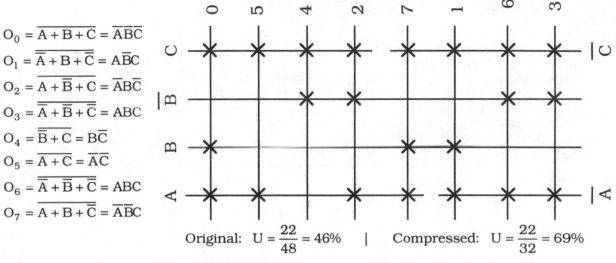

Original: $U = \dfrac{22}{48} = 46\%$ | Compressed: $U = \dfrac{22}{32} = 69\%$

9.44

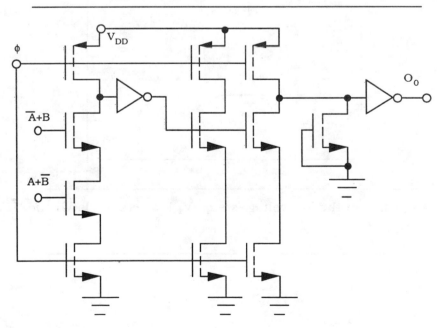

173

```
*PROBLEM 9.44 - Simplified PLA Cross-Section
VCLK 1 0 DC 0 PULSE(0 5 1.5NS 1NS 1NS 25NS)
VIA 3 0 DC 0 PULSE(0 5 3.5NS 1NS 1NS 25NS)
VDD 12 0 DC 5
VIB 5 0 DC 5
MPC1 6 1 12 12 MOSP W=4U L=2U AS=16P AD=16P
MNC1 2 1 0 0 MOSN W=4U L=2U AS=16P AD=16P
MPC2 9 1 12 12 MOSP W=4U L=2U AS=16P AD=16P
MNC2 7 1 0 0 MOSN W=4U L=2U AS=16P AD=16P
MPC3 10 1 12 12 MOSP W=4U L=2U AS=16P AD=16P
MNC3 8 1 0 0 MOSN W=4U L=2U AS=16P AD=16P
MA 4 3 2 0 MOSN W=4U L=2U AS=16P AD=16P
MB 6 5 4 0 MOSN W=16U L=2U AS=64P AD=64P
MN1 13 6 0 0 MOSN W=4U L=2U AS=16P AD=16P
MP1 13 6 12 12 MOSP W=4U L=2U AS=16P AD=16P
MN2 11 10 0 0 MOSN W=4U L=2U AS=16P AD=16P
MP2 11 10 12 12 MOSP W=4U L=2U AS=16P AD=16P
MX 9 13 7 0 MOSN W=4U L=2U AS=16P AD=16P
MY 10 13 8 0 MOSN W=4U L=2U AS=16P AD=16P
MZ 10 0 0 0 MOSN W=4U L=2U AS=16P AD=16P
.OP
.TRAN 0.01NS 10NS
.MODEL MOSN NMOS KP=5E-5 VTO=0.91 GAMMA=0.99
+LAMBDA=.02 TOX=41.5N
+CGSO=330P CGDO=330P CJ=3.9E-4 CJSW=510P
.MODEL MOSP  PMOS  KP=2E-5 VTO=-0.77 GAMMA=0.5
+LAMBDA=.05 TOX=41.5N
+CGSO=315P CGDO=315P CJ=2.0E-4 CJSW=180P
.PROBE V(1) V(3) V(6) V(13) V(10) V(11)
.END
```

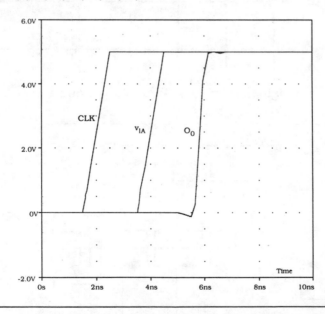

9.45 The inputs are active in the low voltage state. V_1 low sets the latch and V_2 low resets the latch. $\quad V_1 = \overline{S} \quad V_2 = \overline{R}$.

9.46

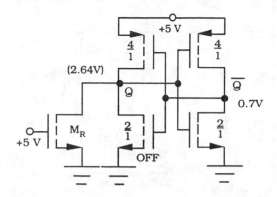

Regenerative switching of the cell will take place when the voltage at Q is pulled low enough by transistor M_R that the voltage at $\overline{Q}$ rises above the NMOS transistor threshold voltage. Equating drain currents for this condition yields the value of V_Q. It appears that the NMOS transistor will be in the linear region, and the PMOS transistor will be saturated.

$$\frac{10^{-5}}{2}\left(\frac{4}{1}\right)\left(5-V_Q-0.7\right)^2 = 25\text{x}10^{-6}\left(\frac{2}{1}\right)\left(V_Q-0.7-\frac{0.7}{2}\right)0.7 \rightarrow V_Q = 2.64\text{V}$$ which agrees with

the assumptions. Now, M_R must be large enough to force $V_Q = 2.64\text{V}$. M_R and the PMOS load transistor are both in the linear region.

$$10^{-5}\left(\frac{4}{1}\right)\left(5-0.7-0.7-\frac{2.36}{2}\right)2.36 \le 25\text{x}10^{-6}\left(\frac{W}{L}\right)_R\left(5-0.7-\frac{2.64}{2}\right)2.64 \rightarrow \left(\frac{W}{L}\right)_R \ge \frac{1.16}{1}$$

9.47

```
*PROBLEM 9.47 - D-Latch
VDD 7 0 DC 5
VI 1 0 DC 5 PULSE(5 0 15NS 1NS 1NS 15NS)
VCLK 2 0 DC 0 PULSE(0 5 3NS 1NS 1NS 10NS)
VNCLK 3 0 DC 0 PULSE(5 0 3NS 1NS 1NS 10NS)
MTN1 1 2 4 0 MOSN W=4U L=2U AS=16P AD=16P
MTP1 1 3 4 7 MOSP W=4U L=2U AS=16P AD=16P
MIN1 5 4 0 0 MOSN W=4U L=2U AS=16P AD=16P
MIP1 5 4 7 7 MOSP W=4U L=2U AS=16P AD=16P
MIN2 6 5 0 0 MOSN W=4U L=2U AS=16P AD=16P
MIP2 6 5 7 7 MOSP W=4U L=2U AS=16P AD=16P
MTN2 6 3 4 0 MOSN W=4U L=2U AS=16P AD=16P
MTP2 6 2 4 7 MOSP W=4U L=2U AS=16P AD=16P
.OP
.TRAN 0.05N 30N
.MODEL MOSN NMOS KP=5E-5 VTO=0.91 GAMMA=0.99
+LAMBDA=.02 TOX=41.5N
+CGSO=330P CGDO=330P CJ=3.9E-4 CJSW=510P
.MODEL MOSP  PMOS  KP=2E-5 VTO=-0.77 GAMMA=0.5
+LAMBDA=.05 TOX=41.5N
+CGSO=315P CGDO=315P CJ=2.0E-4 CJSW=180P
.PROBE V(1) V(2) V(3) V(4) V(5) V(6)
.END
```

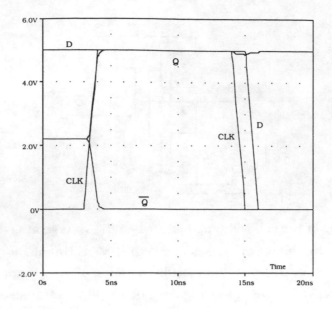

9.48

```
*PROBLEM 9.48 - Master-Slave Flip-Flop
VDD 10 0 DC 5
VI 1 0 DC 5 PWL(0 5 17.4NS 5 17.6NS 0 30NS 0)
VCLK 2 0 DC 0 PULSE(0 5 0NS 2.5NS 2.5NS 7.5NS)
VNCLK 3 0 DC 0 PULSE(5 0 0NS 2.5NS 2.5NS 7.5NS)
MTN1 1 2 4 0 MOSN W=4U L=2U AS=16P AD=16P
MTP1 1 3 4 10 MOSP W=4U L=2U AS=16P AD=16P
MIN1 5 4 0 0 MOSN W=4U L=2U AS=16P AD=16P
MIP1 5 4 10 10 MOSP W=4U L=2U AS=16P AD=16P
MIN2 6 5 0 0 MOSN W=4U L=2U AS=16P AD=16P
MIP2 6 5 10 10 MOSP W=4U L=2U AS=16P AD=16P
MTN2 6 3 4 0 MOSN W=4U L=2U AS=16P AD=16P
MTP2 6 2 4 10 MOSP W=4U L=2U AS=16P AD=16P
*
MTN3 6 3 7 0 MOSN W=4U L=2U AS=16P AD=16P
MTP3 6 2 7 10 MOSP W=4U L=2U AS=16P AD=16P
MIN3 8 7 0 0 MOSN W=4U L=2U AS=16P AD=16P
MIP3 8 7 10 10 MOSP W=4U L=2U AS=16P AD=16P
MIN4 9 8 0 0 MOSN W=4U L=2U AS=16P AD=16P
MIP4 9 8 10 10 MOSP W=4U L=2U AS=16P AD=16P
MTN4 9 2 7 0 MOSN W=4U L=2U AS=16P AD=16P
MTP4 9 3 7 10 MOSP W=4U L=2U AS=16P AD=16P
.IC V(1)=5 V(2)=0 V(3)=5 V(4)=0 V(5)=5 V(6)=0 V(7)=0
+ V(8)=5 V(9)=0 V(10)=5
.TRAN 0.05N 20N UIC
.MODEL MOSN NMOS KP=5E-5 VTO=0.91 GAMMA=0.99
+LAMBDA=.02 TOX=41.5N
+CGSO=330P CGDO=330P CJ=3.9E-4 CJSW=510P
.MODEL MOSP  PMOS  KP=2E-5 VTO=-0.77 GAMMA=0.5
+LAMBDA=.05 TOX=41.5N
+CGSO=315P CGDO=315P CJ=2.0E-4 CJSW=180P
.PROBE V(1) V(2) V(3) V(4) V(6) V(7) V(9)
.END
```

The flip-flop operates normally. Data is transfered to the master following the first clock transistion and to the slave after the second clock transition. The maximum rise and fall times are highly dependent upon the position of the data transistion edge. It is interesting to experiment with the data delay to see the effect. At some point the flip-flop will fail.

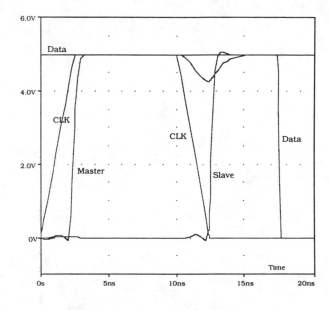

$$N_{opt} = \ln \frac{C_L}{C_o} = \ln(4000) = 8.29 \rightarrow N = 8 \quad | \quad \beta = (4000)^{\frac{1}{8}} = 2.82.$$

The relative sizes of the 8 inverters are: 1, 2.82, 7.95, 22.4, 63.2, 178, 503, 1420.

Each inverter has a delay of $2.82\tau_o$. The total delay is $8(2.82\tau_o) = 22.6\tau_o$

9.50

$$A_T = A_o\left(1 + \beta + \beta^2 + \ldots + \beta^{N-1}\right) = A_o \frac{\beta^N - 1}{\beta - 1}$$

For $N = 6$, $\beta = 1000^{1/6} = 3.1623$ $\quad | \quad A = A_o \frac{1000 - 1}{3.1623 - 1} = 462A_o$

For $N = 7$, $\beta = 1000^{1/7} = 2.6827$ $\quad | \quad A = A_o \frac{1000 - 1}{2.6827 - 1} = 594A_o$

Since the two values of N give similar delays, N = 6 would be used because of it requires significantly less area.

CHAPTER 10

10.1

$$\frac{I_{C2}}{I_{C1}} = \exp\left(\frac{\Delta V_{BE}}{V_T}\right) \Rightarrow \Delta V_{BE} = 0.025 \ln \frac{0.995 \alpha_F I_{EE}}{0.005 \alpha_F I_{EE}} = 0.132V$$

(a) $v_I = V_{REF} + \Delta V_{BE} = -1.25 + 0.132 = -1.12$ V

$v_I = V_{REF} + \Delta V_{BE} = -1.25 - 0.132 = -1.38$ V

(b) $v_I = V_{REF} + \Delta V_{BE} = -2.00 + 0.132 = -1.87$ V

$v_I = V_{REF} + \Delta V_{BE} = -2.00 - 0.132 = -2.13$ V

10.2

Since $V_{REF} = -1.25V$, $v_I = -1.6V \Rightarrow Q_1$ off and Q_2 conducting

$v_{C1} = 0$ V and $v_{C2} = -\alpha_F I_{EE} R_C \approx -I_{EE} R_C = -(2mA)(350\Omega) = -0.700$ V

10.3

Since $V_{REF} = -2V$, $v_I = -1.6V \Rightarrow Q_2$ off and Q_1 conducting

$v_{C2} = 0$ V and $v_{C1} = -\alpha_F I_{EE} R_C \approx -I_{EE} R_C = -(5mA)(350\Omega) = -1.75$ V

Note that Q_1 is beginning to enter the saturation region of operation, but $V_{BC} = +0.15$ V is not really enough to turn on the collector-base diode. (See Problems 10.5 or 5.36.)

10.4

$v_I = V_{REF} + 0.3V \Rightarrow Q_1$ on; Q_2 off. $I_{C1} = \alpha_F I_{EE} \approx I_{EE} = 0.3mA$ | $I_{C2} = 0$

$v_{C1} = 0 - I_{C1}(R_1 + R_C) = -0.3mA(3.33k\Omega + 2k\Omega) = -1.60$ V

$v_{C2} = 0 - I_{C1}R_1 = -0.3mA(3.33k\Omega) = -0.999$ V

10.5 With $V_{BE} = 0.7$ and $V_{BC} = 0.3$, the transistor is technically in the saturation region, but calculating the currents using the transport model in Eq. (5.13) yields

$$\beta_F = \frac{\alpha_F}{1-\alpha_F} = \frac{0.98}{1-0.98} = 49 \mid \beta_R = \frac{\alpha_R}{1-\alpha_R} = \frac{0.2}{1-0.2} = 0.25$$

$$i_C = 10^{-15}\left[\exp\left(\frac{0.7}{0.025}\right) - \exp\left(\frac{0.3}{0.025}\right)\right] - \frac{10^{-15}}{0.25}\left[\exp\left(\frac{0.3}{0.025}\right) - 1\right] = 1.446 \text{ mA}$$

$$i_E = 10^{-15}\left[\exp\left(\frac{0.7}{0.025}\right) - \exp\left(\frac{0.3}{0.025}\right)\right] + \frac{10^{-15}}{49}\left[\exp\left(\frac{0.7}{0.025}\right) - 1\right] = 1.476 \text{ mA}$$

$$i_B = \frac{10^{-15}}{49}\left[\exp\left(\frac{0.7}{0.025}\right) - 1\right] + \frac{10^{-15}}{0.25}\left[\exp\left(\frac{0.3}{0.025}\right) - 1\right] = 29.52 \text{ μA}$$

At 0.3 V, the collector-base junction is not heavily forward-biased compared to the base-emitter junction, and $I_C = 48.99 I_B \approx \beta_F I_B$. The transistor still acts as if it is operating in the forward-active region.

10.6 (a) For Q_2 off, $V_{OH} = 0$ V. For Q_2 on, $I_C \approx I_E$ and

$$I_E = \frac{-0.2 - 0.7 - (-2)}{1.1 \times 10^4} = 100 \ \mu A \qquad V_{OL} \cong -4000 I_E = -0.400 \ V$$

(b) Yes, these voltages are symmetrically positioned above and below V_{REF}, i. e. $V_{REF} \pm 0.2$ V, and the current will be fully switched. See Parts (d) and (e).

(c) For $v_I = 0$ V, $I_C \cong I_E = \dfrac{0 - 0.7 - (-2)}{1.1 \times 10^4} = 118 \ \mu A \qquad R = \dfrac{0.4V}{118 \mu A} = 3.39 \ k\Omega$

(d) Q_2 is cutoff. Q_1 is saturated with $V_{BC} = +0.4$ V.

(e) Q_1 is cutoff. Q_2 is saturated with $V_{BC} = +0.2$ V.

(f) 0.2 V and 0.4 V are not large enough to heavily saturate Q_1 or Q_2. Although the transistors are technically operating in the saturation region, the transistors still behave as if they are in the forward-active region. (See problem 10.5).

10.7

$$V_{OH} = 0 - V_{BE} = -0.7 \ V \quad | \quad V_{OL} = -(5mA)(200\Omega) - 0.5 = -1.70 \ V$$

$$V_{REF} = \frac{V_{OH} + V_{OL}}{2} = -1.2 \ V \quad | \quad \Delta V = (5mA)(200\Omega) = 1 \ V$$

10.8

$$I_{EE} = 5(0.3mA) = 1.5 \ mA \quad | \quad I_3 = I_4 = 5(0.1mA) = 0.5 \ mA \quad | \quad R_C = \frac{2k\Omega}{5} = 400\Omega$$

10.9

(a) $R_C = \dfrac{\Delta V}{I_{EE}} = \dfrac{0.8V}{0.3mA} = 2.67 \ k\Omega \quad | \quad V_{OH} = 0 - V_{BE} = -0.7 \ V \quad | \quad V_{OL} = -0.8 - V_{BE} = -1.5 \ V$

$V_{REF} = \dfrac{V_{OH} + V_{OL}}{2} = -1.10 \ V$

(b) $NM_H = NM_L = \dfrac{\Delta V}{2} - V_T \ln\left(\dfrac{\Delta V}{V_T} - 1\right) = \dfrac{0.8}{2} - 0.025 \ln\left(\dfrac{0.8}{0.025} - 1\right) = 0.314 \ V$

(c) For Q_1: $V_{CB} = -0.8 - (-0.7) = -0.1$ V which represents a slight forward bias, but it is not enough to turn on the diode. For Q_2: $V_{CB} = -0.8 - (-1.10) = +0.3$ V which represents a reverse bias. Both values are satisfactory for operation of the logic gate.

10.10

(b) For Q_1 on and Q_2 off, $I_{C1} = \alpha_F I_{EE} \approx I_{EE} = 0.3mA \quad | \quad I_{C2} = 0$

$v_{OL} = 0 - I_{C1}(R_1 + R_C) - 0.7V = -0.3mA(3.33k\Omega + 2k\Omega) - 0.7V = -2.30 \ V$

$v_{OH} = 0 - I_{C1}R_1 - 0.7V = -0.3mA(3.33k\Omega) - 0.7 = -1.70 \ V$

$\Delta V = V_{OH} - V_{OL} = 0.600 \ V$

(c) $\dfrac{V_{OH} + V_{OL}}{2} = -2.0V = V_{REF} \quad | \quad$ Yes, the input and output voltage levels are

compatible with each other and are symmetrically placed around V_{REF}.

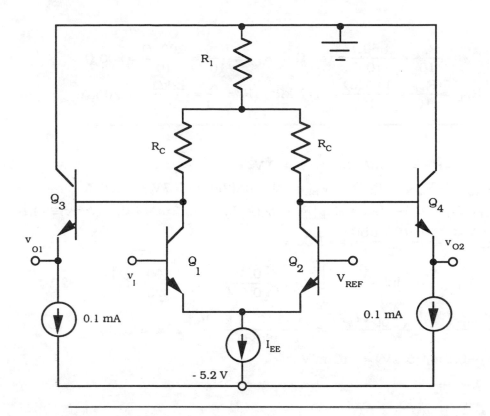

10.11

(a) See Prob. 10.10

(b) $\Delta V = \alpha_F I_{EE} R_C \approx I_{EE} R_C \mid R_C = \dfrac{0.4V}{2mA} = 200\ \Omega$

$V_{OH} = 0 - \alpha_F I_{EE} R_1 - V_{BE} \approx -I_{EE} R_1 - V_{BE} = -2mA(600) - 0.7V = -1.90\ V$

$V_{OL} = 0 - \alpha_F I_{EE}(R_1 + R_C) - V_{BE} \approx -I_{EE}(R_1 + R_C) - V_{BE} = -2mA(800) - 0.7V = -2.30\ V$

$V_{REF} = \dfrac{V_{OH} + V_{OL}}{2} = \dfrac{-1.90 - 2.30}{2} = -2.10\ V$

10.12

$\Delta V = \Delta V_{BE} + \Delta i_{B4} R_C \mid$ Let the Fanout $=$ N and $\beta_F = 20$. Then there will be N base

currents that must be supplied from emitter - follower transistor Q_4: $\Delta i_{E4} = N \dfrac{I_{EE}}{\beta_F + 1}$

$\Delta V_{BE} = V_T \ln \dfrac{I_{C4} + \Delta I_{C4}}{I_{C4}} = V_T \ln \dfrac{I_{E4} + \Delta I_{E4}}{I_{E4}} = V_T \ln\left(1 + \dfrac{\Delta I_{E4}}{I_{E4}}\right) = .025 \ln\left[1 + N \dfrac{I_{EE}}{(\beta_F + 1)I_{E4}}\right]$

$\Delta i_{B4} = \dfrac{\Delta i_{E4}}{\beta_F + 1} = N \dfrac{I_{EE}}{(\beta_F + 1)^2}$. Using a worst case value of $\beta_F = 20$,

$\Delta V = \Delta V_{BE} + \Delta i_{B4} R_C = 0.025 \ln\left(1 + N \dfrac{0.3mA}{21(0.1mA)}\right) + N \dfrac{0.3mA}{(21)^2} 2k\Omega \mid \Delta V \le 0.025$

$0.025 = 0.025 \ln\left(1 + \dfrac{3N}{21}\right) + \dfrac{0.6N}{(21)^2} \mid$ Using MATLAB or HP - Solver: $N \le 6.41 \to N = 6.$

10.13

$$R'_{C1} = \frac{R_{C1}}{10} = \frac{1850\Omega}{10} = 185 \ \Omega \quad | \quad R'_{C2} = \frac{R_{C2}}{10} = \frac{2000\Omega}{10} = 200 \ \Omega$$

$$R'_{EE} = \frac{R_{EE}}{10} = \frac{11.7k\Omega}{10} = 1.17 \ k\Omega \quad | \quad R' = \frac{R}{10} = \frac{42k\Omega}{10} = 4.20 \ k\Omega$$

10.14

$$\Delta V = \alpha_F I_{EE} R_C \approx I_{EE} R_C = 0.2mA(2k\Omega) = 0.400 \ V$$

$$V_{OH} = 0 - \alpha_F I_{EE} R_1 - V_{BE} \approx -I_{EE} R_1 - V_{BE} = -0.2mA(2k\Omega) - 0.7V = -1.10 \ V$$

$$V_{OL} = 0 - \alpha_F I_{EE}(R_1 + R_C) - V_{BE} \approx -I_{EE}(R_1 + R_C) - V_{BE} = -0.2mA(4k\Omega) - 0.7V = -1.50 \ V$$

$$V_{REF} = \frac{V_{OH} + V_{OL}}{2} = \frac{-1.10 - 1.50}{2} = -1.30 \ V$$

$$NM_L = NM_H = V_T\left[\frac{\Delta V}{2V_T} - \ln\left(\frac{\Delta V}{V_T} - 1\right)\right] = 0.025\left[\frac{0.400}{0.050} - \ln\left(\frac{0.400}{0.025} - 1\right)\right] = 0.132 \ V$$

$$I_{E3} + I_{E4} = \frac{[V_{OH} - (-2)] + [V_{OL} - (-2)]}{R} = \frac{(4 - 1.10 - 1.50)V}{50k\Omega} = 28.0 \ \mu A$$

$$\overline{P} = 28\mu A(2V) + 0.2mA(5.2V) = 1.10 \ mW$$

10.15

$$NM_H = V_T\left[\frac{\Delta V}{2V_T} - \ln\left(\frac{\Delta V}{V_T} - 1\right)\right] \quad | \quad 0.1V = 0.025V[20\Delta V - \ln(40\Delta V - 1)]$$

Solving by trial - and - error, HP - Solver, or MATLAB: $\Delta V = 0.3241 \ V$

```
function f=dv15(v)
f=4-20*v+log(40*v-1);

fzero('dv15',0.5)   yields   ans = 0.3241
```

10.16

(a) The change in v_{BE} will be neglected: $\Delta v_{BE} = V_T \ln\dfrac{0.8I_C}{I_C} = -5.6mV$

$$V_{OH} = 0 - V_{BE} = 0 - 0.7 = -0.7 \ V \ - \ \text{no change}$$

$$V_{OL} = 0 - \alpha_F I_{EE} R_C - V_{BE} \approx -I_{EE} R_C - V_{BE} = -0.3mA(1.2)(2k\Omega) - 0.7V = -1.42 \ V$$

V_{OL} has dropped by 0.12V. $\quad | \quad \Delta V = 0.3mA(1.2)(2k\Omega) = 0.72 \ V$

$$NM_H = NM_L = \frac{\Delta V}{2} - V_T \ln\left(\frac{\Delta V}{V_T} - 1\right) = \frac{0.72}{2} - 0.025\ln\left(\frac{0.72}{0.025} - 1\right) = 0.277 \ V$$

(b) At node A: $V_{OH} = 0 - V_{BE} = 0 - 0.7 = -0.7 \ V \ - \ \text{no change}$

$$V_{OL} = 0 - \alpha_F I_{EE} R_C - V_{BE} \approx -I_{EE} R_C - V_{BE} = -\frac{-1.0 - 0.7 - (-5.2)}{1.2(11.7k\Omega)}V(1.2)(2k\Omega) - 0.7V = -1.30 \ V$$

V_{OL} also has not changed! $\quad |$ Similar results hold at node B because the voltages
are set by resistor ratios.

$$NM_H = NM_L = \frac{\Delta V}{2} - V_T \ln\left(\frac{\Delta V}{V_T} - 1\right) = \frac{0.6}{2} - 0.025\ln\left(\frac{0.6}{0.025} - 1\right) = 0.222 \ V, \ \text{unchanged}$$

10.17

$$R'_{C1} = 10R_{C1} = 10(1.85k\Omega) = 18.5 \ k\Omega \ | \ R'_{C2} = 10R_{C2} = 10(2k\Omega) = 20.0 \ k\Omega$$

$$R'_{EE} = 10R_{EE} = 10(11.7k\Omega) = 117 \ k\Omega \ | \ R' = 10R = 10(42k\Omega) = 420 \ k\Omega$$

10.18

(a) $V_{OH} = -0.7V \ | \ \Delta V = 0.8V \ | \ V_{OL} = -0.8 - 0.7 = -1.5V \ | \ V_{REF} = \dfrac{V_{OH} + V_{OL}}{2} = -1.1V$

$$R_{EE} = \frac{-1.1 - 0.7 - (-5.2)}{0.3} \frac{V}{mA} = 11.3 \ k\Omega \ | \ R_{C2} = \frac{0.8V}{0.3mA} = 2.67 \ k\Omega$$

$$I_{E1} = \frac{-0.7 - 0.7 - (-5.2)}{11.3} \frac{V}{k\Omega} = 0.336mA \ | \ R_{C1} = \frac{0.8V}{0.336mA} = 2.38 \ k\Omega$$

(b) $NM_H = NM_L = \dfrac{0.8}{2} - 0.025 \ln\left(\dfrac{0.8}{0.025} - 1\right) = 0.314 \ V$

(c) $V_{CB1} = -0.8 - (-0.7) = -0.1V \ | \ V_{CB2} = -0.8 - (-1.1) = +0.3V$

The collector - base junction of Q_2 is reverse - biased by 0.3 V. Although the collector - base junction of Q_1 is forward - biased by 0.1 V, this is not large enough to cause a problem. Therefore the voltages are acceptable.

10.19

$$NM_H = V_T\left[\frac{\Delta V}{2V_T} - \ln\left(\frac{\Delta V}{V_T} - 1\right)\right] = \frac{\Delta V}{2} - V_T \ln\left(\frac{\Delta V}{V_T} - 1\right)$$

For room temperature, $V_T = 0.025V$: $0.1V = \left[\dfrac{\Delta V}{2} - 0.025V \ln\left(\dfrac{\Delta V}{0.025} - 1\right)\right] \rightarrow \Delta V = 0.324V$

For -55C, $V_T = 0.0188V$: $0.1V = \left[\dfrac{\Delta V}{2} - 0.0188V \ln\left(\dfrac{\Delta V}{0.0188} - 1\right)\right] \rightarrow \Delta V = 0.302V$

For +75C, $V_T = 0.0300V$: $0.1V = \left[\dfrac{\Delta V}{2} - 0.0300V \ln\left(\dfrac{\Delta V}{0.0300} - 1\right)\right] \rightarrow \Delta V = 0.340V$

$\Delta V = 0.340 \ V$

10.20

In the original circuit: $V_{OH} = -2mA(2k\Omega) - 0.7V = -1.1V \ | \ \Delta V = 2mA(2k\Omega) = 0.4V$

$V_{OL} = -1.1V - \Delta V = -1.5V$. V_{OH} amd V_{OL} are symmetrically placed about V_{REF}.

$$R_{EE} = \frac{-1.3 - 0.7 - (-5.2)}{0.2} \frac{V}{mA} = 16.0 \ k\Omega. \ R_1 \text{ and } R_{C2} \text{ remain unchanged.}$$

For Q_1 on and and Q_2 off: $I_{EE} = \dfrac{-1.1 - 0.7 - (-5.2)}{16.0} \dfrac{V}{k\Omega} = 0.2125mA$

$V_{OL1} = -(0.2125mA)(2k\Omega + R_{C1}) - 0.7V \ | \ V_{OL1} = -1.5V \rightarrow R_{C1} = 1.77 \ k\Omega$.

Note that there are only 3 variables $(R_1, R_{C1} \text{ and } R_{C2})$ and four voltage levels. Thus we cannot force them all to the desired level. For this design,

$V_{OH2} = -(0.2125mA)(2k\Omega) - 0.7V = -1.125V$ rather than the desired -1.10V

10.21

$$V_{EQ} = \frac{60k\Omega}{60k\Omega + 44k\Omega}(-5.2V) = -3.0V \quad | \quad R_{EQ} = 60k\Omega\|44k\Omega = 25.38k\Omega$$

$$I_{BS} = \frac{-3.0 - 0.7 - (-5.2)}{25.38 + (\beta_F + 1)30} \frac{V}{k\Omega} \quad | \quad I_{EE} = \beta_F I_{BS} = \beta_F \frac{-3.0 - 0.7 - (-5.2)}{25.38 + (\beta_F + 1)30} \frac{V}{k\Omega}$$

For large β_F, $I_{EE} = \dfrac{-3.0 - 0.7 - (-5.2)}{30} \dfrac{V}{k\Omega} = 50.0~\mu A$ | Forward - active region

requires $V_{CBS} \geq 0V$ | $V_{CBS} = V_{REF} - V_{BE2} - V_{BS} = V_{REF} - 0.7V - (-3V)$

$V_{REF} - 0.7V - (-3V) \geq 0 \rightarrow V_{REF} \geq -2.30~V$

10.22

$$R'_{C1} = 5R_{C1} = 5(1.85k\Omega) = 9.25~k\Omega \quad | \quad R'_{C2} = 5R_{C2} = 5(2k\Omega) = 10.0~k\Omega$$

$$R'_{EE} = 5R_{EE} = 5(11.7k\Omega) = 58.5~k\Omega \quad | \quad R' = 5R = 5(42k\Omega) = 210~k\Omega$$

10.23

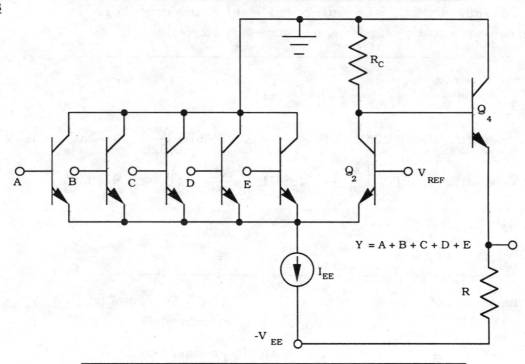

10.24

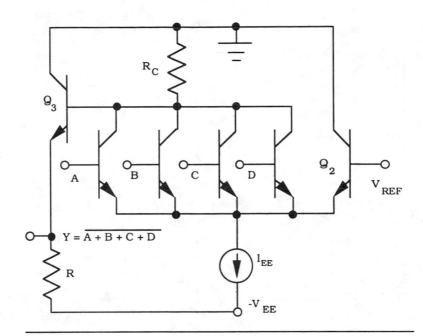

$$Y = \overline{A + B + C + D}$$

10.25

(a) For Q_4 on, $I_{C4} = \alpha_F I_{E4} \cong I_{E4} = \dfrac{-0.7 - (-3.2)}{840} = 2.98$ mA

$V_{OL} = 1.3V - (2.98mA)(390\Omega) - 0.7V = -0.56$ V | For Q_4 off, $V_{OH} = 1.3 - 0.7 = +0.60$ V

(b) For $v_A = 0.6V$, $I_{C2} = \alpha_F I_{E2} \cong I_{E2} = \dfrac{0.6 - 0.7 - (-3.2)}{840} = 3.69$ mA

$\Delta V = 0.60 - (-0.56) = 1.16V$ | $R = \dfrac{\Delta V}{I_{C2}} = \dfrac{1.16V}{3.69mA} = 314 \ \Omega$

10.26

(a) For Q_4 on, $I_{C4} = \alpha_F I_{E4} \cong I_{E4} = \dfrac{-0.7 - (-2.5)}{840} = 2.14$ mA

$V_{OL} = 1.0V - (2.14mA)(390\Omega) - 0.7V = -0.540$ V | For Q_4 off, $V_{OH} = 1.0 - 0.7 = +0.300$ V

(b) For $v_A = 0.3V$, $I_{C2} = \alpha_F I_{E2} \cong I_{E2} = \dfrac{0.3 - 0.7 - (-2.5)}{840} = 2.50$ mA

$\Delta V = 0.30 - (-0.54) = 0.84V$ | $R = \dfrac{\Delta V}{I_{C2}} = \dfrac{0.84V}{2.50mA} = 336 \ \Omega$

10.27

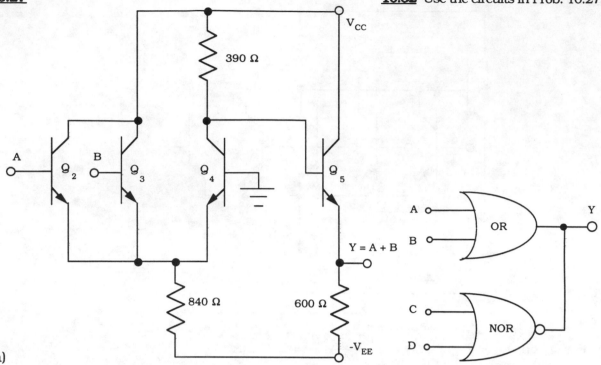

(a)

(b) The Nor output is taken from the collectors of Q_2/Q_3 and the 390Ω resistor is moved.

10.32 Use the circuits in Prob. 10.27.

10.28

$$v_O^{min} = -I_{EE}R_L = -(2.5mA)(1.2k\Omega) = -3.00 \text{ V} \mid I_E = I_{EE} + \frac{v_O}{R_L} = 2.5mA + \frac{4-0.7}{1.2k\Omega} = 5.25 \text{ mA}$$

$V_{BC} = 4 - 5 = -1V$ so transistor is in the forward-active region.

$$I_B = \frac{I_E}{\beta_F + 1} = \frac{5.25mA}{50+1} = 0.103 \text{ mA and } I_C = \beta_F I_B = 5.15 \text{ mA.}$$

10.29 Assuming Q_1 off and using voltage division, $-12 = -15\dfrac{2000}{2000 + R_E} \Rightarrow R_E = 500 \ \Omega$

$$I_E = \frac{12}{2000} + \frac{12 - (-15)}{500} = 60 \text{ mA!}$$

10.30

The outputs act as a "wired-or" connection.

For $v_I = -0.7V$, $v_{O1} = v_{O2} = -0.7$ V $\mid$ $I_{E3} = 0$ $\mid$ $I_{E4} = 0.1mA + 0.1mA = 0.200$ mA

For $v_I = -1.3V$, $v_{O1} = v_{O2} = -0.7$ V $\mid$ $I_{E3} = 0.1mA + 0.1mA = 0.200$ mA $\mid$ $I_{E4} = 0$

10.31 $\quad Y = A + \overline{B} \mid Z = \overline{A} + B$

10.32 See top of page

10.33 Note: In the first printing, the 3.3 kΩ resistor in Fig. 10.25 should be replaced with a 0.3 mA current source. Figure 10.26 is also in error. The correct circuit is given below.

186

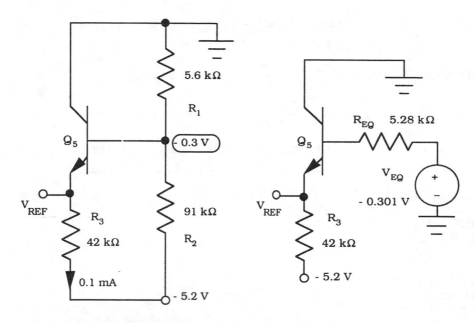

Corrected Figure 10.26 and its equivalent circuit.

$$v_{REF} = -0.301 - 5280i_{B5} - v_{BE5} \approx -0.301 - v_{BE5}$$

$$v_{E2} = v_{REF} - v_{BE2} \approx -0.301 - v_{BE5} - v_{BE2}$$

$$i_{E2} = \frac{v_{E2} - (-5.2)}{11700} = \frac{4.90 - v_{BE5} - v_{BE2}}{11700} = \frac{4.90 - 0.7 - 0.7}{11700} = 0.299 \text{ mA}$$

For a temperature increase of 50C, $\Delta v_{BE} = 50C(-1.8mV/C) = 0.090V$

$$i_{E2} = \frac{4.90 - 0.610 - 0.610}{11700} = 0.315 \text{ mA - a 5.4\% increase.}$$

10.34 See Problem 10.33 for a correction to Fig. 10.26. The new equivelent of the reference source is

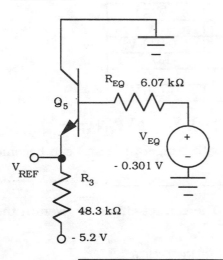

$V_{REF} = -0.301 - 6070i_{B5} - v_{BE5}$
Neglecting the small variations in i_{B5} and v_{BE5}, V_{REF} is essentially unchanged. Since R_{EE}, R_{C2} and R all change by the same factor, V_{OH}, V_{OL}, NM_H, and NM_L all remain unchanged.

10.35 See Problem 10.33 for a correction to Fig. 10.26.

For large β_F, $V_{REF} = -0.301 - 5280i_{B5} - v_{BE5} \approx -0.301 - v_{BE5} =$

At 25C, $v_{BE5} = 0.7V$ and $V_{REF} = -1.00V$

(a) $\Delta T = +60C$ | $\Delta v_{BE5} = 60C\left(-\dfrac{1.8mV}{C}\right) = -0.108V$ | $V_{REF} = -0.892V$

(b) $\Delta T = -80C$ | $\Delta v_{BE5} = -80C\left(-\dfrac{1.8mV}{C}\right) = +0.144V$ | $V_{REF} = -1.14V$

Note: A more exact calculation yields the same answers.

___

10.36

```
*PROBLEM 10.36 - ECL INVERTER VTC
VIN 2 0 DC -1.3
VREF 4 0 -1.0
VEE 8 0 -5.2
Q1 1 2 3 NBJT
Q2 5 4 3 NBJT
Q3 0 1 6 NBJT
Q4 0 5 7 NBJT
REE 3 8 11.7K
RC1 0 1 1.85K
RC2 0 5 2K
R3 6 8 42K
R4 7 8 42K
.DC VIN -1.3 -0.7 .01
.TEMP -55 25 85
.MODEL NBJT NPN BF=40 BR=0.25 VA=50
.PROBE V(2) V(1) V(5) V(6) V(7)
.PRINT DC V(2) V(6) V(7)
.END
```

T	-55C	+25C	+85C
V_T	0.0188 V	0.0257 V	0.0309 V
V_{OH}	-0.846 V	-0.724 V	-0.629 V
V_{OL}	-1.40 V	-1.30 V	-1.22 V
ΔV	0.554 V	0.576 V	0.591 V
V_{REF}	-1.00 V	-1.00 V	-1.00 V
V_{IH}	-0.937 V	-0.921 V	-0.911 V
V_{IL}	-1.06 V	-1.08 V	-1.09 V
N_{MH}	0.091 V	0.197 V	0.282 V
N_{ML}	0.340 V	0.220 V	0.130 V

V_{IH} and V_{IL} were calculated from Eq. 10.29 and 10.30: $V_{REF} \pm V_T \ln\left(\dfrac{\Delta V}{V_T} - 1\right)$

With a fixed reference voltage, the noise margins change with temperature and can become zero for a large enough temperature change.

___

10.37 Note: In the first printing, Fig. 10.26 is in error. The correct circuit is given in the solution to Problem 10.33.

```
*PROBLEM 10.37 - ECL INVERTER VTC WITH REFERENCE
VIN 2 0 DC -1.3
VEE 8 0 -5.2
Q1 1 2 3 NBJT
Q2 5 4 3 NBJT
Q3 0 1 6 NBJT
```

```
Q4 0 5 7 NBJT
REE 3 8 11.7K
RC1 0 1 1.85K
RC2 0 5 2K
R3 6 8 42K
R4 7 8 42K
Q5 0 9 4 NBJT
R1 0 9 5.6K
R2 9 8 91K
RE 4 8 42K
.OP
.DC VIN -1.3 -0.7 .01
.TEMP -55 25 85
.MODEL NBJT NPN BF=40 BR=0.25 VA=50 IS=1FA
.PROBE V(4) V(3) V(2) V(1) V(5) V(6) V(7)
.PRINT DC V(4) V(3) V(2) V(6) V(7)
.END
```

T	-55C	+25C	+85C
V_T	0.0188 V	0.0257 V	0.0309 V
V_{OH}	-0.803 V	-0.665 V	-0.558 V
V_{OL}	-1.35 V	-1.25 V	-1.18 V
ΔV	0.547 V	0.585 V	0.622 V
V_{REF}	-1.11 V	-0.975 V	-0.869 V
V_{IH}	-1.04V	-0.896 V	-0.778 V
V_{IL}	-1.17 V	-1.05 V	-0.960 V
N_{MH}	0.237 V	0.231 V	0.220 V
N_{ML}	0.180 V	0.200 V	0.120 V

V_{IH} and V_{IL} were calculated from Eq. 10.29 and 10.30: $V_{REF} \pm V_T \ln\left(\dfrac{\Delta V}{V_T} - 1\right)$

With a simple temperature dependent reference voltage, V_{REF} stays near the middle of the voltage swing, and the noise margin variation with temperature is significantly reduced.

10.38 Note: In the first printing, Fig. 10.26 is in error. The correct circuit is given in the solution to Problem 10.33.

$R_3 = \dfrac{-2 - (-5.2)}{0.100} \dfrac{V}{mA} = 32 \text{ k}\Omega \; (\rightarrow 33 \text{ k}\Omega \text{ for a discrete design.}) \; | \; I_{B5} = \dfrac{0.1mA}{40 + 1} = 2.44\mu A$

Choose $I_{R_2} \approx 10 I_{B5} \approx 25\mu A \; | \; R_2 = \dfrac{-1.3 - (-5.2)}{25\mu A} = 156 \text{ k}\Omega \; (\rightarrow 160 \text{ k}\Omega \text{ for a discrete design.})$

$I_{R_1} \approx 25\mu A + I_{B5} \approx 27.4\mu A \; | \; R_1 = \dfrac{0 - (-1.3)}{27.4\mu A} = 47.4 \text{ k}\Omega \; (\rightarrow 47 \text{ k}\Omega \text{ for a discrete design.})$

10.39

0, 1, 2 or 3 base currents may be drawn out of the reference depending on the state of each logic gate. Each unit of base current results in a drop

$\Delta V = I_B R = \dfrac{0.3mA}{\beta_F + 1}(2.7k\Omega) = 0.026V. \; V_{REF} = -1 - N\Delta V$ for $N = 0, 1, 2, 3$ yields:

$V_{REF} = -1 \text{ V}, \; -0.974 \text{ V}, \; -0.948 \text{ V}, \; -0.922 \text{ V}$

10.40 Note: In the first printing, the 3.3 kΩ resistor in Fig. 10.25 should be replaced with a 0.3 mA current source.

0, 1, 2, 3 or 4 base currents may be drawn out of the reference depending on the state of each logic gate. The Thevenin equivalent of the bias circuit is (neglecting the small-signal resistance of the diode)

$$V_{EQ} = -5.2V + 0.3mA(11.7k\Omega) + 0.7V = -0.990V \text{ and } R_{EQ} = 11.7k\Omega$$

Each unit of base current results in a drop $\Delta V = I_B R = \dfrac{0.3mA}{\beta_F + 1}(11.7k\Omega) = 0.113V$.

$V_{REF} = -0.990 - N\Delta V$ for $N = 0,1,2,3,4$ yields:

$V_{REF} = -0.990 \text{ V}, \ -0.877 \text{ V}, \ -0.764 \text{ V}, \ -0.651 \text{ V}, \ -0.538 \text{ V}$

10.41

$$i_C = I_S\left[\exp\left(\frac{v_{BE}}{V_T}\right) - \exp\left(\frac{v_{BC}}{V_T}\right)\right] + \frac{I_S}{\beta_R}\left[\exp\left(\frac{v_{BC}}{V_T}\right) - 1\right]$$

$$i_E = I_S\left[\exp\left(\frac{v_{BE}}{V_T}\right) - \exp\left(\frac{v_{BC}}{V_T}\right)\right] + \frac{I_S}{\beta_F}\left[\exp\left(\frac{v_{BE}}{V_T}\right) - 1\right]$$

$v_{BE} > 4V_T$ and $v_{BC} < -4V_T$

$$i_C \approx I_S\left[\exp\left(\frac{v_{BE}}{V_T}\right)\right] \text{ and } i_E = I_S\left(1 + \frac{1}{\beta_F}\right)\left[\exp\left(\frac{v_{BE}}{V_T}\right)\right] = \frac{I_S}{\alpha_F}\left[\exp\left(\frac{v_{BE}}{V_T}\right)\right] \rightarrow i_C \approx \alpha_F i_E$$

$$v_{BE} \approx V_T \ln\left(\frac{i_C}{I_S}\right) = V_T \ln\left(\frac{\alpha_F i_E}{I_S}\right)$$

10.42

$$I_{SD} = \frac{I_S}{\alpha_F} = \frac{1fA}{0.98} = 1.02 \text{ fA}$$

10.43

Both transistors are in the forward-active region. For simplicity, assume $V_A = \infty$.

$I = I_{C1} + I_{B1} + I_{B2}$ | Since the transistors are identical and have the same V_{BE},

$I_{C2} = I_{C1}$ and $I_{B1} = I_{B2}$ | $I = I_{C1} + 2I_{B1} = (\beta_F + 2)I_{B1}$ | $I_{C2} = \beta_F I_{B2} = \beta_F I_{B1}$

$$I_{C2} = \frac{\beta_F}{\beta_F + 2}I = \frac{25}{25 + 2}25\mu A \mid I_{C2} = 23.2 \ \mu A$$

10.44

For Fig. 10.32, $P \approx 0.5mA(5.2V) = 2.6mW = 2600\mu W$. For 20μW, the power must be reduced by 130X. The currents must be reduced by 130X and the resistors must increase by this factor to keep the logic swing the same: $R_C = 130(2k\Omega) = 260k\Omega$.

Using Eq. (10.54), $\tau_P = 0.69(260k\Omega)(2pF) = 359$ ns - rather slow!

10.45

$$R'_C = \frac{R_C}{2} = \frac{2k\Omega}{2} = 1k\Omega \mid \Delta V = 0.3mA(1k\Omega) = 0.3V \mid V_{OH} = 0 - 0.7 = -0.7V$$

$$V_{OL} = V_{OH} - 0.3V = -1.0V \mid V_{REF} = \frac{-0.7 - 1.0}{2}V = -0.850 \text{ V} \mid P \approx 0.5mA(5.2V) = 2.6mW$$

$$\tau_P = 0.69(1k\Omega)(2pF) = 1.38ns \mid PDP = 2.6mW(1.38ns) = 3.59 \text{ pJ}$$

10.46

$$\Delta V = 0.15mA(2k\Omega) = 0.3V \quad | \quad V_{OH} = 0 - 0.7 = -0.7V$$

$$V_{OL} = V_{OH} - 0.3V = -1.0V \quad | \quad V_{REF} = \frac{-0.7-1.0}{2}V = -0.850\ V \quad | \quad P \approx 0.25mA(5.2V) = 1.30mW$$

$$\tau_P = 0.69(2k\Omega)(2pF) = 2.76ns \quad | \quad PDP = 1.30mW(2.76ns) = 3.59\ pJ$$

10.47

(a) At the outputs: $V_{OH} = 0\ V \quad | \quad V_{REF} = V_{OH} - 0.7 - \dfrac{\Delta V}{2} \rightarrow \Delta V = 2(0 - 0.7 - (-1)) = 0.6V$

$V_{OL} = V_{OH} - \Delta V = 0 - .6 = -0.600\ V.$ Ignoring the base currents, the average power is

$$P \approx \left[\frac{(-1.7-(-3.3))V}{1.6k\Omega} + \frac{(-1.0-(-3.3))V}{3.2k\Omega} \right] 3.3V = 5.67\ mW$$

$$R_{C2} = \frac{\Delta V}{I_{EE2}} = \frac{0.6}{\dfrac{-1-0.7-(-3.3)}{1600}} = 600\ \Omega \quad | \quad R_{C1} = \frac{\Delta V}{I_{EE1}} = \frac{0.6}{\dfrac{-0.7-0.7-(-3.3)}{1600}} = 505\ \Omega$$

(b) $\overline{Y} = \overline{A+B+C} \quad Y = A+B+C$ (c) 5 versus 6 transistors

10.48

At the outputs: $V_{OH} = 0\ V \quad | \quad V_{OL} = V_{OH} - \Delta V = 0 - .4 = -0.400\ V.$

At the base of Q_D: $V_{OH} \rightarrow V_{BD} = 0 - 0.7 = -0.7V \quad V_{OL} \rightarrow V_{BD} = -0.4 - 0.7 = -1.10V$

$$V_{REF} = \frac{-0.7-1.1}{2} = -0.90V \quad | \quad V_{EE} \le V_{REF} - 0.7 - 0.6 = -0.9 - 0.7 - 0.6 = -2.20\ V$$

For $V_{EE} = -2.20V$: $R_B = \dfrac{-0.9-(-2.2)}{1}\dfrac{V}{mA} = 1.30\ k\Omega$

$$R_E = \frac{[-0.9-0.7-(-2.2)] + [-0.7-0.7-(-2.2)]}{2} \frac{V}{1mA} = 700\ \Omega$$

$$R_{C1} = \frac{0.4V}{\dfrac{-0.7-0.7-(-2.2)}{700}A} = 350\ \Omega \quad | \quad R_{C2} = \frac{0.4V}{\dfrac{-0.9-0.7-(-2.2)}{700}A} = 467\ \Omega$$

10.49

```
*PROBLEM 10.49 - ECL DELAY
VIN 1 0 PULSE(-0.6 0 0 .01NS .01NS
15NS)
VB 8 0 -0.6
VREF 6 0 -1.0
VEE 7 0 -3.3
QA 0 1 2 NBJT
QB 0 8 2 NBJT
QC 0 8 2 NBJT
QD 4 2 3 NBJT
QE 5 6 3 NBJT
RB 2 7 3.2K
RE 3 7 1.6K
RC1 0 4 505
RC2 0 5 600
.OP
.TRAN 0.1N 30N
.MODEL NBJT NPN BF=40 BR=0.25
+IS=5E-16 TF =0.15NS TR=15NS
+CJC=0.5PF CJE=.25PF CJS=1.0PF
+RB=100 RC=5 RE=1
.PROBE V(2) V(1) V(4) V(5) V(6)
.END
```

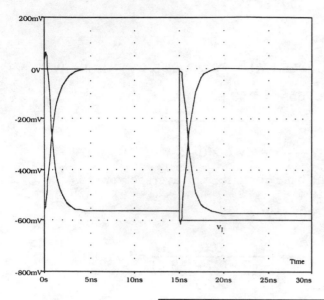

Result: $\tau_P = 0.95$ ns

10.50

One approach is to scale all the resistor values. To reduce the power from 2.7 mW to 1.0 mW, the resistor values should all be increased a factor of 2.7.

$R_{C1} = 2.7(1.85k\Omega) = 5.00$ kΩ | $R_{C2} = 2.7(2k\Omega) = 5.40$ kΩ

$R_{EE} = 2.7(11.7k\Omega) = 31.6$ kΩ | $R = 2.7(42k\Omega) = 113$ kΩ

10.51

Voltage levels remain unchanged: $V_{REF} = -1V$, $V_{OH} = -0.7V$, $V_{OL} = -1.3V$, $I_{EE} = 0.3mA$

$R_{EE} = \dfrac{-1-0.7-(-2)}{0.3}\dfrac{V}{mA} = 1$ kΩ | $R_{C1} = \dfrac{0.6V}{\dfrac{-0.7-0.7-(-2)}{1\ k\Omega}\ A} = \dfrac{0.6V}{0.6mA} = 1$ kΩ

$\bar{I} \approx 2\dfrac{-1-(-2)}{10}\dfrac{V}{k\Omega} + \dfrac{0.3+0.6}{2}$ mA $= 0.650$mA | $P = 0.65$mA$(2V) = 1.30$ mW (-28%)

Note that this gate will now have quite asymmetrical delays at the two outputs since the two collector resistors differ by a factor of two in value.

10.52 The circuit is the pnp version of the ECL gate in Fig. P10.47. | Y = ABC

10.53

$V_{OL} = 0$ | $V_{OH} = V_{OL} + \Delta V = +0.6V$ | $V_{REF} = \dfrac{0.7+1.3}{2} = +1.0V$ | $I = \dfrac{1mW}{3V} = 333\mu A$

The average voltage at the emitter of Q_D is $\dfrac{(1+0.7)+(0.7+0.7)}{2} = 1.55V$

$R_E = \dfrac{(3-1.55)V}{0.9(333\mu A)} = 4.84$ kΩ | $R_B = \dfrac{(3-1)V}{0.1(333\mu A)} = 60.1$ kΩ | $R_C = \dfrac{0.6V}{\dfrac{(3-1.7)V}{4.84k\Omega}} = 2.23$ kΩ

10.54

*Problem 10.54(a) - PNP ECL GATE DELAY
VI 4 0 PULSE(0.6 0 0 .01NS .01NS 25NS)
VB 7 0 DC 0.6
VREF 6 0 DC 1.0
VEE 1 0 DC 3
QA 0 4 3 PBJT
QB 0 7 3 PBJT
QC 0 7 3 PBJT
QD 0 3 2 PBJT
QE 5 6 2 PBJT
RB 1 3 60.1K
RE 1 2 4.84K
RC 5 0 2.23K
.OP
.TRAN 0.1N 50N
.MODEL PBJT PNP BF=40 BR=0.25 IS=5E-16
+TF =0.15NS TR=15NS
+CJC=0.5PF CJE=.25PF CJS=1.0PF
+RB=100 RC=5 RE=1
.PROBE V(4) V(3) V(5)
.END

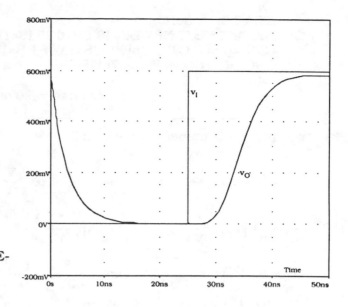

Result: τ_P = 6.0ns. This delay is dominated by a slow charge up at the base of Q_D.

*Problem 10.54(b) - Fig. P10.4
VIN 1 0 PULSE(-2.3 -1.7 0 .01NS .01NS 15NS)
VREF 6 0 -2.0
IEE 2 0 0.0003
Q1 3 1 2 NBJT
Q2 4 6 2 NBJT
R1 0 5 3.33K
RC1 5 3 2K
RC2 5 4 2K
.OP
.TRAN 0.1N 30N
.MODEL NBJT NPN BF=40 BR=0.25 IS=5E-16 TF =0.15NS TR=15NS
+CJC=0.5PF CJE=.25PF CJS=1.0PF RB=100 RC=5 RE=1
.PROBE V(1) V(3) V(4)
.END

Result: τ_P = 2.4 ns.

*Problem 10.54(c) - Fig. P10.14
VIN 1 0 PULSE(-1.5 -1.1 0 .01NS .01NS 15NS)
VREF 6 0 DC -1.30
IEE 2 0 DC 0.0002
Q1 3 1 2 NBJT
Q2 4 6 2 NBJT
Q3 0 3 7 NBJT
Q4 0 4 8 NBJT
R1 0 5 2K
RC1 5 3 2K
RC2 5 4 2K
RE1 7 9 50K
RE2 8 9 50K
VEE 9 0 DC -2

```
.OP
.TRAN 0.1N 30N
.MODEL NBJT NPN BF=40 BR=0.25 IS=1E-17 TF =0.15NS TR=15NS
+CJC=0.5PF CJE=.25PF CJS=1.0PF RB=100 RC=5 RE=1
.PROBE V(1) V(3) V(4) V(7) V(8)
.END
```

Result: $\tau_P = 3.0$ ns.

10.55 Applying the Gummel-Poon model

$$I_C = I_S\left[\exp\left(\frac{V_{BE}}{V_T}\right) - \exp\left(\frac{V_{BC}}{V_T}\right)\right] - \frac{I_S}{\beta_R}\left[\exp\left(\frac{V_{BC}}{V_T}\right) - 1\right]$$

$$I_B = \frac{I_S}{\beta_F}\left[\exp\left(\frac{V_{BE}}{V_T}\right) - 1\right] + \frac{I_S}{\beta_R}\left[\exp\left(\frac{V_{BC}}{V_T}\right) - 1\right]$$

$$I_C = 10^{-15}\left[\exp\left(\frac{0.2}{0.025}\right) - \exp\left(\frac{-4.8}{0.025}\right)\right] - \frac{10^{-15}}{0.25}\left[\exp\left(\frac{-4.8}{0.025}\right) - 1\right] = 2.98 \text{ pA}$$

$$I_B = \frac{10^{-15}}{40}\left[\exp\left(\frac{0.2}{0.025}\right) - 1\right] + \frac{10^{-15}}{0.25}\left[\exp\left(\frac{-4.8}{0.025}\right) - 1\right] = 74.5 \text{ fA}$$

Although the transistor is technically in the forward-active region, (and operating with $I_C = \beta_F I_B$), it is esentially off - its terminal currents are zero for most practical purposes.

10.56

$$\text{For } I_C = 0, \quad V_{CESAT} = V_T \ln\left(\frac{1}{\alpha_R}\right)\frac{1 + \dfrac{I_C}{(\beta_R + 1)I_B}}{1 - \dfrac{I_C}{\beta_F I_B}} = V_T \ln\left(\frac{1}{\alpha_R}\right)$$

$$V_{CESAT} = V_T \ln\left(\frac{\beta_R + 1}{\beta_R}\right) = 0.025 \ln\left(\frac{1.25}{0.25}\right) = 0.402 \text{ V}$$

10.57 (a) For the Gummel-Poon model with $V_{BE} = V_{BC}$, the transport current $i_T = 0$:

$$I_C = \frac{I_S}{\beta_R}\left[\exp\left(\frac{V_{BC}}{V_T}\right) - 1\right] \text{ and } I_E = \frac{I_S}{\beta_F}\left[\exp\left(\frac{V_{BE}}{V_T}\right) - 1\right] \Rightarrow \frac{I_C}{I_E} = \frac{\beta_F}{\beta_R} = \frac{40}{0.25} = 160$$

(b) $v_{BE} = V_B - 0.6$ | $v_{BC} = V_B - 0.8 = v_{BE} - 0.2$

$$i_E = I_S\left[\exp\frac{v_{BE}}{V_T} - \exp\frac{v_{BC}}{V_T}\right] + \frac{I_S}{\beta_F}\left[\exp\frac{v_{BE}}{V_T} - 1\right]$$

$$i_E = I_S\left[\exp\frac{v_{BE}}{V_T} - \exp\frac{v_{BE}}{V_T}\exp\frac{-0.2}{V_T}\right] + \frac{I_S}{\beta_F}\left[\exp\frac{v_{BE}}{V_T} - 1\right]$$

$$i_E \cong I_S\left[\exp\frac{v_{BE}}{V_T} -\right] + \frac{I_S}{\beta_F}\left[\exp\frac{v_{BE}}{V_T}\right] = I_S\left(1 + \frac{1}{\beta_F}\right)\left[\exp\frac{v_{BE}}{V_T}\right] = \frac{I_S}{\alpha_F}\left[\exp\frac{v_{BE}}{V_T}\right]$$

- - - - -

$$i_C = I_S\left[\exp\frac{v_{BE}}{V_T} - \exp\frac{v_{BE}}{V_T}\exp\frac{-0.2}{V_T}\right] - \frac{I_S}{\beta_R}\left[\exp\frac{v_{BE} - 0.2}{V_T} - 1\right]$$

$$i_C \cong I_S\left[\exp\frac{v_{BE}}{V_T}\right] \mid \frac{i_C}{i_E} = \alpha_F = \frac{40}{41} = 0.976$$

(c) $\frac{i_C}{i_E} = -1 \rightarrow i_B = i_E - i_C = 2i_E$ | Both junctions will be forward-biased. Neglect

the -1 terms: $\frac{I_S}{\beta_F}\exp\frac{v_{BE}}{V_T} + \frac{I_S}{\beta_R}\exp\frac{v_{BC}}{V_T} = 2I_S\left(\exp\frac{v_{BE}}{V_T} - \exp\frac{v_{BC}}{V_T}\right) + 2\frac{I_S}{\beta_F}\exp\frac{v_{BE}}{V_T}$

$$v_{BE} - v_{BC} = V_T \ln\frac{2 + \dfrac{1}{\beta_R}}{2 + \dfrac{1}{\beta_F}} = 0.025V\ln\frac{2 + \dfrac{1}{0.25}}{2 + \dfrac{1}{40}} = 27.2mV$$

$$(v_B - v_I) - (v_B - 0.8) = 27.7mV \mid v_I = 0.773 \text{ V}$$

10.58

$$\alpha_F = \frac{\beta_F}{\beta_F + 1} = \frac{40}{41} = 0.976 \quad \alpha_R = \frac{\beta_R}{\beta_R + 1} = \frac{0.25}{1.25} = 0.200$$

$$\tau_S = \frac{0.976(0.4ns + 0.2(12ns))}{1 - 0.976(0.2)} = 3.40ns \quad i_{CMAX} \cong \frac{5V}{2k\Omega} = 2.5 \text{ mA}$$

$$t_S = (3.40ns)\ln\frac{2mA - (-0.5mA)}{\dfrac{2.5mA}{40} - (-0.5mA)} = 5.07 \text{ ns}$$

10.59 (a)

$$I_C = \beta_F I_B \Rightarrow \text{Forward-active region} \mid V_{BE} \cong V_T \ln\frac{I_C}{I_S} = 0.025V\ln\frac{10^{-3}A}{10^{-15}A} = 0.691 \text{ V}$$

(b) $I_C < \beta_F I_B \Rightarrow$ saturation region; V_{BE} is given by Eqn. 5.45

$$V_{BE} = V_T\ln\frac{I_B + (1 - \alpha_R)I_C}{I_S\left[\dfrac{1}{\beta_F} + (1 - \alpha_R)\right]} = V_T\ln\frac{I_B + \left(\dfrac{1}{\beta_R + 1}\right)I_C}{I_S\left[\dfrac{1}{\beta_F} + \left(\dfrac{1}{\beta_R + 1}\right)\right]}$$

$$V_{BE} = 0.025V \ln \frac{25 \times 10^{-6} + \left(\frac{1}{0.25+1}\right)10^{-3}}{10^{-15}\left[\frac{1}{80} + \left(\frac{1}{0.25+1}\right)\right]} = 0.691 \text{ V}$$

(c) $I_C < \beta_F I_B \Rightarrow$ saturation region $\mid V_{BE} = 0.025V \ln \frac{10^{-3} + \left(\frac{1}{0.25+1}\right)10^{-3}}{10^{-15}\left[\frac{1}{40} + \left(\frac{1}{0.25+1}\right)\right]} = 0.710 \text{ V}$

10.60

For $I_C = 0$, $V_{CESAT} = V_T \ln\left(\frac{1}{\alpha_R}\right) = V_T \ln\left(\frac{\beta_R + 1}{\beta_R}\right) = 0.025 \ln\left(\frac{1.25}{0.25}\right) = 40.2 \text{ mV}$

For $I_E = 0$, $V_{ECSAT} = V_T \ln\left(\frac{1}{\alpha_F}\right) = V_T \ln\left(\frac{\beta_F + 1}{\beta_F}\right) = 0.025 \ln\left(\frac{41}{40}\right) = 0.617 \text{ mV}$

10.61

$V_{OH} = V_{CC} = 3.0 \text{ V} \quad V_{OL} = V_{CESAT} = 0.15 \text{ V}$

$V_{IL} = 0.7 - V_{CESAT} = 0.7 - 0.04V = 0.66V \quad V_{IH} \cong V_{BESAT2} = 0.8 \text{ V}$

$V_I = 3V: I_{B1} = \frac{3 - 0.7 - 0.8}{4} \frac{V}{k\Omega} = 375\mu A \mid I_{B2} = 1.25I_{B1} = 469\mu A$

$V_I = 0.15V: I_{IL} = -\frac{3 - 0.8 - 0.15}{4} \frac{V}{k\Omega} = -513\mu A \mid I_{C2SAT} = \frac{3 - 0.15}{2000} A = 1.43mA$

$1.43mA + N(513\mu A) \le 40(469\mu A) \rightarrow N \le 33.8 \rightarrow N \le 33.$

10.62

$v_I = V_{OH}: I = \frac{5 - 0.7 - 0.8}{(0.8)4k\Omega} + \frac{5 - 0.15}{(0.8)2k\Omega} = 4.13mA \mid P = 5(4.13mA) = 20.6 \text{ mW}$

$v_I = V_{OL}: I = \frac{5 - 0.8 - 0.15}{(1.2)4k\Omega} = 0.844mA \mid P = 5(0.844mA) = 4.22 \text{ mW}$

$P_{max} = 20.6 \text{ mW} \quad P_{min} = 4.22 \text{ mW}$

10.63

Using Eqs. 10.55 and 10.58: $V_{CC} - i_C R_C = V_T \ln\left(\frac{1}{\alpha_R}\right)\frac{1 + \frac{i_C}{(\beta_R + 1)i_B}}{1 - \frac{i_C}{\beta_F i_B}}$

$5 - 2000 i_C = 0.025 \ln\left(\frac{1}{.2}\right)\frac{1 + \frac{i_C}{1.25(1.09mA)}}{1 - \frac{i_C}{40(1.09mA)}} \rightarrow i_C = 2.4659 \text{ mA}$

$v_{CESAT} = 5 - 2000 i_C = 0.0682V$

10.64

$V_{OH} = 2.5 \text{ V} \quad V_{OL} = V_{VCESAT} = 0.15 \text{ V}$

$V_{IL} = 0.7 - V_{CESAT} = 0.55V \quad V_{IH} \cong V_{BESAT2} = 0.8 \text{ V}$

$NM_L = 0.55 - 0.15 = 0.40 \text{ V} \quad NM_H = 2.5 - 0.8 = 1.7 \text{ V}$

10.65

For $v_I = V_{OH}$, we require $V_{CC} = V_{BE2SAT} + V_{BC1} + I_{B1}R_B = 0.8 + 0.7 + \Delta V = 1.5V + \Delta V$ where ΔV is the volatge across the base resistor. ΔV must be large enough to abosrb V_{BE} process variations and to establish the base current. 0.5 V should be sufficient. Thus $V_{CC} = 2.0V$ or more is acceptable.

10.66 The VTC transitions are set by the values of v_{BE} and v_{BESAT} and are not changed by the power supply voltage. (b) $V_{IL} = 0.66$ V and $V_{IH} = 0.80$ V. But $V_{OH} = 3V$ and $V_{OL} = 0.15$ V. (c) $NM_H = 3 - 0.8 = 2.2$ V | $NM_L = 0.66 - 0.15 = 0.51$ V.

10.67 We need to reduce the currents by a factor of 11.2. Thus

$$R_B = 11.2\,(4k\Omega) = 44.8\ k\Omega \quad \text{and} \quad R_C = 11.2\,(2k\Omega) = 22.4\ k\Omega$$

10.68 (a)

```
*Problem 10.47 - Prototype TTL Inverter
+Delay
VI 1 0 DC 0 PWL(0 0 0.2N 5 25N 5 25.2N 0
+50N 0)
VCC 5 0 DC 5
Q1 3 2 1 NBJT
Q2 4 3 0 NBJT
RB 5 2 4K
RC 5 4 2K
*RB 5 2 45.2K
*RC 5 4 22.6K
.OP
.TRAN .1N 80N
.MODEL NBJT NPN BF=40 BR=0.25
+IS=5E-16 TF =0.15NS TR=15NS
+CJC=0.5PF CJE=.25PF CJS=1.0PF
+RB=100 RC=5 RE=1
.PROBE V(1) V(2) V(3) V(4)
.END
```

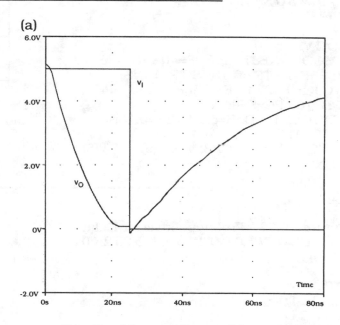

(a)

Results: (a) $\tau_P = 2.9$ ns   (b) $\tau_P = 15.8$ ns.

10.69

$$V_{OH} = 5V \qquad V_{OL} = V_{CE2SAT} = 0.15V$$

(a) $\quad v_I = V_{OL} = 0.15V, \quad I_{IN} = -\dfrac{5 - 0.15 - 0.6}{4000} = -1.06\ \text{mA}$

$\quad\quad v_I = V_{OH} = 5V, \quad I_{IN} = -I_S \cong 0$ where I_S is the diode saturation current.

(b) $\quad I_B = \dfrac{5 - 0.8 - 0.6}{4000} = 0.90\text{mA}; \quad \dfrac{5 - 0.15}{2000} + N(1.06\text{mA}) \le 40(0.9\text{mA}); \quad N \le 31.$

(c) $\quad$ -1.06 mA compared to -1.01 mA and 0 mA compared to 0.22 mA.

10.70 If we assume that the diode on-voltage is 0.7 V to match the base-emitter voltage of the BJT, then the VTC will be the same as that in Fig. 10.47, and both VTC will be the same.

10.71

```
*Figure 10.71 - Prototype TTL Inverter
VTC's
VI 1 0 DC 0
VCC 5 0 DC 5
*DTL
D1A 6 1 D1
D2A 6 7 D1
RBA 5 6 4K
RCA 5 8 2K
Q2A 8 7 0 NBJT
*TTL
Q1B 3 2 1 NBJT
Q2B 4 3 0 NBJT
RBB 5 2 4K
RCB 5 4 2K
.DC VI 0 5 .01
.MODEL NBJT NPN BF=40 BR=0.25
IS=5E-16 TF =0.15NS TR=15NS
+CJC=0.5PF CJE=.25PF CJS=1.0PF
RB=100 RC=5 RE=1
.MODEL D1 D IS=5E-16 TT=0.15NS
CJO=1PF
.PROBE V(1) V(2) V(3) V(4) V(6) V(7) V(8)
.END
```

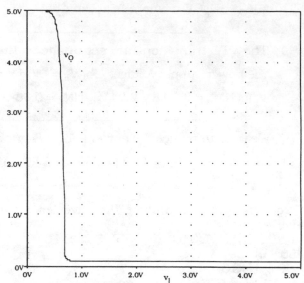

The TTL transition is sharper (more abrupt) and is shifted by approximately 50 mV.

10.72

```
*Figure 10.72 - Prototype Inverter Delays
VI 1 0 DC 0 PWL(0 0 0.2N 5 25N 5 25.2N 0 5
50N 0)
VCC 5 0 DC 5
*DTL
D1A 6 1 D1
D2A 6 7 D1
RBA 5 6 4K
RCA 5 8 2K
Q2A 8 7 0 NBJT
*TTL
Q1B 3 2 1 NBJT
Q2B 4 3 0 NBJT
RBB 5 2 4K
RCB 5 4 2K
.OP
.TRAN 0.1N 100N
.MODEL NBJT NPN BF=40 BR=0.25
IS=5E-16 TF =0.15NS TR=15NS
+CJC=0.5PF CJE=.25PF CJS=1.0PF
RB=100 RC=5 RE=1
.MODEL D1 D IS=5E-16 TT=0.15NS
CJO=1PF
.PROBE V(1) V(2) V(3) V(4) V(6) V(7) V(8)
.END
```

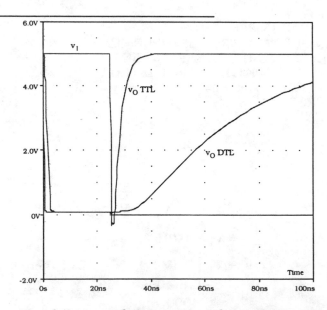

The fall time of the output of the TTL gate is somewhat slower than the DTL gate since transistor Q1 must come out of saturation. However, the rise time of the DTL gate is extremely slow because there is no reverse base current to remove the charge from the transistor base.

10.73

```
*Figure 10.73 - DTL Inverter Delays
VI 1 0 DC 0 PWL(0 0 0.2N 5 25N 5 25.2N 0
50N 0)
VCC 5 0 DC 5
*DTLA
D1A 6 1 D1
D2A 6 7 D1
RBA 5 6 4K
RCA 5 8 2K
Q2A 8 7 0 NBJT
*DTL-B
D1B 2 1 D1
D2B 2 3 D1
Q2B 4 3 0 NBJT
RBB 5 2 4K
RCB 5 4 2K
RB1 3 0 1K
.OP
.TRAN 0.1N 100N
.MODEL NBJT NPN BF=40 BR=0.25
IS=5E-16 TF =0.15NS TR=15NS
+CJC=0.5PF CJE=.25PF CJS=1.0PF
RB=100 RC=5 RE=1
.MODEL D1 D IS=5E-16 TT=0.15NS
CJO=1PF
.PROBE V(1) V(2) V(3) V(4) V(6) V(7) V(8)
.END
```

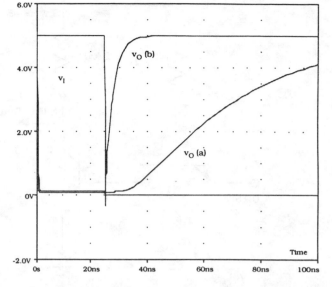

Without the 1 kΩ resistor, the rise time of the DTL gate is extremely slow because there is no reverse base current to remove the charge from the transistor base. The resistor provides an initial reverse base current of -0.7 mA to turn off the transistor and significantly reduces the rise time and propagation delay.

10.74

See problem 10.75. Note that R_3 should be 3 kΩ in the first printing.

10.75

```
*Figure 10.74 - Inverter VTC
VI 1 0 DC 0
VCC 6 0 DC 3.3
Q1 3 2 1 NBJT
Q2 5 3 4 NBJT
Q3 5 4 0 NBJT
R1 6 2 4K
R2 6 5 2K
R3 4 0 3K
.OP
.DC VI 0 3.3 0.01
.MODEL NBJT NPN BF=40 BR=0.25
IS=1E-16 TF =0.15NS TR=15NS
+CJC=0.5PF CJE=.25PF CJS=1.0PF
RB=100 RC=5 RE=1
.PROBE V(1) V(2) V(3) V(4) V(5)
.END
```

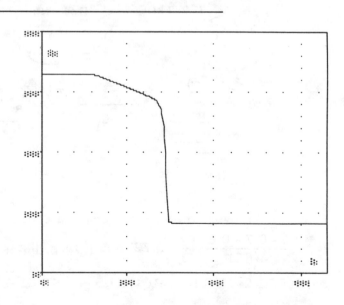

The first break point occurs when the input reaches a voltage large enough to just start turning on Q_2, approximately $V_{CESAT1} + V_{BE2} = 0.04V + 0.6 V = 0.64V$. The second breakpoint occurs when the input reaches $V_{CESAT1} + V_{BE2} + V_{BE3} = 0.04V + 0.7 + 0.6 V = 1.34V$. Note that the shallow slope is set by the ratio of $R_2/R_3 = 2/3$. Also note that Q_3 cannot saturate. $V_{OH} = 3.3 V$, $V_{OL} = V_{BE3} + V_{CESAT2} = 0.80V$. $NM_H = 3.3 - 1.5 = 1.8 V$ $NM_L = 1.4 - 0.8 = 0.60 V$

10.76

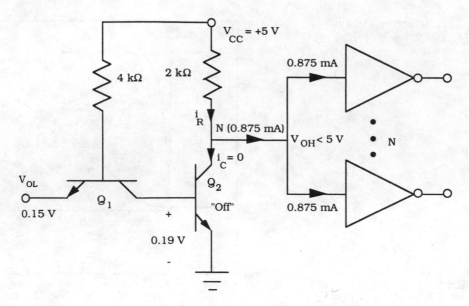

From the analysis in the text, we see that the fanout is limited by the V_{OH} condition.

$$i_{B1} = \frac{5 - 0.7 - 0.8}{4} \frac{V}{k\Omega} = 0.875mA \quad | \quad i_{E1} = -\beta_R i_{B1} = -0.875mA$$

$$5 - 2000(N)(0.875 \times 10^{-3}) \geq 1.5 \rightarrow N \leq 2 \rightarrow \text{Fanout} = 2$$

10.77

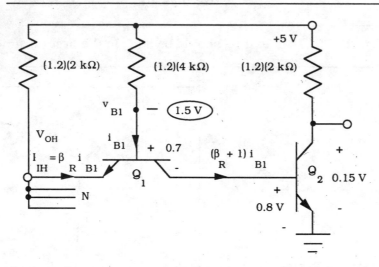

From the analysis in the text, we see that the fanout is limited by the V_{OH} condition.

$$i_{B1} = \frac{5 - 0.7 - 0.8}{4(1.2)} \frac{V}{k\Omega} = 0.729mA \quad | \quad i_{E1} = -\beta_R i_{B1} = -0.25(0.729mA) = 0.182mA$$

$$5 - 2000(1.2)(N)(0.182 \times 10^{-3}) \geq 1.5 \rightarrow N \leq 8.01 \rightarrow \text{Fanout} = 8$$

$$i_{B1} = \frac{5 - 0.7 - 0.8}{4(0.8)} \frac{V}{k\Omega} = 1.09mA \quad | \quad i_{E1} = -\beta_R i_{B1} = -0.25(1.09mA) = 0.273mA$$

$$5 - 2000(0.8)(N)(0.273 \times 10^{-3}) \geq 1.5 \rightarrow N \leq 8.01 \rightarrow \text{Fanout} = 8$$

The result is independent of the tolerance if the resistors track each other.

Note that Eq. 10.83 also yields N = 8 if more digits are used in the calculation.

10.78

From the analysis in the text, we see that the fanout is limited by the V_{OH} condition.

$$5V - 2000\Omega(N)(-i_{E1}) \geq 1.5V \rightarrow (-i_{E1}) \leq \frac{5-1.5}{2000(10)} \frac{V}{\Omega} = 0.175mA$$

$$i_{E1} = -\beta_R i_{B1} \quad | \quad i_{B1} = \frac{0.175mA}{0.25} = 0.700mA \quad | \quad R_B = \frac{5-0.7-0.8}{0.700} \frac{V}{mA} = 5.00 \text{ k}\Omega$$

10.79 (a)

Q_4 is in the forward-active region with $I_E = (\beta_F + 1)I_B$

$$I_E = 101 \frac{5-0.7-0.6}{1600} = 234 \text{ mA}$$

(b)

$$Q_4 \text{ saturates; } I_E = I_B + I_C = \frac{5-0.8-0.6}{1600} + \frac{5-0.6-0.15}{130} = 34.9 \text{ mA}$$

10.80

(a) $P_D = 5V(234mA) = 1.17 \text{ W}$ (b) $P_D = 5V(34.9mA) = 0.175 \text{ W}$

10.81

```
*Problem 10.81 - TTL Output Current
VCC 5 0 DC 5
RB 5 3 1.6K
RS 5 4 130
Q1 4 3 2 NBJT
D1 2 1 D1
IL 1 0 DC 0
```

```
.DC IL 0 30MA 0.01MA
.MODEL NBJT NPN BF=40 BR=0.25 IS=5E-16
TF =0.15NS TR=15NS
+CJC=0.5PF CJE=.25PF CJS=1.0PF RB=100
RC=5 RE=1
.MODEL D1 D IS=5E-16
.PROBE V(1) V(2) V(3) V(4)
.END
```

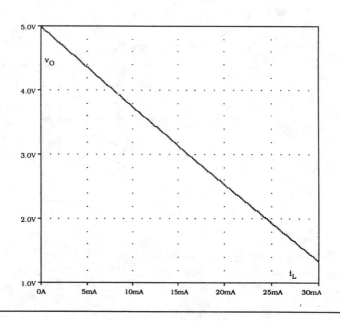

10.82

```
*Problem 10.82 - Modified TTL Inverter
VTC
VI 1 0 DC 0
VCC 9 0 DC 5
```

```
Q1 2 8 1 NBJT
Q2 4 3 0 NBJT
Q3 6 2 3 NBJT
Q4 7 6 5 NBJT
```

D1 5 4 DN
RB 9 8 4K
RC 9 6 1.6K
RS 9 7 130
RL 4 0 100K
Q5 10 11 0 NBJT
RB5 3 11 3K
RC5 3 10 1K
.DC VI 0 5 .01
.MODEL NBJT NPN BF=40 BR=0.25
IS=1E-17 TF =0.25NS TR=25NS
+CJC=0.6PF CJE=.6PF CJS=1.25PF
RB=100 RC=5 RE=1
.MODEL DN D
.PROBE V(1) V(2) V(3) V(4) V(5) V(6)
.END

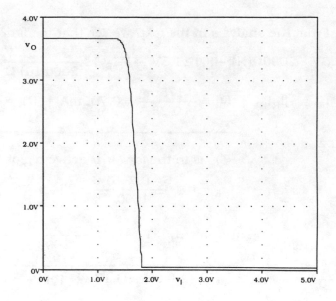

In the modified TTL circuit, Q3 cannot start conducting until its base reaches at lease V_{BE5} + V_{BE6} = 1.2 V.

10.83

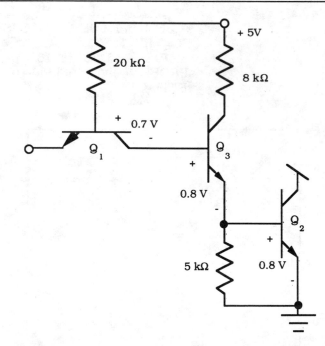

$v_I = V_{OH}$: Q_4 off $- I_{B4} = 0 = I_{C4}$ | Q_2 saturated with $I_{C4} = 0$

$$I_{B1} = \frac{(5 - 0.7 - 0.8 - 0.8)V}{20k\Omega} = 135 \ \mu A \mid I_{E1} = -\beta_R I_{B1} = -0.25(135 \ \mu A) = -33.8 \ \mu A$$

$$I_{C1} = -169 \ \mu A \mid I_{C3} = \frac{(5 - 0.15 - 0.8)V}{8k\Omega} = 506 \ \mu A$$

$$I_{E3} = 506 \mu A + 169 \mu A = 675 \ \mu A \mid I_{B2} = 675 \mu A - \frac{0.8V}{5k\Omega} = 515 \ \mu A$$

$$v_I = V_{OL}: \; Q_2, Q_3 \text{ off}; \; Q_4 \text{ on}$$

$$I_{B1} = \frac{(5 - 0.8 - 0.15)V}{20k\Omega} = 203 \; \mu A = I_{E1} \; | \; I_{C1} = 0$$

10.84   See Problem 10.85.

10.85

*Problem 10.85 - Low Power TTL Inverter
VTC versusTemperature
VI 1 0 DC 0
VCC 9 0 DC 5
Q1 2 8 1 NBJT
Q2 4 3 0 NBJT
Q3 6 2 3 NBJT
Q4 7 6 5 NBJT
D1 5 4 DN
RB 9 8 20K
RC 9 6 8K
RS 9 7 650
RL 4 0 100K
RE 3 0 5K
.DC VI 0 5 .01
.TEMP -55 25 85
.MODEL NBJT NPN BF=40 BR=0.25 IS=1E-
17 TF =0.25NS TR=25NS
+CJC=0.6PF CJE=.6PF CJS=1.25PF
RB=100 RC=5 RE=1
.MODEL DN D
.PROBE V(1) V(2) V(3) V(4) V(5) V(6)
.END

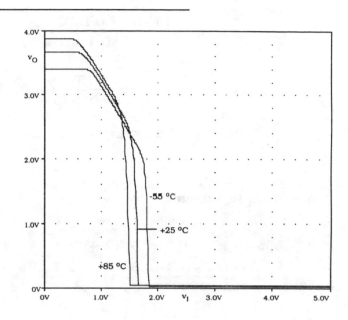

10.86

$$V_{OH} = 5 - 0.7 - 0.7 - \frac{N(I_{IH})}{\beta_F + 1} R_C$$

$$V_{OH} = 3.6 - \frac{N(0.17mA)}{40 + 1}(1600)$$

$$V_{OH} \geq 2.4V \rightarrow N \leq 180$$

10.87

For small β_R, fanout is limited by the $v_O = V_{OL}$ case ($v_I = V_{OH}$).

$$i_{B3} = (\beta_R + 1)i_{B1} = 1.05 \frac{(5 - 0.7 - 0.8 - 0.8)V}{5k\Omega} = 567\mu A$$

$$i_{B2} = i_{E3} - i_{R_E} = \frac{(5 - 0.15 - 0.8)V}{2k\Omega} + 567\mu A - \frac{0.8V}{1.25k\Omega} = 1.95mA$$

$$i_{IL} = -i_{E1} = -i_{B1} = \frac{(5 - 0.8 - 0.15)V}{5k\Omega} = 0.810mA \quad | \quad \alpha_R = \frac{\beta_R}{1 + \beta_R} = \frac{0.05}{1.05} = 0.0476$$

Using Eq. 10.61, $\Gamma = \exp\left(\dfrac{0.15V}{0.025V}\right) = 403.4 \rightarrow \beta_{FOR} = 20 \dfrac{1 - \dfrac{1}{0.0476(403.4)}}{1 + \dfrac{20}{0.05}\dfrac{1}{403.4}} = 9.52$

$$N(0.810mA) \leq 9.52(1.95mA) \rightarrow N = 22$$

10.88

For the $v_O = V_{OL}$ case, the equations are given in Prblem 10.87. For $v_O = V_{OH}$,

$$V_{OH} = 5 - I_{B4}R_C - 0.7 - 0.7 \geq 2.4V$$

$$I_{IH} = \beta_R\left(\frac{5 - 0.7 - 0.8 - 0.8}{4000}\right) = \beta_R\left(\frac{2.7}{4000}\right)$$

$$I_{B4} = \frac{NI_{IH}}{\beta_F + 1} = \frac{N\beta_R}{\beta_F + 1}\left(\frac{2.7}{4000}\right)$$

$$N \leq \frac{1.2(\beta_F + 1)(4000)}{2.7\beta_R(1600)}$$

```
function [N,X]=P1088
br=0;
bf=40;
g=exp(.15/.025);
for i=1:50
      br=br+.1;
      ar=br/(1+br);
      ib3=(1+br)*675;
      ib2=1730+ib3;
      bfor=40*(1-1/(ar*g))/(1+bf/(br*g));
      N1=fix(bfor*ib2/1013);
      N2=1.2*(bf+1)*4000/(2.7*br*1600);
      N(i)=min(N1,N2);
      X(i)=0.1*i;
end

»[Y,X]=p1088;
»plot(X,Y)
```

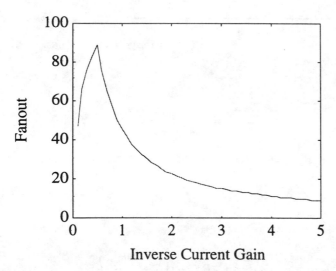

10.89

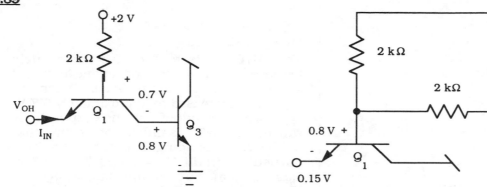

(a) $V_{OH} = 2 - V_{ECSAT2} = 2 - 0.15 = 1.85$ V $\mid$ $V_{OL} = V_{CESAT3} = 0.15$ V

(b) i_{IH}: $i_{B2} \approx 0$ $\mid$ $i_{IH} = 0.25 \dfrac{(2 - 0.7 - 0.8)V}{2k\Omega} = 62.5$ μA

$i_{IL} = -i_{B1} = -\dfrac{(2 - 0.8 - 0.15)V}{2k\Omega} - \dfrac{(2 - 0.8 - 0.8 - 0.15)V}{2k\Omega} = -650$ μA

(c) Assume $\beta_{FOR} \leq 28.3$

For the pnp transistor: $N(62.5\mu A) \leq 28.3 \dfrac{(2 - 0.8 - 0.8 - 0.15)V}{2k\Omega} \rightarrow N = 56$

For the npn transistor: $N(650\mu A) \leq 28.3(1.25) \dfrac{(2 - 0.7 - 0.8)V}{2k\Omega} \rightarrow N = 13$

10.90

(a) $V_{OL} = V_{CESAT3} = 0.15$ V $\mid$ $V_{OH} = 2 - V_{BE2} = 2 - 0.7 = 1.3$ V

(b) $v_I = 0.15V$: $i_{IL} = -(i_{B1} + i_{C1}) = -\left(\dfrac{2 - 0.8 - 0.15}{10000} + \dfrac{2 - 0.15 - 0.15}{12000}\right) = -247$ μA

$v_I = 1.3V$: $i_{IL} = \beta_R i_{B1} = 0.25\left(\dfrac{2 - 0.7 - 0.8}{10^4}\right) = 12.5$ μA

(c) Using $\beta_{FOR} = 28.3$: $i_L = i_{B2} + i_{C2} = \dfrac{2 - 0.8 - 0.15}{6000} + \dfrac{2 - 0.15 - 0.15}{1000} = 1.875$mA

$i_{B3} = \dfrac{2 - 0.8}{12000} + 1.25\left(\dfrac{2 - 0.7 - 0.8}{10000}\right) = 162.5$μA

$28.3(0.1625\text{mA}) \geq N(0.247\text{mA}) + 1.875\text{mA} \rightarrow N = 11$

10.91

(a) $Y = \overline{ABC}$ (b) $V_{OL} = V_{CESAT3} = 0.15$ V $\mid$ $V_{OH} = 3.3 - V_{BE1} - V_D = 3.3 - 1.4 = 1.9$ V

(c) $v_I = 1.9V$, input diode is off and $i_{IH} = 0$. $v_I = 0.15V$, $i_{IL} = -\dfrac{3.3 - 0.7 - 0.15}{6000} = -408$ μA

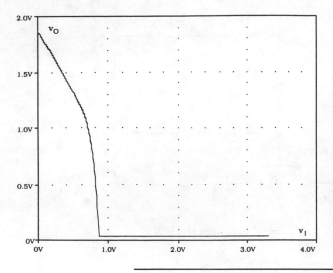

The VTC starts to decrease immediately because Q_2 is ready to conduct due to the 0.7 V drop across the input diode. When the input has increased to approximately 0.7 V, Q_3 begins to conduct and the output drops rapidly. The VTC is much slopier than that of the corresponding TTL gate. For this particular circuit $V_{IL} = 0$ and $V_{IH} = 0.8$ V. Based upon our definitions, $NM_L = 0$. However, the initial slope can be reduced by changing the ratio R_C/R_2 so that $V_{IL} = 0.7$ V.

10.92 (a) If either input A is low or input B is low, V_{B2} will be low. Q_2 will be off, Q_3 will be on and Y will be low. Therefore $\overline{Y} = \overline{A} + \overline{B} \rightarrow Y = AB$.

(b) $V_{OH} = 5 - I_{B5}R_2 - V_{BE5} \approx 5 - V_{BE5} = 5 - 0.7 = 4.30$ V

$V_{OL} = 5 - \alpha_F I_{E3}R_2 - I_{B5}R_2 - V_{BE5} \approx 5 - I_{E3}R_2 - V_{BE5}$

$I_{E3} = \dfrac{+0.7 - 0.7 - (-5)}{5000} = 1.00 \text{mA} \mid V_{OL} = 5 - 0.001(4000) - 0.7 = +0.300$ V

(c) $v_I = 4.3$V: $1.25\left(\dfrac{5 - 0.7 - V_B}{4000}\right) = \dfrac{V_B - (-5)}{10000} + \dfrac{V_B - 0.7 - (-5)}{5000}\dfrac{1}{41} \rightarrow V_B = 1.97$V

$I_{B1} = \dfrac{5 - 0.7 - 1.97}{4000} = 582 \ \mu A \mid I_{E1} = -0.25I_{B1} = -146 \ \mu A \mid I_{IH} = 146 \ \mu A$

$v_I = 0.3$V: $I_{B1} = \dfrac{5 - 0.8 - 0.3}{4000} = 975 \ \mu A \mid I_{C1} = -\dfrac{0.3 + 0.15 - (-5)}{10000} = -545 \ \mu A$

$I_{E1} = I_{B1} + I_{C1} = 430 \ \mu A \mid I_{IL} = -430 \ \mu A$

10.93

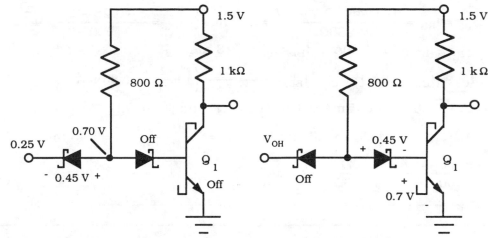

(a) $V_{OH} = V_{CC} = 1.5 \text{ V} \mid V_{OL} = {}"V_{CESAT1}{}" = 0.7 - 0.45 = 0.25 \text{ V}$

(b) For $v_I = 1.5\text{V}$, the input diode is off and $I_{IH} = 0$.

For $v_I = 0.25\text{V}$, $I_{IL} = \dfrac{1.5 - 0.45 - 0.25}{800} = 1.00 \text{ mA}$

(c) Note that Q_1 operates as if it were in the forward-active region:

$$\beta_F I_{B1} \geq N I_{IL} + I_{R_2} \mid 40\left(\frac{1.5 - 0.45 - 0.70}{800}\right) \geq N(0.001) + \frac{1.5 - 0.25}{1000} \rightarrow N = 16$$

10.94

$v_{BE} + v_{D2} - v_{D1} = v_{CE} \mid$ For $v_{D2} \approx v_{D1}$, $v_{CE} = v_{BE} = 0.7 \text{ V}$

Note, the external base current source should be labeled i_{BB}.

$i_C = i_{CC} + i_{DI} \mid i_B = i_{BB} - i_{D1} \mid i_C = \beta_F i_B$

$i_{CC} + i_{D1} = \beta_F(i_{BB} - i_{D1}) \rightarrow i_{D1} = \dfrac{\beta_F i_{BB} - i_{CC}}{\beta_F + 1} = \dfrac{20(0.25) - 1}{21} \text{ mA} = 0.191 \text{ mA}$

$i_{D2} = i_{BB} - i_{D1} = 0.25 - 0.191 = 0.059 \text{ mA} \mid i_C = 20 i_B = 20 i_{D2} = 1.18 \text{ mA}$

10.95

In this circuit as drawn, the collector-base junction of Q_1 is bypassed by a Schottky diode. Q_1 will be "off" with $V_{BC} = +0.45 \text{ V}$.

$i_{B1} = \dfrac{5 - 0.45 - 0.7}{4000} = 963 \text{ } \mu A \mid I_{IN} = 0 \mid i_{B2} = i_{B1} = 963 \text{ } \mu A$

10.96

$i_{B1} = \dfrac{5 - 0.7 - 0.25}{4000} = 1.01 \text{ mA} \mid I_{IN} = -i_{B1} = -1.01 \text{ mA} \mid i_{B2} = 0$

10.97

For $v_I = 5\text{V}$, the Schottky diode bypasses the collector-base junction, $I_{IH} \approx 0$,

and $i_{B2} = i_{B1} = \dfrac{5 - .45 - 0.7}{4000} = 963 \mu A$

For $v_I = 0.25\text{V}$, $I_{IL} = -\dfrac{5 - 0.7 - 0.25}{4000} = -1.01 \text{ mA}$

$40(963 \mu A) \geq N(1.01\text{mA}) + \dfrac{5 - 0.25}{2000} \rightarrow N = 35$

10.98

(a) $v_I = V_{OH}$: $i_{B3} = i_{RB} = \dfrac{5 - 0.45 - 0.7 - 0.7}{2800} = 1.13$ mA | $i_{C3} = \dfrac{5 - 0.25 - 0.7}{900} = 4.50$ mA

$i_{E3} = 0$ | $i_{C1} = -i_{B3} = -1.13$ mA | $i_{B1} = i_{B3} = 1.13$ mA

$i_{B2} = i_{B3} + i_{C3} - (i_{C6} + i_{B6})$ | $(i_{C6} + i_{B6}) = \dfrac{0.7 - 0.25}{250}\left(1 + \dfrac{1}{40}\right) = 1.85$ mA

$i_{B2} = 1.13\text{mA} + 4.50\text{mA} - 1.85\text{mA} = 3.78$ mA | Q_4 and Q_5 are off.

(b) $v_I = V_{OL}$: Q_2, Q_3, Q_4 and Q_6 are all off. $i_{B1} = i_{RB} = \dfrac{5 - 0.7 - 0.25}{2800} = 1.45$ mA

$i_{E5} = \dfrac{5 - 900i_{B5} - 0.7}{3500} \approx \dfrac{5 - 0.7}{3500} = 1.23$ mA

10.99

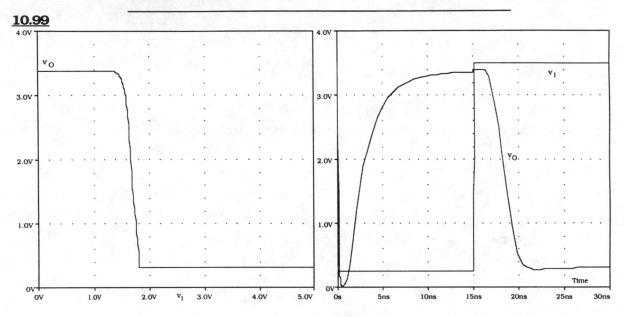

Result: $\tau_P = 3.0$ ns

```
*Problem 10.99 - Schottky TTL Inverter VTC
VI 1 0 DC 3.5 PWL(0 3.5 0.2N 0.25 15N 0.25 15.2N 3.5 30N 3.5)
VCC 9 0 DC 5
Q1 2 8 1 NBJT
D1 2 8 DS
Q2 4 3 0 NBJT
D2 3 4 DS
Q3 6 2 3 NBJT
D3 2 6 DS
Q4 7 5 4 NBJT
Q5 7 6 5 NBJT
D5 6 7 DS
RB 9 8 2.8K
RC 9 6 900
RS 9 7 50
R5 5 0 3.5K
RL 4 0 100K
Q6 10 11 0 NBJT
D6 11 10 DS
R2 3 11 500
R6 3 10 250
```

.OP
.DC VI 0 5 .01
.TRAN .025N 30N
.MODEL NBJT NPN BF=40 BR=0.25 IS=1E-17 TF =0.15NS TR=15NS
+CJC=1PF CJE=.5PF CJS=1PF RB=100 RC=10 RE=1
.MODEL DS D IS=1E-12
.PROBE V(1) V(2) V(3) V(4) V(5) V(6)
.END

10.100

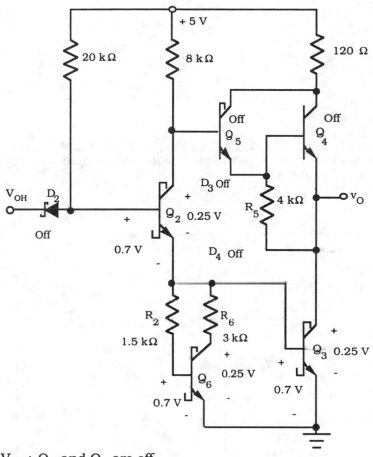

(a) $v_I = V_{OH}$: Q_4 and Q_5 are off.

$$i_{B2} = \frac{5 - 0.7 - 0.7}{20000} = 180 \text{ µA} \quad | \quad i_{C2} = \frac{5 - 0.25 - 0.7}{8000} = 506 \text{ µA}$$

$$i_{B3} = i_{B2} + i_{C2} - (i_{C6} + i_{B6}) \quad | \quad (i_{C6} + i_{B6}) = \frac{0.7 - 0.25}{3000}\left(1 + \frac{1}{40}\right) = 154 \text{ µA}$$

$$i_{B3} = 180\text{µA} + 506\text{µA} - 154\text{µA} = 532 \text{ µA}$$

(b) $v_I = V_{OL}$: Q_2, Q_3, Q_4, Q_5 and Q_6 are all off.

10.101

*Problem 10.101 - Low Power Schottky TTL Inverter VTC
VI 1 0 DC 3.5 PWL(0 3.5 0.2N 0.25 10N 0.25 10.2N 3.5 20n 3.5)
VCC 9 0 DC 5
DS1 8 1 DS
Q3 4 3 0 NBJT
D3 3 4 DS
Q2 6 8 3 NBJT

```
D2 8 6 DS
Q4 7 5 4 NBJT
Q5 7 6 5 NBJT
D5 6 7 DS
DS3 5 6 DS
DS4 4 6 DS
RB 9 8 20K
RC 9 6 8K
RS 9 7 120
R5 5 4 4K
Q6 10 11 0 NBJT
D6 11 10 DS
R2 3 11 1.5K
R6 3 10 3K
RL 4 0 100K
.OP
.DC VI 0 5 .01
.TRAN .025N 20N
.TEMP -55 +25 +85
.MODEL NBJT NPN BF=40 BR=0.25 IS=1E-17 TF =0.25NS TR=25NS
+CJC=0.6PF CJE=.6PF CJS=1.25PF RB=100 RC=5 RE=1
.MODEL DS D  IS=1E-12
.PROBE V(1) V(2) V(3) V(4) V(5) V(6)
.END
```

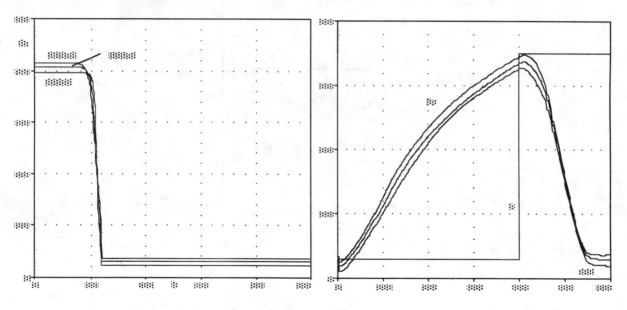

Result: τ_p = 13 ns. Note that the delays are dependent upon the specific BJT models used in SPICE.

10.102   In the first printing, see solution to Problem 10.101.

```
*Problem 10.102 - Advanced Low Power Schottky TTL Inverter VTC
VI 1 0 DC 4 PWL(0 4 0.2N 0.3 125N 0.3 125.2N 4 150N 4)
VCC 9 0 DC 5
Q4 0 1 2 PBJT
R1 9 2 40K
Q1 12 2 8 NBJT
D1 2 12 DS
```

```
R2 9 12 60K
DS1 8 1 DS
Q8 4 3 0 NBJT
D8 3 4 DS
Q6 6 8 3 NBJT
D6 8 6 DS
Q3 7 5 4 NBJT
Q2 7 6 5 NBJT
D2 6 7 DS
DS3 4 6 DS
R3 9 6 15K
R4 9 7 50
R5 5 4 4K
Q7 10 11 0 NBJT
D7 11 10 DS
R6 3 11 3K
R7 3 10 6K
RL 4 0 100K
.OP
*.DC VI 0 5 .01
.TRAN .05N 150N
.TEMP -55 +25 +85
.MODEL NBJT NPN BF=40 BR=0.25 IS=1E-17 TF =0.15NS TR=15NS
+CJC=1PF CJE=.5PF CJS=1PF RB=100 RC=10 RE=1
.MODEL PBJT PNP BF=40 BR=0.25 IS=1E-17 TF =0.15NS TR=15NS
+CJC=1PF CJE=.5PF CJS=1PF RB=100 RC=10 RE=1
.MODEL DS D  IS=1E-12
.PROBE V(1) V(3) V(4) V(5) V(6)
.END
```

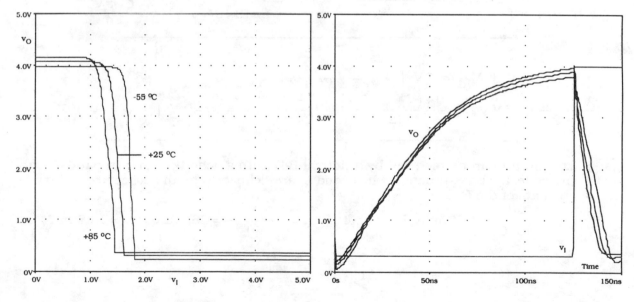

Result: τ_P = 22 ns. Note that the delays are highly dependent upon the specific BJT models used in SPICE.

10.103 Note that Prob. 10.103 in the first printing is a duplicate of Prob. 10.101.

$$Y = A + B + C \mid V_{OH} = 0 \text{ V} \mid V_{OL} = -540 I_C = -540 \frac{V_{REF} - 0.7 - (-3)}{750} = -0.72(V_{REF} + 2.3)$$

$$\frac{V_{OH} + V_{OL}}{2} = V_{REF} - 0.7 + 0.4 + 0.7 = V_{REF} + 0.4$$

$$\frac{0 - 0.72(V_{REF} + 2.3)}{2} = V_{REF} + 0.4 \rightarrow V_{REF} = -0.903V \mid V_{OL} = -0.72(-.903 + 2.3) = -1.01 \text{ V}$$

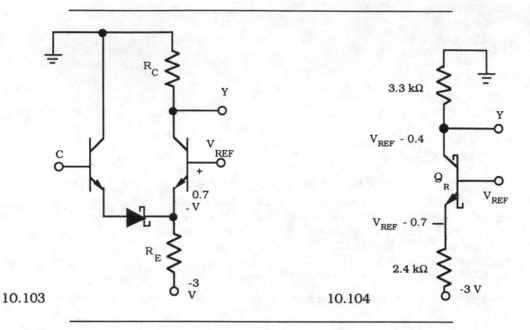

10.103   10.104

10.104

$$Y = A + B + C \mid V_{OH} = 0 \text{ V} \mid V_{OL} = V_{REF} - 0.4$$

$$\frac{V_{OH} + V_{OL}}{2} = V_{REF} \mid \frac{0 + (V_{REF} - 0.4)}{2} = V_{REF} \rightarrow V_{REF} = -0.40 \text{ V} \mid V_{OL} = -0.80V$$

10.105 The circuit can be modeled by a normal BJT with a schottky diode in parallel with the collector base junction. If i_C and i_B are defined to be the collector- and base-currents of the BJT,

$$i_C + i_B = \frac{5 - 0.7}{4000} = 1.075mA \mid i_C \approx \beta_F i_B \rightarrow i_B = \frac{1.075mA}{40} = 26.9 \text{ μA} \mid i_C = 1.05 \text{ mA}$$

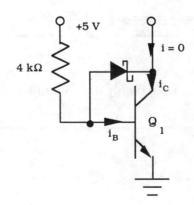

CHAPTER 11

11.1

A/C temperature
Automobile
    coolant temperature
    gasoline level
    oil pressure
    sound intensity
    inside temperature
Battery charge level
Battery voltage
Fluid level
Computer display
    hue
    contrast
    brightness
Electrical variables
    voltage amplitude
    voltage phase

current amplitude
current phase
power
power factor
spectrum
Fan speed
Humidity
Lawn mower speed
Light intensity
Oven temperature
Refrigerator temperature
Sewing machine speed
Stereo volume
Stove temperature
Time
TV picture brightness
TV sound level
Wind velocity

11.2

(a) $20 \log (125) = 41.9$ dB | $20 \log (50) = 34.0$ dB | $20 \log (5000) = 94.0$ dB

$20 \log(100000) = 100$ dB | $20 \log(0.85) = -1.41$ dB

(b) $20 \log (600) = 55.6$ dB | $20 \log (3000) = 69.5$ dB | $20 \log (10^6) = 120$ dB

$20 \log(200000) = 106$ dB | $20 \log(0.95) = -0.446$ dB

(c) $10 \log (2 \times 10^9) = 93.0$ dB | $10 \log (4 \times 10^5) = 56.0$ dB

$10 \log (6 \times 10^8) = 87.8$ dB | $10 \log(10^{10}) = 100$ dB

11.3

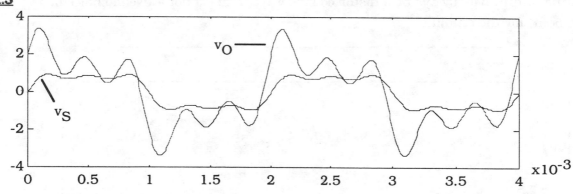

(b) 500 Hz: $1 \angle 0°$ | 1500 Hz: $0.333 \angle 0°$ | 2500 Hz: $0.200 \angle 0°$

(c) 500 Hz: $2 \angle 30°$ | 1500 Hz: $1 \angle 30°$ | 2500 Hz: $1 \angle 30°$

(d) 500 Hz: $2 \angle 30°$ | 1500 Hz: $3 \angle 30°$ | 2500 Hz: $5 \angle 30°$

(e) Yes

11.4

$$V_s = 0.005V \mid P_O = 40W \mid V_o = \sqrt{2P_OR_L} = \sqrt{2(40)(8)} = 25.3V$$

$$|A_V| = \frac{25.3}{.005} = 5060 \mid 20 \log (5060) = 74.1 \text{ dB}$$

$$I_s = \frac{0.005V}{5k\Omega + 50k\Omega} = 90.91\text{nA} \mid I_o = \frac{V_o}{8\Omega} = \frac{25.3V}{8\Omega} = 3.162A$$

$$|A_I| = \frac{3.162A}{90.91\text{nA}} = 3.48 \times 10^7 \mid 20 \log \left(3.48 \times 10^7\right) = 151 \text{ dB}$$

$$A_P = \frac{40W}{\dfrac{.005V(90.91\text{nA})}{2}} = 1.76 \times 10^{11} \mid 10 \log \left(1.76 \times 10^{11}\right) = 112 \text{ dB}$$

11.5 In the dc steady state, the internal circuit voltages cannot exceed the power supply limits. (a) +15 V (b) -9 V

11.6

$$\text{For } V_B = 0.6V, \ V_O = +8V \mid A_V = \left.\frac{dv_O}{dv_I}\right|_{v_I=0.6V} = \frac{12-4}{0.5-0.7} = -40$$

$$|A_V| = 32 \text{ dB} \ \angle A_V = 180° \mid V_M \leq 0.100 \text{ V for linear operation}$$

11.7

$$\text{For } V_B = 0.8V, \ V_O = +3V \mid A_V = \left.\frac{dv_O}{dv_I}\right|_{v_I=0.8V} = \frac{4-2}{0.7-0.9} = -10$$

$$|A_V| = 20\text{dB} \ \angle A_V = 180° \mid V_M \leq 0.100 \text{ V for linear operation}$$

11.8

For $V_B = 0.5V$, $V_O = +12V$ | $\dfrac{dv_O}{dv_I}$ is different for positive and negative values of $V_M \sin 1000t$. Thus, the gain is different for positive and negative signal excursions and the output will always be a distorted sine wave. This is not a useful choice of bias point for the amplifier.

11.9

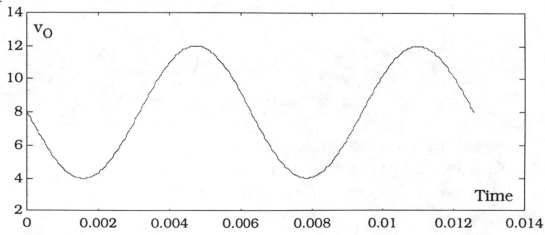

The amplifier is operating in a linear region. $v_O = 8 - 4 \sin 1000t$. There are only two spectral components: 8 V at dc and -4 V at 159 Hz

---

11.10

$$\text{For } \sin 1000t \geq 0, \; v_O = 12 - 4 \sin 1000t$$
$$\text{For } \sin 1000t < 0, \; v_O = 12 - 1 \sin 1000t$$

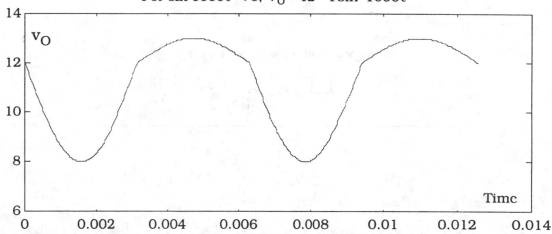

Using the MATLAB FFT capability with a fundamental frequency of $1000/2\pi$ Hz:

```
t=linspace(0,2*pi/1000,1000);
y=12-4*sin(1000*t).*(sin(1000*t)>=0)-sin(1000*t).*(sin(1000*t)<0);
z=fftshift(fft(y))/1000;
```

yields the following series:

$$v_O(t) = 11.05 - 2.50 \sin(1000t) + 0.638 \cos(2000t) + 0.127 \cos(4000t) + 0.0546 \cos(6000t)$$

Note: It is worth plotting this function to see if it is correct.

The Fourier coefficients may also be calculated directly using MATLAB. For example, for the cosine terms:

Define a function:
```
        function y=four(t)
        y=cos(fn*1000*t).*(12-4*sin(1000*t).*(sin(1000*t)>=0)-
            sin(1000*t).*(sin(1000*t)<0));
```

```
global fn
fn=0;  quad('four',0,pi/500)*1000/pi
```

11.11

$$g_{11} = \left.\frac{i_1}{v_1}\right|_{i_2=0} \qquad g_{12} = \left.\frac{i_1}{i_2}\right|_{v_1=0} \qquad g_{21} = \left.\frac{v_2}{v_1}\right|_{i_2=0} \qquad g_{22} = \left.\frac{v_2}{i_2}\right|_{v_1=0}$$

For $i_2 = 0$: $\quad y_{21}v_1 = -y_{22}v_2 \quad$ and $\quad i_1 = y_{11}v_1 + y_{12}v_2$

$$g_{11} = \left.\frac{i_1}{v_1}\right|_{i_2=0} = y_{11} - y_{12}\frac{y_{21}}{y_{22}} \to y_{11} \quad | \quad g_{21} = \left.\frac{v_2}{v_1}\right|_{i_2=0} = -\frac{y_{21}}{y_{22}}$$

For $v_1 = 0$: $\quad i_1 = y_{12}v_2 \quad$ and $\quad i_2 = y_{22}v_2$

$$g_{12} = \left.\frac{i_1}{i_2}\right|_{v_1=0} = \frac{y_{12}}{y_{22}} \to 0 \quad | \quad g_{22} = \left.\frac{v_2}{i_2}\right|_{v_1=0} = \frac{1}{y_{22}}$$

11.12

$$h_{11} = \left.\frac{\mathbf{v_1}}{\mathbf{i_1}}\right|_{\mathbf{v_2}=0} \qquad h_{12} = \left.\frac{\mathbf{v_1}}{\mathbf{v_2}}\right|_{\mathbf{i_1}=0} \qquad h_{21} = \left.\frac{\mathbf{i_2}}{\mathbf{i_1}}\right|_{\mathbf{v_2}=0} \qquad h_{22} = \left.\frac{\mathbf{i_2}}{\mathbf{v_2}}\right|_{\mathbf{i_1}=0}$$

For $\mathbf{v_2} = 0$: $\mathbf{i_1} = y_{11}\mathbf{v_1}$ and $\mathbf{i_2} = y_{21}\mathbf{v_1}$

$$h_{11} = \left.\frac{\mathbf{v_1}}{\mathbf{i_1}}\right|_{\mathbf{v_2}=0} = \frac{1}{y_{11}} \quad | \quad h_{21} = \left.\frac{\mathbf{i_2}}{\mathbf{i_1}}\right|_{\mathbf{v_2}=0} = \frac{y_{21}}{y_{11}}$$

For $\mathbf{i_1} = 0$: $y_{11}\mathbf{v_1} = -y_{12}\mathbf{v_2}$ and $\mathbf{i_2} = y_{21}\mathbf{v_1} + y_{22}\mathbf{v_2}$

$$h_{12} = \left.\frac{\mathbf{v_1}}{\mathbf{v_2}}\right|_{\mathbf{i_1}=0} = -\frac{y_{12}}{y_{11}} \to 0 \quad | \quad h_{22} = \left.\frac{\mathbf{i_2}}{\mathbf{v_2}}\right|_{\mathbf{i_1}=0} = y_{22} - \frac{y_{21}y_{12}}{y_{11}} \to y_{22}$$

11.13

$$h_{11} = \left.\frac{\mathbf{v_1}}{\mathbf{i_1}}\right|_{\mathbf{v_2}=0} \qquad h_{12} = \left.\frac{\mathbf{v_1}}{\mathbf{v_2}}\right|_{\mathbf{i_1}=0} \qquad h_{21} = \left.\frac{\mathbf{i_2}}{\mathbf{i_1}}\right|_{\mathbf{v_2}=0} \qquad h_{22} = \left.\frac{\mathbf{i_2}}{\mathbf{v_2}}\right|_{\mathbf{i_1}=0}$$

For $\mathbf{v_2} = 0$: $g_{21}\mathbf{v_1} = -g_{22}\mathbf{i_2}$ and $\mathbf{i_1} = g_{11}\mathbf{v_1} + g_{12}\mathbf{i_2}$

$$h_{11} = \left.\frac{\mathbf{v_1}}{\mathbf{i_1}}\right|_{\mathbf{v_2}=0} = \left[g_{11} - g_{12}\frac{g_{21}}{g_{22}}\right]^{-1} \to \frac{1}{g_{11}} \quad | \quad h_{21} = \left.\frac{\mathbf{i_2}}{\mathbf{i_1}}\right|_{\mathbf{v_2}=0} = \left[g_{12} - g_{11}\frac{g_{22}}{g_{21}}\right]^{-1} \to -\frac{g_{21}}{g_{11}g_{22}}$$

For $\mathbf{i_1} = 0$: $g_{11}\mathbf{v_1} = -g_{12}\mathbf{i_2}$ and $\mathbf{v_2} = g_{21}\mathbf{v_1} + g_{22}\mathbf{i_2}$

$$h_{12} = \left.\frac{\mathbf{v_1}}{\mathbf{v_2}}\right|_{\mathbf{i_1}=0} = \left[g_{21} - g_{22}\frac{g_{11}}{g_{12}}\right]^{-1} \to 0 \quad | \quad h_{22} = \left.\frac{\mathbf{i_2}}{\mathbf{v_2}}\right|_{\mathbf{i_1}=0} = \left[g_{22} - g_{21}\frac{g_{12}}{g_{11}}\right]^{-1} \to \frac{1}{g_{22}}$$

11.14

$$g_{11} = \left.\frac{\mathbf{i_1}}{\mathbf{v_1}}\right|_{\mathbf{i_2}=0} \qquad g_{12} = \left.\frac{\mathbf{i_1}}{\mathbf{i_2}}\right|_{\mathbf{v_1}=0} \qquad g_{21} = \left.\frac{\mathbf{v_2}}{\mathbf{v_1}}\right|_{\mathbf{i_2}=0} \qquad g_{22} = \left.\frac{\mathbf{v_2}}{\mathbf{i_2}}\right|_{\mathbf{v_1}=0}$$

For $\mathbf{i_2} = 0$: $\mathbf{v_1} = z_{11}\mathbf{i_1}$ and $\mathbf{v_2} = z_{21}\mathbf{i_1}$

$$g_{11} = \left.\frac{\mathbf{i_1}}{\mathbf{v_1}}\right|_{\mathbf{i_2}=0} = \frac{1}{z_{11}} \quad | \quad g_{21} = \left.\frac{\mathbf{v_2}}{\mathbf{v_1}}\right|_{\mathbf{i_2}=0} = \frac{z_{21}}{z_{11}}$$

For $\mathbf{v_1} = 0$: $z_{11}\mathbf{i_1} = -z_{12}\mathbf{i_2}$ and $\mathbf{v_2} = z_{21}\mathbf{i_1} + z_{22}\mathbf{i_2}$

$$g_{12} = \left.\frac{\mathbf{i_1}}{\mathbf{i_2}}\right|_{\mathbf{v_1}=0} = -\frac{z_{12}}{z_{11}} \to 0 \quad | \quad g_{22} = \left.\frac{\mathbf{v_2}}{\mathbf{i_2}}\right|_{\mathbf{v_1}=0} = z_{22} - z_{21}\frac{z_{12}}{z_{11}} \to z_{22}$$

11.15

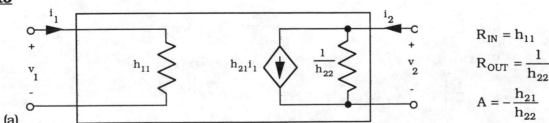

(a)

$$R_{IN} = h_{11}$$

$$R_{OUT} = \frac{1}{h_{22}}$$

$$A = -\frac{h_{21}}{h_{22}}$$

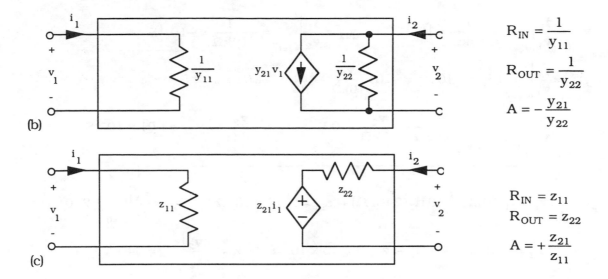

$$R_{IN} = \frac{1}{y_{11}}$$

$$R_{OUT} = \frac{1}{y_{22}}$$

$$A = -\frac{y_{21}}{y_{22}}$$

(b)

$$R_{IN} = z_{11}$$
$$R_{OUT} = z_{22}$$

$$A = +\frac{z_{21}}{z_{11}}$$

(c)

11.16

$$g_{11} = \left.\frac{\mathbf{i_1}}{\mathbf{v_1}}\right|_{\mathbf{i_2}=0} : \mathbf{v_1} = 10^4\mathbf{i_1} + 101\,\mathbf{i_1}(240k\Omega) \rightarrow g_{11} = 4.124 \times 10^{-8}\,S = 4.12 \times 10^{-8}\,S$$

$$g_{12} = \left.\frac{\mathbf{i_1}}{\mathbf{i_2}}\right|_{\mathbf{v_1}=0} : \mathbf{i_1} = -\frac{240k\Omega}{240k\Omega + 10k\Omega}(\mathbf{i_2} + 100\mathbf{i_1}) \rightarrow g_{12} = -9.90 \times 10^{-3}$$

$$g_{21} = \left.\frac{\mathbf{v_2}}{\mathbf{v_1}}\right|_{\mathbf{i_2}=0} : \mathbf{v_2} = 101\mathbf{i_1}(240k\Omega) \;|\; \mathbf{i_1} = g_{11}\mathbf{v_1} \rightarrow g_{21} = 1.00$$

$$g_{22} = \left.\frac{\mathbf{v_2}}{\mathbf{i_2}}\right|_{\mathbf{v_1}=0} : \mathbf{i_2} = \frac{\mathbf{v_2}}{240k\Omega} + \frac{\mathbf{v_2}}{10k\Omega} + 100\frac{\mathbf{v_2}}{10k\Omega} \rightarrow g_{22} = 99.0\,\Omega$$

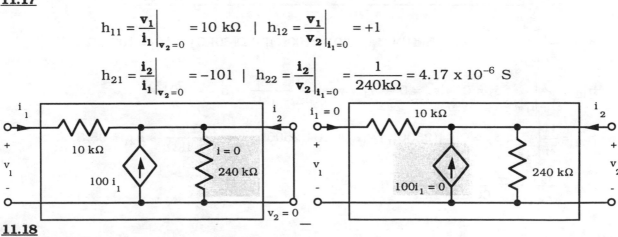

11.17

$$h_{11} = \left.\frac{\mathbf{v_1}}{\mathbf{i_1}}\right|_{\mathbf{v_2}=0} = 10\ k\Omega \;|\; h_{12} = \left.\frac{\mathbf{v_1}}{\mathbf{v_2}}\right|_{\mathbf{i_1}=0} = +1$$

$$h_{21} = \left.\frac{\mathbf{i_2}}{\mathbf{i_1}}\right|_{\mathbf{v_2}=0} = -101 \;|\; h_{22} = \left.\frac{\mathbf{i_2}}{\mathbf{v_2}}\right|_{\mathbf{i_1}=0} = \frac{1}{240k\Omega} = 4.17 \times 10^{-6}\,S$$

11.18

$$y_{11} = \frac{i_1}{v_1}\bigg|_{v_2=0} = \frac{1}{10k\Omega} = 10^{-4}\,S \quad | \quad y_{12} = \frac{i_1}{v_2}\bigg|_{v_1=0} = -\frac{1}{10k\Omega} = -10^{-4}\,S$$

$$y_{21} = \frac{i_2}{v_1}\bigg|_{v_2=0} : i_2 = -101i_1 = -101\frac{v_1}{10k\Omega} \rightarrow y_{21} = -1.01 \times 10^{-2}\,S$$

$$y_{22} = \frac{i_2}{v_2}\bigg|_{v_1=0} : i_2 = \frac{v_2}{240k\Omega} + \frac{v_2}{10k\Omega} - 100i_1 \quad | \quad i_1 = \frac{-v_2}{10k\Omega} \rightarrow y_{22} = 1.01 \times 10^{-2}\,S$$

11.19

$$z_{11} = \frac{v_1}{i_1}\bigg|_{i_2=0} : v_1 = i_1(10k\Omega) + 101i_1(240k\Omega) \rightarrow z_{11} = 2.43 \times 10^7\,\Omega \quad | \quad z_{12} = \frac{v_1}{i_2}\bigg|_{i_1=0} = 240\ k\Omega$$

$$z_{21} = \frac{v_2}{i_1}\bigg|_{i_2=0} : v_2 = -101i_1(240k\Omega) \rightarrow z_{21} = 2.42 \times 10^7\,\Omega \quad | \quad z_{22} = \frac{v_2}{i_2}\bigg|_{i_1=0} = 240\ k\Omega$$

11.20

$$g_{11} = \frac{i_1}{v_1}\bigg|_{i_2=0} = \frac{1}{2.5k\Omega + 1k\Omega} = 0.286\ mS \quad | \quad g_{12} = \frac{i_1}{i_2}\bigg|_{v_1=0} = -\frac{1k\Omega}{2.5k\Omega + 1k\Omega} = -0.286$$

$$g_{21} = \frac{v_2}{v_1}\bigg|_{i_2=0} : v_2 = v_1\frac{1k\Omega}{2.5k\Omega + 1k\Omega} + v_1\frac{2.5k\Omega}{2.5k\Omega + 1k\Omega}(-0.04)(60k\Omega) \rightarrow g_{21} = -1710$$

$$g_{22} = \frac{v_2}{i_2}\bigg|_{v_1=0} : v_2 = (i_2 - 0.04v_a)60k\Omega + i_2(1k\Omega\|2.5k\Omega) \quad | \quad v_a = -i_2(1k\Omega\|2.5k\Omega)$$

$$g_{22} = 1.78 \times 10^6\ \Omega$$

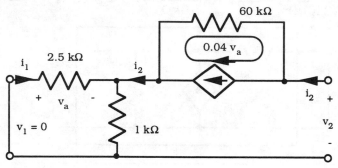

11.21

$$h_{11} = \frac{v_1}{i_1}\bigg|_{v_2=0} : v_1 = i_1(2.5k\Omega) + (i_1 + 0.04(2500i_1))(1k\Omega\|60k\Omega) \rightarrow h_{11} = 102\ k\Omega$$

$$h_{12} = \frac{v_1}{v_2}\bigg|_{i_1=0} : i_1 = 0 \rightarrow v_a = 0 \rightarrow v_1 = v_2\frac{1k\Omega}{60k\Omega + 1k\Omega} \rightarrow h_{12} = 0.0164$$

$$h_{21} = \frac{i_2}{i_1}\bigg|_{v_2=0} : i_2 = 0.04(2500i_1) - (i_1 + 0.04(2500i_1))\frac{1k\Omega}{60k\Omega + 1k\Omega} \rightarrow h_{21} = 98.3$$

$$h_{22} = \frac{i_2}{v_2}\bigg|_{i_1=0} = \frac{1}{60k\Omega + 1k\Omega} = 16.4\ \mu S$$

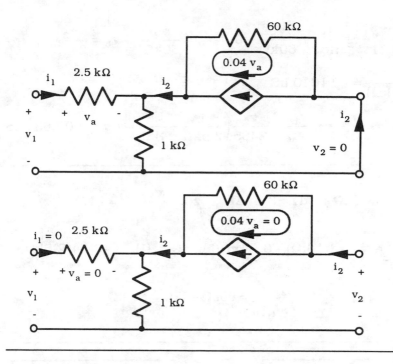

11.22

$$0.04\mathbf{v_a} = 0.04(2500\mathbf{i_1}) = 100\mathbf{i_1} \quad | \quad y_{11} = \left.\frac{\mathbf{i_1}}{\mathbf{v_1}}\right|_{\mathbf{v_2}=0} \quad : \mathbf{v_1} = 2500\mathbf{i_1} + \left[\mathbf{i_1} + 100\mathbf{i_1}\right](1k\Omega\|60k\Omega)$$

$$y_{11} = \frac{1}{2500 + 101(1k\Omega\|60k\Omega)} = 9.82 \ \mu S$$

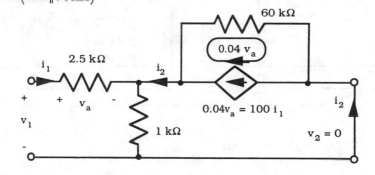

$$y_{21} = \left.\frac{\mathbf{i_2}}{\mathbf{v_1}}\right|_{\mathbf{v_2}=0} \quad : \mathbf{i_2} = 100\mathbf{i_1} - 101\mathbf{i_1}\frac{1k\Omega}{1k\Omega + 60k\Omega} \quad | \quad \mathbf{i_2} = 98.34\mathbf{i_1} \quad | \quad \mathbf{i_1} = y_{11}\mathbf{v_1}$$

$$y_{21} = 98.34\left(9.82\text{x}10^{-6}\right) = 0.9656 \ mS$$

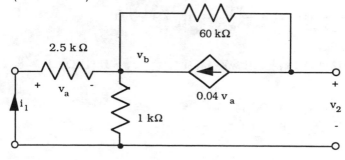

$$y_{12} = \frac{i_1}{v_2}\bigg|_{v_1=0} : \quad \frac{v_b}{2.5k\Omega} + \frac{v_b}{1k\Omega} + \frac{v_b}{60k\Omega} + 0.04v_b = \frac{v_2}{60k\Omega} \rightarrow v_b = \frac{v_2}{2485} \quad | \quad i_1 = -\frac{v_b}{2.5k\Omega}$$

$$y_{12} = -\frac{1}{2485(2.5k\Omega)} = -0.1610 \ \mu S$$

$$y_{22} = \frac{i_2}{v_2}\bigg|_{v_1=0} : \quad i_2 = \frac{v_b}{2.5k\Omega} + \frac{v_b}{1k\Omega} = \frac{v_2}{2485}\left(\frac{1}{2.5k\Omega} + \frac{1}{1k\Omega}\right) \rightarrow y_{22} = 0.5634 \ \mu S$$

11.23

$$z_{11} = \frac{v_1}{i_1}\bigg|_{i_2=0} = 2.5k\Omega + 1k\Omega = 3.5 \ k\Omega \quad | \quad z_{12} = \frac{v_1}{i_2}\bigg|_{i_1=0} = 1 \ k\Omega$$

$$z_{21} = \frac{v_2}{i_1}\bigg|_{i_2=0} \quad | \quad v_2 = i_1(1k\Omega) - 0.04v_a(60k\Omega) = i_1(1k\Omega) - 0.04(2.5k\Omega)i_1(60k\Omega)$$

$$z_{21} = -6.00 \ M\Omega \quad | \quad z_{22} = \frac{v_2}{i_2}\bigg|_{i_1=0} = 60k\Omega + 1k\Omega = 61 \ k\Omega$$

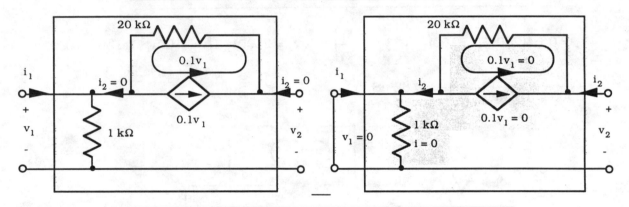

11.24

$$g_{11} = \frac{i_1}{v_1}\bigg|_{i_2=0} = \frac{1}{1k\Omega} = 1.00 \ mS \quad | \quad g_{12} = \frac{i_1}{i_2}\bigg|_{v_1=0} = -1$$

$$g_{21} = \frac{v_2}{v_1}\bigg|_{i_2=0} : \quad v_2 = v_1 + 0.1v_1(20k\Omega) \rightarrow g_{21} = +2001 \quad | \quad g_{22} = \frac{v_2}{i_2}\bigg|_{v_1=0} = 20k\Omega$$

11.25

$$h_{11} = \frac{v_1}{i_1}\bigg|_{v_2=0} : \quad i_1 = \frac{v_1}{1k\Omega} + 0.1v_1 + \frac{v_1}{20k\Omega} \rightarrow h_{11} = 9.90 \ \Omega$$

$$h_{12} = \frac{v_1}{v_2}\bigg|_{i_1=0} : \quad v_2 = (i_2 + 0.1v_1)(20k\Omega) + i_2(1k\Omega) \quad | \quad v_1 = i_2(1k\Omega) \quad | \quad \frac{v_2}{i_2} = 2.02 \times 10^6$$

$$h_{12} = \frac{v_1}{v_2} = \frac{1000i_2}{v_2} = \frac{1}{2020} = 0.000495$$

$$h_{21} = \frac{i_2}{i_1}\bigg|_{v_2=0} : i_2 = -\left(0.1v_1 + \frac{v_1}{20k\Omega}\right) \mid v_1 = h_{11}i_1 = 9.896i_1 \rightarrow h_{21} = -0.990$$

$$h_{22} = \frac{i_2}{v_2}\bigg|_{i_1=0} : i_2 = \frac{v_1}{1k\Omega} \mid v_1 = h_{12}v_2 = \frac{v_2}{2020} \mid h_{22} = \frac{1}{2020(1000\Omega)} = 0.495 \ \mu S$$

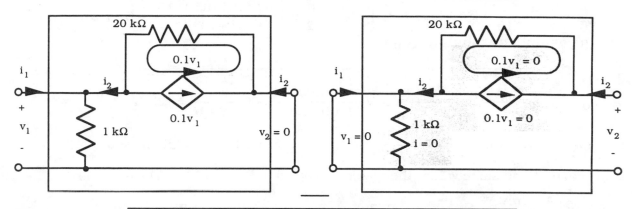

11.26

$$y_{11} = \frac{i_1}{v_1}\bigg|_{v_2=0} : i_1 = \frac{v_1}{1k\Omega} + 0.1v_1 + \frac{v_1}{20k\Omega} \rightarrow y_{11} = 0.101 \ S \mid y_{12} = \frac{i_1}{v_2}\bigg|_{v_1=0} = -\frac{1}{20k\Omega} = -50.0 \ \mu S$$

$$y_{21} = \frac{i_2}{v_1}\bigg|_{v_2=0} : i_2 = -0.1v_1 - \frac{v_1}{20k\Omega} \rightarrow y_{21} = -0.100 \ S \mid y_{22} = \frac{i_2}{v_2}\bigg|_{v_1=0} = \frac{1}{20k\Omega} = 50.0 \ \mu S$$

11.27

$$z_{11} = \frac{v_1}{i_1}\bigg|_{i_2=0} = 1k\Omega \mid z_{12} = \frac{v_1}{i_2}\bigg|_{i_1=0} = 1 \ k\Omega$$

$$z_{21} = \frac{v_2}{i_1}\bigg|_{i_2=0} : v_2 = i_1(1k\Omega) + 0.1v_1(20k\Omega) = i_1(1k\Omega) + 0.1[i_1(1k\Omega)](20k\Omega) \rightarrow z_{21} = 2.00 \ M\Omega$$

$$z_{22} = \frac{v_2}{i_2}\bigg|_{i_1=0} : v_2 = i_2(1k\Omega) + 0.1v_1(20k\Omega) = i_2(1k\Omega) + 0.1[i_2(1k\Omega)]20k\Omega \rightarrow z_{22} = 2.00 \ M\Omega$$

11.28

(a) $V_O = V_S \dfrac{R_{IN}}{R_{IN} + R_S} A \dfrac{R_L}{R_L + R_{OUT}} \mid A = 10^{\frac{54}{20}} = 501.2$

$$A_V = \frac{10^6}{10^3 + 10^6}(501.2)\frac{16}{0.5 + 16} = 485.5 \mid A_{VdB} = 20 \log(485.5) = 53.7 \ dB$$

$$A_I = \frac{I_O}{I_S} = \frac{\dfrac{485.5V_S}{16}}{\dfrac{V_S}{10^3 + 10^6}} = 3.041 \times 10^7 \mid A_{IdB} = 20 \log(3.041 \times 10^7) = 150 \ dB$$

$$A_P = \frac{V_O I_O}{V_S I_S} = \frac{485.5V_S \dfrac{485.5V_S}{16}}{V_S \dfrac{V_S}{10^3 + 10^6}} = 485.5(3.041 \times 10^7) = 1.478 \times 10^{10}$$

$A_{PdB} = 10 \log(1.478 \times 10^{10}) = 102$ dB

(b) $1 = \dfrac{V_O^2}{2(16)} \rightarrow V_O = 5.657$ V $\mid$ $V_S = \dfrac{5.657}{485.5} = 11.65$ mV

(c) R_{OUT} and R_L see the same current. $P = \dfrac{I_O^2}{2} R_L \rightarrow \dfrac{I_O^2}{2} = \dfrac{1}{16}$

$P_{R_{OUT}} = \dfrac{I_O^2}{2} R = \dfrac{1}{16} 0.5 = 31.25$ mW $\mid$ $P_{R_{IN}} = \dfrac{I_S^2}{2} R_{IN} = \left(\dfrac{0.01165}{10^3 + 10^6}\right)^2 \dfrac{10^6}{2} = 67.7$ pW

$P = 31.25\text{mW} + 67.7\text{pW} = 31.3$ mW

11.29

(a) $V_O = V_S \dfrac{R_{IN}}{R_{IN} + R_S} A \dfrac{R_L}{R_L + R_{OUT}} = V_S \dfrac{1000}{1000 + 1000} (500) \dfrac{16}{16 + 16} = 125 V_S$

$1 = \dfrac{V_O^2}{2(16)} \rightarrow V_O = 5.66\text{V} \mid V_S = \dfrac{5.66}{125} = 45.3$ mV $\mid$ Since R_{OUT} and R_L have the

same current and same value, the power dissipated in R_{OUT} is 1 W. The power lost

in R_{IN} is $\left(\dfrac{45.3\text{mV}}{2}\right)^2 \dfrac{1}{2(1000)} = 0.257\mu\text{W} \mid P_D = 0.257\mu\text{W} + 1.00\text{W} = 1.00$ W

11.30

$R_{IN} = \infty \mid R_{OUT} = 0\ \Omega \mid v_O = Av_S = -1000v_S \mid v_O = 0.01\text{V}(-1000) = -10$ V

$P = \dfrac{V_O^2}{2R_L} = \dfrac{10^2}{2(16)} = 3.13$ W $\mid$ $A_P = \dfrac{3.13\text{W}}{0} = \infty$

11.31

$A_V = -10^{\frac{77}{20}} = -7079 \mid -7079 = \dfrac{20\text{k}\Omega}{20\text{k}\Omega + 2\text{k}\Omega} A \dfrac{2\text{k}\Omega}{2\text{k}\Omega + 0.1\text{k}\Omega} \rightarrow A = -8176 \mid A = -8180$

11.32

$I_O = I_S \dfrac{R_S}{R_S + R_{IN}} \beta \dfrac{R_{OUT}}{R_{OUT} + R_L} \mid 200 = \dfrac{200\text{k}\Omega}{200\text{k}\Omega + 20\text{k}\Omega} \beta \dfrac{300\text{k}\Omega}{300\text{k}\Omega + 50\text{k}\Omega} \rightarrow \beta = 257$

11.33

$R_{IN} = 0\Omega \mid R_{OUT} = \infty \mid P = \dfrac{I_O^2}{2} R_L = \dfrac{[10^{-6}(5000)A]^2}{2} 10^4 \Omega = 125$ mW $\mid$ $A_P = \dfrac{125\text{mW}}{0} = \infty$

11.34

$V_O = V_S \dfrac{R_{IN}}{R_{IN} + R_S} A \dfrac{R_{IN}}{R_{IN} + R_{OUT}} A \dfrac{R_L}{R_L + R_{OUT}}$

$A_V = \dfrac{5000}{5000 + 1000} (-1000) \dfrac{5000}{5000 + 250} (-1000) \dfrac{100}{100 + 250} = +2.27 \times 10^5$

$A_I = \dfrac{I_O}{I_S} = \dfrac{2.27 \times 10^5 V_S}{100} \dfrac{1}{\dfrac{V_S}{6000}} = +1.36 \times 10^7$

$A_P = \dfrac{2.27 \times 10^5 V_S(+1.36 \times 10^7 I_S)}{V_S I_S} = +3.09 \times 10^{12}$

11.35

$$A_P = \frac{V_O I_O}{V_S I_S} = \frac{V_O \dfrac{V_O}{R_L}}{V_S \dfrac{V_S}{R_S + R_{IN}}} = \left(\frac{V_O}{V_S}\right)^2 \frac{R_S + R_{IN}}{R_L}$$

$$A_{PdB} = 10\log\left[\left(\frac{V_O}{V_S}\right)^2 \frac{R_S + R_{IN}}{R_L}\right] = 10\log\left(\frac{V_O}{V_S}\right)^2 + 10\log\left(\frac{R_S + R_{IN}}{R_L}\right)$$

$$A_{PdB} = 20\log\left(\frac{V_O}{V_S}\right) - 10\log\left(\frac{R_L}{R_S + R_{IN}}\right) = A_{VdB} - 10\log\left(\frac{R_L}{R_S + R_{IN}}\right)$$

$$A_P = \frac{V_O I_O}{V_S I_S} = \frac{I_O R_L I_O}{I_S(R_S + R_{IN})I_S} = \left(\frac{I_O}{I_S}\right)^2 \frac{R_L}{R_S + R_{IN}}$$

$$A_{IdB} = 10\log\left[\left(\frac{I_O}{I_S}\right)^2 \frac{R_L}{R_S + R_{IN}}\right] = 10\log\left(\frac{I_O}{I_S}\right)^2 + 10\log\left(\frac{R_L}{R_S + R_{IN}}\right)$$

$$A_{PdB} = 20\log\left(\frac{I_O}{I_S}\right) + 10\log\left(\frac{R_L}{R_S + R_{IN}}\right) = A_{IdB} + 10\log\left(\frac{R_L}{R_S + R_{IN}}\right)$$

Note: $\quad A_{PdB} = \dfrac{A_{VdB} + A_{IdB}}{2}$

11.36

(a) $A_I(s) = \dfrac{3\times10^9 s^2}{\left(s^2 + 51s + 50\right)\left(s^2 + 13000s + 3\times10^7\right)} = \dfrac{3\times10^9 s^2}{(s+1)(s+50)(s+3000)(s+10000)}$

Zeros: $s = 0$, $s = 0$ | Poles: $s = -1$, $s = -50$, $s = -3000$, $s = -10000$

(b) $A_V(s) = \dfrac{10^5\left(s^2 + 51s + 50\right)}{s^5 + 1000s^4 + 50000s^3 + 20000s^2 + 13000s + 3\times10^7}$ | Zeros: $s = -1$, $s = -50$

Using MATLAB to find the poles:

```
Av=[1 1000 50000 20000 13000 3e7];
roots(Av)
```

$\quad$ ans = -947.24 -52.13 -9.170 4.27 + j6.93 4.27 - j6.93

11.37

$$A_V = \frac{2\pi \times 10^7 s}{(s + 20\pi)(s + 2\pi \times 10^4)} = \frac{1000s}{(s + 20\pi)\left(1 + \dfrac{s}{2\pi \times 10^4}\right)} \quad | \quad A_{mid} = +1000 = 60 \text{ dB}$$

$f_L = \dfrac{20\pi}{2\pi} = 10 \text{ Hz}$ | $f_H = \dfrac{2\pi \times 10^4}{2\pi} = 10 \text{ kHz}$ | BW = 10kHz − 10Hz = 9.99 kHz

Bandpass Amplifier

11.38

$$A_V = \frac{2\pi \times 10^6}{s + 20\pi} = \frac{10^5}{1 + \frac{s}{20\pi}} \rightarrow \text{Low - pass Amplifier} \mid A_{mid} = +10^5 = 100 \text{ dB}$$

$$f_L = 0 \text{ Hz} \mid f_H = \frac{20\pi}{2\pi} = 10 \text{ Hz} \mid BW = 10Hz - 0Hz = 10 \text{ Hz}$$

11.39

$$A_V = \frac{10^4 s}{s + 100\pi} \mid \text{High - pass Amplifier} \mid A_{mid} = +10^4 = 80 \text{ dB}$$

$$f_L = \frac{100\pi}{2\pi} = 50 \text{ Hz} \mid f_H = \infty \mid BW = \infty$$

11.40

$$A_V(s) = \frac{10^7 s}{s^2 + 10^5 s + 10^{14}} = 10^2 \frac{10^5 s}{s^2 + 10^5 s + 10^{14}} = A_{mid} \frac{s\frac{\omega_o}{Q}}{s^2 + s\frac{\omega_o}{Q} + \omega_o^2}$$

$$\text{Bandpass Amplifier} \mid A_{mid} = 100 = 40 \text{ dB} \mid f_O = \frac{10^7}{2\pi} = 1.592 \text{ MHz} \mid Q = \frac{\omega_o}{10^5} = 100$$

$$BW = \frac{1.592MHz}{100} = 15.92 \text{ kHz} \mid \text{For a high Q circuit:}$$

$$f_L \approx f_o - \frac{BW}{2} = 1.592MHz - 15.92kHz = 1.584 \text{ MHz}$$

$$f_H \approx f_o + \frac{BW}{2} = 1.592MHz + 15.92kHz = 1.600 \text{ MHz}$$

11.41

$$A_V(s) = -20 \frac{s^2 + 10^{12}}{s^2 + 10^4 s + 10^{12}} = A_{mid} \frac{s^2 + \omega_o^2}{s^2 + s\frac{\omega_o}{Q} + \omega_o^2} \mid \text{Notch Filter}$$

$$\text{Note: } A_V(s) = -20\left(1 - \frac{s\frac{\omega_o}{Q}}{s^2 + s\frac{\omega_o}{Q} + \omega_o^2}\right) \text{ where } \frac{s\frac{\omega_o}{Q}}{s^2 + s\frac{\omega_o}{Q} + \omega_o^2} \text{ is a bandpass function.}$$

$$A_{mid} = -20 = 20 \text{ dB but } A_V = 0 \text{ at } f_o \mid f_O = \frac{\omega_o}{2\pi} = \frac{10^6}{2\pi} = 159.2 \text{ kHz} \mid Q = \frac{\omega_o}{10^4} = 100$$

$$\text{The width of the null } = BW = \frac{159.2kHz}{100} = 1.592 \text{ kHz} \mid \text{For a high Q circuit:}$$

$$f_L \approx f_o - \frac{BW}{2} = 159.2Hz - 1.592kHz = 157.6 \text{ kHz}$$

$$f_H \approx f_o - \frac{BW}{2} = 159.2Hz + 1.592kHz = 160.8 \text{ kHz}$$

11.42

$$A_V(s) = \frac{4\pi^2 \times 10^{14} s^2}{(s + 20\pi)(s + 50\pi)(s + 2\pi \times 10^5)(s + 2\pi \times 10^6)}$$

$$A_V(s) = \frac{10^3 s^2}{(s + 20\pi)(s + 50\pi)\left(1 + \dfrac{s}{2\pi \times 10^5}\right)\left(1 + \dfrac{s}{2\pi \times 10^6}\right)} \quad | \quad A_{mid} = 1000 = 60 \text{ dB}$$

Zeros: $s = 0$, $s = 0$ | Poles: $s = -20\pi$, $s = -50\pi$, $s = -2\pi \times 10^5$, $s = -2\pi \times 10^6$

For $s \gg 50\pi$, $A_V(s) \approx \dfrac{10^3}{\left(1 + \dfrac{s}{2\pi \times 10^5}\right)\left(1 + \dfrac{s}{2\pi \times 10^6}\right)}$

Since the two high frequency poles are separated in frequency by a decade,

$$f_H \approx \frac{2\pi \times 10^5}{2\pi} = 100 \text{ kHz} \quad | \quad \text{However, we are not that lucky at low frequencies.}$$

For $s \ll 2\pi \times 10^5$, $A_V(s) \approx \dfrac{10^3 s^2}{(s + 20\pi)(s + 50\pi)} \quad | \quad |A_V(j\omega_L)| = \dfrac{10^3 \omega_L^2}{\sqrt{\left(\omega_L^2 + (20\pi)^2\right)\left(\omega_L^2 + (50\pi)^2\right)}} = \dfrac{10^3}{\sqrt{2}}$

$$\omega_L^4 - \left[(20\pi)^2 + (50\pi)^2\right]\omega_L^2 - (20\pi)^2(50\pi)^2 = 0 \rightarrow \omega_L = \pm 178 \quad | \quad f_L = \frac{178}{2\pi} = 28.3 \text{ Hz}$$

11.43

Using MATLAB: n=[2e7*pi 0]; d=[1 (20*pi+2e4*pi) 40e4*pi^2]; bode(n,d)

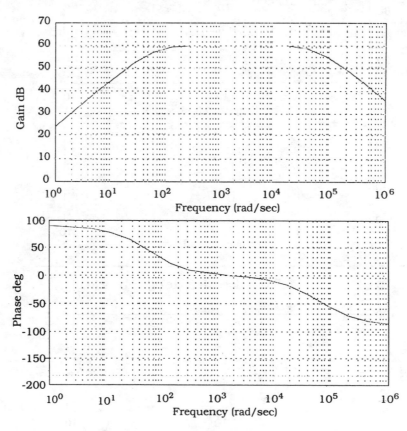

11.44   Using MATLAB: n=[2e6*pi]; d=[1   20*pi]; bode(n,d)

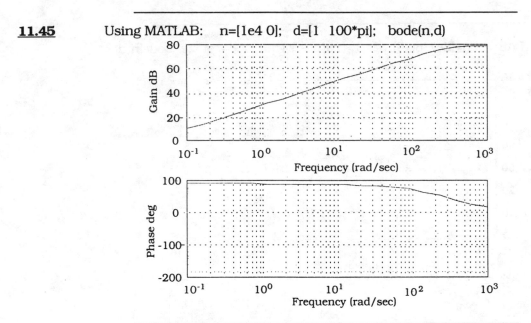

11.45   Using MATLAB: n=[1e4 0]; d=[1   100*pi];   bode(n,d)

11.46   Using MATLAB: n=[1e7 0]; d=[1 1e5 1e14];   bode(n,d)

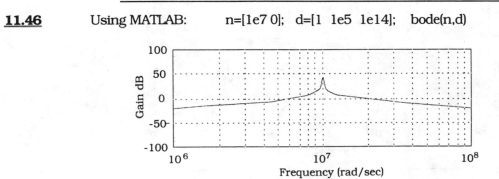

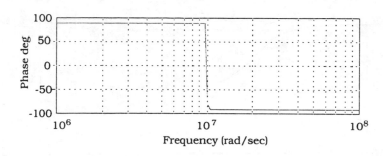

11.47   Using MATLAB: n=[-20 0 -2e13];   d=[1 1e4 1e12];   bode(n,d)

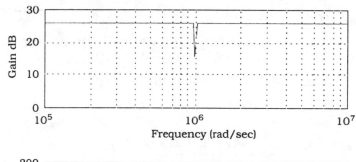

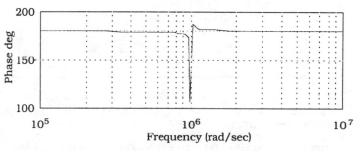

11.48   Using MATLAB:

```
n=[4e14*pi^2  0  0];
p1=[1 20*pi];   p2=[1 50*pi];   p3=[1 2e5*pi];   p4=[1 2e6*pi];
d=conv(conv(p1,p2),conv(p3,p4));
bode(n,d)
```

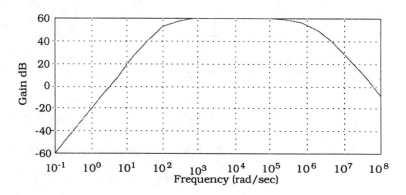

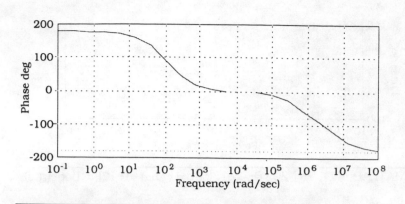

11.49   Using MATLAB:

     n=[2e7*pi 0]; d=conv([1 20*pi],[1 2e4*pi]); w=2*pi*[5 500 50000];
     a=freqs(n,d,w); am=abs(a); ap=angle(a)*180/pi

     Magnitudes: 447.2135   998.5526   196.1161

     Phases: 63.4063   -1.7166   -78.6786

$$\text{(a) } v_O = 0.447 \sin\left(10\pi t + 63.4°\right) \text{ V}$$

$$\text{(b) } v_O = 0.999 \sin\left(1000\pi t - 1.72°\right) \text{ V}$$

$$\text{(c) } v_O = 0.196 \sin\left(10^5 \pi t - 78.7°\right) \text{ V}$$

11.50   Using MATLAB:

     n=[2e6*pi]; d=[1 20*pi]; w=2*pi*[2 2000 200000]; a=freqs(n,d,w);
     am=abs(a); ap=angle(a)*180/pi

     Magnitudes: 9.8058e+04   4.9999e+02   5.0000e+00

     Phases: -11.3099   -89.7135   -89.9971

$$\text{(a) } v_O = 0.981 \sin\left(4\pi t - 11.3°\right) \text{ V}$$

$$\text{(b) } v_O = 5.00 \sin\left(4000\pi t - 89.7°\right) \text{ mV}$$

$$\text{(c) } v_O = 50.0 \sin\left(4\text{x}10^5 \pi t - 90.0°\right) \text{ μV}$$

11.51

$$A_V(s) = \frac{10^4 s}{s + 100\pi} \quad | \quad A_V(j\omega) = \frac{10^4 j\omega}{j\omega + 100\pi} = \frac{10^4 jf}{jf + 50}$$

$$\left|A_V(j\omega)\right| = \frac{10^4 f}{\sqrt{f^2 + 50^2}} \quad | \quad \angle A_V(j\omega) = 90° - \tan^{-1}\frac{f}{50}$$

(a) 1 Hz: $\left|A_V(j\omega)\right| = 200$ | $\angle A_V(j\omega) = 88.9°$ | $v_O = 0.06 \sin\left(2\pi t + 88.9°\right)$ V

(b) 50 Hz: $\left|A_V(j\omega)\right| = 7071$ | $\angle A_V(j\omega) = 45.0°$ | $v_O = 2.12 \sin\left(100\pi t + 45.0°\right)$ V

(c) 5 kHz: $\left|A_V(j\omega)\right| = 10^4$ | $\angle A_V(j\omega) = 0.573°$ | $v_O = 3.00 \sin\left(10^4 \pi t + 0.573°\right)$ V

11.52 In the first printing, the transfer function should refer to Problem 11.42.

Using MATLAB:
```
n=[4e14*pi^2  0  0];
p1=[1 20*pi];  p2=[1 50*pi];  p3=[1 2e5*pi];  p4=[1 2e6*pi];
d=conv(conv(p1,p2),conv(p3,p4));
w=2*pi*[5 500 50000];
a=freqs(n,d,w);
am=abs(a)
ap=angle(a)*180/pi
```

Magnitudes: 87.7058 998.5400 893.3111

Phases: 142.1219   3.6930 -29.3873

$$\text{(a) } v_O = 87.7\sin\left(10\pi t + 142°\right) \text{ mV}$$

$$\text{(b) } v_O = 0.999\sin\left(1000\pi t + 3.69°\right) \text{ V}$$

$$\text{(c) } v_O = 0.893\sin\left(10^5\pi t - 29.4°\right) \text{ V}$$

11.53   In the first printing, the transfer function should refer to Problem 11.40.

Using MATLAB:
```
n=[-1e7 0];  d=[1 1e5 1e14];
w=2*pi*[1.59e6 1e6 5e6];
a=freqs(n,d,w);
am=abs(a)
ap=angle(a)*180/pi
```

Magnitudes: 98.1550 1.0381 0.3542

Phases: -168.9767 -90.5948   90.2029

$$\text{(a) } v_O = 0.491\sin\left(3.18\text{x}10^6\pi t - 169°\right) \text{ V}$$

$$\text{(b) } v_O = 5.19\sin\left(2\text{x}10^6\pi t - 90.6°\right) \text{ mV}$$

$$\text{(c) } v_O = 1.77\sin\left(10^7\pi t + 90.2°\right) \text{ mV}$$

11.54   In the first printing, the transfer function should refer to Problem 11.41.

Using MATLAB:
```
n=[-20  0 -2e13];  d=[1 1e4 1e12];
w=2*pi*[1.59e5 5e4 2e5];
a=freqs(n,d,w);
am=abs(a)
ap=angle(a)*180/pi
```

Magnitudes: 3.8242 19.9999 19.9953

Phases: 101.0233 179.8003 -178.7570

$$\text{(a) } v_O = 95.6\sin\left(3.18\text{x}10^5\pi t + 101°\right) \text{ mV}$$

$$\text{(b) } v_O = 0.500\sin\left(10^5\pi t + 180\right) \text{ V}$$

$$\text{(c) } v_O = 0.500\sin\left(4\text{x}10^5\pi t - 179°\right) \text{ V}$$

11.55

(a) $A_{mid} = +10^{\frac{20}{20}} = +10$ | $A_V = \dfrac{10}{1 + \dfrac{s}{2\pi \times \left(5 \times 10^6\right)}} = \dfrac{10}{1 + \dfrac{s}{10^7 \pi}} = \dfrac{10^8 \pi}{s + 10^7 \pi}$

(b) $A_{mid} = -10^{\frac{20}{20}} = -10$ | $A_V = -\dfrac{10^8 \pi}{s + 10^7 \pi}$

11.56

(a) $A_V(s) = 100 \dfrac{s}{(s + 200\pi)\left(1 + \dfrac{s}{2\pi \times 10^5}\right)} = \dfrac{2\pi \times 10^7 s}{(s + 200\pi)(s + 2\pi \times 10^5)}$

(b) $A_V(s) = -\dfrac{2\pi \times 10^7 s}{(s + 200\pi)(s + 2\pi \times 10^5)}$

11.57

$A_V(s) = -1000\left(\dfrac{50000\pi}{s + 50000\pi}\right)^2 = -1000\left(\dfrac{1}{1 + \dfrac{s}{50000\pi}}\right)^2$ | $A_{mid} = -1000$

$f_H = 0.64 \ f_1 = 0.644(25\text{kHz}) = 16.1 \text{ kHz}$ | $2\left(-20\dfrac{\text{dB}}{\text{dec}}\right) = -40\dfrac{\text{dB}}{\text{dec}}$

Using MATLAB:
```
n=1000*(50000*pi)^2;
d=[1  2*50000*pi  (50000*pi)^2 ];
bode(n,d)
```

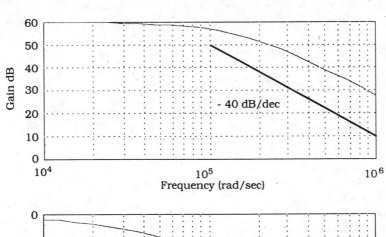

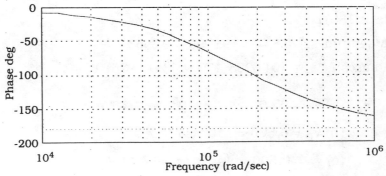

11.58

$$A_V(s) = A_o\left(\frac{\omega_1}{s + \omega_1}\right)^3 \quad | \quad \left|A_V(j\omega_H)\right| = A_o\left(\frac{\omega_1}{\sqrt{\omega_H^2 + \omega_1^2}}\right)^3 = \frac{A_o}{\sqrt{2}} \quad | \quad BW = f_H$$

$$\sqrt{2}^{\frac{1}{3}} = \sqrt{1 + \left(\frac{f_H}{f_1}\right)^2} \rightarrow f_H = f_1\sqrt{2^{\frac{1}{3}} - 1} = 25\text{kHz}(0.5098) = 12.8 \text{ kHz} \quad | \quad 3\left(-20\frac{dB}{dec}\right) = -60\frac{dB}{dec}$$

Using MATLAB:

```
n=2500*(50000*pi)^3;
d=[1  3*50000*pi  3*(50000*pi)^2  (50000*pi)^3];
bode(n,d)
```

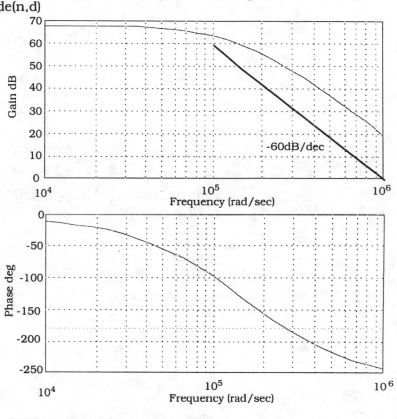

11.59 (a) To avoid distortion of the waveform, the phase shift must be proportional to frequency. $30°$ at 1500 Hz and $50°$ at 2500 Hz.

(b) $v_O = 10\sin(1000\pi t + 10°) + 3.33\sin(3000\pi t + 30°) + 2.00\sin(5000\pi t + 50°)$

(c) Using MATLAB:
```
t=linspace(0,.004);
vs=sin(1000*pi*t)+0.333*sin(3000*pi*t)+0.200*sin(5000*pi*t);
vo=10*sin(1000*pi*t+pi/18)+3.33*sin(3000*pi*t+3*pi/18)+
       2.00*sin(5000*pi*t+5*pi/18);
plot(t,10*vs,t,vo)
```

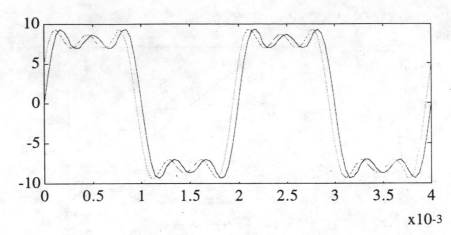

CHAPTER 12

12.1

$$\mathbf{v_o} = \mathbf{v_s} \frac{1M\Omega}{1M\Omega + 5k\Omega}(1000)\frac{1k\Omega}{1k\Omega + 0.5\Omega} \quad | \quad A_V = \frac{\mathbf{v_o}}{\mathbf{v_s}} = 990 \text{ or } 59.9 \text{ dB}$$

$$\mathbf{i_s} = \frac{\mathbf{v_s}}{1M\Omega + 5k\Omega} \text{ and } \mathbf{i_o} = \frac{990\mathbf{v_s}}{1k\Omega} \quad | \quad A_I = \frac{\mathbf{i_o}}{\mathbf{i_s}} = \frac{990}{1000}10^6 = 9.9 \times 10^5 \text{ or } 120 \text{ dB}$$

$$A_P = A_V A_I = 990\left(9.9 \times 10^5\right) = 9.8 \times 10^8 \text{ or } 89.9 \text{ dB} \quad | \quad \mathbf{v_s} = \frac{\mathbf{v_o}}{A_V} = \frac{5V}{990} = 5.05 \text{ mV}$$

12.2

$$\mathbf{v_o} = \mathbf{v_s} \frac{5k\Omega}{5k\Omega + 5k\Omega}(31.6)\frac{1k\Omega}{1k\Omega + 1k\Omega} \text{ and } A_V = \frac{\mathbf{v_o}}{\mathbf{v_s}} = 7.91 \text{ or } 18.0 \text{ dB}$$

$$\mathbf{v_s} = \frac{\mathbf{v_o}}{A_V} = \frac{10V}{7.91} = 1.27 \text{ V} \quad \text{Since } R_{OUT} \text{ has the same value as } R_L, \text{ the power}$$

dissipated in R_{OUT} is also 0.5W. The power dissipated in R_{ID} will be

$$P_I = \frac{V_{ID}^2}{2R_{ID}} = \frac{\left(\frac{V_S}{2}\right)^2}{2R_{ID}} = \frac{V_S^2}{8R_{ID}} \quad \text{where } V_S = \frac{V_O}{7.91} \text{ and } V_O = \sqrt{2(0.5W)(1000\Omega)} = 31.6V$$

$$P_I = \frac{4^2}{8(5000)} = 0.4 \text{mW}. \quad \text{The total power dissipated in the amplifier is}$$

$$P = 500\text{mW} + 0.4\text{mW} = 500 \text{ mW}.$$

12.3

$$0.99\text{mV} \geq 1\text{mV}\frac{R_{ID}}{R_{ID} + 50k\Omega} \Rightarrow R_{ID} \geq 4.95 \text{ M}\Omega$$

12.4

$$I_o = \sqrt{\frac{2(100W)}{50\Omega}} = 2A \text{ and } \frac{I_o^2 R_{OUT}}{2} \leq 5W \text{ or } R_{OUT} \leq 2.5\Omega$$

12.5

$$\mathbf{v_{ID}} = \frac{\mathbf{v_o}}{A} = \frac{10V}{10^5} = 0.1 \text{ mV} \quad | \quad \frac{10V}{A} \leq 10^{-6}V \text{ requires } A \geq 10^7 \text{ or } 140 \text{ dB}$$

12.6

$$\mathbf{v_{ID}} = \frac{\mathbf{v_o}}{A} = \frac{15V}{10^6} = 15 \text{ } \mu V \quad | \quad \frac{15V}{A} \leq 10^{-6}V \text{ requires } A \geq 15 \times 10^6 \quad | \quad \mathbf{i_+} = \frac{15\mu V}{1M\Omega} = 15 \text{ pA}$$

12.7

$$A_v = -\frac{R_2}{R_1} = -\frac{220k\Omega}{4.7k\Omega} = -46.8 \quad | \quad 20\log(46.8) = 33.4 \text{ dB} \quad | \quad R_{IN} = R_1 = 4.7 \text{ k}\Omega \quad | \quad R_{OUT} = 0 \text{ } \Omega$$

12.8

$$A_v = -\frac{R_2}{R_1} = -\frac{8200\Omega}{910\Omega} = -9.01$$

$$V_O = -9.01(0.05V) = -0.451V \quad | \quad v_o(t) = -0.451\sin(4638t)\ V$$

$$I_s = \frac{V_s}{R_1} = \frac{0.05V}{910\Omega} = 54.9\mu A \quad | \quad i_s(t) = 54.9\sin(4638t)\ \mu A$$

12.9

$$A_v = 1 + \frac{R_2}{R_1} = 1 + \frac{680k\Omega}{8.2k\Omega} = 83.9 \quad | \quad 20\log(83.9) = 38.5\ dB \quad | \quad R_{IN} = \infty \quad | \quad R_{OUT} = 0\ \Omega$$

12.10

$$A_v = 1 + \frac{R_2}{R_1} = 1 + \frac{8200\Omega}{910\Omega} = 10.0 \mid V_O = 10.0(0.05V) = 0.500V \mid v_o(t) = 0.500\sin(9125t)\ V$$

12.11

$$v_O = -\frac{R_3}{R_1}v_1 - \frac{R_3}{R_2}v_2 = -\frac{51k\Omega}{1k\Omega}v_1 - \frac{51k\Omega}{2k\Omega}v_2 = -51v_1 - 25.5v_2$$

$$v_O(t) = -51(0.01\sin 3770t) - 25.5(0.04\sin 10000t)$$

$$v_O(t) = (0.510\sin 3770t - 1.02\sin 10000t)\ V \quad \text{and} \quad v_-(t) \equiv 0.$$

12.12

(a) $A_v^{nom} = 1 + \dfrac{R_2}{R_1} = 1 + \dfrac{47k\Omega}{0.18k\Omega} = 262 \quad | \quad 20\log(262) = 48.4\ dB$

$R_{IN} = 10k\Omega + \infty = \infty \quad | \quad R_{OUT} = 0\ \Omega$

(b) $A_v^{max} = 1 + \dfrac{47k\Omega(1.1)}{0.18k\Omega(0.9)} = 320 \quad | \quad A_v^{min} = 1 + \dfrac{47k\Omega(0.9)}{0.18k\Omega(1.1)} = 215$

$\dfrac{A_v^{max} - A_v^{nom}}{A_v^{nom}} = \dfrac{320 - 262}{262} = 0.22 \quad | \quad \dfrac{A_v^{min} - A_v^{nom}}{A_v^{nom}} = \dfrac{215 - 262}{262} = -0.18$

(c) Tolerances: $+22\%,\ -18\%$ (d) $\dfrac{320}{215} = 1.49:1$

(e) function count=c;
```
   c=0;
   for i=1:500,
        r1=180*(1+0.2*(rand-0.5));
        r2=47000*(1+0.2*(rand-0.5));
        a=1+r2/r1;
        anom=1+47000/180;
        if (a>=0.95*anom & a<=1.05*anom), c=c+1; end;
   end
   c
```
Executing this function twenty times yields 44% .

12.13

(a) Using Eq. 12.36: $A_V = -\dfrac{10R}{R} = -10$

(b) $R_2 = \dfrac{v_2}{i_2}\Big|_{v_1=0} = 11R = 110\ k\Omega \quad | \quad R_1 = \dfrac{v_1}{i_1}\Big|_{v_2=0} = R = 10\ k\Omega$.

12.14

$$i_{TH} = \frac{v_-}{R_{TH}} + \frac{v_- - v_o}{R} \quad \text{but } v_- = 0 \text{ because it is a virtual ground } (v_- = v_+ = 0)$$

$$i_{TH} = -\frac{v_o}{R} \quad | \quad v_o = -i_{TH}R \quad | \quad V_O = -I_{TH}R \quad | \quad \text{This circuit is known as a}$$

current - to - voltage converter or transresistance amplifier.

12.15

(a) $A_v = -\dfrac{R_2}{R_1} = -\dfrac{100k\Omega}{20k\Omega} = -5.00 \quad | \quad R_{IN} = R_1 = 20 \text{ k}\Omega$

(b) $A_v = 1 + \dfrac{R_2}{R_1} = 1 + \dfrac{100k\Omega}{20k\Omega} = +6.00 \quad | \quad R_{IN} = 27k\Omega \| \infty = 27 \text{ k}\Omega$

(c) $A_v = -\dfrac{R_2}{R_1} = -\dfrac{0}{33k\Omega} = 0 \quad | \quad R_{IN} = R_1 = 33 \text{ k}\Omega$ (This is not a very useful circuit.)

12.16 The inverting terminal of the op-amp represents a virtual ground and

(a) $I_O = I_{DS} = \dfrac{V_- - (-V_{EE})}{R} = \dfrac{0 - (-10)}{10} = 1 \text{ A.}$

(b) Saturation requires $V_{DS} \geq V_{GS} - V_{TN}$ where $V_{DS} = V_{DD} - V_- = V_{DD}$ and

$$V_{GS} - V_{TN} = \sqrt{\frac{2I_{DS}}{K_n}} = \sqrt{\frac{2(1)}{0.25}} = 2.83V \rightarrow V_{DD} \geq 2.83V.$$

(c) $P_R = I^2 R = (1)^2 10 = 10W.$ So the resistor must dissipate 10 W.

(A 15W resistor would provide a reasonable safety margin.)

12.17 The inverting terminal of the op-amp represents a virtual ground.

(a) $I_O = I_C = \alpha_F I_E = \dfrac{\beta_F}{1 + \beta_F} \dfrac{V_- - (-V_{EE})}{R} = \dfrac{30}{31} \dfrac{0 - (-15)}{30} = 0.484 \text{ A.}$

(b) $V_O = V_- + V_{BE} = 0 + V_{BE} = V_{BE} = V_T \ln \dfrac{I_C}{I_S} = 0.025V \ln \dfrac{0.484}{10^{-13}} = 0.730V$

(c) Forward - active region operation requires $V_{CE} \geq V_{BE}$ but $V_{CE} = V_{CC} - V_- = V_{CC}$
Therefore $V_{CC} \geq 0.730$ V.

(d) $P_R = I^2 R = (0.484)^2 30 = 7.03W.$ So the resistor must dissipate 7.03 W.

(A 10W resistor would provide a reasonable safety margin.)

$$P_D = I_C V_{CE} + I_B V_{BE} = 0.484(15) + \dfrac{0.484}{30} 0.730 = 7.27 \text{ W.}$$

12.18

$$\frac{V_S - V_+}{R} + \frac{V_O - V_+}{KR} = sCV_+ \quad \text{and} \quad V_+ = V_- = V_O \frac{R_1}{R_1 + KR_1} = \frac{V_O}{1 + K}$$

Combining these expressions yields: $A_V(s) = \dfrac{V_O}{V_S} = +\dfrac{1 + K}{sRC}$, a non - inverting integrator.

12.19 (a) Applying ideal op-amp assumption 1, the voltage at the top end of R is v_1 and the voltage at the bottom end of R is v_2. Applying op-amp assumption 2, the current i_o must also equal the current in R, and

$$i_o = \frac{v_1 - v_2}{R}$$

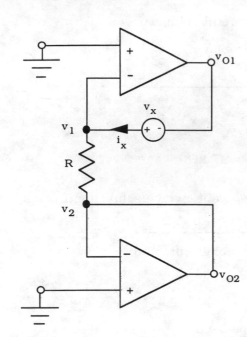

(b) $i_x = \dfrac{0V - 0V}{R} = 0$ | $R_{OUT} = \dfrac{v_x}{i_x} = \infty$

$v_{O1} = A\big(0 - (v_{O1} + v_x)\big)$ $v_{O2} = A(0 - v_{O2}) \Rightarrow v_{O2} = 0$

$v_{O1} = -v_x \dfrac{A}{1 + A}$ | $v_1 = v_{O1} + v_x = \dfrac{v_x}{1 + A}$

$i_x = \dfrac{v_1 - v_2}{R} = \dfrac{v_x}{(1 + A)R}$ | $R_{OUT} = \dfrac{v_x}{i_x} = (1 + A)R$

12.20

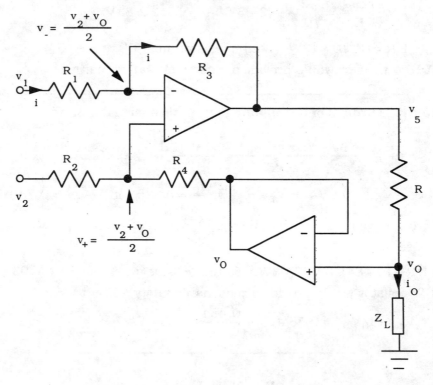

(a)

$i_o = \dfrac{v_5 - v_O}{R}$ | $v_5 = v_- - i\,R_3 = v_- - \dfrac{v_1 - v_-}{R_1}\,R_3 = 2v_- - v_1$ since $R_1 = R_3$

$v_- = \dfrac{v_2 + v_O}{2}$ and $v_5 = v_2 - v_1 + v_O$ | $i_o = \dfrac{v_2 - v_1 + v_O - v_O}{R} = \dfrac{v_2 - v_1}{R}$

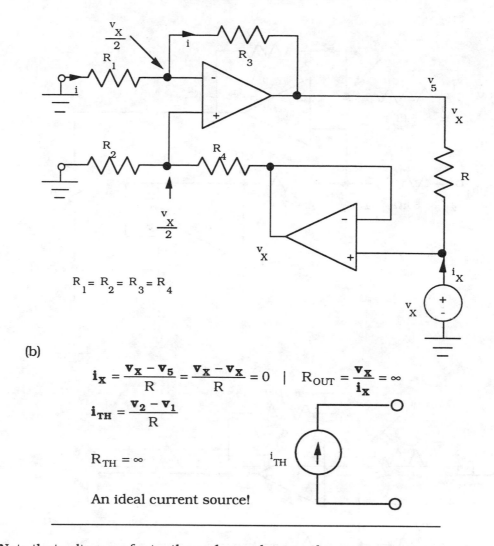

(b)

$$i_X = \frac{v_X - v_5}{R} = \frac{v_X - v_X}{R} = 0 \quad | \quad R_{OUT} = \frac{v_X}{i_X} = \infty$$

$$i_{TH} = \frac{v_2 - v_1}{R}$$

$$R_{TH} = \infty \qquad\qquad i_{TH}$$

An ideal current source!

12.21 (a) Note that voltages refer to the node numbers on the next page

Using voltage division since $i_+ = 0$, $\quad v_2 = v_4 + 6\,\dfrac{4.99k\Omega}{4.99k\Omega + 5.00k\Omega}$

$$v_2 = v_4 + \left(6 - v_4\right)\frac{4.99k\Omega}{4.99k\Omega + 5.00k\Omega} = 0.5005v_4 + 2.997V$$

Since $v_{id} = 0$, $\quad v_1 = v_2$ $\quad$ and $\quad v_5 = v_1 - \dfrac{4 - v_1}{5k\Omega}(5.01k\Omega)$

Solving for v_5 yields $\quad v_5 = 1.992V + 1.002v_4$

$$i_o = \frac{v_5 - v_4}{10k\Omega} = 199\mu A + 2\times10^{-7}v_4$$

v_4 is unknown; let us assume $2\times10^{-7}v_4 \ll 199\times10^{-6}$ A
which requires $v_4 \ll 995V$. So for $v_4 < 100V$, which should almost always be true in transistor circuits, $i_o = 199\mu A$.

For $Z_L = 10$ kΩ, $\quad v_4 = 1.99$ V, $\quad v_2 = 3.99$ V, $\quad v_1 = 3.99$ V, $\quad v_5 = 3.99$ V

Note that $v_5 - v_4 = 2$ V $= (6V - 4V)$

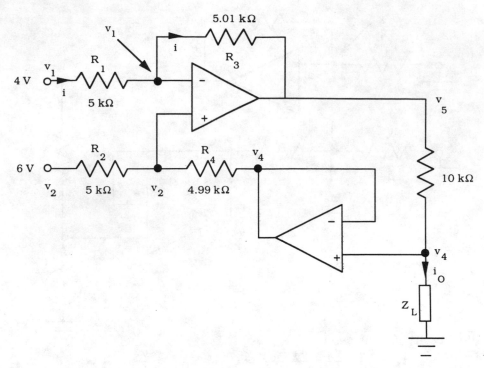

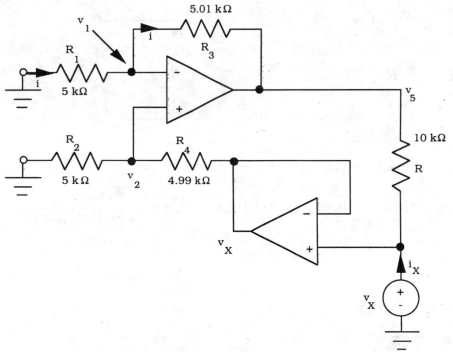

12.21 (b)

$$R_{OUT} = \frac{\mathbf{v_x}}{\mathbf{i_x}} \quad \text{and} \quad \mathbf{i_x} = \frac{\mathbf{v_x} - \mathbf{v_5}}{10\text{k}\Omega} \quad \text{So we need to find } i_X, \text{ and hence } v_5, \text{ in terms of } v_X$$

$$\mathbf{v_1} = \mathbf{v_2} = \mathbf{v_x} \frac{5.00\text{k}\Omega}{4.99\text{k}\Omega + 5.00\text{k}\Omega} = 0.5005\mathbf{v_x}$$

$$\mathbf{v_5} = \mathbf{v_1} + \mathbf{i}\,(5.01\text{k}\Omega) = \mathbf{v_1} + \frac{\mathbf{v_1}}{5\text{k}\Omega}(5.01\text{k}\Omega) = 2.002\mathbf{v_1} = 1.002\mathbf{v_x}$$

$$\mathbf{i_x} = \frac{\mathbf{v_x} - \mathbf{v_5}}{10\text{k}\Omega} = \frac{\mathbf{v_x} - 1.002\mathbf{v_x}}{10\text{k}\Omega} = -\frac{0.002\mathbf{v_x}}{10\text{k}\Omega} \quad \text{and} \quad R_{OUT} = -5\ \text{M}\Omega\ ! \quad \text{A negative output resistance!}$$

12.22 Using ideal op-amp assumption 2, $V_S = I_S R_1 + I_L Z_L$, and using ideal op-amp assumption 1, the voltage across R_2 must equal the voltage across R_1 which requires

$$I_2 R_2 = I_S R_1 \quad \text{or} \quad I_2 = I_S \frac{R_1}{R_2}.$$

$$V_S = I_S R_1 + I_S \left(1 + \frac{R_1}{R_2}\right) Z_L \quad \text{and} \quad Z_{IN} = \frac{V_S}{I_S} = R_1 + \left(1 + \frac{R_1}{R_2}\right) Z_L$$

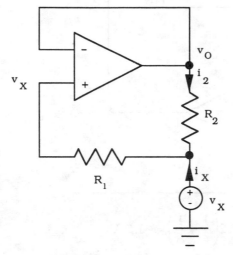

$$R_{OUT} = \frac{\mathbf{v_x}}{\mathbf{i_x}} \quad \text{where}$$

$$\mathbf{i_x} = \frac{\mathbf{v_x} - \mathbf{v_o}}{R_2} = \frac{\mathbf{v_x} - \mathbf{v_x}}{R_2} = 0$$

$$R_{OUT} = \frac{\mathbf{v_x}}{\mathbf{i_x}} = \infty$$

Note, for the case of finite gain A,

$$R_{OUT} = \frac{\mathbf{v_x}}{\mathbf{i_x}} \quad \text{where} \quad \mathbf{i_x} = \frac{\mathbf{v_x} - \mathbf{v_o}}{R_2} \quad \text{and} \quad \mathbf{v_o} = \mathbf{v_x} \frac{A}{1 + A}$$

$$\mathbf{v_x} - \mathbf{v_o} = \frac{\mathbf{v_x}}{1 + A} \quad \text{and} \quad R_{OUT} = R_2 (1 + A)$$

12.23 For $Z_L = 3.6 \text{ k}\Omega$, $R_{IN} = 10 \text{k}\Omega + 3.6 \text{k}\Omega \left(1 + \frac{10 \text{k}\Omega}{1 \text{k}\Omega}\right) = 49.6 \text{ k}\Omega$

12.24 Applying op-amp assumption 1 to the circuit on the next page, the voltage at the top of R_2 is v_{O2}, and applying op-amp assumption 2,

$$\frac{\mathbf{v_s}}{R_1} = -\frac{\mathbf{v_{O2}}}{R_2} \quad \text{or} \quad \mathbf{v_{O2}} = -\mathbf{v_s} \frac{R_2}{R_1}$$

Since the op-amp input currents are zero, and

$$\mathbf{i} = \frac{\mathbf{v_s}}{R_1}, \quad \mathbf{v_{O1}} = -\mathbf{i}R_2 - \mathbf{i}R_3 = -\left(\frac{R_2}{R_1} + \frac{R_3}{R_1}\right)\mathbf{v_s}$$

Alternatively, the voltage at the bottom of R_2 is zero, so

$$\mathbf{v_{O1}} = \left(1 + \frac{R_3}{R_2}\right)\mathbf{v_{O2}} = \left(1 + \frac{R_3}{R_2}\right)\left(-\frac{R_2}{R_1}\right)\mathbf{v_s} = -\left(\frac{R_2}{R_1} + \frac{R_3}{R_1}\right)\mathbf{v_s}$$

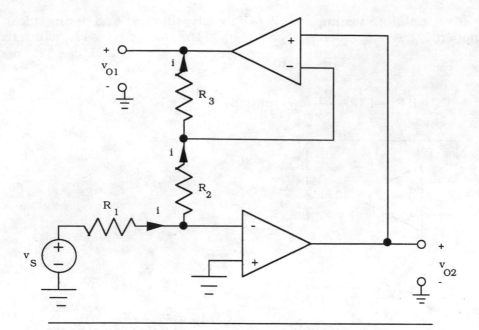

12.25

$$V_O = -V_{REF}\left(\frac{R}{4R} + \frac{R}{8R}\right) = -3.2\left(\frac{1}{4} + \frac{1}{8}\right) = -1.2 \text{ V}$$

$$V_O = -V_{REF}\left(\frac{R}{2R} + \frac{R}{16R}\right) = -3.2\left(\frac{1}{2} + \frac{1}{16}\right) = -1.8 \text{ V}$$

0000	0.000 V
0001	-0.200 V
0010	-0.400 V
0011	-0.600 V
0100	-0.800 V
0101	-1.00 V
0110	-1.20 V
0111	-1.40 V
1000	-1.60 V
1001	-1.80 V
1010	-2.00 V
1011	-2.20 V
1100	-2.40 V
1101	-2.60 V
1110	-2.80 V
1111	-3.00 V

12.26 Desire $R_{on} \leq 0.01(10 \text{ k}\Omega) = 100 \ \Omega$.

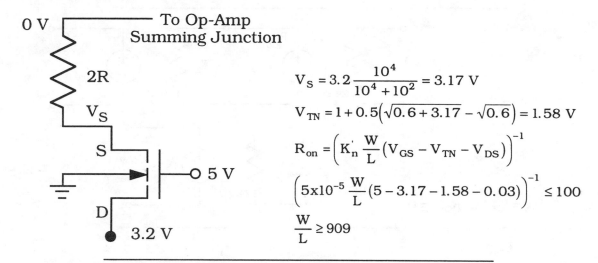

$$V_S = 3.2 \frac{10^4}{10^4 + 10^2} = 3.17 \text{ V}$$

$$V_{TN} = 1 + 0.5\left(\sqrt{0.6 + 3.17} - \sqrt{0.6}\right) = 1.58 \text{ V}$$

$$R_{on} = \left(K_n' \frac{W}{L}\left(V_{GS} - V_{TN} - V_{DS}\right)\right)^{-1}$$

$$\left(5 \times 10^{-5} \frac{W}{L}(5 - 3.17 - 1.58 - 0.03)\right)^{-1} \leq 100$$

$$\frac{W}{L} \geq 909$$

12.27 Consider the error for each bit acting by itself:

$$V_{REF}\left[\frac{R(1 + \varepsilon_0)}{2R(1 - \varepsilon_1)}\right] - \frac{V_{REF}}{2} \approx V_{REF}\left[\frac{(1 + \varepsilon_0 + \varepsilon_1)}{2} - \frac{1}{2}\right] = V_{REF}\frac{(\varepsilon_0 + \varepsilon_1)}{2}$$

$$V_{REF}\left[\frac{R(1 + \varepsilon_0)}{4R(1 - \varepsilon_2)}\right] - \frac{V_{REF}}{4} \approx V_{REF}\frac{(\varepsilon_0 + \varepsilon_2)}{4}$$

$$V_{REF}\left[\frac{R(1 + \varepsilon_0)}{8R(1 - \varepsilon_3)}\right] - \frac{V_{REF}}{8} \approx V_{REF}\frac{(\varepsilon_0 + \varepsilon_3)}{8}$$

$$V_{REF}\left[\frac{R(1 + \varepsilon_0)}{16R(1 - \varepsilon_4)}\right] - \frac{V_{REF}}{16} \approx V_{REF}\frac{(\varepsilon_0 + \varepsilon_4)}{16}$$

Adding these together yields

$$V_{REF}\frac{(\varepsilon_0 + \varepsilon_1)}{2} + V_{REF}\frac{(\varepsilon_0 + \varepsilon_2)}{4} + V_{REF}\frac{(\varepsilon_0 + \varepsilon_3)}{8} + V_{REF}\frac{(\varepsilon_0 + \varepsilon_4)}{16} = 0.05 V_{REF}$$

$$\frac{15}{16}\varepsilon_0 + \frac{\varepsilon_1}{2} + \frac{\varepsilon_2}{4} + \frac{\varepsilon_3}{8} + \frac{\varepsilon_4}{16} = 0.05$$

Giving each term the same weight:

$$\frac{15}{16}\varepsilon_0 = 1\% \text{ and } \varepsilon_0 = 1.07\% \mid \frac{\varepsilon_1}{2} = 1\% \text{ and } \varepsilon_1 = 2\% \quad \varepsilon_2 = 4\% \quad \varepsilon_3 = 8\% \quad \varepsilon_4 = 16\%$$

12.28 An n-bit DAC requires (n+1) resistors. Ten bits requires 11 resistors.

$$\frac{2^{10}R}{R} = \frac{2^{10}}{1} \quad \text{or} \quad 1024:1$$

A wide range of resistor values is required but it could be done. For R = 1 kΩ, 1024R = 1.024 MΩ.

12.29 Taking successive Thévenin equivalent circuits at each ladder node yields:

$$-\frac{V_{REF}}{16} = -0.3V \mid -\frac{V_{REF}}{8} = -0.6V \mid -\frac{V_{REF}}{4} = -1.2V \mid -\frac{V_{REF}}{2} = -2.4V$$

    Combine amplifiers A & B;   Combine amplifiers B & C

12.31

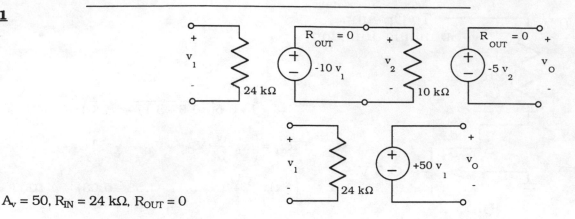

$A_v = 50$, $R_{IN} = 24$ kΩ, $R_{OUT} = 0$

12.32

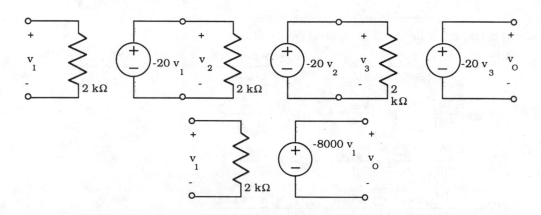

12.33   (a) Driving the output of the circuit in Fig. 12.21 with a current source of value i_X:

$$\mathbf{i_X} = \mathbf{i_O} + \mathbf{i_2} \quad | \quad \mathbf{i_2} = \frac{\mathbf{v_X}}{R_1 + R_2} \quad ; \quad \mathbf{i_O} = \frac{\mathbf{v_X} - A\mathbf{v_{id}}}{R_O} \quad ; \quad \mathbf{v_{id}} = -\mathbf{i_2}R_1$$

$$\mathbf{i_O} = \frac{\mathbf{v_X} + A\mathbf{i_2}R_1}{R_O} = \mathbf{v_X}\frac{1 + A\beta}{R_O} \quad \text{where} \quad \beta = \frac{R_1}{R_1 + R_2}$$

$$\mathbf{i_X} = \mathbf{v_X}\frac{1 + A\beta}{R_O} + \frac{\mathbf{v_X}}{R_1 + R_2} \quad \text{and} \quad R_{OUT} = \frac{\mathbf{v_X}}{\mathbf{i_X}} = \frac{R_O}{1 + A\beta}\|(R_1 + R_2)$$

(b) This approach places two potentially unequal value voltage sources in parallel which is not permitted.

12.34   Assume $i_- \ll i_2$:

$$\mathbf{i_-} = -\mathbf{i_X} = -\frac{\mathbf{v_X}}{R_{ID}(1 + A\beta)} = -\frac{0.1V}{10^6\Omega\left(1 + 10^5\dfrac{1}{48}\right)} = -48.0 \text{ pA}$$

$$\mathbf{i_1} \approx \mathbf{i_2} = \frac{\mathbf{v_O}}{R_1 + R_2} = \frac{0.1V(1 + 47)}{48k\Omega} = 100 \text{ μA} \quad \text{and} \quad \mathbf{i_-} \ll \mathbf{i_2}$$

12.35

$$\text{Setting } v_2 = 0, \quad R_{IN1} = R_{ID}(1 + A\beta) = (500k\Omega)\left(1 + 4x10^4 \frac{2R_1}{2R_1 + 49R_1}\right) = 785 \text{ M}\Omega$$

$$\text{By symmetry, } R_{IN2} = R_{IN1} = 785 \text{ M}\Omega \quad | \quad R_{OUT} = R_{OUT3} = \frac{R_O}{(1 + A\beta)} = \frac{75}{\left(1 + \dfrac{4x10^4}{2}\right)} = 3.75 \text{ m}\Omega$$

12.36
$$\text{FGE} = 1 - \frac{A}{1 + A} = \frac{1}{1 + A} \leq 10^{-4} \quad \text{requires } A \geq 10,000 \text{ (80 dB)}$$

12.37   Op-amp parameters: $R_{ID} = 500 \text{ k}\Omega, \quad R_O = 35 \ \Omega, \quad A = 50,000$
Amplifier Requirements: $A_V = 200, \ R_{IN} \geq 200 \text{ M}\Omega, \ R_{OUT} \leq 0.2 \ \Omega.$

We must immediately discard the inverting amplifier case. $R_{IN} = R_1$ requires $R_1 \geq 200$ MΩ which can be achieved, but then R_2 must be $200 \ R_1 \geq 40$ GΩ which is out of the question (see values in Appendix C).   So, working with the non-inverting amplifier:

$$A_V = 200 \Rightarrow \beta = \frac{R_1}{R_1 + R_2} = \frac{1}{200} \quad \text{and} \quad A\beta = \frac{50000}{200} = 250 \gg 1$$

$$R_{OUT} = \frac{R_O}{1 + A\beta} \cong \frac{35}{250} = 0.14\Omega \quad \text{meets the specification}$$

$$R_{IN} = R_{ID}(1 + A\beta) \cong 500k\Omega(250) = 125M\Omega \quad \text{does not meet the requirements.}$$

So the specifications cannot be met using a single-stage amplifier built using the op-amp that was given to us.

12.38 The non-inverting amplifier is the only one that can hope to achieve both the required gain and input resistance (see Prob. 12.37):

$$A_{CL} = \frac{1}{\beta} = 200 \quad \text{and} \quad A\beta = \frac{10^4}{200} = 50$$

$$R_{IN} = R_{ID}(1 + A\beta) = 1M\Omega(51) = 51 \text{ M}\Omega \ - \text{ too small}$$

$$R_{OUT} = \frac{R_O}{(1 + A\beta)} = \frac{100\Omega}{51} = 1.96\Omega \ - \quad \text{too large}$$

If the gain specification is met, the input and output resistance specifications will not be met.

12.39 The open circuit voltage is $\mathbf{v_{th}} = \mathbf{v_s}\left(-\dfrac{R_2}{R_1}\right)\left(\dfrac{A\beta}{1 + A\beta}\right)$. Checking the loop-gain:

$$A\beta = \left(5x10^4\right)\left(\frac{6.8k\Omega}{6.8k\Omega + 110k\Omega}\right) = 2910 \gg 1 \quad \text{so } \mathbf{v_{th}} = \mathbf{v_s}\left(-\frac{R_2}{R_1}\right) = -\mathbf{v_s}\left(\frac{110k\Omega}{6.8k\Omega}\right) = -16.2v_S$$

$$R_{th} = R_{OUT} = \frac{R_O}{1 + A\beta} \approx \frac{R_O}{A\beta} = \frac{250\Omega}{2910} = 85.9 \text{ m}\Omega$$

12.40 The open circuit voltage is $\mathbf{v_{th}} = \dfrac{A}{1 + A\beta} \mathbf{v_s}$. Checking the loop-gain:

$$A\beta = 10^4 \left(\frac{0.39\text{k}\Omega}{0.39\text{k}\Omega + 56\text{k}\Omega} \right) = 69.2 \gg 1 \quad \text{so } \mathbf{v_{th}} \cong \mathbf{v_s} \left(1 + \frac{R_2}{R_1} \right) = \mathbf{v_s} \left(1 + \frac{56\text{k}\Omega}{0.39\text{k}\Omega} \right) = 145 \ \mathbf{v_s}$$

or more exactly: $\mathbf{v_{th}} = \mathbf{v_s} \dfrac{A}{1 + A\beta} = \mathbf{v_s} \dfrac{10^4}{1 + 69.2} = 143 \ \mathbf{v_s}$ | $R_{th} = R_{OUT} = \dfrac{R_O}{1 + A\beta} = \dfrac{200\Omega}{70.2} = 2.85 \ \Omega$

12.41 Applying the definition of fractional gain error,

$$\text{FGE} = \frac{-\dfrac{R_2}{R_1} - \left[-\dfrac{R_2(1 \pm \varepsilon)}{R_1(1 \mp \varepsilon)} \right] \dfrac{A\beta}{1 + A\beta}}{-\dfrac{R_2}{R_1}} = 1 - \left[\frac{(1 \pm \varepsilon)}{(1 \mp \varepsilon)} \right] \frac{A\beta}{1 + A\beta} \approx 1 - (1 \pm 2\varepsilon) \frac{A\beta}{1 + A\beta}$$

$$\text{FGE} \approx 1 - \frac{A\beta}{1 + A\beta} \mp 2\varepsilon \frac{A\beta}{1 + A\beta} = \frac{1}{1 + A\beta} \mp 2\varepsilon \frac{A\beta}{1 + A\beta}$$

For $A\beta \gg 1$, $\text{FGE} \approx \dfrac{1}{A\beta} \mp 2\varepsilon$ which must be ≤ 0.01

$\dfrac{1}{A\beta} \mp 2\varepsilon = \dfrac{1}{\left(2\text{x}10^5 \right) \dfrac{1}{1000}} \mp 2\varepsilon \leq 0.01$ | Taking the positive sign, $2\varepsilon \leq 0.005$ and $\varepsilon \leq 0.25\%$

12.42 Using the results from problem 12.41:

For $A\beta = \dfrac{4\text{x}10^4}{50} = 800 \gg 1$, so $\text{FGE} \approx \dfrac{1}{A\beta} \mp 2\varepsilon$ which must be ≤ 0.02

$\dfrac{1}{A\beta} \mp 2\varepsilon = \dfrac{1}{800} \mp 2\varepsilon \leq 0.02$ | Taking the positive sign, $2\varepsilon \leq 0.01875$ and $\varepsilon \leq 0.938\%$

12.43 One worst-case tolerance assignment is given below. The second is found by reversing the resistor values.

$$v_+ = \mathbf{v_{ic}} \frac{9.995}{10.005 + 9.995} = 0.49975\mathbf{v_{ic}} \ | \ \mathbf{i} = \frac{\mathbf{v_{ic}} - \mathbf{v_-}}{9.995\text{k}\Omega} = \frac{\mathbf{v_{ic}} - \mathbf{v_+}}{9.995\text{k}\Omega} = \frac{0.50025}{9.995\text{k}\Omega} \mathbf{v_{ic}}$$

$$\mathbf{v_O} = \mathbf{v_-} - \mathbf{i}(10.005\text{k}\Omega) = \mathbf{v_+} - \mathbf{i}(10.005\text{k}\Omega) = 0.49975\mathbf{v_{ic}} - \frac{0.50025}{9.995\text{k}\Omega} \mathbf{v_{ic}}(10.005\text{k}\Omega)$$

$\mathbf{v_O} = -0.001\mathbf{v_{ic}}$ and $A_{cm} = \dfrac{\mathbf{v_O}}{\mathbf{v_{ic}}} = -0.001$ | The value of $A_{dm} = 1$ is not affected by the

small tolerances. $CMRR = \left|\dfrac{A_{dm}}{A_{cm}}\right| = 1000$ | $CMRR_{dB} = 60$ dB

12.44

$V_{IC} = \dfrac{5 + 5.01}{2} = 5.005V$. The maximum equivalent input error is

$\dfrac{V_{IC}}{CMRR} = \dfrac{5.005}{10^4} = 0.500$ mV, but the sign is unknown. Therefore the meter reading

may be anywhere in the range 9.50 mV $\leq V_{meter} \leq 10.5$ mV.

12.45

$v_{ic} = \dfrac{v_1 + v_2}{2} = 10\sin 120\pi t$ V and $v_{id} = v_1 - v_2 = 0.50\sin 5000\pi t$ V

$v_+ = \mathbf{v_{ic}}\dfrac{99k\Omega}{10.1k\Omega + 99k\Omega} = 0.90742\mathbf{v_{ic}}$ | $\mathbf{i} = \dfrac{\mathbf{v_{ic}} - \mathbf{v_-}}{9.9k\Omega} = \dfrac{\mathbf{v_{ic}} - \mathbf{v_+}}{9.9k\Omega} = \dfrac{0.09258}{9.9k\Omega}\mathbf{v_{ic}}$

$\mathbf{v_O} = \mathbf{v_-} - \mathbf{i}(101k\Omega) = \mathbf{v_+} - \mathbf{i}(101k\Omega) = 0.90742\mathbf{v_{ic}} - \dfrac{0.09258}{9.9k\Omega}\mathbf{v_{ic}}(101k\Omega)$

$\mathbf{v_O} = -0.037\mathbf{v_{ic}}$ and $A_{cm} = \dfrac{\mathbf{v_O}}{\mathbf{v_{ic}}} = -0.037$ | The value of $A_{dm} = -10$ is not

affected by the small tolerances. $CMRR = \left|\dfrac{A_{dm}}{A_{cm}}\right| = 270$ - a paltry 48.6 dB

$v_O = A_{dm}v_{id} + A_{cm}v_{ic} = -0.370\sin(120\pi t) - 5.00\sin(5000\pi t)$ V

12.46

Setting $v_2 = 0$, $R_{IN1} = R_{ID}(1 + A\beta)\|2R_{IC} = (1M\Omega)\left(1 + 7.5\times10^4\dfrac{2k\Omega}{2k\Omega + 24k\Omega}\right)\|2(500M\Omega) = 852$ MΩ

By symmetry, $R_{IN2} = R_{IN1} = 852$ MΩ | $R_{OUT} = R_{OUT3} = \dfrac{R_O}{(1 + A\beta)} = \dfrac{100}{\left(1 + \dfrac{75000}{2}\right)} = 2.67$ mΩ

12.47 See figure on next page for labels.

$V_O = (V_{OS} - I_{B1}R_1)\left(1 + \dfrac{R_2}{R_3}\right) - I_{B2}R_3\left(-\dfrac{R_2}{R_3}\right) = (V_{OS} - I_{B1}R_1)\left(1 + \dfrac{R_2}{R_3}\right) + I_{B2}R_2$

$V_O = (\pm0.001 - 10^{-7}10^5)\left(1 + \dfrac{10^6}{10^5}\right) + 0.95\times10^{-7}10^6 = \pm.011 - .015V$

Worst case V_O = -0.026 mV, Ideal output = 0 V. Error = -26 mV

Yes R_1 should be $R_2\|R_3 = 90.9$ kΩ.

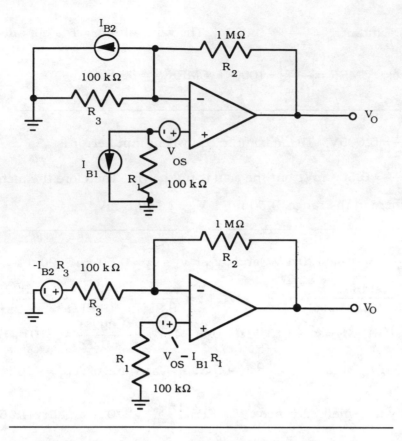

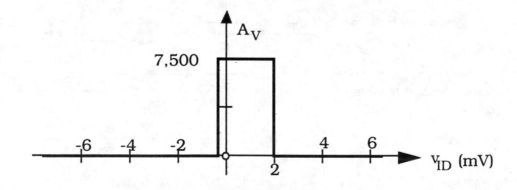

12.48

$$v_O = A_V(v_{ID} + V_{OS}) \mid A_V = \frac{dv_O}{dv_{ID}} = \frac{10-(-5)}{2-0}\frac{V}{mV} = +7,500$$

When $v_O = 0$, $v_{ID} = -V_{OS}$ and so $V_{OS} = -0.667$ mV.

12.49

12.50

For $I_{B2} = 0$: Since v_+ must $= v_- = V_{OS}$, the current through C is $i_C(t) = \dfrac{V_{OS}}{R}$

$$v_O(t) = V_{OS} + \frac{1}{C}\int_0^t i_C(t)\,dt = V_{OS} + \frac{1}{C}\int_0^t \frac{V_{OS}}{R}\,dt = V_{OS} + \frac{V_{OS}}{RC}t$$

For $V_{OS} = 0$, $i_C(t) = I_{B2}$ since $v_- = v_+ = 0$.

$$v_O(t) = \frac{1}{C}\int_0^t i_C(t)\,dt = \frac{1}{C}\int_0^t I_{B2}\,dt = \frac{I_{B2}}{C}t \quad | \quad \text{Summing these two results yields}$$

Eq. (12.100): $v_O(t) = V_{OS} + \dfrac{V_{OS}}{RC}t + \dfrac{I_{B2}}{C}t \quad | \quad$ Note that $v_C(0) = 0$ for both cases.

12.51

$$40\text{dB} = 100 = 1 + \frac{R_2}{R_1} \quad \text{or} \quad \frac{R_2}{R_1} = 99 \quad | \quad \text{For bias current compensation, } R_1 \| R_2 = 10\text{k}\Omega$$

$$\frac{R_1 R_2}{R_1 + R_2} = \frac{R_2}{1 + \dfrac{R_2}{R_1}} = 10\text{k}\Omega \quad | \quad R_2 = 10\text{k}\Omega(1 + 99) = 1.00\text{ M}\Omega \quad \text{and} \quad R_1 = \frac{1\text{M}\Omega}{99} = 10.1\text{k}\Omega$$

The nearest 5% values would be 1 MΩ and 10 kΩ.

12.52

$$v_{cm} = \frac{v_a + v_b}{2} = \frac{4.99 + 5.01}{2} = 5\text{V} \quad v_{dm} = v_a - v_b = 4.99 - 5.01 = -0.02\text{V}$$

$$v_2 = v_a = 4.99\text{V} \quad v_3 = v_b = 5.01\text{V} \quad i_{32} = \frac{v_3 - v_2}{200\Omega} = \frac{0.02\text{V}}{200\Omega} = 10^{-4}\text{A}$$

$$v_1 = v_2 - 10^{-4}(4900) = 4.99 - 0.49 = 4.50\text{V}$$

$$v_4 = v_3 + 10^{-4}(4900) = 5.01 + 0.49 = 5.50\text{V}$$

$$i_2 = -\left(i_{32} + \frac{v_4}{10.01\text{k}\Omega + 9.99\text{k}\Omega}\right) = -\left(10^{-4} + \frac{5.50}{20\text{k}\Omega}\right) = -3.75\text{x}10^{-4}\text{A}$$

$$v_5 = v_6 = v_4 \frac{9.99\text{k}\Omega}{10.01\text{k}\Omega + 9.99\text{k}\Omega} = 2.747\text{V}$$

$$i_1 = i_{32} - \frac{v_1 - v_5}{9.99\text{k}\Omega} = 10^{-4} - \frac{4.50 - 2.747}{9.99\text{k}\Omega} = -75.5\text{x}10^{-4}\text{A}$$

$$v_O = v_5 - \frac{v_1 - v_5}{9.99\text{k}\Omega}(10.01\text{k}\Omega) = 2.747 - \frac{4.50 - 2.747}{9.99\text{k}\Omega}(10.01\text{k}\Omega) = 0.990\text{V}$$

The common-mode and differential mode inputs to the differential subtractor are $v_{cms} = \dfrac{v_1 + v_2}{2} = 5.00\text{V}$ and $v_{dms} = v_1 - v_2 = -0.100\text{V}$. The subtractor outputs for the common-mode and differential mode inputs are:

For the common-mode signal, $v_5 = v_6 = 5\dfrac{9.99\text{k}\Omega}{10.01\text{k}\Omega + 9.99\text{k}\Omega}$

$$v_{Ocm} = v_5 + \frac{v_1 - v_5}{9.99\text{k}\Omega}(10.01\text{k}\Omega) = 5\frac{9.99\text{k}\Omega}{10.01\text{k}\Omega + 9.99\text{k}\Omega} - \frac{5 - 5\dfrac{9.99\text{k}\Omega}{10.01\text{k}\Omega + 9.99\text{k}\Omega}}{9.99\text{k}\Omega}(10.01\text{k}\Omega)$$

$$v_{Ocm} = -.0100\text{V} \quad \text{and} \quad A_{cm} = \frac{-.01}{5} = -.002$$

For the differential mode signal, $v_5 = v_6 = 0.5\dfrac{9.99\text{k}\Omega}{10.01\text{k}\Omega + 9.99\text{k}\Omega}$

$$v_{Odm} = v_5 + \frac{v_1 - v_5}{9.99\text{k}\Omega}(10.01\text{k}\Omega) = v_5 - \frac{-0.5 - v_5}{9.99\text{k}\Omega}(10.01\text{k}\Omega)$$

$$v_{Odm} = +1.00\text{V} \quad \text{and} \quad A_{dm} = \frac{1.00}{-.02} = -50 \quad \text{CMRR} = \left|\frac{A_{dm}}{A_{cm}}\right| = 25,000$$

12.53

(a) Ideal $V_O = -0.005V\left(1 + \dfrac{100k\Omega}{1.1k\Omega}\right) = -0.460V$

(b) $V_O = (-0.005V - 0.001V)\dfrac{A}{1 + A\beta} = (-0.005V - 0.001V)\dfrac{10^4}{1 + 10^4\dfrac{1.1}{101.1}} = -0.546V$

(c) Error $= \dfrac{-0.460 - (-0.546)}{-0.460} = -0.187$ or -18.7%

12.54

Inverting Amplifier: $v_O = A_V v_S = -6.2v_S$ as long as $|v_O| \le 10V$ as constrained by the op-amp power supply voltages

(a) $V_O = -6.2(1) = -6.2V$, feedback loop is working and $V_- = 0$

(b) $V_O = -6.2(-3) = +18V$; V_O saturates at $V_O = +10V$

The feedback loop is broken since the open-loop gain is now 0.

(The output voltage does not change when the input changes so $A = 0$)

By superposition, $V_- = -3\dfrac{6.2k\Omega}{7.2k\Omega} + 10\dfrac{1k\Omega}{10k\Omega} = -1.19V$

12.55

Non-inverting Amplifier: $v_O = A_V v_S = +40v_S$ as long as $|v_O| \le 15V$

(a) $V_O = 40(0.25V) = +10V$, feedback loop is working and $V_{ID} = 0$

(b) $V_O = 40(0.5V) = 20V$; V_O saturates at $V_O = +15V$

The feedback loop is broken since the open-loop gain is now 0.

(The output voltage does not change when the input changes so $A = 0$)

$V_{ID} = V_+ - V_- = 0.5V - 15\dfrac{1k\Omega}{1k\Omega + 39k\Omega} = 0.125V.$

12.56

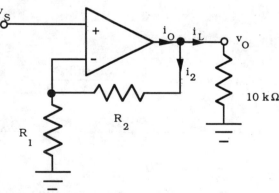

$i_O = i_L + i_2$ and $|i_O| \le 1.5mA$. The output voltage requirement gives $|i_L| \le \dfrac{10V}{10k\Omega} = 1.00mA$

which leaves 0.500mA as the maximum value of i_2. $i_2 = \dfrac{10V}{R_1 + R_2}$ gives $(R_1 + R_2) \ge 20k\Omega$.

The closed-loop gain of 40db $(A_V = 100)$ requires $\dfrac{R_2}{R_1} = 99$.

The closest ratio from the resistor tables appears to be $\frac{R_2}{R_1} = 100$ which is within 1%

of the desired ratio. (This is close enough since we are using 5% resistors.)

There are many many choices that meet both $\frac{R_2}{R_1} = 100$ and $(R_1 + R_2) \geq 20k\Omega$.

However, the choice, $R_1 = 200\Omega$ and $R_2 = 20k\Omega$ is not acceptable because its

minimum value does not meet the requirements: $20.2k\Omega(1 - 0.05) = 19.2k\Omega$.

The smallest acceptable pair is $R_1 = 220\Omega$ and $R_2 = 22k\Omega$.

12.57

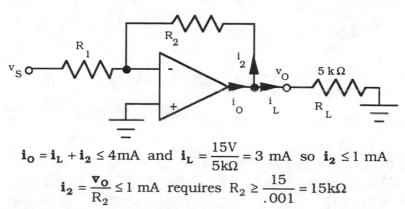

$$i_o = i_L + i_2 \leq 4mA \quad \text{and} \quad i_L = \frac{15V}{5k\Omega} = 3 \text{ mA} \quad \text{so} \quad i_2 \leq 1 \text{ mA}$$

$$i_2 = \frac{v_o}{R_2} \leq 1 \text{ mA} \quad \text{requires} \quad R_2 \geq \frac{15}{.001} = 15k\Omega$$

To account for the resistor tolerance, $0.95R_2 \geq 15k\Omega$ requires $R_2 \geq 15.8k\Omega$. For $A_V = 46$ dB = 200, $R_2 = 200 R_1$, and one acceptable resistor pair would be $R_1 = 1 \ k\Omega$ and $R_2 = 20 \ k\Omega$. Many acceptable choices exist. An input resistance constraint might set a lower limit on R_1.

12.58 The maximum base current will be 5 mA, and the maximum emitter current will be I_E

$= (\beta_F+1)I_B = 51(5mA) = 255$ mA. Since $I_E = 10V/R$, $R \leq 10V/0.255A = 39.2$ Ω.

12.59 Referring to the figure used in the solution to problem 12.57:

$$i_o = i_L + i_2 \leq \frac{10V}{4k\Omega} = 2.5 \text{ mA} \quad \text{and} \quad i_L = \frac{10V}{5k\Omega} = 2 \text{ mA} \quad \text{so} \quad i_2 \leq 0.5 \text{ mA}$$

$$R_2 \geq \frac{10V}{0.5mA} = 20k\Omega \quad A_V = 46dB \Rightarrow \frac{R_2}{R_1} = 200$$

One possible choice would be $R_2 = 20 \ k\Omega$ and $R_1 - 100 \ \Omega$. However, the op-amp would not be able to supply enough output current if tolerances are take into acount. Better choices would be $R_2 = 22 \ k\Omega$ and $R_1 - 110 \ \Omega$ or $R_2 = 200 \ k\Omega$ and $R_1 - 1 \ k\Omega$ which would give the amplifier a much higher input resistance.

(b) $V = \frac{|v_{o max}|}{200} = \frac{10V}{200} = 50$ mV   (c) $R_{IN} = R_1 = 110 \ \Omega$ and $1 \ k\Omega$ for the two designs given above.

12.60

Using the expressions in Table 12.4:

First stage: $\beta = \dfrac{24k\Omega}{24k\Omega + 240k\Omega} = \dfrac{1}{11}$ | $A_{V1} = -\dfrac{240k\Omega}{24k\Omega}\dfrac{\dfrac{10^5}{11}}{1+\dfrac{10^5}{11}} = -10.0$

$R_{IN} = 24k\Omega + 500k\Omega\| \dfrac{240k\Omega}{1+10^5} = 24.0 \text{ k}\Omega$ | $R_{OUT} = \dfrac{100}{1+\dfrac{10^5}{11}} = 11.0 \text{ m}\Omega$

Second stage: $\beta = \dfrac{10k\Omega}{10k\Omega + 50k\Omega} = \dfrac{1}{6}$ | $A_{V1} = -\dfrac{50k\Omega}{10k\Omega}\dfrac{\dfrac{10^5}{6}}{1+\dfrac{10^5}{6}} = -5.00$

$R_{IN} = 10k\Omega + 500k\Omega\| \dfrac{240k\Omega}{1+10^5} = 10.0 \text{ k}\Omega$ | $R_{OUT} = \dfrac{100}{1+\dfrac{10^5}{6}} = 6.00 \text{ m}\Omega$

Overall amplifier:

$A_V = -10.0\dfrac{10k\Omega}{10.0k\Omega + 11.0m\Omega}(-5.00) = +50.0$ | $R_{IN} = 24.0 \text{ k}\Omega$ | $R_{OUT} = 6.00 \text{ m}\Omega$

For all practical purposes, the numbers the same. $R_{OUT} = 6.00 \text{ m}\Omega$ is a good approximation of 0Ω.

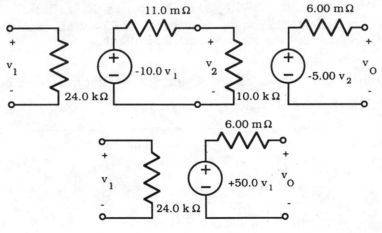

12.61

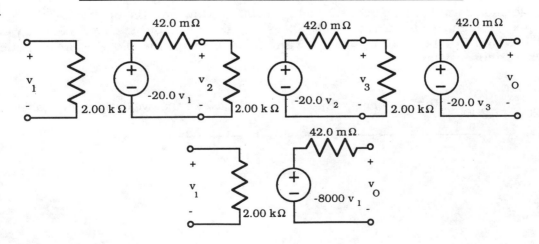

Use the expressions in Table 12.4. All three amplifier stages are the same.

$$\beta = \frac{2k\Omega}{2k\Omega + 40k\Omega} = \frac{1}{21} \quad | \quad A_{V1} = -\frac{40k\Omega}{2k\Omega} \frac{\frac{10^5}{21}}{1 + \frac{10^5}{21}} = -20.0$$

$$R_{IN} = 2k\Omega + 250k\Omega \| \frac{40k\Omega}{1 + 10^5} = 2.00 \text{ k}\Omega \quad | \quad R_{OUT} = \frac{200}{1 + \frac{10^5}{21}} = 42.0 \text{ m}\Omega$$

For the overall amplifier: $A_V = \left(-20.0 \frac{2k\Omega}{2k\Omega + 42.0m\Omega}\right)\left(-20.0 \frac{2k\Omega}{2k\Omega + 42.0m\Omega}\right)(-20.0) = -8000$

$R_{IN} = 2.00 \text{ k}\Omega \quad | \quad R_{OUT} = 42.0 \text{ m}\Omega \quad |$ For all practical purposes, the numbers the same.
$R_{OUT} = 42.0 \text{ m}\Omega$ is a good approximation of 0Ω.

12.62

$50^2 < 5000 < 50^3 \quad |$ Three stages will be required to keep the gain of each stage ≤ 50. However, the input and output resistance requirements could further constrain the gains and must be checked as well. $A = 10^{\frac{85}{20}} = 1.778 \times 10^4$

For $R_{OUT} = \frac{R_O}{1 + A\beta}$: $\frac{100\Omega}{1 + A\beta} \leq 0.1\Omega \rightarrow A\beta \geq 999 \rightarrow \beta \geq 0.0562 \rightarrow \frac{1}{\beta} \leq 17.8$.

For $R_{IN} = R_{ID}(1 + A\beta)\|2R_{IC}$: $1M\Omega(1 + A\beta)\|2G\Omega \geq 10M\Omega \rightarrow A\beta \geq 9 \rightarrow\rightarrow \frac{1}{\beta} \leq 1976$

$17.8(50)(50) > 5000$ so three stages is still sufficient.

12.63

$$V_s = V_o \frac{R_1}{R_1 + \frac{\frac{SC}{R_2} }{R_2 + \frac{1}{SC}}} = V_o \frac{(SCR_2 + 1)R_1}{(SCR_2 + 1)R_1 + R_2} \quad | \quad A_V(s) = \frac{V_o}{V_s} = \left(1 + \frac{R_2}{R_1}\right)\frac{SC(R_1\|R_2) + 1}{SCR_2 + 1}$$

12.64

$$A_V(s) = -\frac{R_2}{R_1} \frac{1}{sCR_2 + 1} \quad A_V(0) = -\frac{R_2}{R_1} \quad f_H = \frac{1}{2\pi CR_2}$$

$$A_V^{nom} = -\frac{330k\Omega}{10k\Omega} = -33 \quad A_V^{max} = -\frac{330k\Omega(1.1)}{10k\Omega(0.9)} = -40.3 \quad A_V^{max} = -\frac{330k\Omega(0.9)}{10k\Omega(1.1)} = -27.0$$

$$f_H^{nom} = \frac{1}{2\pi(10^{-10})3.3\times10^5} = 4.83\text{kHz} \quad f_H^{max} = \frac{1}{2\pi(10^{-10})(0.5)3.3\times10^5(0.9)} = 10.7\text{kHz}$$

$$f_H^{min} = \frac{1}{2\pi(10^{-10})(1.2)3.3\times10^5(1.1)} = 3.65\text{kHz}$$

12.65

$-60db$ / decade requires 3 poles $3(-20db$ / decade$)$. Using three identical amplifiers: $A_V = \sqrt[3]{1000} = 10$ and $f_{H1} = \frac{f_{H3}}{\sqrt{2^{\frac{1}{3}} - 1}} = 1.96(20\text{kHz}) = 39.2\text{kHz}$.

$$R_2C = \frac{1}{2\pi\left(39.2\text{x}10^3\right)} = 4.06\text{x}10^{-6}\text{s}. \quad \text{One possible choice would be}$$

$C = 200$ pF, $R_2 = 20$ kΩ and $R_1 = 1$ kΩ giving $A_V = 10$ and $f_H = 39.8$ kHz.

12.66

$$A(s) = \frac{\omega_T}{s + \omega_B} \quad | \quad \omega_T = A_o\omega_B \quad | \quad Z_{OUT} = \frac{R_O}{1 + A(s)\beta} = \frac{R_O}{1 + \dfrac{\omega_T}{s + \omega_B}\beta} = R_O\frac{s + \omega_B}{s + \omega_B + \omega_T\beta}$$

$$Z_{OUT} = R_O\frac{s + \omega_B}{s + \omega_B(1 + A_o\beta)} = \frac{R_O}{(1 + A_o\beta)}\frac{1 + \dfrac{s}{\omega_B}}{1 + \dfrac{s}{\omega_B(1 + A_o\beta)}} \approx \frac{R_O}{(1 + A_o\beta)}\frac{1 + \dfrac{s}{\omega_B}}{1 + \dfrac{s}{\beta\omega_T}}$$

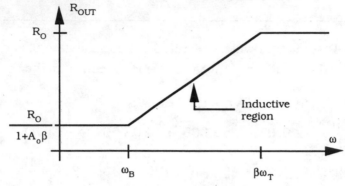

12.67 Using MATLAB:

```
b=1/11; ro=100; wt=2*pi*1e6; wb=wt/1e5;
n=ro*[1 wb]; d=[1 b*wt];w=logspace(0,7);
r=freqs(n,d,w);
mag=abs(r); phase=angle(r)*180/pi;
subplot(212);semilogx(w,phase)
subplot(211);loglog(w,mag)
```

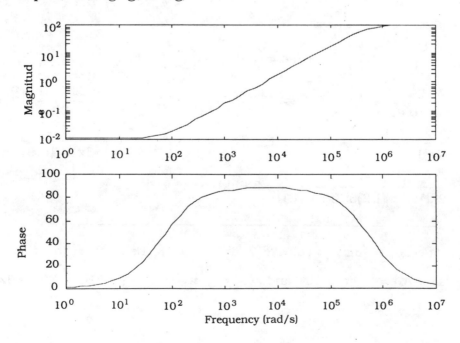

12.68

$$Z_{IN} = R_1 + R_{ID} \left\| \frac{R_2}{1 + A(s)} \right. = R_1 + R_{ID} \left\| \frac{R_2}{1 + \dfrac{\omega_T}{s + \omega_B}} \right. = R_1 + R_{ID} \left\| R_2 \frac{(s + \omega_B)}{s + \omega_B + \omega_T} \right.$$

$$Z_{IN} = R_1 + \frac{R_{ID} R_2 \dfrac{(s + \omega_B)}{s + \omega_B + \omega_T}}{R_{ID} + R_2 \dfrac{(s + \omega_B)}{s + \omega_B + \omega_T}} = R_1 + \frac{R_{ID} R_2 (s + \omega_B)}{R_{ID}(s + \omega_B + \omega_T) + R_2(s + \omega_B)}$$

$$Z_{IN} = R_1 + \frac{R_{ID} R_2 \omega_B \left(1 + \dfrac{s}{\omega_B}\right)}{R_{ID}\omega_B(1 + A_o) + R_2\omega_B + s(R_{ID} + R_2)} = R_1 + \frac{R_{ID}\dfrac{R_2}{(1 + A_o)}}{R_{ID} + \dfrac{R_2}{(1 + A_o)}} \frac{\left(1 + \dfrac{s}{\omega_B}\right)}{1 + \dfrac{s}{\omega_B(1 + A_O)}\dfrac{R_{ID} + R_2}{R_{ID} + \dfrac{R_2}{(1 + A_o)}}}$$

$$Z_{IN} = R_1 + \left(R_{ID} \left\| \frac{R_2}{(1 + A_o)} \right.\right) \frac{\left(1 + \dfrac{s}{\omega_B}\right)}{1 + \dfrac{s}{\omega_B(1 + A_O)}\dfrac{R_{ID} + R_2}{R_{ID} + \dfrac{R_2}{(1 + A_o)}}}$$

12.69 Using MATLAB:

```
n1=1e6; d1=[1 2000];
n2=1e6; d2=[1 4000];
n3=1e12; d3=[1 6000 8e6];
w=logspace(2,5);
[m1,p1,w]=bode(n1,d1,w);
[m2,p2,w]=bode(n2,d2,w);
[m3,p3,w]=bode(n3,d3,w);
subplot(211)
loglog(w,m1,w,m2,w,m3)
subplot(212)
semilogx(w,p1,w,p2,w,p3)
```

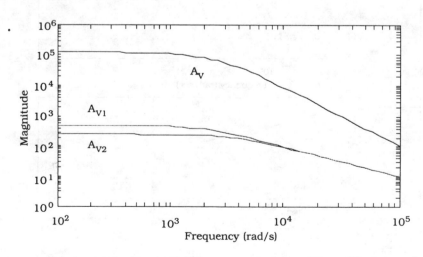

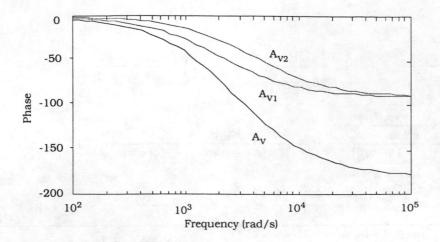

$$A_V = -\frac{Z_2}{Z_1}\frac{A\beta}{1+A\beta} \qquad \beta = \frac{Z_1}{Z_1+Z_2} \qquad A = \frac{\omega_T}{s+\omega_o} \qquad Z_1 = R_1 \qquad Z_2 = \frac{R_2}{sCR_2+1}$$

$$A_V(s) = -\frac{\dfrac{R_2}{R_1}\omega_T}{s^2R_2C + s\left(1+\dfrac{R_2}{R_1}+R_2C(\omega_o+\omega_T)\right)+\omega_o\left(1+\dfrac{R_2}{R_1}\right)+\omega_T}$$

$$A_V(s) = -\frac{3.653\text{x}10^{13}}{s^2+3.142\text{x}10^7 s+1.916\text{x}10^{12}}$$

Using MATLAB:

```
bode(-3.653e13,[1 3.142e7 1.916e12])
```

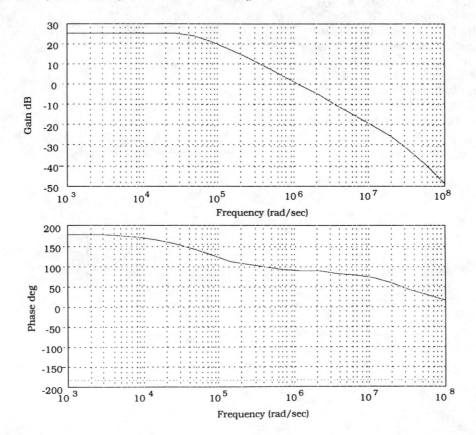

12.71

(a) $\dfrac{\mathbf{V_s}(s)}{R} = -sC\mathbf{V_o}(s) \mid A_V(s) = \dfrac{\mathbf{V_o}(s)}{\mathbf{V_s}(s)} = -\dfrac{1}{sRC}$ which is the transfer function of an integrator

(b) Generalizing Eq. (12.119): $A_V(s) = -\dfrac{Z_2}{Z_1}\dfrac{A(s)\beta}{1+A(s)\beta} \mid Z_2 = \dfrac{1}{sC} \mid Z_1 = R_1 \mid \beta = \dfrac{Z_1}{Z_1+Z_2}$

$$\beta = \dfrac{R_1}{R_1+\dfrac{1}{sC}} = \dfrac{sCR}{sCR+1} \mid A(s)\beta = \dfrac{\omega_T}{s+\omega_B}\dfrac{sRC}{sRC+1} \mid A_V(s) = -\dfrac{1}{sRC}\dfrac{\dfrac{\omega_T}{s+\omega_B}\dfrac{sRC}{sRC+1}}{1+\dfrac{\omega_T}{s+\omega_B}\dfrac{sRC}{sRC+1}}$$

$$A_V(s) = -\dfrac{1}{sRC}\dfrac{sRC\omega_T}{(s+\omega_B)(sRC+1)+sRC\omega_T} = -\dfrac{\omega_T}{(s+\omega_B)(sRC+1)+sRC\omega_T}$$

$$A_V(s) = -\dfrac{\dfrac{\omega_T}{RC}}{s^2+s\left(\omega_B+\omega_T+\dfrac{1}{RC}\right)+\dfrac{\omega_B}{RC}} \approx -\dfrac{\dfrac{\omega_T}{RC}}{(s+\omega_T)\left(s+\dfrac{\omega_B}{\omega_T RC}\right)} = -\dfrac{\dfrac{\omega_T}{RC}}{(s+\omega_T)\left(s+\dfrac{1}{A_oRC}\right)}$$

using dominant root factorization where it is assumed $\omega_T \gg \omega_B$ and $\omega_T \gg \dfrac{1}{RC}$.

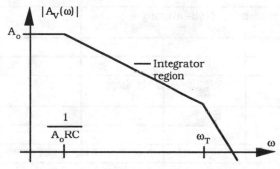

12.72

```
wrc=1/(1e4*470e-12); wt=2*pi*5e6; wb=2*pi*50;
n=wt*wrc; d=[1 wt+wb+wrc wb*wrc];
bode(n,d)
```

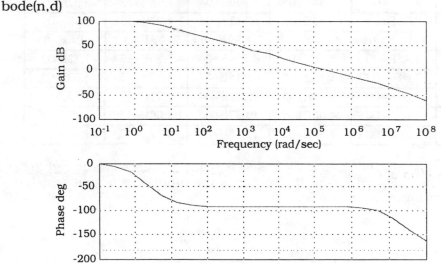

12.73

$$20\text{dB} \rightarrow A_V = -10 = -\frac{R_2}{R_1} \quad R_{IN} = R_1 = 20 \text{ k}\Omega \quad R_2 = 10R_1 = 200 \text{ k}\Omega$$

$$C = \frac{1}{2\pi f_H R_2} = \frac{1}{2\pi(1000)(200\text{k}\Omega)} = 796 \text{ pF} \rightarrow 820 \text{ pF using values in Appendix C}$$

12.74

$$\beta = \frac{2\text{k}\Omega}{2\text{k}\Omega + 40\text{k}\Omega} = \frac{1}{21} \quad | \quad A\beta = \frac{10^5}{21} = 4760 \gg 1$$

(a) $A_V = -\dfrac{R_2}{R_1} = -\dfrac{40\text{k}\Omega}{2\text{k}\Omega} = -20 \quad | \quad f_H = \beta f_T = \dfrac{3\times10^6 \text{Hz}}{21} = 143\text{kHz}$

(b) $A_V = (-20)^3 = -8000 \; (78\text{dB}) \quad | \quad f_{H3} = 0.51 f_H = 72.9\text{kHz}$

12.75 The table below follows the approach used in Table 12.8. The only change is the required gain $= A_V = 10^{\frac{85}{20}} = 1.778 \times 10^4$.

# of Stages	Cascade of Identical Non-Inverting Amplifiers				
	$A_V(0)$	F_H	F_H	R_{IN}	R_{OUT}
	Gain per Stage	Single Stage	N Stages		
	$1/\beta$	$\beta \times F_T$			
1	2.00E+04	5.00E+01	5.000E+01	6.00E+09	8.33E+00
2	1.41E+02	7.07E+03	4.551E+03	7.08E+11	7.06E-02
3	2.71E+01	3.68E+04	1.878E+04	3.69E+12	1.36E-02
4	1.19E+01	8.41E+04	3.658E+04	8.41E+12	5.95E-03
5	7.25E+00	1.38E+05	5.320E+04	1.38E+13	3.62E-03
6	5.21E+00	1.92E+05	6.717E+04	1.92E+13	2.60E-03
7	**4.12E+00**	**2.43E+05**	**7.839E+04**	**2.43E+13**	**2.06E-03**
8	3.45E+00	2.90E+05	8.724E+04	2.90E+13	1.72E-03
9	3.01E+00	3.33E+05	9.415E+04	3.33E+13	1.50E-03
10	2.69E+00	3.71E+05	9.951E+04	3.71E+13	1.35E-03
11	2.46E+00	4.06E+05	1.037E+05	4.06E+13	1.23E-03
12	2.28E+00	4.38E+05	1.068E+05	4.38E+13	1.14E-03

We see from the spreadsheet that a cascade of seven identical stages is required to achieve the bandwidth specification. Fortuitously, it also meets the input and output resistance specs. For the non-inverting amplifier cascade:

$$A_V = 1 + \frac{R_2}{R_1} = 4.12 \rightarrow \frac{R_2}{R_1} = 3.12$$

A similar spreadsheet for the cascade of identical inverting amplifiers indicates that it is impossible to meet the bandwidth requirement.

12.76

(a) From Problem 12.75, $A_V = 1 + \dfrac{R_2}{R_1} = 4.12 \rightarrow \dfrac{R_2}{R_1} = 3.12$ | Exploring the 5% resistor

tables, we find $R_2 = 62k\Omega$ and $R_1 = 20k\Omega$ yields $\dfrac{R_2}{R_1} = 3.10$ as a reasonable pair.

The nominal gain of the cascade is then $A_V = (4.10)^7 = 1.948 \times 10^4$.

$A_V = 86db \pm 1dB \Rightarrow 1.778 \times 10^4 \le A_V \le 2.239 \times 10^4$ and the gain is well within this range. Many amplifiers will probably fail due to tolerances with 5% resistors. A Monte Carlo analysis would tell us. If we resort to 1% resistors to limit the tolerance spread, $R_2 = 30.9\ k\Omega$ and $R_1 = 10.0\ k\Omega$ is one of many possible pairs.

(b) For $R_2 = 62k\Omega$ and $R_1 = 20k\Omega$, $\beta = \dfrac{1}{4.1}$ | $f_{H1} = \beta f_T = \dfrac{5 \times 10^6}{4.1} = 1.22$ MHz

$f_H = 1.22 \text{MHz} \sqrt{2^{\frac{1}{7}} - 1} = 394$ kHz

12.77   Two stages - See problem 12.78

12.78   One possibility: Use a cascade of two non-inverting amplifiers, and shunt the input of the first amplifier to define the input resistance.

$60db \rightarrow A_V = 1000$ | A single - stage amplifier with a gain of 1000 would have a bandwidth of only 5 kHz using this op - amp. Two stages should be sufficient if R_{IN} and R_{OUT} can also be met. A design with $f_{H2} \gg f_{H1}$ will be tried.

First stage: Non - inverting with bandwidth of 20 kHz

$\beta_1 = \dfrac{f_{H1}}{f_T} = \dfrac{20\text{kHz}}{5\text{MHz}} = 0.004 \quad A_{V1} = \dfrac{1}{\beta_1} = 250 \rightarrow A_{V2} = 4 \rightarrow \beta_2 = 0.25 \rightarrow f_{H2} = 1.25\text{MHz}$

Since $f_{H2} \gg f_{H1}$, $f_H = f_{H1} = 20$kHz. $A_o = 85$dB $= 17800$

Checking $R_{OUT} = \dfrac{R_{O2}}{1 + A_o\beta_2} = \dfrac{100}{1 + 17800(0.25)} = 0.0225\Omega$ which is ok.

Choosing resistors from the Appendix, a possible set is

Amplifier 1: $R_1 = 1.2k\Omega$, $R_2 = 300k\Omega$ and shunt the input with $R_3 = 27k\Omega$

Amplifier 2: $R_1 = 3.3k\Omega$, $R_2 = 10k\Omega$

Checking gain: $A_V = \dfrac{17800}{1 + \dfrac{17800}{251}}\left(\dfrac{17800}{1 + \dfrac{17800}{4.03}}\right) = 997.5 = 60.0$dB

12.79

```
function sg=Prob79(tol);
sg=0;
  for j=1:10
    ao=100000; ft=1e6*sqrt(2^(1/6)-1);
      for i=1:500,
              r1=22000*(1+2*tol*(rand-0.5));r2=130000*(1+2*tol*(rand-0.5));
              beta=r1/(r1+r2);g1=ao/(1+ao*beta); b1=beta*ft;
              r1=22000*(1+2*tol*(rand-0.5));r2=130000*(1+2*tol*(rand-0.5));
              beta=r1/(r1+r2);g2=ao/(1+ao*beta); b2=beta*ft;
              r1=22000*(1+2*tol*(rand-0.5));r2=130000*(1+2*tol*(rand-0.5));
              beta=r1/(r1+r2);g3=ao/(1+ao*beta); b3=beta*ft;
              r1=22000*(1+2*tol*(rand-0.5));r2=130000*(1+2*tol*(rand-0.5));
              beta=r1/(r1+r2);g4=ao/(1+ao*beta); b4=beta*ft;
              r1=22000*(1+2*tol*(rand-0.5));r2=130000*(1+2*tol*(rand-0.5));
              beta=r1/(r1+r2);g5=ao/(1+ao*beta); b5=beta*ft;
              r1=22000*(1+2*tol*(rand-0.5));r2=130000*(1+2*tol*(rand-0.5));
              beta=r1/(r1+r2);g6=ao/(1+ao*beta); b6=beta*ft;
              gain(i)=g1*g2*g3*g4*g5*g6; bw(i)=(b1+b2+b3+b4+b5+b6)/6;
      end;
    sg=sg+sum(gain<1e5 | bw<5e4);
    end;
  end
```

(a) For 5000 test cases with tol = 0.05, 33.5% of the amplifiers failed to meet either the gain or bandwith requirement.

(b) For 10000 test cases with tol = 0.015, 0.1% of the amplifiers failed to meet either the gain or bandwith requirement.

12.80

(a) $\left(\dfrac{1}{\beta}\right)^N = G \rightarrow \beta = \dfrac{1}{G^{\frac{1}{N}}}$ | $f_{H1} = \beta f_T$ | $f_H = \dfrac{f_T}{G^{\frac{1}{N}}}\sqrt{2^{\frac{1}{N}}-1}$ | $\dfrac{f_H}{f_T} = \dfrac{\sqrt{2^{\frac{1}{N}}-1}}{G^{\frac{1}{N}}} = \dfrac{\left(2^Z-1\right)^{\frac{1}{2}}}{G^Z}$ for $Z = \dfrac{1}{N}$

For $2^Z = e^{Z\ln 2}$ and $G^Z = e^{Z\ln G}$: $\dfrac{d}{dz}\left(\dfrac{f_H}{f_T}\right) = \dfrac{G^Z\left[\frac{1}{2}\left(2^Z-1\right)^{-\frac{1}{2}}2^Z\ln 2\right] - \left(2^Z-1\right)^{\frac{1}{2}}G^Z\ln G}{G^{2Z}}$

Setting $\dfrac{d}{dz}\left(\dfrac{f_H}{f_T}\right) = 0 \rightarrow G^Z\left[\frac{1}{2}\left(2^Z-1\right)^{-\frac{1}{2}}2^Z\ln 2\right] - \left(2^Z-1\right)^{\frac{1}{2}}G^Z\ln G = 0 \rightarrow 2^Z\ln 2 = 2\left(2^Z-1\right)\ln G$

$2^Z = -\dfrac{2\ln G}{\ln 2 - 2\ln G} \rightarrow Z\ln 2 = \ln\left(-\dfrac{2\ln G}{\ln 2 - 2\ln G}\right)$

$Z = \dfrac{\ln\left(-\dfrac{\ln G}{\ln G - \ln\sqrt{2}}\right)}{\ln 2} \rightarrow N_{opt} = \dfrac{\ln 2}{\ln\left(\dfrac{\ln G}{\ln G - \ln\sqrt{2}}\right)}$

(b) $N_{opt} = \dfrac{\ln 2}{\ln\left(\dfrac{\ln 10^5}{\ln 10^5 - \ln\sqrt{2}}\right)} = 22.7$ which agrees with the spreadsheet in Table 12.8

$f_{Hopt} = 106.0$ kHz

12.81

$$\beta_{nom} = \frac{22k\Omega}{22k\Omega + 130k\Omega} = \frac{1}{6.91} \qquad A\beta = \frac{5 \times 10^4}{6.91} = 7240 \gg 1$$

(a) $A_V^{nom} = 1 + \frac{R_2}{R_1} = 1 + \frac{130k\Omega}{22k\Omega} = 6.91$

$$A_V^{max} = 1 + \frac{R_2}{R_1} = 1 + \frac{130k\Omega(1.05)}{22k\Omega(0.95)} = 7.53 \quad | \quad A_V^{min} = 1 + \frac{R_2}{R_1} = 1 + \frac{130k\Omega(0.95)}{22k\Omega(1.05)} = 6.35$$

$$f_H^{nom} = \beta_{nom} f_T = \frac{10^6 Hz}{6.91} = 145 \text{ kHz} \quad | \quad f_H^{max} = \frac{10^6 Hz}{6.36} = 157 \text{ kHz} \quad | \quad f_H^{min} = \frac{10^6 Hz}{7.53} = 133 \text{ kHz}$$

12.82

```
function [gain,bw]=Prob82a
ao=50000; ft=1e6;
    for i=1:500,
                r1=22000*(1+0.1*(rand-0.5));
                r2=130000*(1+0.1*(rand-0.5));
                beta=r1/(r1+r2);
                gain(i)=ao/(1+ao*beta); bw(i)=beta*ft;
    end;
end
```

```
[gain,bw]=prob82a;
mean(gain)    ans = 6.9140    std(gain)      ans = 0.2339
mean(bw)      ans = 1.4478e+05   std(bw)      ans = 4.8969e+03
```

Three sigma limits: $6.21 \le A_V \le 7.62$ $130 \text{ kHz} \le BW \le 150 \text{ kHz}$

```
function [gain,bw]=Prob82b
    for i=1:500,
                ao=100000*(1+1.0*(rand-0.5));
                ft=2e6*(1+1.0*(rand-0.5));
                r1=22000*(1+0.1*(rand-0.5));
                r2=130000*(1+0.1*(rand-0.5));
                 beta=r1/(r1+r2);
                gain(i)=ao/(1+ao*beta); bw(i)=beta*ft;
    end;
end
```

```
[gain,bw]=prob82b;
mean(gain)    ans = 6.9201    std(gain)      ans = 0.2414
mean(bw)      ans = 2.8925e+05   std(bw)      ans = 8.5536e+04
```

Note that the bandwidth is essentially a uniform distribution.

3σ: $6.20 \le A_V \le 7.64$ 98.9% of the values fall between: $146 \text{ kHz} \le BW \le 439 \text{ kHz}$

12.83 $SR \ge V_O \omega = (15V)(2\pi)(2 \times 10^4 Hz) = 1.89 \times 10^6 \frac{V}{s}$ or $1.89 \frac{V}{\mu s}$

12.84 $f = \frac{SR}{2\pi V_o} = \frac{10V}{10^{-6} s} \frac{1}{20\pi V} = 159 \text{ kHz}$

12.85 The negative transistion requires the largest slew rate: $SR = \dfrac{\Delta V}{\Delta t} = \dfrac{20V}{2\mu s} = 10\,\dfrac{V}{\mu s}$

12.86

(a) For the circuit in Fig. 12.44: $R_{ID} = 250k\Omega$ | $R = 1k\Omega$ – an arbitrary choice

$\omega_B = \dfrac{2\pi(5x10^6)}{8x10^4} = 125\pi$ | $C = \dfrac{1}{\omega_B R} = \dfrac{1}{(125\pi)1000} = 2.55\mu F$ | $R_O = 50\Omega$ | $A_o = 80,000$

(b) Add a resistor from each input terminal to ground of value $2R_{IC} = 1G\Omega$ (See Prob. 12.87)

12.87 Two possibilities:

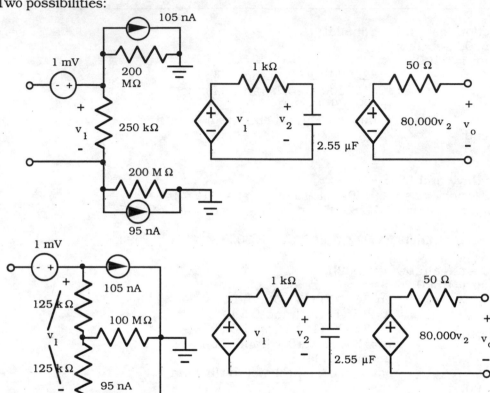

12.88

$\omega_1:\ C = \dfrac{1}{\omega_1 R_1} = \dfrac{1}{2\pi(10^3)(100)} = 1.592\ \mu F$ – setting R_1 arbitrarily to 100Ω.

$\omega_2:\ R_2 = \dfrac{1}{\omega_2 C} = \dfrac{1}{2\pi(10^5)(1.592\ \mu F)} = 1\ \Omega$ – Using the same value of C.

12.89

```
*PROBLEM 12.89 - Six-Stage Amplifier
VS 1 0 AC 1
XA1 1 2 0 AMP
XA2 2 3 0 AMP
XA3 3 4 0 AMP
XA4 4 5 0 AMP
XA5 5 6 0 AMP
XA6 6 7 0 AMP
.SUBCKT AMP 1 2 7
        RID 1 3 1E9
        RO 6 2 50
        E2 6 7 5 7 1E5
        E1 4 7 1 3 1
        R4 5 1K
        C 5 7 15.915UF
        R2 2 3 130K
        R1 3 7 22K
.ENDS
.TF V(7) VS
.AC DEC 40 1 1MEG
.PRINT AC V(1) V(2) V(3) V(4) V(5) V(6) V(7)
.PROBE V(1) V(2) V(3) V(4) V(5) V(6) V(7)
.END
```

12.90

```
*PROBLEM 12.90 - Six Stage Amplifier
VS 1 0 AC 1
XA1 1 2 0 AMP
XA2 2 3 0 AMP
XA3 3 4 0 AMP
XA4 4 5 0 AMP
XA5 5 6 0 AMP
XA6 6 7 0 AMP
.SUBCKT AMP 1 2 8
        RID 1 3 1E9
        RO 7 2 50
        E2 7 8 6 8 1E5
        *Two dummy loops provide separate control of Gain & BW tolerances
        G1 8 4 1 3 .001
        R11 4 8 RG 1000
        E1 5 8 4 8 1
        RC 5 6 1000
        C 6 8 CC 15.915UF
        *
        R2 2 3 RR 130K
        R1 3 8 RR 22K
.ENDS
.MODEL RR RES (R=1 DEV=5%)
.MODEL RG RES (R=1 DEV=50%)
.MODEL CC CAP (C=1 DEV=50%)
.AC DEC 20 1E3 1E6
.PROBE V(7)
.PRINT AC V(7)
.MC 1000 AC V(7) MAX OUTPUT(EVERY 20)
*.MC 1000 AC V(7) MAX OUTPUT(RUNS 77 573 597 777)
.END
```

Maximum gain = 103 dB;   Minimum gain = 98.5 dB
Maximum Bandwidth = 65 kHz;   Minimum bandwidth = 38 kHz (These are approximate.)

12.91

$$A_o = 200,000 \quad | \quad R_{ID} = 10^{12}\,\Omega \quad | \quad R_O \text{ unspecified} \quad | \quad R = 1\text{ k}\Omega$$

$$C = \frac{1}{\omega_o R} \quad | \quad \omega_o = \frac{\omega_T}{A_o} = \frac{2\pi(2.5 \times 10^6)}{2 \times 10^5} = 25\pi \quad | \quad C = \frac{1}{25\pi(1000)} = 12.7\ \mu F$$

12.92

$$A_{OL} \geq 15000 \qquad CMRR \geq 80\text{dB} \qquad PSRR \geq 80\text{dB} \qquad V_{OS} \leq 13\text{mV} \qquad I_B \leq 8\text{nA} \qquad I_{OS} \leq 2\text{nA}$$

Power supply voltages: ± 18 V R_{ID} – lower bound not given ($10^{12}\,\Omega$ typical)

SR – lower bound not given (50V / μs typical)

GBW – lower bound not given (20 MHz typical)

12.93

(a) $C_2 = C = 0.005\mu F \quad | \quad C_1 = 2C = 0.01\mu F \quad | \quad R = \dfrac{1}{\sqrt{2}\,\omega_o C} = \dfrac{1}{\sqrt{2}(40000\pi)0.005\mu F} = 1.13\text{k}\Omega$

For $Q = \dfrac{1}{\sqrt{2}}$: $A_V(s) = \dfrac{\omega_o^2}{s^2 + \sqrt{2}\,\omega_o s + \omega_o^2} \quad | \quad A(0) = 1 \quad | \quad \left|A(j\omega_o)\right| = \dfrac{1}{\sqrt{2}} \rightarrow \omega_H = \omega_o! \quad | \quad f_H = 20\text{kHz}$

(b) For $f_O = 40$kHz: $C' \rightarrow \dfrac{C}{2}$: $C_1' = 0.005\mu F \quad | \quad C_2' = 0.0025\mu F \quad | \quad R = 1.13\text{k}\Omega$

12.94 (a)

```
r1=1130;  r2=1130;  c1=1e-8;  c2=5e-9;
wo=1/sqrt(r1*r2*c1*c2)
n=wo*wo;
d=[1 2/(r1*c1) wo*wo];
bode(n,d)
```

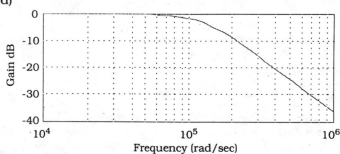

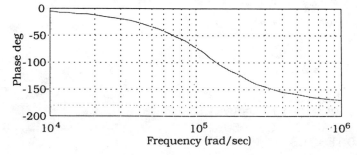

(b)

```
*PROBLEM 12.94 - Low-pass Filter
VS 1 0 AC 1
R1 1 2 1.125K
R2 2 3 1.125K
C1 2 6 0.01UF
```

```
C2 3 0 0.005UF
ISEN 3 6 DC 0
EC 4 0 3 6 1
RC 4 5 1K
CC 5 0 15.915UF
E1 6 0 5 0 100000
.AC DEC 40 1 1MEG
.PRINT AC IM(VS) IP(VS) VDB(6) VP(6)
.PROBE I(VS) V(6)
.END
```

(c) The magnitude response is very similar to the ideal case. However, note the excess phase shift as one approaches the f_T of the amplifier. In this case, it is not causing a problem, but for higher gain filters the situation would be different.

12.95

Using Eq. 12.134: $\mathbf{V}_1(s) = \dfrac{G_1 \mathbf{V_S}(s)(sC_2 + G_2)}{s^2 C_1 C_2 + sC_2(G_1 + G_2) + G_1 G_2}$ | $\mathbf{I_S} = G_1(\mathbf{V_S} - \mathbf{V}_1)$

$$\mathbf{I_S} = G_1 \mathbf{V_S}\left(1 - \frac{G_1(sC_2 + G_2)}{s^2 C_1 C_2 + sC_2(G_1 + G_2) + G_1 G_2}\right) = G_1 \mathbf{V_S} \frac{s^2 C_1 C_2 + sC_2 G_2}{s^2 C_1 C_2 + sC_2(G_1 + G_2) + G_1 G_2}$$

$$Z_S(s) = \frac{\mathbf{V_S}}{\mathbf{I_S}} = R_1 \frac{s^2 C_1 C_2 + sC_2(G_1 + G_2) + G_1 G_2}{s^2 C_1 C_2 + sC_2 G_2} = R_1 \frac{s^2 + s\dfrac{\omega_o}{Q} + \omega_o^2}{s\left(s + \dfrac{1}{R_2 C_1}\right)}$$

$$\omega_o^2 = \frac{1}{R_1 R_2 C_1 C_2} \quad | \quad \frac{\omega_o}{Q} = \frac{1}{C_1}\left(\frac{1}{R_1} + \frac{1}{R_2}\right)$$

12.96

```
r1=2260; r2=2260; c1=2e-8; c2=1e-8;
wsq=1/(r1*r2*c1*c2);
n=r1*[1 2/(r1*c1) wsq];
d=[1 1/(r1*c1) 0];
bode(n,d)
```

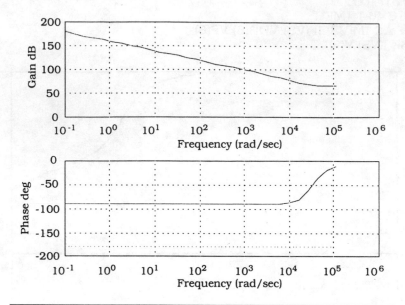

12.97

$$G_1 \mathbf{V_s} = (sC_1 + G_1 + G_2)\mathbf{V_1} - s(KC_1 + G_2)\mathbf{V_2}$$

$$0 = -G_2\mathbf{V_1} + (sC_2 + G_2)\mathbf{V_2}$$

$$\mathbf{V_O} = K\mathbf{V_2} \quad | \quad \frac{\mathbf{V_O}}{\mathbf{V_s}} = \frac{K}{s^2 R_1 R_2 C_1 C_2 + s\left[R_1 C_1(1-K) + C_2(R_1 + R_2)\right] + 1}$$

$$\omega_O = \frac{1}{\sqrt{R_1 R_2 C_1 C_2}} \quad | \quad Q = \frac{\omega_O^3}{\left[\dfrac{1-K}{R_2 C_2} + \dfrac{1}{(R_1 \| R_2)C_1}\right]}$$

For $R_1 = R_2 = R$ and $C_1 = C_2 = C$, $\quad \omega_O = \dfrac{1}{RC} \quad Q = \dfrac{\omega_O^2}{3-K} \quad S_K^Q = \dfrac{K}{3-K}$

12.98

$$\omega_o = \frac{1}{\sqrt{R_1 R_2 C_1 C_2}} \quad | \quad S_{R_1}^{\omega_o} = \frac{R_1}{\omega_o}\frac{\partial \omega_o}{\partial R_1} = \frac{R_1}{\omega_o}\frac{1}{\sqrt{R_2 C_1 C_2}}\left(-\frac{1}{2}\right)(R_1)^{-\frac{3}{2}} = \frac{R_1}{\omega_o}\left(-\frac{1}{2}\frac{\omega_o}{R_1}\right) = -\frac{1}{2}$$

$$S_{R_1}^{\omega_o} = -\frac{1}{2} \quad | \quad \text{By symmetry, } S_{C_1}^{\omega_o} = -\frac{1}{2}$$

12.99

(a) For $C_1 = C = C_2$: $\quad \omega_o = \dfrac{1}{C\sqrt{R_1 R_2}} \quad | \quad Q = \dfrac{1}{2}\sqrt{\dfrac{R_2}{R_1}} \quad | \quad \omega_o = \dfrac{1}{2R_1 CQ}$

$$S_Q^{\omega_o} = \frac{Q}{\omega_o}\frac{\partial \omega_o}{\partial Q} = \frac{Q}{\omega_o}\left(-\frac{1}{2R_1 CQ^2}\right) = \frac{Q}{\omega_o}\left(-\frac{\omega_o}{Q}\right) = -1 \quad \text{(b) } S_Q^{\omega_o} = -1$$

12.100

As noted in Example 12.11, the maximally flat response corresponds to $Q = \frac{1}{\sqrt{2}}$.

For $Q = \frac{1}{\sqrt{2}}$: $A_V(s) = \frac{\omega_o^2}{s^2 + \sqrt{2}\omega_o s + \omega_o^2}$ | $A(0) = 1$ | $\left|A(j\omega_o)\right| = \frac{1}{\sqrt{2}} \rightarrow \omega_H = \omega_o$ | $\therefore f_H = 1\text{kHz}$

$R_1 = R = R_2$ and $C_1 = 2C_2 = 2C$ yields $Q = \frac{1}{\sqrt{2}}$ | $\omega_o = \frac{1}{\sqrt{2R^2C^2}} = \frac{1}{\sqrt{2}RC}$

$RC = \frac{1}{2\pi\sqrt{2}(1000)} = 1.125 \times 10^{-4}$ | For $C = 0.001\ \mu F$, $R = 112.5\ k\Omega$. The

nearest 5% value is $110\ k\Omega$. The nearest 1% value is $113\ k\Omega$. Using 1% values,
$C_1 = 0.002\ \mu F$ | $C_2 = 0.001\ \mu F$ | $R_1 = R_2 = 113\ k\Omega$

12.101

Using the $R_1 = R_2 = R$ and $C_1 = C_2 = C$ case, $A_{HP}(s) = K\dfrac{s^2}{s^2 + s\dfrac{\omega_o}{Q} + +\omega_o^2}$

$\omega_o = \dfrac{1}{RC}$ | $Q = \dfrac{1}{3-K}$ | $Q = 1 \rightarrow K = 2$ | $A_{HP}(s) = 2\dfrac{s^2}{s^2 + s\omega_o + +\omega_o^2}$

We need to find the relationship between ω_L and ω_o.

$\dfrac{2}{\sqrt{2}} = 2\dfrac{\omega_L^2}{\sqrt{\left(\omega_o^2 - \omega_L^2\right)^2 + \left(\omega_L\omega_o\right)^2}} \rightarrow \omega_o^4 - 2\omega_o^2\omega_L^2 + \omega_L^4 + \omega_o^2\omega_L^2 = 2\omega_L^4$ | $\omega_L^4 + \omega_o^2\omega_L^2 - \omega_o^4 = 0$

$\omega_L^2 = \dfrac{-\omega_o^2 \pm \sqrt{\omega_o^4 + 4\omega_o^4}}{2} \rightarrow \omega_L^2 = \omega_o^2\dfrac{\sqrt{5}-1}{2}$ | $\omega_L = 0.7862\omega_o$ | $2\pi(20\text{kHz}) = 0.7862\omega_o$

$\omega_o = 1.599 \times 10^5$ | $RC = \dfrac{1}{\omega_o} = 6.256 \times 10^{-6}$ | For $C = 270\ pF$, $R = 23.17\ k\Omega$

The nearest 1% resistor value is $23.2\ k\Omega$.
Final design: $C_1 = C_2 = 270\ pF$ | $R_1 = R_2 = 23.2\ k\Omega$

12.102

(a) $Q = \dfrac{1}{2}\sqrt{\dfrac{R_2}{R_1}} = \dfrac{1}{2}\sqrt{\dfrac{200k\Omega}{1k\Omega}} = \dfrac{10}{\sqrt{2}}$ | $f_o = \dfrac{1}{2\pi\sqrt{10^3\left(2\times10^5\right)\left(2.2\times10^{-10}\right)^2}} = 51.2\ \text{kHz}$

$BW = \dfrac{f_o}{Q} = 7.23\ \text{kHz}$

(b) $K_M = \dfrac{3.3k\Omega}{1k\Omega} = 3.3$ | $R_1 = 3.3(1k\Omega) = 3.3\ k\Omega$ | $R_2 = 3.3(200k\Omega) = 660\ k\Omega$

$C_1 = C_2 = \dfrac{220pF}{3.3} = 66.7\ pF$

(b) $K_F = \dfrac{2f_o}{f_o} = 2$ | $C_1 = C_2 = \dfrac{220pF}{2} = 110\ pF$ | $R_1 = 1\ k\Omega$ | $R_2 = 200\ k\Omega$

(a) $BW = \dfrac{f_o}{Q} = \dfrac{1000 \text{Hz}}{5} = 200 \text{ Hz}$ | $C_1 = C_2 = C$ | $Q = \dfrac{1}{2}\sqrt{\dfrac{R_2}{R_1}} = 5 \rightarrow \dfrac{R_2}{R_1} = 100$

Choose $R_1 = 1 \text{ k}\Omega \rightarrow R_2 = 100 \text{ k}\Omega$ | $C = \dfrac{1}{\omega_o \sqrt{R_1 R_2}} = \dfrac{1}{2\pi(10^3)(10^4)} = 0.0159 \ \mu\text{F}$

$\omega_o = \dfrac{1}{10 R_1 C}$: Checking the nearest standard values:

$C = 0.015 \ \mu\text{F} \rightarrow R_1 = 1.06 \text{k}\Omega$ - not good; $C = 0.01 \ \mu\text{F} \rightarrow R_1 = 1.6 \text{ k}\Omega$ | $R_2 = 160 \text{ k}\Omega$

(b) $C' = \dfrac{C}{2.25} = 0.004 \ \mu\text{F}$ | $R_1 = 1.6 \text{ k}\Omega$ | $R_2 = 160 \text{ k}\Omega$

12.104

```
r1=1000; r2=2e5; c=2.2e-10;
wo=1/sqrt(r1*r2*c*c);  q=sqrt(r2/r1)/2;
n=[-2*q*wo 0];  d=[1 wo/q wo*wo];
w=logspace(4,7,300);
bode(n,d,w)
```

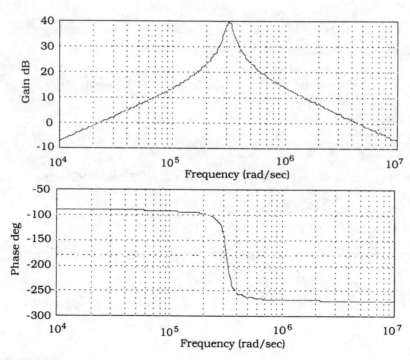

```
*PROBLEM 12.104 - Band-pass Filter
VS 1 0 AC 1
R1 1 2 1K
R2 3 6 200K
C1 2 6 220PF
C2 2 3 220PF
EC 4 0 0 3 1
RC 4 5 1K
CC 5 0 7.977UF
E1 6 0 5 0 50120
.AC DEC 500 1K 1MEG
.PRINT AC VDB(6) VP(6)
.PROBE V(6)
.END
```

SPICE yields: fo = 38.9 kHz, Q = 8, Center frequency gain = 38.8 dB. These values are off due to the finite bandwidth of the op-amp and its excess phase shift at the center frequency of the filter.

12.105

(a) $BW = \dfrac{\omega_o}{Q} = \dfrac{1}{3}$ | $\omega_L = 0.833 \dfrac{rad}{s}$ | $\omega_H = 1.167 \dfrac{rad}{s}$

$BW' = BW\sqrt{2^{\frac{1}{2}} - 1} = 0.215 \dfrac{rad}{s}$ | $\omega_o' = \omega_o = 1 \dfrac{rad}{s}$ | $Q' = \dfrac{1}{0.215} = 4.65$

$C_1 = C_2 = C: \quad \omega_o = \dfrac{1}{C\sqrt{R_1 R_2}}$ | $Q = \dfrac{1}{2}\sqrt{\dfrac{R_2}{R_1}}$ | $\dfrac{1}{R_1 C} = 2Q\omega_o$

(b) $A(s) = \left(\dfrac{-2Q\omega_o}{s^2 + s\dfrac{\omega_o}{Q} + 1} \right)^2 = \left(\dfrac{-6s}{s^2 + \dfrac{s}{3} + 1} \right)^2$

12.106   n=conv([-6 0],[-6,0]); d=conv([1 1/3 1],[1 1/3 1]); bode(n,d)

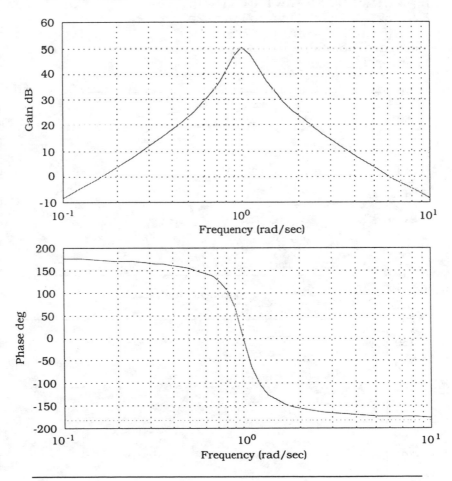

12.107

Using normalized frequency: 5 kHz $\rightarrow \omega_O = 1$ and 6 kHz $\rightarrow \omega_O = 1.1$

$$A(s) = \left(\frac{-10s}{s^2 + 0.2s + 1}\right)\left(\frac{-12s}{s^2 + 0.24s + 1.44}\right) = \frac{120s^2}{s^4 + 0.44s^3 + 2.484s^2 + 0.528s + 1.44}$$

At the new center frequency $s = j\omega_O$, $-0.44\omega_O^3 + 0.528\omega_O = 0 \rightarrow \omega_O = 1.095$

and $\left|A(j\omega_O)\right| = 1429 \approx 63.1$ dB

The bandwidth points can be found using MATLAB:

```
w=linspace(.9,1.5,250);
[m,p,w]=bode([120 0 0],[1 .44 2.484 .528 1.44],w);
20*log10(max(m))
        ans = 63.098

((20*log10(a))>60.098).*(w.');
```

From this last vector one can easily find: $\omega_o = 1.095 \rightarrow 5.48$ kHz, $\omega_L = 0.970 \rightarrow 4.85$ kHz, $\omega_H = 1.237 \rightarrow 6.19$ kHz, BW = 1.34 kHz, Q = 4.09

12.108

```
w1=2*pi*5000; q1=5; w2=2*pi*6000; q2=5;
n1=[-2*q1*w1 0]; d1=[1 w1/q1 w1*w1];
n2=[-2*q2*w2 0]; d2=[1 w2/q2 w2*w2];
n=conv(n1,n2); d=conv(d1,d2);
w=logspace(4,5,100);
bode(n,d,w)
```

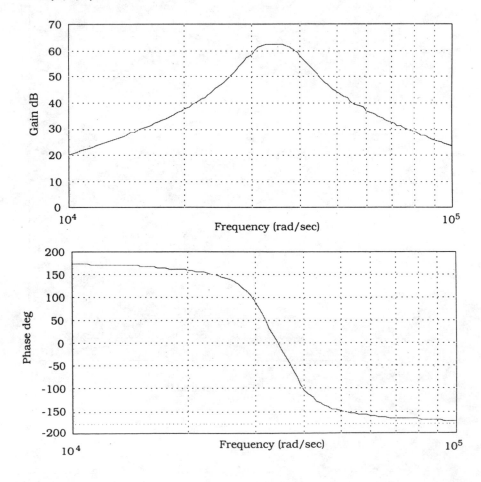

Using $A_V = 20$ dB at the center frequency: $R_{IN} = R_1 = 10$ kΩ | $10 = KQ = \dfrac{R_2}{R_1}$

$R_2 = 100$ kΩ | $K = \dfrac{10}{Q} = 2$ | $R = KR_1 = 20$ kΩ | $C = \dfrac{1}{\omega_o R} = \dfrac{1}{2\pi(600\text{Hz})20\text{k}\Omega} = 0.0133$ μF.

12.110   Q is set independently of C in the Tow-Thomas biquad. $S_C^Q = 0$.

12.111

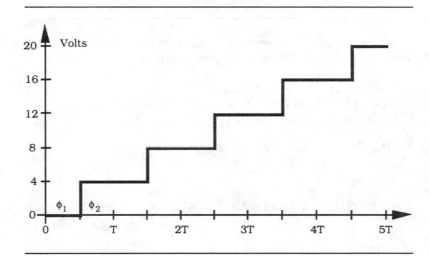

12.112

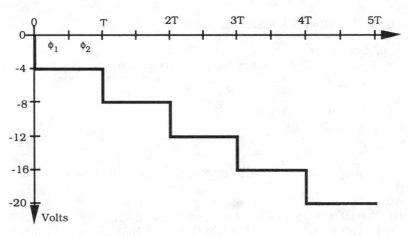

12.113

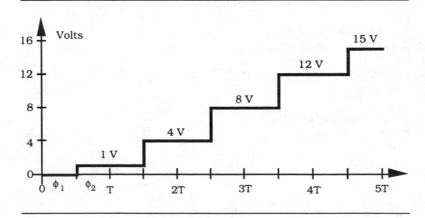

12.114 In the first printing, the problem should state that there are 0.1pF stray capacitances from each end of C_1 to ground. C_{GS} and C_{GD} should be ignored.

(a) In this case, the sampling capacitor has an effective value of 1.1pF.

$A_V = -\dfrac{1.1pF}{0.2pF} = 5.5$ whereas the ideal gain is $A_V = \dfrac{1.0pF}{0.2pF} = -5$ | Gain error -0.5 or 10%

(b) The stray insensitive integrator eliminates the effects of the stray capacitances.

Therefore $A_V = -5$ and there is no gain error.

12.115 Note: It is very important to observe and discuss the effects of clock feedthrough in the simulation results in both parts of this problem.

```
*PROBLEM 12.115(a) - SC Integrator
VCLK 2 0 DC 0 PULSE(0 5 0U 0.5US 0.5US 4US 10U)
VNCLK 4 0 DC 5 PULSE(0 5 5U 0.5US 0.5US 4US 10U)
VS 1 0 DC 1
M1 3 2 1 0 MOSN W=4U L=2U AS=16P AD=16P
C1 3 0 1PF
*Stray capacitance CS
CS 3 0 0.1PF
M2 3 4 5 0 MOSN W=4U L=2U AS=16P AD=16P
C2 5 6 0.2PF
E1 6 0 0 0 5 1E5
RID 5 0 1MEG
RL 6 0 10K
.OPTIONS VNTOL=1E-9 RELTOL=1E-6
.OP
.TRAN 0.025U 20U
.MODEL MOSN NMOS KP=5E-5 VTO=0.91 GAMMA=0.99
+LAMBDA=.02 TOX=41.5N
+CGSO=330P CGDO=330P CJ=3.9E-4 CJSW=510P
.PROBE V(1) V(2) V(3) V(4) V(5) V(6)
.PRINT TRAN V(3) V(6)
.END
```

Note that the output in part (a) is really only valid during Phase-1 times because of clock feedthrough.

```
*PROBLEM 12.115(b) - Stray Insensitive SC Integrator
VCLK 2 0 DC 0 PULSE(0 5 0U 0.5US 0.5US 4US 10U)
VNCLK 4 0 DC 5 PULSE(0 5 5U 0.5US 0.5US 4US 10U)
VS 1 0 DC 1
M1 3 2 1 0 MOSN W=4U L=2U
M3 7 2 5 0 MOSN W=4U L=2U
C1 3 7 1PF
*Stray capacitances CS1 and CS2
CS1 3 0 0.1PF
CS2 7 0 0.1PF
M2 3 4 0 0 MOSN W=4U L=2U
M4 7 4 0 0 MOSN W=4U L=2U
C2 5 6 0.2PF
E1 6 0 0 0 5 1E5
RID 5 0 1MEG
RL 6 0 10K
.OPTIONS VNTOL=1E-9 RELTOL=1E-6
```

```
.OP
.TRAN 0.025U 30U
.MODEL MOSN NMOS KP=5E-5 VTO=0.91 GAMMA=0.99
+LAMBDA=.02 TOX=41.5N
+CGSO=330P CGDO=330P CJ=3.9E-4 CJSW=510P
.PROBE V(1) V(2) V(3) V(4) V(5) V(6)
.PRINT TRAN V(3) V(6)
.END
```

Note that the output in part (b) is really only valid during Phase-2 times because of clock feedthrough.

12.116

$$f_o = f_C \sqrt{\frac{C_3 C_4}{C_1 C_2}} = 10^5 \sqrt{\frac{1pF(0.1pF)}{0.4pF(0.4pF)}} = 79.1 \text{ kHz}$$

$$Q = \sqrt{\frac{C_3}{C_4}} \frac{\sqrt{C_1 C_2}}{C_1 + C_2} = \sqrt{\frac{1pF}{0.1pF}} \frac{\sqrt{0.4pF(0.4pF)}}{0.4pF + 0.4pF} = 1.58$$

12.117

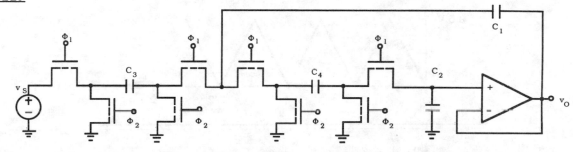

12.118

$$\frac{V_1}{10k\Omega} = I_S \exp\frac{-V_{o1}}{V_T} \quad | \quad V_{O1} = -V_T \ln\frac{V_1}{10^4 I_S} \quad | \quad V_{O2} = -V_T \ln\frac{V_2}{10^4 I_S}$$

$$V_{O3} = -(V_{O1} + V_{O2}) = V_T\left(\ln\frac{V_1}{10^4 I_S} + \ln\frac{V_2}{10^4 I_S}\right) = V_T \ln\frac{V_1 V_2}{10^8 I_S^2}$$

$$V_O = -10^4 I_D = -10^4 I_S \exp\frac{V_D}{V_T} = -10^4 I_S \exp\left(\ln\frac{V_1 V_2}{10^8 I_S^2}\right) = -\frac{V_1 V_2}{10^4 I_S}$$

12.119

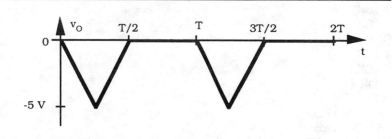

271

12.120

The waveform going into the low - pass filter is the same as that in Prob. 12.119

except the amplitude will be $V_M = 1V\left(-\dfrac{8.2k\Omega}{2.7k\Omega}\right) = -3.037$ V.

The average value of the waveform is $\overline{V} = \left(-\dfrac{10k\Omega}{10k\Omega}\right)\dfrac{\dfrac{1}{2}\dfrac{T}{2}(-3.037)}{T} = +0.759$ V

12.121

The Fourier series converges very rapidly since only the even terms exist for $n \geq 2$ and the terms decrease as $1/n^2$. Thus the RMS value will be dominated by the first term ($n = 1$).

Require: $\dfrac{\pi}{2}\dfrac{1}{\sqrt{1+\left(\dfrac{\omega}{\omega_o}\right)^2}} \leq 0.01 \mid (50\pi)^2 \leq 1+\left(\dfrac{\omega}{\omega_o}\right)^2 \mid \omega_o \geq \dfrac{\omega}{157} = \dfrac{120\pi}{157} = 2.40$ Hz

12.122

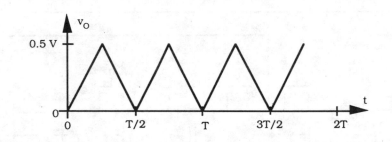

12.123

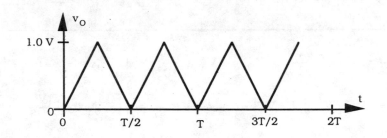

12.124

```
*PROBLEM 12.124 - RECTIFIER
VS 1 0 PWL(0 0 1M 1 3M -1 5M 1 7M -1 8M 0)
R1 1 2 10K
R2 4 5 10K
R3 5 6 10K
R4 2 4 10K
R5 1 5 20K
D1 3 2 DIODE
D2 4 3 DIODE
EOP1 3 0 0 2 1E5
EOP2 6 0 0 5 1E5
.MODEL DIODE D IS=1E-12A
.TRAN .01M 8M
.PRINT TRAN V(6)
.PROBE V(1) V(2) V(3) V(4) V(5) V(6)
.END
```

12.125

```
*PROBLEM 12.125 - RECTIFIER
VS 1 0 PWL(0 0 1M 1 3M -1 5M 1 7M -1 8M 0)
R1 0 2 10K
R2 4 5 10K
R3 5 6 20K
R4 2 4 10K
D1 3 2 DIODE
D2 4 3 DIODE
EOP1 3 0 1 2 1E5
EOP2 6 0 1 5 1E5
.MODEL DIODE D IS=1E-12A
.TRAN .01M 8M
.PRINT TRAN V(6)
.PROBE V(1) V(2) V(3) V(4) V(5) V(6)
.END
```

12.126

Simplify the circuit by taking a Thevenin equivalent of the 5V source and two 10kΩ

resistors: $V_{TH} = 5V \dfrac{10k\Omega}{10k\Omega + 10k\Omega} = 2.5V$ | $R_{TH} = 10k\Omega \| 10k\Omega = 5k\Omega$

$V_O = 5V$ – Using superposition: $V_+ = 2.5 \dfrac{100k\Omega}{100k\Omega + 5k\Omega} + 5 \dfrac{5k\Omega}{100k\Omega + 5k\Omega} \doteq 2.62V$

$V_O = 0V$: $V_+ = 2.5 \dfrac{100k\Omega}{100k\Omega + 5k\Omega} = 2.38V$ $V_N = 2.62 - 2.38 = 0.24V$

12.127

$$V_O = -10V: \quad V_+ = -10 \frac{4.3k\Omega}{4.3k\Omega + 39k\Omega} = -0.993 \text{ V}$$

$$V_O = 10V: \quad V_+ = 10 \frac{4.3k\Omega}{4.3k\Omega + 39k\Omega} = 0.993 \text{ V}$$

$$V_N = 0.993 - (-0.993) = 1.99 \text{ V}$$

12.128

$$\text{For } V_O = 4.3 + 0.6 = 4.9V: \quad V_+ = 4.9 \frac{4.3k\Omega}{4.3k\Omega + 39k\Omega} = 0.487 \text{ V}$$

$$\text{For } V_O = -4.3 - 0.6 = -4.9V: \quad V_+ = -4.9 \frac{4.3k\Omega}{4.3k\Omega + 39k\Omega} = -0.487 \text{ V}$$

$$V_N = 0.487 - (-0.487) = 0.974 \text{ V}$$

12.129 Note: The design needs to use the circuit in Fig. 12.126.

For $V_O = 0$: $V_+ = V_{TH} \dfrac{R_2}{R_{TH} + R_2} = 1 - \dfrac{0.05}{2} = 0.975V$ | $R_{TH} = R_3 \| R_4$ | $V_{TH} = 5 \dfrac{R_4}{R_3 + R_4}$

For $V_O = 5$: $V_+ = V_{TH} \dfrac{R_2}{R_{TH} + R_2} + 5 \dfrac{R_{TH}}{R_{TH} + R_2} = 1 + \dfrac{0.05}{2} = 1.025V$

Subtracting: $5 \dfrac{R_{TH}}{R_{TH} + R_2} = 0.05V \rightarrow \dfrac{R_{TH}}{R_{TH} + R_2} = 0.01 \rightarrow \dfrac{R_2}{R_{TH}} = 99$

$\dfrac{V_{TH} \dfrac{R_2}{R_{TH} + R_2}}{\dfrac{R_{TH}}{R_{TH} + R_2}} = \dfrac{0.975}{0.01} \rightarrow V_{TH} \dfrac{R_2}{R_{TH}} = 97.5 \rightarrow V_{TH} = \dfrac{97.5}{99} = 0.985V$

$0.985 = 5 \dfrac{R_4}{R_3 + R_4} \rightarrow \dfrac{R_3}{R_4} = 4.077$ | Choosing $R_4 = 2k\Omega \rightarrow R_3 = 8.154k\Omega$

$R_{TH} = 8.154k\Omega \| 2k\Omega = 1.606k\Omega$ | $R_2 = 99(1.606k\Omega) = 159k\Omega$

Choosing standard values: $R_2 = 160\ k\Omega$ | $R_3 = 8.2k\Omega$ | $R_4 = 2\ k\Omega$

12.130

For $v_O = +12V$: $V_+ = 6 \dfrac{24k\Omega}{3.4k\Omega + 24k\Omega} + 12 \dfrac{3.4k\Omega}{3.4k\Omega + 24k\Omega} = 6.74\ V$

For $v_O = 0V$: $V_+ = 6 \dfrac{24k\Omega}{3.4k\Omega + 24k\Omega} = 5.26\ V$

$v(t) = V_F - (V_F - V_I) \exp\left(-\dfrac{t}{RC}\right)$

$6.74 = 12 - (12 - 5.26)\exp\left(-\dfrac{T_1}{RC}\right) \rightarrow T_1 = 6200(3.3 \times 10^{-8}) \ln \dfrac{6.74}{5.26} = 50.7\ \mu s$

$5.26 = 0 - (0 - 6.74)\exp\left(-\dfrac{T_2}{RC}\right) \rightarrow T_2 = 6200(3.3 \times 10^{-8}) \ln \dfrac{6.74}{5.26} = 50.7\ \mu s$

$f = \dfrac{1}{50.7\mu s + 50.7\mu s} = 9.86\ kHz$

12.131 $f = 0$. The circuit does not oscillate. $V_O = 0$ is a stable state.

12.132

(a) Let $R_1 = R_2$ | $\beta = \dfrac{R_1}{R_1 + R_2} = \dfrac{1}{2}$ | $T = 2RC \ln \dfrac{1+\beta}{1-\beta} = 2RC \ln 3 = 2.197RC$

During steady - state oscillation, the maximum output current from the op - amp is

$I = \dfrac{5}{R_1 + R_2} + \dfrac{5 - (-2.5)}{R}$ | Let $R = R_1 = R_2$ | $\dfrac{5}{2R} + \dfrac{7.5}{R} \le 1mA \rightarrow R \ge 10k\Omega$

$RC = \dfrac{0.001s}{2.197} = 4.55 \times 10^{-4} s$ | Selecting $C = 0.015\mu F$, $R = 30.3k\Omega \rightarrow 30 \ k\Omega$ (5% values)

Final values: $R = R_1 = R_2 = 30 \ k\Omega$ | $C = 0.015 \ \mu F$ | $f = \dfrac{1}{2.197(30 \ k\Omega)(0.015\mu F)} = 1.01 \ kHz$

(b) $\beta = \dfrac{1}{1 + \dfrac{R_2}{R_1}}$ | $\beta_{max} = \dfrac{1}{1 + \dfrac{30k\Omega(0.95)}{30k\Omega(1.05)}} = 0.525$ | $\beta_{min} = \dfrac{1}{1 + \dfrac{30k\Omega(1.05)}{30k\Omega(0.95)}} = 0.475$

$T_{max} = 2(30k\Omega)(1.05)(0.015\mu F)(1.1) \ln \dfrac{1 + 0.525}{1 - 0.525} = 1.213 \times 10^{-3} s \rightarrow f_{min} = 825 \ Hz$

$T_{min} = 2(30k\Omega)(0.95)(0.015\mu F)(0.90) \ln \dfrac{1 + 0.475}{1 - 0.475} = 7.949 \times 10^{-4} s \rightarrow f_{min} = 1.26 \ kHz$

(c) For $v_O = +4.75V$: $V_+ = 4.75\beta = \dfrac{4.75}{2} = 2.375V$

For $v_O = -5.25V$: $V_+ = -5.25\beta = \dfrac{-5.25}{2} = -2.625V$

$v(t) = V_F - (V_F - V_1) \exp\left(-\dfrac{t}{RC}\right)$

$2.375 = 4.75 - (4.75 - (-2.625)) \exp\left(-\dfrac{T_1}{RC}\right) \rightarrow T_1 = RC \ln \dfrac{7.375}{2.375} = 1.133RC$

$-2.625 = -5.25 - (-5.25 - 2.375) \exp\left(-\dfrac{T_2}{RC}\right) \rightarrow T_2 = RC \ln \dfrac{7.625}{2.625} = 1.066RC$

$T = 2.199RC = 2.199(30k\Omega)(0.015\mu F) = 9.896 \times 10^{-4} s \rightarrow f = 1.01 \ kHz$ – Very little change

---

12.133

For a triangular waveform with peak amplitude V_S and $\omega_o = 2000\pi$:

$v(t) = \displaystyle\sum_{n=1}^{\infty} \dfrac{8V_S}{n^2\pi^2} \sin \dfrac{n\pi}{2} \sin n\omega_o t$

For the low - pass filter: $A_V(s) = -\dfrac{1}{1 + \dfrac{s}{3000\pi}}$ | $|A_V(jf)| = \dfrac{1}{\sqrt{1 + \left(\dfrac{f}{1500}\right)^2}}$

$|A_V(j1000)| = 0.832$ | $|A_V(j3000)| = 0.447$ | $|A_V(j5000)| = 0.287$

For a 5V fundamental: $\dfrac{8V_S}{\pi^2} 0.832 = 5 \rightarrow V_S = \dfrac{1}{0.832} \dfrac{5}{8} \pi^2 = 7.41 \ V$

This series contains only odd harmonics: For $n = 2$, $V_{2000} = 0$.

For $f = 3 \ kHz$, $n = 3$: $V_{3000} = 0.447 \left(\dfrac{5}{.832}\right) \dfrac{1}{3^2} = 0.298 \ V$

For $f = 5 \ kHz$, $n = 5$: $V_{5000} = 0.287 \left(\dfrac{5}{.832}\right) \dfrac{1}{5^2} = 69.0 \ mV$

12.134

$$T = RC \ln \frac{1 + \dfrac{V_{on}}{V_{CC}}}{1 - \beta} \quad | \quad \beta = \frac{15k\Omega}{15k\Omega + 27k\Omega} = 0.357 \quad | \quad (51k\Omega)(0.033\mu F) \ln \frac{1 + \dfrac{0.6}{10}}{1 - 0.357} = 841\ \mu s$$

$$T_r = RC \ln \frac{1 + \beta\dfrac{V_{CC}}{V_{EE}}}{1 - \dfrac{V_{on}}{V_{EE}}} = (51k\Omega)(0.033\mu F) \ln \frac{1 + 0.357\left(\dfrac{10}{10}\right)}{1 - \dfrac{0.6}{10}} = 416\ \mu s$$

12.135

$$T = RC \ln \frac{1 + \dfrac{V_{on}}{V_{CC}}}{1 - \beta} \quad | \quad T_r = RC \ln \frac{1 + \beta\dfrac{V_{CC}}{V_{EE}}}{1 - \dfrac{V_{on}}{V_{EE}}} \quad | \quad \ln \frac{1 + \dfrac{V_{on}}{V_{CC}}}{1 - \beta} = \frac{T}{T_r} \ln \frac{1 + \beta\dfrac{V_{CC}}{V_{EE}}}{1 - \dfrac{V_{on}}{V_{EE}}}$$

$$\ln \frac{1 + \dfrac{0.6}{5}}{1 - \beta} = \frac{10\mu s}{5\mu s} \ln \frac{1 + \beta\dfrac{5}{5}}{1 - \dfrac{0.6}{5}} \quad | \quad \ln\left(\frac{1.12}{1 - \beta}\right) = 2 \ln \frac{1 + \beta}{0.88} \quad | \quad \left(\frac{1.12}{1 - \beta}\right) = \left(\frac{1 + \beta}{0.88}\right)^2$$

MATLAB gives $\beta = 0.6998 \rightarrow \dfrac{R_1}{R_2} = 2.33$ | $R_2 = 13$ kΩ | $R_2 = 30.3$k$\Omega \rightarrow 30$ kΩ

$$RC = \frac{10^{-5}}{\ln \dfrac{1 + \dfrac{0.6}{5}}{1 - 0.6998}} = 7.595\mu s \quad | \quad C = 150\ pF \quad | \quad R = 50.6k\Omega \rightarrow 51\ k\Omega$$

CHAPTER 13

13.1 Assuming linear operation:

$$v_{BE} = 0.700 + 0.005 \sin 2000\pi t \text{ V}$$

$$v_{ce} = \left(\frac{5mV}{8mV}\right)(-1.65 \sin 2000\pi t) = -1.03 \sin 2000\pi t \text{ V}$$

$$v_{CE} = 5.00 - 1.03 \sin 2000\pi t \text{ V}; \quad 10 - 3300 I_C \geq 0.700 \rightarrow I_C \leq 2.82 \text{ mA}$$

13.2 Assuming linear operation:

$$v_{GS} = 3.50 + 0.25 \sin 2000\pi t \text{ V}$$

$$v_{ds} = \frac{0.25V}{0.50V}(-2 \sin 2000\pi t) = -1.00 \sin 2000\pi t \text{ V}$$

$$v_{DS} = 4.80 - 1.00 \sin 2000\pi t \text{ V}$$

$$v_{DS} \geq v_{GS} - V_{TN} \rightarrow 10 - 3300 I_{DS} - 1.00 \sin 2000\pi t \geq 3.50 + 0.25 \sin 2000\pi t - 1$$

For $\sin 2000\pi t = 1$, $I_{DS} \leq \dfrac{10 - 1 - 3.5 - 0.25 + 1}{3300} \dfrac{V}{\Omega} = 1.89 \text{ mA}$

13.3 (a) C_1 is a bypass capacitor. C_2 is a coupling capacitor that couples the ac component of v_0 into the amplifier. C_0 is a coupling capacitor which couples the ac component of the signal at the collector to the output v_O. (b) The signal voltage at the base will be $v_b = 0$.

13.4 (a) C_1 is a coupling capacitor that couples the ac component of v_S into the amplifier. C_2 is a bypass capacitor. C_3 is a coupling capacitor which couples the ac component of the signal at the collector to the output v_O. (b) The signal voltage at the emitter will be $v_e = 0$.

13.5 (a) C_1 is a coupling capacitor that couples the ac component of v_S into the amplifier. C_2 is a bypass capacitor. C_3 is a coupling capacitor which couples the ac component of the signal at the drain to the output v_O. (b) The signal voltage at the source will be $v_s = 0$.

13.6 (a) C_1 is a coupling capacitor that couples the ac component of v_S into the amplifier. C_2 is a coupling capacitor which couples the ac component of the signal at the drain to the output v_O. (b) C_1 is a coupling capaictor that couples the ac component of v_S into the amplifier. C_2 is a coupling capacitor which couples the ac component of the signal at the drain to the output v_O.

13.7 (a) C_1 is a coupling capacitor that couples the ac component of v_S into the amplifier. C_2 is a bypass capacitor. C_3 is a coupling capacitor which couples the ac component of the signal at the drain to the output v_O. (b) The signal voltage at the source will be $v_s = 0$.

13.8 (a) C_1 is a coupling capacitor that couples the ac component of v_S into the amplifier. C_2 is a bypass capacitor. C_3 is a coupling capacitor which couples the ac component of the signal at the collector to the output v_O. (b) The signal voltage at the emitter will be $v_e = 0$.

13.9

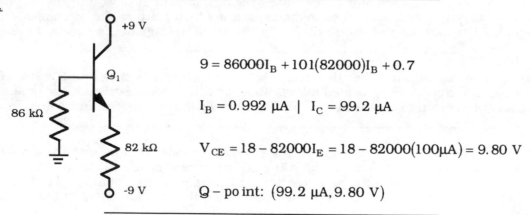

$$V_{EQ} = -12V + \frac{5k\Omega}{5k\Omega + 10k\Omega} 24V = -4V$$

$$R_{EQ} = 5k\Omega \| 10k\Omega = 3.33k\Omega$$

$$-4 = 3330I_B + 0.7 + 76(4000)I_B - 12$$

$$I_B = 23.8\ \mu A \ | \ I_C = 1.78\ mA \ | \ I_E = 1.81\ mA$$

$$V_{CE} = 12 - 6000I_C - 4000I_E - (-12) = 6.08\ V$$

$$Q - point: \ (1.78\ mA, 6.08\ V)$$

13.10

```
*Problem 13.10 - Common-Emitter Amplifier - Figure P13.1
VCC 7 0 DC 12
VEE 8 0 DC -12
R1 3 8 5K
R2 7 3 10K
RE 4 8 4K
RC 7 5 6K
Q1 5 3 4 NBJT
.OP
.MODEL NBJT NPN IS=1E-15 BF=75 VA=75
.END
```

Results: IC   1.78E-03   VCE   6.14E+00 VBE   7.28E-01

13.11

$$9 = 86000I_B + 101(82000)I_B + 0.7$$

$$I_B = 0.992\ \mu A \ | \ I_C = 99.2\ \mu A$$

$$V_{CE} = 18 - 82000I_E = 18 - 82000(100\mu A) = 9.80\ V$$

$$Q - point: \ (99.2\ \mu A, 9.80\ V)$$

13.12

```
*Problem 13.12 - Common-Collector Amplifier - Figure P13.2
VCC 5 0 DC 9
VEE 8 0 DC -9
R1 3 6 43K
R2 6 0 43K
RE 4 8 82K
Q1 5 3 4 NBJT
.OP
.MODEL NBJT NPN IS=1E-16 BF=100 VA=75
.END
```

Results: IC   9.93E-05   VCE   9.79E+00   VBE   7.12E-01

13.13

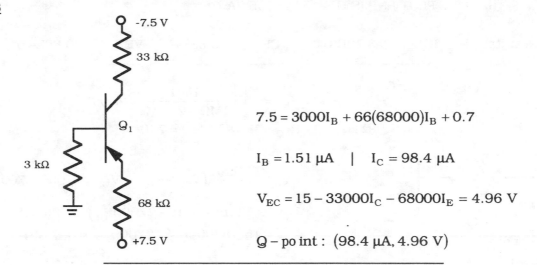

$$7.5 = 3000I_B + 66(68000)I_B + 0.7$$

$$I_B = 1.51 \ \mu A \quad | \quad I_C = 98.4 \ \mu A$$

$$V_{EC} = 15 - 33000I_C - 68000I_E = 4.96 \ V$$

$$Q-\text{point}: \ (98.4 \ \mu A, \ 4.96 \ V)$$

13.14

*Problem 13.14 - Common-Base Amplifier - Figure P13.3
VEE 1 0 DC 7.5
VCC 5 0 DC -7.5
RC 5 4 33K
RB 3 0 3K
RE 1 2 68K
Q1 4 3 2 PBJT
.OP
.MODEL PBJT PNP IS=1E-16 BF=65 VA=75
.END

Results: IC   -9.83E-05   VCE   -4.97E+00   VBE   -7.13E-01

13.15

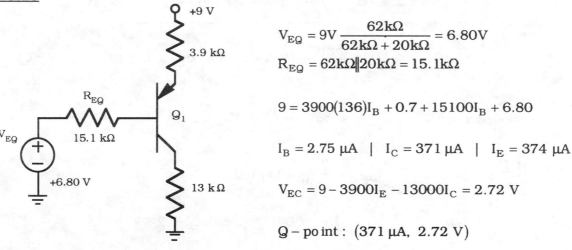

$$V_{EQ} = 9V \ \frac{62k\Omega}{62k\Omega + 20k\Omega} = 6.80V$$
$$R_{EQ} = 62k\Omega \| 20k\Omega = 15.1k\Omega$$

$$9 = 3900(136)I_B + 0.7 + 15100I_B + 6.80$$

$$I_B = 2.75 \ \mu A \quad | \quad I_C = 371 \ \mu A \quad | \quad I_E = 374 \ \mu A$$

$$V_{EC} = 9 - 3900I_E - 13000I_C = 2.72 \ V$$

$$Q-\text{point}: \ (371 \ \mu A, \ 2.72 \ V)$$

13.16

*Problem 13.16 - Common-Emitter Amplifier - Figure P13.4
VCC 4 0 DC 9
RC 1 0 13K
R2 2 0 62K
R1 4 2 20K
RE 4 3 3.9K

Q1 1 2 3 PBJT
.OP
.MODEL PBJT PNP IS=1E-15 BF=135 VA=75
.END

Results: IC   -3.73E-04   VCE   -2.68E+00   VBE   -6.88E-01

13.17

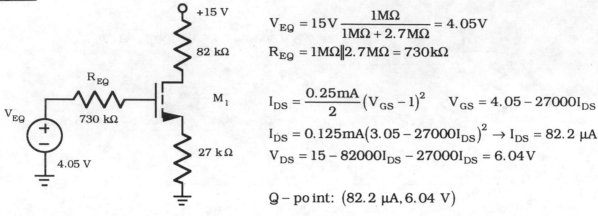

$$V_{EQ} = 15V \frac{1M\Omega}{1M\Omega + 2.7M\Omega} = 4.05V$$

$$R_{EQ} = 1M\Omega \| 2.7M\Omega = 730k\Omega$$

$$I_{DS} = \frac{0.25mA}{2}(V_{GS} - 1)^2 \qquad V_{GS} = 4.05 - 27000I_{DS}$$

$$I_{DS} = 0.125mA(3.05 - 27000I_{DS})^2 \rightarrow I_{DS} = 82.2\ \mu A$$

$$V_{DS} = 15 - 82000I_{DS} - 27000I_{DS} = 6.04V$$

$$Q - point: (82.2\ \mu A, 6.04\ V)$$

13.18

*Problem 13.18 - Common-Source Amplifier - Figure P13.5
VDD 4 0 DC 15
RD 4 3 82K
R2 4 2 2.7MEG
R1 2 0 1MEG
R4 1 0 27K
M1 3 2 1 1 NFET
.OP
.MODEL NFET NMOS KP=250U VTO=1
.END

Results: ID   8.29E-05   VDS   5.96E+00   VGS   1.81E+00

13.19

$$I_{DS} = \frac{5 \times 10^{-4}}{2}(V_{GS} + 2)^2 \quad | \quad V_{GS} = -3900I_{DS}$$

$$V_{GS} = -3900 \frac{5 \times 10^{-4}}{2}(V_{GS} + 2)^2 \rightarrow V_{GS} = -0.990V$$

$$I_{DS} = -\frac{V_{GS}}{3900} = 254\ \mu A$$

$$V_{DS} = 15 - 4300I_{DS} - 3900I_{DS} = 12.9V$$

$$Q - point: (254\ \mu A,\ 12.9\ V)$$

13.20

*Problem 13.20 - Common-Gate Amplifier - Figure P13.6
VDD 3 0 DC 15
RD 3 2 4.3K

```
R1 1 0 3.9K
M1 2 0 1 1 NDMOS
.OP
.MODEL NDMOS NMOS KP=500U VTO=-2
.END
```

Results: ID   2.54E-04   VDS   1.29E+01   VGS   -9.92E-01

13.21

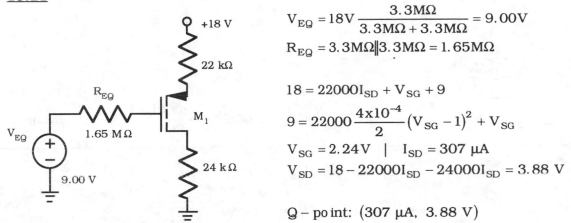

$$V_{EQ} = 18V \frac{3.3M\Omega}{3.3M\Omega + 3.3M\Omega} = 9.00V$$

$$R_{EQ} = 3.3M\Omega \| 3.3M\Omega = 1.65M\Omega$$

$$18 = 22000 I_{SD} + V_{SG} + 9$$

$$9 = 22000 \frac{4x10^{-4}}{2} (V_{SG} - 1)^2 + V_{SG}$$

$$V_{SG} = 2.24V \quad | \quad I_{SD} = 307 \ \mu A$$

$$V_{SD} = 18 - 22000 I_{SD} - 24000 I_{SD} = 3.88 \ V$$

$$Q - po\,int: \ (307 \ \mu A, \ 3.88 \ V)$$

13.22

```
*Problem 13.22 - Common-Source Amplifier - Figure P13.7
VDD 4 0 DC 18
RD 1 0 24K
R2 4 2 3.3MEG
R1 2 0 3.3MEG
R4 4 3 22K
M1 1 2 3 3 PFET
.OP
.MODEL PFET PMOS KP=400U VTO=-1
.END
```

Results: ID   -3.07E-04   VDS   -3.86E+00   VGS   -2.24E+00

13.23

$$I_{SD} = \frac{12 - V_{SG}}{33000} = \frac{200x10^{-6}}{2} (V_{SG} + 1)^2$$

$$V_{SG} = 0.84V \quad | \quad I_{SD} = 338 \ \mu A$$

$$V_{SD} = 12 - 33000 I_{SD} - 22000 I_{SD} - (-12)$$

$$V_{SD} = 5.41 \ V$$

$$Q - po\,int: \ (338 \ \mu A, \ 5.41 \ V)$$

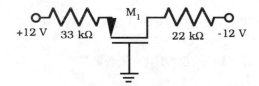

+12 V   33 kΩ M_1 22 kΩ   -12 V

13.24

```
*Problem 13.24 - Common-Gate Amplifier - Figure P13.8
VDD 4 0 DC 12
VSS 1 0 DC -12
RD 2 1 22K
```

R1 4 3 33K
M1 2 0 3 3 PFET
.OP
.MODEL PFET PMOS KP=200U VTO=+1
.END

Results: ID   -3.38E-04   VDS   -5.40E+00   VGS   -8.39E-01

13.25

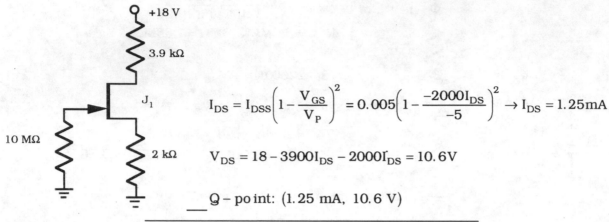

$$I_{DS} = I_{DSS}\left(1 - \frac{V_{GS}}{V_P}\right)^2 = 0.005\left(1 - \frac{-2000I_{DS}}{-5}\right)^2 \rightarrow I_{DS} = 1.25\text{mA}$$

$$V_{DS} = 18 - 3900I_{DS} - 2000I_{DS} = 10.6V$$

$$Q - \text{point: } (1.25 \text{ mA}, 10.6 \text{ V})$$

13.26

For the JFET: $V_{TO} = V_P$ and $\beta = \dfrac{I_{DSS}}{V_P^2} = \dfrac{0.005}{25} = 200\dfrac{\mu A}{V^2}$

*Problem 13.26 - Common-Source Amplifier - Figure P13.9
VDD 4 0 DC 18
RD 4 3 3.9K
RG 2 0 10MEG
R1 1 0 2K
J1 3 2 1 NFET
.OP
.MODEL NFET NJF BETA=200U VTO=-5
.END

Results: ID   1.25E-03   VDS   1.06E+01   VGS   -2.50E+00

13.27

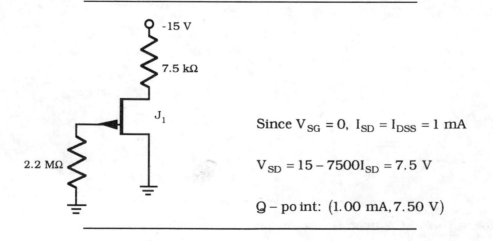

Since $V_{SG} = 0$, $I_{SD} = I_{DSS} = 1$ mA

$$V_{SD} = 15 - 7500I_{SD} = 7.5 \text{ V}$$

$$Q - \text{point: } (1.00 \text{ mA}, 7.50 \text{ V})$$

<u>**13.28**</u>

*Problem 13.28 - Common-Source Amplifier - Figure P13.10
VDD 4 0 DC -15
RD 4 3 7.5K
RG 2 0 2.2MEG
J1 3 2 0 PFET
.OP
*Note that JFET model requires negative sign on VP
.MODEL PFET PJF BETA=111U VTO=-3
.END

Results: ID   -9.99E-04   VDS   -7.51E+00 VGS   -1.65E-05

<u>**13.29**</u>

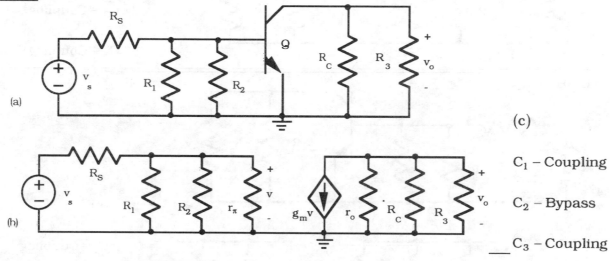

(c)

C_1 – Coupling

C_2 – Bypass

C_3 – Coupling

<u>**13.30 (a)**</u>

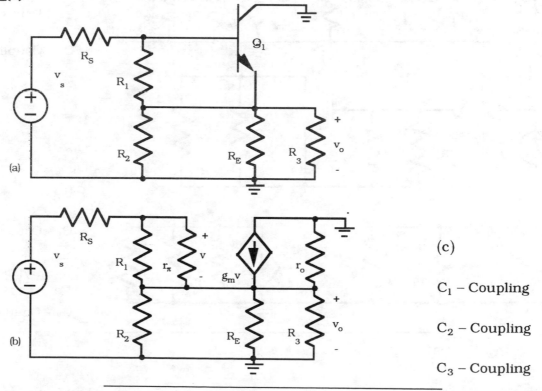

(c)

C_1 – Coupling

C_2 – Coupling

C_3 – Coupling

13.30 (b)

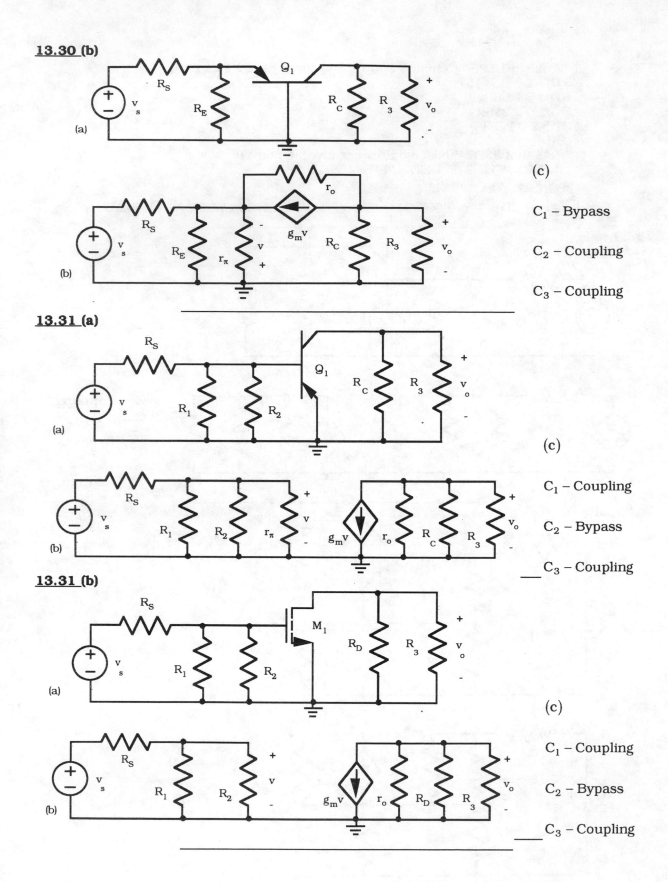

(a)

(b)

(c)

C_1 – Bypass

C_2 – Coupling

C_3 – Coupling

13.31 (a)

(a)

(b)

(c)

C_1 – Coupling

C_2 – Bypass

C_3 – Coupling

13.31 (b)

(a)

(b)

(c)

C_1 – Coupling

C_2 – Bypass

C_3 – Coupling

284

13.32 (a)

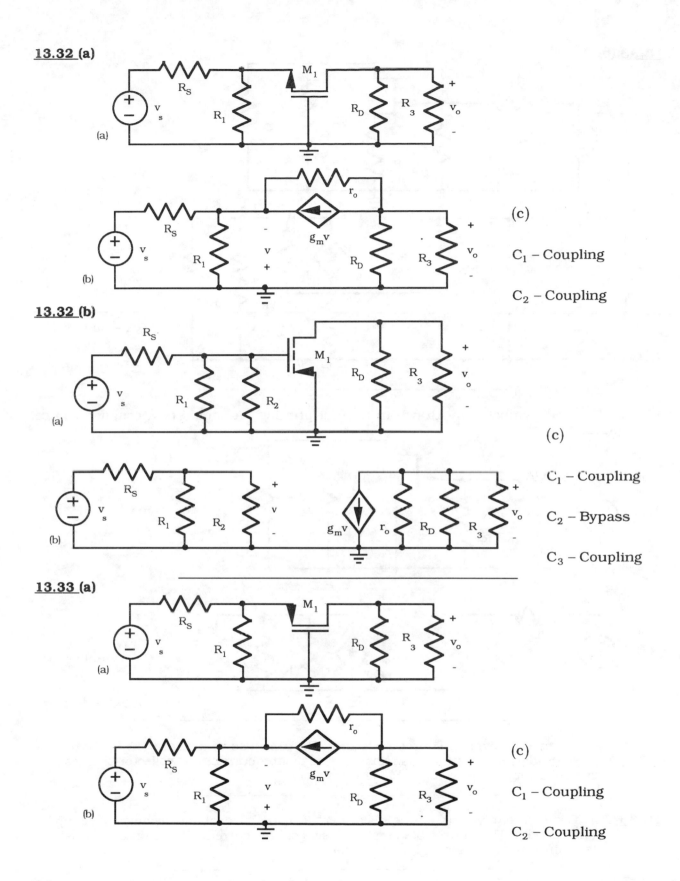

(c)

C$_1$ – Coupling

C$_2$ – Coupling

13.32 (b)

(c)

C$_1$ – Coupling

C$_2$ – Bypass

C$_3$ – Coupling

13.33 (a)

(c)

C$_1$ – Coupling

C$_2$ – Coupling

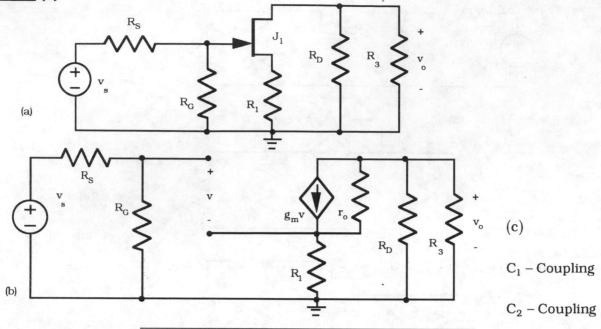

(a)

(b)

(c)

C_1 – Coupling

C_2 – Coupling

13.34 The JFET symbol is misdrawn in the first printing. It should be a common source circuit.

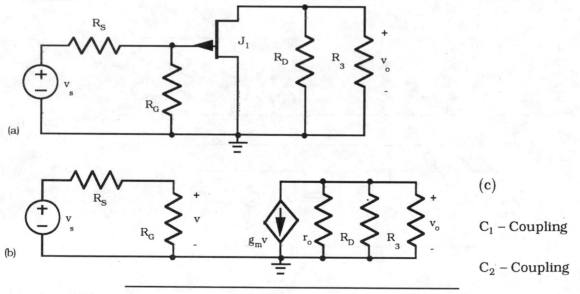

(a)

(b)

(c)

C_1 – Coupling

C_2 – Coupling

13.35 R_S: Thévinen equivalent source resistance; R_1: base bias voltage divider; R_2: base bias voltage divider; R_E: emitter bias resistor - sets emitter current; R_C: collector bias resistor - sets collector-emitter voltage; R_3: load resistor

13.36 R_S: Thévinen equivalent source resistance; R_1: gate bias voltage divider; R_2: gate bias voltage divider; R_4: source bias resistor - sets source current; R_D: drain bias resistor - sets drain-source voltage; R_3: load resistor

13.37 R_S: Thévinen equivalent source resistance: R_1: gate bias voltage divider; R_2: gate bias voltage divider; R_4: source bias resistor - sets source current; R_D: drain bias resistor - sets drain-source voltage; R_3: load resistor

13.38

(a) $r_d = \dfrac{V_T}{I_D + I_S}$ | $I_D = 10^{-14}\left(\exp\left(\dfrac{0.6}{0.025}\right) - 1\right) = 264.9\mu A$ | $r_d = \dfrac{0.025}{264.9\mu A + 10fA} = 94.4 \ \Omega$

(b) $I_D = 0$ $r_d = \dfrac{0.025}{10fA} = 2.50 \ T\Omega$ (c) $\dfrac{0.025}{I_D + I_S} > 10^{15} \rightarrow I_D + I_S < 2.5 \times 10^{-17} A$

$V_D < V_T \ln \dfrac{I_D + I_S}{I_S} = 0.025 \ln \dfrac{2.5 \times 10^{-17}}{10^{-14}} = -0.150 \ V$

13.39

$$V_T = \frac{kT}{q} = \frac{1.38 \times 10^{-23}}{1.60 \times 10^{-19}} T = 8.63 \times 10^{-5} T \ | \ r_d \cong \frac{V_T}{I_D} = 1000 V_T$$

T	75K	100K	200K	300K	400K
V_T	6.47 mV	8.63 mV	17.3 mV	25.9 mV	34.5 mV
r_d	6.47 Ω	8.63 Ω	17.3 Ω	25.9 Ω	34.5 Ω

13.40

$\dfrac{r_D}{20k\Omega + r_D} = \dfrac{1}{10} \rightarrow r_D = 2.22k\Omega$ | $40 I_D = \dfrac{1}{2.22k\Omega} \rightarrow I_D = 11.3 \ \mu A$ | $v_s = 10(5mV) = 50 \ mV$

13.41

(a) $\exp\left(\dfrac{0.005}{0.025}\right) - 1 = 0.221$ | $\dfrac{0.005}{0.025} = 0.200 \rightarrow +10.7\%$ error

$\exp\left(-\dfrac{0.005}{0.025}\right) - 1 = -0.181$ | $-\dfrac{0.005}{0.025} = -0.200 \rightarrow -9.37\%$ error

(b) $\exp\left(\dfrac{0.010}{0.025}\right) - 1 = 0.492$ | $\dfrac{0.010}{0.025} = 0.400 \rightarrow +23.0\%$ error

$\exp\left(-\dfrac{0.010}{0.025}\right) - 1 = -0.330$ | $-\dfrac{0.010}{0.025} = -0.400 \rightarrow -17.5\%$ error

13.42 $\qquad\qquad\qquad I_C = \dfrac{g_m}{40} = \dfrac{0.03}{40} = 0.750 \ mA = 750 \ \mu A$

13.43

$I_C = \dfrac{\beta_o V_T}{r_\pi} = \dfrac{75(0.025V)}{10^4 \Omega} = 187.5 \ \mu A$ | Q - point: $(188 \ \mu A, V_{CE} > 0.7 \ V)$

$g_m = 40 I_C = 40\left(1.875 \times 10^{-4}\right) = 7.50 \ mS$ | $r_o = \dfrac{V_A + V_{CE}}{I_C} \approx \dfrac{V_A}{I_C} = \dfrac{100V}{187.5 \ \mu A} = 533 \ k\Omega$

13.44

$r_o = \dfrac{V_A + V_{CE}}{I_C}$; solving for V_A: $V_A = I_C r_o - V_{CE}$

Using the values from row 1: $V_A = 0.002(40000) - 10 = 70 \ V$

Using the values from the second row: $\beta_o = g_m r_\pi = 0.12(500) = 60$ and $\beta_F = \beta_o = 60$.

Row 1: $g_m = 40I_C = 40(0.002) = 0.08$ S | $r_\pi = \dfrac{\beta_o}{g_m} = \dfrac{60}{0.08} = 750\ \Omega$

$\mu_F = g_m r_o = 0.08(40000) = 3200$

Row 2: $I_C = \dfrac{g_m}{40} = \dfrac{0.12}{40} = 3$ mA | $r_o = \dfrac{V_A + V_{CE}}{I_C} = \dfrac{80}{0.003} = 26.7$ kΩ

$\mu_F = g_m r_o = 0.12(26700) = 3200$

Row 3: $g_m = \dfrac{\beta_o}{r_\pi} = \dfrac{60}{4.8 \times 10^5} = 1.25 \times 10^{-4}$ S | $I_C = \dfrac{g_m}{40} = \dfrac{1.25 \times 10^{-4}}{40} = 3.13\ \mu$A

$r_o = \dfrac{V_A + V_{CE}}{I_C} = \dfrac{80}{3.13 \times 10^{-6}} = 25.6$ MΩ | $\mu_F = g_m r_o = 1.25 \times 10^{-4}(25.6 \times 10^6) = 3200$

13.45

(a) $\exp\left(\dfrac{0.005}{0.025}\right) - 1 = 0.221$ | $\dfrac{0.005}{0.025} = 0.200 \rightarrow +10.7\%$ error

$\exp\left(-\dfrac{0.005}{0.025}\right) - 1 = -0.181$ | $-\dfrac{0.005}{0.025} = -0.200 \rightarrow -9.37\%$ error

(b) $\exp\left(\dfrac{0.0075}{0.025}\right) - 1 = 0.350$ | $\dfrac{0.0075}{0.025} = 0.300 \rightarrow +16.7\%$ error

$\exp\left(-\dfrac{0.0075}{0.025}\right) - 1 = -0.259$ | $-\dfrac{0.0075}{0.025} = -0.300 \rightarrow -13.6\%$ error

(c) $\exp\left(\dfrac{0.0025}{0.025}\right) - 1 = 0.105$ | $\dfrac{0.0025}{0.025} = 0.100 \rightarrow +5.17\%$ error

$\exp\left(-\dfrac{0.0025}{0.025}\right) - 1 = -0.0952$ | $-\dfrac{0.0025}{0.025} = -0.100 \rightarrow -4.84\%$ error

---

13.46

$I_C = \dfrac{\beta_o V_T}{r_\pi} = \dfrac{75(0.025\text{V})}{10^6\ \Omega} = 1.875\ \mu$A | Q-point: $(1.88\ \mu\text{A}, V_{CE} > 0.7\text{ V})$

$g_m = 40I_C = 40(1.875 \times 10^{-6}) = 75.0\ \mu$S | $r_o = \dfrac{V_A + V_{CE}}{I_C} \approx \dfrac{V_A}{I_C} = \dfrac{100\text{V}}{1.875\ \mu\text{A}} = 53.3$ MΩ

13.47

(a) $\beta_F = \dfrac{I_C}{I_B} \cong \dfrac{350\mu\text{A}}{4\mu\text{A}} \cong 90$ | $\beta_o = \dfrac{\Delta I_C}{\Delta I_B} \cong \dfrac{600\mu\text{A} - 125\mu\text{A}}{6\mu\text{A} - 2\mu\text{A}} \cong 120$

(b) $\beta_F \cong \dfrac{750\mu\text{A}}{8\mu\text{A}} \cong 95$ | $\beta_o \cong \dfrac{900\mu\text{A} - 600\mu\text{A}}{4\mu\text{A}} \cong 75$

13.48

(a)
```
t=linspace(0,.004,1024);
ic=.001*exp(40*.005*sin(2000*pi*t));
IC=fft(ic);
z=abs(IC(1:26)/1024);
z(1)
ans = 0.001
plot(t,ic)
```

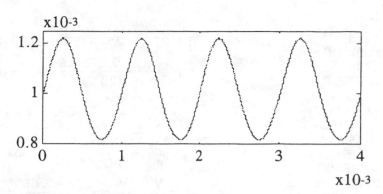

```
        z([5 9 13])
            ans = 0.0001    0.0000    0.0000
```

(b) t=linspace(0,.004,1024);
    ic=.001*exp(40*.005*sin(2000*pi*t));
    IC=fft(ic);
    z=abs(IC(1:26)/1024);
    z(1)
        ans = 0.0023
    plot(t,ic)

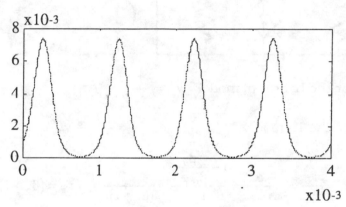

```
        z([5 9 13])
            ans = 0.0016    0.0007    0.0002
```

13.49 (a)

```
NAME        Q1
MODEL       NBJT
IB          2.21E-05
IC          1.78E-03
VBE         7.28E-01
VBC        -5.41E+00
VCE         6.14E+00
BETADC      8.04E+01
GM          6.87E-02
RPI         1.17E+03
RX          0.00E+00
RO          4.52E+04
BETAAC      8.04E+01
```

$T = 27C \mid V_T = 8.625 \times 10^{-5}(300) = 25.9 \text{mV}$

$g_m = \dfrac{I_C}{V_T} = \dfrac{1.78\text{mA}}{25.9\text{mV}} = 68.7 \text{ mS}$

$\beta_o = \beta_{FO}\left(1 + \dfrac{V_{CE}}{V_A}\right) = 75\left(1 + \dfrac{6.14}{75}\right) = 81.1$

$r_\pi = \dfrac{\beta_o}{g_m} = \dfrac{81.1}{0.0687} = 1180 \ \Omega$

$r_o = \dfrac{V_A + V_{CE}}{I_C} = \dfrac{75 + 6.14}{1.78\text{mA}} = 45.6 \text{ k}\Omega$

13.49 (b)

MODEL	PBJT
IB	-2.69E-06
IC	-3.73E-04
VBE	-6.88E-01
VBC	1.99E+00
VCE	-2.68E+00
BETADC	1.39E+02
GM	1.44E-02
RPI	9.61E+03
RX	0.00E+00
RO	2.06E+05
BETAAC	1.39E+02

$T = 27C \quad | \quad V_T = 8.625 \times 10^{-5}(300) = 25.9 mV$

$$g_m = \frac{I_C}{V_T} = \frac{0.373 mA}{25.9 mV} = 14.4 \; mS$$

$$\beta_o = \beta_{FO}\left(1 + \frac{V_{CE}}{V_A}\right) = 135\left(1 + \frac{2.68}{75}\right) = 140$$

$$r_\pi = \frac{\beta_o}{g_m} = \frac{140}{0.0144} = 9.72 \; k\Omega$$

$$r_o = \frac{V_A + V_{CE}}{I_C} = \frac{75 + 2.68}{0.373 mA} = 208 \; k\Omega$$

Note: The SPICE model actually is using V_{CB} instead of V_{CE}

$$\text{(a) } \beta_o = 75\left(1 + \frac{5.41}{75}\right) = 80.4 \quad \text{(b) } \beta_o = 135\left(1 + \frac{1.99}{75}\right) = 139$$

13.50

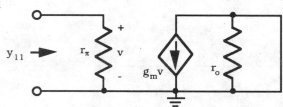 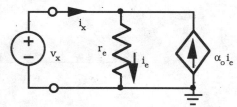

For the hybrid pi model: $y_{11} = \dfrac{1}{r_\pi}$

For the T - model: $i_x = \dfrac{v_x}{r_e} - \alpha_o \dfrac{v_x}{r_e} = \dfrac{1 - \alpha_o}{r_e} v_x$

$$y_{11} = \frac{i_x}{v_x} = \frac{1 - \alpha_o}{r_e} = \frac{1 - \dfrac{\beta_o}{\beta_o + 1}}{r_e} = \frac{1}{(\beta_o + 1)r_e} \rightarrow r_\pi = (\beta_o + 1)r_e$$

$$r_e = \frac{r_\pi}{(\beta_o + 1)} = \frac{\beta_o}{g_m(\beta_o + 1)} = \frac{\alpha_o}{g_m} = \frac{\alpha_o V_T}{I_C} = \frac{V_T}{I_E}$$

13.51

$$A_v \cong -10V_{CC} = -10(12) = -120$$

13.52

$$A_v \cong -10\left(V_{CC} + V_{EE}\right) = -10(15 + 15) = -300$$

13.53

$$A_v = -10\left(V_{CC} + V_{EE}\right) = -10(1.5 + 1.5) = -30; \text{ This estimate says no.}$$

However, if we look a bit deeper,

$$A_V = -40\left(I_C R_C\right) = -40 V_{R_C}, \text{ and we let } V_{R_C} = \frac{\left(V_{CC} + V_{EE}\right)}{2} = 1.5V,$$

then we can achieve $A_V = -40(1.5) = -60$.

So with careful design we can probably achieve a gain of 50.

13.54   Using our rule-of-thumb estimate:

$$A_v \cong -10V_{CC} = -10(1.5) = -15 \; ; \; A_v = -10(1) = -10$$

Note that this result really assumes that I_C varies with V_{CC}.

13.55

$$i_c = \frac{5V}{10k\Omega} = 0.5 \text{ mA, but } i_c \leq 0.2I_C \text{ for small-signal operation, or } I_C \geq 5i_c = 2.5 \text{ mA.}$$

$$V_{CC} \geq V_{BE} + i_c R_L + I_C R_L = 0.7 + 5 + 25 = 30.7 \text{ V}$$

13.56 $A_v = 40dB = 100 \; | \; v_o = 100v_{be} = 100(0.005V) = 0.500V.$

13.57

(a) $V_{EQ} = -9 + \dfrac{20k\Omega}{62k\Omega + 20k\Omega} 18 = -4.61V \; | \; R_{EQ} = 20k\Omega \| 62k\Omega = 15.1k\Omega$

$I_B = \dfrac{-4.61 - 0.7 - (-9)}{15.1k\Omega + 136(3.9k\Omega)} = 6.76\mu A \; | \; I_C = 135I_B = 913\mu A$

$V_{CE} = 9 - 13000I_C - 3900I_E - (-9) = 2.54V$

$g_m = 40I_C = 0.0365S \; | \; r_\pi = \dfrac{135}{g_m} = 3.70k\Omega \; | \; r_o = \infty$

$A_V = -\left(\dfrac{2.97k\Omega}{1k\Omega + 2.97k\Omega}\right)(0.0365)(11.5k\Omega) = -314$

(b) For $V_{CC} = 18V$, the answers are the same: $I_C = 913\mu A \; | \; V_{EC} = 2.54V \; | \; A_V = -314$

13.58

For common-emitter stage: $A_V = 50dB \rightarrow A_V = -316$

$|v_{be}| = \dfrac{15V}{316} = 47.5mV$ which is far too big for small-signal operation.

The will be significant distortion of the sine wave.

13.59

$g_m = 40(50\mu A) = 2.00mS \; | \; r_\pi = \dfrac{100}{2.00mS} = 50k\Omega \; | \; r_o = \dfrac{75V + 10V}{50\mu A} = 1.70M\Omega$

$R_{BB} = 100k\Omega \| 50k\Omega = 33.3k\Omega$

$A_V = -\left(\dfrac{33.3k\Omega}{33.3k\Omega + 0.75k\Omega}\right)(2mS)(1.70M\Omega \| 100k\Omega \| 100k\Omega) = -95.0$

13.60

For $\beta_o = 100$, see Prob. 13.59.

$r_\pi = \dfrac{60}{2.00mS} = 30k\Omega \; | \; R_{BB} = 100k\Omega \| 30k\Omega = 23.1k\Omega$

$A_V = -\left(\dfrac{23.1k\Omega}{23.1k\Omega + 0.75k\Omega}\right)(2mS)(1.70M\Omega \| 100k\Omega \| 100k\Omega) = -94.1$

$-95.0 \leq A_V \leq -94.1$ – only a small variation

13.61

$$g_m = 40(2.5\text{mA}) = 0.100\text{S} \quad | \quad r_\pi = \frac{75}{0.1\text{S}} = 750\Omega \quad | \quad r_o = \frac{50 + 7.5}{2.5\text{mA}} = 23.0\text{k}\Omega$$

$$R_{th} = 4.7\text{k}\Omega \| 50\Omega = 49.5\Omega \quad | \quad v_{th} = \frac{4700}{4700 + 50} v_s = 0.990 v_s$$

$$A_V = -0.990 \left(\frac{750\Omega}{750\Omega + 49.5\Omega} \right) (0.1\text{S})(23.0\text{k}\Omega \| 4.3\text{k}\Omega \| 10\text{k}\Omega) = -247$$

13.62

$$g_m = 40(1\mu\text{A}) = 40\mu\text{S} \quad | \quad r_\pi = \frac{40}{40\mu\text{S}} = 1\text{M}\Omega \quad | \quad r_o = \frac{50 + 1.5}{1\mu\text{A}} = 51.5\text{M}\Omega$$

$$R_{th} = 10\text{k}\Omega \| 5\text{M}\Omega = 9.98\text{k}\Omega \quad | \quad v_{th} = \frac{5\text{M}\Omega}{5\text{M}\Omega + 10\text{k}\Omega} v_s = 0.998 v_s$$

$$A_V = -0.998 \left(\frac{1\text{M}\Omega}{1\text{M}\Omega + 9.98\text{k}\Omega} \right) (40\mu\text{S})(51.5\text{M}\Omega \| 1.5\text{M}\Omega \| 3.3\text{M}\Omega) = -40.0$$

13.63

```
*Problem 13.63 - Common-Emitter Amplifier - Figure 13.23
VCC 7 0 DC 12
VS 1 0 AC 1
RS 1 2 1K
C1 2 3 100U
R1 3 0 10K
R2 7 3 30K
RE 4 0 1.3K
C3 4 0 100U
RC 7 5 4.3K
C2 5 6 100U
R3 6 0 100K
Q1 5 3 4 NBJT
.OP
.AC DEC 20 1HZ 10KHZ
.MODEL NBJT NPN IS=1E-16 BF=100 VA=75
.PRINT AC VM(6) VP(6)
.END
```

Results: $I_C = 1.60$ mA, $V_{CE} = 3.03$ V, $A_V = -135$ -- I_C differs by 10% - A_V is off by 4%

13.64

$$\left[10(V_{CC})\right]^N = \left[10(10)\right]^N \geq 20000 \rightarrow N \geq \frac{\log(20000)}{\log(100)} = 2.15 \rightarrow N = 3 \text{ (or possibly 2)}$$

13.65

```
*Problem 13.65 - Common-Emitter Amplifier - Figure P13.4
VCC 7 0 DC 9
VS 1 0 AC 1
RS 1 2 1K
C1 2 3 100U
R1 7 3 20K
R2 3 0 62K
RE 7 4 3.9K
C 7 4 100U
RC 5 0 13K
C3 5 6 100U
R3 6 0 100K
```

```
Q1 5 3 4 PBJT
.OP
.MODEL PBJT PNP IS=1E-15 BF=135 VA=75
.AC DEC 10  100Hz 10000Hz
.PRINT AC VM(6) VDB(6) VP(6)
.END
```

Results: $I_C = 373\ \mu A$, $V_{EC} = 2.68V$, $A_V = -134$

Hand calculations in Prob. 13.15 yielded (371 μA, 2.72V)

$$g_m = 40(371\mu A) = 14.8mS \ | \ r_\pi = \frac{135}{14.8mS} = 9.12k\Omega \ | \ r_o = \infty$$

$$R_{th} = 15.1k\Omega \| 1k\Omega = 938\Omega \ | \ v_{th} = \frac{15.1k\Omega}{15.1\Omega + 1k\Omega} v_s = 0.938v_s$$

$$A_V = -0.938\left(\frac{9.12k\Omega}{9.12k\Omega + 938\Omega}\right)(14.8mS)\left(\infty\|13k\Omega\|100k\Omega\right) = -145$$

SPICE A_V result is lower because r_o is included.

13.66   Using the information from Row 1:

$$\frac{1}{\lambda} = I_{DS}r_o - V_{DS} = \left(8x10^{-4}\right)\left(4x10^4\right) - 6 = 26V \ ; \ \lambda = 0.0385V^{-1}$$

From Row 2: $K_n = \dfrac{g_m^2}{2I_{DS}(1 + \lambda V_{DS})} = \dfrac{\left(2x10^{-4}\right)^2}{2\left(5x10^{-5}\right)\left(1 + \dfrac{6}{26}\right)} = 3.25x10^{-4}\ \dfrac{A}{V^2}$

Row 1: $g_m = \sqrt{2K_nI_{DS}(1 + \lambda V_{DS})} = \sqrt{2\left(3.25x10^{-4}\right)\left(8x10^{-4}\right)\left(1 + \dfrac{6}{26}\right)} = 8x10^{-4}S$

$$\mu_f = g_m r_o = 8x10^{-4}\left(4x10^4\right) = 32$$

$$0.2(V_{GS} - V_{TN}) = 0.2\sqrt{\frac{2I_{DS}}{K_n(1 + \lambda V_{DS})}} = 0.2\sqrt{\frac{2\left(8x10^{-4}\right)}{3.25x10^{-4}\left(1 + \dfrac{6}{26}\right)}} = 0.40V$$

Row 2: $r_o = \dfrac{\dfrac{1}{\lambda} + V_{DS}}{I_{DS}} = \dfrac{26 + 6}{5x10^{-5}} = 640k\Omega \ | \ \mu_f = g_m r_o = 2x10^{-4}\left(6.4x10^5\right) = 128$

$$0.2(V_{GS} - V_{TN}) = 0.2\sqrt{\frac{2I_{DS}}{K_n(1 + \lambda V_{DS})}} = 0.2\sqrt{\frac{2\left(5x10^{-5}\right)}{3.25x10^{-4}\left(1 + \dfrac{6}{26}\right)}} = 0.10V$$

Row 3: $g_m = \sqrt{2K_nI_{DS}(1 + \lambda V_{DS})} = \sqrt{2\left(3.25x10^{-4}\right)\left(10^{-2}\right)\left(1 + \dfrac{6}{26}\right)} = 2.83x10^{-3}S$

$$r_o = \dfrac{\dfrac{1}{\lambda} + V_{DS}}{I_{DS}} = \dfrac{26 + 6}{0.01} = 3.2k\Omega \ | \ \mu_f = g_m r_o = 2.83x10^{-3}\left(3.2x10^3\right) = 9.06$$

$$0.2(V_{GS} - V_{TN}) = 0.2\sqrt{\frac{2I_{DS}}{K_n(1 + \lambda V_{DS})}} = 0.2\sqrt{\frac{2\left(10^{-2}\right)}{3.25x10^{-4}\left(1 + \dfrac{6}{26}\right)}} = 1.41V$$

MOSFET Small-Signal Parameters				
I_{DS}	g_m (S)	r_o (Ω)	μ_f	Small-Signal Limit v_{gs} (V)
0.8 mA	0.0008	40,000	32	0.40
50 µA	0.0002	640,000	128	0.10
10 mA	0.00283	3200	9.06	1.41

13.67

$$\mu_f = \left(\frac{1}{\lambda} + V_{DS}\right)\sqrt{\frac{2K_n(1+\lambda V_{DS})}{I_{DS}}} \cong \left(\frac{1}{\lambda}\right)\sqrt{\frac{2K_n}{I_{DS}}} \quad | \quad \left(\frac{1}{.02}\right)\sqrt{\frac{2(2.5\times 10^{-4})}{I_{DS}}} \le 1 \to I_{DS} \ge 1.25 \text{ A}$$

13.68

$$(1+0.2)^2 - 1 = 0.44 \quad | \quad 2(0.2) = 0.40 \to 10\% \text{ error}$$

$$(1+0.4)^2 - 1 = 0.96 \quad | \quad 2(0.4) = 0.80 \to 20\% \text{ error}$$

13.69 From the results of Problem 13.18:

ID = 8.29E-05, VGS = 1.81E+00, VDS=5.96E+00, GM = 2.04E-04, GDS = 0.00E+00

$$g_m = \frac{2I_{DS}}{V_{GS} - V_{TN}} = \frac{2(82.9\mu A)}{1.81-1} = 205 \text{ µS} \quad | \quad \lambda = 0 \to r_o = \infty$$

13.70 From the results of Problem 13.22:

ID = 3.07E-04, VGS = -2.24E+00, VDS=-3.86E+00, GM = 4.96E-04, GDS = 0.00E+00

$$g_m = \frac{2I_{SD}}{V_{SG} + V_{TP}} = \frac{2(307\mu A)}{2.24-1} = 495 \text{ µS} \quad | \quad \lambda = 0 \to r_o = \infty$$

13.71 At virtually any Q-point. R_{IN} is set by R_G which can be any value desired since there is no gate current. (Note this is not the case with a BJT for which base current must be considered.)

13.72

$$R_{OUT} = \frac{R_D r_o}{R_D + r_o} \quad | \quad \text{Using } V_{DS} = \frac{V_{DD}}{2} \quad | \quad R_D = \frac{9V}{I_{DS}} \quad | \quad r_o = \frac{50V + 9V}{I_{DS}} \to R_{OUT} = \frac{7.8V}{I_{DS}}$$

$$I_{DS} = \frac{7.8V}{50k\Omega} = 156\mu A \to R_D = 57.6k\Omega \quad | \quad r_o = 378k\Omega \quad | \quad Q\text{-point}: (156 \text{ µA}, 9 \text{ V})$$

13.73

$$i_{DS} = I_{DSS}\left(1 - \frac{v_{GS}}{V_P}\right)^2 = \frac{1}{2}\left(\frac{2I_{DSS}}{V_P^2}\right)(V_P - v_{GS})^2 = \frac{1}{2}\left(\frac{2I_{DSS}}{V_P^2}\right)(v_{GS} - V_P)^2 = \frac{1}{2}K_n(v_{GS} - V_{TN})^2$$

13.74
(a) t=linspace(0,.004,1024);
    id=.005*(1-0.5*.4*sin(2000*pi*t)).^2;
    ID=fft(id);
    y=abs(ID(1:26)/1024);
    y(1)
      ans = 0.0051
    plot(t,id)

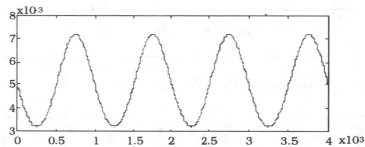

y([5 9 13])
  ans = 1.0e-03 * 0.9995   0.0500   0.0007

(b) t=linspace(0,.004,1024);
    id=.005*(1-0.5*.4*sin(2000*pi*t)).^2;
    ID=fft(id);
    y=abs(ID(1:26)/1024);
    y(1)
      ans = 0.0056
    plot(t,id)

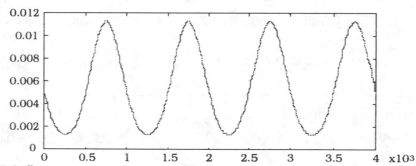

y([5 9 13 17 21])
  ans = 0.0025   0.0003   0.0000

13.75

$$g_m = \frac{2}{|V_P|}\sqrt{I_{DSS}I_{DS}} \rightarrow I_{DSS} = \frac{1}{5x10^{-5}}\left[\frac{5x10^{-4}(2.5)}{2}\right]^2 = 7.81 \text{ mA}$$

$$\frac{1}{\lambda} = I_{DS}r_o - V_{DS} = 10\text{mA}(15\text{k}\Omega) - 6\text{V} = 144\text{V} \rightarrow \lambda = 6.94x10^{-3}\text{V}^{-1}$$

Row 1: $g_m = \frac{2}{2.5}\sqrt{7.81\text{mA}(1\text{mA})} = 2.24$ mS | $r_o = \frac{150\text{V}}{1\text{mA}} = 150$ kΩ | $\mu_f = g_m r_o = 335$

$$0.2(V_{GS} - V_P) = 0.2\sqrt{\frac{I_D}{I_{DSS}}} = 0.2\sqrt{\frac{1\text{mA}}{7.81\text{mA}}} = 71.6 \text{ mV}$$

Row 2: $g_m = 0.5$ mS $|$ $r_o = \dfrac{150V}{50\mu A} = 3.00$ MΩ $|$ $\mu_f = g_m r_o = 15000$

$$0.2\sqrt{\dfrac{I_D}{I_{DSS}}} = 0.2\sqrt{\dfrac{50\mu A}{7.81mA}} = 16.0 \text{ mV}$$

Row 3: $g_m = \dfrac{2}{2.5}\sqrt{7.81mA(10mA)} = 7.07$ mS $|$ $r_o = 15$ kΩ $|$ $\mu_f = g_m r_o = 106$

$$0.2\sqrt{\dfrac{10mA}{7.81mA}} = 226 \text{ mV}$$

Note that the gate -channel diode is forward-biased by 0.33 V in the last case.

JFET Small-Signal Parameters				
I_{DS}	g_m (S)	r_o (Ω)	μ_f	Small-Signal Limit v_{gs} (V)
1 mA	0.00224	150,000	335	0.0716
50 μA	0.0005	3,000,000	1500	0.0160
10 mA	0.00707	15,000	106	0.226

13.76 From the results of Problem 13.26:

ID = 1.25E-03, VGS = -2.50E+00, VDS=1.06E+01, GM = 1.00E-03, GDS = 0.00E+00

$$g_m = \dfrac{2I_{DS}}{V_{GS} - V_P} = \dfrac{2(1.25mA)}{-2.50 - (-5)} = 1.00 \text{ mS} \;|\; \lambda = 0 \rightarrow r_o = \infty \;|\; QED$$

13.77 From the results of Problem 13.26:

ID = -9.99E-04, VGS = -1.65E-05, VDS=-7.51E+00, GM = 6.66E-04, GDS = 0.00E+00

$$g_m = \dfrac{2I_{SD}}{V_{SG} + V_P} = \dfrac{2(0.999mA)}{16.5\mu V + 3V} = 666 \text{ } \mu S \;|\; \lambda = 0 \rightarrow r_o = \infty \;|\; QED$$

13.78

Note that $i_G \cong 0$ for this device.

Load line: $400 = 133000 i_P + v_{PK}$ and $v_{GK} = -1.5V$

Two points (i_P, v_{PK}): $(3mA, 0V)$ and $(0mA, 400V) \rightarrow$ Q - pt:$(1.4 \text{ mA}, 215 \text{ V})$

$r_o = \dfrac{250V - 200V}{2.15mA - 1.25mA} = 55.6k\Omega$ $|$ $g_m = \dfrac{2.3mA - 0.7mA}{-1V - (-2V)} = 1.6$mS $|$ $\mu_f = 89.0$

$A_V = -g_m\left(R_P \| r_o\right) = -1.6mS(133k\Omega \| 55.6k\Omega) = -62.7$

13.79

BJT: $I_C = g_m V_T = 0.5S(0.025V) = 12.5mA$ | MOSFET: $I_{DS} = \dfrac{g_m^2}{2K_n} = \dfrac{(0.5S)^2}{2(25mA/V^2)} = 5\ A!$

The BJT can achieve the required transconductance at a 400 times lower current than the MOSFET. For a given power supply voltage, the BJT will therefore use 400 times less power.

Note, however, that r_π is small for the BJT: $r_\pi = \dfrac{60}{0.5} = 120\Omega$ versus ∞ for the FET.

13.80 Since a relatively high input resistance is required at a relatively high current, a FET should be used. If a BJT were selected, it would be very difficult to achieve the required input resistance because its value of r_π is low:

$$r_\pi = \frac{\beta_o V_T}{I_C} = \frac{100(.025V)}{10mA} = 250\ \Omega$$

13.81

$$40(V_A + V_{CE}) = \left(\frac{1}{\lambda} + V_{DS}\right)\sqrt{\frac{2K_n(1 + \lambda V_{DS})}{I_{DS}}}$$

$$40(35) = 60\sqrt{\frac{2(0.025)(1.2)}{I_{DS}}} \rightarrow I_{DS} = 111\ \mu A\ |\ \mu_f = 40(35) = 1400$$

13.82 Either transistor could be used. For a BJT operating in the common-emitter configuration or a FET operating in the common-source configuration:

For the BJT : $R_{IN} \approx r_\pi$ | $I_C = \dfrac{\beta_o V_T}{r_\pi} \cong \dfrac{100(0.025V)}{75\Omega} = 33.3\ mA$ - A reasonable current.

For the FET, $R_{IN} = R_G$ and setting $R_G = 75\ \Omega$ is satisfactory, particularly if a

depletion - mode MOSFET is available.

(Note that common-base and common-gate amplifiers from Chapter 14 could also be used.)

13.83

$$A_V \approx -\frac{V_{DD}}{V_{GS} - V_{TN}} = -\frac{(12)}{1} = -12\ \text{ or }\ 21.6\ dB$$

13.84

$v_d = \dfrac{15}{2} = 7.5V_{peak}$ | $15dB \rightarrow A_V = -5.62$ | $v_{gs} = \dfrac{7.5V}{5.62} = 1.34V$ | $V_{GS} - V_{TN} \geq 5(1.34) = 6.70V$

Yes, it is possible although the required value of V_{GS}-V_{TN} is getting rather large.

13.85

For $V_{DS} = \dfrac{V_{DD}}{2}$, $A_V = -\dfrac{V_{DD}}{V_{GS} - V_{TN}}$ | $30 = \dfrac{15}{V_{GS} - V_{TN}}$ | $V_{GS} - V_{TN} = 0.5\ V$

$I_{DS} = \dfrac{1mA}{2}(V_{GS} - V_{TN})^2 = 125\mu A$ | Q - point: $(125\ \mu A, 7.5\ V)$

13.86

$$A_V \approx \frac{V_{DD}}{V_{GS} - V_{TN}} \quad | \quad \frac{9}{V_{GS} - V_{TN}} \geq 30 \rightarrow V_{GS} - V_{TN} \leq 0.300 \text{ V}$$

13.87

$$v_{gs} \leq 0.2(V_{GS} - V_{TN}) \text{ requires } (V_{GS} - V_{TN}) \geq \frac{0.5}{0.2} = 2.5V$$

$A_V = 20dB \rightarrow A_V = -10.$ Using the rule-of-thumb estimate to select V_{DD}:

$$A_V = -\frac{V_{DD}}{V_{GS} - V_{TN}} \quad \text{and} \quad V_{DD} = 10(2.5) = 25 \text{ V}$$

13.88

$$v_{gs} \leq 0.2(V_{GS} - V_{TN}) \text{ requires } (V_{GS} - V_{TN}) \geq \frac{0.1}{0.2} = 0.5V$$

$A_V = 35dB \rightarrow A_V = -56.2.$ Using the rule-of-thumb estimate to select V_{DD}:

$$A_V = -\frac{V_{DD}}{V_{GS} - V_{TN}} \quad \text{and} \quad V_{DD} = 56.2(0.5V) = 28 \text{ V}$$

13.89

We desire $\left(\frac{V_{DD}}{V_{GS} - V_{TN}}\right)^N \geq 1000; \left(\frac{10}{V_{GS} - V_{TN}}\right)^N \geq 1000$

For $V_{GS} - V_{TN} = 1V$, $N = 3$ meets the requirements, but with no safety margin.

For $V_{GS} - V_{TN} = 0.75V$, $N = 3$ easily meets the requirements.

13.90

For the bias network : $V_{TH} = 10V \dfrac{430k\Omega}{430k\Omega + 560k\Omega} = 4.343V \quad | \quad R_{TH} = 430k\Omega \| 560k\Omega = 243k\Omega$

$I_{DS} = \dfrac{5 \times 10^{-4}}{2}(V_{GS} - 1)^2 \quad | \quad V_{GS} = 4.343 - 2 \times 10^4 I_{DS} \rightarrow V_{GS} = 1.72 \text{ V} \quad | \quad I_{DS} = 131 \text{ } \mu A$

$V_{DS} = 10 - 63k\Omega(131\mu A) = 1.75V \geq V_{GS} - V_{TN}$ so saturation region is ok.

$g_m = \sqrt{2(5 \times 10^{-4})(131\mu A)} = 362\mu S \quad | \quad r_o = \dfrac{\left(\dfrac{1}{0.0133} + 1.75\right)V}{131\mu A} = 586k\Omega$

$A_V = -\dfrac{243k\Omega}{243k\Omega + 1k\Omega}(362\mu S)(586k\Omega \| 43k\Omega \| 100k\Omega) = -10.3 \quad | \quad$ Original $A_V = -4.69$

A_V increases because $\dfrac{g_m}{I_{DS}}$ increases as current decreases.

13.91

$$g_m = \sqrt{2\left(500 \frac{\mu A}{V^2}\right)(100\mu A)(1 + 0.02(5))} = 332\mu S \quad | \quad r_o = \frac{50 + 5V}{100\mu A} = 550k\Omega$$

$$A_V = -\left(\frac{6.8M\Omega}{6.8M\Omega + 0.1M\Omega}\right)(332\mu S)(550k\Omega \| 50k\Omega \| 120k\Omega) = -10.9$$

$$g_m^{max} = \sqrt{2(700\mu A / V^2)(100\mu A)} = 374\mu S \quad | \quad g_m^{min} = \sqrt{2(300\mu A / V^2)(100\mu A)} = 245\mu S$$

$$A_V = -\left(\frac{6.8M\Omega}{6.8M\Omega + 0.1M\Omega}\right)(g_m)(550k\Omega\|50k\Omega\|120k\Omega) = (-32.7k\Omega)(g_m)$$

$$A_V^{max} = -12.2 \quad | \quad A_V^{min} = -8.01$$

13.93

$$g_m = \sqrt{2(100\mu A / V^2)(10\mu A)(1 + 0.02(5))} = 46.9\mu S \quad | \quad r_o = \frac{50 + 5V}{10\mu A} = 5.50M\Omega$$

$$A_V = -\left(\frac{10M\Omega}{10M\Omega + 0.1M\Omega}\right)(46.9\mu S)(5.50M\Omega\|560k\Omega\|2.2M\Omega) = -19.2$$

13.94

$$g_m = \sqrt{2K_n I_{DS}(1 + \lambda V_{DS})} = \sqrt{2(0.001)(0.002)(1 + 0.015(7.5))} = 2.11\times10^{-3}S$$

$$r_o = \frac{\dfrac{1}{\lambda} + V_{DS}}{I_{DS}} = \frac{\dfrac{1}{0.015} + 7.5}{0.002} = 37.1k\Omega$$

$$v_{th} = \frac{10^6\Omega}{10^6\Omega + 10^4\Omega}v_s = 0.990v_s \quad | \quad R_{th} = 10k\Omega\|1M\Omega = 9.90 \ k\Omega$$

$$A_{vth} = -g_m\left(r_o\|R_D\|R_3\right) = -2.11\times10^{-3}\left(37.1k\Omega\|3.9k\Omega\|270k\Omega\right)$$

$$A_v = -2.11\times10^{-3}(3.48k\Omega)(0.990) = -7.27$$

13.95

```
*Problem 13.95 - Common-Source Amplifier - Figure P13.5
VDD 7 0 DC 15
*FOR OUTPUT RESISTANCE
*VO 6 0 AC 1
*VS 1 0 AC 0
*
VS 1 0 AC 1
RS 1 2 1K
C1 2 3 100UF
R1 3 0 1MEG
R2 7 3 2.7MEG
R4 4 0 27K
C2 4 0 100UF
RD 7 5 82K
C3 5 6 100UF
R3 6 0 470K
M1 5 3 4 4 NFET
.OP
.MODEL NFET NMOS KP=250U VTO=1
.AC LIN 1 1000 1000
.PRINT AC VM(6) VDB(6) VP(6) IM(VS) IP(VS)
*.PRINT AC IM(C3) IP(C3)
.END
```

Results: ID = 8.29E-05   VGS = 1.81E+00   VDS = 5.96E+00

VM(6) = 1.420E+01   VP(6) = -1.800E+02   IM(VS) = 1.369E-06   IP(VS) = -1.800E+02

VM(3) = 9.986E-01   VP(3) = 1.248E-04   IM(C3) = 1.220E-05   IP(C3) = -1.800E+02

$$A_V = -14.6 \mid R_{IN} = \frac{VM(3)}{IM(VS)} = \frac{0.9986}{1.369\mu A} = 729 \text{ k}\Omega \mid R_{OUT} = \frac{1}{IM(C3)} = \frac{1}{12.20\mu A} = 82.0 \text{ k}\Omega$$

13.96

```
*Problem 13.96 - Common-Source Amplifier - Figure P13.7
VDD 7 0 DC 18
*FOR OUTPUT RESISTANCE
*VO 6 0 AC 1
*VS 1 0 AC 0
*
VS 1 0 AC 1
RS 1 2 1K
C1 2 3 100U
R2 7 3 3.3MEG
R1 3 0 3.3MEG
R4 7 4 22K
C2 7 4 100U
RD 5 0 24K
C3 5 6 100U
R3 6 0 470K
M1 5 3 4 4 PFET
.OP
.MODEL PFET PMOS KP=500U VTO=-1
.AC LIN 1 1000 1000
.PRINT AC VM(6) VDB(6) VP(6) IM(VS) IP(VS) VM(3) VP(3)
*.PRINT AC IM(C3) IP(C3)
.END
```

Results: ID = -3.13E-04   VGS = -2.12E+00   VDS = -3.61E+00

VM(6) = 12.76E+01   VP(6) = -1.799E+02   IM(VS) = 6.057E-07   IP(VS) = -1.800E+02

VM(3) = 9.994E-01 VP(3) = 5.523E-05 IM(C3) = 4.167E-05   IP(C3) = -1.800E+02

$$A_V = -12.8 \mid R_{IN} = \frac{VM(3)}{IM(VS)} = \frac{0.9994V}{0.6057\mu A} = 1.65 \text{ M}\Omega \mid R_{OUT} = \frac{1}{IM(C3)} = \frac{1}{41.67\mu A} = 24.0 \text{ k}\Omega$$

13.97

```
*Problem 13.97 - Common-Source Amplifier - Figure P13.9
VDD 7 0 DC 18
*FOR OUTPUT RESISTANCE
*VO 6 0 AC 1
*VS 1 0 AC 0
*
VS 1 0 AC 1
RS 1 2 10K
C1 2 3 100UF
RG 3 0 10MEG
R1 4 0 2K
C3 4 0 100UF
RD 7 5 3.9K
C2 5 6 100UF
R3 6 0 36K
J1 5 3 4 NFET
.OP
.MODEL NFET NJF BETA=200U VTO=-5
.AC LIN 1 1000 1000
.PRINT AC VM(6) VDB(6) VP(6) IM(VS) IP(VS) VM(3) VP(3)
```

```
*.PRINT AC IM(C2) IP(C2)
.END
```

Results: ID = 1.25E-03   VGS = -2.50E+00   VDS = -1.06E+01

VM(6) = 3.515E+00   VP(6) = -1.799E+02   IM(VS) = 9.991E-08   IP(VS) = -1.800E+02

VM(3) = 9.990E-01   VP(3) = 9.106E-06   IM(C3) = 2.564E-04   IP(C3) = -1.800E+02

$$A_V = -3.52 \mid R_{IN} = \frac{VM(3)}{IM(VS)} = \frac{0.9990V}{99.91nA} = 10.0 \text{ M}\Omega \mid R_{OUT} = \frac{1}{IM(C3)} = \frac{1}{256.4\mu A} = 3.90 \text{ k}\Omega$$

13.98

```
*Problem 13.98 - Common-Source Amplifier - Figure P13.10
VDD 7 0 DC -15
*FOR OUTPUT RESISTANCE
*VO 6 0 AC 1
*VS 1 0 AC 0
*
VS 1 0 AC 1
RS 1 2 10K
C1 2 3 100U
RG 3 0 2.2MEG
RD 7 5 7.5K
C2 5 6 100U
R3 6 0 220K
J1 5 3 0 PFET
.OP
*Note that JFET model requires negative sign on VP
.MODEL PFET PJF  BETA=111U VTO=-3
.AC LIN 1 1000 1000
.PRINT AC VM(6) VDB(6) VP(6) IM(VS) IP(VS) VM(3) VP(3)
*.PRINT AC IM(C2) IP(C2)
.END
```

Results: ID = -9.99E-04   VGS = -1.65E+05   VDS = -7.51E+00

VM(6) = 4.809E+01   VP(6) = -1.800E+02   IM(VS) = 4.525E-07   IP(VS) = -1.800E+02

VM(3) = 9.955E-01   VP(3) = 4.126E-05   IM(C3) = 1.333E-04   IP(C3) = -1.800E+02

$$A_V = -4.81 \mid R_{IN} = \frac{VM(3)}{IM(VS)} = \frac{0.9955V}{0.4525\mu A} = 2.20 \text{ M}\Omega \mid R_{OUT} = \frac{1}{IM(C3)} = \frac{1}{133.3\mu A} = 7.50 \text{ k}\Omega$$

13.99 $i_{ds} \leq 0.4 I_{DS}$ and $i_{ds}R_D = 5V$ or $i_{ds} = \dfrac{5V}{15k\Omega} = 333\mu A \rightarrow I_{DS} = 833 \text{ }\mu A$

13.100

$$g_m = \frac{2}{3}\sqrt{1mA(1mA)[1 + 0.015(9)]} = 710\mu S \quad \mid \quad r_o = \frac{\frac{1}{0.015} + 9V}{1mA} = 75.7k\Omega$$

$$A_V = -\left(\frac{1M\Omega}{1M\Omega + 10k\Omega}\right)(710\mu S)(75.7k\Omega\|7.5k\Omega\|160k\Omega) = -4.60$$

13.101

$$r_\pi = \frac{100}{2.00\text{mS}} = 50\text{k}\Omega \quad | \quad r_o = \frac{75\text{V} + 10\text{V}}{50\mu\text{A}} = 1.70\text{M}\Omega$$

$$R_{IN} = R_B \| r_\pi = 100\text{k}\Omega \| 50\text{k}\Omega = 33.3\text{k}\Omega \quad | \quad R_{OUT} = 1.7\text{M}\Omega \| 100\text{k}\Omega = 94.4\text{k}\Omega$$

13.102

$$R_{IN} = R_B \| r_\pi \quad | \quad r_\pi^{min} = \frac{60}{40(50\mu\text{A})} = 30\text{ k}\Omega \quad | \quad r_\pi^{max} = \frac{100}{40(50\mu\text{A})} = 50\text{ k}\Omega$$

$$R_{IN}^{min} = R_B \| r_\pi = 100\text{k}\Omega \| 30\text{k}\Omega = 23.1\text{k}\Omega \quad | \quad R_{IN}^{max} = R_B \| r_\pi = 100\text{k}\Omega \| 50\text{k}\Omega = 33.3\text{ k}\Omega$$

$$R_{OUT} = R_C \| r_o = 100\text{k}\Omega \left\| \frac{75 + 10}{50\mu\text{A}} \right. = 100\text{k}\Omega \| 1.7\text{M}\Omega = 94.4\text{ k}\Omega \text{ independent of } \beta_o$$

13.103

$$r_\pi = \frac{75(0.025\text{V})}{2.5\text{mA}} = 750\Omega \quad | \quad r_o = \frac{50 + 7.5}{2.5}\frac{\text{V}}{\text{mA}} = 23.0\text{k}\Omega$$

$$R_{IN} = R_B \| r_\pi = 4.7\text{k}\Omega \| 0.75\text{k}\Omega = 647\text{ }\Omega \quad | \quad R_{OUT} = R_C \| r_o = 4.3\text{k}\Omega \| 23\text{k}\Omega = 3.62\text{k}\Omega$$

13.104

$$r_\pi = \frac{40(0.025\text{V})}{1\mu\text{A}} = 1.00\text{M}\Omega \quad | \quad r_o = \frac{50 + 1.5}{1}\frac{\text{V}}{\mu\text{A}} = 51.5\text{M}\Omega$$

$$R_{IN} = R_B \| r_\pi = 5\text{M}\Omega \| 1\text{M}\Omega = 833\text{ k}\Omega \quad | \quad R_{OUT} = R_C \| r_o = 1.5\text{M}\Omega \| 51.5\text{M}\Omega = 1.46\text{ M}\Omega$$

13.105

$$r_\pi = \frac{40(0.025\text{V})}{1\mu\text{A}} = 1.00\text{M}\Omega \quad | \quad r_o = \frac{50 + 1.5}{1}\frac{\text{V}}{\mu\text{A}} = 51.5\text{M}\Omega$$

$$z_{11} = \left.\frac{\mathbf{v_1}}{\mathbf{i_1}}\right|_{\mathbf{i_2}=0} = R_B \| r_\pi = 5\text{M}\Omega \| 1\text{M}\Omega = 833\text{ k}\Omega \quad | \quad z_{12} = \left.\frac{\mathbf{v_1}}{\mathbf{i_2}}\right|_{\mathbf{i_1}=0} = 0$$

$$z_{21} = \left.\frac{\mathbf{v_2}}{\mathbf{i_1}}\right|_{\mathbf{i_2}=0} = (R_B \| r_\pi)(-g_m)(r_o \| R_C) = (833\text{ k}\Omega)(-40\text{x}10^{-6})(51.5\text{M}\Omega \| 1.5\text{M}\Omega) = -48.7\text{ M}\Omega$$

$$z_{22} = \left.\frac{\mathbf{v_2}}{\mathbf{i_2}}\right|_{\mathbf{i_1}=0} = R_C \| r_o = 1.5\text{M}\Omega \| 51.5\text{M}\Omega = 1.46\text{ M}\Omega$$

13.106

$$g_m = \sqrt{2K_n I_{DS}(1 + \lambda V_{DS})} = \sqrt{2(0.001)(0.002)(1 + 0.015(7.5))} = 2.11\text{x}10^{-3}\text{S}$$

$$r_o = \frac{\frac{1}{\lambda} + V_{DS}}{I_{DS}} = \frac{\frac{1}{0.015} + 7.5}{0.002} = 37.1\text{k}\Omega \quad | \quad z_{11} = \left.\frac{\mathbf{v_1}}{\mathbf{i_1}}\right|_{\mathbf{i_2}=0} = R_G = 1\text{ M}\Omega \quad | \quad z_{12} = \left.\frac{\mathbf{v_1}}{\mathbf{i_2}}\right|_{\mathbf{i_1}=0} = 0$$

$$z_{22} = \left.\frac{\mathbf{v_2}}{\mathbf{i_2}}\right|_{\mathbf{i_1}=0} = R_D \| r_o = 3.9\text{k}\Omega \| 37.1\text{k}\Omega = 3.53\text{ k}\Omega$$

$$z_{21} = \left.\frac{\mathbf{v_2}}{\mathbf{i_1}}\right|_{\mathbf{i_2}=0} = (1\text{M}\Omega)(-2.11\text{mS})(3.53\text{k}\Omega) = -7.45\text{ M}\Omega$$

13.107

From Prob. 13.90: Q-Point $= (131\mu A, 1.75V)$

$R_{IN} = R_1 \| R_2 = 430k\Omega \| 560k\Omega = 243$ kΩ | $R_{OUT} = 43k\Omega \| r_o$

$$r_o = \frac{\left(\dfrac{1}{0.0133} + 1.75\right)V}{0.131mA} = 587k\Omega \quad | \quad R_{OUT} = 43k\Omega \| 587k\Omega = 40.1k\Omega$$

At the input there is no change in voltage division. However, at the output the voltage division between R_{OUT} and R_3 is much worse due to the higher output resistance (40.1kΩ versus 3.98kΩ). This is more than compensated for by the increase in g_m / I_{DS}.

13.108

$$R_{IN} = R_G = 6.8M\Omega \quad | \quad R_{OUT} = 50k\Omega \| r_o$$

$$r_o = \frac{(50+5)V}{0.1mA} = 550k\Omega \quad | \quad R_{OUT} = 50k\Omega \| 550k\Omega = 45.8k\Omega$$

13.109

$R_{IN} = R_G = 6.8M\Omega$ which is independent of K_n | $R_{OUT} = R_D \| r_o$

$$r_o = \frac{\left(\dfrac{1}{0.02} + 5\right)V}{0.1mA} = 550k\Omega \quad | \quad R_{OUT} = 50k\Omega \| 550k\Omega = 45.8 \text{ k}\Omega, \text{ also independent of } K_n$$

13.110

$$R_{IN} = R_G = 10M\Omega \quad | \quad R_{OUT} = R_D \| r_o \quad | \quad r_o = \frac{\left(\dfrac{1}{0.02} + 5\right)V}{10\mu A} = 5.50 \text{ M}\Omega$$

$$R_{OUT} = 560k\Omega \| 5.50M\Omega = 508 \text{ k}\Omega$$

13.111

$$R_{IN} = R_G = 1M\Omega \quad | \quad R_{OUT} = R_D \| r_o \quad | \quad r_o = \frac{\left(\dfrac{1}{0.015} + 7.5\right)V}{2mA} = 37.1 \text{ k}\Omega$$

$$R_{OUT} = 3.9k\Omega \| 37.1k\Omega = 3.53 \text{ k}\Omega$$

13.112

$$R_{IN} = R_G = 1M\Omega \quad | \quad R_{OUT} = R_D \| r_o \quad | \quad r_o = \frac{\left(\dfrac{1}{0.015} + 9\right)V}{1mA} = 75.7 \text{ k}\Omega$$

$$R_{OUT} = 7.5k\Omega \| 75.7k\Omega = 6.82 \text{ k}\Omega$$

13.113

$$g_m = 40(50\mu A) = 2.00mS \quad | \quad r_\pi = \frac{100}{2.00mS} = 50k\Omega \quad | \quad r_o = \frac{75V + 10V}{50\mu A} = 1.70M\Omega$$

$$R_{BB} = R_B \| r_\pi = 100k\Omega \| 50k\Omega = 33.3k\Omega$$

$$\mathbf{v_{th}} = -\mathbf{v_s}\left(\frac{33.3k\Omega}{33.3k\Omega + 0.75k\Omega}\right)(2mS)(1.70M\Omega \| 100k\Omega) = -185\mathbf{v_s}$$

$$R_{th} = 1.70M\Omega \| 100k\Omega = 94.4 \text{ k}\Omega$$

13.114

$$g_m = 40(2.5\text{mA}) = 100\text{mS} \quad | \quad r_\pi = \frac{75}{100\text{mS}} = 750\Omega \quad | \quad r_o = \frac{50\text{V} + 7.5\text{V}}{2.5\text{mA}} = 23.0\text{k}\Omega$$

$$R_{BB} = R_B \| r_\pi = 4.7\text{k}\Omega \| 0.75\text{k}\Omega = 647\Omega$$

$$\mathbf{v_{th}} = -\mathbf{v_s}\left(\frac{647\Omega}{647\Omega + 50\Omega}\right)(100\text{mS})(23.0\text{k}\Omega \| 4.3\text{k}\Omega) = -336\mathbf{v_s}$$

$$R_{th} = 23.0\text{k}\Omega \| 4.3\text{k}\Omega = 3.62 \text{ k}\Omega$$

13.115

$$g_m = \sqrt{2\left(500\mu\text{A}/\text{V}^2\right)(100\mu\text{A})(1 + 0.02(5))} = 332\mu\text{S} \quad | \quad r_o = \frac{(50+5)\text{V}}{100\mu\text{A}} = 550\text{k}\Omega$$

$$\mathbf{v_{th}} = -\mathbf{v_s}\left(\frac{6.8\text{M}\Omega}{6.8\text{M}\Omega + 0.1\text{M}\Omega}\right)(332\mu\text{S})(550\text{k}\Omega \| 50\text{k}\Omega) = -15.0\mathbf{v_s}$$

$$R_{th} = 550\text{k}\Omega \| 50\text{k}\Omega = 45.8 \text{ k}\Omega$$

13.116

$$g_m = \sqrt{2\left(100\mu\text{A}/\text{V}^2\right)(10\mu\text{A})(1 + 0.02(5))} = 46.9\mu\text{S} \quad | \quad r_o = \frac{(50+5)\text{V}}{10\mu\text{A}} = 5.50\text{M}\Omega$$

$$\mathbf{v_{th}} = -\mathbf{v_s}\left(\frac{10\text{M}\Omega}{10\text{M}\Omega + 0.1\text{M}\Omega}\right)(46.9\mu\text{S})(5.50\text{M}\Omega \| 560\text{k}\Omega) = -23.6\mathbf{v_s}$$

$$R_{th} = 5.50\text{M}\Omega \| 560\text{k}\Omega = 508 \text{ k}\Omega$$

13.117

$$g_m = \frac{2}{|-3|}\sqrt{1\text{mA}(1\text{mA})(1 + 0.015(9))} = 710\mu\text{S} \quad | \quad r_o = \frac{\left(\frac{1}{0.015} + 9\right)\text{V}}{1\text{mA}} = 75.7\text{k}\Omega$$

$$\mathbf{v_{th}} = -\mathbf{v_s}\left(\frac{1\text{M}\Omega}{1\text{M}\Omega + 0.01\text{M}\Omega}\right)(710\mu\text{S})(75.7\text{k}\Omega \| 7.5\text{k}\Omega) = -4.79\mathbf{v_s}$$

$$R_{th} = 75.7\text{k}\Omega \| 7.5\text{k}\Omega = 6.82 \text{ k}\Omega$$

13.118   Note: f = 1000 Hz is more nearly midband

```
*Problem 13.118 - Common-Emitter Amplifier - Figure 13.42
VCC 7 0 DC 5
VEE 8 0 DC -5
VS 1 0 AC 1
*VO 6 0 AC 1
*VS 1 0 AC 0
RS 1 2 330
C1 2 3 100U
RB 3 0 100K
RE 4 8 16K
C2 4 0 100U
RC 7 5 10K
C3 5 6 100U
R4 6 0 220K
Q1 5 3 4 NBJT
.OP
.AC LIN 1 1000HZ 1000HZ
.MODEL NBJT NPN IS=1E-16 BF=65 VA=50
.PRINT AC VM(6) VP(6) IM(VS) IP(VS) VM(3) VP(3)
```

Results: IC = 2.41E-04   VCE = 3.68E+00

VM(6) = 8.148E+01   VP(6) = -1.792E+02   IM(VS) = 1.388E-04   IP(VS) = -1.793E+02

VM(3) = 9.542E-01   VP(3) = -2.259E-02   IM(C3) = 1.046E-04   IP(C3) = -1.800E+02

$$A_V = -81.5 \mid R_{IN} = \frac{VM(3)}{IM(VS)} = \frac{0.9542V}{138.8\mu A} = 6.88 \text{ k}\Omega \mid R_{OUT} = \frac{1}{IM(C3)} = \frac{1}{106.4\mu A} = 9.40 \text{ k}\Omega$$

The results are quite close. The variations are caused by small differences in the values of the small-signal parameters due to T = 27 C and β_o.

13.119

$$I_B = \frac{(5-0.7)V}{10000\Omega + 66(1600)\Omega} = 37.2 \text{ }\mu A \mid I_C = 65I_B = 2.42 \text{ mA} \mid I_E = 66I_B = 2.46 \text{ mA}$$

$$V_{CE} = 10 - 1000I_C - 1600I_E - (-5) = 8.64 \text{ V}$$

$$g_m = 40(0.00242) = 0.0968S \mid r_\pi = \frac{65}{0.0968S} = 672\Omega \mid r_o = \frac{50+8.64}{0.00242} = 24.2\text{k}\Omega$$

$$R_{IN} = R_B \| r_\pi = 10\text{k}\Omega \| 672\Omega = 630\Omega \mid R_{OUT} = 1\text{k}\Omega \| 24.2\text{k}\Omega = 960 \text{ }\Omega$$

$$A_V = -\left(\frac{630}{330+630}\right)(0.0968)\left(1\text{k}\Omega \| 24.2\text{k}\Omega \| 220\text{k}\Omega\right) = -60.7$$

Note that the gain has been reduced by 25% by the lower value of R_{IN}. Also note that R_{IN} and R_{OUT} have changed directly with the current.

13.120

Note: f = 10 kHz is more nearly midband because of the smaller resistor values.

```
*Problem 13.120 - Common-Emitter Amplifier - Figure 13.119
VCC 7 0 DC 5
VEE 8 0 DC -5
VS 1 0 AC 1
*VO 6 0 AC 1
*VS 1 0 AC 0
RS 1 2 330
C1 2 3 100U
RB 3 0 10K
RE 4 8 1.6K
C2 4 0 100U
RC 7 5 1K
C3 5 6 100U
R4 6 0 220K
Q1 5 3 4 NBJT
.OP
.AC LIN 1 10KHZ 10KHZ
.MODEL NBJT NPN IS=1E-16 BF=65 VA=50
.PRINT AC VM(6) VP(6) IM(VS) IP(VS) VM(3) VP(3)
*.PRINT AC IM(C3) IP(C3)
.END
```

Results: IC = 2.38E-03   VCE = 3.76E+00

VM(6) = 5.942E+01   VP(6) = -1.794E+02   IM(VS) = 9.738E-04   IP(VS) = -1.795E+02

VM(3) = 6.787E-01   VP(3) = -2.345E-01   IM(C3) = 1.045E-03   IP(C3) = -1.800E+02

$$A_V = -59.4 \mid R_{IN} = \frac{VM(3)}{IM(VS)} = \frac{0.6787V}{973.8\mu A} = 697\ \Omega \mid R_{OUT} = \frac{1}{IM(C3)} = \frac{1}{1.045mA} = 957\ \Omega$$

The results are quite close. The variations are caused by small differences in the values of the small-signal parameters due to T = 27 C and β_o.

13.121

$$I_B = \frac{5 - 0.7}{10^6 + 66(160k\Omega)} = 0.372\ \mu A \mid I_C = 65I_B = 24.2\ \mu A \mid I_E = 66I_B = 24.6\ \mu A$$

$$V_{CE} = 10 - 10^5 I_C - 1.6 \times 10^5 I_E - (-5) = 3.64\ V$$

$$g_m = 40(24.2\ \mu A) = 968\mu S \mid r_\pi = \frac{65}{968\mu S} = 67.1k\Omega \mid r_o = \frac{50 + 8.64}{24.2\ \mu A} = 2.42M\Omega$$

$$R_{IN} = R_B \| r_\pi = 1M\Omega \| 67.1k\Omega = 62.9\ k\Omega \mid R_{OUT} = 100k\Omega \| 2.42M\Omega = 96.0\ k\Omega$$

$$A_V = -\left(\frac{62.9k\Omega}{0.330k\Omega + 62.9k\Omega}\right)(968\mu S)(100k\Omega \| 2.42M\Omega \| 220k\Omega) = -64.4$$

Note that the gain has been increased due to the higher value of R_{IN} relative to that of R_S, but gain has been lost ecause R_{OUT} is now larger relative to the 220kΩ load resistor. Also note that R_{IN} and R_{OUT} have changed directly with the current.

13.122

```
*Problem 13.122 - Common-Emitter Amplifier - Figure 13.121
VCC 7 0 DC 5
VEE 8 0 DC -5
VS 1 0 AC 1
*VO 6 0 AC 1
*VS 1 0 AC 0
RS 1 2 330
C1 2 3 100U
RB 3 0 1MEG
RE 4 8 160K
C2 4 0 100U
RC 7 5 100K
C3 5 6 100U
R4 6 0 220K
Q1 5 3 4 NBJT
.OP
.AC LIN 1 1000HZ 1000HZ
.MODEL NBJT NPN IS=1E-16 BF=65 VA=50
.PRINT AC VM(6) VP(6) IM(VS) IP(VS) VM(3) VP(3)
*.PRINT AC IM(C3) IP(C3)
.END
```

Results: IC = 2.44E-05   VCE = 3.59E+00

VM(6) = 6.264E+01   VP(6) = -1.799E+02   IM(VS) = 1.467E-05   IP(VS) = -1.799E+02

VM(3) = 9.952E-01   VP(3) = 9.552E-04   IM(C3) = 1.046E-05   IP(C3) = -1.800E+02

$$A_V = -62.6 \mid R_{IN} = \frac{VM(3)}{IM(VS)} = \frac{0.9952V}{14.67\mu A} = 67.8\ k\Omega \mid R_{OUT} = \frac{1}{IM(C3)} = \frac{1}{10.46\mu A} = 95.6\ k\Omega$$

The results are quite close. The variations are caused by small differences in the values of the small-signal parameters due to T = 27 C and β_o.

13.123 $A_V = -g_m R$; We need to increase g_m by a factor or 10. Since g_m is proportional to the square root of K_n, K_n must increase by a factor of 100: $K_n = 50$ mA/V^2.

$$V_{GS} = V_{TN} + \sqrt{\frac{2I_{DS}}{K_n(1 + \lambda V_{DS})}} = 1 + \sqrt{\frac{2(250\mu A)}{0.05A(1 + 0.0167(5))}} = 1.096 \text{ V} \quad | \quad V_{GS} - V_{TN} = 0.096 \text{ V}$$

(Not really strong inversion) $\quad | \quad V_{GS} = \frac{R_{G1}}{R_{G1} + 3M\Omega}(10 - 5)V \rightarrow R_{G1} = 842 \text{ k}\Omega$

13.124 (a)

$$\beta_F = \beta_{FO}\left(1 + \frac{V_{CE}}{V_A}\right) \quad | \quad I_C = \beta_F \frac{5 - 0.7}{100000 + (\beta_F + 1)16000} \quad | \quad I_E = (\beta_F + 1)\frac{5 - 0.7}{100000 + (\beta_F + 1)16000}$$

$$V_{CE} = 10 - 10000I_C - 16000I_E$$

Iterative procedure: Pick V_{CE}, then calculate β_F, I_C, I_E and find the updated value of V_{CE}.

Results: $I_C = 243$ µA $\quad V_{CE} = 3.62$ V compared to $I_C = 241$ µA $\quad V_{CE} = 3.67$ V

(b)
```
                    *Problem 13.124 - Common-Emitter Amplifier - Figure P13.42
          *Monte Carlo Analysis for the Q-Point
          VEE 8 0 DC -5
          VCC 7 0 DC 5
          RC 7 5 RRAN 10K
          RB 3 0 RRAN 100K
          RE 4 8 RRAN 16K
          Q1 5 3 4 NBJT
          .OP
          .DC VCC 5 5 0.01
          .MODEL NBJT NPN IS=1E-16 BF=65 VA=50
          .MODEL RRAN RES R=1 DEV 10%
          .MC 500 DC IC(Q1) YMAX OUTPUT(ALL)
          *.MC 500 DC VCE(Q1) YMAX OUTPUT(ALL)
          .END
```

Results: Nominal IC = 241 µA Mean IC = 240 µA σ = 12.5 µA 3σ limits: 240 ± 37.5 µA

Nominal VCE = 3.68 V Mean VCE = 3.68 V σ = 0.185 V 3σ limits: 3.68 ± 0.555 V

Adding V_A to the hand calcualtions makes only a small change in our estimate of the Q-point, and the change is far smaller than that caused by the circuit tolerances. The added complexity in the hand calculations is not worth the extra effort.

13.125
```
          *Problem 13.125 - Common-Emitter Amplifier - Figure P13.42
          *Monte Carlo Analysis
          *Generate VCC and VEE with 5% Tolerances
          ICC 0 9 DC 5
          RCC 9 0 RRA 1
          ECC 7 0 9 0 1
          *
          IEE 10 0 DC 5
          REE 10 0 RRA 1
          EEE 8 0 10 0 1
          *
          VS 1 0 AC 1
          RS 1 2 RRB 330
          C1 2 3 100U
          RC 7 5 RRB 10K
```

```
RB 3 0 RRB 100K
RE 4 8 RRB 16K
C2 4 0 100U
C3 5 6 100U
R4 6 0 RRB 220K
Q1 5 3 4 NBJT
.OP
.AC LIN 1 1000 1000
.PRINT AC VM(6) VP(6)
.MODEL NBJT NPN IS=1E-16 BF=70 DEV 42.86% VA=65 DEV 23.08%
.MODEL RRA RES R=1 DEV 5%
.MODEL RRB RES R=1 DEV 10%
.MC 250 AC VM(6) YMAX OUTPUT(ALL)
.END
```

Results: Nominal Gain = 82.9   Mean Gain = 82.3 $\sigma = 7.22$ 3σ limits: 82.3 ± 21.7

13.126

```
*Problem 13.126 - Common-Source Amplifier - Figure 13.52
VDD 7 0 DC 10
VS 1 0 AC 1
*VO 6 0 AC 1
*VS 1 0 AC 0
RS 1 2 10K
C1 2 3 100U
RG1 3 0 2MEG
RG2 3 4 2MEG
C2 4 0 100U
RG3 4 5 1MEG
RD 7 5 20K
C3 5 6 100U
R3 6 0 100K
M1 5 3 0 0 NFET
.OP
.MODEL NFET NMOS KP=500U VTO=1 LAMBDA=0.0167
.AC LIN 1 1000HZ 1000HZ
.PRINT AC VM(6) VP(6) IM(VS) IP(VS) VM(3) VP(3)
*.PRINT AC IM(C3) IP(C3)
.END
```
Results: IDS = 2.53E-04   VDS = 4.92E+00

VM(6) = 7.983E+00   VP(6) = -1.800E+02   IM(VS) = 9.901E-07   IP(VS) = -1.800E+02

VM(3) = 9.901E-01   VP(3) = 9.370E-05   IM(C3) = 5.491E-05   IP(C3) = -1.800E+02

$$A_V = -79.8 \mid R_{IN} = \frac{VM(3)}{IM(VS)} = \frac{0.9901V}{0.9901\mu A} = 1.00 \text{ M}\Omega \mid R_{OUT} = \frac{1}{IM(C3)} = \frac{1}{54.91\mu A} = 18.2 \text{ k}\Omega$$

The results are almost identical.

13.127

```
*Problem 13.127 - Common-Source Amplifier - Figure P13.90
VDD 7 0 DC 10
*FOR OUTPUT RESISTANCE
*VO 6 0 AC 1
*VS 1 0 AC 0
*
VS 1 0 AC 1
RS 1 2 1K
```

```
C1 2 3 100U
R1 3 0 430K
R2 7 3 560K
R4 4 0 20K
C3 4 0 100U
RD 7 5 43K
C2 5 6 100U
R3 6 0 100K
M1 5 3 4 4 NFET
.OP
.MODEL NFET NMOS KP=500U VTO=1 LAMBDA=0.0133
.AC LIN 1 1000 1000
.PRINT AC VM(6) VDB(6) VP(6) VM(3) VP(3) IM(VS) IP(VS)
*.PRINT AC IM(C2) IP(C2)
.END
```

Results: IDS = 1.31E-04   VDS = 1.73E+00

VM(6) = 1.044E+01   VP(6) = -1.800E+02   IM(VS) = 4.094E-06   IP(VS) = -1.800E+02

VM(3) = 9.959E-01   VP(3) = 3.734E-04   IM(C3) = 2.496E-05   IP(C3) = -1.800E+02

$$A_V = -10.4 \mid R_{IN} = \frac{VM(3)}{IM(VS)} = \frac{0.9959V}{4.094\mu A} = 243 \text{ k}\Omega \mid R_{OUT} = \frac{1}{IM(C3)} = \frac{1}{24.96\mu A} = 40.1 \text{ k}\Omega$$

13.128 For the JFET model, $\beta = I_{DSS}/V_P^2$.

```
*Problem 13.128 - Common-Source Amplifier - Figure P13.59
VDD 7 0 DC 12
*FOR OUTPUT RESISTANCE
*VO 6 0 AC 1
*VS 1 0 AC 0
*
VS 1 0 AC 1
RS 1 2 1K
C1 2 3 100U
RG 3 0 1MEG
R1 4 0 2K
C2 4 0 100U
RD 7 5 27K
C3 5 6 100U
R3 6 0 100K
J1 5 3 4 NFET
.OP
.MODEL NFET NJF BETA=1M VTO=-1 LAMBDA=0.02
.AC LIN 1 1000 1000
.PRINT AC VM(6) VDB(6) VP(6) IM(VS) IP(VS) VM(3) VP(3)
*.PRINT AC IM(C3) IP(C3)
.END
```

Results: IDS = 2.57E-04   VDS = 4.54E+00

VM(6) = 2.045E+01   VP(6) = -1.799E+02   IM(VS) = 9.990E-07   IP(VS) = -1.800E+02

VM(3) = 9.990E-01   VP(3) = 9.110E-05   IM(C3) = 4.175E-05   IP(C3) = -1.800E+02

$$A_V = -20.5 \mid R_{IN} = \frac{VM(3)}{IM(VS)} = \frac{0.9990V}{0.9990\mu A} = 1.00 \text{ M}\Omega \mid R_{OUT} = \frac{1}{IM(C3)} = \frac{1}{41.75\mu A} = 24.0 \text{ k}\Omega$$

The results are almost identical.

13.129

$I_B = 3.71\mu A \quad I_C = 241\mu A \quad I_E = 245\mu A \quad V_{CE} = 3.67V$

$P_{R_B} = I_B^2 R_B = (3.71\mu A)^2 (100k\Omega) = 1.38 \ \mu W \ | \ P_{R_C} = I_C^2 R_C = (241\mu A)^2 (10k\Omega) = 0.581 \ mW$

$P_{R_E} = I_E^2 R_E = (245\mu A)^2 (16k\Omega) = 0.960 \ mW$

$P_{BJT} = I_C V_{CE} + I_B V_{BE} = (241\mu A)(3.67V) + (3.71\mu A)(0.7V) = 0.887 \ mW$

$P_S = 5V(241\mu A) + (-5V)(-245\mu A) = 2.43 \ mW \ | \ P_S = P_{R_B} + P_{R_C} + P_{R_E} + P_Q$

13.130

$I_{DS} = 250\mu A \quad V_{DS} = 4.75V$

$P_{JFET} = I_{DS} V_{DS} = (250\mu A)(4.75V) = 1.19 \ mW \ | \ P_{R_D} = I_{DS}^2 R_D = (250\mu A)^2 (27k\Omega) = 1.69 \ mW$

$P_{R_4} = I_{DS}^2 R_4 = (250\mu A)^2 (2k\Omega) = 0.125 \ mW \ | \ P_{R_G} = 0$

$P_S = 12V(250\mu A) = 3.00 \ mW \ | \ P_{JFET} + P_{R_D} + P_{R_4} + P_{R_G} = 3.00 \ mW$

13.131 Use values from Prob. 13.9

$I_B = 23.8\mu A \quad I_C = 1.78mA \quad I_E = 1.81mA \quad V_{CE} = 6.08V \quad V_B = -4.09V$

$P_{R_1} = \dfrac{V_1^2}{R_1} = \dfrac{(-4.09 - (-12))^2 \ V^2}{5000\Omega} = 12.5 \ mW \ | \ P_{R_2} = \dfrac{V_2^2}{R_2} = \dfrac{(12 - (-4.09))^2 \ V^2}{10000\Omega} = 25.9 \ mW$

$P_{R_C} = I_C^2 R_C = (1.78mA)^2 (6k\Omega) = 19.0 \ mW \ | \ P_{R_E} = I_E^2 R_E = (1.81mA)^2 (4k\Omega) = 13.0 \ mW$

$P_{BJT} = I_C V_{CE} + I_B V_{BE} = (1.78mA)(6.08V) + (23.8\mu A)(0.7V) = 10.8 \ mW$

$P_S = 12V \left[1.78mA + \dfrac{12 - (-4.09)V}{10000\Omega} \right] + 12V \left[1.81mA + \dfrac{-4.09 - (-12)V}{5000\Omega} \right] = 81.3 \ mW$

$P_S = P_{R_1} + P_{R_2} + P_{R_C} + P_{R_E} + P_{BJT} = 81.2 \ mW$

13.132 Use values from Prob. 13.13

$I_B = 1.51\mu A \quad I_C = 98.4\mu A \quad I_E = 99.9\mu A \quad V_{CE} = 6.96V$

$P_{R_B} = I_B^2 R_B = (1.51\mu A)^2 \ 3k\Omega = 6.84 \ nW \ | \ P_{R_C} = I_C^2 R_C = (98.4\mu A)^2 (33k\Omega) = 0.320 \ mW$

$P_{R_E} = I_E^2 R_E = (99.9\mu A)^2 (68k\Omega) = 0.679 \ mW$

$P_{BJT} = I_C V_{CE} + I_B V_{BE} = (98.4\mu A)(6.96V) + (1.51\mu A)(0.7V) = 0.489 \ mW$

$P_S = 7.5(98.4\mu A) + 7.5V(99.9\mu A) = 1.49 \ mW \ | \ P_S = P_{R_B} + P_{R_C} + P_{R_E} + P_{BJT} = 1.49 \ mW$

13.133 Use values from Prob. 13.17

$I_{DS} = 82.2\mu A \quad V_{DS} = 6.04V$

$P_{FET} = I_{DS} V_{DS} = (82.2\mu A)(6.04V) = 0.497 \ mW \ | \ P_{R_D} = I_{DS}^2 R_D = (82.2\mu A)^2 (82k\Omega) = 0.554 \ mW$

$P_{R_4} = I_{DS}^2 R_4 = (82.2\mu A)^2 (27k\Omega) = 0.182 \ mW \ | \ I_2 = \dfrac{15V}{3.7M\Omega} = 4.05\mu A$

$P_{R_1} = I_2^2 R_1 = (4.05\mu A)^2 (1M\Omega) = 16.4 \ \mu W \ | \ P_{R_2} = I_2^2 R_2 = (4.05\mu A)^2 (2.7M\Omega) = 44.3 \ \mu W$

$P_S = 15V(82.2\mu A + 4.05\mu A) = 1.29 \ mW \ | \ P_{FET} + P_{R_D} + P_{R_4} + P_{R_1} + P_{R_2} = 1.29 \ mW$

13.134 Use values from Prob. 13.21

$I_{SD} = 307\mu A \quad V_{SD} = 3.88V$

$P_{FET} = I_{SD}V_{SD} = (307\mu A)(3.88V) = 1.19 \text{ mW} \mid P_{R_D} = I_{SD}^2 R_D = (307\mu A)^2(24k\Omega) = 2.26 \text{ mW}$

$P_{R_4} = I_{SD}^2 R_4 = (307\mu A)^2(22k\Omega) = 2.07 \text{ mW} \mid I_2 = \dfrac{18V}{6.6M\Omega} = 2.73\mu A$

$P_{R_1} = I_2^2 R_1 = (2.73\mu A)^2(3.3M\Omega) = 24.6 \text{ }\mu W \mid P_{R_2} = I_2^2 R_2 = (2.73\mu A)^2(3.3M\Omega) = 24.6 \text{ }\mu W$

$P_S = 18V(307\mu A + 2.73\mu A) = 5.58 \text{ mW} \mid P_{FET} + P_{R_D} + P_{R_4} + P_{R_1} + P_{R_2} = 5.57 \text{ mW}$

13.135 Use values from Prob. 13.25

$I_{DS} = 1.25mA \quad V_{DS} = 10.6V$

$P_{JFET} = I_{DS}V_{DS} = (1.25mA)(10.6V) = 13.3 \text{ mW} \mid P_{R_D} = I_{DS}^2 R_D = (1.25mA)^2(3.9k\Omega) = 6.09 \text{ mW}$

$P_{R_4} = I_{DS}^2 R_4 = (1.25mA)^2(2k\Omega) = 3.13 \text{ mW} \mid P_{R_G} = 0$

$P_S = 18V(1.25mA) = 22.5 \text{ mW} \mid P_{JFET} + P_{R_D} + P_{R_4} + P_{R_G} = 22.5 \text{ mW}$

13.136

$$I_C = \frac{V_{CC}}{3R_C} \mid i_c \leq 0.2I_C \mid v_c = i_c R_C \leq 0.2\frac{V_{CC}}{3R_C}R_C = \frac{V_{CC}}{15}$$

13.137

$|i_{ds}| \leq 0.4I_{DS} \mid I_{DS} = \dfrac{500\text{x}10^{-6}}{2}(0 - (-1.5))^2 = 563 \text{ }\mu A$

$|v_{gs}| \leq 0.2(V_{GS} - V_{TN}) = 0.2(0 - (-1.5)) = 0.3 \text{ V}$

$v_{ds} = i_{ds}R_D \leq 0.4(563\mu A)(15k\Omega) = 3.38 \text{ V}$

To insure saturation: $v_{DS} \geq v_{GS} - V_{TN} = v_{gs} - V_{TN} = 0.3 - (-1.5) = 1.8 \text{ V}$

$V_{DD} \geq 1.8 + 3.38 + (563\mu A)(15k\Omega) = 13.6 \text{ V}$

13.138

$$|v_o| \leq \frac{V_{CC}}{2} \mid P_{dc} = V_{CC}\left(\frac{V_{CC}}{2R_L}\right) = \frac{V_{CC}^2}{2R_L} \mid P_{ac} = \frac{1}{2}\left(\frac{V_{CC}}{2}\right)^2\frac{1}{R_L} = \frac{V_{CC}^2}{8R_L} \mid \varepsilon = 100\%\frac{\frac{V_{CC}^2}{8R_L}}{\frac{V_{CC}^2}{2R_L}} = 25 \text{ \%}$$

13.139

The Q-point from problem 13.9 is $(1.78mA, 6.08V)$.

$|i_c| \leq 0.2I_C = 0.356 \text{ mA} \mid |v_c| \leq 0.2I_C R_L = 0.356mA(100k\Omega\|6k\Omega) = 2.02V$

13.140

The Q-point from problem 13.9 is $(371\mu A, 2.72V)$.

$|v_o| \leq g_m|v_{be}|(r_o\|R_C\|R_3) = 40(371\mu A)(5mV)(\infty\|13k\Omega\|100k\Omega) = 0.854 \text{ V}$

13.141

The Q-point from Problem 13.17 is $(82.2\mu A, 6.04V)$.

$|i_{ds}| \leq 0.4I_{DS} = 32.9\mu A \mid |v_{ds}| \leq 0.4I_{DS}R_L = 32.9\mu A(\infty\|82k\Omega\|420k\Omega) = 2.30V$

13.142

The Q - point from Problem 13.21 is $(307\mu A, 3.88V)$.

$|i_{sd}| \le 0.4 I_{SD} = 307\mu A$ | $|v_o| \le 0.4 I_{SD} R_L = 307\mu A(\infty \| 24k\Omega \| 470k\Omega) = 2.80V$

Checking the bias point: $V_{R_D} = 307\mu A(24k\Omega) = 7.37V$ | $2.80 < 7.37$ & $2.80 < 3.88 - 1$

13.143

The Q - point from Problem 13.25 is $(1.25mA, 10.6V)$

$|i_{ds}| \le 0.4 I_{DS} = 0.500mA$ | $|v_{ds}| \le 0.4 I_{DS} R_L = 0.500mA(\infty \| 3.9k\Omega \| 36k\Omega) = 1.76V$

Checking the bias point: $I_{DS} R_D = 1.25mA(3.9k\Omega) = 4.88V$ & $V_{DS} = 10.6$ V

13.144

The Q - point from Problem 13.27 is $(1.00mA, 7.50V)$.

$|i_{sd}| \le 0.4 I_{SD} = 0.400\mu A$ | $|v_o| \le 0.4 I_{SD} R_L = 307\mu A(\infty \| 7.5k\Omega \| 2200k\Omega) = 2.90V$

Checking the bias point: $V_{R_D} = 1.25mA(7.5k\Omega) = 9.38V$ | $2.90 < 9.38$ & $2.90 < 7.50 - 3$

13.145

$V_{CE} = 20 - 20000 I_C$: Two points on the load line $(0mA, 20V)$, $(1mA, 0V)$

At $I_B = 2\mu A$, the maximum swing is approximately 2.5 V limited by V_{R_C}.

For $I_B = 5\mu A$, the maximum swing is approximately -8.5 V limited by V_{CE}.

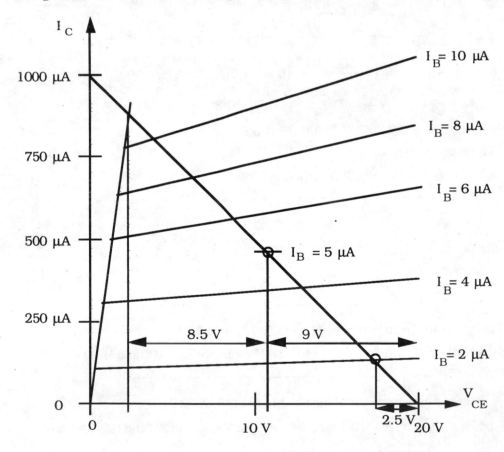

CHAPTER 14

14.1 (a) Common-collector Amplifier (Emitter-follower)

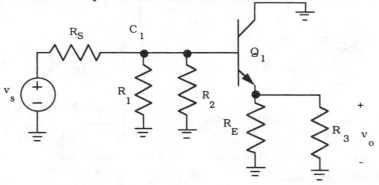

14.1 (b) Common-gate Amplifier

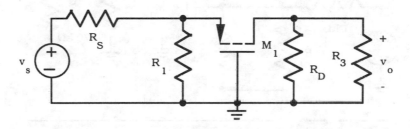

14.1 (c) Common-collector Amplifier (Emitter-follower)

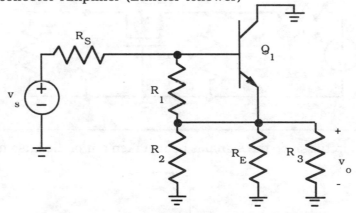

14.1 (d) Not a useful circuit because the signal is injected into the drain of the transistor.

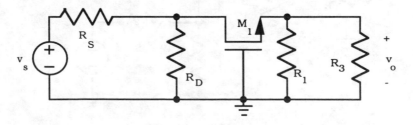

14.1 (e) Common-emitter Amplifier

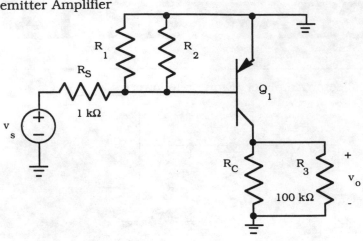

14.1 (f) Common-source Amplifier

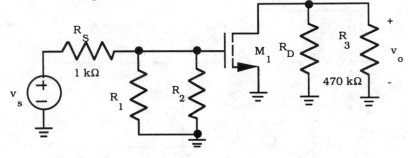

14.1 (g) Common-gate Amplifier

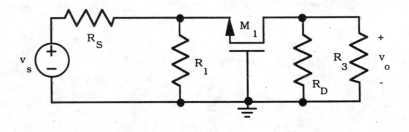

14.1 (h) Not a useful circuit since the signal is being taken out of the base terminal.

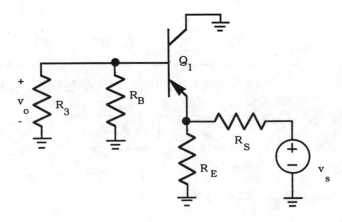

314

14.1 (i) Common-source Amplifier

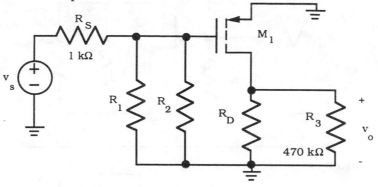

14.1 (j) Common-source Amplifier

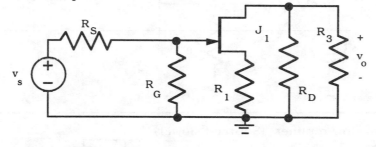

14.1 (k) Common-base Amplifier

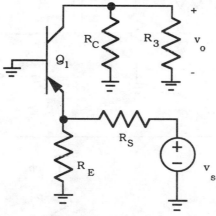

14.1 (l) Not a useful circuit because the signal is injected into the drain of the transistor.

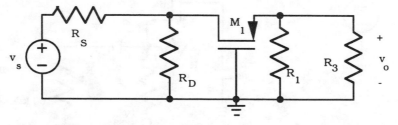

Note that the resistor labels on R_D and R_1 were reversed in the first printing.

14.1 (m) Common-source Amplifier

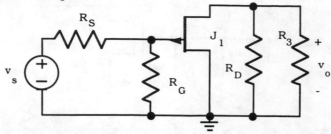

14.1 (n) Common-emitter Amplifier

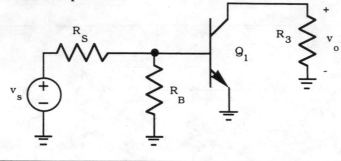

14.1 (o) Common-drain Amplifier (Source-follower)

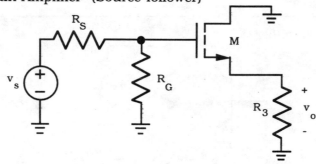

14.2

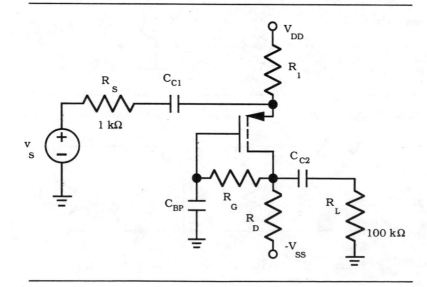

14.3

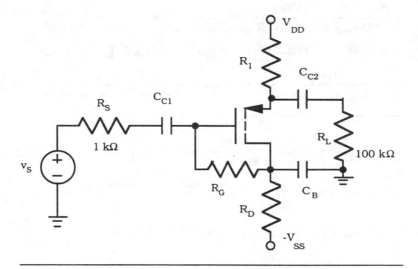

14.4

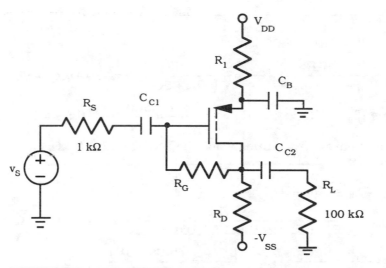

14.5

(a) Neglecting R_{OUT}: $A_{Vth} = -\dfrac{g_m R_L}{1 + g_m R_5} = -\dfrac{(0.005S)(2000\Omega)}{1 + (0.005S)(200\Omega)} = -5.00 \mid R_{IN} = \infty$

$R_{OUT} = r_o(1 + g_m R_5) = 10k\Omega[1 + (0.005S)(200\Omega)] = 20.0 \text{ k}\Omega \gg 2k\Omega \mid A_{Ith} = \infty$

(b) $A_{Vth} = -g_m R_L = -(0.005S)(2k\Omega\|10k\Omega) = -8.33 \mid R_{IN} = \infty \mid R_{OUT} = r_o = 10.0 \text{ k}\Omega \mid A_{Ith} = \infty$

14.6

(a) $g_m = 0.02S \mid r_\pi = \dfrac{75}{.02} = 3750\Omega \mid R_{IN} = r_\pi + (\beta_o + 1)R_5 = 3750\Omega + 76(200\Omega) = 19.0 \text{ k}\Omega$

Neglecting R_{OUT}: $A_{Vth} = -\dfrac{\beta_o R_L}{R_{th} + r_\pi + (\beta_o + 1)R_5} = -\dfrac{75(12k\Omega)}{500\Omega + 3750\Omega + 76(200\Omega)} = -46.3$

$R_{OUT} = r_o\left(1 + \dfrac{\beta_o R_5}{R_{th} + r_\pi + R_5}\right) = 100k\Omega\left[1 + \dfrac{75(200\Omega)}{500\Omega + 3750\Omega + 200\Omega}\right] = 437 \text{ k}\Omega \gg 12k\Omega$

$A_{Ith} = -\beta_o = -75$

(b) $A_{Vth} = -\dfrac{75(12k\Omega)}{500\Omega + 3750\Omega + 76(560\Omega)} = -19.2$

$R_{IN} = r_\pi + (\beta_o + 1)R_5 = 3750\Omega + 76(560\Omega) = 46.3 \text{ k}\Omega \quad | \quad A_{Ith} = -\beta_o = -75$

$R_{OUT} = r_o\left(1 + \dfrac{\beta_o R_5}{R_{th} + r_\pi + R_5}\right) = 100\text{k}\Omega\left[1 + \dfrac{75(560\Omega)}{500\Omega + 3750\Omega + 560\Omega}\right] = 973 \text{ k}\Omega$

14.7

(a) For large β_o: $A_V \cong -\dfrac{R_L}{R_5} = -\dfrac{8.2\text{k}\Omega\|47\text{k}\Omega}{330\Omega + 680\Omega} = -6.91 \quad |$ (b) Place a bypass capacitor in

parallel with the 330Ω resistor. Then $A_V \cong -\dfrac{R_L}{R_5} = -\dfrac{8.2\text{k}\Omega\|47\text{k}\Omega}{680\Omega} = -10.3 \quad |$ (c) Place a

bypass capacitor in parallel with the 680Ω resistor. Then $A_V \cong -\dfrac{8.2\text{k}\Omega\|47\text{k}\Omega}{330\Omega} = -21.2$

(d) Place a bypass capacitor from the emitter to ground. (e) $A_V \cong -10V_{CC} = -120$.

14.8

$R_{IN} = r_\pi + (\beta_o + 1)R_5 = 500 \text{ k}\Omega$

$A_{Vth} = -\dfrac{\beta_o R_L}{R_{th} + r_\pi + (\beta_o + 1)R_5} = -\dfrac{75R_L}{100\Omega + 500\text{k}\Omega} = -10 \rightarrow R_L = 66.7 \text{ k}\Omega$

Assuming $(\beta_o + 1)R_5 \gg r_\pi$, $R_5 \approx \dfrac{500 \text{ k}\Omega}{\beta_o + 1} = \dfrac{500 \text{ k}\Omega}{76} = 6.58 \text{ k}\Omega$

Note: The nearest 5% values would be 68 kΩ and 6.8 kΩ.

14.9

$R_{IN} = r_\pi = 500 \text{ k}\Omega$

$A_{Vth} = -\dfrac{\beta_o R_L}{R_{th} + r_\pi} = -\dfrac{75R_L}{100\Omega + 500\text{k}\Omega} = -10 \quad | \quad R_L = 66.7 \text{ k}\Omega$

$r_\pi = \dfrac{\beta_o}{g_m} = \dfrac{\beta_o V_T}{I_C} \quad | \quad I_C = \dfrac{\beta_o V_T}{r_\pi} = \dfrac{75(0.025V)}{500\text{k}\Omega} = 3.75 \text{ μA}$

14.10

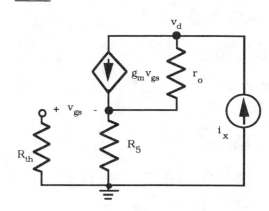

$$\begin{bmatrix} i_x - g_m v_{gs} \\ +g_m v_{gs} \end{bmatrix} = \begin{bmatrix} g_o & -g_o \\ -g_o & g_o + G_5 \end{bmatrix} \begin{bmatrix} v_d \\ v_s \end{bmatrix} \mid v_{gs} = -v_s$$

$$\begin{bmatrix} i_x \\ 0 \end{bmatrix} = \begin{bmatrix} g_o & -(g_m + g_o) \\ -g_o & g_m + g_o + G_5 \end{bmatrix} \begin{bmatrix} v_d \\ v_s \end{bmatrix}$$

$$\Delta = g_o G_5 \mid v_d = (g_m + g_o + G_5)\frac{i_x}{\Delta} = \frac{(g_m + g_o + G_5)}{g_o G_5} i_x$$

$$R_{OUT} = \frac{v_d}{i_x} = R_5\left(1 + \frac{g_m}{g_o} + \frac{G_5}{g_o}\right) = R_5\left(1 + \mu_f + \frac{r_o}{R_5}\right)$$

$$R_{OUT} = r_o + (1 + \mu_f)R_5 \cong r_o + \mu_f R_5 = r_o(1 + g_m R_5)$$

14.11

$$\begin{bmatrix} i_x + g_m' v_e \\ -g_m' v_e \end{bmatrix} = \begin{bmatrix} g_o & -g_o \\ -g_o & g_o + G_5 + G_1 \end{bmatrix} \begin{bmatrix} v_x \\ v_e \end{bmatrix} \mid \begin{bmatrix} i_x \\ 0 \end{bmatrix} = \begin{bmatrix} g_o & -(g_m' + g_o) \\ -g_o & g_m' + g_o + G_5 + G_1 \end{bmatrix} \begin{bmatrix} v_x \\ v_e \end{bmatrix}$$

$$\Delta = g_o(G_5 + G_1) \mid v_x = (g_m' + g_o + G_5 + G_1)\frac{i_x}{\Delta} = \frac{(g_m' + g_o + (G_5 + G_1))}{g_o(G_5 + G_1)} i_x$$

$$R_{OUT} = \frac{v_x}{i_x} = (R_5 \| R_1)\left(1 + \frac{g_m'}{g_o} + \frac{G_5 + G_1}{g_o}\right) = (R_5 \| R_1)\left(1 + g_m' r_o + \frac{r_o}{(R_5 \| R_1)}\right)$$

$$R_{OUT} = (R_5 \| R_1) + r_o + r_o\frac{g_m r_\pi}{R_{th} + r_\pi}\frac{R_5(R_{th} + r_\pi)}{R_{th} + r_\pi + R_5} = (R_5 \| R_1) + r_o\left(1 + \frac{\beta_o R_5}{R_{th} + r_\pi + R_5}\right)$$

14.12

$$V_{EQ} = 12\frac{62k\Omega}{20k\Omega + 62k\Omega} = 9.07V \mid R_{EQ} = 20k\Omega \| 62k\Omega = 15.1k\Omega$$

$$I_B = \frac{(12 - 0.7 - 9.07)V}{15.1k\Omega + (75 + 1)3.9k\Omega} = 7.16\mu A \mid I_C = 537\,\mu A \mid V_{EC} = 12 - 3900I_E - 8200I_C = 5.47\ V$$

Forward − active region is correct. $\mid r_\pi = \frac{75(0.025V)}{537\mu A} = 3.49k\Omega$

$$\mathbf{v_{th}} = \mathbf{v_s}\frac{15.1k\Omega}{1k\Omega + 15.1k\Omega} = 0.938\mathbf{v_s} \mid R_{th} = 1k\Omega \| 15.1k\Omega = 0.938k\Omega$$

$$R_L = r_o \| 8.2k\Omega \| 100k\Omega \cong 8.2k\Omega \| 100k\Omega = 7.58k\Omega \mid A_{Vth} = -\frac{75(7.58k\Omega)}{0.938k\Omega + 3.49k\Omega} = -128$$

$$A_V = 0.938A_{Vth} = -120 \mid A_I = -75\frac{15.1k\Omega}{15.1k\Omega + 3.49k\Omega} = -60.9$$

$$R_{IN} = 15.1k\Omega \| 3.49k\Omega = 2.83\ k\Omega \mid R_{OUT} = r_o \| 8.2k\Omega \cong 8.2k\Omega$$

$$\mathbf{v_{be}} = 0.938\mathbf{v_s}\frac{3.49k\Omega}{0.938k\Omega + 3.49k\Omega} = 0.739\mathbf{v_s} \mid \mathbf{v_s} = \frac{5.00mV}{0.739} = 6.76\ mV$$

$$A_V \cong -10V_{CC} = -10(12) = -120. \mid \text{Gain is identical to the rule - of - thumb estimate.}$$

14.13

$$V_{EQ} = 18 \frac{500k\Omega}{1.4M\Omega + 500k\Omega} = 4.74V \mid R_{EQ} = 500k\Omega \| 1.4M\Omega = 368k\Omega$$

$$4.74 = V_{GS} + 27000I_{DS} = 1 + \sqrt{\frac{2I_{DS}}{250 \times 10^{-6}}} + 27000I_{DS} \rightarrow I_{DS} = 104\mu A$$

$$V_{DS} = 18 - I_{DS}(75k\Omega + 27k\Omega) = 7.39V \mid \text{Saturation region is correct.}$$

$$g_m = \sqrt{2(250 \times 10^{-6})(104 \times 10^{-6})} = 0.228mS$$

$$\mathbf{v_{th}} = \mathbf{v_s} \frac{368k\Omega}{1k\Omega + 368k\Omega} = 0.997\mathbf{v_s} \mid R_{th} = 1k\Omega \| 368k\Omega = 0.997k\Omega$$

$$R_L = r_o \| 75k\Omega \| 470k\Omega \cong 75k\Omega \| 470k\Omega = 64.7k\Omega \mid A_{Vth} = -(0.228mS)(64.7k\Omega) = -14.8$$

$$A_V = 0.997A_{Vth} = -14.7 \mid A_I = 368k\Omega(-g_m)\frac{75k\Omega}{75k\Omega + 470k\Omega} = -11.6$$

$$R_{IN} = 368 \ k\Omega \mid R_{OUT} = r_o \| 75k\Omega \cong 75k\Omega$$

$$\mathbf{v_{gs}} = 0.997\mathbf{v_s} \mid V_{GS} - V_{TN} = \sqrt{\frac{2(104\mu A)}{250\mu A / V^2}} = 0.912V \mid \mathbf{v_s} = 0.2\frac{0.912V}{0.997} = 0.183 \ V$$

$$A_V \cong -\frac{V_{DD}}{V_{GS} - V_{TN}} = -\frac{18}{0.912} = -19.7 \mid \text{The rule-of-thumb estimate assumes } V_{R_L} = \frac{V_{DD}}{2}.$$

We have $V_{R_L} = 104\mu A(75k\Omega) = 7.80V = 0.433V_{DD}$

The estimate also doesn't account for the presence of R_3.

14.14

$$V_{EQ} = 18 \frac{2.2M\Omega}{2.2M\Omega + 2.2M\Omega} = 9.00V \mid R_{EQ} = 2.2M\Omega \| 2.2M\Omega = 1.10M\Omega$$

$$18 = 22000I_{SD} + V_{SG} + 9 \mid 9 = 22000I_{SD} + 1 + \sqrt{\frac{2I_{SD}}{400 \times 10^{-6}}} \rightarrow I_{SD} = 307\mu A$$

$$V_{SD} = 18 - I_{SD}(22k\Omega + 18k\Omega) = 5.72V \mid \text{Saturation region is correct.}$$

$$g_m = \sqrt{2(400 \times 10^{-6})(307 \times 10^{-6})} = 0.496mS$$

$$\mathbf{v_{th}} = \mathbf{v_s} \frac{1.1M\Omega}{1k\Omega + 1.1M\Omega} = 0.999\mathbf{v_s} \mid R_{th} = 1k\Omega \| 1.1M\Omega = 0.999k\Omega$$

$$R_L = r_o \| 18k\Omega \| 470k\Omega \cong 18k\Omega \| 470k\Omega = 17.3k\Omega \mid A_{Vth} = -(0.496mS)(17.3k\Omega) = -8.60$$

$$A_V = 0.999A_{Vth} = -8.59 \mid R_{IN} = 1.10 \ M\Omega \mid R_{OUT} = r_o \| 18k\Omega \cong 18k\Omega$$

$$A_I = A_V \frac{R_{IN}}{R_3} = -8.59\frac{1.1M\Omega}{470k\Omega} = -20.1$$

$$\mathbf{v_{gs}} = 0.999\mathbf{v_s} \mid V_{GS} - V_{TN} = \sqrt{\frac{2(307\mu A)}{400\mu A / V^2}} = 1.24V \mid \mathbf{v_s} = 0.2\frac{1.24V}{0.999} = 0.248 \ V$$

14.15

$$V_{GS} = -(11k\Omega)I_{DS} = -(11k\Omega)(20mA)\left(1 - \frac{V_{GS}}{-4}\right)^2 \rightarrow V_{GS} = -3.50V, \ I_{DS} = -\frac{V_{GS}}{11k\Omega} = 318 \ \mu A$$

$$V_{DS} = 20 - I_{DS}(11k\Omega + 39k\Omega) = 4.10V \mid \text{Saturation region is correct.}$$

$$g_m = \frac{2}{|-4|}\sqrt{20mA(318\mu A)} = 1.26mS \mid \mathbf{v_{th}} = \mathbf{v_s} \frac{1M\Omega}{0.5k\Omega + 1M\Omega} = 1.00\mathbf{v_s}$$

$$R_{th} = 0.5k\Omega \| 1M\Omega = 0.500k\Omega \quad | \quad R_L = 39k\Omega \| 500k\Omega = 36.2k\Omega$$

$$A_V = A_{Vth} = -\frac{1.26mS(36.2k\Omega)}{1 + 1.26mS(11k\Omega)} = -3.07 \quad | \quad R_{IN} = 1.00 \ M\Omega \quad | \quad R_{OUT} = 39k\Omega$$

$$A_I = -R_G \frac{g_m}{1 + g_m R_1} = -\left(10^6\right)\frac{1.26mS}{1 + 1.26mS(11k\Omega)} = -84.8$$

$$\mathbf{v_{th}} = 1.00\mathbf{v_s} \quad | \quad V_{GS} - V_P = -3.5 - (-4) = 0.500V \quad | \quad \mathbf{v_s} = 0.2(0.5)\left[1 + 1.26mS(11k\Omega)\right] = 1.49 \ V$$

14.16

$$V_{SG} = 0 \rightarrow I_{SD} = I_{DSS} = 5.00mA \quad | \quad V_{DS} = 16 - 1800 I_{DS} = 7.00V$$

$$\text{Saturation region is correct.} \quad | \quad g_m = \frac{2}{|-5|}\sqrt{5mA(5mA)} = 2.00mS$$

$$\mathbf{v_{th}} = \mathbf{v_s}\frac{10M\Omega}{5k\Omega + 10M\Omega} = 1.00\mathbf{v_s} \quad | \quad A_V = \frac{10M\Omega}{10M\Omega + 5k\Omega}(-2.00mS)(1.8k\Omega \| 36k\Omega) = -3.43$$

$$R_{IN} = 10.0 \ M\Omega \quad | \quad R_{OUT} = 1.80 \ k\Omega \quad | \quad A_I = (10M\Omega)(-2.00mS)\frac{1.8k\Omega}{1.8k\Omega + 36k\Omega} = -952$$

$$\mathbf{v_{gs}} = \mathbf{v_s}\frac{10M\Omega}{10M\Omega + 5k\Omega} \leq 0.2|V_{SG} + V_P| \rightarrow \mathbf{v_s} \leq 1 \ V$$

14.17

$$I_B = \frac{(10 - 0.7)V}{20k\Omega + (80 + 1)9.1k\Omega} = 12.3\mu A \quad | \quad I_C = 983 \ \mu A \quad | \quad V_{CE} = 20 - 9100 I_E = 11.0 \ V \quad | \quad \text{Forward -}$$

$$\text{active region is correct.} \quad | \quad r_\pi = \frac{80(0.025V)}{983\mu A} = 2.04k\Omega \quad | \quad r_o = \frac{(100 + 11.0)V}{983\mu A} = 113k\Omega$$

$$\mathbf{v_{th}} = \mathbf{v_s}\frac{20k\Omega}{20k\Omega + 250\Omega} = 0.988\mathbf{v_s} \quad | \quad R_{th} = 20k\Omega \| 250\Omega = 247\Omega$$

$$R_L = r_o \| 1M\Omega = 113k\Omega \| 1M\Omega = 102k\Omega \quad | \quad A_{Vth} = -\frac{80(102k\Omega)}{247\Omega + 2.04k\Omega} = -3570$$

$$A_V = 0.988 A_{Vth} = -3530 \quad | \quad A_I = \frac{20k\Omega}{20k\Omega + 2.04k\Omega}(-80)\frac{113k\Omega}{113k\Omega + 1M\Omega} = -7.37$$

$$R_{IN} = 20k\Omega \| 2.04k\Omega = 1.85 \ k\Omega \quad | \quad R_{OUT} = 113 \ k\Omega$$

$$\mathbf{v_{be}} = 0.988\mathbf{v_s}\frac{2.04k\Omega}{247\Omega + 2.04k\Omega} = 0.881\mathbf{v_s} \quad | \quad \mathbf{v_s} = \frac{5.00mV}{0.881} = 5.67 \ mV$$

14.18

$$A_{Ith} = +81 \quad | \quad r_\pi = \frac{80}{0.4S} = 200\Omega \quad | \quad A_{Vth} = -\frac{81(1k\Omega)}{47k\Omega + 200\Omega + 81(1k\Omega)} = 0.632$$

$$R_{IN} = 200\Omega + 81(1k\Omega) = 81.2 \ k\Omega \quad | \quad R_{OUT} = \frac{0.988}{0.4S} + \frac{47k\Omega}{81} = 583 \ \Omega$$

14.19

$$A_{Vth} = -\frac{0.01(1k\Omega)}{1 + 0.01(1k\Omega)} = 0.909 \quad | \quad A_{Ith} = \infty \quad | \quad R_{IN} = \infty \quad | \quad R_{OUT} = \frac{1}{10mS} = 100 \ \Omega$$

14.20   Defining v_1 as the source node:

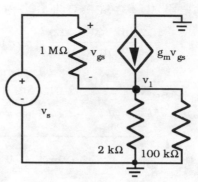

(a) $2k\Omega \| 100k\Omega = 1.96k\Omega$

$$\frac{(v_s - v_1)}{10^6} + 3.54\times10^{-3}(v_s - v_1) = \frac{v_1}{1960}$$

$$3.541\times10^{-3}v_s = 4.051\times10^{-3}v_1$$

$$v_1 = 0.874v_s \mid A_V = 0.874$$

$$R_{IN} = \frac{v_s}{i_s} = \frac{v_s}{10^{-6}(v_s - v_1)} = 7.94 \text{ M}\Omega$$

Driving the output with current source i_x:

$$R_{OUT}: i_x = \frac{v_1}{10^6} + \frac{v_1}{2000} + 3.54\times10^{-3}v_1$$

$$R_{OUT} = \frac{v_1}{i_x} = 247\ \Omega \mid \text{(b) } R_{IN} = \infty$$

14.21

$$V_{EQ} = 18\frac{51k\Omega}{51k\Omega + 100k\Omega} = 6.08V \mid R_{EQ} = 51k\Omega\|100k\Omega = 33.8k\Omega$$

$$I_B = \frac{(6.08 - 0.7 + 18)V}{33.8k\Omega + (126)(4.7k\Omega)} = 37.3\mu A \mid I_C = 4.67 \text{ mA} \mid V_{CE} = 36 - 2000I_C - 4700I_E = 4.54 \text{ V}$$

Forward - active region is correct. $\mid r_\pi = \frac{125(0.025V)}{4.67mA} = 669\Omega \mid r_o = \frac{(50 + 4.54)V}{4.67mA} = 11.7k\Omega$

$$v_{th} = v_s\frac{33.8\Omega}{500\Omega + 33.8k\Omega} = 0.985v_s \mid R_{th} = 33.8k\Omega\|500\Omega = 493\Omega$$

$$R_L = 24k\Omega\|4.7k\Omega\|11.7k\Omega = 2.94k\Omega \mid A_{Vth} = -\frac{126(2.94k\Omega)}{0.493k\Omega + 0.669k\Omega + 126(2.94k\Omega)} = 0.997$$

$$A_V = 0.985A_{Vth} = 0.982 \mid R_{IN} = 33.8k\Omega\|[0.669k\Omega + 126(2.94k\Omega)] = 31.0 \text{ k}\Omega$$

$$A_I = A_V\frac{R_S + R_{IN}}{R_3} = 0.982\frac{0.5k\Omega + 31.0k\Omega}{24.0k\Omega} = 1.29 \mid R_{OUT} = \frac{493\Omega + 669\Omega}{126}\|2.94k\Omega = 9.19\ \Omega$$

$$v_{be} = 0.982v_s\frac{0.669k\Omega}{0.493k\Omega + 0.669k\Omega + 126(2.94k\Omega)} = 0.00177v_s \mid v_s = \frac{5.00mV}{0.00177} = 2.83 \text{ V}$$

14.22

$$I_B = \frac{(5 - 0.7)V}{1M\Omega + (100 + 1)430k\Omega} = 96.8nA \mid I_C = 9.68\mu A \mid V_{CE} = 10 - 430000I_E = 5.80V \mid \text{Forward -}$$

active region is correct. $r_\pi = \frac{100(0.025V)}{9.68\mu A} = 258k\Omega \mid r_o = \frac{(60 + 5.80)V}{9.68\mu A} = 6.80M\Omega$ - neglected

In the ac model, R_1 appears in parallel with r_π. The circuit appears to have a transistor

with $r'_\pi = 500k\Omega\|r_\pi = 170k\Omega$ and $\beta'_o = g_m r'_\pi = 40(9.68\mu A)170k\Omega = 65.8$

$v_{th} = v_s \mid R_{th} = 500\Omega \mid R_L = 500k\Omega\|430k\Omega\|500k\Omega = 158k\Omega$

$$A_V = -\frac{66.8(158k\Omega)}{0.500k\Omega + 170k\Omega + 66.8(158k\Omega)} = 0.984 \mid R_{IN} = 170k\Omega + 66.8(158k\Omega) = 10.7 \text{ M}\Omega$$

$$A_I = A_V \frac{R_S + R_{IN}}{R_3} = 0.984 \frac{500\Omega + 10.7M\Omega}{500k\Omega} = 21.1$$

$$R_{OUT} = \frac{500\Omega + 170k\Omega}{66.8} \| 500k\Omega \| 430k\Omega = 2.53 \text{ k}\Omega$$

$$\mathbf{v_{be}} = \mathbf{v_s} \frac{170k\Omega}{0.500k\Omega + 170k\Omega + 66.8(158k\Omega)} = 0.0159\mathbf{v_s} \mid \mathbf{v_s} \le \frac{5.00mV}{0.0159} = 0.315 \text{ V}$$

14.23

$$V_{GS} = 5V \mid I_{DS} = \frac{4\times10^{-4}}{2}(5-1)^2 = 3.2mA \mid V_{DS} = 5 - (-5) = 10V \quad - \text{ Saturation region}$$

operation is correct. $\mid g_m = \sqrt{2(4\times10^{-4})(3.2mA)[1 + 0.02(10)]} = 1.75mS$

$$r_o = \frac{\frac{1}{0.02} + 10}{3.2mA} = 18.8k\Omega \quad - \text{ Cannot neglect!} \mid R_L = 18.8k\Omega \| 100k\Omega = 15.8k\Omega$$

$$A_V = \frac{10^6}{10^6 + 10^4} \frac{1.75mS(15.8k\Omega)}{1 + 1.75mS(15.8k\Omega)} = 0.956 \mid A_I = 10^6 \frac{1.75mS(15.8k\Omega)}{1 + 1.75mS(15.8k\Omega)} \frac{1}{10^5} = 9.56$$

$$R_{IN} = R_G = 1 \text{ M}\Omega \mid R_{OUT} = \frac{1}{g_m} \| r_o = 555 \ \Omega$$

$$\mathbf{v_{gs}} = \mathbf{v_s} \frac{10^6}{10^6 + 10^4} \frac{1}{1 + 1.75mS(15.8k\Omega)} = 0.0346\mathbf{v_s} \mid \mathbf{v_s} \le \frac{0.2(5-1)}{0.0346} = 23.2 \text{ V} \quad \text{But,}$$

v_{DS} must exceed $v_{GS} - V_{TN} \cong V_{GS} - V_{TN} = 4V$ for saturation.

$$V_{DS} = 10 - \mathbf{v_o} = 10 - 0.956\mathbf{v_s} \ge 4 \rightarrow \mathbf{v_s} \le 6.28 \text{ V} \quad - \text{ Limited by the Q - point voltages}$$

14.24

$$\beta_o = g_m r_\pi = 3.54mS(1M\Omega) = 3540 \mid R_L = 2k\Omega \| 100k\Omega = 1.96k\Omega$$

$$A_V = \frac{(\beta_o + 1)R_L}{r_\pi + (\beta_o + 1)R_L} = \frac{(3540 + 1)(1.96k\Omega)}{1M\Omega + (3540 + 1)(1.96k\Omega)} = 0.874$$

$$R_{IN} = r_\pi + (\beta_o + 1)R_L = 1M\Omega + (3540 + 1)(1.96k\Omega) = 7.94 \text{ M}\Omega$$

$$R_{OUT} = \frac{r_\pi}{(\beta_o + 1)} \| 2k\Omega = \frac{10^6}{(3541)} \| 2k\Omega = 247 \ \Omega$$

14.25

$$\mathbf{v_s} \le 0.005(1 + g_m R_L) \mid R_L = R_4 \| R_7 \cong R_4$$

$$\mathbf{v_s} \le 0.005(1 + g_m R_L) = 0.005(1 + g_m R_4) = 0.005\left(1 + \frac{I_C R_4}{V_T}\right)$$

$$\mathbf{v_s} \le 0.005\left(1 + \alpha_F \frac{I_E R_4}{V_T}\right) \cong 0.005\left(1 + \frac{I_E R_4}{V_T}\right)$$

$$\mathbf{v_s} \le 0.005\left(1 + \frac{V_{R_4}}{V_T}\right) = 0.005\left(1 + \frac{V_{R_4}}{0.025}\right) = 0.005 + \frac{V_{R_4}}{5}$$

14.26

(a) $\mathbf{v_{be}} = \mathbf{v_s} - \mathbf{v_o}$ | $0.005 \le 5 - \mathbf{v_o} \to A_V = \dfrac{\mathbf{v_o}}{\mathbf{v_s}} \ge \dfrac{4.995}{5} = 0.999$

(b) $A_V = \dfrac{(\beta_o+1)R_E}{r_\pi+(\beta_o+1)R_E} = \dfrac{1}{1+\dfrac{r_\pi}{(\beta_o+1)R_E}} = \dfrac{1}{1+\dfrac{\beta_o}{(\beta_o+1)}\dfrac{r_\pi}{\beta_o R_E}} = \dfrac{1}{1+\dfrac{\alpha_o}{g_m R_E}} = \dfrac{1}{1+\dfrac{V_T}{I_E R_E}}$

$\dfrac{1}{1+\dfrac{V_T}{I_E R_E}} \ge 0.999 \to \dfrac{V_T}{I_E R_E} \le 0.001 \to I_E R_E \ge \dfrac{0.025V}{0.001} = 25.0 \text{ V}$

14.27

$\mathbf{v_{be}} = \mathbf{v_s} - \mathbf{v_o} = (1-A_V)\mathbf{v_s}$ | $0.005 \le (1-A_V)7.5 \to A_V = \dfrac{\mathbf{v_o}}{\mathbf{v_s}} \ge \dfrac{7.5-0.005}{7.5} = 0.999333$

From Prob. 14.26, $A_V = \dfrac{1}{1+\dfrac{V_T}{I_E R_L}}$ | $R_L = R_E \| 500\Omega = \dfrac{500 R_E}{500+R_E}$ | $A_V = \dfrac{1}{1+\dfrac{V_T}{I_E R_E}\left(\dfrac{500+R_E}{500}\right)}$

$\dfrac{1}{1+\dfrac{V_T}{I_E R_E}\left(\dfrac{500+R_E}{500}\right)} \ge 0.999333 \to \dfrac{V_T}{I_E R_E}\left(\dfrac{500+R_E}{500}\right) \le 6.67 \times 10^{-4}$

$\dfrac{500 I_E R_E}{500+R_E} \ge \dfrac{0.025V}{6.67\times10^{-4}} = 37.5V$ | $V_{CC} \ge I_E R_E + 0.7 + 7.5$

Some design possibilities are listed in the table below.

R_E	I_E	V_{CC}	$V_{CC} I_E$
100 Ω	450 mA	53 V	24 W
250 Ω	225 mA	64 V	16 W
360 Ω	179 mA	73 V	13 W
500 Ω	150 mA	83 V	12 W
750 Ω	125 mA	102 V	13 W
1000 Ω	113 mA	120 V	14 W
2000 Ω	93.8 mA	196 V	18 W

Using a result near the minimum power case in the table:
$R_E = 510~\Omega, I_E = 149\text{mA}$ and $V_{CC} = 85\text{V}$.

Assumining $\beta_F = 50$: $I_B \cong \dfrac{149\text{mA}}{51} = 2.92 \text{ mA}$ | Set $I_{R_1} = 5I_B = 14.6\text{mA} \cong 15\text{mA}$

$R_1 = \dfrac{V_E + V_{BE}}{I_{R_1}} = \dfrac{149\text{mA}(510\Omega)+0.7}{15\text{mA}} = 5.07\text{k}\Omega \to 5.1 \text{ k}\Omega$ | $I_{R_2} = I_{R_1} + I_B \cong 18\text{mA}$

$R_2 = \dfrac{85 - V_{BE} - V_{BE}}{I_{R_2}} = \dfrac{8.3V}{18\text{mA}} = 462\Omega \to 470 ~\Omega$

It is very difficult to achieve the required level of linearity!

14.28

(a) $A_{Vth} = \dfrac{g_m R_L}{1 + g_m R_{th}} = \dfrac{0.5mS(100k\Omega)}{1 + 0.5mS(50\Omega)} = 48.8$ | $R_{IN} = \dfrac{1}{g_m} = \dfrac{1}{0.5mS} = 2.00 \text{ k}\Omega$

$R_{OUT} = \infty$ (since $\lambda = 0$) | $A_{Ith} = 1$

(b) $A_{Vth} = \dfrac{0.5mS(100k\Omega)}{1 + 0.5mS(5k\Omega)} = 14.3$ | $R_{IN} = 2.00 \text{ k}\Omega$ | $R_{OUT} = \infty$ | $A_{Ith} = 1$

14.29

(a) $r_\pi = \dfrac{100(0.025V)}{12.5\mu A} = 200k\Omega$ | $g_m = 40(12.5\mu A) = 0.5mS$

$A_{Vth} = \dfrac{g_m R_L}{1 + g_m R_{th}} = \dfrac{0.5mS(100k\Omega)}{1 + 0.5mS(50\Omega)} = 48.8$ | $R_{IN} = \dfrac{r_\pi}{\beta_o + 1} = 1.98 \text{ k}\Omega$

$R_{OUT} = r_o(1 + g_m R_{th}) = \dfrac{60V}{12.5\mu A}\left[1 + 0.5mS(50\Omega)\right] = 4.92 \text{ M}\Omega$ | $A_{Ith} = \alpha_o = 0.990$

(b) $A_{Vth} = \dfrac{0.5mS(100k\Omega)}{1 + 0.5mS(2.2k\Omega)} = 23.8$ | $R_{IN} = 1.98 \text{ k}\Omega$

$R_{OUT} = \dfrac{60V}{12.5\mu A}\left[1 + 0.5mS(2.2k\Omega)\right] = 10.1 \text{ M}\Omega$

14.30 $A_V \approx 0$; The signal is injected into the collector and taken out of the emitter. This is not a useful amplifier circuit.

14.31

$V_{SG} = 12 - (33k\Omega)I_{SD}$ | $V_{SG} = 12 - \dfrac{\left(3.3x10^4\right)\left(2x10^{-4}\right)}{2}\left(V_{SG} - 1\right)^2$

$V_{SG} = 2.68V$ & $I_{SD} = \dfrac{\left(2x10^{-4}\right)}{2}\left(V_{SG} - 1\right)^2 = 282\mu A$

$V_{SD} = 24 - I_{SD}(33k\Omega + 24k\Omega) = 7.93 \text{ V}$ - Saturation region operation is correct.

$g_m = \sqrt{2\left(2x10^{-4}\right)\left(2.82x10^{-4}\right)} = 3.36x10^{-4}\text{S}$ | $\mathbf{v}_{th} = \dfrac{33k\Omega}{0.5k\Omega + 33k\Omega}\mathbf{v_s} = 0.985\mathbf{v_s}$

$R_{th} = 0.5k\Omega \| 33k\Omega = 493\Omega$

$R_L = 24k\Omega \| 100k\Omega = 19.4k\Omega$ | $A_V = 0.985\dfrac{3.36x10^{-4}\text{S}(19.4k\Omega)}{1 + 3.36x10^{-4}\text{S}(493\Omega)} = 5.51$

$A_I = \dfrac{33k\Omega}{33k\Omega + \dfrac{1}{g_m}}\dfrac{24k\Omega}{24k\Omega + 100k\Omega} = 0.178$ | $R_{IN} = 33k\Omega\left\|\dfrac{1}{g_m}\right. = 2.73k\Omega$ | $R_{OUT} = R_D = 24k\Omega$

$\mathbf{v}_{sg} = \mathbf{v_s}\dfrac{R_{IN}}{R_S + R_{IN}} \le 0.2(V_{SG} - 1)$ | $\mathbf{v_s}\dfrac{2.73k\Omega}{0.5k\Omega + 2.73k\Omega} \le 0.2(2.68 - 1) \rightarrow \mathbf{v_s} \le 0.398 \text{ V}$

14.32 Note: This problem should refer to Fig. P14.1(g).

$V_{GS} = -3900I_{DS} = -3900\dfrac{\left(5x10^{-4}\right)}{2}\left(V_{GS} + 2\right)^2$ | $V_{GS} = -0.975\left(V_{GS} + 2\right)^2 \rightarrow V_{GS} = -0.9915V$

$I_{SD} = \dfrac{\left(5x10^{-4}\right)}{2}\left(V_{GS} + 2\right)^2 = 254\mu A$ | $V_{DS} = 15 - 23.9k\Omega I_{DS} = 8.92V$ - Saturated.

$$g_m = \frac{2(254\mu A)}{2 - 0.992} = 0.504mS \quad | \quad R_{IN} = 3.9k\Omega\left\|\frac{1}{g_m}\right. = 1.32k\Omega \quad | \quad R_{OUT} = R_D = 20k\Omega$$

$$R_L = 20k\Omega\|51k\Omega = 14.4k\Omega \quad | \quad A_V = \frac{R_{IN}}{R_S + R_{IN}}g_m R_L = \frac{1.32k\Omega}{1k\Omega + 1.32k\Omega}(0.504mS)(14.4k\Omega) = 4.11$$

$$A_I = \frac{3.9k\Omega}{3.9k\Omega + \dfrac{1}{g_m}}(1)\frac{20k\Omega}{20k\Omega + 51k\Omega} = 0.187$$

$$\mathbf{v_{sg}} = \mathbf{v_s}\frac{1.32k\Omega}{1k\Omega + 1.32k\Omega} \le 0.2(V_{GS} + 2) \quad | \quad \mathbf{v_s}\frac{1.32k\Omega}{1k\Omega + 1.32k\Omega} \le 0.2(-0.992 + 2) \to \mathbf{v_s} \le 0.354 \text{ V}$$

___

14.33

$$I_B = \frac{(9 - 0.7)V}{100k\Omega + (50 + 1)82k\Omega} = 1.94\mu A \mid I_C = 96.9 \ \mu A$$

$$V_{CE} = 18 - 82000I_E - 39000I_C = 6.12 \text{ V} \quad | \quad \text{Forward - active region is correct.}$$

$$g_m = 40I_C = 3.88mS \quad | \quad r_\pi = \frac{\beta_o}{g_m} = 12.9k\Omega \quad | \quad r_o = \frac{(50 + 6.12)V}{96.9\mu A} = 579k\Omega \ - \text{ neglected}$$

$$\mathbf{v_{th}} = \mathbf{v_s}\frac{82k\Omega}{0.5k\Omega + 82k\Omega} = 0.994\mathbf{v_s} \mid R_{th} = 0.5k\Omega\|82k\Omega = 497\Omega \mid R_L = 39k\Omega\|100k\Omega = 28.1k\Omega$$

$$A_V = 0.994\frac{50(28.1k\Omega)}{12.9k\Omega + 51(0.497k\Omega)} = 36.5 \quad | \quad R_{IN} = 82k\Omega\left\|\frac{r_\pi}{\beta_o + 1}\right. = 253\Omega$$

$$A_I = A_V\frac{R_S + R_{IN}}{R_3} = 36.5\frac{500\Omega + 253\Omega}{100k\Omega} = 0.275 \quad | \quad R_{OUT} = R_C = 39.0 \ k\Omega$$

$$\mathbf{v_{eb}} = \mathbf{v_s}\frac{R_{IN}}{R_S + R_{IN}} \le 5.00mV \mid \quad 0.336\mathbf{v_s} \le 5.00mV \mid \quad \mathbf{v_s} \le 14.9 \text{ mV}$$

___

14.34

$$I_B = \frac{(9 - 0.7)V}{1000k\Omega + (50 + 1)820k\Omega} = 194nA \mid I_C = 9.69 \ \mu A$$

$$V_{CE} = 18 - 820000I_E - 390000I_C = 6.12 \text{ V} \quad | \quad \text{Forward - active region is correct.}$$

$$g_m = 40I_C = 0.388mS \quad | \quad r_\pi = \frac{\beta_o}{g_m} = 129k\Omega \quad | \quad r_o = \frac{(50 + 6.12)V}{9.69\mu A} = 5.79M\Omega \ - \text{ neglected}$$

$$\mathbf{v_{th}} = \mathbf{v_s}\frac{820k\Omega}{5k\Omega + 820k\Omega} = 0.994\mathbf{v_s} \mid R_{th} = 5k\Omega\|820k\Omega = 4.97k\Omega \mid R_L = 390k\Omega\|1M\Omega = 281k\Omega$$

$$A_V = 0.994\frac{50(281k\Omega)}{129k\Omega + 51(4.97k\Omega)} = 36.5 \quad | \quad R_{IN} = 820k\Omega\left\|\frac{r_\pi}{\beta_o + 1}\right. = 2.52k\Omega$$

$$A_I = A_V\frac{R_S + R_{IN}}{R_3} = 36.5\frac{5k\Omega + 2.52k\Omega}{1M\Omega} = 0.275 \quad | \quad R_{OUT} = R_C = 390 \ k\Omega$$

$$\mathbf{v_{eb}} = \mathbf{v_s}\frac{R_{IN}}{R_S + R_{IN}} \le 5.00mV \mid \quad 0.335\mathbf{v_s} \le 5.00mV \mid \quad \mathbf{v_s} \le 14.9 \text{ mV}$$

___

14.35 **Note:** $V_{TP} = -1 V.$

$$I_{SD} = \frac{\left(2 \times 10^{-4}\right)}{2}\left(V_{SG} - 1\right)^2 \mid \frac{15 - V_{SG}}{68k\Omega} = 10^{-4}\left(V_{SG} - 1\right)^2 \rightarrow V_{SG} = 2.363V$$

$$I_{SD} = \frac{15 - V_{SG}}{68k\Omega} = 186\mu A \mid V_{SD} = 30 - (68k\Omega + 43k\Omega)I_{SD} = 9.35V \mid \text{Saturation region}$$

is correct. $\mid g_m = \frac{2(186\mu A)}{2.36 - 1} = 0.274mS \mid R_{IN} = 68k\Omega \left\| \frac{1}{g_m} = 3.46k\Omega \right.$

$$R_{OUT} = R_D = 43k\Omega \mid R_L = 43k\Omega \| 200k\Omega = 35.4k\Omega$$

$$A_V = \frac{R_{IN}}{R_S + R_{IN}} g_m R_L = \frac{3.46k\Omega}{0.250k\Omega + 3.46k\Omega}(0.274mS)(35.4k\Omega) = 9.05$$

$$A_I = \frac{68k\Omega}{68k\Omega + \frac{1}{g_m}}(1)\frac{43k\Omega}{43k\Omega + 200k\Omega} = 0.168 \mid \mathbf{v_{gs}} = \mathbf{v_s} \frac{3.46k\Omega}{0.250k\Omega + 3.46k\Omega} \leq 0.2(V_{SG} - 1)$$

$$\mathbf{v_s} \frac{3.46k\Omega}{0.250k\Omega + 3.46k\Omega} \leq 0.2(2.36 - 1) \rightarrow \mathbf{v_s} \leq 0.292 \ V$$

14.36

For $R_{th} \ll \frac{1}{g_m}$, $A_{Vth} \cong g_m R_L$ All of the input voltage appeas across the gate - source terminals of the transistor.

For $R_{th} \gg \frac{1}{g_m}$, $A_{Vth} \cong \frac{R_L}{R_{th}}$ For large R_{th}, all of the Thevenin equivalent source

current, $\frac{v_{th}}{R_{th}}$, goes into the transistor source terminal.

14.37

$$R_{IN} = \frac{r_\pi + 1.5k\Omega}{\beta_o + 1} \mid r_\pi = \frac{75(0.025V)}{1mA} = 1.88k\Omega \mid R_{IN} = \frac{1.88k\Omega + 1.5k\Omega}{76} = 44.5 \ \Omega$$

14.38

$$g_m = \frac{2}{|-2|}\sqrt{1mA(5mA)} = 2.24mS \mid R_{IN} = \frac{1}{g_m} = 447 \ \Omega$$

14.39

$$g_m = \sqrt{2(1.25mA)(1mA)} = 1.58mS \mid R_{IN} = \frac{1}{g_m} = 633 \ \Omega$$

14.40

(a) $R_{OUT} = r_o\left[1 + \frac{\beta_o R_E}{r_\pi + R_E}\right] \mid I_E = \frac{15V - 0.7V}{143k\Omega} = 100\mu A \mid$ For $\beta_F = 100$, $I_C = 99.0\mu A$

$$r_\pi = \frac{100(0.025V)}{99.0\mu A} = 25.3k\Omega \mid r_o \cong \frac{50V}{99.0\mu A} = 505k\Omega$$

$$R_{OUT} = 505k\Omega\left[1 + \frac{100(143k\Omega)}{25.3k\Omega + 143k\Omega}\right] = 43.4 \ M\Omega \qquad \text{(b) 0 V}$$

(c) $I_E = \dfrac{15V - 0.7V}{15k\Omega} = 953\mu A$ | For $\beta_F = 100$, $I_C = 944\mu A$ | $r_\pi = \dfrac{100(0.025V)}{944\mu A} = 2.65k\Omega$

$r_o \cong \dfrac{50V}{944\mu A} = 53.0k\Omega$ | $R_{OUT} = 53.0k\Omega\left[1 + \dfrac{100(15k\Omega)}{15k\Omega + 2.65k\Omega}\right] = 4.56 \text{ M}\Omega$ | $V_{CB} \geq 0$ V

14.41

$$R_{OUT} = (\beta_o + 1)r_o = (\beta_o + 1)\frac{V_A + V_{CE}}{I_C} = 126\frac{50 + 10.7}{49.6\mu A} = 154 \text{ M}\Omega$$

14.42

$R_{IN} = 5M\Omega$ | $A_V = 10^{\frac{30}{20}} = 31.6$ | Large R_{IN}, moderate gain

These requirements are easily met by a common-source amplifier.

For example, $A_V \cong \dfrac{V_{DD}}{V_{GS} - V_{TN}} = \dfrac{15V}{0.5V} = 30.$

A common-emitter stage operating at a low collector current is a second possibility.

14.43

$R_{IN} = 1M\Omega$ | $A_V = 10^{\frac{52}{20}} = 398$ | Large R_{IN}, large gain

A common-emitter amplifier operating at a low current can achieve both a large gain and input resistance. $A_V \cong 20V_{CC} \to V_{CC} = 20V$

Achieving this gain with an FET is much more difficult:

$A_V \cong \dfrac{V_{DD}}{V_{GS} - V_{TN}} = \dfrac{V_{DD}}{0.25V} \to V_{DD} \cong 100V$ which is unreasonably large.

14.44

An inverting amplifier with a gain of 40 dB is most easily achieved with a common-emitter stage: $A_V \cong 10V_{CC} \to V_{CC} = 10$ V. The input resistance can be achieved by shunting the input with a 5Ω resistor. Setting $r_\pi = 5\Omega$ would require $I_C \cong \dfrac{100(0.025V)}{5\Omega} = 0.5A$ and would waste a large amount of power to achieve the required input resistance.

14.45

0 dB corresponds to a follower.

For an emitter-follower, $R_{IN} \cong (\beta_o + 1)R_L \cong 101(10k\Omega) = 1.01M\Omega$. So an BJT does not meet the input resistance requirement. A source follower provides a gain of approximately 1 and can easily achieve the required input resistance.

14.46

A gain of 0.98 and an input resistance of $250k\Omega$ should be achievable with either a source-follower or emitter-follower. For the FET, $A_V = \dfrac{g_m R_S}{1 + g_m R_S} = 0.98$

requires $g_m R_L = 49$: $\dfrac{2I_{DS}R_S}{V_{GS} - V_{TN}} = 49 \to I_{DS}R_S = 12.3V$ for a design with $V_{GS} - V_{TN} = 0.5V$.

The BJT can achieve the required gain with a much lower power supply and can still meet the R_{IN} requirement: $R_{IN} \geq \beta_o R_L \cong 100(5k\Omega) = 500k\Omega$.

$$A_V = \frac{(\beta_o + 1)R_E}{r_\pi + (\beta_o + 1)R_E} \cong \frac{\dfrac{g_m R_E}{\alpha_o}}{1 + \dfrac{g_m R_E}{\alpha_o}} = 0.98 \quad | \quad \frac{g_m R_E}{\alpha_o} = 49 \rightarrow I_E R_E = 49(0.025) = 1.23V.$$

14.47

A non-inverting amplifier with a gain of 10 and an input resistance of 2kΩ should be readily achievable with either a common-base or common-gate amplifier with proper choice of operating point. The gain of 10 is easily achieved with either the FET or BJT design estimate: $A_V \cong \dfrac{V_{DD}}{V_{GS} - V_{TN}}$ or $A_V \cong 10V_{CC}$. $R_{IN} \cong \dfrac{1}{g_m} = 2k\Omega$ is within easy reach of either device.

14.48

$A_V = 10^{\frac{80}{20}} = 10,000$. This value of voltage gain excceds the amplification factor of even the best BJTs: $A_V \leq \mu_f = 40V_A = 40(150V) = 6000$. Such a large gain requirement cannot be met with a single-transistor amplifier. An FET typically has a much lower μ_f and is at an even worse disadvantage.

14.49

$$R_{OUT} = \frac{R_{th} + r_\pi}{\beta_o + 1} \geq \frac{R_{th}}{\beta_o + 1} = \frac{250}{151} = 1.66\Omega$$

14.50

$$R_{IN} = r_\pi + (\beta_o + 1)R_E \cong r_\pi + \beta_o R_E = r_\pi(1 + g_m R_E) \quad | \quad r_\pi' = r_\pi(1 + g_m R_E)$$

$$g_m' = \frac{i_c}{v_s} = \frac{\beta_o}{r_\pi + (\beta_o + 1)R_E} \cong \frac{\beta_o}{r_\pi + \beta_o R_E} = \frac{\beta_o}{r_\pi(1 + g_m R_E)} = \frac{g_m}{1 + g_m R_E}$$

$$r_o' = \frac{i_c}{v_c}\bigg|_{v_s = 0} = r_o\left(1 + \frac{\beta_o R_E}{r_\pi + R_E}\right) \cong r_o\left(1 + \frac{\beta_o R_E}{r_\pi}\right) = r_o(1 + g_m R_E) \text{ for } r_\pi \gg R_E$$

$$\beta_o' = g_m' r_\pi' = \left(\frac{g_m}{1 + g_m R_E}\right)r_\pi(1 + g_m R_E) = \beta_o \quad | \quad \mu_f' = g_m' r_o' = \left(\frac{g_m}{1 + g_m R_E}\right)r_o(1 + g_m R_E) = \mu_f$$

14.51

```
*Problem 14.51 - Common-Emitter Amplifier 5mV
VCC 6 0 DC 9
VEE 4 0 DC -9
VS 1 0 SIN(0 0.005 1K)
C1 1 2 1U
RB 2 0 10K
RC 6 5 3.6K
RE 3 4 2K
C2 3 0 50U
C3 5 7 1U
R3 7 0 10K
Q1 5 2 3 NBJT
.OP
```

```
.TRAN 1U 5M
.FOUR 1KHZ V(7)
.MODEL NBJT NPN IS=1E-16 BF=100 VA=70
.PROBE V(7)
.END
*Problem 14.51 - Common-Emitter Amplifier 10mV
VCC 6 0 DC 9
VEE 4 0 DC -9
VS 1 0 SIN(0 0.01 1K)
C1 1 2 1U
RB 2 0 10K
RC 6 5 3.6K
RE 3 4 2K
C2 3 0 50U
C3 5 7 1U
R3 7 0 10K
Q1 5 2 3 NBJT
.OP
.TRAN 1U 5M
.FOUR 1KHZ V(7)
.MODEL NBJT NPN IS=1E-16 BF=100 VA=70
.PROBE V(7)
.END
*Problem 14.51 - Common-Emitter Amplifier 15mV
VCC 6 0 DC 9
VEE 4 0 DC -9
VS 1 0 SIN(0 0.015 1K)
C1 1 2 1U
RB 2 0 10K
RC 6 5 3.6K
RE 3 4 2K
C2 3 0 50U
C3 5 7 1U
R3 7 0 10K
Q1 5 2 3 NBJT
.OP
.TRAN 1U 5M
.FOUR 1KHZ V(7)
.MODEL NBJT NPN IS=1E-16 BF=100 VA=70
.PROBE V(7)
.END
```

Results:

	1 kHz	2 kHz	3 kHz	THD
5 mV	5.8 mV	0.335 mV (5.7%)	0.043 mV (0.74%	5.9%
10 mV	12.4 mV	1.54 mV (12.5%)	0.258 mV (2.1%)	12.8%
15 mV	20.6 mV	4.32 mV (21%)	1.18 mV (5.4%)	22%

14.52

```
*Problem 14.52 - Output Resistance
VCC 2 0 DC 10
IB1 0 1 DC 10U
Q1 2 1 0 NBJT
IB2 0 3 DC 10U
RE 4 0 10K
Q2 2 3 4 NBJT
.OP
.DC VCC 10 20 .025
```

```
.MODEL NBJT NPN IS=1E-16 BF=60 VA=20
.PRINT DC IC(Q1) IC(Q2)
.PROBE IC(Q1) IC(Q2)
.END
```

Results: A small value of Early voltage has been used deliberately to accentuate the results. Note that the transistors have significantly different values of β_F because of the collector-emitter voltage differences and low value of V_A.

```
NAME        Q1        Q2
MODEL       NBJT      NBJT
IB          1.00E-05  1.00E-05
IC          8.77E-04  6.72E-04
VBE         7.61E-01  7.61E-01
VBC         -9.24E+00 -2.41E+00
VCE         1.00E+01  3.18E+00
BETADC      8.77E+01  6.72E+01
GM          3.39E-02  2.60E-02
RPI         2.59E+03  2.59E+03
RO          3.33E+04  3.33E+04
```

From SPICE: $R_{OUT1} = \dfrac{(20-10)}{(1.17-0.877)}\dfrac{V}{mA} = 34.1\ k\Omega$ | $R_{OUT2} = \dfrac{(20-10)}{(903-673)}\dfrac{V}{\mu A} = 43.5\ k\Omega$

For circuit 1: $R_{OUT1} = r_{o1} = 33.3\ k\Omega$

For circuit 2: $R_{OUT2} = r_{o2}\left(1 + \dfrac{\beta_o R_E}{R_{th}+r_\pi+R_E}\right) + (R_{th}+r_\pi)\|R_E$ (See Eq. 14.26)

But $R_{th} = \infty \rightarrow R_{OUT2} = r_{o2} + R_E = 33.3k\Omega + 10k\Omega = 43.3\ k\Omega$

14.53

$$\mathbf{v_{th}} = G_m R_{th} = -\frac{g_m}{1+g_m R_5}\left[r_o(1+g_m R_5)\right]\mathbf{v_s} = -\mu_f\mathbf{v_s}\ \ |\ \ R_{th} = r_o(1+g_m R_5) = r_o + \mu_f R_5$$

14.54

$$\mathbf{v_{th}} = \mathbf{v_s}\frac{r_\pi}{R_S+r_\pi}(1+g_m r_o) = \frac{r_\pi}{R_S+r_\pi}(1+\mu_f)\mathbf{v_s}\ \ |\ \ R_{th} \cong r_o\left(1+\frac{\beta_o R_S}{R_S+r_\pi}\right)$$

14.55

$$\mathbf{v_{th}} = \mathbf{v_s}\frac{(\beta_o+1)r_o}{R_s+r_\pi+(\beta_o+1)r_o} = \mathbf{v_s}\frac{1}{\dfrac{R_s}{(\beta_o+1)r_o}+\dfrac{r_\pi}{(\beta_o+1)r_o}+1} = \mathbf{v_s}\frac{1}{\dfrac{g_m R_s}{(\beta_o+1)\mu_f}+\dfrac{\beta_o}{(\beta_o+1)\mu_f}+1} \cong \mathbf{v_s}$$

$$R_{th} \cong \frac{R_s+r_\pi}{\beta_o+1}\|r_o \cong \frac{R_s+r_\pi}{\beta_o+1}$$

14.56

(a) $y_{21} = \left.\dfrac{\mathbf{i_2}}{\mathbf{v_1}}\right|_{\mathbf{v_2}=0}\ \ |\ \ \mathbf{i_2} = -g_m\mathbf{v_1}\ \ |\ \ y_{21} = -g_m$

$y_{12} = \left.\dfrac{\mathbf{i_1}}{\mathbf{v_2}}\right|_{\mathbf{v_1}=0}\ \ |\ \ \mathbf{i_1} = 0\ \ |\ \ y_{12} = 0\ \ |\ \ \dfrac{y_{12}}{y_{21}} = 0$

331

(b) $y_{21} = \dfrac{i_2}{v_1}\Big|_{v_2=0}$ $\quad|\quad i_2 = -(\beta_o + 1)i_b = -(\beta_o + 1)\dfrac{v_1}{r_\pi}$ $\quad|\quad y_{21} = -\dfrac{(\beta_o + 1)}{\beta_o}\dfrac{\beta_o}{r_\pi} = -\dfrac{g_m}{\alpha_o} \cong -g_m$

$y_{12} = \dfrac{i_1}{v_2}\Big|_{v_1=0}$ $\quad|\quad i_1 = -i_b = -\dfrac{v_2}{r_\pi}$ $\quad|\quad y_{12} = -g_\pi$ $\quad|\quad \dfrac{y_{12}}{y_{21}} = \dfrac{\alpha_o}{g_m}g_\pi = \dfrac{\alpha_o}{\beta_o} = \dfrac{1}{\beta_o + 1} \ll 1$

(c) $y_{21} = \dfrac{i_2}{v_1}\Big|_{v_2=0}$ $\quad|\quad i_2 = -(g_m + g_o)v_1$ $\quad|\quad y_{21} = -(g_m + g_o)$

$y_{12} = \dfrac{i_1}{v_2}\Big|_{v_1=0}$ $\quad|\quad i_1 = -g_o v_2$ $\quad|\quad y_{21} = -g_o$ $\quad|\quad \dfrac{y_{12}}{y_{21}} = \dfrac{-g_o}{-(g_m + g_o)} = \dfrac{1}{\mu_f + 1} \ll 1$

(d) $y_{21} = \dfrac{i_2}{v_1}\Big|_{v_2=0}$ $\quad|\quad i_2 = -g_m v_1$ $\quad|\quad y_{21} = -g_m$

$y_{12} = \dfrac{i_1}{v_2}\Big|_{v_1=0}$ $\quad|\quad i_1 = -g_o v_2$ $\quad|\quad y_{21} = -g_o$ $\quad|\quad \dfrac{y_{12}}{y_{21}} = \dfrac{-g_o}{-g_m} = \dfrac{1}{\mu_f} \ll 1$

(e) $y_{21} = \dfrac{i_2}{v_1}\Big|_{v_2=0}$ $\quad|\quad i_2 = \dfrac{\beta_o}{r_\pi + (\beta_o + 1)R_5}v_1$ $\quad|\quad y_{21} = \dfrac{\beta_o}{r_\pi + (\beta_o + 1)R_5}$

$y_{12} = \dfrac{i_1}{v_2}\Big|_{v_1=0}$ $\quad|\quad i_1 = -i_2\dfrac{R_5}{R_5 + r_\pi} = -\dfrac{v_2}{R_{OUT}}\dfrac{R_5}{R_5 + r_\pi} \cong -\dfrac{v_2}{r_o\left(1 + \dfrac{\beta_o R_5}{R_5 + r_\pi}\right)}\dfrac{R_5}{R_5 + r_\pi}$

$y_{12} \cong -\dfrac{1}{(\beta_o + 1)r_o}$ for $(\beta_o + 1)R_5 \gg r_\pi$

$\dfrac{y_{12}}{y_{21}} = -\dfrac{1}{(\beta_o + 1)r_o}\dfrac{r_\pi + (\beta_o + 1)R_5}{\beta_o} \cong \dfrac{R_5}{\beta_o r_o}$ for $(\beta_o + 1)R_5 \gg r_\pi$ $\quad|\quad \dfrac{R_5}{\beta_o r_o} = \dfrac{g_m R_5}{\beta_o \mu_f} \ll 1$

(f) $y_{21} = \dfrac{i_2}{v_1}\Big|_{v_2=0}$ $\quad|\quad i_2 = \dfrac{g_m}{1 + g_m R_5}v_1$ $\quad|\quad y_{21} = \dfrac{g_m}{1 + g_m R_5}$

$y_{12} = \dfrac{i_1}{v_2}\Big|_{v_1=0}$ $\quad|\quad i_1 = 0$ $\quad|\quad y_{12} = 0$ $\quad|\quad \dfrac{y_{12}}{y_{21}} = 0$

14.57

At the output node v_o: $\quad g_m v_x = (g_o + G_L)v_o - g_o v_x$ $\quad|\quad v_o = \dfrac{g_m + g_o}{g_o + G_L}v_x$

$i_x = g_m v_x + g_o(v_x - v_o)$ $\quad|\quad \dfrac{i_x}{v_x} = g_m + g_o\left(1 - \dfrac{g_m + g_o}{g_o + G_L}\right) = g_m + g_o\left(\dfrac{G_L - g_m}{g_o + G_L}\right)$

$\dfrac{i_x}{v_x} = g_m + g_o\left(\dfrac{G_L - g_m}{g_o + G_L}\right) = G_L\dfrac{g_m + g_o}{g_o + G_L}$ $\quad|\quad R_{IN} = \dfrac{v_x}{i_x} = \dfrac{1}{g_m}\dfrac{1 + \dfrac{R_L}{r_o}}{1 + \dfrac{1}{\mu_f}} \cong \dfrac{1}{g_m}\left(1 + \dfrac{R_L}{r_o}\right)$

14.58

$$I_C = 100\frac{5 - 0.7}{10^4 + 101(10^3)} = 3.87\text{mA} \mid g_m = 40I_C = 0.155\text{S} \mid r_\pi = \frac{100}{g_m} = 645\Omega$$

$$R_L = 1\text{k}\Omega\|20\text{k}\Omega = 952\Omega \mid R_E = 1\text{k}\Omega\|20\text{k}\Omega = 952\Omega$$

$$A_{V1} = -\frac{\beta_o R_L}{r_\pi + (\beta_o + 1)R_E} = -\frac{100(952\Omega)}{645\Omega + 101(952\Omega)} = -0.984$$

$$A_{V2} = \frac{(\beta_o + 1)R_E}{r_\pi + (\beta_o + 1)R_E} = \frac{101(952\Omega)}{645\Omega + 101(952\Omega)} = 0.993$$

The small-signal requirement limits the output signal to:

$$v_{be} = v_s - v_{o2} = v_s(1 - 0.993) = 0.007v_s \mid v_s \le \frac{0.005}{0.007} = 0.714\text{V}$$

$$v_{o1} \le 0.984(0.714\text{V}) = 0.703\text{V}$$

We also need to check V_{CB}: $V_C = 5 - 3.87\text{mA}(1\text{k}\Omega) = 1.13\text{V}$ and $V_B = -10^4 I_B = -0.387\text{V}$.

The total collector-base voltage of the transistor is therefore: $V_{CB} = 1.52\text{V} - 0.984v_s - v_s$.

We require $V_{CB} \ge 0$ for forward-active region operation. Therefore: $v_s \le 0.766$ V.

The small-signal limit is the most restrictive.

14.59

```
    *Problem 14.59 - Common-Collector Amplifier 14.1(a)
    VCC 6 0 DC 18
    VEE 7 0 DC -18
    VS 1 0 AC 1
    *For Output Resistance
    *VS 1 0 AC 0
    *VO 8 0 AC 1
    RS 1 2 500
    C1 2 3 10UF
    R1 3 0 51K
    R2 6 3 100K
    RE 4 7 4.7K
    RC 6 5 2K
    C3 5 0 10UF
    C2 4 8 47UF
    R3 8 0 24K
    Q1 5 3 4 NBJT
    .OP
    .AC LIN 1 10KHZ 10KHZ
    .MODEL NBJT NPN IS=1E-16 BF=125 VA=50
    .PRINT AC VM(8) VP(8) VM(3) VP(3) IM(VS) IP(VS) IM(C2) IP(C2)
    .END
```

Results: Q-point: (4.67 mA, 4.57 V), $A_V = 0.982$, $R_{IN} = 31.1$ kΩ, $R_{OUT} = 9.12$ Ω

For hand calculations see Problem 14.21: $A_V = 0.982$, $R_{IN} = 31.0$ kΩ, $R_{OUT} = 9.19$ Ω

14.60

```
    *Problem 14.60 - Common-Gate Amplifier - 14.1(b)
    VSS 5 0 DC 12
    VDD 6 0 DC -12
    VS 1 0 AC 1
    *For Output Resistance
    *VS 1 0 AC 0
    *VO 7 0 AC 1
```

```
RS 1 2 500
C1 2 3 10U
R1 5 3 33K
RD 6 4 24K
C2 4 7 47U
R3 7 0 100K
M1 4 0 3 3 PFET
.OP
.AC LIN 1 50KHZ 50KHZ
.MODEL PFET PMOS KP=200U VTO=-1 LAMBDA=0.02
.PRINT AC VM(7) VP(7) VM(3) VP(3) IM(VS) IP(VS) IM(C2) IP(C2)
.END
```

Results: Q-point: (286 μA, 7.72V), A_V = +5.50, R_{IN} = 2.73 kΩ, R_{OUT} = 21.8 kΩ

For hand calculations see Problem 14.31: A_V = +5.51, R_{IN} = 2.73 kΩ

$$R_{OUT} = R_O^{CG} \| R_D \quad | \quad r_o = \frac{50 + 7.93}{282 \times 10^{-6}} = 205k\Omega \quad | \quad R_{OUT}^{CG} = r_o(1 + g_m R_{th})$$

$$R_{OUT}^{CG} = 205k\Omega\left[1 + \left(3.36 \times 10^{-4}\right)(493)\right] = 239k\Omega \quad | \quad R_{OUT} = 239k\Omega \| 24k\Omega = 21.8 \ k\Omega$$

14.61

```
*Problem 14.61 - Common-Collector Amplifier - 14.1(c)
VCC 7 0 DC 5
VEE 8 0 DC -5
VS 1 0 AC 1
*For Output Resistance
*VS 1 0 AC 0
*VO 6 0 AC 1
RS 1 2 500
C1 2 3 10UF
R1 3 5 500K
R2 5 0 500K
RE 4 8 430K
C2 4 5 47UF
C3 4 6 10UF
R3 6 0 500K
Q1 7 3 4 NBJT
.OP
.AC LIN 1 10KHZ 10KHZ
.MODEL NBJT NPN IS=1E-16 BF=100 VA=60
.PRINT AC VM(6) VP(6) VM(3) VP(3) IM(VS) IP(VS) IM(C3) IP(C3)
.END
```

Results: Q-point: (9.81 μA, 5.74V), A_V = 0.983, R_{IN} = 11.0 MΩ, R_{OUT} = 2.58 kΩ

For hand calculations see Problem 14.22: A_V = 0.984, R_{IN} = 10.7 MΩ, R_{OUT} = 2.53 kΩ

14.62

```
*Problem 14.62 - Common-Emitter Amplifier - 14.1(e)
VCC 6 0 DC 12
VS 1 0 AC 1
*VS 1 0 AC 0
*VO 7 0 AC 1
RS 1 2 1K
C1 2 3 2.2UF
R1 6 3 20K
R2 3 0 62K
RE 6 4 3.9K
C2 6 4 47UF
```

RC 5 0 8.2K
C3 5 7 10UF
R3 7 0 100K
Q1 5 3 4 PBJT
.OP
.AC LIN 1 5KHZ 5KHZ
.MODEL PBJT PNP IS=1E-16 BF=75 VA=60
.PRINT AC VM(7) VP(7) VM(3) VP(3) IM(VS) IP(VS) IM(C3) IP(C3)
.END

Results: Q-point: (525 µA, 5.62V), A_V = -110, R_{IN} = 3.16kΩ, R_{OUT} = 7.69 kΩ

For hand calculations see Problem 14.12: Q-point: (537 µA, 5.47V), R_{IN} = 2.84 kΩ

$$r_o = \frac{60 + 5.47}{537 \times 10^{-6}} = 122 k\Omega \quad | \quad R_L = r_o \| 8.2 k\Omega \| 100 k\Omega = 122 k\Omega \| 8.2 k\Omega \| 100 k\Omega = 7.14 k\Omega$$

$$A_{Vth} = -\frac{75(7.14 k\Omega)}{0.938 k\Omega + 3.49 k\Omega} = -121 \quad | \quad A_V = 0.938 A_{Vth} = -113 \quad | \quad R_{OUT} = r_o \| 8.2 k\Omega = 7.68 k\Omega$$

14.63

*Problem 14.63 - Common-Source Amplifier - 14.1(f)
VDD 4 0 DC 18
VS 1 0 AC 1
*For output resistance
*VS 1 0 AC 0
*VO 7 0 AC 1
RS 1 2 1K
C1 2 3 2.2U
R1 3 0 500K
R2 4 3 1.4MEG
R4 6 0 27K
C2 6 0 47U
RD 4 5 75K
C3 5 7 10U
R3 7 0 470K
M1 5 3 6 6 NMOSFET
.OP
.AC LIN 1 5KHZ 5KHZ
.MODEL NMOSFET NMOS VTO=1 KP=250U LAMBDA=0.02
.PRINT AC VM(3) VP(3) VM(7) VP(7) IM(VS) IP(VS) IM(C3) IP(C3)
.END

Results: Q-point: (106µA, 7.14V), A_V = -14.2, R_{IN} = 369kΩ, R_{OUT} = 65.8 kΩ

For hand calculations see Problem 14.13: Q-point: (104 µA, 7.39V), R_{IN} = 368 kΩ

$$r_o = \frac{50 + 7.39}{104 \times 10^{-6}} = 552 k\Omega \quad | \quad R_L = r_o \| R_D \| 470 k\Omega = 552 k\Omega \| 75 k\Omega \| 470 k\Omega = 57.9 k\Omega$$

$$R_{OUT} = r_o \| 75 k\Omega = 66.0 \ k\Omega \quad | \quad v_{th} = v_s \frac{368 k\Omega}{1 k\Omega + 368 k\Omega} = 0.997 v_s$$

$$A_V = -0.997 g_m R_L = -0.997(0.228 mS)(57.9 k\Omega) = -13.2$$

14.64

*Problem 14.64 - Common-Gate Amplifier - 14.1(g)
VDD 5 0 DC 15
VS 1 0 AC 1
*For output resistance

```
*VS 1 0 AC 0
*VO 6 0 AC 1
RS 1 2 1K
C1 2 3 2.2U
R1 3 0 3.9K
RD 4 5 20K
C2 4 6 47U
R3 6 0 51K
M1 4 0 3 3 NMOSFET
.OP
.AC LIN 1 20KHZ 20KHZ
.MODEL NMOSFET NMOS VTO=-2 KP=500U LAMBDA=0.02
.PRINT AC VM(3) VP(3) VM(6) VP(6) IM(VS) IP(VS) IM(C2) IP(C2)
.END
```

Results: Q-point: (268µA, 8.60V), A_V = 4.26, R_{IN} = 1.27 kΩ, R_{OUT} = 18.8 kΩ

For hand calculations see Problem 14.32: Q-point: (254 µA, 8.92V), R_{IN} = 1.32 kΩ

$$r_o = \frac{50 + 8.92}{254 \times 10^{-6}} = 232k\Omega \quad | \quad R_{OUT}^{CG} = r_o(1 + g_m R_{th}) = 232k\Omega(1 + 0.504mS(3.9k\Omega\|1k\Omega)) = 325k\Omega$$

$$R_L \cong R_D\|R_3 = 51k\Omega\|20k\Omega = 14.4k\Omega \quad | \quad R_{OUT} = R_{OUT}^{CG}\|20k\Omega = 18.8 \text{ k}\Omega$$

$$v_{th} = v_s \frac{3.9k\Omega}{1k\Omega + 3.9k\Omega} = 0.796v_s$$

$$A_V = -0.796\frac{g_m R_L}{1 + g_m R_{th}} = 0.796\frac{0.504mS(14.4k\Omega)}{1 + 0.504mS(3.9k\Omega\|1k\Omega)} = 4.12$$

14.65

```
*Problem 14.65 - Common-Source Amplifier 14.1(i)
VDD 6 0 DC 18
VS 1 0 AC 1
*For output resistance
*VS 1 0 AC 0
*VO 7 0 AC 1
RS 1 2 1K
C1 2 3 2.2UF
R2 6 3 2.2MEG
R1 3 0 2.2MEG
R4 6 4 22K
C2 6 4 47UF
RD 5 0 18K
C3 5 7 10UF
R3 7 0 470K
M1 5 3 4 4 PFET
.OP
.AC LIN 1 7.5KHZ 7.5KHZ
.MODEL PFET PMOS KP=400U VTO=-1 LAMBDA=0.02
.PRINT AC VM(3) VP(3) VM(7) VP(7) IM(VS) IP(VS) IM(C3) IP(C3)
.END
```

Results: Q-point: (268µA, 8.60V), A_V = -8.29, R_{IN} = 1.10kΩ, R_{OUT} = 16.4 kΩ

For hand calculations see Problem 14.32: Q-point: (307 µA, 5.72V), R_{IN} = 1.10 kΩ

$$r_o = \frac{50 + 5.72}{307 \times 10^{-6}} = 182\text{k}\Omega \quad | \quad R_L = r_o \| R_D \| 470\text{k}\Omega = 182\text{k}\Omega \| 18\text{k}\Omega \| 470\text{k}\Omega = 15.8\text{k}\Omega$$

$$R_{OUT} = r_o \| 18\text{k}\Omega = 16.4 \text{ k}\Omega \quad | \quad v_{th} = v_s \frac{1.1\text{M}\Omega}{1\text{k}\Omega + 1.1\text{k}\Omega} = 0.999 v_s$$

$$A_V = -0.999 g_m R_L = -0.999(0.496\text{mS})(15.8\text{k}\Omega) = -7.82$$

14.66

```
*Problem 14.66 - Common-Source Amplifier - 14.1(j)
VDD 6 0 DC 20
VS 1 0 AC 1
*For output resistance
*VS 1 0 AC 0
*VO 7 0 AC 1
RS 1 2 500
C1 2 3 2.2UF
RG 3 0 1MEG
R4 4 0 11K
C2 5 7 47UF
RD 6 5 39K
R3 7 0 500K
J1 5 3 4 NJFET
.OP
.AC LIN 1 4KHZ 4KHZ
.MODEL NJFET NJF BETA=1.25M VTO=-4 LAMBDA=0.02
.PRINT AC VM(3) VP(3) VM(7) VP(7) IM(VS) IP(VS) IM(C2) IP(C2)
.END
```

Results: Q-point: (319 μA, 4.03V), A_V = -3.02, R_{IN} = 1.00 MΩ, R_{OUT} = 38.4 kΩ

For hand calculations see Problem 14.15: Q-point: (318 μA, 4.10V), R_{IN} = 1.00 MΩ

$$r_o = \frac{50 + 4.10}{318 \times 10^{-6}} = 170\text{k}\Omega \quad | \quad R_{OUT}^{CS} = r_o(1 + g_m R_1) = 170\text{k}\Omega[1 + 1.26\text{mS}(11\text{k}\Omega)] = 253\text{k}\Omega$$

$$R_L = R_{OUT}^{CS} \| R_D \| R_3 = 253\text{k}\Omega \| 39\text{k}\Omega \| 500\text{k}\Omega = 31.7\text{k}\Omega \quad | \quad R_{OUT} = R_{OUT}^{CS} \| 39\text{k}\Omega = 33.8 \text{ k}\Omega$$

$$v_{th} = v_s \frac{1\text{M}\Omega}{0.5\text{k}\Omega + 1\text{M}\Omega} = v_s \quad | \quad A_V = -g_m R_L = -(1.26\text{mS})(31.7\text{k}\Omega) = -3.99$$

14.67

```
*Problem 14.67 - Common-Base Amplifier - 14.1(k
VCC 7 0 DC -9
VEE 4 0 DC 9
VS 1 0 AC 1
*For output resistance
*VS 1 0 AC 0
*VO 8 0 AC 1
RS 1 2 500
C2 2 3 47UF
RB 5 0 100K
RE 3 4 82K
C1 5 0 4.7UF
RC 7 6 39K
C3 6 8 10UF
R3 8 0 100K
Q1 6 5 3 PBJT
.OP
.AC LIN 1 12KHZ 12KHZ
.MODEL PBJT PNP IS=1E-16 BF=50 VA=50
```

```
.PRINT AC VM(3) VP(3) VM(8) VP(8) IM(VS) IP(VS) IM(C3) IP(C3)
.END
```

Results: Q-point: (97.2 µA, 6.10V), $A_V = 35.5$, $R_{IN} = 273$ Ω, $R_{OUT} = 38.1$ kΩ

For hand calculations see Problem 14.33: Q-point: (96.9 µA, 6.12V), $R_{IN} = 253$ Ω

$$r_o = \frac{50 + 6.12}{96.9 \times 10^{-6}} = 579k\Omega \quad | \quad R_{OUT}^{CB} = r_o\left(1 + \frac{\beta_o R_{th}}{r_\pi + R_{th}}\right) = 579k\Omega\left(1 + \frac{50(497\Omega)}{12.9k\Omega + 497\Omega}\right) = 1.65M\Omega$$

$$R_L = R_{OUT}^{CB}\|R_D\|R_3 = 1.65M\Omega\|39k\Omega\|100k\Omega = 26.6k\Omega \quad | \quad R_{OUT} = R_{OUT}^{CB}\|39k\Omega = 38.1 \ k\Omega$$

$$v_{th} = v_s \frac{82k\Omega}{0.5k\Omega + 82k\Omega} = 0.994v_s$$

$$A_V = -0.994\frac{g_m R_L}{1 + g_m R_{th}} = 0.994\frac{3.88mS(26.6k\Omega)}{1 + 3.88mS(0.497k\Omega)} = 34.9$$

14.68

```
*Problem 14.68 - JFET Common-Source Amplifier - 14.1(m)
VDD 5 0 DC -16
VS 1 0 AC 1
*For output resistance
*VS 1 0 AC 0
*VO 6 0 AC 1
RS 1 2 5K
C1 2 3 2.2U
R1 3 0 10MEG
RD 4 5 1.8K
C2 4 6 10U
R3 6 0 36K
J1 4 3 0 PJFET
.OP
.AC LIN 1 3KHZ 3KHZ
.MODEL PJFET PJF BETA=200U VTO=-5 LAMBDA=0.02
.PRINT AC VM(3) VP(3) VM(6) VP(6) IM(VS) IP(VS) IM(C2) IP(C2)
.END
```

Results: Q-point: (5.59 µA, 5.93 V), $A_V = -3.27$, $R_{IN} = 10.0$ MΩ, $R_{OUT} = 1.53$ kΩ

For hand calculations see Problem 14.16: Q-point: (5.00 mA, 7.00V), $R_{IN} = 10.0$ MΩ

$$r_o = \frac{50 + 7.00}{5 \times 10^{-3}} = 11.4k\Omega \quad | \quad R_L = r_o\|R_D\|R_3 = 11.4k\Omega\|1.8k\Omega\|36k\Omega = 1.48k\Omega$$

$$R_{OUT} = r_o\|R_D = 11.4k\Omega\|1.8k\Omega = 1.56k\Omega$$

$$v_{th} = v_s \frac{10M\Omega}{5k\Omega + 10M\Omega} = v_s \quad | \quad A_V = -g_m R_L = -(2.00mS)(1.48k\Omega) = -2.96$$

14.69

```
*Problem 14.69 - Common-Emitter Amplifier - 14.1(n)
VCC 7 0 DC 10
VEE 6 0 DC -10
VS 1 0 AC 1
*For output resistance
*VS 1 0 AC 0
*VO 8 0 AC 1
RS 1 2 250
C1 2 3 4.7UF
RB 3 0 20K
```

```
R4 4 6 9.1K
C2 4 0 100UF
L 7 5 1H
C3 5 8 1UF
R3 8 0 1MEG
Q1 5 3 4 NBJT
.OP
.AC LIN 1 500KHZ 500KHZ
.MODEL NBJT NPN IS=1E-16 BF=80 VA=100
.PRINT AC VM(3) VP(3) VM(8) VP(8) IM(VS) IP(VS) IM(C3) IP(C3)
.END
```

Note: L needs to be 1H to reach midband performance at 500kHz.

Results: Q-point: (979 µA, 11.0 V), A_V = -3420, R_{IN} = 2.09 kΩ, R_{OUT} = 113 kΩ

For hand calculations see Problem 14.17: Q-point: (983 µA, 11.0V), R_{IN} = 1.85 kΩ

$$r_o = \frac{100 + 11.0}{983 \times 10^{-6}} = 113k\Omega \quad | \quad R_L = r_o \| R_3 = 113k\Omega \| 1M\Omega = 102k\Omega \quad | \quad R_{OUT} = r_o = 113k\Omega$$

$$v_{th} = v_s \frac{20k\Omega}{250\Omega + 20k\Omega} = 0.988 v_s \quad | \quad A_V = -0.988 \frac{\beta_o R_L}{R_{th} + r_\pi} = -0.988 \frac{80(102k\Omega)}{247\Omega + 2.04k\Omega} = -3530$$

14.70

```
*Problem 14.70 - Source Follower - 14.1(o)
VDD 5 0 DC 5
VSS 6 0 DC -5
VS 1 0 AC 1
*For output resistance
*VS 1 0 AC 0
*VO 7 0 AC 1
RS 1 2 10K
C1 2 3 2.2U
R1 3 0 1MEG
L 4 6 100mH
C3 4 7 4.7U
R3 7 0 100K
M1 5 3 4 4 NMOSFET
.OP
.AC LIN 1 100KHZ 100KHZ
.MODEL NMOSFET NMOS VTO=1 KP=400U LAMBDA=0.02
.PRINT AC VM(3) VP(3) VM(7) VP(7) IM(VS) IP(VS) IM(C3) IP(C3)
.END
```

Results: Q-point: (3.84 mA, 10.0 V), A_V = 0.953, R_{IN} = 1.00 MΩ, R_{OUT} = 504 Ω

For hand calculations see Problem 14.23: Q-point: (3.20 mA, 10.0V),

$$A_V = 0.956, \quad R_{IN} = 1.00 M\Omega, R_{OUT} = 555 \Omega$$

14.71

$$A_V = \frac{g_m R_L}{1 + g_m R_L} \geq 0.95 \rightarrow g_m R_L \geq 19 \quad | \quad g_m = \sqrt{2K_n I_{DS}} \quad | \quad V_{GS} - V_{TN} = \sqrt{\frac{2I_{DS}}{K_n}} = 0.5V$$

$$I_{DS} = \frac{(0.5)^2 (0.03)}{2} = 3.75mA \quad | \quad R_L \geq \frac{19}{\sqrt{2(0.03)(0.00375)}} = 1.27k\Omega$$

$$R_L = R_S \| 3k\Omega \rightarrow R_S \geq 2.19 k\Omega \quad | \quad V_{SS} = V_{GS} + (3.75mA)R_S \quad | \quad \text{Possible designs:}$$

$2.4 k\Omega, 11.5V ; 2.7k\Omega, 12.6V ; 3.0k\Omega, 13.75V$ - Making a choice which uses a nearly minimum value of supply voltage gives: $V_{SS} = 12$ V, $R_S = 2.4$ kΩ.

14.72

$$R_{IN} \cong r_\pi = \frac{\beta_o V_T}{I_C} \quad | \quad I_C = \frac{100(0.025V)}{75\Omega} = 33.3 \text{ mA}$$

14.73 The base voltage should remain half way between the positive and negative power supply voltages. If $V_{EE} = +10V$ and $V_{CC} = 0V$, then V_B should $= 5$ V which can be obtained using a resistive voltage divider from the +10V supply. We now have the standard four-resistor bias circuit. The base curent is 327 μA/80 = 4 μA.

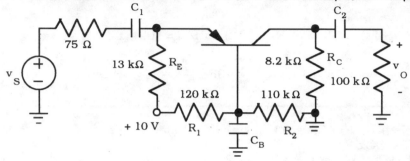

Setting the current in R_1 to $10I_B = 40\mu A$, $R_1 = \dfrac{5V}{40\mu A} = 125k\Omega \rightarrow 120k\Omega$. The

current in $R_2 = 11I_B = 44\mu A$, and $R_2 = \dfrac{5V}{44\mu A} = 114k\Omega \rightarrow 110k\Omega$.

Note that the base terminal must now be bypassed with a capacitor.

14.74

$$R_{IN} \cong \frac{1}{g_m} \rightarrow g_m = \sqrt{2K_n I_{DS}} = 0.1S \quad | \quad I_{DS} = \frac{0.01}{2K_n} \quad | \quad \text{(a)} \ I_{DS} = \frac{0.01}{2(0.005)} = 1 \text{ A}$$

(b) $I_{DS} = \dfrac{0.01}{2(0.5)} = 10.0$ mA $|$ The second FET achieves the desired input resistance

at much lower current and hence much lower power for a given supply voltage.

14.75

This analysis assumes that the source and load resistors are fixed, and that only

the amplifier parameters are changing. $A_{Vth} = \dfrac{R_L}{\dfrac{1}{g_m} + \dfrac{R_{th}}{\alpha_o}} \quad | \quad \alpha_o = \dfrac{80}{81} = 0.988 \quad | \quad R_{th} = R_E \| 75\Omega$

Since $R_E \gg 75\Omega$, $R_{th} = 75\Omega$ is essentially constant. To achieve A_{Vth}^{max}, $R_L \rightarrow R_L^{max}$, $g_m \rightarrow g_m^{max}$

which requires $I_C \rightarrow I_C^{max} = 0.988 \dfrac{(5.25 - 0.7)V}{13k\Omega(0.95)} = 364\mu A \ | \ R_L^{max} = 8.2k\Omega(1.05)\|100k\Omega = 7.93k\Omega$

$$A_{Vth}^{max} = \frac{7.93k\Omega}{\dfrac{1}{40(364\mu A)} + \dfrac{75}{0.988}} = 54.8 \quad | \quad \text{To achieve } A_{Vth}^{min}, \ R_L \to R_L^{min}, g_m \to g_m^{min} \text{ which requires}$$

$$I_C \to I_C^{min} = 0.988\frac{(4.75 - 0.7)V}{13k\Omega(1.05)} = 293\mu A \quad | \quad R_L^{min} = 8.2k\Omega(0.95)\|100k\Omega = 7.23k\Omega$$

$$A_{Vth}^{min} = \frac{7.23k\Omega}{\dfrac{1}{40(293\mu A)} + \dfrac{75}{0.988}} = 44.8 \quad | \quad 44.8 \le A_V \le 54.8 \quad | \quad \text{The range is only slightly larger}$$

than that observed in the Monte Carlo analysis in Table 14.16.

14.76

```
*Problem 14.76 - Common-Base Amplifier - Monte Carlo Analysis
*Generate Voltage Sources with 5% Tolerances
IEE 0 8 DC 5
REE 8 0 RTOL 1
EEE 6 0 8 0 1
*
ICC 0 9 DC 5
RCC 9 0 RTOL 1
ECC 7 0 9 0 -1
*
VS 1 0 AC 1
RS 1 2 75
C1 2 3 47U
RE 3 6 RTOL 13K
Q1 4 0 3 PBJT
RC 4 7 RTOL 8.2K
C2 4 5 4.7U
R3 5 0 100K
.OP
.AC LIN 1 10KHZ 10KHZ
.PRINT AC VM(5) VP(5)
.MODEL PBJT PNP (BF=80 DEV 25%) (VA = 60 DEV 33.33%)
.MODEL RTOL RES (R=1 DEV 5%)
.MC 1000 AC VM(5) YMAX
.END
```

Results: Mean value $A_V = 47.5$; 3σ limits: $42.5 \le A_V \le 52.5$. However, the worst-case values observed in the analysis are $A_V^{min} = 43.2$ and $A_V^{max} = 51.9$. The mean is 5% lower than the design value. The width of the distribution is approximately the same as that in Table 14.16.

14.77 (a)

This analysis assumes that the source and load resistors are fixed, and that only the amplifier parameters are changing. $A_{Vth} = \dfrac{R_L}{\dfrac{1}{g_m} + \dfrac{R_{th}}{\alpha_o}}$ | $\alpha_o = \dfrac{80}{81} = 0.988$ | $R_{th} = R_E\|75\Omega$

Since $R_E \gg 75\Omega$, $R_{th} = 75\Omega$ is essentially constant. To achieve A_{Vth}^{max}, $R_L \to R_L^{max}, g_m \to g_m^{max}$ which requires $I_C \to I_C^{max} = 0.988\dfrac{(5.10 - 0.7)V}{13.3k\Omega(0.99)} = 330\mu A$ | $R_L^{max} = 8.25k\Omega(1.01)\|100k\Omega = 7.69k\Omega$

$$A_{Vth}^{max} = \frac{7.69k\Omega}{\dfrac{1}{40(330\mu A)} + \dfrac{75}{0.988}} = 50.7 \quad | \quad \text{To achieve } A_{Vth}^{min}, \ R_L \to R_L^{min}, g_m \to g_m^{min} \text{ which requires}$$

$$I_C \to I_C^{min} = 0.988\frac{(4.90-0.7)V}{13.3k\Omega(1.01)} = 309\mu A \quad | \quad R_L^{min} = 8.25k\Omega(0.99)\|100k\Omega = 7.55k\Omega$$

$$A_{Vth}^{min} = \frac{7.55k\Omega}{\dfrac{1}{40(309\mu A)} + \dfrac{75}{0.988}} = 48.2 \quad | \quad 48.2 \le A_V \le 50.7$$

Using a Spreadsheet similar to Table 14.16: Mean value $A_V = 49.6$; 3σ limits: $48.2 \le A_V \le$ 50.9. The worst-case values observed in the analysis are $A_V^{min} = 48.4$ and $A_V^{max} = 50.8$.

14.78

```
*Problem 14.76 - Common-Base Amplifier - Monte Carlo Analysis
*Generate Voltage Sources with 2% Tolerances
IEE 0 8 DC 5
REE 8 0 RTOL 1
EEE 6 0 8 0 1
*
ICC 0 9 DC 5
RCC 9 0 RTOL 1
ECC 7 0 9 0 -1
*
VS 1 0 AC 1
RS 1 2 75
C1 2 3 100U
RE 3 6 RR 13.3K
Q1 4 0 3 PBJT
RC 4 7 RR 8.25K
C2 4 5 1U
R3 5 0 100K
.OP
.AC LIN 1 10KHZ 10KHZ
.PRINT AC VM(5) VP(5) IM(VS) IP(VS)
.MODEL PBJT PNP (BF=80 DEV 25%) (VA = 60 DEV 33.33%)
.MODEL RTOL RES (R=1 DEV 2%)
.MODEL RR RES (R=1 DEV 1%)
.MC 1000 AC VM(5) YMAX
*.MC 1000 AC IM(VS) YMAX
.END
```

Results: Mean value: $A_V = 47.2$; 3σ limits: $45.7 \le A_V \le 48.5$
 Mean value: $R_{IN} = 83.4\ \Omega$; 3σ limits: $79.5\ \Omega \le A_V \le 87.6\ \Omega$

14.79

$$R_{IN} = R_E \left\| \frac{1}{g_m} = \frac{R_E}{1 + g_m R_E} = \frac{R_E}{1 + 40 I_C R_E} = \frac{R_E}{1 + 40 \frac{80}{81} I_E R_E} = \frac{R_E}{1 + 39.5 I_E R_E}$$

$$I_E R_E = 2.5 - 0.7 = 1.8V \quad | \quad 75 = \frac{R_E}{1 + 39.5(1.8)} \rightarrow R_E = 5.41k\Omega$$

$$I_C = \frac{80}{81} \frac{1.8V}{5.41k\Omega} = 329\mu A \quad | \quad R_{th} = 75\Omega \| 5.41k\Omega = 74.0\Omega \quad | \quad g_m = 40(329\mu A) = 13.2mS$$

$$v_{th} = v_s \frac{5410}{75 + 5410} = 0.986 v_s \quad | \quad A_V = 0.986 \frac{R_L}{\frac{1}{g_m} + \frac{R_{th}}{\alpha_o}} \rightarrow R_L = 7.64k\Omega$$

$7.64k\Omega = R_C \| 100k\Omega \rightarrow R_C = 8.27k\Omega \mid V_C = -2.5V + I_C R_C = +0.221V \mid$ Oops! We are violating our definition of the forward-active region. If we use the nearest 5% values, $R_E = 5.6k\Omega$ and $R_C = 8.2k\Omega$, $I_C = 318\mu A$ and $V_C = +0.108V$. The transistor is entering saturation.

14.80

Using a Spreadsheet similar to Table 14.16:

Mean value: $A_V = 0.960$; 3σ limits: $0.942 \leq A_V \leq 0.979$

Mean value: $I_{DS} = 4.91$ mA; 3σ limits: 4.27 mA $\leq I_{DS} \leq 5.55$ mA

Mean value: $V_{DS} = 7.03$ V; 3σ limits: 4.52 V $\leq V_{DS} \leq 9.54$ V

```
*Problem 14.80 - Common-Drain Amplifier - fig. 14.40
*Generate Voltage Sources with 5% Tolerances
IDD 0 7 DC 5
RDD 7 0 RTOL 1
EDD 5 0 7 0 1
*
ISS 0 8 DC 20
RSS 8 0 RTOL 1
ESS 6 0 8 0 -1
*
VGG 1 0 DC 0 AC 1
C1 1 2 4.7U
RG 2 0 RTOL 22MEG
RS 3 6 RTOL 3.6K
C2 3 4 68U
R3 4 0 3K
M1 5 2 3 3 NMOSFET
.OP
.AC LIN 1 10KHZ 10KHZ
.DC VGG 0 0 1
.MODEL NMOSFET NMOS (VTO=1.5 DEV 33.33%) (KP=20M DEV 50%)
LAMBDA=0.02
.MODEL RTOL RES (R=1 DEV 5%)
.PRINT AC VM(4) VP(4) IM(VGG) IP(VGG)
.MC 1000 DC ID(M1) YMAX
*.MC 1000 DC VDS(M1) YMAX
*.MC 1000 AC IM(VGG) YMAX
*.MC 1000 AC VM(4) YMAX
.END
```

Results: Mean value: $I_{DS} = 4.97$ mA; 3σ limits: 4.32 mA $\leq I_{DS} \leq 5.62$ mA

Mean value: $V_{DS} = 7.19$ V; 3σ limits: 6.18 V $\leq V_{DS} \leq 8.20$ V

Mean value: $R_{IN} = 22.0$ MΩ; 3σ limits: $20.3\ \Omega \le R_{IN} \le 24.0\ \Omega$

Mean value: $A_V = 0.956$; 3σ limits: $0.936 \le A_V \le 0.976$

14.81

(a) $A_{Vth} = \dfrac{g_m R_L}{1 + g_m(1+\eta)R_L} = \dfrac{0.01S(1k\Omega)}{1 + 0.01S(1+0.5)(1k\Omega)} = 0.625 \ \ | \ \ R_{IN} = \infty$

$R_{OUT} = \dfrac{1}{g_m(1+\eta)} = \dfrac{1}{0.01S(1+0.5)} = 66.7\Omega \ \ | \ \ A_{Ith} = \infty$

(b) A_{Vth} is worse; R_{OUT} is improved.

14.82

(a) $A_{Vth} = -\dfrac{g_m R_L}{1 + g_m(1+\eta)R_5} = -\dfrac{0.01S(2k\Omega)}{1 + 0.01S(1+0.75)(200\Omega)} = -4.44 \ \ | \ \ R_{IN} = \infty$

$R_{OUT} = r_o\left[1 + g_m(1+\eta)R_5\right] = 10k\Omega\left[1 + 0.01S(1.75)(200\Omega)\right] = 45.0\ k\Omega \ \ | \ \ A_{Ith} = \infty$

(b) A_{Vth} is reduced; R_{OUT} is increased.

14.83

(a) $A_{Vth} = \dfrac{g_m(1+\eta)R_L}{1 + g_m(1+\eta)R_{th}} = \dfrac{0.5mS(1+1)(100k\Omega)}{1 + 0.5mS(1+1)(50\Omega)} = 95.2$

$R_{IN} = \dfrac{1}{g_m(1+\eta)} = \dfrac{1}{0.5mS(1+1)} = 1000\ \Omega$

$R_{OUT} = r_o\left[1 + g_m(1+\eta)R_{th}\right] = r_o\left[1 + 0.5mS(1+1)(50\Omega)\right] = 1.05r_o \ \ (= \infty \text{ for } \lambda = 0)$

(b) A_V is larger; R_{IN} is smaller.

CHAPTER 15

15.1

The bypass capacitors do not affect R_{IN}: $R_{IN} = R_G = 1$ MΩ | $A_{V1} = -\dfrac{g_{m1}R_{L1}}{1 + g_{m_1}R_5}$

$R_{L1} = \left(620\Omega \| 78k\Omega \| 22k\Omega\right) \| \left(r_{\pi2} + (\beta_{o2} + 1)1.6k\Omega\right) = 598\Omega \| \left(2.39k\Omega + (151)1.6k\Omega\right) = 597\Omega$

$A_{V1} = -\dfrac{0.01(597)}{1 + (0.01)200} = -1.99$ | $A_{V2} = -\dfrac{\beta_{o2}R_{L2}}{r_{\pi2} + (\beta_{o2} + 1)1.6k\Omega} = -\dfrac{150(3.54k\Omega)}{2.39k\Omega + (151)1.6k\Omega} = -2.18$

$A_{V3} = +0.950$ | $A_v = -1.99(-2.18)(0.950) = +4.12$

$R_{OUT} = (3300\Omega) \left\| \left(\dfrac{R_{th3} + r_{\pi3}}{\beta_{o3} + 1}\right)\right.$ | $R_{th3} = R_{I3} \| R_{o2} = R_{I3} \left\| r_{o2}\left(1 + \dfrac{\beta_{o2}R_{E2}}{R_{th2} + r_{\pi2} + R_{E2}}\right) \cong R_{I3} = 4.31k\Omega\right.$

$R_{OUT} = (3.30k\Omega) \left\| \left(\dfrac{4.31 + 1.00}{81}k\Omega\right)\right. = 64.3\Omega$

15.2

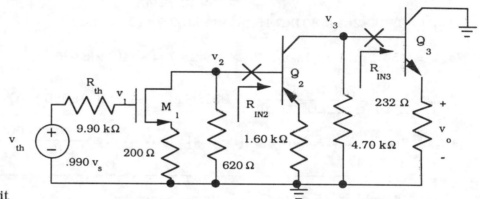

Ac equivalent circuit

The Q-points and small-signal parameter values have already been found in the text.

$\dfrac{v_o}{v_s} = \left(\dfrac{v_o}{v_3}\right)\left(\dfrac{v_3}{v_2}\right)\left(\dfrac{v_2}{v_1}\right)\left(\dfrac{v_1}{v_{th}}\right)\left(\dfrac{v_{th}}{v_s}\right)$ | $\left(\dfrac{v_o}{v_3}\right) = \dfrac{(\beta_{o3} + 1)R_{L3}}{r_{\pi3} + (\beta_{o3} + 1)R_{L3}} = \dfrac{(81)\,232}{1500 + (81)232} = 0.926$

$\left(\dfrac{v_3}{v_2}\right) = -\dfrac{\beta_{o2}\left(4700 \| R_{IN3}\right)}{r_{\pi2} + (\beta_{o2} + 1)R_{E2}}$ | $R_{IN3} = r_{\pi3} + (\beta_{o3} + 1)R_{L3} = 1500 + (81)232 = 20.3k\Omega$

$\left(\dfrac{v_3}{v_2}\right) = -\dfrac{150(4.70k\Omega \| 20.3k\Omega)}{2.50k\Omega + (151)1.60k\Omega} = -2.35$ | $\left(\dfrac{v_2}{v_1}\right) = -\dfrac{g_{m1}\left(R_{I1} \| R_{IN2}\right)}{1 + g_{m1}R_{S1}}$ | $R_{IN2} = r_{\pi2} + (\beta_{o2} + 1)R_{E2}$

$R_{IN2} = 2.50k\Omega + (151)1.60k\Omega = 244k\Omega$ | $\left(\dfrac{v_2}{v_1}\right) = -\dfrac{0.01(620\Omega \| 244k\Omega)}{1 + 0.01(200\Omega)} = -2.06$

$\left(\dfrac{v_1}{v_{th}}\right) = 1$ | $\left(\dfrac{v_{th}}{v_s}\right) = 0.990$ | $\dfrac{v_o}{v_s} = (0.926)(-2.35)(-2.06)(1)(0.990) = +4.44$

$$M_1: \quad I_{DS} = \frac{0.01}{2}\left(V_{GS} + 2\right)^2 \quad | \quad V_{GS} = -9000 I_{DS} \rightarrow V_{GS} = -1.80V$$

$$I_{DS} = \frac{0.01}{2}\left(-1.8 + 2\right)^2 = 200 \ \mu A \quad | \quad V_{DS} = 15 - (15k\Omega + 9k\Omega)I_{DS} = 10.2 \ V$$

$$g_m = \sqrt{2\left(10mA / V^2\right)(0.2mA)} = 2mS \quad | \quad r_o = \frac{(50 + 10.2)V}{0.2mA} = 301k\Omega$$

$$Q_2: \quad V_{EQ2} = 15\frac{43k\Omega}{43k\Omega + 160k\Omega} = 3.18V \quad | \quad R_{EQ2} = 160k\Omega \| 43k\Omega = 33.9k\Omega$$

$$I_{C2} = 150\frac{3.18 - 0.7}{33.9k\Omega + 151(1.6k\Omega)} = 1.35 \ mA \quad | \quad V_{CE2} = 15 - \left(4.7k\Omega + \frac{151}{150}1.6k\Omega\right)I_C = 6.49 \ V$$

$$g_{m2} = 40(1.35mA) = 54.0mS \quad | \quad r_{\pi 2} = \frac{150}{54.0mS} = 2.78k\Omega \quad | \quad r_{o2} = \frac{(80 + 6.49)V}{1.35mA} = 64.1k\Omega$$

$$Q_3: \quad V_{EQ3} = 15\frac{120k\Omega}{120k\Omega + 91k\Omega} = 8.53V \quad | \quad R_{EQ3} = 120k\Omega \| 91k\Omega = 51.8k\Omega$$

$$I_{C3} = 80\frac{8.53 - 0.7}{51.8k\Omega + 81(2.2k\Omega)} = 2.72 \ mA \quad | \quad V_{CE3} = 15 - \left(\frac{81}{80}2.2k\Omega\right)I_C = 8.93 \ V$$

$$g_{m3} = 40(2.72mA) = 109mS \quad | \quad r_{o3} = \frac{(60 + 8.93)V}{2.72mA} = 25.3k\Omega \quad | \quad r_{\pi 3} = \frac{80}{109mS} = 734\Omega$$

$$A_{V1} = -0.990(2mS)\left(301k\Omega \| 15k\Omega \| 33.9k\Omega \| 2.78k\Omega\right) = -4.312$$

$$A_{V2} = (-54.0mS)\left[64.1k\Omega \| 4.7k\Omega \| 51.8k\Omega \|\left(734 + 81(2.2k\Omega \| 250\Omega)\right)\right] = -180$$

$$A_{V3} = \frac{81(2.2k\Omega \| 250\Omega)}{734 + 81(2.2k\Omega \| 250\Omega)} = 0.961 \quad | \quad A_V = -4.312(-180)(0.961) = 748$$

$$\mathbf{v_{be3}} = \mathbf{v_{b3}}\left(1 - A_{v3}\right) = A_{V1}A_{V2}\mathbf{v_s}\left(1 - A_{v3}\right) \leq 5mV \quad | \quad \mathbf{v_s} \leq \frac{0.005}{4.312(180)(1 - 0.961)} = 165\mu V$$

```
*Problem 15.4/15.5 - Multistage Amplifier
VCC 12 0 DC 15
VS 1 0 AC 1
*For output resistance
*VS 1 0 AC 0
*VO 11 0 AC 1
RS 1 2 10K
C1 2 3 22U
RG 3 0 1MEG
M1 5 3 4 4 NMOSFET
RS1 4 0 9K
C2 4 0 22U
RD 12 5 15K
C3 5 6 22U
R1 12 6 160K
R2 6 0 43K
Q2 8 6 7 NBJT1
RC 12 8 4.7K
RE2 7 0 1.6K
C4 7 0 22U
C5 8 9 22U
R3 12 9 91K
R4 9 0 120K
```

Q3 12 9 10 NBJT2
RE3 10 0 2.2K
C6 10 11 22U
RL 11 0 250
.MODEL NMOSFET NMOS VTO=-2 KP=.01 LAMBDA=0.02
.MODEL NBJT1 NPN IS=1E-16 BF=150 VA=80
.MODEL NBJT2 NPN IS=1E-16 BF=80 VA=60
.OPTIONS TNOM=17.2
.OP
.AC LIN 1 2KHZ 2KHZ
.PRINT AC VM(3) VP(3) IM(VS) IP(VS) VM(11) VP(11) IM(C6) IP(C6)
.END

Results: $A_V = VM(11) = +879$ | $R_{IN} = \dfrac{VM(3)}{IM(VS)} = 1.00 \text{ M}\Omega$ | $R_{OUT} = \dfrac{1}{IM(C6)} = 51.8 \ \Omega$

15.5 *Problem 15.5 - Use the listing from Problem 15.4, but remove C2 and C4.

Result: $A_V = VM(11) = +2.20$

15.6

Q_1: $V_{EQ1} = 15 \dfrac{100\text{k}\Omega}{100\text{k}\Omega + 820\text{k}\Omega} = 1.63\text{V}$ | $R_{EQ1} = 100\text{k}\Omega \| 820\text{k}\Omega = 89.1\text{k}\Omega$

$I_{C1} = 100 \dfrac{1.63 - 0.7}{89.1\text{k}\Omega + 101(2\text{k}\Omega)} = 319 \ \mu\text{A}$ | $V_{CE1} = 15 - \left(18\text{k}\Omega + \dfrac{101}{100} 2\text{k}\Omega\right)I_C = 8.61 \text{ V}$

$g_{m1} = 40(319 \ \mu\text{A}) = 12.8\text{mS}$ | $r_{\pi1} = \dfrac{100}{12.8\text{mS}} = 7.81\text{k}\Omega$ | $r_{o1} = \dfrac{(70 + 8.61)\text{V}}{319 \ \mu\text{A}} = 246\text{k}\Omega$

Q_2: $V_{EQ2} = 15 \dfrac{43\text{k}\Omega}{43\text{k}\Omega + 160\text{k}\Omega} = 3.18\text{V}$ | $R_{EQ2} = 160\text{k}\Omega \| 43\text{k}\Omega = 33.9\text{k}\Omega$

$I_{C2} = 100 \dfrac{3.18 - 0.7}{33.9\text{k}\Omega + 101(1.6\text{k}\Omega)} = 1.27 \text{ mA}$ | $V_{CE2} = 15 - \left(4.7\text{k}\Omega + \dfrac{101}{100} 1.6\text{k}\Omega\right)I_C = 6.98 \text{ V}$

$g_{m2} = 40(1.27\text{mA}) = 50.8\text{mS}$ | $r_{\pi2} = \dfrac{100}{50.8\text{mS}} = 1.97\text{k}\Omega$ | $r_{o2} = \dfrac{(70 + 6.98)\text{V}}{1.27\text{mA}} = 60.6\text{k}\Omega$

M_3: $V_{EQ3} = 15 \dfrac{1.2\text{M}\Omega}{1.2\text{M}\Omega + 910\text{k}\Omega} = 8.53\text{V}$ | $R_{EQ3} = 1.2\text{M}\Omega \| 910\text{k}\Omega = 518\text{k}\Omega$

$8.53 = V_{GS3} + 3000I_{DS3} = 1 + \sqrt{\dfrac{2I_{DS3}}{0.001}} + 3000I_{DS3} \rightarrow I_{DS3} = 1.87\text{mA}$ | $V_{GS3} - V_{TN3} = 1.93\text{V}$

$V_{DS3} = 15 - 3000I_{DS3} = 9.39\text{V}$ | $g_{m3} = \sqrt{2(0.001)(0.00187)} = 1.93\text{mS}$

$\mathbf{v_{th}} = \mathbf{v_s} \dfrac{89.1\text{k}\Omega}{89.1\text{k}\Omega + 10\text{k}\Omega} = 0.899\mathbf{v_s}$ | $R_{th} = 89.1\text{k}\Omega \| 10\text{k}\Omega = 8.99\text{k}\Omega$

$A_{V1} = -0.899 \dfrac{\beta_{o1}\left(R_{C1} \| R_{B2} \| r_{\pi2}\right)}{R_{th} + r_{\pi1}} = -0.899 \dfrac{100(18\text{k}\Omega \| 33.9\text{k}\Omega \| 1.97\text{k}\Omega)}{8.99\text{k}\Omega + 7.81\text{k}\Omega} = -9.03$

$A_{V2} = -g_{m2}\left(R_{C2} \| R_{G3}\right) = -50.8\text{mS}(4.7\text{k}\Omega \| 518\text{k}\Omega) = -237$

$A_{V3} = \dfrac{g_{m3}\left(R_{E3} \| R_L\right)}{1 + g_{m3}\left(R_{E3} \| R_L\right)} = \dfrac{1.93\text{mS}(3.0\text{k}\Omega \| 250\Omega)}{1 + 1.93\text{mS}(3.0\text{k}\Omega \| 250\Omega)} = 0.308$ | $A_V = -9.03(-237)(0.308) = 659$

$\mathbf{v_{gs3}} = \mathbf{v_{g3}}(1 - A_{V3}) = A_{V1}A_{V2}\mathbf{v_s}(1 - A_{v3}) \le 0.2(V_{GS3} - V_{TN3})$ | $\mathbf{v_s} \le \dfrac{0.2(1.93)}{9.03(237)(1 - 0.308)} = 261\mu\text{V}$

```
*Problem 15.7/15.8 - Multistage Amplifier
VCC 12 0 DC 15
VS 1 0 AC 1
RS 1 2 10K
*For output resistance
*VS 1 0 AC 0
*VO 11 0 AC 1
C1 2 3 22U
R1 12 3 820K
R2 3 0 100K
Q1 5 3 4 NBJT
RE1 4 0 2K
C2 4 0 22U
RC1 12 5 18K
C3 5 6 22U
R3 12 6 160K
R4 6 0 43K
Q2 8 6 7 NBJT
RC 12 8 4.7K
RE2 7 0 1.6K
C4 7 0 22U
C5 8 9 22U
R5 12 9 910K
R6 9 0 1.2MEG
M3 12 9 10 10 NMOSFET
RE3 10 0 3K
C6 10 11 22U
RL 11 0 250
.OP
.AC LIN 1 3KHZ 3KHZ
.MODEL NMOSFET NMOS VTO=1 KP=.001 LAMBDA=0.02
.MODEL NBJT NPN IS=1E-16 BF=100 VA=70
.PRINT AC VM(3) VP(3) IM(VS) IP(VS) VM(11) VP(11) IM(C6) IP(C6)
.END
```

Results: $A_V = VM(11) = +711 \quad | \quad R_{IN} = \dfrac{VM(3)}{IM(VS)} = 8.29 \text{ k}\Omega \quad | \quad R_{OUT} = \dfrac{1}{IM(C6)} = 401 \ \Omega$

15.8

$R_1 \| R_2 = 100\text{k}\Omega \| 820\text{k}\Omega = 89.1\text{k}\Omega$

$\mathbf{v_{th}} = \mathbf{v_s} \dfrac{89.1\text{k}\Omega}{89.1\text{k}\Omega + 10\text{k}\Omega} = 0.899\mathbf{v_s} \quad | \quad R_{th} = 89.1\text{k}\Omega \| 10\text{k}\Omega = 8.99\text{k}\Omega$

$A_{V1} = -0.899 \dfrac{\beta_{o1}\left(R_{C1} \| R_{B2} \| R_{I2}\right)}{R_{th} + r_{\pi1} + (\beta_{o1}+1)R_{E1}} \quad | \quad R_{I2} = r_{\pi2} + (\beta_{o2}+1)R_{E2} = 1.97\text{k}\Omega + 101(1.6\text{k}\Omega) = 164\text{k}\Omega$

$R_3 \| R_4 = 43\text{k}\Omega \| 160\text{k}\Omega = 33.9\text{k}\Omega \quad | \quad A_{V1} = -0.899 \dfrac{100(18\text{k}\Omega \| 33.9\text{k}\Omega \| 164\text{k}\Omega)}{8.99\text{k}\Omega + 7.81\text{k}\Omega + 101(2\text{k}\Omega)} = -4.51$

$R_5 \| R_6 = 1.2\text{M}\Omega \| 910\text{k}\Omega = 518\text{k}\Omega \quad | \quad A_{V2} = -\dfrac{\beta_{o2}\left(R_{C2} \| R_{G3}\right)}{r_{\pi2} + (\beta_{o2}+1)R_{E1}} = -\dfrac{100(4.7\text{k}\Omega \| 518\text{k}\Omega)}{1.97\text{k}\Omega + 101(1.6\text{k}\Omega)} = -2.84$

$A_{V3} = \dfrac{g_{m3}\left(R_{E3} \| R_L\right)}{1 + g_{m3}\left(R_{E3} \| R_L\right)} = \dfrac{1.93\text{mS}(3.0\text{k}\Omega \| 250\Omega)}{1 + 1.93\text{mS}(3.0\text{k}\Omega \| 250\Omega)} = 0.308 \quad | \quad A_V = -4.51(-2.84)(0.308) = 3.95$

15.9 Note that the dc equivalent circuits are identical for Q_1 and Q_2.

$$V_{EQ} = \frac{180k\Omega}{180k\Omega + 300k\Omega} 15V = 5.63V \quad | \quad R_{EQ} = 180k\Omega\|300k\Omega = 113 \ k\Omega$$

$$I_B = \frac{5.63 - 0.7}{113 + 101(20)} \frac{V}{k\Omega} = 2.31\mu A \quad | \quad I_C = 100I_{B1} = 232\mu A \quad | \quad I_E = 101I_{B1} = 234\mu A$$

$$V_{CE} = 15 - 2 \times 10^4 I_E - 2 \times 10^4 I_C = 5.71V$$

$$r_\pi = \frac{100(0.025V)}{232\mu A} = 10.8k\Omega \quad | \quad r_o = \frac{(70 + 5.71)V}{232\mu A} = 326k\Omega \quad - \quad \text{Neglected}$$

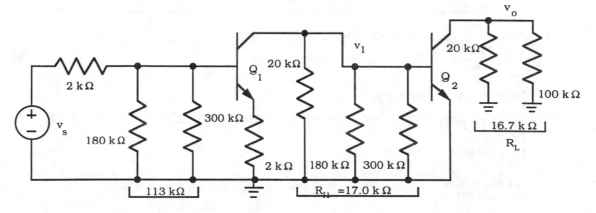

$$v_{th} = v_s \frac{113k\Omega}{113k\Omega + 2k\Omega} = 0.983v_s \quad | \quad R_{th} = 113k\Omega\|2k\Omega = 1.97k\Omega$$

$$\frac{v_1}{v_s} = -0.983 \frac{\beta_{o1}(R_{I1}\|r_{\pi2})}{R_{th} + r_{\pi1} + (\beta_{o1} + 1)R_5} = -0.983 \frac{100(17k\Omega\|10.8k\Omega)}{1.97k\Omega + 10.8k\Omega + (101)2k\Omega} = -3.02v_s$$

$$\frac{v_o}{v_1} = -g_{m2}R_L \quad | \quad R_L = 100k\Omega\|20k\Omega = 16.7k\Omega \quad | \quad \frac{v_o}{v_1} - 40(232\mu A)(16.7k\Omega) = -154v_1$$

$$A_v = \frac{v_o}{v_s} = (-3.02)(-154) = +465 \quad | \quad R_{OUT} = 20k\Omega\|r_{o2} \cong 20k\Omega$$

$$R_{IN} = R_{B1}\|(r_{\pi1} + (\beta_{o1} + 1)R_5) = 113k\Omega\|[10.8k\Omega + (101)2k\Omega] = 73.8k\Omega$$

15.10 The ac equivalent circuit from Problem 15.9 becomes:

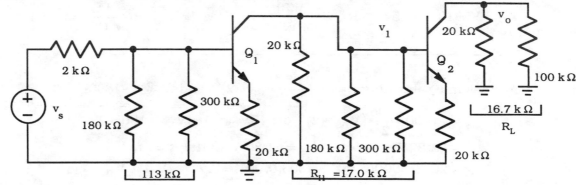

$$\frac{v_1}{v_s} = -0.983 \frac{\beta_o\left(R_{I1} \| r_{\pi2} + (\beta_{o2}+1)R_6\right)}{R_{th} + r_{\pi1} + (\beta_{o1}+1)R_5} = -0.983 \frac{100\left[17k\Omega \| (10.8k\Omega + (101)20k\Omega)\right]}{1.97k\Omega + 10.8k\Omega + (101)20k\Omega} = -0.816$$

$$\frac{v_o}{v_1} = -\frac{\beta_{o2}R_L}{r_{\pi2} + (\beta_{o2}+1)R_6} = -\frac{100(16.7k\Omega)}{10.8k\Omega + (101)20k\Omega} = -0.822$$

$$A_v = \frac{v_o}{v_s} = (-0.816)(-0.822) = +0.671 \quad | \quad \text{The voltage gain is completely lost.} \quad | \quad R_{OUT} = 20k\Omega$$

$$R_{IN} = 113k\Omega \| \left(r_{\pi1} + (\beta_{o1}+1)R_5\right) = 113k\Omega \| (10.8k\Omega + (101)20k\Omega) = 107k\Omega$$

15.11

```
*Problem 15.11 - Multistage Amplifier
VCC 11 0 DC 15
VS 1 0 AC 1
RS 1 2 2K
*For output resistance
*VS 1 0 AC 0
*VO 100 0 AC 1
C1 2 3 10U
R1 3 0 180K
R2 11 3 300K
Q1 6 3 4 NBJT
RE1 4 5 2K
RE2 5 0 18K
C2 5 0 10U
RC1 11 6 20K
C3 6 7 10U
R3 7 0 180K
R4 11 7 300K
Q2 9 7 8 NBJT
RC2 11 9 20K
RE3 8 0 20K
C4 8 0 10U
C5 9 10 10U
RL 10 0 100K
.OP
.AC LIN 1 5KHZ 5KHZ
.MODEL NMOSFET NMOS VTO=1 KP=.001 LAMBDA=0.02
.MODEL NBJT NPN IS=1E-16 BF=100 VA=70
.PRINT AC VM(3) VP(3) IM(VS) IP(VS) VM(10) VP(10) IM(C5) IP(C5)
.END
```

Results:
$$A_v = VM(10) = +454 \quad | \quad R_{IN} = \frac{VM(3)}{IM(VS)} = 74.7 \text{ k}\Omega \quad | \quad R_{OUT} = \frac{1}{IM(C5)} = 18.8 \text{ k}\Omega$$

15.12

M_1: Assume saturation: $I_{DS} = \frac{0.05}{2}(V_{GS}+2)^2$ and $V_{GS} = -1800I_D$

$$V_{GS} = -1800\frac{0.05}{2}(V_{GS}+2)^2 \quad \text{or} \quad 45V_{GS}^2 + 181V_{GS} + 180 = 0$$

$$V_{GS} = -2.22V, -1.80V \quad | \quad V_{GS} = -1.80 \text{ V} \text{ and } I_{DS} = 1 \text{ mA}$$

$$V_{DS} = 20 - 15000(0.001) - 1800(0.001) = 3.2 \text{ V} > V_{GS} - V_{TN}$$

M_2: Assume saturation: $I_{DS} = \frac{0.05}{2}(V_{GS}+2)^2$ and $V_{GS} = -2500I_D$

$$V_{GS} = -2500 \frac{0.05}{2} \left(V_{GS} + 2\right)^2 \quad \text{or} \quad 62.5V_{GS}^2 + 251V_{GS} + 250 = 0$$

$$V_{GS} = -1.83 \text{ V} \quad \text{and} \quad I_{DS} = 0.723 \text{ mA}$$

$$V_{DS} = 20 - 2500(0.723\text{mA}) = 18.2 \text{ V} > V_{GS} - V_{TN}$$

$$g_{m1} = \sqrt{2(0.05)(0.001)} = 10.0\text{mS} \quad | \quad g_{m2} = \sqrt{2(0.05)\left(7.23\text{x}10^{-4}\right)} = 8.50\text{mS}$$

$$R_{IN} = 1800 \left\| \frac{1}{g_{m1}} = 1800 \| 100 = 94.7\Omega \quad | \quad R_{OUT} = 2500 \left\| \frac{1}{g_{m2}} = 2500 \| 118 = 113\Omega$$

$$A_{V1} = +g_{m1}\left(15\text{k}\Omega \| 1\text{M}\Omega\right) = 0.01\text{S}(14.8\text{k}\Omega) = 148$$

$$A_{V2} = +\frac{g_{m2}\left(2.5\text{k}\Omega \| 10\text{k}\Omega\right)}{1 + g_{m2}\left(2.5\text{k}\Omega \| 10\text{k}\Omega\right)} = +\frac{8.5\text{x}10^{-3}\left(2.5\text{k}\Omega \| 10\text{k}\Omega\right)}{1 + 8.5\text{x}10^{-3}\left(2.5\text{k}\Omega \| 10\text{k}\Omega\right)} = 0.944$$

$$A_V = A_{V1}A_{V2} = +140$$

15.13 (a) $R_{D1} = 750 \, \Omega$

I_{DS1} does not depend upon R_{D1} and is unchanged.

$$V_{D1} = 15 - 750\left(I_{DS1} - I_{B2}\right) \cong 15 - 750I_{DS1} = 15 - 750(0.005) = 11.3\text{V}$$

$$V_{DS1} = 11.3 - 1.00 = 10.3\text{V}$$

$$I_{E2} = \frac{15 - 0.7 - 11.3}{1600} = 1.88 \text{ mA} \quad | \quad V_{EC2} = 11.3 + .7 - (1.87\text{mA})4.7\text{k}\Omega = 3.21\text{V}$$

$$I_{B2} = 12.6\mu\text{A} \ll I_{D1}$$

$$I_{E3} = \frac{4700\left(I_{C2} - I_{B3}\right) - 0.7}{3300} \cong \frac{4700I_{C2} - 0.7}{3300} = \frac{4.7\text{k}\Omega(1.88\text{mA}) - 0.7}{3300} = 2.47\text{mA}$$

$$I_{B3} = \frac{I_{E3}}{81} = 30.9\mu\text{A} \ll I_{C2} \quad | \quad V_{CE3} = 15 - 3300I_{E3} = 6.86\text{V}$$

$$Q - Pt_1: \ (5\text{mA}, \ 10.3\text{V}) \ | \ Q - Pt_2: \ (1.88\text{mA}, \ 3.21\text{V}) \ | \ Q - Pt_3: \ (2.47\text{mA}, \ 6.86\text{V})$$

(b) $R_{D1} = 910 \, \Omega$

$$V_{D1} \cong 15 - 910I_{D1} = 15 - 910(0.005) = 10.5\text{V} \quad | \quad Q - Pt_1: \ (5\text{mA}, \ 9.45\text{V})$$

$$I_{E2} = \frac{15 - 0.7 - 10.5}{1600} = 2.38 \text{ mA} \quad | \quad V_{EC2} = 10.5 + .7 - (2.36\text{mA})4.7\text{k}\Omega = 0.108\text{V}$$

Q_2 is saturated! - The circuit will no longer operate as an amplifier.

$$I_{E3} = \frac{V_{C2} - 0.7}{3300} \cong \frac{10.5 + 0.7 - 0.1 - 0.7}{3300} = 3.15\text{mA}$$

$$Q - Pt_3: \ (3.15\text{mA}, \ 4.60\text{V})$$

15.14

$$I_{C1} = 80 \frac{0.7 - (-9)}{100 + 81(24)} \frac{\text{V}}{\text{k}\Omega} = 325\mu\text{A} \quad | \quad V_{EQ2} = 9 - 9100I_{C1} = 6.04\text{V} \quad | \quad R_{EQ2} = 9.1\text{k}\Omega$$

$$I_{C2} = 80 \frac{9 - 0.7 - 6.04}{9.1 + 81(12)} \frac{\text{V}}{\text{k}\Omega} = 184\mu\text{A} \quad | \quad V_{C1} = 9 - 9.1\text{k}\Omega\left(I_{C1} - I_{B2}\right) = 6.06\text{V}$$

$$V_{E1} = -9 + I_{E1}(24\text{k}\Omega) = -1.10\text{V} \quad | \quad V_{CE1} = 6.06 - (-1.10) = 7.16\text{V}$$

$$V_{C2} = -9 + I_{C2}(43\text{k}\Omega) = -1.09\text{V} \quad | \quad V_{E2} = V_{C1} + 0.7 = 6.76\text{V} \quad | \quad V_{EC2} = 7.85\text{V}$$

$$Q_1: \ (325\mu\text{A}, 7.16\text{V}) \quad Q_2: \ (184\mu\text{A}, 7.85\text{V})$$

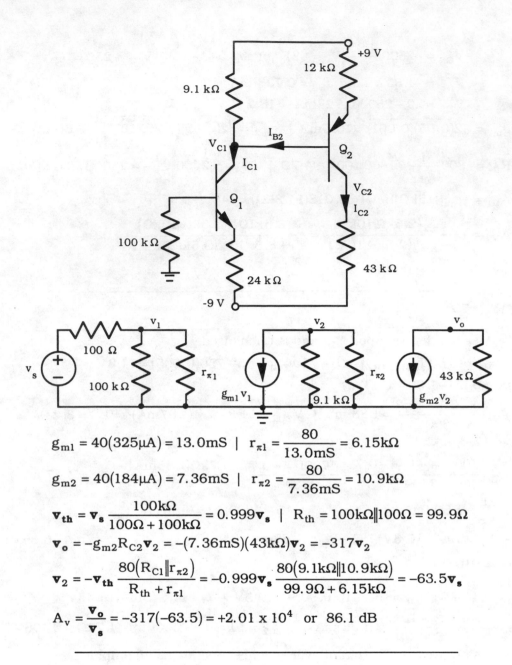

$$g_{m1} = 40(325\mu A) = 13.0mS \quad | \quad r_{\pi 1} = \frac{80}{13.0mS} = 6.15k\Omega$$

$$g_{m2} = 40(184\mu A) = 7.36mS \quad | \quad r_{\pi 2} = \frac{80}{7.36mS} = 10.9k\Omega$$

$$\mathbf{v_{th}} = \mathbf{v_s}\frac{100k\Omega}{100\Omega + 100k\Omega} = 0.999\mathbf{v_s} \quad | \quad R_{th} = 100k\Omega\|100\Omega = 99.9\Omega$$

$$\mathbf{v_o} = -g_{m2}R_{C2}\mathbf{v_2} = -(7.36mS)(43k\Omega)\mathbf{v_2} = -317\mathbf{v_2}$$

$$\mathbf{v_2} = -\mathbf{v_{th}}\frac{80(R_{C1}\|r_{\pi 2})}{R_{th} + r_{\pi 1}} = -0.999\mathbf{v_s}\frac{80(9.1k\Omega\|10.9k\Omega)}{99.9\Omega + 6.15k\Omega} = -63.5\mathbf{v_s}$$

$$A_v = \frac{\mathbf{v_o}}{\mathbf{v_s}} = -317(-63.5) = +2.01 \times 10^4 \quad or \quad 86.1 \, dB$$

15.15

```
*Problem 15.15 - Two-stage Amplifier
VCC 8 0 DC 9
VEE 9 0 DC -9
VS 1 0 AC 1
RS 1 2 100
*For output resistance
*VS 1 0 AC 0
*IO 0 6 AC 1
C1 2 3 10U
RB 3 0 100K
Q1 5 3 4 NBJT
RE1 4 9 24K
C2 4 9 10U
RC1 8 5 9.1K
Q2 6 5 7 PBJT
```

RE2 8 7 12K
C3 7 8 10U
RC2 6 9 43K
*C4 6 10 10U - Not needed
.OP
.AC LIN 1 2.5KHZ 2.5KHZ
.MODEL NBJT NPN IS=1E-16 BF=80
.MODEL PBJT PNP IS=1E-16 BF=80
.PRINT AC VM(3) VP(3) IM(VS) IP(VS) VM(6) VP(6)
.END

Results: $A_V = VM(6) = +1.86 \times 10^4$ | $R_{IN} = \dfrac{VM(3)}{IM(VS)} = 6.04$ kΩ | $R_{OUT} = VM(6) = 43.0$ kΩ

15.16 Assuming that M_1 remains in saturation, then its drain current does not change when the circuit is modified, and using the results from Prob. 15.12: $I_{DS1} = 1$ mA and $V_{DS1} = +5$ V.

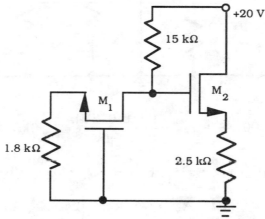

Assume that M_2 is saturated:

$$I_{DS2} = \frac{0.05}{2}\left(V_{GS2} + 2\right)^2 \quad | \quad V_{GS2} = 5 - 2500 I_{D2} \quad | \quad \text{Solving these}$$

two simultaneous equations gives $V_{GS2} = -1.67$V and $I_{DS2} = 2.67$mA.

15.17 dc equivalent circuit:

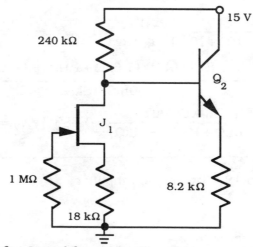

We assume saturation for J_1 and forward-active region operation for Q_2.

$$I_{DS1} = I_{DSS}\left(1 - \frac{V_{GS1}}{V_P}\right)^2 \quad | \quad I_{DS1} = 0.005\left(1 - \frac{-18000 I_{DS1}}{-1}\right)^2 \rightarrow I_{DS1} = 50\mu A$$

$$V_{EQ2} = 15 - I_{DS1}(240k\Omega) = 3.00V \quad | \quad R_{EQ2} = 240k\Omega \quad | \quad I_{C2} = 100\frac{3 - 0.7}{240 + 101(8.2)}\frac{V}{k\Omega} = 215\ \mu A$$

$$V_{CE2} = 15 - 8200 I_{E2} = 13.2\ V \quad | \quad \text{Checking } V_{DS1}: V_{D1} = 15 - (50 + 2.15)(\mu A)(240k\Omega) = 2.48\ V$$

$$V_{DS1} = 2.48 - (50\mu A)(18k\Omega) = 1.58\ V \quad | \quad V_{GS1} - V_P = -(50\mu A)(18k\Omega) + 1 = 0.1\ V \rightarrow M_1 \text{ is saturated.}$$

ac equivalent circuit:

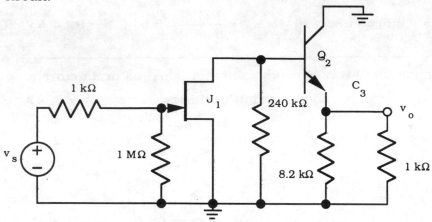

$$g_{m1} = \frac{2}{|-1|}\sqrt{(5mA)50\mu A} = 1.00mS \quad | \quad r_{\pi 2} = \frac{100(0.025V)}{215\mu A} = 11.6k\Omega$$

$$A_{V1} = \frac{\mathbf{v_1}}{\mathbf{v_s}} = -\frac{10^6}{10^6 + 10^3}g_{m1}R_{L1} = -\frac{10^6}{10^6 + 10^3}g\left[R_{D1}\|\left(r_{\pi 2} + (\beta_{o2} + 1)R_{L2}\right)\right]$$

$$R_{L2} = R_{E2}\|R_L = 8.2k\Omega\|1k\Omega = 891\Omega \quad | \quad A_{V1} = (-1.00mS)\left[240k\Omega\|(11.6k\Omega + 101(891\Omega))\right] = -71.4$$

$$A_{V2} = \frac{\mathbf{v_o}}{\mathbf{v_1}} = +\frac{101(0.891k\Omega)}{11.6k\Omega + 101(0.891k\Omega)} = 0.886 \quad | \quad A_V = -71.4(0.866) = -63.2 \quad | \quad R_{IN} = 1\ M\Omega$$

$$R_{OUT} = R_{E2}\left\|\frac{R_{th2} + r_{\pi 2}}{\beta_{o2} + 1}\right. = 8.2k\Omega\left\|\frac{240k\Omega + 11.6k\Omega}{101}\right. = 8.2k\Omega\|2.49k\Omega = 1.91\ k\Omega$$

Note: R_{OUT} and A_V would be lower if r_{o1} were also included.

$$(b)\ A_{V1} = \frac{\mathbf{v_1}}{\mathbf{v_s}} = -\frac{10^6}{10^6 + 10^3}\frac{g_{m1}R_{L1}}{1 + g_{m1}R_5}$$

$$A_{V1} = -0.999\frac{(1.00mS)\left[240k\Omega\|(11.6k\Omega + 101(0.891k\Omega))\right]}{1 + (1.00mS)(18k\Omega)} = -3.75$$

$$A_{V2} = \frac{\mathbf{v_o}}{\mathbf{v_1}} = +\frac{101(0.891k\Omega)}{11.6k\Omega + 101(0.891k\Omega)} = 0.886 \quad | \quad A_V = -3.75(0.866) = -3.25$$

15.18

*Problem 15.18 - Two-stage Amplifier
VCC 8 0 DC 15
VS 1 0 AC 1
RS 1 2 1K
*For output resistance

```
*VS 1 0 AC 0
*VO 7 0 AC 1
C1 2 3 33U
RG 3 0 1MEG
J1 5 3 4 NJFET
RS1 4 0 18K
C2 4 0 33U
RD 8 5 240K
Q2 8 5 6 NBJT
RE 6 0 8.2K
C3 6 7 33U
RL 7 0 1K
.OP
.AC LIN 1 1KHZ 1KHZ
.MODEL NBJT NPN IS=1E-16 BF=100
.MODEL NJFET NJF BETA=0.005 VTO=-1
.PRINT AC VM(3) VP(3) IM(VS) IP(VS) VM(7) VP(7) IM(C3) IP(C3)
.END
```

Results: $A_V = VM(7) = -63.1$ | $R_{IN} = \dfrac{VM(3)}{IM(VS)} = 1.00 \ M\Omega$ | $R_{OUT} = \dfrac{1}{IM(C3)} = 1.91 \ k\Omega$

15.19 Using the dc equivalent circuit:

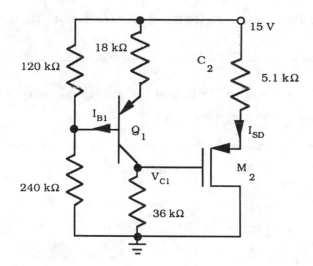

$$V_{TH} = \frac{240k\Omega}{240k\Omega + 120k\Omega} 15V = 10.0V \ | \ R_{TH} = 240k\Omega \| 120k\Omega = 80.0k\Omega$$

$$I_{B1} = \frac{15 - 10 - 0.7}{80 + 76(18)} \frac{V}{k\Omega} = 2.97 \ \mu A \ | \ I_{c1} = 75I_{B1} = 223 \ \mu A$$

$$V_{E1} = 15 - 18000I_{E1} = 10.9V \ | \ V_{C1} = 36000I_{C1} = 8.03 \ V \ | \ V_{EC1} = 10.9 - 8.03 = 2.87 \ V$$

$$I_{SD2} = \frac{15 - V_{SG2} - 8.03}{5.1k\Omega} \ | \ I_{SD2} = \frac{0.004}{2}\left(V_{SG2} + 4\right)^2 \Rightarrow V_{SG2} = -3.01 \ V, \ I_{SD2} = 1.96 \ mA$$

$$V_{SD2} = 15 - 5.1k\Omega(1.96mA) = 5.00 \ V \ | \ V_{SG} + V_P = -3.01 + 4 = 0.99V \ | \ M_2 \text{ is saturated.}$$

Using the ac equivalent circuit:

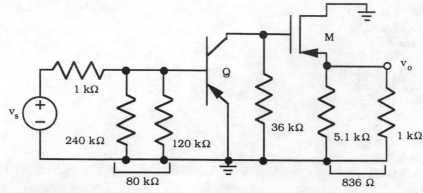

$$r_{\pi 1} = \frac{75(0.025V)}{223\mu A} = 8.41k\Omega \quad | \quad g_{m2} = \sqrt{2(4x10^{-3})(1.96x10^{-3})} = 3.96mS$$

$$A_{v1} = \frac{v_1}{v_s} = 0.988 \frac{-\beta_{o1}R_I}{R_{th} + r_{\pi 1}} = 0.988 \frac{-75(36000)}{988 + 8410} = -284$$

$$A_{v2} = \frac{v_o}{v_1} = \frac{g_{m2}R_L}{1 + g_{m2}R_L} = \frac{(3.96mS)(0.836k\Omega)}{1 + (3.96mS)(0.836k\Omega)} = 0.768$$

$$A_v = 0.768(-284) = -218 \quad | \quad R_{IN} = R_B \| r_{\pi 1} = 7.61 \text{ k}\Omega \quad | \quad R_{OUT} = 5100 \left\| \frac{1}{g_{m2}} \right. = 241 \ \Omega$$

(b) If the bypass capacitor is removed from the 18 kΩ resistor, then

$$A_{v1} = \frac{v_1}{v_s} = 0.988 \frac{-\beta_{o1}R_I}{R_{th} + r_{\pi 1} + (\beta_{o1} + 1)18k\Omega} = 0.988 \frac{-75(36000)}{988 + 8410 + 76(18k\Omega)} = -1.94$$

$$A_v = 0.768(-1.94) = -1.49 \quad | \quad \text{Note that the input resistance will increase to}$$

$$R_{IN} = 80k\Omega \| [8410 + 76(18k\Omega)] = 75.6k\Omega$$

15.20

```
*Problem 15.20 - Two-stage Amplifier
VCC 8 0 DC 15
VS 1 0 AC 1
RS 1 2 1K
*For output resistance
*VS 1 0 AC 0
*VO 7 0 AC 1
C1 2 3 20U
R1 3 0 240K
R2 8 3 120K
Q1 4 3 5 PBJT
RE1 8 5 18K
C2 8 5 20U
RC 4 0 36K
M2 0 4 6 6 PFET
RS2 8 6 5.1K
C3 6 7 20U
RL 7 0 1K
.OP
.AC LIN 1 2KHZ 2KHZ
.MODEL PBJT PNP IS=1E-16 BF=75
.MODEL PFET PMOS KP=.004 VTO=4
.PRINT AC VM(3) VP(3) IM(VS) IP(VS) VM(7) VP(7) IM(C3) IP(C3)
.END
```

Results: $A_V = VM(7) = -210$ | $R_{IN} = \dfrac{VM(3)}{IM(VS)} = 7.92\ k\Omega$ | $R_{OUT} = \dfrac{1}{IM(C3)} = 240\ \Omega$

15.21

(a) For $\beta_F = \infty$, $I_{B1} = 0 = I_{B2}$ | $V_{BE1} = 0.7V = V_{BE2}$ | $V_{C1} = V_{BE2} + (300k\Omega)I_{B1} + V_{BE1} = 1.40V$

$I_{C1} + I_{B2} = \dfrac{3 - 1.4}{360}\dfrac{V}{k\Omega} = 4.44\mu A$ | $I_{C1} = 4.44\ \mu A$ | $I_{C2} = I_{E2} - I_{B2} = \dfrac{0.7V}{30k\Omega} - 0 = 23.3\ \mu A$

$Q_1 : (4.44\mu A, 1.40V)$ | $Q_2 : (23.3\mu A, 2.30V)$

(b) Writing an equation for the current through the 300 kΩ resistor:

$I_{B1} = \dfrac{3V - 360k\Omega(I_{C1} + I_{B2}) - 0.7V - 0.7V}{300k\Omega}$ and also $I_{B1} = \dfrac{(I_{E2} - I_{B1})(30k\Omega) - 0.7V}{300k\Omega}$

Solving these two simultaneous equations with $I_{C1} = 75I_{B1}$, $I_{C2} = 75I_{B2}$ yields $I_{B1} = 54.5nA$, $I_{C1} = 4.08\mu A$, $I_{B2} = 315nA$, $I_{C2} = 23.6\mu A$ | $Q_1 : (4.08\mu A, 1.42V)$ | $Q_2 : (23.6\mu A, 2.28V)$

15.22

$I_{C2} = \beta_F I_{E1} = \beta_F \dfrac{\beta_F + 1}{\beta_F} I_{C1} = (\beta_F + 1)I_{C1}$ | $r_{\pi1} = (\beta_o + 1)r_{\pi2}$ | $y_{11} = \dfrac{i_1}{v_1}\bigg|_{v_2 = 0}$

$\mathbf{v_1} = \mathbf{i_1}[r_{\pi1} + (\beta_{o1} + 1)r_{\pi2}] = 2r_{\pi1}$ | $y_{11} = \dfrac{1}{2r_{\pi1}}$ | $y_{12} = \dfrac{i_1}{v_2}\bigg|_{v_1 = 0} = 0$

$\mathbf{i_{b2}} \cong \dfrac{\mathbf{v_2}}{r_{o1}(1 + g_{m1}r_{\pi2})} \cong \dfrac{\mathbf{v_2}}{2r_{o1}}$ | $\mathbf{i_1} \cong -\dfrac{\mathbf{v_2}}{2r_{o1}}\dfrac{r_{\pi2}}{r_{\pi1} + r_{\pi2}} = -\dfrac{\mathbf{v_2}}{2r_{o1}(\beta_{o1} + 1)}$ | $y_{12} \cong -\dfrac{1}{2\beta_{o1}r_{o1}}$

$y_{21} = \dfrac{i_2}{v_1}\bigg|_{v_2 = 0} \cong \dfrac{i_{C2}}{v_1}\bigg|_{v_2 = 0} = \dfrac{(\beta_{o1} + 1)r_{\pi2}}{r_{\pi1} + (\beta_{o1} + 1)r_{\pi2}} g_{m2} = \dfrac{g_{m2}}{2}$

$y_{22} = \dfrac{i_2}{v_2}\bigg|_{v_1 = 0}$ | $\mathbf{i_2} = \dfrac{\mathbf{v_2}}{r_{o2}} + \beta_{o2}i_{e1} + i_{c1} = \dfrac{\mathbf{v_2}}{r_{o2}} + \beta_{o2}\dfrac{\beta_{o1} + 1}{\beta_{o1}}i_{c1} + i_{c1} \cong \dfrac{\mathbf{v_2}}{r_{o2}} + \beta_{o2}i_{c1}$

$\mathbf{i_{c1}} = \dfrac{\mathbf{v_2}}{r_{o1}\left(1 + \dfrac{\beta_{o1}R_E}{r_{\pi1} + R_E}\right)} = \dfrac{\mathbf{v_2}}{r_{o1}\left(1 + \dfrac{\beta_{o2}r_{\pi2}}{r_{\pi1} + r_{\pi2}}\right)} \cong \dfrac{\mathbf{v_2}}{r_{o1}\left(1 + \dfrac{\beta_{o2}r_{\pi2}}{(\beta_{o2} + 2)r_{\pi2}}\right)} = \dfrac{\mathbf{v_2}}{2r_{o1}}$

$y_{22} = \dfrac{1}{r_{o2}} + \dfrac{\beta_{o2}}{2r_{o1}} = \dfrac{1}{r_{o2}} + \dfrac{1}{2r_{o2}} = \dfrac{3}{2r_{o2}}$

15.23

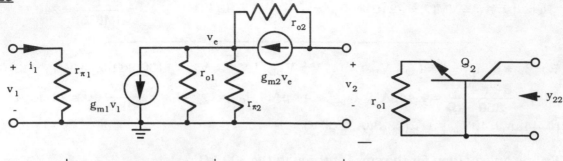

$$y_{11} = \left.\frac{i_1}{v_1}\right|_{v_2=0} = \frac{1}{r_{\pi 1}} \quad \Big| \quad y_{12} = \left.\frac{i_1}{v_2}\right|_{v_1=0} = 0 \quad \Big| \quad y_{21} = \left.\frac{i_2}{v_1}\right|_{v_2=0} = g_{m1}\frac{g_{m2} + g_{o2}}{g_{m2} + g_{o2} + g_{\pi 2} + g_{o1}}$$

$$I_{C2} = \alpha_F I_{C1} \cong I_{C1} \rightarrow g_{m2} = g_{m1} \quad \Big| \quad g_{o2} = g_{o1} \quad \Big| \quad y_{21} \cong g_{m1}\frac{1 + \dfrac{1}{\mu_{f2}}}{1 + \dfrac{1}{\mu_{F2}} + \dfrac{1}{\beta_{o2}} + \dfrac{1}{\mu_{f1}}} \cong g_{m1}$$

$$y_{12} = \left.\frac{i_2}{v_2}\right|_{v_1=0} = \frac{1}{r_{o2}\left(1 + \dfrac{\beta_{o2}R_E}{r_{\pi 2} + R_E}\right)} = \frac{1}{r_{o2}\left(1 + \dfrac{\beta_{o2}r_{o1}}{r_{\pi 2} + r_{o1}}\right)} \cong \frac{1}{r_{o2}(\beta_{o2} + 1)}$$

15.24

$$y_{11} = \left.\frac{i_1}{v_1}\right|_{v_2=0} = 0 \quad \Big| \quad y_{12} = \left.\frac{i_1}{v_2}\right|_{v_1=0} = 0 \quad \Big| \quad y_{21} = \left.\frac{i_2}{v_1}\right|_{v_2=0} = g_{m1}(1) = g_{m1}$$

$$y_{12} = \left.\frac{i_2}{v_2}\right|_{v_1=0} = \frac{1}{r_{o2}(1 + g_{m2}r_{o1})} \cong \frac{1}{\mu_{f2}r_{o1}} \quad \Big| \quad I_{DS2} = I_{DS1}$$

15.25

$$I_{C2} = \beta_{F2}I_{C1} \rightarrow g_{m2} = \beta_{o2}g_{m1}$$

$$g'_m = \left.\frac{i_2}{v_1}\right|_{v_2=0} = g_{m1}(\beta_{o2} + 1) = g_{m2}\frac{\beta_{o2} + 1}{\beta_{o2}} \cong g_{m2} = g_m$$

$$r'_\pi = r_{\pi 1} = \frac{\beta_{o1}}{g_{m1}} = \frac{\beta_{o1}}{g_{m2}}\beta_{o2} = \beta_{o1}r_{\pi 2} = \beta_o r_\pi \quad \Big| \quad \beta'_o = \beta_{o1}(\beta_{o2} + 1) \cong \beta_{o1}\beta_{o2}$$

$$r'_o = r_{o2}\left\|\frac{r_{o1} + r_{\pi 2}}{\beta_{o2} + 1}\right. = r_{o2}\left\|\frac{\beta_{o2}r_{o2} + r_{\pi 2}}{\beta_{o2} + 1}\right. \cong r_{o2}\|r_{o2} = \frac{r_o}{2} \quad \Big| \quad \mu'_f = g_m\frac{r_o}{2} = \frac{\mu_f}{2}$$

15.26

$$A_V = G_m R_o \cong -\alpha_{o2}g_{m1}(\beta_{o2}r_{o2}) = -g_{m2}(\beta_{o2}r_{o2}) = -\beta_{o2}\mu_{f2} = -100(40)(75) = -3 \times 10^5 \ !$$

15.27

$$\text{Assume } I_{C2} = \beta_{F2}I_{C1} \rightarrow g_{m2} = \beta_{o2}g_{m1} \quad \Big| \quad I'_C = I_{C2} = I_C \quad \Big| \quad I'_B = I_{B1} = \frac{I_{C2}}{\beta_{F1}\beta_{F2}}$$

$$g'_m = -\beta_{o2}g_{m1} = -\beta_{o2}\frac{g_{m2}}{\beta_{o2}} = g_{m2} = g_m \quad \Big| \quad r'_\pi = r_{\pi 1} = \beta_o r_\pi \quad \Big| \quad \beta'_o = g_m\beta_o r_\pi = \beta_o^2$$

$$r'_o = r_{o2} \quad \Big| \quad \mu'_f = g_m r_o = \mu_f$$

For forward - active region operation, we require $V_{CB} \geq 0$. $V_{CB} = -V_{GS} - (-I_B R_B)$

$V_{CB} = -V_{GS} + \dfrac{I_{EE}}{\beta_F + 1} R_B$ | For the JFET, $V_{GS} \leq 0 \rightarrow V_{CB} \geq \dfrac{I_{EE}}{\beta_F + 1} R_B$. So the BJT will be

in the forward active region for as long as $I_{EE} \leq I_{DSS} = 1mA$ or $0 \leq I_{EE} \leq 1$ mA

15.29

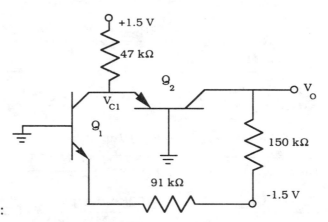

Dc equivalent circuit $(v_S = 0)$:

Q_1: $I_{C1} = \beta_{F1} I_{B1} = 100 \dfrac{1.5V - 0.7V}{200k\Omega + 101(91k\Omega)} = 8.52$ μA

$V_{CE1} = V_{C1} - V_{E1} = +0.7 - \left[-1.5V + 91k\Omega(I_{E1}) \right] = 1.42V$ | Q - point: $(8.52\mu A, 1.42V)$

Q_2: $I_{E2} = \dfrac{1.5V - 0.7V}{47k\Omega} - I_{C1} = 17.0 - 8.52 = 8.48$ μA | $I_{C2} = \alpha_{F2} I_{E2} = \dfrac{100}{101} 8.48$ μA $= 8.40$ μA

$V_{EC2} = V_{E2} - V_{C2} = +0.7 - \left[-1.5 + 8.40\mu A(1.5 \times 10^5) \right] = 0.940V$ | Q - point: $(8.40\mu A, 0.940V)$

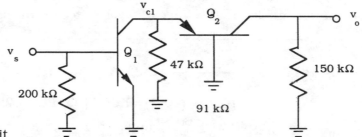

Ac equivalent circuit

$A_V = \left(\dfrac{v_o}{v_{c1}} \right) \left(\dfrac{v_{c1}}{v_s} \right)$ | $\dfrac{v_{c1}}{v_s} = -g_{m1} \left(47k\Omega \left\| \dfrac{1}{g_{m2}} \right) = -40(8.52\mu A) \left(47k\Omega \left\| \dfrac{1}{40(8.40\mu A)} \right) = -0.954$

$\dfrac{v_o}{v_{c1}} = g_{m2} R_L = 40(8.40\mu A)(1.5 \times 10^5) = 50.4$ | $A_V = -48.1$

The two stage common-emitter/common-base cascade is usually called a cascode amplifier.

15.30

(a) $I_C = \alpha_F I_E = \dfrac{1}{2} \dfrac{\beta_F}{\beta_F + 1} \dfrac{12 - V_{BE}}{R_{EE}} = \dfrac{1}{2} \dfrac{100}{101} \dfrac{12 - 0.7}{2.7 \times 10^5} = 20.7$ μA | $V_C = 12 - 3.3 \times 10^5 I_C = 5.17V$

$V_{CE} = V_C - (-0.7V) = 5.87V$ | Q - Point $= (20.7\mu A, \; 5.87V)$

(b) $A_{dd} = -g_m R_C = -40(20.7\mu A)(330k\Omega) = -273$

$$R_{ID} = 2r_\pi = 2\frac{\beta_o V_T}{I_C} = 2\frac{100(0.025V)}{20.7\mu A} = 243 \text{ k}\Omega \quad | \quad R_{OD} = 2R_C = 660 \text{ k}\Omega$$

(c) $A_{cc} = -\dfrac{\beta_o R_C}{r_\pi + (\beta_o + 1)2R_{EE}} = -\dfrac{100(330k\Omega)}{122k\Omega + 2(101)270k\Omega} = -0.604$

$$A_{dd} = -\frac{g_m R_C}{2} = -137 \quad | \quad A_{cd} = A_{cc} \quad | \quad CMRR = \left|\frac{-137}{-0.604}\right| = 227$$

$$R_{IC} = \frac{r_\pi + (\beta_o + 1)2R_{EE}}{2} = \frac{122k\Omega + 2(101)270k\Omega}{2} = 27.3 \text{ M}\Omega$$

15.31

(a) $I_C = \alpha_F I_E = \dfrac{1}{2}\dfrac{\beta_F}{\beta_F + 1}\dfrac{12 - V_{BE}}{R_{EE}} = \dfrac{1}{2}\dfrac{100}{101}\dfrac{12 - 0.7}{2.7 \times 10^5} = 20.7 \ \mu A$

$V_{C1} = V_{C2} = 12 - 3.9 \times 10^5 I_C = 3.93V \quad | \quad V_{CE} = V_C - (-0.7V) = 4.63V$

$Q - Point = (20.7\mu A, \ 4.63V) \quad | \quad r_\pi = \dfrac{100(0.025V)}{20.7 \ \mu A} = 121k\Omega$

$A_{cc} = -\dfrac{\beta_o R_C}{r_\pi + (\beta_o + 1)2R_{EE}} = \dfrac{100(390k\Omega)}{121k\Omega + (101)540k\Omega} = -0.714 \quad | \quad v_{ic} = \dfrac{5.000 + 5.000}{2} = 5.00V$

$v_{C1} = v_{C2} = 3.93 + A_{cc}v_{ic} = 3.93 - 0.714(5) = 0.360 \text{ V}$

(b) $I_C = \alpha_F I_E = \dfrac{1}{2}\dfrac{\beta_F}{\beta_F + 1}\dfrac{5V - V_{BE} - (-12V)}{R_{EE}} = \dfrac{1}{2}\dfrac{100}{101}\dfrac{17V - 0.7V}{2.7 \times 10^5} = 29.9 \ \mu A$

$V_{C1} = V_{C2} = 12 - 3.9 \times 10^5 I_C = 0.339 \text{ V} \quad | \quad$ Part (a) is in error by 0.021 V

(c) The common - mode signal voltage applied to the base - emitter junction is

$$V_{be} = V_{IC}\frac{r_\pi}{r_\pi + (\beta_o + 1)2R_{EE}} = 5\frac{121k\Omega}{121k\Omega + (101)540k\Omega} = 11.1 \text{ mV} > 5\text{mV}.$$

A common - mode input voltage of 5 volts exceeds the small - signal limit.

15.32

(a) $I_E = \dfrac{1}{2}\dfrac{1.5 - 0.7}{75 \times 10^3}\dfrac{V}{\Omega} = 5.33\mu A \quad | \quad I_C = \alpha_F I_E = \dfrac{60}{61}I_E = 5.25\mu A$

$V_{CE} = 1.5 - 10^5 I_C - (-0.7) = 1.68V \quad | \quad$ Q - Pt: $(5.25\mu A, 1.68V)$

(b) $g_m = 40I_C = 0.210\text{mS} \quad | \quad r_\pi = \dfrac{60}{g_m} = 286k\Omega \quad | \quad A_{dd} = -g_m R_C = -0.210\text{mS}(100k\Omega) = -21.0$

$A_{cc} = -\dfrac{\beta_o R_C}{r_\pi + (\beta_o + 1)2R_{EE}} = -\dfrac{60(100k\Omega)}{286k\Omega + 61(150k\Omega)} = -0.636$

For differential output: $CMRR = \left|\dfrac{-21.0}{0}\right| = \infty$

For single-ended output: CMRR $= \left| \dfrac{\dfrac{-21.0}{2}}{-0.636} \right| = 16.5$, a paltry 24.4 dB!

$$R_{ID} = 2r_\pi = 572k\Omega \quad | \quad R_{IC} = \dfrac{r_\pi + (\beta_o + 1)2R_{EE}}{2} = \dfrac{286 + 61(150)}{2}k\Omega = 4.72 \text{ M}\Omega$$

$$R_{OD} = 2R_C = 200 \text{ k}\Omega \quad | \quad R_{OC} = \dfrac{R_C}{2} = 50k\Omega$$

15.33

```
*Problem 15.33
VCC 2 0 DC 12
VEE 1 0 DC -12
VIC 8 0 DC 0
VID1 4 8 AC 0.5
VID2 6 8 AC -0.5
RC1 2 3 330K
RC2 2 7 330K
Q1 3 4 5 NBJT
Q2 7 6 5 NBJT
REE 5 1 270K
.MODEL NBJT NPN BF=100 VA=60 IS=1FA
.OP
.AC LIN 1 1KHZ 1KHZ
.PRINT AC IM(VID1) IP(VID1) VM(3,7) VP(3,7)
.TF V(7) VIC
.END
```

Results: $A_{dd} = \text{VM}(3,7) = -241 \quad | \quad R_{ID} = \dfrac{1}{\text{IM(VID1)}} = 269 \text{ k}\Omega \quad | \quad A_{cc} = -0.602 \quad | \quad R_{IC} = 23.2 \text{ M}\Omega$

15.34 (a)

$$I_E = \dfrac{1.5V - 0.7V}{2(4.7 \times 10^4 \Omega)} = 8.51\mu A \quad | \quad I_C = \alpha_F I_E = \dfrac{100}{101}I_E = 8.43\mu A$$

$$V_{CE} = 1.5 - 10^5 I_C - (-0.7) = 1.36V \,| \text{ Q-point: } (8.43\mu A, 1.36V)$$

$$g_m = 40I_C = 0.337mS \quad | \quad r_\pi = \dfrac{100}{g_m} = 297k\Omega \quad | \quad A_{dd} = -g_m R_C = -0.337mS(100k\Omega) = -33.7$$

$$A_{cc} = -\dfrac{\beta_o R_C}{r_\pi + (\beta_o + 1)2R_{EE}} = -\dfrac{100(100k\Omega)}{297k\Omega + 101(94k\Omega)} = -1.02$$

For differential output: CMRR $= \left| \dfrac{-33.7}{0} \right| = \infty$

For single-ended output: CMRR $= \left| \dfrac{\dfrac{-33.7}{2}}{-1.02} \right| = 16.5$, a paltry 24.4 dB!

$$R_{ID} = 2r_\pi = 594k\Omega \quad | \quad R_{IC} = \dfrac{r_\pi + (\beta_o + 1)2R_{EE}}{2} = \dfrac{297 + 101(94)}{2}k\Omega = 4.90 \text{ M}\Omega$$

$$R_{OD} = 2R_C = 200 \text{ k}\Omega \quad | \quad R_{OC} = \dfrac{R_C}{2} = 50 \text{ k}\Omega$$

15.35 We should first check the feasibility of the design using the Rule-of-Thumb estimates similar to those developed in Chapter 13 (Eq. 13.59):

The required $A_{dd} = 200$ (46 db). Assuming we drop half the power supply voltage across R_C:

$$A_{dd} = g_m R_C = 40 I_C R_L = 40 \frac{V_{CC}}{2} = 20 V_{CC} = 240. \text{ Thus, a gain of 200 appears feasible.}$$

$$R_{ID} = 2r_\pi = 1 M\Omega \rightarrow r_\pi = 500 k\Omega \mid I_C = \frac{\beta_o V_T}{r_\pi} = \frac{100(0.025 V)}{500 k\Omega} = 5.00 \ \mu A$$

$$I_E = \frac{I_C}{\alpha_F} = \frac{101}{100} I_C = 5.05 \mu A \mid R_{EE} = \frac{V_{EE} - V_{BE}}{2 I_E} = \frac{(12 - 0.7)V}{2(5.05 \mu A)} = 1.12 M\Omega$$

$$A_{dd} = -g_m R_C = -200 \ (46 dB) \mid R_C = \frac{200}{g_m} = \frac{200}{40(5 \times 10^{-6})} = 1.00 M\Omega$$

Checking the collector voltage: $V_C = 12 - (990 k\Omega)(5\mu A) = 7V$ | Picking the closest 5% values from the table in the Appendix: $R_{EE} = 1.1 \ M\Omega$ and $R_C = 1 \ M\Omega$ are the final design values. These values give $I_C = 5.09 \mu A$ and $A_{dd} = -204 \ (46.2 dB)$

15.36 We should first check the feasibility of the design using the Rule-of-Thumb estimates similar to those developed in Chapter 13 (Eq. 13.59):

The required $A_{dd} = 794$ (58 db). (This sounds pretty large - a significant fraction of the BJT amplification factor μ_f.) Even assuming we choose to drop all of the positive power supply voltage across R_C (which provides no common-mode input range):

$$A_{dd} = g_m R_C = 40 I_C R_L \le 40 V_{CC} = 40(9) = 360.$$

Thus, a gain of 794 is not feasible with this topology!

15.37

$$I_C = \alpha_F I_E = \alpha_F \frac{I_{EE}}{2} = \frac{100}{101} \frac{400 \mu A}{2} = 198 \mu A \mid V_{CE} = 12 - 3.9 \times 10^4 I_C - (-0.7) = 4.98 V$$

Q-point: $(198 \mu A, 4.98 V)$ | $g_m = 40 I_C = 7.92 mS$ | $r_\pi = \frac{100}{g_m} = 12.6 k\Omega$

$$A_{dd} = -g_m R_C = -7.92 mS(39 k\Omega) = -309$$

$$A_{cc} = -\frac{\beta_o R_C}{r_\pi + (\beta_o + 1) 2 R_{EE}} = -\frac{100(39 k\Omega)}{12.6 k\Omega + 101(400 k\Omega)} = -0.0965$$

For differential output: $\text{CMRR} = \left| \frac{-309}{0} \right| = \infty$

For single-ended output: $\text{CMRR} = \left| \frac{\frac{-309}{2}}{-0.0965} \right| = 1600$ or 64.1 dB

$$R_{ID} = 2r_\pi = 25.2 \ k\Omega \mid R_{IC} = \frac{r_\pi + (\beta_o + 1) 2 R_{EE}}{2} = \frac{12.6 k\Omega + 101(400 k\Omega)}{2} k\Omega = 20.2 \ M\Omega$$

(Note that this value is approaching the $\beta_o r_o$ limit and hence is not really correct.)

$$R_{OD} = 2R_C = 78.0 \ k\Omega \mid R_{OC} = \frac{R_C}{2} = 19.5 \ k\Omega$$

15.38

$$I_C = \alpha_F I_E = \alpha_F \frac{I_{EE}}{2} = \frac{75}{76} \frac{400\mu A}{2} = 197\mu A \quad | \quad V_{C1} = V_{C2} = 12 - 3.9 \times 10^4 I_C = 4.32V$$

$$V_{CE} = 4.32 - (-0.7) = 5.02V \quad | \quad Q\text{-point:} \quad (197\mu A, 5.02V)$$

$$g_m = 40I_C = 7.88mS \quad | \quad r_\pi = \frac{75}{g_m} = 9.52k\Omega \quad | \quad A_{dd} = -g_m R_C = -7.88mS(39k\Omega) = -307$$

$$A_{cc} = -\frac{\beta_o R_C}{r_\pi + (\beta_o + 1)2R_{EE}} = -\frac{75(39k\Omega)}{9.52k\Omega + 76(400k\Omega)} = -0.0962$$

$$v_{id} = 2.005 - 1.995 = 0.01V \quad | \quad v_{ic} = \frac{2.005 + 1.995}{2} = 2.00V$$

$$v_{C1} = V_{C1} + A_{dd}\frac{v_{id}}{2} + A_{cc}v_{ic} = 4.32V - 307\frac{0.01V}{2} - 0.0962(2V) = 2.593 \text{ V}$$

$$v_{C2} = V_{C2} - A_{dd}\frac{v_{id}}{2} + A_{cc}v_{ic} = 4.32V + 307\frac{0.01V}{2} - 0.0962(2V) = 5.663 \text{ V}$$

$$v_{OD} = 2.593 - 5.663 = -3.07 \text{ V}$$

$$V_{CB} = V_{C1} + A_{cc}V_{IC} - V_{IC} \geq 0 \quad | \quad V_{IC} \leq \frac{4.32}{1 + 0.0962} = 3.94 \text{ V}$$

15.39

$$R_{ID} = 2r_\pi = \frac{2\beta_o V_T}{I_C} \rightarrow I_C \frac{2(100)(0.025V)}{5M\Omega} = 1.00\mu A \quad | \quad I_{EE} = 2\frac{I_C}{\alpha_F} = 2\frac{101}{100}(1\mu A) = 2.02 \ \mu A$$

$$CMRR = g_m R_{EE} = 10^5 \rightarrow R_{EE} = \frac{10^5}{40(1.00\mu A)} = 2.5 \text{ G}\Omega \ !$$

15.40

(a) $I_C = \alpha_F I_E = \alpha_F \frac{I_{EE}}{2} = \frac{100}{101}\frac{20\mu A}{2} = 9.90\mu A \quad | \quad V_{C2} = 10 - 9.1 \times 10^5 I_C = 0.991V$

$$g_m = 40I_C = 0.396mS \quad | \quad A_{dd} = -g_m R_C = -0.396mS(910k\Omega) = -360 \quad | \quad R_{EE} = \infty \rightarrow A_{cc} \cong 0$$

$$v_{C2} = V_{C2} - A_{dd}\frac{v_{ID}}{2} + A_{cc}v_{IC} \quad | \quad \text{For } v_s = 0: \ v_{C2} = V_{C2} = 0.991$$

For $v_s = 2mV$: $v_{C2} = 0.991V + 360(0.001V) - 0(0.001V) = +1.35 \text{ V}$

(b) $|v_s| \leq \frac{0.991V}{180} = 5.51 \text{ mV}$

15.41

(a) $I_C = \alpha_F I_E = \alpha_F \frac{I_{EE}}{2} = \frac{120}{121}\frac{200\mu A}{2} = 99.2\mu A \quad | \quad V_O = 10 - 1.10 \times 10^5 I_C = 1.09 \text{ V}$

$$g_m = 40I_C = 3.97mS \quad | \quad A_{dd} = -g_m R_C = -3.97mS(110k\Omega) = -437 \quad | \quad R_{EE} = \infty \rightarrow A_{cc} \cong 0$$

For $v_s = 0$: $V_O = 1.09 \text{ V}$ and $v_o = -A_{dd}\frac{v_{id}}{2} = 0$

For $v_s = 1mV$: $V_O = 1.09 \text{ V}$ and $v_o = -(-437)\frac{0.001V}{2} = 0.219 \text{ V}$

(b) For $v_{CB} \geq 0$, $|v_s| \leq \frac{V_O}{-\dfrac{A_{dd}}{2}} = 2\frac{1.09}{437} = 5.00 \text{ mV}$

15.42

```
*Problem 15.42
VCC 2 0 DC 12
VEE 1 0 DC -12
V1 3 7 AC 1
V2 5 7 AC 0
VIC 7 0 DC 0
RC 2 6 110K
Q1 2 3 4 NBJT
Q2 6 5 4 NBJT
IEE 4 1 DC 200U
.MODEL NBJT NPN **VA=60V** BF=120
.OP
.AC LIN 1 1KHz 1KHZ
.PRINT AC IM(V1) IP(V1) VM(6) VP(6)
.TF V(6) VIC
.END
```

Results: $A_{dd} = VM(6) = -193 \mid R_{ID} = \dfrac{1}{IM(V1)} = 82.0 \text{ k}\Omega \mid A_{cc} = +0.0123 \mid R_{IC} = 45.8 \text{ M}\Omega$

15.43

$$I_C = \alpha_F I_E = \frac{150}{151} \frac{15 - 0.7}{2(150\text{k}\Omega)} = 47.4\mu\text{A} \mid V_{EC} = 0.7 - \left(-15 + 2\text{x}10^5 I_C\right) = 6.22\text{V}$$

$$\text{Q - points: } (47.4\mu\text{A}, 6.22\text{V}) \mid g_m = 40 I_C = 1.90\text{mS} \mid r_\pi = \frac{150}{g_m} = 79.0\text{k}\Omega$$

$$A_{dd} = -g_m R_C = -1.90\text{mS}(200\text{k}\Omega) = -380$$

$$A_{cc} = -\frac{\beta_o R_C}{r_\pi + (\beta_o + 1)2R_{EE}} = -\frac{150(200\text{k}\Omega)}{79.0\text{k}\Omega + 151(300\text{k}\Omega)} = -0.661$$

$$R_{ID} = 2r_\pi = 158\text{k}\Omega \mid R_{IC} = \frac{r_\pi + (\beta_o + 1)2R_{EE}}{2} = \frac{79.0\text{k}\Omega + 151(300\text{k}\Omega)}{2} = 22.7 \text{ M}\Omega$$

For a differential output: $A_{dm} = A_{dd} = -380 \mid A_{cm} = 0 \mid \text{CMRR} = \infty$

For a single - ended output: $A_{dm} = \dfrac{A_{dd}}{2} = -190 \mid A_{cm} = A_{cc} = -0.661$

$$\text{CMRR} = \left| \frac{-190}{-0.661} \right| = 287 \text{ or } 49.2\text{dB}$$

15.44

$$I_C = \alpha_F I_E = \frac{100}{101} \frac{10 - 0.7}{2(430\text{k}\Omega)} = 10.7\mu\text{A} \mid V_{C1} = V_{C2} = -10 + 5.6\text{x}10^5 I_C = -4.01\text{V}$$

$$V_{EC} = 0.7 - (-4.01) = 4.71\text{V} \mid g_m = 40 I_C = 0.428\text{mS} \mid r_\pi = \frac{100}{g_m} = 234\text{k}\Omega$$

$$A_{dd} = -g_m R_C = -0.428\text{mS}(560\text{k}\Omega) = -240$$

$$A_{cc} = -\frac{\beta_o R_C}{r_\pi + (\beta_o + 1)2R_{EE}} = -\frac{100(560\text{k}\Omega)}{234\text{k}\Omega + 101(860\text{k}\Omega)} = -0.643$$

$$v_{id} = 1 - 0.99 = 0.01\text{V} \mid v_{ic} = \frac{1 + 0.99}{2} = 0.995\text{V}$$

$$v_{C1} = V_{C1} + A_{dd}\frac{v_{id}}{2} + A_{cc}v_{ic} = -4.01V - 240\frac{0.01V}{2} - 0.643(0.995V) = -5.850 \text{ V}$$

$$v_{C2} = V_{C2} - A_{dd}\frac{v_{id}}{2} + A_{cc}v_{ic} = -4.01V + 240\frac{0.01V}{2} - 0.643(0.995V) = -3.450 \text{ V}$$

$$v_{OD} = -5.850 - (-3.450) = -2.40 \text{ V} \mid \text{Note: } A_{dd}v_{id} = -2.40V \text{ and } v_{OC} = \frac{-5.850 - 3.450}{2} = 4.65$$

Also note: $v_{OC} = V_C + A_{cc}v_{ic} = -4.01 - 0.643(0.995V) = -4.65V$

15.45

```
*Problem 15.45
VCC 2 0 DC 10
VEE 1 0 DC -10
V1 4 8 AC 1
V2 6 8 AC 0
VIC 8 0 DC 0
RC1 5 1 560K
RC2 7 1 560K
Q1 5 4 3 PBJT
Q2 7 6 3 PBJT
REE 2 3 430K
.MODEL PBJT PNP VA=60V BF=100
.OP
.AC LIN 1 5KHz 5KHZ
.PRINT AC IM(V1) IP(V1) VM(5,7) VP(5,7)
.TF V(7) VIC
.END
```

$$A_{dd} = VM(5,7) = -213 \mid R_{ID} = \frac{1}{IM(V1)} = 511 \text{ k}\Omega$$

Results:

$$A_{cc} = -0.642 \mid R_{IC} = 37.5 \text{ M}\Omega \mid CMRR = \frac{213}{0.642} = 332 \rightarrow 50.4dB$$

15.46

$$I_C = \alpha_F \frac{I_{EE}}{2} = \frac{80}{81}\frac{10\mu A}{2} = 4.94\mu A \mid V_{EC} = 0.7 - \left(-3 + 3.9x10^5 I_C\right) = 1.77V$$

$$Q\text{-points: } (4.94\mu A, 1.77V) \mid g_m = 40I_C = 0.198mS \mid r_\pi = \frac{80}{g_m} = 404k\Omega$$

$$A_{dd} = -g_m R_C = -0.198mS(390k\Omega) = -77.2$$

$$A_{cc} = -\frac{\beta_o R_C}{r_\pi + (\beta_o + 1)2R_{EE}} = -\frac{80(390k\Omega)}{404k\Omega + 81(10M\Omega)} = -0.0385$$

$$R_{ID} = 2r_\pi = 808k\Omega \mid R_{IC} = \frac{r_\pi + (\beta_o + 1)2R_{EE}}{2} = \frac{808k\Omega + 81(10M\Omega)}{2} = 405 \text{ M}\Omega$$

Note that R_{IC} is similar to $\frac{\beta_o r_o}{2}$ so that $R_{IC} = 405$ MΩ will not be fully acheived.

For example, if $V_A = 80V$, $\frac{\beta_o r_o}{2} \cong \frac{80}{2}\frac{80}{4.94\mu A} = 648$ MΩ

For a differential output: $A_{dm} = A_{dd} = -77.2$ | $A_{cm} = 0$ | CMRR = ∞

For a single - ended output: $A_{dm} = \dfrac{A_{dd}}{2} = -38.6$ | $A_{cm} = A_{cc} = -0.661$

CMRR = $\left| \dfrac{-38.6}{-0.0385} \right| = 1000$ or 60.0dB | $V_{BC} \geq 0$ requires $V_{IC} \geq V_C = -1.07V$ and

Without detailed knowledge of I_{EE}, we can only estimate that V_{IC} should not exceed $V_{IC} + 0.7 \leq V_{CC} - 0.7V$ which allows 0.7V for biasing $I_{EE} \rightarrow -1.07V \leq V_{IC} \leq +1.6V$.

15.47

$I_C = \alpha_F \dfrac{I_{EE}}{2} = \dfrac{120}{121} \dfrac{1mA}{2} = 496\mu A$ | $V_{C1} = V_{C2} = -22 + 1.5 \times 10^4 I_C = -14.6V$

Checking $V_{EC} = 0.7 - (-14.6) = 15.3V$ | $g_m = 40 I_C = 19.8mS$ | $r_\pi = \dfrac{120}{g_m} = 6.06k\Omega$

$A_{dd} = -g_m R_C = -19.8mS(15k\Omega) = -297$

$A_{cc} = -\dfrac{\beta_o R_C}{r_\pi + (\beta_o + 1)2R_{EE}} = -\dfrac{120(15k\Omega)}{6.06k\Omega + 121(1M\Omega)} = -0.0149$

$v_{id} = 0.01 - 0 = 0.01V$ | $v_{ic} = \dfrac{0.01 + 0}{2} = 0.005V$

$v_{C1} = V_{C1} + A_{dd}\dfrac{v_{id}}{2} + A_{cc}v_{ic} = -14.6V - 297\dfrac{0.01V}{2} - 0.0149(0.005V) = -16.09$ V

$v_{C2} = V_{C2} - A_{dd}\dfrac{v_{id}}{2} + A_{cc}v_{ic} = -14.6V + 297\dfrac{0.01V}{2} - 0.0149(0.005V) = -13.12$ V

$v_{OD} = -16.09 - (-13.12) = -2.97$ V | Note: $A_{dd}v_{id} = -2.97V$

Also note: $v_{OC} = \dfrac{-16.09 - 13.12}{2} = -14.6$ and

$v_{OC} = V_C + A_{cc}v_{ic} = -14.60 - 0.0149(0.005V) = -14.6V$

15.48

$I_C = \alpha_F I_E = \dfrac{100}{101} \dfrac{15V - 0.7V}{2(100k\Omega)} = 70.8\mu A$ | $g_m = 40 I_C = 2.83mS$ | $r_\pi = \dfrac{100}{g_m} = 35.3k\Omega$

$A_{dd} = \dfrac{\mathbf{v_{od}}}{\mathbf{v_{id}}}$ | $\mathbf{v_{od}} = \mathbf{v_{c1}} - \mathbf{v_{c2}} = \mathbf{i_{c1}}\left(R + \dfrac{\Delta R}{2}\right) - \mathbf{i_{c2}}\left(R - \dfrac{\Delta R}{2}\right)$

$\mathbf{v_{od}} = -gm\dfrac{\mathbf{v_{id}}}{2}\left(R + \dfrac{\Delta R}{2}\right) - \left(-gm\dfrac{\mathbf{v_{id}}}{2}\right)\left(R - \dfrac{\Delta R}{2}\right) = -g_m R \mathbf{v_{id}}$ | $A_{dd} = -g_m R = -283$

$A_{cd} = \dfrac{\mathbf{v_{od}}}{\mathbf{v_{ic}}}$ | $\mathbf{v_{od}} = \mathbf{v_{c1}} - \mathbf{v_{c2}} = \mathbf{i_{c1}}\left(R + \dfrac{\Delta R}{2}\right) - \mathbf{i_{c2}}\left(R - \dfrac{\Delta R}{2}\right)$

For common - mode input, $\mathbf{i_{c1}} = \mathbf{i_{c2}} = \dfrac{\beta_o}{r_\pi + (\beta_o + 1)2R_{EE}} \mathbf{v_{ic}}$

$\mathbf{v_{od}} = -\dfrac{\beta_o}{r_\pi + (\beta_o + 1)2R_{EE}} \mathbf{v_{ic}}\left[\left(R + \dfrac{\Delta R}{2}\right) - \left(R - \dfrac{\Delta R}{2}\right)\right] = \mathbf{v_{od}} = -\dfrac{\beta_o \Delta R}{r_\pi + (\beta_o + 1)2R_{EE}} \mathbf{v_{ic}}$

$A_{cd} = -\dfrac{\Delta R}{R} \dfrac{\beta_o R}{r_\pi + (\beta_o + 1)2R_{EE}} = -0.01\dfrac{100(100k\Omega)}{35.3k\Omega + (101)200k\Omega} = -.00494$

CMRR = $\left| \dfrac{-283}{-0.00494} \right| = 57300$ or 95.2 dB

15.49

```
*Problem 15.49
VCC 2 0 DC 15
VEE 1 0 DC -15
V1 4 8 AC 0.5
V2 6 8 AC -0.5
VIC 8 0 DC 0
RC1 2 5 100.5K
RC2 2 7 99.5K
Q1 5 4 3 NBJT
Q2 7 6 3 NBJT
REE 3 1 100K
.MODEL NBJT NPN BF=100
.OP
.AC LIN 1 100 100
.PRINT AC IM(V1) IP(V1) VM(5,7) VP(5,7)
.TF V(5,7) VIC
.END
```

Results: $A_{dd} = VM(5,7) = -274 \mid A_{cd} = -0.00494 \mid$ CMRR $= 55500$ or 94.9 dB

15.50

For a differential - mode input:

$$\mathbf{v}_{od} = -\left(\frac{\mathbf{v}_{id}}{2} - \mathbf{v}_e\right)\left(g_m + \frac{\Delta g_m}{2}\right)R + \left(-\frac{\mathbf{v}_{id}}{2} - \mathbf{v}_e\right)\left(g_m - \frac{\Delta g_m}{2}\right)R = -g_m R\,\mathbf{v}_{id} + \Delta g_m R \mathbf{v}_e$$

$$\mathbf{v}_{od} = -g_m R\left(\mathbf{v}_{id} + \frac{\Delta g_m}{g_m}\mathbf{v}_e\right) \mid \text{ At the emitter node:}$$

$$\left(\frac{\mathbf{v}_{id}}{2} - \mathbf{v}_e\right)\left(g_m + \frac{\Delta g_m}{2} + g_\pi\right) + \left(-\frac{\mathbf{v}_{id}}{2} - \mathbf{v}_e\right)\left(g_m - \frac{\Delta g_m}{2} + g_\pi\right) - G_{EE}\mathbf{v}_e = 0$$

$$\mathbf{v}_e = \frac{1}{2}\frac{\Delta g_m}{g_m}\frac{\beta_o R_{EE}}{r_\pi + (\beta_o + 1)2R_{EE}}\mathbf{v}_{id} \cong \frac{1}{4}\frac{\Delta g_m}{g_m}\mathbf{v}_{id} << \mathbf{v}_{id} \mid \mathbf{v}_{od} \cong -g_m R\,\mathbf{v}_{id} \mid A_{dd} \cong -g_m R = -300$$

For a common - mode input:

$$\mathbf{v}_{od} = -(\mathbf{v}_{ic} - \mathbf{v}_e)\left(g_m + \frac{\Delta g_m}{2}\right)R + (\mathbf{v}_{ic} - \mathbf{v}_e)\left(g_m - \frac{\Delta g_m}{2}\right)R = -\Delta g_m R(\mathbf{v}_{ic} - \mathbf{v}_e) = -\frac{\Delta g_m}{g_m}g_m R(\mathbf{v}_{ic} - \mathbf{v}_e)$$

At the emitter node:

$$(\mathbf{v}_{ic} - \mathbf{v}_e)\left(g_m + \frac{\Delta g_m}{2} + g_\pi + g_m - \frac{\Delta g_m}{2} + g_\pi\right) - G_{EE}\mathbf{v}_e = 0$$

$$\mathbf{v}_e = \frac{(\beta_o + 1)2R_{EE}}{r_\pi + (\beta_o + 1)2R_{EE}}\mathbf{v}_{ic} \mid \mathbf{v}_{ic} - \mathbf{v}_e = \frac{r_\pi}{r_\pi + (\beta_o + 1)2R_{EE}}\mathbf{v}_{ic}$$

$$A_{cd} = \frac{\mathbf{v}_{od}}{\mathbf{v}_{ic}} = -\frac{\Delta g_m}{g_m}\frac{\beta_o R}{r_\pi + (\beta_o + 1)2R_{EE}} \cong -\frac{\Delta g_m}{g_m}\frac{g_m R}{1 + 2g_m R_{EE}} = -\frac{\Delta g_m}{g_m}\frac{g_m R}{1 + 2g_m R_{EE}} = -0.00499$$

$$\text{CMRR} \cong 2g_m R_{EE}\left[\frac{\Delta g_m}{g_m}\right]^{-1} = 60000 \text{ or } 95.6 \text{ dB}$$

367

The MATLAB m-file listed below 'FET Bias' can be used to help find the drain currents in the FET circuits in Problems 15.51 - 15. Use fzero('FET Bias',0) to find ids.

```
function f=bias(ids)
kn=4e-4; vto=1; gamma=0.0;
rss=62e3; vss=15;
vsb=2*ids*rss;
vtn=vto+gamma*(sqrt(vsb+0.6)-sqrt(0.6));
f=vss-vtn-sqrt(2*ids/kn)-vsb;
```

15.51   This solution made use of the m-file above. The solution to Problem 15.52 gives an example of direct hand calculation.

$$V_{SS} - V_{GS} = 2I_{DSS}R_{SS} \mid V_{GS} = V_{TN} + \sqrt{\frac{2I_{DS}}{K_n}} \mid V_{SS} = 2I_{DSS}R_{SS} + V_{TN} + \sqrt{\frac{2I_{DS}}{K_n}}$$

$$15 = 2I_{DSS}\left(62 \times 10^3\right) + 1 + \sqrt{\frac{2I_{DS}}{4 \times 10^{-4}}} \to I_{DS} = 107\mu A \mid V_{GS} - V_{TN} = 0.731V$$

$$V_{DS} = 15 - (62k\Omega)I_{DS} - (-V_{GS}) = 10.1V > 0.731V \text{ - Saturated } \mid Q\text{-pt: } (107\mu A, 10.1V)$$

$$g_m = \frac{2I_{DS}}{V_{GS} - V_{TN}} = \frac{2(107\mu A)}{0.731V} = 0.293mS \mid A_{dd} = -g_m R_D = -(0.293mS)(62k\Omega) = -18.2$$

$$A_{cc} = -\frac{g_m R_D}{1 + 2g_m R_{SS}} = -\frac{(0.293mS)(62k\Omega)}{1 + 2(0.293mS)(62k\Omega)} = -0.487$$

For a differential output: $A_{dm} = A_{dd} = -18.2 \mid A_{cm} = 0 \mid CMRR = \infty$

For a single-ended output: $A_{dm} = \frac{A_{dd}}{2} = -9.10 \mid A_{cm} = A_{cc} = -0.487$

$$CMRR = \frac{9.10}{0.487} = 18.7 \mid CMRR_{db} = 25.4 \text{ dB} \mid R_{ID} = \infty \mid R_{IC} = \infty$$

15.52

$$2I_S = \frac{12 - V_{GS}}{220k\Omega} \Rightarrow 2\frac{K_n}{2}\left(V_{GS} - V_{TN}\right)^2 = \frac{12 - V_{GS}}{220k\Omega} \text{ and for } K_n = 400\frac{\mu A}{V^2} \text{ and } V_{TN} = 1V$$

$$12 - V_{GS} = 88\left(V_{GS}^2 - 2V_{GS} + 1\right) \text{ or } 88V_{GS}^2 - 175V_{GS} + 76 = 0 \text{ and } V_{GS} = 1.348V$$

$$I_D = I_S = \frac{1}{2}\left(\frac{12 - 1.35}{220k\Omega}\right) = 24.2\mu A. \quad V_D = 12 - 3.3 \times 10^5(I_D) = 4.01V$$

$$V_{DS} = 4.01 - (-V_{GS}) = 5.36V \ (> V_{GS} - V_{TN}). \quad Q\text{-Point} = (24.2\mu A, 5.36V)$$

$$g_m = \frac{2I_D}{V_{GS} - V_{TN}} = \frac{2\left(24.2 \times 10^{-6}\right)}{0.348} = 1.39mS \mid A_{dd} = -g_m R_D = -1.39ms(330k\Omega) = -45.9$$

$$A_{cc} = -\frac{g_m R_D}{1 + 2g_m R_{SS}} = \frac{1.39ms(330k\Omega)}{1 + 2(1.39ms)(220k\Omega)} = -0.738$$

For a differential output: $A_{dm} = A_{dd} = -45.9 \mid A_{cm} = 0 \mid CMRR = \infty$

For a single-ended output: $A_{dm} = \frac{A_{dd}}{2} = -23.0 \mid A_{cm} = A_{cc} = -0.738$

$$CMRR = \frac{23.0}{0.738} = 31.2 \mid CMRR_{db} = 29.8 \text{ dB} \mid R_{ID} = \infty \mid R_{IC} = \infty$$

15.53

```
*Problem 15.53
VCC 2 0 DC 12
VEE 1 0 DC -12
VIC 8 0 DC 0
VID1 4 8 AC 0.5
VID2 6 8 AC -0.5
RD1 2 3 330K
RD2 2 7 330K
M1 3 4 5 5 NFET
M2 7 6 5 5 NFET
REE 5 1 220K
.MODEL NFET NMOS KP=400U VTO=1
.OP
.AC LIN 1 1KHZ 1KHZ
.PRINT AC IM(VID1) IP(VID1) VM(3,7) VP(3,7)
.TF V(7) VIC
.END
```

Results: $A_{dd} = VM(3,7) = -45.9 \mid A_{cc} = -0.738 \mid CMRR = 31.1 \mid R_{ID} = \infty \mid R_{IC} = \infty$

15.54

$R_{OD} = 2R_D = 5k\Omega \rightarrow R_D = 2.5k\Omega \mid$ Selecting closest 5% value: $R_D = 2.4k\Omega$

$A_{dd} = -g_m R_D = 10^{\frac{20}{20}} = 10 \mid g_m = \dfrac{10}{2400} = 4.17mS = \sqrt{2K_n I_{DS}}$

$I_{DS} = \dfrac{\left(4.17 \times 10^{-3}\right)^2}{2\left(25 \times 10^{-3}\right)} = 348\mu A \mid V_{GS} = V_{TN} + \sqrt{\dfrac{2I_{DS}}{K_n}} = 1.16V$

$R_{SS} = \dfrac{V_{SS} - V_{GS}}{2R_{SS}} = \dfrac{5 - 1.16}{2(348\mu A)} = 5.52k\Omega \mid$ Selecting closest 5% value: $R_{SS} = 5.6k\Omega$

15.55 This solution made use of the m-file above Problem 15.51.

$V_{SS} - V_{GS} = 2I_{DSS}R_{SS} \mid V_{GS} = V_{TN} + \sqrt{\dfrac{2I_{DS}}{K_n}} \mid V_{SS} = 2I_{DSS}R_{SS} + V_{TN} + \sqrt{\dfrac{2I_{DS}}{K_n}}$

$V_{TN} = V_{TO} + \gamma\left(\sqrt{V_{SB} + 0.6} - \sqrt{0.6}\right) = V_{TO} + \gamma\left(\sqrt{2I_{DSS}R_{SS} + 0.6} - \sqrt{0.6}\right)$

Solving iteratively with $R_{SS} = 62k\Omega \mid K_n = 400\dfrac{\mu A}{V^2} \mid V_{TO} = 1V \mid \gamma = 0.75\sqrt{V}$ yields

$I_{DS} = 91.3\mu A \mid V_{GS} - V_{TN} = 0.676V \mid V_{TN} = 3.01V \mid V_{GS} = 3.69V$

$V_{DS} = 15 - (62k\Omega)I_{DS} - (-V_{GS}) = 12.9V > 0.676V$ - Saturated $\mid$ Q-pt: $(91.3\mu A, 12.9V)$

$g_m = \dfrac{2I_{DS}}{V_{GS} - V_{TN}} = \dfrac{2(91.3\mu A)}{0.676V} = 0.270mS \mid A_{dd} = -g_m R_D = -(0.270mS)(62k\Omega) = -16.7$

$A_{cc} = -\dfrac{g_m R_D}{1 + 2g_m(1+\eta)R_{SS}} = -\dfrac{(0.270mS)(62k\Omega)}{1 + 2(0.270mS)(62k\Omega)} = -0.486$ assuming $\eta = 0$

For a differential output: $A_{dm} = A_{dd} = -16.7 \mid A_{cm} = 0 \mid CMRR = \infty$

For a single-ended output: $A_{dm} = \dfrac{A_{dd}}{2} = -8.35 \mid A_{cm} = A_{cc} = -0.486$

$CMRR = \dfrac{8.35}{0.486} = 17.2 \mid CMRR_{db} = 24.7 \text{ dB} \mid R_{ID} = \infty \mid R_{IC} = \infty$

15.56

```
*Problem 15.56
VCC 2 0 DC 15
VEE 1 0 DC -15
VIC 8 0 DC 0
VID1 4 8 AC 0.5
VID2 6 8 AC -0.5
RD1 2 3 62K
RD2 2 7 62K
M1 3 4 5 1 NFET
M2 7 6 5 1 NFET
REE 5 1 62K
.MODEL NFET NMOS KP=400U VTO=1 PHI=0.6 GAMMA=0.75
.OP
.AC LIN 1 1KHZ 1KHZ
.PRINT AC IM(VID1) IP(VID1) VM(3,7) VP(3,7)
.TF V(7) VIC
.END
```

Results: $A_{dd} = VM(3,7) = -16.8 \mid A_{cc} = -0.439 \mid CMRR = 25.6 \mid R_{ID} = \infty \mid R_{IC} = \infty$

15.57 This solution made use of the m-file above Problem 15.51.

$$V_{SS} - V_{GS} = 2I_{DSS}R_{SS} \mid V_{GS} = V_{TN} + \sqrt{\frac{2I_{DS}}{K_n}} \mid V_{SS} = 2I_{DSS}R_{SS} + V_{TN} + \sqrt{\frac{2I_{DS}}{K_n}}$$

$$V_{TN} = V_{TO} + \gamma\left(\sqrt{V_{SB} + 0.6} - \sqrt{0.6}\right) = V_{TO} + \gamma\left(\sqrt{2I_{DSS}R_{SS} + 0.6} - \sqrt{0.6}\right)$$

Solving iteratively with $R_{SS} = 220k\Omega \mid K_n = 400\frac{\mu A}{V^2} \mid V_{TO} = 1V \mid \gamma = 0.75\sqrt{V}$ yields

$$I_{DS} = 20.3\mu A \mid V_{GS} - V_{TN} = 0.319V \mid V_{TN} = 2.74V \mid V_{GS} = 3.05V$$

$$V_{DS} = 12 - (330k\Omega)I_{DS} - (-V_{GS}) = 8.35V > 0.319V \text{ - Saturated} \mid Q\text{-pt: } (20.3\mu A, 8.35V)$$

$$g_m = \frac{2I_{DS}}{V_{GS} - V_{TN}} = \frac{2(20.3\mu A)}{0.319V} = 0.127mS \mid A_{dd} = -g_m R_D = -(0.127mS)(330k\Omega) = -41.9$$

$$A_{cc} = -\frac{g_m R_D}{1 + 2g_m(1+\eta)R_{SS}} = -\frac{(0.127mS)(330k\Omega)}{1 + 2(0.127mS)(220k\Omega)} = -0.737 \text{ assuming } \eta = 0$$

For a differential output: $A_{dm} = A_{dd} = -41.9 \mid A_{cm} = 0 \mid CMRR = \infty$

For a single-ended output: $A_{dm} = \frac{A_{dd}}{2} = -21.0 \mid A_{cm} = A_{cc} = -0.737$

$$CMRR = \frac{21.0}{0.737} = 28.4 \mid CMRR_{db} = 29.1 \text{ dB} \mid R_{ID} = \infty \mid R_{IC} = \infty$$

15.58

$$I_{DS} = \frac{I_{SS}}{2} = 150\mu A \mid V_{GS} = V_{TN} + \sqrt{\frac{2I_{DS}}{K_n}} = 1 + \sqrt{\frac{2(1.5\times10^{-4})}{4\times10^{-4}}} = 1.866V \mid V_{GS} - V_{TN} = 0.866V$$

$$V_{DS} = 15 - (75k\Omega)I_{DS} - (-V_{GS}) = 5.62V > 0.866V \text{ - Saturated} \mid Q\text{-pt: } (150\mu A, 5.62V)$$

$$g_m = \frac{2I_{DS}}{V_{GS} - V_{TN}} = \frac{2(150\mu A)}{0.866V} = 0.346mS \mid A_{dd} = -g_m R_D = -(0.346mS)(75k\Omega) = -26.0$$

$$A_{cc} = -\frac{g_m R_D}{1 + 2g_m R_{SS}} = -\frac{(0.346mS)(75k\Omega)}{1 + 2(0.346mS)(160k\Omega)} = -0.232$$

For a differential output: $A_{dm} = A_{dd} = -26.0$ | $A_{cm} = 0$ | CMRR $= \infty$

For a single-ended output: $A_{dm} = \dfrac{A_{dd}}{2} = -13.0$ | $A_{cm} = A_{cc} = -0.232$

$\text{CMRR} = \dfrac{13.0}{0.232} = 56.0$ | $\text{CMRR}_{db} = 35.0 \text{ dB}$ | $R_{ID} = \infty$ | $R_{IC} = \infty$

15.59

$I_{DS} = \dfrac{I_{SS}}{2} = 20\mu A$ | $V_{GS} = V_{TN} + \sqrt{\dfrac{2I_{DS}}{K_n}} = 1 + \sqrt{\dfrac{2\left(2\times10^{-5}\right)}{4\times10^{-4}}} = 1.316V$ | $V_{GS} - V_{TN} = 0.316V$

$V_{DS} = 9 - (300k\Omega)I_{DS} - (-V_{GS}) = 4.32V > 0.316V$ - Saturated | Q-pt: $(20\mu A, 4.32V)$

$g_m = \dfrac{2I_{DS}}{V_{GS} - V_{TN}} = \dfrac{2(20\mu A)}{0.316V} = 0.127mS$ | $A_{dd} = -g_m R_D = -(0.127mS)(300k\Omega) = -38.0$

$A_{cc} = -\dfrac{g_m R_D}{1 + 2g_m R_{SS}} = -\dfrac{(0.127mS)(300k\Omega)}{1 + 2(0.127mS)(1.25M\Omega)} = -0.120$

For a differential output: $A_{dm} = A_{dd} = -38.0$ | $A_{cm} = 0$ | CMRR $= \infty$

For a single-ended output: $A_{dm} = \dfrac{A_{dd}}{2} = -19.0$ | $A_{cm} = A_{cc} = -0.120$

$\text{CMRR} = \dfrac{19.0}{0.120} = 158$ | $\text{CMRR}_{db} = 44.0 \text{ dB}$ | $R_{ID} = \infty$ | $R_{IC} = \infty$

15.60

$I_{DS} = \dfrac{I_{SS}}{2} = 150\mu A$ | $V_{GS} = V_{TN} + \sqrt{\dfrac{2I_{DS}}{K_n}} = V_{TN} + \sqrt{\dfrac{2\left(1.5\times10^{-4}\right)}{4\times10^{-4}}} = V_{TN} + 0.866V$

$V_{TN} = V_{TO} + \gamma\left(\sqrt{V_{SB} + 0.6} - \sqrt{0.6}\right) = V_{TO} + \gamma\left(\sqrt{15 - V_{GS} + 0.6} - \sqrt{0.6}\right)$

$V_{GS} - 0.866 = 1 + 0.75\left(\sqrt{15 - V_{GS} + 0.6} - \sqrt{0.6}\right) \rightarrow V_{GS} = 3.86V$ | $V_{TN} = 2.99V$

$V_{DS} = 15 - (75k\Omega)I_{DS} - (-V_{GS}) = 7.61V > 0.866V$ - Saturated | Q-pt: $(150\mu A, 7.61V)$

$g_m = \dfrac{2I_{DS}}{V_{GS} - V_{TN}} = \dfrac{2(150\mu A)}{0.866V} = 0.346mS$ | $A_{dd} = -g_m R_D = -(0.346mS)(75k\Omega) = -26.0$

$A_{cc} = -\dfrac{g_m R_D}{1 + 2g_m(1 + \eta)R_{SS}} = -\dfrac{(0.346mS)(75k\Omega)}{1 + 2(0.346mS)(160k\Omega)} = -0.233$ assuming $\eta = 0$

For a differential output: $A_{dm} = A_{dd} = -26.0$ | $A_{cm} = 0$ | CMRR $= \infty$

For a single-ended output: $A_{dm} = \dfrac{A_{dd}}{2} = -13.0$ | $A_{cm} = A_{cc} = -0.233$

$\text{CMRR} = \dfrac{13.0}{0.233} = 55.8$ | $\text{CMRR}_{db} = 34.9 \text{ dB}$ | $R_{ID} = \infty$ | $R_{IC} = \infty$

15.61

$I_{DS} = \dfrac{I_{SS}}{2} = 20\mu A$ | $V_{GS} = V_{TN} + \sqrt{\dfrac{2I_{DS}}{K_n}} = V_{TN} + \sqrt{\dfrac{2\left(2\times10^{-5}\right)}{4\times10^{-4}}} = V_{TN} + 0.316V$

$V_{TN} = V_{TO} + \gamma\left(\sqrt{V_{SB} + 0.6} - \sqrt{0.6}\right) = 1 + 0.75\left(\sqrt{9 - V_{GS} + 0.6} - \sqrt{0.6}\right)$

$V_{GS} - 0.316 = 1 + 0.75\left(\sqrt{9 - V_{GS} + 0.6} - \sqrt{0.6}\right) \rightarrow V_{GS} = 2.71V$ | $V_{TN} = 2.39V$

$V_{DS} = 9 - (300k\Omega)I_{DS} - (-V_{GS}) = 5.71V > 0.316V$ - Saturated | Q - pt: $(20\mu A, 5.71V)$

$g_m = \dfrac{2I_{DS}}{V_{GS} - V_{TN}} = \dfrac{2(20\mu A)}{0.316V} = 0.127mS$ | $A_{dd} = -g_m R_D = -(0.127mS)(300k\Omega) = -38.1$

$A_{cc} = -\dfrac{g_m R_D}{1 + 2g_m(1+\eta)R_{SS}} = -\dfrac{(0.127mS)(300k\Omega)}{1 + 2(0.127mS)(1.25M\Omega)} = -0.120$ assuming $\eta = 0$

For a differential output: $A_{dm} = A_{dd} = -38.1$ | $A_{cm} = 0$ | CMRR $= \infty$

For a single - ended output: $A_{dm} = \dfrac{A_{dd}}{2} = -19.0$ | $A_{cm} = A_{cc} = -0.120$

CMRR $= \dfrac{19.0}{0.120} = 158$ | CMRR$_{db} = 44.0$ dB | $R_{ID} = \infty$ | $R_{IC} = \infty$

15.62

$A_{dd} = -g_m R_D = 10^{\frac{30}{20}} = 31.6$ | $g_m R_D = 31.6 = \dfrac{2I_{DS}R_D}{V_{GS} - V_{TN}}$

Maximum common - mode range requires minimum $I_{DS}R_D \Rightarrow$ minimum $V_{GS} - V_{TN}$

Choosing $V_{GS} - V_{TN} = 0.25V$ to insure strong inversion operation,

$I_{DS}R_D = \dfrac{0.25(31.6)}{2} = 3.95V$ | $0.25V = \sqrt{\dfrac{2I_{DS}}{K_n}} \rightarrow I_{DS} = \dfrac{(0.25)^2(0.005)}{2} = 156\mu A$

$I_{SS} = 2I_{DS} = 312 \mu A$ | $R_D = \dfrac{3.95V}{156\mu A} = 25.3k\Omega \rightarrow 27k\Omega$, the nearest 5% value.

15.63

$I_{SD} = \dfrac{1}{2}\left(\dfrac{18 - V_{SG}}{56k\Omega}\right) \Rightarrow \dfrac{K_n}{2}(V_{SG} + V_{TP})^2 = \dfrac{18 - V_{SG}}{112k\Omega}$ and for $K_n = 200 \dfrac{\mu A}{V^2}$ and $V_{TP} = -1V$

$18 - V_{SG} = 11.2(V_{SG} - 1)^2 \rightarrow V_{SG} = 2.19V$ | $V_{SG} + V_{TP} = 1.19V$ | $I_{SD} = 142\mu A$

$V_{SD} = V_{SG} - [(91k\Omega)I_{SD} - (-18)] = 7.27V > 1.19V$ – Saturated | Q - Point $= (142\mu A, 7.27V)$

$g_m = \sqrt{2(2x10^{-4})(1.42x10^{-4})} = 0.238mS$ | $A_{dd} = -g_m R_D = -0.238mS(91k\Omega) = -21.7$

$A_{cc} = -\dfrac{g_m R_D}{1 + 2g_m R_{SS}} = \dfrac{0.238mS(91k\Omega)}{1 + 2(0.238mS)(56k\Omega)} = -0.785$

For a differential output: $A_{dm} = A_{dd} = -21.7$ | $A_{cm} = 0$ | CMRR $= \infty$

For a single - ended output: $A_{dm} = \dfrac{A_{dd}}{2} = -10.9$ | $A_{cm} = A_{cc} = -0.785$

CMRR $= \dfrac{10.9}{0.785} = 13.9$ | CMRR$_{db} = 22.9$ dB | $R_{ID} = \infty$ | $R_{IC} = \infty$

15.64

```
*Problem 15.64
VCC 2 0 DC 18
VEE 1 0 DC -18
VIC 8 0 DC 0
V1 4 8 AC 0.5
V2 6 8 AC -0.5
RD1 5 1 91K
RD2 7 1 91K
M1 5 4 3 3 PFET
M2 7 6 3 3 PFET
```

REE 2 3 56K
.MODEL PFET PMOS KP=200U VTO=-1
.OP
.AC LIN 1 3KHZ 3KHZ
.PRINT AC IM(V1) IP(V1) VM(5,7) VP(5,7)
.TF V(7) VIC
.END

Results: $A_{dd} = VM(5,7) = -21.6 \mid A_{cc} = -0.783 \mid CMRR = 13.8 \mid R_{ID} = \infty \mid R_{IC} = \infty$

15.65

$$I_{SD} = \frac{I_{SS}}{2} = 20\mu A \mid V_{SG} = -V_{TP} + \sqrt{\frac{2I_{SD}}{K_p}} = -V_{TP} + \sqrt{\frac{2(2\times10^{-5})}{2\times10^{-4}}} = -V_{TP} + 0.447V$$

$$V_{TP} = V_{TO} - \gamma\left(\sqrt{V_{BS} + 0.6} - \sqrt{0.6}\right) = -1 - 0.6\left(\sqrt{10 - V_{SG} + 0.6} - \sqrt{0.6}\right)$$

$$V_{SG} - 0.447 = 1 + 0.6\left(\sqrt{10.6 - V_{SG}} - \sqrt{0.6}\right) \rightarrow V_{SG} = 2.67V \mid V_{TP} = -2.23V$$

$$V_{SD} = V_{SG} - \left[-10 + (300k\Omega)I_{SG}\right] = 6.67V > 0.447V \text{ - Saturated} \mid Q\text{-pt: } (20\mu A, 6.67V)$$

$$g_m = \sqrt{2(2\times10^{-5})(2\times10^{-4})} = 89.4\mu S \mid A_{dd} = -g_m R_D = -(89.4\mu S)(300k\Omega) = -26.8$$

$$A_{cc} = -\frac{g_m R_D}{1 + 2g_m(1+\eta)R_{SS}} = -\frac{(89.4\mu S)(300k\Omega)}{1 + 2(89.4\mu S)(1.25M\Omega)} = -0.119 \text{ assuming } \eta = 0$$

For a differential output: $A_{dm} = A_{dd} = -26.8 \mid A_{cm} = 0 \mid CMRR = \infty$

For a single-ended output: $A_{dm} = \frac{A_{dd}}{2} = -13.4 \mid A_{cm} = A_{cc} = -0.119$

$$CMRR = \frac{13.4}{0.119} = 113 \mid CMRR_{db} = 41.0 \text{ dB} \mid R_{ID} = \infty \mid R_{IC} = \infty$$

15.66

Note: V_{SS} and V_{DD} should be 12V and $V_P = +2V$

(a) $I_{SD} = \frac{I_{SS}}{2} = 10\mu A \mid V_O = -12 + (820k\Omega)I_{SD} = -3.80V \mid$ For $v_S = 0$, $v_O = V_O = -3.80$ V

$$V_{SG} = V_P\left(\sqrt{\frac{I_{SD}}{I_{DSS}}} - 1\right) = 2\left(\sqrt{\frac{10\mu A}{1mA}} - 1\right) = -1.8V \mid V_{SG} + V_P = 0.2V \mid V_{SD} > 0.2V \text{ for pinchoff}$$

So $V_D \leq -2$ for pinchoff.

$$g_m = \frac{1}{|-2V|}\sqrt{2(1mA)(10\mu A)} = 70.7\mu S \mid A_{dd} = -g_m R_D = -(70.7\mu S)(820k\Omega) = -58.0$$

$$A_{cc} = 0 \text{ for } R_{SS} \text{ and } r_o = \infty \mid v_O = V_O - \frac{A_{dd}}{2}v_{id} = -3.80 - \frac{-58.0}{2}(0.02 - 0) = -1.22V$$

$$\frac{v_1}{2} \leq 0.2(V_{SG} + V_P) = 0.2(0.2) = 40.0mV \mid v_1 \leq 80.0 \text{ mV from small-signal limit}$$

Also $v_O = V_O - \frac{A_{dd}}{2}v_{id} = -3.80 - 29.0v_{id} \leq -2V$ for pinchoff $\rightarrow v_{id} \leq 62.1mV \mid v_1 \leq 62.1mV$

15.67

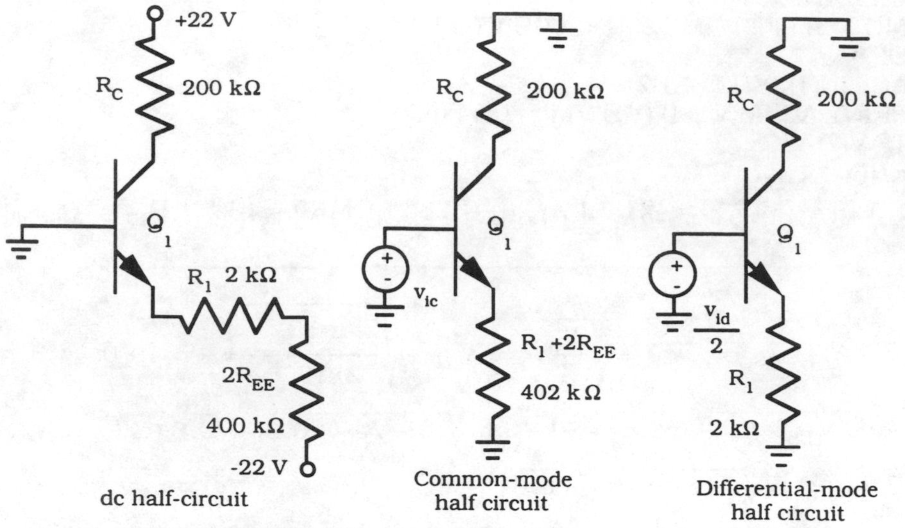

+22 V
R_C
200 kΩ
Q_1
R_1 2 kΩ
2R_EE
400 kΩ
-22 V
dc half-circuit
R_C
200 kΩ
Q_1
v_ic
R_1 +2R_EE
402 k Ω
Common-mode
half circuit
R_C
200 kΩ
Q_1
v_id / 2
R_1
2 kΩ
Differential-mode
half circuit

(a) $I_C = \alpha_F I_E = \frac{150}{151}\frac{22-0.7}{402k\Omega} = 52.6\ \mu A$ | $V_{CE} = 22 - (200k\Omega)I_C - (-0.7) = 12.2\ V$

$Q-Point = (52.6\mu A, 12.2V)$ for both transistors | $r_\pi = \frac{150(0.025V)}{52.6\mu A} = 71.3k\Omega$

(b) $A_{cc} = -\frac{\beta_o R_C}{r_\pi + (\beta_o+1)(R_1+2R_{EE})} = -\frac{150(200k\Omega)}{71.3k\Omega + (151)402k\Omega} = -0.494$

$A_{dd} = -\frac{\beta_o R_C}{r_\pi + (\beta_o+1)R_1} = -\frac{150(200k\Omega)}{71.3k\Omega + (151)2k\Omega} = -80.4$

$R_{ID} = 2\left[r_\pi + (\beta_o+1)R_1\right] = 2\left[71.3k\Omega + (151)2k\Omega\right] = 747k\Omega$

15.68

```
*Problem 15.68
VCC 2 0 DC 22
VEE 1 0 DC -22
VIC 10 0 DC 0
V1 4 10 AC 0.5
V2 8 10 AC -0.5
RC1 2 5 200K
RC2 2 9 200K
Q1 5 4 3 NBJT
Q2 9 8 7 NBJT
RE1 3 6 2K
RE2 7 6 2K
REE 6 1 200K
.MODEL NBJT NPN BF=150
.OP
.AC LIN 1 1KHZ 1KHZ
.PRINT AC IM(V1) IP(V1) VM(5,9) VP(5,9)
.TF V(9) VIC
.END
```

Results: $A_{dd} = VM(5,9) = -79.9$ | $A_{cc} = -0.494$ | $R_{ID} = \frac{1}{IM(V1)} = 751\ k\Omega$

15.69 (a)

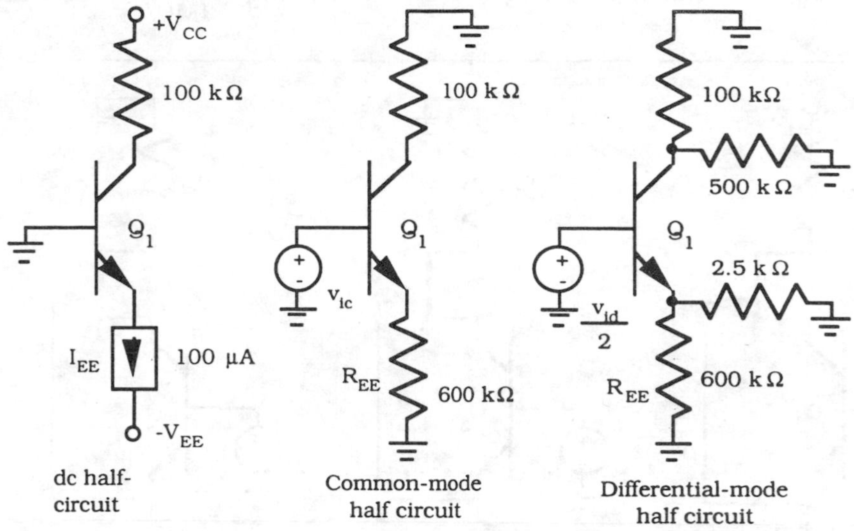
+V_CC
100 kΩ
Q1
I_EE
100 μA
-V_EE
dc half-circuit
100 kΩ
Q1
v_ic
R_EE
600 kΩ
Common-mode half circuit
100 kΩ
500 kΩ
Q1
2.5 kΩ
v_id/2
R_EE
600 kΩ
Differential-mode half circuit

(b) $I_C = \alpha_F I_E = \frac{100}{101}(100\mu A) = 99.0\ \mu A \quad V_{CE} = 20 - 10^5 I_C - (-0.7) = 10.8\ V$

$Q - \text{Point} = (99.0\mu A, 10.8V)$ for both transistors $|\ r_\pi = \frac{100(0.025V)}{99.0\ \mu A} = 25.3k\Omega$

$$A_{cc} = -\frac{\beta_o R_L'}{r_\pi + (\beta_o + 1)R_{EE}} = -\frac{100k\Omega}{25.3k\Omega + 101(600k\Omega)} = -0.165$$

$$A_{dd} = -\frac{\beta_o R_L}{r_\pi + (\beta_o + 1)R_5} \ |\ R_L = 100k\Omega \| 500k\Omega = 83.3k\Omega \ |\ R_5 = 600k\Omega \| 2.5k\Omega = 2.49k\Omega$$

$$A_{dd} = -\frac{100(83.3k\Omega)}{25.3k\Omega + 101(2.49k\Omega)} = -30.1$$

$$R_{ID} = 2[r_\pi + (\beta_o + 1)R_5] = 2[25.3k\Omega + 101(2.49k\Omega)] = 554k\Omega$$

15.70

```
*Problem 15.70
VCC 2 0 DC 20
VEE 1 0 DC -20
VIC 9 0 DC 0
V1 4 9 AC 0.5
V2 7 9 AC -0.5
RC1 2 5 100K
RC2 2 8 100K
RL 5 8 1MEG
Q1 5 4 3 NBJT
Q2 8 7 6 NBJT
REE 3 6 5K
IEE1 3 1 67.8U
RE1 3 1 600K
IEE2 6 1 67.8U
RE2 6 1 600K
.MODEL NBJT NPN BF=100
.OP
.AC LIN 1 1KHZ 1KHZ
.PRINT AC IM(V1) IP(V1) VM(5,8) VP(5,8)
.TF V(8) VIC
.END
```

Results: $A_{dd} = VM(5,8) = -30.0 \mid A_{cc} = -0.165 \mid R_{ID} = \dfrac{1}{IM(V1)} = 555 \text{ k}\Omega$

15.71 (a)

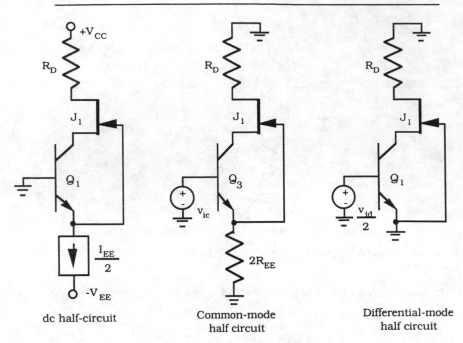

dc half-circuit   Common-mode half circuit   Differential-mode half circuit

Note: Use $R_D = 75 \text{ k}\Omega$

(b) $I_C = \alpha_F \dfrac{I_{EE}}{2} = \dfrac{100}{101}(100\mu A) = 99.0 \ \mu A \mid 99.0\mu A = 200\mu A\left(1 - \dfrac{V_{GS}}{-4}\right)^2 \rightarrow V_{GS} = -1.19V$

$V_{CE} = -V_{GS} = 1.19V \mid V_{DS} = 15 - 7.5 \times 10^4 I_C - V_{CE} - (-0.7) = 7.09 \ V$

BJT Q – Points = $(99.0\mu A, 1.19V) \mid$ JFET Q – Points = $(99.0\mu A, 7.09V)$

$r_\pi = \dfrac{100(0.025V)}{99.0 \ \mu A} = 25.3\text{k}\Omega \mid A_{cc} = -- \dfrac{\beta_o R_L}{r_\pi + (\beta_o + 1)(2R_{EE})} = -\dfrac{100(75\text{k}\Omega)}{25.3\text{k}\Omega + 101(1.2M\Omega)} = -0.0619$

$A_{dd} = -g_m R_D = -40(99.0 \ \mu A)(75\text{k}\Omega) = -297 \mid R_{ID} = 2r_\pi = 50.5\text{k}\Omega$

15.72 Note: The sources of M_1 and M_2 should be connectd in Fig. P15.72.

$I_{DS1} = I_2 = 400\mu A \mid V_{GS1} = V_{TN} + \sqrt{\dfrac{2I_{DS1}}{K_n}} = 1 + \sqrt{2\dfrac{4 \times 10^{-4}}{10^{-3}}} = 1.894V \mid V_{GS1} - V_{TN} = 0.894V$

$I_{SD3} = I_1 - I_{DS1} = 500\mu A - 400\mu A = 100\mu A \mid V_{DS1} = V_{SG3} = 1 + \sqrt{2\dfrac{10^{-4}}{4 \times 10^{-4}}} = 1.710V$

$V_{SG3} + V_{TP} = 0.710V \mid V_{SD3} = V_{S1} + V_{SG3} - \left[-6 + (30\text{k}\Omega)I_{SD3}\right] = -1.89 + 1.71 + 6 - 3 = 2.82V$

Both M_1 and M_3 are saturated. Q - points: M_1: $(400\mu A, 1.71V)$ M_3: $(100\mu A, 2.82V)$

$A_{dd} = -g_m R_D = -\sqrt{2(4 \times 10^{-4})(10^{-3})}(30\text{k}\Omega) = -26.8 \mid$ For $r_o = \infty$, $A_{cc} = 0 \mid R_{ID} = \infty$

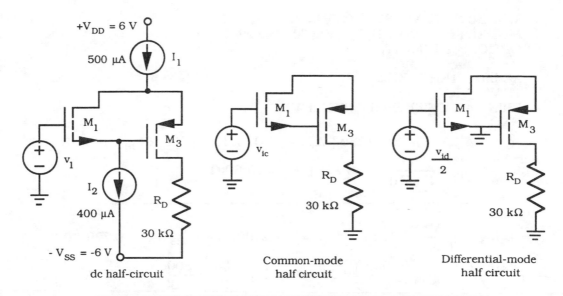

+V_DD = 6 V

500 μA I_1

M_1

M_3

v_1

I_2

400 μA

R_D

30 kΩ

- V_SS = -6 V

dc half-circuit

M_1

M_3

v_{ic}

R_D

30 kΩ

Common-mode
half circuit

M_1

M_3

$\dfrac{v_{id}}{2}$

R_D

30 kΩ

Differential-mode
half circuit

15.73

(a) $I_{C1} = \alpha_F \dfrac{I_1}{2} = \dfrac{100}{101}\dfrac{50\mu A}{2} = 24.8\ \mu A \mid V_{CE2} = 12 - V_{EB3} - \left(-V_{BE2}\right) = 12\ V$

For $V_O = 0 \rightarrow V_{EC3} = 12\ V \mid I_{C3} = \dfrac{12V}{24k\Omega} = 500\ \mu A$

Q - points: $(24.8\ \mu A, 12V)\ (24.8\ \mu A, 12V)\ (500\ \mu A, 12V) \mid R_{C1} = \dfrac{0.7V}{24.8\mu A} = 28.2k\Omega$

(b) $R_{C2} = \dfrac{V_{EB3}}{I_{C2} - I_{B3}} = \dfrac{0.7V}{24.8\mu A - 5\mu A} = 35.4k\Omega \mid r_{\pi 2} = \dfrac{100(0.025V)}{24.8\mu A} = 101k\Omega$

$r_{o2} = \dfrac{60+12}{24.8\mu A} = 2.90M\Omega \mid r_{\pi 3} = \dfrac{100(0.025V)}{500\mu A} = 5k\Omega \mid r_{o3} = \dfrac{60+12}{500\mu A} = 144k\Omega$

$A_{dm} = \dfrac{g_{m2}}{2}\left(r_{o2}\|R_{C2}\|r_{\pi 3}\right)g_{m3}\left(r_{o3}\|R\right)$

$A_{dm} = \dfrac{40(24.8\mu A)}{2}\left(2.90M\Omega\|35.4k\Omega\|5k\Omega\right)(40)(500\mu A)\left(144k\Omega\|24k\Omega\right) = 893$

$R_{ID} = 2r_{\pi 2} = 202\ k\Omega \mid$ (c) $R_O = r_{o3}\|R = 20.6\ k\Omega$

(d) $R_{IC} \cong \dfrac{(\beta_o + 1)r_{o2}}{2} = \dfrac{(101)2.90M\Omega}{2} = 147\ M\Omega \mid$ (e) v_2 is the non - inverting input

---

15.74 Note that the parameters of the transistors and values of R_C have been carefully
adjusted to permit open-loop operation and achieve $V_O = 0$.

*Problem 15.74 - Two Stage Amplifier
VCC 1 0 DC 12
VEE 2 0 DC -12
RC1 1 5 28.2K
RC2 1 7 33.9K
Q1 5 4 3 NBJT
Q2 7 6 3 NBJT
I1 3 2 DC 50U
Q3 8 7 1 PBJT
R 8 2 24K
V1 4 10 AC 0.5
V2 6 10 AC -0.5
VIC 10 0 DC 0

.MODEL NBJT NPN BF=100 VA=60
.MODEL PBJT PNP BF=100 VA=60 IS=0.288F
.OPTIONS TNOM=17.2
.OP
.AC LIN 1 1KHZ 1KHZ
.TF V(8) VIC
.PRINT AC VM(8) VP(8) IM(V1) IP(V1)
.END

Results:

$$A_{dm} = VM(8) = 1030 \mid A_{cm} = -6.07 \times 10^{-3} \mid CMRR_{dB} = 105 \text{ dB}$$

$$R_{ID} = \frac{1}{IM(V1)} = 239 \text{ k}\Omega \mid R_O = 20.6 \text{ k}\Omega$$

15.75

(a) For $V_O = 0$, $I_{C3} = \dfrac{15V}{50k\Omega} = 300\mu A \mid V_{C2} = 15 - 2400I_{E3} - V_{EB3} = 15 - 0.729 - 0.7 = 13.6V$

$$I_{C1} = I_{C2} = \alpha_F\left(\frac{200\mu A}{2}\right) = \frac{80}{81}\left(\frac{200\mu A}{2}\right) = 98.8\mu A \mid I_{B3} = \frac{I_{C3}}{\beta_{F3}} = \frac{300\mu A}{80} = 3.75\mu A$$

$$V_{CE1} = V_{CE2} = 13.6 - (-0.7) = 14.3V \mid V_{EC3} = 15 - 2400I_{E3} - V_O = 14.3V$$

Q - points: $(98.8\mu A, 14.3V)$ $(98.8\mu A, 14.3V)$ $(300\mu A, 14.3V)$

$$R_C = \frac{15 - 13.6}{(98.8 - 3.75)} \frac{V}{\mu A} = 15.1k\Omega \quad r_{\pi3} = \frac{80(0.025V)}{0.3mA} = 6.67k\Omega$$

(b) $A_{v1} = \dfrac{\mathbf{v_{c2}}}{\mathbf{v_{id}}} = -\left(\dfrac{g_{m1}}{2}\right)\left[R_C \| \left[r_{\pi3} + (\beta_{o3} + 1)R_E\right]\right]$

$$A_{v1} = -\left(\frac{40(98.8\mu A)}{2}\right)\left[15.1k\Omega \| (6.67k\Omega + 81(2.4k\Omega))\right] = -27.7$$

$$A_{v2} = \frac{\mathbf{v_o}}{\mathbf{v_{c2}}} = -\frac{\beta_{o3}R_L}{r_{\pi3} + (\beta_{o3} + 1)R_E} = -\frac{80(50k\Omega)}{6.67k\Omega + 81(2.4k\Omega)} = -19.9$$

$$A_v = \frac{\mathbf{v_{c2}}}{\mathbf{v_{id}}}\frac{\mathbf{v_o}}{\mathbf{v_{c2}}} = -27.7(-19.9) = 551$$

$$R_{ID} = 2r_{\pi1} = 2\frac{\beta_{o1}V_T}{I_{C1}} = 2\frac{80(0.025V)}{98.8\mu A} = 40.5k\Omega \mid r_{o3} = \frac{70 + 14.3}{0.3mA} = 281k\Omega$$

(c) $R_{OUT} = 50k\Omega \| r_{o3}\left(1 + \dfrac{\beta_o R_E}{R_C + r_{\pi3} + R_E}\right) = 50k\Omega \| 281k\Omega\left[1 + \dfrac{80(2.4k\Omega)}{15.1k\Omega + 6.67k\Omega + 2.4k\Omega}\right] = 49.0k\Omega$

(d) $R_{IC} = \dfrac{(\beta_{o1} + 1)r_{o1}}{2} = \dfrac{81}{2}\left(\dfrac{70 + 14.3}{98.8\mu A}\right) = 34.6M\Omega \mid$ (e) v_2 is the non - inverting (+) input.

15.76

(a) For $V_O = 0$, $I_{C3} = \dfrac{15V}{50k\Omega} = 300\mu A \quad V_{EC3} = 15 - V_O = 15 - 0 = 15V$

$$I_{C1} = I_{C2} = \alpha_F\left(\frac{200\mu A}{2}\right) = \frac{80}{81}\left(\frac{200\mu A}{2}\right) = 98.8\mu A \quad I_{B3} = \frac{I_{C3}}{\beta_{F3}} = \frac{300\mu A}{80} = 3.75\mu A$$

$$V_{CE1} = 15 - V_{EB3} - (-V_{BE1}) = 15.0V$$

Q - points: $(98.8\mu A, 15.0V)$ $(98.8\mu A 15.0V)$ $(300\mu A, 15.0V)$

$$R_C = \frac{0.7}{(98.8 - 3.75)} \frac{V}{\mu A} = 7.37k\Omega \mid r_{\pi3} = \frac{80(0.025V)}{0.3mA} = 6.67k\Omega \mid r_{o3} = \frac{70V + 15V}{0.3mA} = 283k\Omega$$

(b) $A_{v1} = \dfrac{v_{c2}}{v_{id}} = -\left(\dfrac{g_{m1}}{2}\right)\left(R_C \| r_{\pi3} \| 2r_{o1}\right) g_{m3}\left(R \| r_{o3}\right) \cong -\left(\dfrac{g_{m1}}{2}\right)\left(R_C \| r_{\pi3}\right) g_{m3}(R)$

$A_{v1} = \dfrac{40(98.8\mu A)}{2}\left(7.37k\Omega \| 6.67k\Omega\right)(40)(300\mu A)(50k\Omega) = 3530$

$R_{ID} = 2r_{\pi1} = 2\dfrac{\beta_{o1}V_T}{I_{C1}} = 2\dfrac{80(0.025V)}{98.8\mu A} = 40.5k\Omega$

(c) $R_{IC} = \dfrac{(\beta_{o1}+1)r_{o1}}{2} = \dfrac{81}{2}\left(\dfrac{70+15}{98.8\mu A}\right) = 34.8M\Omega$

15.77

For $V_O = 0$, $I_{C3} = \dfrac{15V}{50k\Omega} = 300\mu A$ | $I_{B3} = \dfrac{I_{C3}}{\beta_{F3}} = \dfrac{300\mu A}{80} = 3.75\mu A$ | $I_{E3} = \dfrac{81}{80}I_{C3} = 304\mu A$

$I_{C1} = I_{C2} = \alpha_F\left(\dfrac{200\mu A}{2}\right) = \dfrac{80}{81}\left(\dfrac{200\mu A}{2}\right) = 98.8\mu A$ | $R_C = \dfrac{0.7V + I_{E3}R_E}{I_{C1} - I_{B3}} = \dfrac{0.7V + (304\mu A)R_E}{98.8\mu A - 3.75\mu A}$

$V_{C2} = 15 - 2400 I_{E3} - V_{EB3} = 15 - 0.729 - 0.7 = 13.6V$

$A_{Vth3} = -\dfrac{g_{m1}}{2}R_C = -20(98.8\mu A)R_C = -1.976 \times 10^{-3}R_C$ | $R_{th} = R_C$

$A_{V2} = -\dfrac{\beta_o R_L}{R_{th} + r_{\pi3} + (\beta_o + 1)R_E}$ | $R_L = R \left\| r_{o3}\left(1 + \dfrac{\beta_o R_R}{R_{th} + r_{\pi3} + R_E}\right)\right.$ | $A_V = A_{Vth3}A_{V2}$

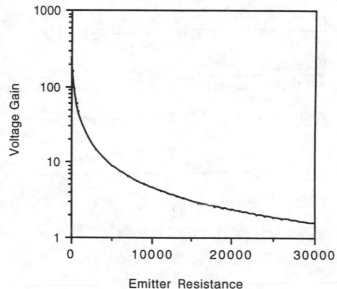

15.78

$R_{OUT} = R \| r_{o3}$ | $\dfrac{1}{R_{OUT}} = \dfrac{1}{R} + \dfrac{1}{r_{o3}} = \dfrac{1}{R} + \dfrac{I_{C3}}{V_A + V_{EC3}} = \dfrac{1}{R} + \dfrac{1}{R}\dfrac{I_{C3}R}{V_A + V_{EC3}}$ | $V_O = 0V$

$10^{-3} = \dfrac{1}{R}\left(1 + \dfrac{9}{70+9}\right) \rightarrow R = 1.11\ k\Omega$ | $I_{C3} = \dfrac{9}{R} = 8.11mA$ | $r_{\pi3} = \dfrac{100(0.025V)}{8.11mA} = 308\Omega$

$A_{V2} = -g_{m3}R_{OUT} = -40(8.11mA)(1k\Omega) = -324$ | $A_{V1} = \dfrac{A_V}{A_{V2}} = \dfrac{2000}{-324} = -6.165$

$$A_{V1} = -\frac{g_{m2}}{2}\left(R_C\|r_{\pi3}\right) = -20\frac{I_{C2}R_Cr_{\pi3}}{R_C + r_{\pi3}} = -20\frac{I_{C2}R_C}{\dfrac{R_C}{r_{\pi3}}+1} \cong -20\frac{0.7}{\dfrac{R_C}{r_{\pi3}}+1} \quad \text{neglecting } I_{B3}$$

$$-20\frac{0.7}{\dfrac{R_C}{308}+1} = -6.165 \rightarrow R_C = 391\Omega \;\Big|\; I_{C1} = \frac{0.7V}{391\Omega} + I_{B3} = \frac{0.7V}{391\Omega} + \frac{8.11mA}{100} = 1.87mA$$

Selecting the closest 5% values: $R = 1.1\,k\Omega$, $R_C = 390\,\Omega$, $I_1 = 3.74\,mA$

15.79

(a) For $V_O = 0$, $I_{C3} = I_2 = 300\mu A$ $\quad V_{C2} = 15 - 2400I_{E3} - V_{EB3} = 15 - 0.729 - 0.7 = 13.6V$

$$I_{C1} = I_{C2} = \alpha_F\left(\frac{200\mu A}{2}\right) = \frac{80}{81}\left(\frac{200\mu A}{2}\right) = 98.8\mu A \quad I_{B3} = \frac{I_{C3}}{\beta_{F3}} = \frac{300\mu A}{80} = 3.75\mu A$$

$$V_{CE1} = V_{CE2} = 13.6 - (-0.7) = 14.3V \;\Big|\; V_{EC3} = 15 - 2400I_{E3} - V_O = 14.3V$$

Q - points: $(98.8\mu A, 14.3V)$ $(98.8\mu A, 14.3V)$ $(300\mu A, 14.3V)$

$$R_C = \frac{15 - 13.6}{(98.8 - 3.75)}\frac{V}{\mu A} = 15.1k\Omega \quad r_{\pi3} = \frac{80(0.025V)}{0.3mA} = 6.67k\Omega$$

(b) $A_{v1} = \dfrac{v_{c2}}{v_{id}} = -\left(\dfrac{g_{m1}}{2}\right)\left[R_C\|\left(r_{\pi3} + (\beta_{o3}+1)R_E\right)\right]$

$$A_{v1} = -\left(\frac{40(98.8\mu A)}{2}\right)\left[15.1k\Omega\|\left(6.67k\Omega + 81(2.4k\Omega)\right)\right] = -27.8$$

$$A_{v2} = \frac{v_o}{v_{c2}} = -\frac{\beta_{o3}R_L}{r_{\pi3} + (\beta_{o3}+1)R_E} \;\Big|\; R_L = r_{o3}\left(1 + \frac{\beta_o R_E}{R_C + r_{\pi3} + R_E}\right) \;\Big|\; r_{o3} = \frac{70 + 14.3}{300\mu A} = 281k\Omega$$

$$R_L = 281k\Omega\left(1 + \frac{80(2.4k\Omega)}{15.1k\Omega + 6.67k\Omega + 2.4k\Omega}\right) = 2.51M\Omega \;\Big|\; A_{v2} = -\frac{80(2.51M\Omega)}{6.67k\Omega + 81(2.4k\Omega)} = -999$$

$$A_v = \frac{v_{c2}}{v_{id}}\frac{v_o}{v_{c2}} = -27.8(-999) = 27800 \;\Big|\; R_{ID} = 2r_{\pi1} = 2\frac{\beta_{o1}V_T}{I_{C1}} = 2\frac{80(0.025V)}{98.8\mu A} = 40.5k\Omega$$

$$R_O = R_L = 2.51\,M\Omega$$

15.80

$$I_{C1} = I_{C2} = \alpha_F\left(\frac{200\mu A}{2}\right) = \frac{100}{101}\left(\frac{200\mu A}{2}\right) = 99.0\mu A \;\Big|\; V_{CE1} = V_{CE2} = 15 - V_{EB3} - (-V_{BE1}) = 15V$$

For $V_O = 0$, $I_{C3} = I_2 = 300\mu A$ $\quad V_{EC3} = 15 - V_O = 15V$

Q - points: $(99.0\mu A, 15.0V)$ $(99.0\mu A, 15.0V)$ $(300\mu A, 15.0V)$

15.81

$$A_V = A_{V1}A_{V2} \;\Big|\; A_{V1} = -\frac{g_{m1}}{2}\left[R_C\|r_{\pi3} + (\beta_{o3}+1)R_E\right]$$

$$A_{V2} = -\frac{\beta_o R_{OUT}}{r_{\pi3} + (\beta_o+1)R_E} = -\frac{\beta_o R_{OUT}}{r_{\pi3} + (\beta_o+1)R_E}r_{o3}\left(1 + \frac{\beta_o R_E}{R_{th} + r_{\pi3} + R_E}\right)$$

$$I_{C1} = I_{C2} = \alpha_F \frac{I_1}{2} = \frac{80}{81} \frac{200\mu A}{2} = 98.8\mu A \quad | \quad \text{For } V_O = 0, \ I_{C3} = I_2 = 300\mu A$$

$$I_{B3} = \frac{I_{C3}}{\beta_{F3}} = \frac{300\mu A}{80} = 3.75\mu A \quad | \quad I_{E3} = \frac{81}{80} I_{C3} = 303.8\mu A \quad | \quad V_{EC3} = 15 - I_{E3}R_E$$

$$R_C = \frac{0.7V + I_{E3}R_E}{I_{C1} - I_{B3}} = \frac{0.7V + (303.8\mu A)R_E}{98.8\mu A - 3.75\mu A}$$

$$r_{\pi3} = \frac{80(0.025V)}{300\mu A} = 6.67k\Omega \quad | \quad g_{m1} = 40(98.8\mu A) = 3.95mS \quad | \quad r_{o3} = \frac{70 + 15 - (303.8\mu A)R_E}{300\mu A}$$

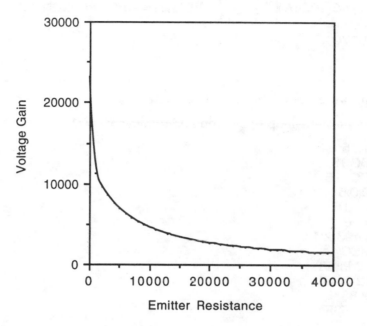

Emitter Resistance

15.82

$$I_{SD2} = \frac{500\mu A}{2} = 250\mu A \quad | \quad V_S = V_{SG} = -V_{TP} + \sqrt{\frac{2I_{SD2}}{K_p}} = 1 + \sqrt{\frac{2(2.5\times10^{-4})}{5\times10^{-3}}} = 1.32V$$

$$V_D = -15 + 0.7 = -14.3V \ | \ V_{SD} = V_S - V_D = 1.32 - (-14.3) = 15.6V \ | \ Q\text{-pt:}(250\mu A, 15.6V)$$

$$I_{C3} = 500\mu A \ | \ V_{CE3} = V_{C3} - V_{E3} = 0 - (-15) = 15V \ | \ Q\text{-pt:}(500\mu A, 15V)$$

$$R_D = \frac{V_{BE}}{I_{D2} - I_{B3}} = \frac{0.7V}{250\mu A - \dfrac{500\mu A}{80}} = 2.87k\Omega$$

$$g_{m2} = \sqrt{2(0.005)(0.00025)} = 1.58\times10^{-3}S \quad | \quad r_{\pi3} = \frac{80(0.025V)}{0.5mA} = 4k\Omega$$

$$A_V = \frac{\mathbf{v_{d2}}}{\mathbf{v_{id}}} \frac{\mathbf{v_o}}{\mathbf{v_{d2}}} = A_{V1}A_{V2} \quad | \quad A_{V1} = -\frac{g_{m2}}{2}\left(R_D \| r_{\pi3}\right) = -\frac{1.58mS}{2}\left(2.87k\Omega \| 4k\Omega\right) = -1.30$$

$$A_{V2} = -g_{m3}\left(r_{o3} \| R_2\right) = -40(0.5mA)\left(\frac{75V + 15V}{0.5mA} \| 2M\Omega\right) = -0.02(180k\Omega \| 2M\Omega) = -3300$$

$$A_V = -1.30(-3300) = 4300 \quad | \quad R_{IN} = \infty \quad | \quad R_{OUT} = r_{o3} \| R_2 = 180k\Omega \| 2M\Omega = 165k\Omega$$

v_2 is the non-inverting (+) input

15.83

$$A_V = \frac{v_{d2}}{v_{id}}\frac{v_o}{v_{d2}} = A_{V1}A_{V2} \quad | \quad A_{V1} = -\frac{g_{m2}}{2}(R_D\|r_{\pi3}) \quad | \quad I_{C3} = 100\mu A \quad | \quad r_{\pi3} = \frac{80(0.025V)}{100\mu A} = 20k\Omega$$

$$I_{DS2} = \frac{500\mu A}{2} = 250\mu A \quad | \quad g_{m2} = \sqrt{2(0.005)(0.00025)} = 1.58 \times 10^{-3}S$$

$$R_D = \frac{V_{BE}}{I_{DS2} - I_{B3}} = \frac{0.7V}{250\mu A - \dfrac{100\mu A}{80}} = 2.81k\Omega \quad | \quad A_{V1} = -\frac{1.58mS}{2}(2.81k\Omega\|20k\Omega) = -1.95$$

$$A_{V2} = -g_{m3}(r_{o3}\|R_2) = -40(100\mu A)\left(\frac{75V + 5V}{100\mu A}\|10M\Omega\right) = -0.02(800k\Omega\|10M\Omega) = -2960$$

$$A_V = -1.95(-2960) = 5770$$

15.84 Note that the parameters of the transistors and values of R_D have been carefully adjusted to permit open-loop operation and achieve $V_O = 0$.

```
*Problem 15.84
VCC 7 0 DC 15
VEE 8 0 DC -15
V1 1 9 AC 0.5
V2 3 9 AC -0.5
VIC 9 0 DC 0
I1 7 2 DC 493.2U
R1 7 2 2MEG
M1 4 1 2 2 PFET
M2 5 3 2 2 PFET
RD1 4 8 2.863K
RD2 5 8 2.863K
Q3 6 5 8 NBJT
I2 7 6 DC 492.5U
R2 7 6 2MEG
.MODEL PFET PMOS KP=5M VTO=-1
.MODEL NBJT NPN BF=80 VA=75 IS=0.2881FA
.OP
.AC LIN 1 1000 1000
.TF V(6) VIC
.PRINT AC IM(V1) IP(V1) VM(6) VP(6)
.OPTIONS TNOM=17.2
.END
```

$$A_{dm} = VM(6) = 4630 \quad | \quad A_{cm} = -1.46 \quad | \quad CMRR_{dB} = 70.0 \text{ dB}$$

Results:
$$R_{ID} = \frac{1}{IM(V1)} = \infty \quad | \quad R_O = 164 \text{ k}\Omega$$

15.85

(a) $$I_{SD2} = \frac{500\mu A}{2} = 250\mu A \quad | \quad V_S = V_{SG} = -V_{TP} + \sqrt{\frac{2I_{SD2}}{K_p}} = 1 + \sqrt{\frac{2(2.5 \times 10^{-4})}{5 \times 10^{-3}}} = 1.32V$$

$$V_D = -5 + 0.7 + 0.7 = -3.6V \quad | \quad V_{SD} = V_S - V_D = 1.32 - (-3.6) = 4.92V \quad | \quad Q\text{-pt:}(250\mu A, 4.92V)$$

$$I_{C3} + I_{C4} = 500\mu A \quad | \quad I_{C3} + \beta_F I_{E3} = (\beta_F + 2)I_{C3} = 500\mu A \rightarrow I_{C3} = 6.10\mu A \quad | \quad I_{C4} = 494\mu A$$

For $V_O = 0$, $V_{CE4} = 5V$ and $V_{CE3} = 5 - 0.7 = 4.30V$

Q-pts: $(250\mu A, 4.92V)$ $(250\mu A, 4.92V)$ $(6.10\mu A, 4.30V)$ $(494\mu A, 5.00V)$

$$R_D = \frac{V_{BE3} + V_{BE4}}{I_{D2} - I_{B3}} = \frac{1.4V}{250\mu A - \frac{6.10\mu A}{80}} = 5.60k\Omega \quad | \quad \text{Based upon results for the Darlington}$$

circuit in (Eq. 15.53): $A_{V1} = \frac{g_{m1}}{2}\left(R_D\|2r_{\pi 3}\right) \quad | \quad r_{\pi 3} = \frac{80(0.025V)}{6.10\mu A} = 328k\Omega$

$$g_{m1} = \sqrt{2(0.005)(0.00025)} = 1.58mS \quad | \quad A_{V1} = -\frac{1.58mS}{2}(5.60k\Omega\|656k\Omega) = -4.39$$

$$A_{V2} = -\frac{g_{m4}}{2}\left(\frac{2}{3}r_{o4}\|R_2\right) = -\frac{40(494\mu A)}{2}\left(\frac{2}{3}\frac{75V+5V}{494\mu A}\|1M\Omega\right) = -9.88mS(108k\Omega\|1M\Omega) = -963$$

$$A_V = -4.39(-963) = 4230 \quad | \quad R_{ID} = \infty \quad | \quad R_{OUT} = \frac{2}{3}r_{o4}\|R_2 = 108k\Omega\|1M\Omega = 97.5 \ k\Omega$$

15.86

```
*Problem 15.86
*Vos (the dc value of V2) has been carefully adjusted to set Vo ≈ 0
VCC 8 0 DC 5
VEE 9 0 DC -5
V1 1 10 AC 0.5
V2 3 10 DC 1.21M AC -0.5
VIC 10 0 DC 0
I1 8 2 DC 496.3U
R1 8 2 1MEG
M1 4 1 2 2 PFET
M2 5 3 2 2 PFET
RD1 4 9 5.6K
RD2 5 9 5.6K
Q3 7 5 6 NBJT
Q4 7 6 9 NBJT
I2 8 7 DC 495U
R2 8 7 1MEG
.OP
.MODEL PFET PMOS KP=5M VTO=-1
.MODEL NBJT NPN BF=80 VA=75
.AC LIN 1 1000 1000
.TF V(7) VIC
.PRINT AC IM(V1) IP(V1) VM(7) VP(7)
.END
```

$$A_{dm} = VM(7) = 4080 \ | \ A_{cm} = -2.58 \ | \ CMRR_{dB} = 64.0 \ dB$$

Results: $R_{ID} = \dfrac{1}{IM(V1)} = \infty \ | \ R_O = 96.2 \ k\Omega$

15.87

(a) $I_{C1} = I_{C2} = \alpha_F \dfrac{I_1}{2} = \dfrac{100}{101}\dfrac{100\mu A}{2} = 49.5\mu A \ | \ V_{EC2} = +0.7V - (-15V + 0.7V) = 15.0V$

For $V_O = 0$, $I_{C4} = \alpha_F I_3 = \dfrac{100}{101}1.00mA = 990\mu A \ | \ V_{EC4} = 0 - (-15V) = 15.0V$

$I_{C3} = I_2 + I_{B4} = 350\mu A + \dfrac{1mA}{101} = 360\mu A \ | \ V_{CE3} = V_O - 0.7V - (-15) = 14.3$

Q – pts: $(49.5\mu A, 15.0V) \ (49.5\mu A, 15.0V) \ (360\mu A, 14.3V) \ (990\mu A, 15.0V)$

(b) $R_C = \dfrac{0.7V}{I_{C2} - I_{B3}} = \dfrac{0.7V}{(49.5 - 3.60)\mu A} = 15.3k\Omega$ | $r_{\pi 3} = \dfrac{100(0.025V)}{360\mu A} = 6.94k\Omega$

$r_{o3} = \dfrac{50 + 14.3}{360\mu A} = 179k\Omega$ | $A_V = A_{V1}A_{V2}A_{V3} = \dfrac{g_{m1}}{2}(R_C\|r_{\pi 3})(g_{m3}r_{o3})(1) = \dfrac{g_{m1}}{2}(R_C\|r_{\pi 3})\mu_{f3}$

$A_V = \dfrac{40(49.5\mu A)}{2}(15.3k\Omega\|6.94k\Omega)(40)(64.3) = 12200$ | $R_{ID} = 2r_{\pi 1} = 2\dfrac{100(0.025V)}{49.5\mu A} = 101\ k\Omega$

(c) $R_O = \dfrac{r_{o3} + r_{\pi 4}}{\beta_{o4} + 1}$ | $r_{\pi 4} = \dfrac{100(0.025V)}{990\mu A} = 2.53k\Omega$ | $R_O = \dfrac{179k\Omega + 2.53k\Omega}{101} = 1.80\ k\Omega$

(d) $R_{IC} = \dfrac{(\beta_{o1} + 1)r_{o1}}{2}$ | $r_{o1} = \dfrac{50V + 15V}{49.5\mu A}\ 1.31M\Omega$ | $R_{IC} = \dfrac{101(1.31M\Omega)}{2} = 66.3\ M\Omega$ (e) v_2

15.88

```
*Problem 15.88
*RC and Vos (see V2) have been carefully adjusted to set Vo ≈ 0
VCC 7 0 DC 15
VEE 8 0 DC -15
V1 1 9 DC 0.117M AC 0.5
V2 3 9 AC -0.5
VIC 9 0 DC 0
I1 7 2 DC 100U
Q1 4 1 2 PBJT
Q2 5 3 2 PBJT
RC1 4 8 15.8K
RC2 5 8 15.8K
Q3 6 5 8 NBJT
I2 7 6 DC 350U
Q4 8 6 10 PBJT
I3 7 10 DC 1M
.MODEL PBJT PNP BF=100 VA=50
.MODEL NBJT NPN BF=100 VA=50
.NODESET V(10)=0
.OP
.AC LIN 1 1000 1000
.TF V(10) VIC
.PRINT AC IM(V1) IP(V1) VM(10) VP(10)
.END
```

$A_{dm} = VM(10) = 13800$ | $A_{cm} = -0.0804$ | $CMRR_{dB} = 105\ dB$

Results: $R_{ID} = \dfrac{1}{IM(V1)} = 133\ k\Omega$ | $R_O = 1.37\ k\Omega$

15.89

(a) Working backwards from the output: $V_{DS4} = V_{DD} - V_O = 12 - 0 = 12.0V$ | $I_{DS4} = I_3 = 5.00mA$

$V_{GS4} = V_{TN} + \sqrt{\dfrac{2I_{DS4}}{K_n}} = 0.75 + \sqrt{\dfrac{2(0.005)}{0.005}} = 2.16V$ | $V_{SD3} = V_{DD} - V_{GS4} = 12 - 2.16 = 9.84V$

$I_{SD3} = I_2 = 2.00mA$ | $V_{SG3} = -V_{TP} + \sqrt{\dfrac{2I_{DS4}}{K_n}} = 0.75V + \sqrt{\dfrac{2(0.002)}{0.002}} = 2.16V$

$V_{D2} = V_{DD} - V_{SG3} = 12V - 2.16V = 9.84V$ | $I_{DS1} = I_{DS2} = \dfrac{I_1}{2} = 250\mu A$

$$V_{GS2} = 0.75V + \sqrt{\frac{2(2.5 \times 10^{-4})}{5 \times 10^{-3}}} = 1.07V \quad | \quad V_{DS1} = V_{DS2} = 9.84V - (-1.07V) = 10.9V$$

$$Q-pts: \quad (250\mu A, 10.9V) \quad (250\mu A, 10.9V) \quad (2.00mA, 9.84V) \quad (5.00mA, 12.0V)$$

(b) $A_{dm} = \dfrac{g_{m1}}{2} R_D (g_{m3}r_{o3}) \dfrac{g_{m4}r_{o4}}{1 + g_{m4}r_{o4}} = \dfrac{g_{m1}}{2} R_D \mu_{f3} \dfrac{\mu_{f4}}{1 + \mu_{f4}} \quad | \quad R_D = \dfrac{2.16V}{0.25mA} = 8.64k\Omega$

$$g_{m1} = \sqrt{2(5 \times 10^{-3})(2.5 \times 10^{-4})[1 + 0.02(10.9)]} = 1.75mS \quad | \quad r_{o3} = \frac{\frac{1}{0.015} + 9.84}{2mA} = 38.3k\Omega$$

$$g_{m3} = \sqrt{2(2 \times 10^{-3})(2 \times 10^{-3})[1 + 0.015(9.84)]} = 3.03mS \quad | \quad r_{o4} = \frac{\frac{1}{0.02} + 12}{5mA} = 12.4k\Omega$$

$$g_{m4} = \sqrt{2(5 \times 10^{-3})(5 \times 10^{-3})[1 + 0.02(12)]} = 7.87mS \quad | \quad \mu_{f3} = g_{m3}r_{o3} = 116 \quad | \quad \mu_{f4} = 97.6$$

$$A_{dm} = \frac{1.75ms}{2}(8.64k\Omega)(116)\frac{97.6}{1 + 97.6} = 868 \quad | \quad R_{ID} = \infty \quad | \quad R_O = \frac{1}{g_{m4}} = 127\Omega$$

15.90

```
*Problem 15.90
*The values of RD have been adjusted to bring the offset voltage to ≈ 0
VCC 8 0 DC 12
VEE 9 0 DC -12
V1 1 10 AC 1
V2 3 10 AC 1
VIC 10 0 DC 0
I1 2 9 DC 500U
M1 4 1 2 2 NFET
M2 5 3 2 2 NFET
RD1 8 4 8.28K
RD2 8 5 8.28K
M3 6 5 8 8 PFET
M4 8 6 7 7 NFET
I2 6 9 DC 2M
I3 7 9 DC 5M
.MODEL PFET PMOS KP=2M VTO=-0.75 LAMBDA=0.015
.MODEL NFET NMOS KP=5M VTO=0.75 LAMBDA=0.02
.OP
.AC LIN 1 1000 1000
.TF V(7) VIC
.PRINT AC VM(7) VP(7) IM(V1) IP(V1)
.END
```

Results:
$$A_{dm} = VM(7) = 802 \quad | \quad A_{cm} = -4.74 \times 10^{-7} \cong 0 \quad | \quad CMRR_{dB} = \infty$$
$$R_{ID} = \frac{1}{IM(V1)} = 10^{30} \cong \infty \quad | \quad R_O = 126 \; \Omega$$

15.91

(a) Working backwards from the output: $V_{SD4} = V_O - V_{SS} = 0 - (-5) = 5.00V$

$$I_{SD4} = I_3 = 2.00mA \quad | \quad V_{SG4} = -V_{TP} + \sqrt{\frac{2I_{SD4}}{K_p}} = 0.7 + \sqrt{\frac{2(0.002)}{0.002}} = 2.11V$$

$$V_{DS3} = V_O - V_{SG4} + V_{SS} = 0 - 2.11 + 5 = 2.89V$$

$$I_{DS3} = I_2 = 500\mu A \quad | \quad V_{GS3} = V_{TN} + \sqrt{\frac{2I_{DS4}}{K_n}} = 0.75V + \sqrt{\frac{2(5 \times 10^{-4})}{5 \times 10^{-3}}} = 1.15V$$

$$V_{D2} = -V_{SS} + V_{GS3} = -5 + 1.15V = -3.85V \quad | \quad I_{SD1} = I_{SD2} = \frac{I_1}{2} = 300\mu A$$

$$V_{SG1} = V_{SG2} = 0.7V + \sqrt{\frac{2(3 \times 10^{-4})}{2 \times 10^{-3}}} = 1.25V \quad | \quad V_{SD2} = V_{SD2} = 1.25 - (3.85) = 5.10V$$

$$Q = pts: \ (300\mu A, 5.10V) \ (300\mu A, 5.10V) \ (500\mu A, 2.89V) \ (2.00mA, 5.00V)$$

$$(b) \ A_{dm} = \frac{g_{m1}}{2} R_D (g_{m3} r_{o3}) \frac{g_{m4} r_{o4}}{1 + g_{m4} r_{o4}} = \frac{g_{m1}}{2} R_D \mu_{f3} \frac{\mu_{f4}}{1 + \mu_{f4}} \quad | \quad R_D = \frac{1.15V}{0.3mA} = 8.83k\Omega$$

$$g_{m1} = \sqrt{2(2 \times 10^{-3})(3 \times 10^{-4})[1 + 0.015(5.10)]} = 1.14mS \quad | \quad r_{o3} = \frac{\frac{1}{0.02} + 2.89}{0.5mA} = 106k\Omega$$

$$g_{m3} = \sqrt{2(5 \times 10^{-3})(5 \times 10^{-4})[1 + 0.02(2.89)]} = 2.30mS \quad | \quad r_{o4} = \frac{\frac{1}{0.015} + 5.00}{2mA} = 35.8k\Omega$$

$$g_{m4} = \sqrt{2(2 \times 10^{-3})(2 \times 10^{-3})[1 + 0.015(15)]} = 2.93mS \quad | \quad \mu_{f3} = g_{m3} r_{o3} = 244 \quad | \quad \mu_{f4} = 105$$

$$A_{dm} = \frac{1.14ms}{2} (8.83k\Omega)(244) \frac{105}{1 + 105} = 1220 \quad | \quad R_{ID} = \infty \quad | \quad R_O = \frac{1}{g_{m4}} = 341\Omega$$

15.92 Note: Use $R_E = 1k\Omega$

(a) Working backwards from the output with $V_O = 0$: $V_{DS4} = V_{CC} - V_O = 5 - 0 = 5V$

$$I_{DS4} = I_3 = 2mA \quad | \quad V_{GS4} = -V_P \left(\sqrt{\frac{I_{DS4}}{I_{DSS4}}} - 1 \right) = -5 \left(\sqrt{\frac{2mA}{5mA}} - 1 \right) = -2.76V \quad | \quad I_{C3} = I_2 = 500\mu A$$

$$V_{EC3} = 5 - I_{E3} R_E - V_{GS4} = 5V - \frac{101}{100}(500\mu A)1k\Omega - (-2.76V) = 7.26V$$

$$V_{CE2} = 5 - I_{E3} R_E - V_{EB3} - (-V_{BE2}) = 5 - 0.505 - 0.7 + 0.7 = 4.50V$$

$$I_{C1} = I_{C2} = \alpha_F \frac{I_1}{2} = \frac{100}{101} \frac{200\mu A}{2} = 99.0\mu A \quad | \quad R_C = \frac{I_{E3} R_E + V_{EB3}}{I_{C2} - I_{B3}} = \frac{0.505V + 0.7V}{(99.0 - 5.00)\mu A} = 12.8k\Omega$$

$$V_{CE1} = 5 - I_{C1} R_C - (-V_{BE2}) = 5 - 99.0\mu A(12.8k\Omega) + 0.7 = 4.43V$$

$$Q = pts: \ (99.0\mu A, 4.43V) \ (99.0\mu A, 4.50V) \ (500\mu A, 7.26V) \ (2.00mA, 5.00V)$$

(b) Using current division at the collector of Q_2:

$$A_{dm} = \frac{g_{m1}}{2} \frac{R_C}{R_C + r_{\pi3} + (\beta_{o3} + 1)R_E} \beta_{o3} r_{o3} \left(1 + \frac{\beta_{o3} R_E}{R_C + r_{\pi3} + R_E} \right) \frac{g_{m4} R_L}{1 + g_{m4} R_L}$$

$$r_{\pi3} = \frac{100(0.025V)}{500\mu A} = 5.00k\Omega \quad | \quad r_{o3} = \frac{50V + 7.26V}{500\mu A} =$$

$$g_{m4} = \frac{2I_{DS4}}{V_{GS4} - V_P} = \frac{2(2mA)}{-2.76 + 5} = 1.79mS \quad | \quad \frac{g_{m4} R_L}{1 + g_{m4} R_L} = \frac{1.79mS(5k\Omega)}{1 + 1.79mS(5k\Omega)} = 0.890$$

$$A_{dm} = \frac{40(99.0\mu A)}{2} \frac{12.8k\Omega(100)}{12.8k\Omega + 5.00k\Omega + (101)1k\Omega}(115k\Omega) \left(1 + \frac{(101)1k\Omega}{12.8k\Omega + 5.00k\Omega + 1k\Omega} \right) 0.890$$

$$A_{dm} = 13900 \quad | \quad R_{ID} = 2r_{\pi1} = 2\frac{100(0.025V)}{99.0\mu A} = 50.5 \ k\Omega \quad | \quad R_O = \frac{1}{g_{m4}} = 559 \ \Omega$$

15.93

(a) Working backwards from the output with $V_O = 0$: $V_{DS4} = V_{CC} - V_O = 5 - 0 = 5V$

$$I_{DS4} = I_3 = 2mA \mid V_{GS4} = V_{TN} + \sqrt{\frac{2I_{DS4}}{K_n}} = 0.7 + \sqrt{\frac{2(0.002)}{0.005}} = 1.59V \mid I_{C3} = I_2 = 500\mu A$$

$$V_{EC3} = 5 - V_{GS4} = 5 - 1.59 = 3.41V \mid V_{CE2} = 5 - V_{EB3} - (-V_{BE2}) = 5 - 0.7 + 0.7 = 5.00V$$

$$I_{C1} = I_{C2} = \alpha_F \frac{I_1}{2} = \frac{100}{101}\frac{200\mu A}{2} = 99.0\mu A \mid R_C = \frac{V_{EB3}}{I_{C2} - I_{B3}} = \frac{0.7V}{(99.0 - 5.00)\mu A} = 7.45k\Omega$$

$$V_{CE1} = 5 - I_{C1}R_C - (-V_{BE2}) = 5 - 99.0\mu A(7.45k\Omega) + 0.7 = 4.96V$$

$Q = pts$: $(99.0\mu A, 4.96V)$ $(99.0\mu A, 5.00V)$ $(500\mu A, 3.41V)$ $(2.00mA, 5.00V)$

(b) Using current division at the collector of Q_2:

$$A_{dm} = \frac{g_{m1}}{2}\frac{R_C}{R_C + r_{\pi 3}}\beta_{o3}r_{o3}\frac{g_{m4}R_L}{1 + g_{m4}R_L} = \frac{g_{m1}}{2}(R_C \| r_{\pi 3})\mu_{f3}\frac{g_{m4}R_L}{1 + g_{m4}R_L}$$

$$r_{\pi 3} = \frac{100(0.025V)}{500\mu A} = 5.00k\Omega \mid g_{m4} = \sqrt{2(0.005)(0.002)} = 4.47mS$$

$$A_{dm} = \frac{40(99.0\mu A)}{2}(7.45k\Omega \| 5.00k\Omega)(40)(50 + 3.41)\frac{4.47mS(2k\Omega)}{1 + 4.47mS(2k\Omega)} = 11400$$

$$R_{ID} = 2r_{\pi 1} = 2\frac{100(0.025V)}{99.0\mu A} = 50.5 \ k\Omega \mid R_O = \frac{1}{g_{m4}} = 224 \ \Omega$$

15.94

```
*Problem 15.94
*The values of RC have been adjusted to set Vo ≈ 0.
VCC 8 0 DC 5
VEE 9 0 DC -5
VIC 10 0 DC 0
V1 1 10 AC 0.5
V2 3 10 AC -0.5
I1 2 9 DC 200U
Q1 4 1 2 NBJT
Q2 5 3 2 NBJT
RC1 8 4 8.00K
RC2 8 5 8.00K
Q3 6 5 8 PBJT
I2 6 9 DC 500U
M4 8 6 7 7 NFET
I3 7 9 DC 2M
RL 7 0 2K
.MODEL NBJT NPN BF=100 VA=50
.MODEL PBJT PNP BF=100 VA=50
.MODEl NFET NMOS KP=5M VTO=0.70
.OP
.AC LIN 1 2KHZ 2KHZ
.PRINT AC VM(7) VP(7) IM(V1) IP(V1)
.TF V(7) VIC
.END
```

$$A_{dm} = VM(7) = 11200 \mid A_{cm} = -0.0957 \mid CMRR_{dB} = 101 \ dB$$

Results: $R_{ID} = \frac{1}{IM(V1)} = 56.4 \ k\Omega \cong \infty \mid R_O = 201 \ \Omega$

15.95

(a) $I_{C1} = I_{C2} = \alpha_F \dfrac{I_1}{2} = \dfrac{100}{101} \dfrac{10\mu A}{2} = 4.95 \ \mu A \ | \ \ I_{C3} = I_{C4} = \alpha_F \dfrac{I_2}{2} = \dfrac{50}{51} \dfrac{50\mu A}{2} = 24.5 \ \mu A$

$V_{CE2} = V_{CC} - (I_{C2} - I_{B3})R_C - (-V_{BE2}) = 3V - \left(4.95\mu A - \dfrac{24.5 \ \mu A}{50}\right)300k\Omega - (-0.7) = 2.36V$

For $V_O = 0$: $I_{C5} = \alpha_F I_3 \dfrac{50}{51}(250\mu A) = 245\mu A \ | \ V_{EC5} = 3.00 \ V \ | \ V_{C4} = -0.7V$

$V_{C1} = 3 - \left(4.95\mu A - \dfrac{24.5 \ \mu A}{50}\right)300k\Omega = 1.66V \ | \ V_{EC3} = V_{EC4} = 1.66 + 0.7 - (-0.7) = 3.06V$

Q - pts: $(4.95\mu A, 2.36V) \ (4.95\mu A, 2.36V) \ (24.5\mu A, 3.06V) \ (24.5\mu A, 3.06V) \ (245\mu A, 3.00V)$

(b) $A_{dm} = g_{m1}\left(R_{C1} \| r_{\pi 3}\right)\dfrac{g_{m3}}{2}\left(R_{C2} \| [r_{\pi 5} + (\beta_{o5} + 1)R_L]\right)\dfrac{(\beta_{o5} + 1)R_L}{r_{\pi 5} + (\beta_{o5} + 1)R_L}$

$r_{\pi 3} = \dfrac{50(0.025V)}{24.5\mu A} = 51.0k\Omega \ | \ r_{\pi 5} = \dfrac{50(0.025V)}{245\mu A} = 5.10k\Omega$

$\dfrac{(\beta_{o5} + 1)R_L}{r_{\pi 5} + (\beta_{o5} + 1)R_L} = \dfrac{51(2k\Omega)}{5.10k\Omega + 51(2k\Omega)} = 0.952$

$A_{dm} = 40(4.95\mu A)(300k\Omega \| 51.0k\Omega)\dfrac{(40)(24.5\mu A)}{2}\left(78k\Omega \| [5.10k\Omega + 51(2k\Omega)]\right)0.952 = 182$

$R_{ID} = 2r_{\pi 1} = 2\dfrac{100(0.025V)}{4.95\mu A} = 1.01 \ M\Omega \ | \ R_O = \dfrac{R_{C2} + r_{\pi 5}}{\beta_{o5} + 1} = \dfrac{78 + 5.10}{51} k\Omega = 1.63 \ k\Omega$

(c) v_A is the non - inverting input - v_B is the inverting input

(d) $A_V = (10V_{CC})(10V_{CC}) = 30^2 = 900 \ | \ r_{\pi 3} \ll R_C$ is substantailly reducing the gain
Also, the input resistance of the emitter follower is low, $R_{IN5} = 107k\Omega \approx R_{C2}$, and
is reducing the gain by an additional factor of almost 2.

15.96

(a) $I_{C1} = I_{C2} = \alpha_F \dfrac{I_1}{2} = \dfrac{100}{101} \dfrac{100\mu A}{2} = 49.5 \ \mu A \ | \ \ I_{C3} = I_{C4} = \alpha_F \dfrac{I_2}{2} = \dfrac{50}{51} \dfrac{200\mu A}{2} = 98.0 \ \mu A$

$V_{CE2} = V_{CC} - (I_{C2} - I_{B3})R_C - (-V_{BE2}) = 18V - \left(49.5\mu A - \dfrac{98.0 \ \mu A}{50}\right)120k\Omega - (-0.7) = 13.0V$

For $V_O = 0$: $I_{C5} = \alpha_F I_3 \dfrac{50}{51}(750\mu A) = 735\mu A \ | \ V_{EC4} = 18 \ V \ | \ V_{C4} = -0.7V$

$V_{C1} = 18 - \left(49.5\mu A - \dfrac{98.0 \ \mu A}{50}\right)120k\Omega = 12.3V \ | \ V_{EC3} = V_{EC4} = 12.3 + 0.7 - (-0.7) = 13.7V$

Q - pts: $(49.5\mu A, 13.0V) \ (49.5\mu A, 13.0V) \ (98.0\mu A, 13.7V) \ (98.0\mu A, 13.7V) \ (735\mu A, 18.0V)$

(b) $A_{dm} = g_{m1}\left(R_{C1} \| r_{\pi 3}\right)\dfrac{g_{m3}}{2}\left(R_{C2} \| [r_{\pi 5} + (\beta_{o5} + 1)R_L]\right)\dfrac{(\beta_{o5} + 1)R_L}{r_{\pi 5} + (\beta_{o5} + 1)R_L}$

$r_{\pi 3} = \dfrac{50(0.025V)}{98.0\mu A} = 12.8k\Omega \ | \ r_{\pi 5} = \dfrac{50(0.025V)}{735\mu A} = 1.70k\Omega$

$\dfrac{(\beta_{o5} + 1)R_L}{r_{\pi 5} + (\beta_{o5} + 1)R_L} = \dfrac{51(2k\Omega)}{1.70k\Omega + 51(2k\Omega)} = 0.984$

$$A_{dm} = 40(49.5\mu A)(120k\Omega\|12.8k\Omega)\frac{(40)(98.0\mu A)}{2}\left(170k\Omega\|[1.70k\Omega + 51(2k\Omega)]\right)0.984 = 2840$$

$$R_{ID} = 2r_{\pi 1} = 2\frac{100(0.025V)}{49.5\mu A} = 101 \ k\Omega \ | \ R_O = \frac{R_{C2} + r_{\pi 5}}{\beta_{o5} + 1} = \frac{170 + 1.70}{51} k\Omega = 3.37 \ k\Omega$$

(c) For positive V_{IC}, $V_{IC} \le V_{C1} = 12.3V$ | For negative V_{IC}, the characteristics of I_1 will deterimine V_{IC}. For the ideal current source, the negative limit of V_{IC} is not defined.

(d) The actual voltage at the collector of Q_4 would be

$$V_{C4} = -18V + (I_{C4} + I_{B5})R_{C2} = -18V + \left(98.0\mu A + \frac{735\mu A}{50}\right)170k\Omega = 1.16V \text{ and } V_O = +1.86V$$

should be - 0.7V. The value of offset voltage required to bring the output back to zero is

$$V_{OS} = \frac{\Delta V_O}{A_V} = \frac{1.86V}{2840} = 0.655 \text{ mV}.$$

15.97

(a) $I_{C1} = I_{C2} = \alpha_F \dfrac{I_1}{2} = \dfrac{100}{101}\dfrac{70\mu A}{2} = 34.7\mu A$ | For $V_O = 0$: $I_{DS4} = I_{C3} = 1mA$

$V_{CE1} = +0.7 - (-5) = 5.7V$ | $V_{CE2} = +0.7 - (-5 + .7) = 5.0V$

$$V_{GS4} = V_P\left(1 - \sqrt{\frac{I_{DS4}}{I_{DSS4}}}\right) = -5\left(1 - \sqrt{\frac{1mA}{5mA}}\right) = -2.76V \ | \ V_{CE3} = -V_{GS4} = 2.76V$$

$V_{DS4} = V_O - (-V_{EE} - V_{GS4}) = 0 - (-5 + 2.76) = 2.24V$

$Q = pts: (34.7\mu A, 5.70V) (34.7\mu A, 5.00V) (1.00mA, 2.76V) (1.00mA, 2.24V)$

(b) $A_{dm} = \dfrac{g_{m2}}{2}(R_C\|r_{\pi 3})g_{m3}R_O = \dfrac{g_{m2}}{2}(R_C\|r_{\pi 3})g_{m3}(R_2\|\mu_{f4}r_{o3})$ | $r_{\pi 3} = \dfrac{100(0.025V)}{34.7\mu A} = 72.1k\Omega$

$$R_C = \frac{V_{BE3}}{I_{C2} - I_{B3}} = \frac{0.7V}{(34.7 - 10.0)\mu A} = 28.3 \ k\Omega \ | \ r_{o3} = \frac{50V + 2.76V}{1mA} = 52.8k\Omega$$

$$\mu_{f4} = g_{m4}r_{o4} = \left(\frac{2}{5}\sqrt{1mA(5mA)}\right)\left(\frac{50V + 2.24V}{1mA}\right) = 46.7$$

$$A_{dm} = \frac{40(34.7 \times 10^{-6})}{2}(28.3 \ k\Omega\|72.1k\Omega)(40)(0.001)[5M\Omega\|(46.7)(52.8k\Omega)] = 9.31 \times 10^5 \ !$$

$$R_{ID} = 2r_{\pi 1} = 2\frac{100(0.025V)}{34.7\mu A} = 144 \ k\Omega \ | \ R_O = R_2\|\mu_{f4}r_{o3} = 5M\Omega\|(46.7)(52.8k\Omega) = 1.65 \ M\Omega$$

15.98

(a) $I_{C1} = I_{C2} = \alpha_F \dfrac{I_1}{2} = \dfrac{100}{101}\dfrac{200\mu A}{2} = 99.0\mu A$ | For $V_O = 0$: $I_{C3} = \alpha_F I_{E3} = \dfrac{100}{101}\dfrac{12V}{12k\Omega} = 990\mu A$

$V_{CE3} = 12V - 0V = 12.0V$ | $V_{CE2} = +0.7 - (-0.7) = 1.4V$

$$R_C = \frac{12V - 0.7V}{I_{C2} + I_{B3}} = \frac{0.7V}{(99.0 + 9.90)\mu A} = 104 \ k\Omega \ | \ V_{CE1} = 12 - 99.0\mu A(104k\Omega) - (-0.7) = 2.40V$$

Q - points: $(99.0\mu A, 2.40V) (99.0\mu A, 1.40V) (990\mu A, 12V)$

(b) $A_{dm} = \dfrac{g_{m2}}{2}\left(R_C \| \left[r_{\pi 3} + (\beta_{o3}+1)R\right]\right)\dfrac{(\beta_{o3}+1)R}{r_{\pi 3}+(\beta_{o3}+1)R}$ $\quad | \quad r_{\pi 3} = \dfrac{100(0.025V)}{990\mu A} = 2.53k\Omega$

$A_{dm} = \dfrac{40(99.0\mu A)}{2}\left(104k\Omega\|2.53k\Omega + (101)12k\Omega\right)\dfrac{(101)12k\Omega}{2.53k\Omega + (101)12k\Omega} = 189$

$R_{ID} = 2r_{\pi 1} = 2\dfrac{100(0.025V)}{99.0\mu A} = 50.5\ k\Omega$ $\quad | \quad R_O = \dfrac{R_C + r_{\pi 3}}{\beta_{o3}+1} = \dfrac{104k\Omega + 2.53k\Omega}{101} = 1.06\ k\Omega$

15.99

$300k\Omega = 2r_{\pi 1} \rightarrow I_{C1} = 2\dfrac{100(0.025V)}{300k\Omega} = 16.7\mu A$ For $V_O = 0$, $V_{C1} = 0.7V$

$R_C = \dfrac{12-0.7}{I_{C1}+I_{B3}} \cong \dfrac{11.3V}{I_{C1}} = \dfrac{11.3V}{16.7\mu A} = 677k\Omega$ $\quad | \quad R_O = \dfrac{R_C + r_{\pi 3}}{\beta_{o3}+1} \geq \dfrac{677k\Omega}{101} = 6.7k\Omega$

The R_O specification cannot be meet if the R_{ID} specification is met and vice - versa.
Either R_{ID} must be reduced or R_O must be increased, or both must be changed.

15.100

$1M\Omega = 2r_{\pi 1} \rightarrow I_{C1} = 2\dfrac{100(0.025V)}{1M\Omega} = 5.00\mu A$ $\quad | \quad$ For $V_O = 0$, $V_{C1} = 0.7V$

$R_C = \dfrac{9-0.7}{I_{C1}+I_{B3}} \cong \dfrac{8.3V}{I_{C1}} = \dfrac{8.3V}{5.00\mu A} = 1.66M\Omega$ $\quad | \quad R_O = \dfrac{R_C + r_{\pi 3}}{\beta_{o3}+1} \geq \dfrac{1.66M\Omega}{101} = 16.4k\Omega$

The R_O specification cannot be meet if the R_{ID} specification is met and vice - versa.
Either R_{ID} must be reduced or R_O must be increased, or both must be changed.

15.101

(a) For $V_O = 0$, $I_{C6} = \alpha_F I_{E6} = \alpha_F I_3 = \dfrac{100}{101}5mA = 4.95mA$

$I_{C5} = \alpha_F I_{E5} = \alpha_F \dfrac{I_{C6}}{\beta_{F6}} = \dfrac{4.95mA}{101} = 49.0\mu A$ $\quad | \quad I_{C4} + I_{C3} = I_2 + I_{B5} = 500\mu A + \dfrac{49.0\mu A}{100} = 500\mu A$

$\beta_{F4}\dfrac{I_{C3}}{\alpha_{F3}} + I_{C3} = (\beta_{F3}+2)I_{C3} = 500\mu A \rightarrow I_{C3} = 9.62\mu A$ $\quad | \quad I_{C4} = 500\mu A - I_{C3} = 490\mu A$

$I_{C1} = I_{C2} = \alpha_F \dfrac{I_1}{2} = \dfrac{100}{101}\dfrac{50\mu A}{2} = 24.8\mu A$ $\quad | \quad V_{CE6} = 18 - 0 = 18V$ $\quad | \quad V_{CE5} = V_{CE6} - V_{BE6} = 17.3V$

$V_{EC4} = 18 - V_{BE5} - V_{BE6} = 16.6V$ $\quad | \quad V_{EC3} = V_{EC4} - V_{EB4} = 15.9V$

$V_{CE1} = V_{CE2} = 18 - V_{EB4} - V_{EB3} - (-V_{EB2}) = 17.3V$

$Q-pts: (24.8\mu A, 17.3V)\ (24.8\mu A, 17.3V)\ (9.62\mu A, 15.9V)\ (490\mu A, 16.6V)$

$(49.0\mu A, 17.3V)\ (4.95mA, 18.0V)$ $\quad | \quad R_C = \dfrac{1.4V}{I_{C2}-I_{B3}} = \dfrac{1.4V}{\left(24.8 + \dfrac{9.62}{50}\right)\mu A} = 56.9k\Omega$

(b) Using the properties of the Darlington configuration (Eq. 15.54):

Note that the correct expressions are: $r_o' = \dfrac{2}{3}r_{o2}$ and $\mu_f' = \dfrac{\mu_{f2}}{3}$

$A_{dm} = \dfrac{g_{m2}}{2}\left(R_C\|R_{IN3}\right)\dfrac{g_{m4}}{2}\left(\dfrac{2}{3}r_{o4}\|R_{IN5}\right)\dfrac{\beta_{o5}\beta_{o6}R_L}{2r_{\pi 5} + \beta_{o5}\beta_{o6}R_L}$

$$R_{IN3} \cong 2\beta_{o3}r_{\pi4} = 2(50)\frac{50(0.025V)}{490\mu A} = 255k\Omega$$

$$R_{IN5} \cong 2\beta_{o5}r_{\pi6} + \beta_{o5}\beta_{o6}R_L = 2(100)\frac{100(0.025V)}{4.95mA} + 100(100)(2k\Omega) = 20.1M\Omega$$

$$R_{IN5} >> r_{o4} = \frac{70V+16.6V}{490\mu A} = 177k\Omega \quad | \quad A_{dm} = \frac{40(24.8\mu A)}{2}\left(56.9k\Omega\|255k\Omega\right)\frac{\mu_{f4}}{3}\frac{20M\Omega}{20.1M\Omega}$$

$$\frac{\mu_{f4}}{3} = \frac{40(70+11.6)}{3} = 1155 \quad | \quad A_{dm} = 26500 \; (88.5dB) \quad | \quad R_{ID} = 2r_{\pi1} = 2\frac{100(0.025V)}{24.8\mu A} = 202\ k\Omega$$

$$R_O = \frac{R_{th5}+2r_{\pi5}}{\beta_{o5}\beta_{o6}} = \frac{\frac{2}{3}r_{o4}+2r_{\pi5}}{\beta_{o5}\beta_{o6}} = \frac{\frac{2}{3}118k\Omega + 2\frac{100(0.025V)}{49.0\mu A}}{100(100)} = 18.1\ \Omega$$

15.102

(a) For $V_O = 0$, $I_{C6} = \alpha_F I_{E6} = \alpha_F I_3 = \frac{100}{101}5mA = 4.95mA$

$$I_{C5} = \alpha_F I_{E5} = \alpha_F \frac{I_{C6}}{\beta_{F6}} = \frac{4.95mA}{101} = 49.0\mu A \quad | \quad I_{C4} + I_{C3} = I_2 + I_{B5} = 500\mu A + \frac{49.0\mu A}{100} = 500\mu A$$

$$\beta_{F4}\frac{I_{C3}}{\alpha_{F3}} + I_{C3} = (\beta_{F3}+2)I_{C3} = 500\mu A \rightarrow I_{C3} = 9.62\mu A \quad | \quad I_{C4} = 500\mu A - I_{C3} = 490\mu A$$

$$I_{C1} = I_{C2} = \alpha_F\frac{I_1}{2} = \frac{100}{101}\frac{50\mu A}{2} = 24.8\mu A \quad | \quad V_{CE6} = 22-0 = 22V \quad | \quad V_{CE5} = V_{CE6} - V_{BE6} = 21.3V$$

$$V_{EC4} = 22 - V_{BE5} - V_{BE6} = 20.6V \quad | \quad V_{EC3} = V_{EC4} - V_{EB4} = 19.9V$$

$$V_{CE1} = V_{CE2} = 22 - V_{EB4} - V_{EB3} - (-V_{EB2}) = 21.3V$$

Q $-$ pts: $(24.8\mu A, 21.3V)$ $(24.8\mu A, 21.3V)$ $(9.62\mu A, 19.9V)$ $(490\mu A, 20.6V)$

$$(49.0\mu A, 21.3V) \; (4.95mA, 22.0V) \quad | \quad R_C = \frac{1.4V}{I_{C2}-I_{B3}} = \frac{1.4V}{\left(24.8+\frac{9.62}{50}\right)\mu A} = 56.9k\Omega$$

(b) Using the properties of the Darlington configuration (Eq. 15.54):

Note that the correct expressions are: $r_o' = \frac{2}{3}r_{o2}$ and $\mu_f' = \frac{\mu_{f2}}{3}$

$$A_{dm} = A_{V1}A_{V2}A_{V3} = \left[\frac{g_{m2}}{2}\left(R_C\|R_{IN3}\right)\right]\left[\frac{g_{m4}}{2}\left(\frac{2}{3}r_{o4}\|R_{IN5}\right)\right]\left[\frac{\beta_{o5}\beta_{o6}R_L}{2r_{\pi5}+\beta_{o5}\beta_{o6}R_L}\right]$$

$$R_{IN3} \cong 2\beta_{o3}r_{\pi4} = 2(50)\frac{50(0.025V)}{490\mu A} = 255k\Omega$$

$$R_{IN5} \cong 2\beta_{o5}r_{\pi6} + \beta_{o5}\beta_{o6}R_L = 2(100)\frac{100(0.025V)}{4.95mA} + 100(100)(2k\Omega) = 20.1M\Omega$$

$$R_{IN5} >> r_{o4} = \frac{70V+20.6V}{490\mu A} = 185k\Omega \quad | \quad A_{dm} = \frac{40(24.8\mu A)}{2}\left(56.9k\Omega\|255k\Omega\right)\frac{\mu_{f4}}{3}\frac{20M\Omega}{20.1M\Omega}$$

$$\frac{\mu_{f4}}{3} = \frac{40(70+20.6)}{3} = 1208 \quad | \quad A_{dm} = 27700 \; (88.9dB) \quad | \quad R_{ID} = 2r_{\pi1} = 2\frac{100(0.025V)}{24.8\mu A} = 202\ k\Omega$$

$$R_O = \frac{R_{th5}+2r_{\pi5}}{\beta_{o5}\beta_{o6}} = \frac{\frac{2}{3}r_{o4}+2r_{\pi5}}{\beta_{o5}\beta_{o6}} = \frac{\frac{2}{3}185k\Omega + 2\frac{100(0.025V)}{49.0\mu A}}{100(100)} = 22.5\ \Omega$$

15.103

Since the transistor parameters are the same, $V_{GS1} = V_{SG2} = \dfrac{2.2V}{2} = 1.1V$

$$I_{SD2} = I_{DS1} = \frac{6\times10^{-4}}{2}(1.1-0.75)^2 = 36.8 \ \mu A$$

15.104

$$2.2V = V_{GS1} + V_{SG2} = V_{TN} + \sqrt{\frac{2I_{DS1}}{K_n}} - V_{TP} + \sqrt{\frac{2I_{SD2}}{K_p}} \quad \text{where} \quad I_{SD2} = I_{DS1}$$

$$2.2 = 0.7 + 0.8 + \sqrt{I_{DS1}}\left(\sqrt{\frac{2}{6\times10^{-4}}} + \sqrt{\frac{2}{4\times10^{-4}}}\right) \ | \ \sqrt{I_{DS1}} = \frac{0.7}{128.5} \rightarrow I_{SD2} = I_{DS1} = 29.7 \mu A$$

15.105

Since the values of I_S and I_E are the same, $V_{BE1} = V_{EB2}$

$$1.35 = V_{BE1} + V_{EB2} = 2V_T \ln\frac{I_C}{I_S} \ | \ I_C = 10^{-15}\exp\frac{1.35}{2(0.025V)} = 196 \ \mu A$$

15.106

$$1.35 = V_{BE1} + V_{EB2} = V_T \ln\frac{I_C}{I_{S1}} + V_T \ln\frac{I_C}{I_{S2}} = V_T \ln\frac{I_C^2}{I_{S1}I_{S2}}$$

$$I_C = \sqrt{\left(5\times10^{-15}\right)\left(10^{-15}\right)}\exp\frac{1.35}{0.025} = 438 \ \mu A$$

15.107

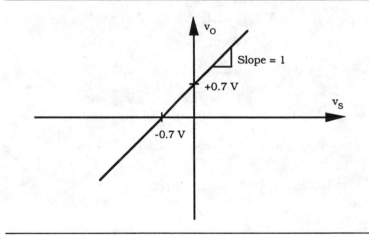

15.108

```
*Problem 15.108
VCC 3 0 DC 10
VEE 5 0 DC -10
VBB 2 1 DC 1.3
VS 1 0 DC 0
Q1 3 2 4 NBJT
Q2 5 1 4 PBJT
RL 4 0 1K
.MODEL NBJT NPN IS=5FA BF=60
.MODEL PBJT PNP IS=1FA BF=50
.OP
.DC VS -10 +8.7 0.01
.PROBE
```

.END

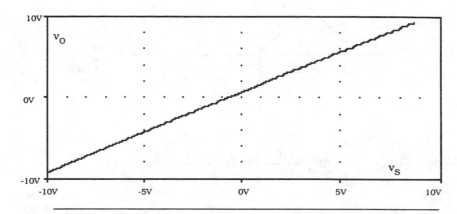

15.109

Since the base currents are zero $(\beta_F = \infty)$, $V_{BE1} + V_{EB2} = (250\mu A)(5k\Omega) = 1.25V$

$$1.25V = V_T \ln \frac{I_C}{I_{S1}} + V_T \ln \frac{I_C}{I_{S2}} = V_T \ln \frac{I_C^2}{I_{S1}I_{S2}} \quad | \quad I_C = \sqrt{(10^{-15})(10^{-16}) \exp \frac{1.25}{0.025}} = 22.8 \ \mu A$$

15.110

$$V_{GS1} + V_{SG2} = (0.5mA)(4k\Omega) = 2.00V \quad | \quad 2.00V = V_{TN} + \sqrt{\frac{2I_{DS1}}{K_n}} - V_{TP} + \sqrt{\frac{2I_{SD2}}{K_p}} \quad | \quad I_{SD2} = I_{DS1}$$

$$2.00 = 0.75 + 0.75 + \sqrt{I_{DS1}}\left(\sqrt{\frac{2}{5x10^{-4}}} + \sqrt{\frac{2}{2x10^{-4}}}\right) \quad | \quad \sqrt{I_{DS1}} = \frac{0.5}{163.3} \rightarrow I_{SD2} = I_{DS1} = 9.38 \ \mu A$$

15.111

$$I_S \geq \frac{5V}{R_L} = \frac{5V}{1k\Omega} = 5.00mA \quad | \quad i_S = I_S + i_s$$

$$i_S^{max} = I_S + \frac{5V}{1k\Omega} = I_S + 5.00mA \quad | \quad i_S^{min} = I_S - \frac{5V}{1k\Omega} = I_S - 5.00mA$$

For $I_S = 5.00mA$, $i_S^{max} = 10.0mA$ | $i_S^{min} = 0$ | $i_{DS} = 0.005(1 + \sin 2000\pi t)$ A

Power delivered from the supplies: $P(t) = 10V(i_{DS}) + 10V(I_S) = 0.05(2 + \sin 2000\pi t)$ W

$$P_{av} = \frac{1}{T}\int_0^T 0.05(2 + \sin 2000\pi t)dt = 100mW$$

Signal power developed in R_L: $P_{ac} = \left(\frac{5}{\sqrt{2}}\right)^2 \frac{1}{1k\Omega} = 12.5mW \quad | \quad \eta = 100\% \frac{12.5mW}{100mW} = 12.5\%$

15.112

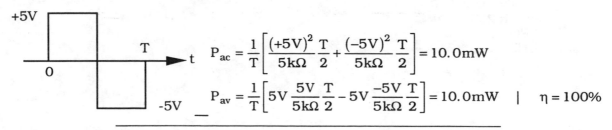

$$P_{ac} = \frac{1}{T}\left[\frac{(+5V)^2}{5k\Omega}\frac{T}{2} + \frac{(-5V)^2}{5k\Omega}\frac{T}{2}\right] = 10.0mW$$

$$P_{av} = \frac{1}{T}\left[5V\frac{5V}{5k\Omega}\frac{T}{2} - 5V\frac{-5V}{5k\Omega}\frac{T}{2}\right] = 10.0mW \quad | \quad \eta = 100\%$$

15.113

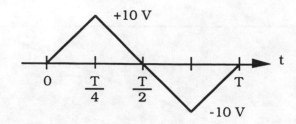

$$P_{ac} = \frac{1}{T}\int_0^T \frac{v^2(t)}{R}\,dt = \frac{4}{T}\int_0^{\frac{T}{4}} \frac{\left(\frac{40t}{T}\right)^2}{R}\,dt = \frac{6400}{T^3R}\int_0^{\frac{T}{4}} t^2\,dt = \frac{100}{3R}$$

$$P_{av} = \frac{1}{T}\int_0^T 10i(t)\,dt = \frac{20}{T}\int_0^{\frac{T}{2}} i(t)\,dt = \frac{40}{T}\int_0^{\frac{T}{4}} \frac{40t}{TR}\,dt = \frac{1600}{T^2R}\int_0^{\frac{T}{4}} t\,dt = \frac{50}{R} \quad | \quad \eta = 100\%\frac{\frac{100}{3R}}{\frac{50}{R}} = 66.7\%$$

15.114

```
*Problem 15.114(a) VBB = 0 V
VCC 3 0 DC 10
VEE 5 0 DC -10
VBB 2 1 DC 0
VS 1 0 DC 0 SIN(0 4 2000)
Q1 3 2 4 NBJT
Q2 5 1 4 PBJT
RL 4 0 2K
.MODEL NBJT NPN IS=5FA BF=60
.MODEL PBJT PNP IS=1FA BF=50
.OP
.TRAN 1U 2M
.FOUR 2000 V(4)
.PROBE
.END
*Problem 15.114(b) VBB = 1.3 V
VCC 3 0 DC 10
VEE 5 0 DC -10
VBB 2 1 DC 1.3
VS 1 0 DC 0 SIN(0 4 2000)
Q1 3 2 4 NBJT
Q2 5 1 4 PBJT
RL 4 0 2K
.MODEL NBJT NPN IS=5FA BF=60
.MODEL PBJT PNP IS=1FA BF=50
.OP
.TRAN 1U 2M
.FOUR 2000 V(4)
.PROBE
.END
```

HARMONIC NO	FREQUENCY (HZ)	FOURIER COMPONENT	NORMALIZED COMPONENT	PHASE (DEG)	NORMALIZED PHASE (DEG)
1	2.000E+03	3.056E+00	1.000E+00	-4.347E-01	0.000E+00
2	4.000E+03	2.693E-02	8.811E-03	-1.300E+02	-1.296E+02
3	6.000E+03	2.112E-01	6.910E-02	-1.744E+02	-1.740E+02
4	8.000E+03	3.473E-02	1.136E-02	-1.550E+02	-1.545E+02
5	1.000E+04	7.718E-02	2.525E-02	-1.678E+02	-1.674E+02
6	1.200E+04	4.064E-02	1.330E-02	-1.679E+02	-1.675E+02
7	1.400E+04	3.179E-02	1.040E-02	-1.580E+02	-1.576E+02
8	1.600E+04	4.109E-02	1.345E-02	-1.736E+02	-1.731E+02
9	1.800E+04	2.127E-02	6.960E-03	-1.568E+02	-1.564E+02

TOTAL HARMONIC DISTORTION =   7.831458E+00 PERCENT

HARMONIC NO	FREQUENCY (HZ)	FOURIER COMPONENT	NORMALIZED COMPONENT	PHASE (DEG)	NORMALIZED PHASE (DEG)
1	2.000E+03	3.853E+00	1.000E+00	2.544E-01	0.000E+00
2	4.000E+03	1.221E-02	3.169E-03	6.765E+01	6.740E+01
3	6.000E+03	1.537E-02	3.990E-03	9.046E+01	9.020E+01
4	8.000E+03	1.504E-02	3.903E-03	5.520E+01	5.495E+01
5	1.000E+04	1.501E-02	3.897E-03	5.500E+01	5.475E+01
6	1.200E+04	1.531E-02	3.973E-03	4.231E+01	4.206E+01
7	1.400E+04	1.435E-02	3.726E-03	3.680E+01	3.654E+01
8	1.600E+04	1.467E-02	3.807E-03	2.823E+01	2.798E+01
9	1.800E+04	1.382E-02	3.587E-03	2.087E+01	2.062E+01

TOTAL HARMONIC DISTORTION =   1.064939E+00 PERCENT

15.115

The current begins to limit at $i_E = \dfrac{V_{BE2}}{R} = \dfrac{0.7V}{10\Omega} = 70.0$ mA.

$$v_S = 1000i_B + V_{BE1} + V_{BE2} + 250i_E = 1000\frac{0.07}{101} + 0.7 + 0.7 + 250(0.07) = 19.6 \text{ V}$$

15.116 Note: The current limiting will be much more dramatic if R_1 is increased to 10kΩ.

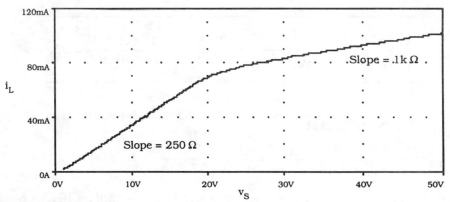

```
*Problem 15.116
VCC 3 0 DC 50
VS 1 0 DC 1
R1 1 2 1K
Q1 3 2 4 NBJT
```

```
Q2 2 4 5 NBJT
R 4 5 10
RL 5 0 250
.MODEL NBJT NPN IS=1FA BF=100
.OP
.DC VS 1 50 .05
.PROBE
.END
```

15.117

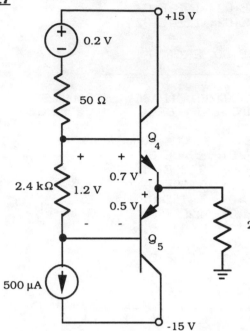

For $V_{BE4} = 0.7V$, $V_{EB5} = I_2R_B - V_{BE4}$

$V_{EB5} = 1.2 - 0.7 = 0.5V$ and Q_5 is off.

$V_{EQ} = 15 - 0.2 - 500\mu A(50\Omega) = 14.8V$

$R_{EQ} = 50\Omega$

$I_{C4} = 100\dfrac{(14.8 - 0.7)V}{50\Omega + 101(2k\Omega)} = 6.98\ mA$

15.118

$$I_2 R_G = V_{GS4} - V_{SG5} \mid (0.25mA)(7k\Omega) = V_{TN4} + \sqrt{\dfrac{2I_{DS4}}{0.005}} - V_{TP5} + \sqrt{\dfrac{2I_{SD5}}{0.002}} \mid I_{SD5} = I_{DS4}$$

$$1.75 - 0.75 - 0.75 = \sqrt{I_{DS4}}\left(\sqrt{\dfrac{2}{0.005}} + \sqrt{\dfrac{2}{0.002}}\right) \rightarrow I_{SD5} = I_{DS4} = 23.5\ \mu A$$

15.119

$$R_{OUT} = \dfrac{1}{n^2}\dfrac{r_\pi}{\beta_o + 1} = \dfrac{1}{100}\dfrac{\beta_o}{\beta_o + 1}\dfrac{V_T}{I_C} = \dfrac{1}{100}\dfrac{V_T}{I_E} = \dfrac{1}{100}\dfrac{0.025V}{10mA} = 25.0\ m\Omega$$

15.120

$$I_C = 100 I_B = 100\dfrac{9 - 0.7}{200k\Omega + 101(82k\Omega)}\dfrac{V}{\Omega} = 97.9\ \mu A \mid \text{Looking back into the}$$

transformer: $R_{th} = \dfrac{1}{n^2}\left(\dfrac{r_\pi}{\beta_o + 1}\right) \mid \dfrac{r_\pi}{\beta_o + 1} = \dfrac{1}{101}\dfrac{100(0.025V)}{97.9\mu A} = 253\Omega$

Desire to match the Thevenin equivalent resistance to R_L: $\dfrac{1}{n^2}253\Omega = 10\Omega \rightarrow n = 5.03$

$$\mathbf{v_{th}} = \dfrac{(\beta_o + 1)n^2 R_L}{r_\pi + (\beta_o + 1)n^2 R_L}\mathbf{v_s} = \dfrac{(101)253}{25.6k\Omega + (101)253}\mathbf{v_s} = 0.500\mathbf{v_s} \mid \text{Using the ideal transformer}$$

relationships: $\mathbf{v_{th}} = \mathbf{i_1}R_{th} + n\mathbf{v_o}$ | $\mathbf{i_1} = \dfrac{1}{n}\mathbf{i_2} = \dfrac{1}{n}\dfrac{\mathbf{v_o}}{R_L}$ | $\mathbf{v_{th}} = \dfrac{1}{n}\dfrac{\mathbf{v_o}}{R_L}R_{th} + n\mathbf{v_o}$

$$\mathbf{v_o} = \dfrac{\mathbf{v_{th}}}{n + \dfrac{R_{th}}{nR_L}} \quad | \quad \mathbf{v_o} = \dfrac{0.500\mathbf{v_s}}{5.03 + \dfrac{253\Omega}{5.03(10\Omega)}} = 0.0497\mathbf{v_s} \quad | \quad v_o = 0.0497\sin 2000\pi t$$

$$P_o = \left(\dfrac{0.0497}{\sqrt{2}}\right)^2 \dfrac{1}{10} = 0.124 \text{ mW}$$

15.121

$$V_{EQ} = -12V \dfrac{2M\Omega}{2M\Omega + 2M\Omega} = -6V \quad | \quad R_{EQ} = 2M\Omega \| 2M\Omega = 1M\Omega$$

$$I_O = 100 I_B = 100 \dfrac{-6 - 0.7 - (-12)}{1M\Omega + 101(220k\Omega)}\dfrac{V}{\Omega} = 22.8 \ \mu A \quad | \quad r_\pi = \dfrac{100(0.025V)}{22.8\mu A} = 110k\Omega$$

$$V_{CE} = 12 - I_E(220k\Omega) = 12 - \dfrac{101}{100}(22.8\mu A)(220k\Omega) = 6.93V \quad | \quad r_o = \dfrac{(50 + 6.93)V}{22.8\mu A} = 2.50M\Omega$$

$$R_{OUT} = r_o\left(1 + \dfrac{\beta_o R_E}{R_{th} + r_\pi + R_E}\right) = 110k\Omega\left(1 + \dfrac{100(220k\Omega)}{1M\Omega + 110k\Omega + 220k\Omega}\right) = 43.9 \ M\Omega$$

15.122

The dc analysis is the same as Problem 15.121. However, the bypass capacitor provides as ac ground at the base of the transistor so that $R_{th} = 0$.

$$R_{OUT} = r_o\left(1 + \dfrac{\beta_o R_E}{r_\pi + R_E}\right) = 110k\Omega\left(1 + \dfrac{100(220k\Omega)}{110k\Omega + 220k\Omega}\right) = 169 \ M\Omega$$

15.123

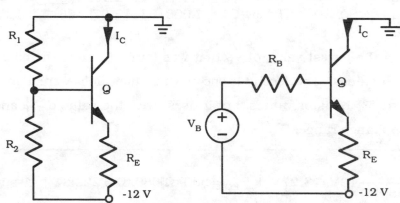

A spread sheet will be used to assist in this design using $\beta_F = \beta_o = 100$ & $V_A = 70V$
The maximum current in the two bias resistors is $0.2mA$. To allow
some room for tolerances, choose $I_1 \cong 0.15mA$. Neglecting the transistor base current,

$$R_1 + R_2 = \dfrac{12V}{0.15mA} = 80k\Omega \quad | \quad R_2 = \dfrac{V_B}{12}(R_1 + R_2) = \dfrac{V_B}{12}80k\Omega \quad | \quad R_B = R_1 \| R_2$$

$$I_C = 100\dfrac{(V_B - 0.7)}{R_B + 101R_E} \quad \text{or} \quad R_E = \dfrac{1}{101}\left(\dfrac{100(V_B - 0.7)}{I_C} - R_B\right) \quad | \quad V_{CE} = 12 - I_E R_E$$

$$r_o = \dfrac{70 + V_{CE}}{I_C} \quad | \quad R_{OUT} = r_o\left(1 + \dfrac{\beta_o R_E}{R_B + r_\pi + R_E}\right)$$

Now, a spreadsheet MATLAB, MATHCAD, etc. can be used to explore the design space with V_B as the primary design variable.

V_B	R_2	R_1	R_B	R_E	r_O	R_{out}	
0.500	3.33E+03	7.67E+04	3.19E+03	-2.30E+02	-1.74E+05	5.57E+05	
0.600	4.00E+03	7.60E+04	3.80E+03	-1.37E+02	-8.00E+04	9.73E+04	
0.700	4.67E+03	7.53E+04	4.39E+03	-4.35E+01	1.41E+04	5.13E+03	
0.800	5.33E+03	7.47E+04	4.98E+03	4.97E+01	1.08E+05	1.80E+05	
0.900	6.00E+03	7.40E+04	5.55E+03	1.43E+02	2.03E+05	5.56E+05	
1.000	6.67E+03	7.33E+04	6.11E+03	2.37E+02	2.97E+05	1.09E+06	
1.100	7.33E+03	7.27E+04	6.66E+03	3.30E+02	3.91E+05	1.75E+06	
1.200	8.00E+03	7.20E+04	7.20E+03	4.24E+02	4.86E+05	2.52E+06	
1.300	8.67E+03	7.13E+04	7.73E+03	5.18E+02	5.81E+05	3.38E+06	
1.400	9.33E+03	7.07E+04	8.24E+03	6.11E+02	6.76E+05	4.31E+06	
1.500	1.00E+04	7.00E+04	8.75E+03	7.05E+02	7.71E+05	5.32E+06	
1.600	1.07E+04	6.93E+04	9.24E+03	8.00E+02	8.66E+05	6.38E+06	
1.700	1.13E+04	6.87E+04	9.73E+03	8.94E+02	9.61E+05	7.50E+06	
1.800	1.20E+04	6.80E+04	1.02E+04	9.88E+02	1.06E+06	8.68E+06	
1.900	1.27E+04	6.73E+04	1.07E+04	1.08E+03	1.15E+06	9.90E+06	
2.000	1.33E+04	6.67E+04	1.11E+04	1.18E+03	1.25E+06	1.12E+07	
	Two possible solutions						IO
0.916	6.20E+03	7.50E+04	5.73E+03	1.50E+02	2.10E+05	5.85E+05	1.04E-03
1.800	1.20E+04	6.80E+04	1.02E+04	1.00E+03	1.07E+06	8.86E+06	9.89E-04

The first solution is the lowest value of V_B that was found to meet the output specification using the nearest 5% values. The second is one in which the values were found to be very close to existing standard 5% resistor values, but it uses twice the value of V_B and has a smaller output voltage compliance range.

15.124

$$V_{EQ} = \frac{330k\Omega}{330k\Omega + 680k\Omega} 10V = 3.27V \quad | \quad R_{EQ} = 330k\Omega \| 680k\Omega = 222k\Omega \quad | \quad \text{Assume saturation:}$$

$$V_{GS} = 3.27 - (30k\Omega)I_{DS} = 3.27 - \left(\frac{5x10^{-4}}{2}\right)(V_{GS} - 1)^2 \Rightarrow V_{GS} = 1.488V \quad | \quad I_O = I_{DS} = 59.4 \ \mu A$$

$$V_{DS} = 10 - (30k\Omega)I_{DS} = 8.22V \quad | \quad r_o = \frac{100 + 8.22}{59.4} \frac{V}{\mu A} = 1.82 \ M\Omega$$

$$g_m = \sqrt{2(5x10^{-4})(59.4x10^{-6})[1 + (0.01)8.22]} = 0.254 \ mS$$

$$R_{OUT} = r_o[1 + g_m(3x10^4)] = 1.82M\Omega[1 + 0.254mS(30k\Omega)] = 16.0 \ M\Omega$$

15.125

$$V_{EQ} = 15V \frac{200k\Omega}{200k\Omega + 100k\Omega} = 10V \quad | \quad R_{EQ} = 200k\Omega \| 100k\Omega = 66.7k\Omega$$

$$I_O = 75I_B = 75\frac{15 - 0.7 - 10}{66.7k\Omega + 76(43k\Omega)}\frac{V}{\Omega} = 96.7\ \mu A \quad | \quad r_\pi = \frac{75(0.025V)}{96.7\mu A} = 19.4k\Omega$$

$$V_{EC} = 15 - I_E R_E = 15 - \frac{76}{75}(96.7\ \mu A)(43k\Omega) = 10.8V \quad | \quad r_o = \frac{(50 + 10.8)V}{96.7\mu A} = 629k\Omega$$

$$R_{OUT} = r_o\left(1 + \frac{\beta_o R_E}{R_{th} + r_\pi + R_E}\right) = 629k\Omega\left(1 + \frac{75(43k\Omega)}{66.7k\Omega + 19.4k\Omega + 43k\Omega}\right) = 16.3\ M\Omega$$

15.126

$$V_{EQ} = 9V \frac{2M\Omega}{2M\Omega + 1M\Omega} = 6V \quad | \quad R_{EQ} = 2M\Omega \| 1M\Omega = 667k\Omega \quad | \quad 9 - 10^5 I_{SD} - V_{SG} = 6$$

$$V_{SG} = -V_{TP} + \sqrt{\frac{2I_{SD}}{K_p}} \quad | \quad 10^5 I_{SD} = 3 - \left(0.75 + \sqrt{\frac{2I_{SD}}{7.5x10^{-4}}}\right) \Rightarrow I_O = I_{SD} = 20.2\ \mu A$$

$$V_{SD} = 9 - 10^5 I_{SD} = 6.98V \quad | \quad r_o = \frac{100 + 6.98}{20.2}\frac{V}{\mu A} = 5.30\ M\Omega$$

$$g_m = \sqrt{2(7.5x10^{-4})(20.2x10^{-6})[1 + 0.01(6.98)]} = 0.180mS$$

$$R_{OUT} = r_o(1 + g_m R_S) = [1 + 0.180mS(10^5)] = 5.30M\Omega(1 + 0.180mS(10^5)) = 101\ M\Omega$$

15.127

Estimating $R_{OUT} \cong r_o(1 + g_m R_5) \cong \frac{50V}{1.75x10^{-4}}\left(1 + \sqrt{2(2x10^{-4})(1.75x10^{-4})}R_5\right)$

Note that including λ in the g_m expression will increase R_{OUT} above this estimate. Hence neglecting it is a conservative simplification.

$$286k\Omega(1 + 2.65x10^{-4}R_E) \geq 2.5M\Omega \Rightarrow R_5 \geq 29.2k\Omega \quad | \quad \text{Choose } R_5 \cong 33k\Omega$$

$$V_G = V_{DD} - I_D R_5 - V_{SG} = 12 - 1.75x10^{-4}(3.3x10^4) - \left(1 + \sqrt{\frac{2(1.75x10^{-4})}{2x10^{-4}}}\right) = 3.90V$$

$$\frac{R_4}{R_3 + R_4}12 = 3.90 \quad | \quad I_2 \leq 25\mu A \quad | \quad \text{Assign } I_2 = 20\mu A \quad | \quad R_3 + R_4 = \frac{12V}{20\mu A} = 600k\Omega$$

$$R_4 = \frac{3.90}{12}(R_3 + R_4) = 195k\Omega \Rightarrow R_4 = 200k\Omega \quad | \quad R_3 = 430k\Omega$$

15.128

$$V_{EQ} = -12V \frac{68k\Omega}{68k\Omega + 33k\Omega} = -8.08V \quad | \quad R_{EQ} = 68k\Omega \| 33k\Omega = 22.2k\Omega \quad | \quad V_B = -8.08 - (I_{B1} + I_{B2})R_{TH}$$

$$V_B = -8.08 - \left(\frac{V_B - 0.7 - (-12)}{126(20k\Omega)} + \frac{V_B - 0.7 - (-12)}{126(100k\Omega)}\right)22.2k\Omega \rightarrow V_B = -8.11V$$

$$I_{C1} = \alpha_F I_{E1} = \frac{125}{126}\left(\frac{V_B - 0.7 - (-12)}{20k\Omega}\right) = 158\ \mu A \quad | \quad I_{C2} = \alpha_F I_{E2} = \frac{125}{126}\left(\frac{V_B - 0.7 - (-12)}{100k\Omega}\right) = 31.7\ \mu A$$

$$V_{CE} = 0 - (-8.11 - 0.7) = 8.87V \quad | \quad r_{o1} = \frac{(50 + 8.11)V}{158\mu A} = 368k\Omega \quad | \quad R_{th1} = R_{EQ}\|[r_{\pi 2} + (\beta_o + 1)(100k\Omega)]$$

$$r_{\pi 1} = \frac{125(0.025V)}{158\ \mu A} = 19.8k\Omega \quad | \quad r_{\pi 2} = \frac{125(0.025V)}{31.7\mu A} = 98.6k\Omega$$

$$R_{th1} = 22.2k\Omega \| [98.6k\Omega + (126)(100k\Omega)] = 22.2k\Omega$$

$$R_{OUT1} = r_{o1}\left(1 + \frac{\beta_o R_E}{R_{th} + r_{\pi 1} + R_E}\right) = 368k\Omega\left(1 + \frac{125(20k\Omega)}{22.2k\Omega + 19.8k\Omega + 20k\Omega}\right) = 15.2\ M\Omega$$

$$r_{o2} = \frac{(50 + 8.11)V}{31.7\mu A} = 1.83M\Omega \quad | \quad R_{th2} = R_{TH} \| [r_{\pi 1} + (\beta_o + 1)(20k\Omega)]$$

$$R_{th2} = 22.2k\Omega \| [19.8k\Omega + (126)(20k\Omega)] = 22.0k\Omega$$

$$R_{OUT2} = r_{o2}\left(1 + \frac{\beta_o R_E}{R_{th} + r_{\pi 2} + R_E}\right) = 1.83M\Omega\left(1 + \frac{125(100k\Omega)}{22.0k\Omega + 98.6k\Omega + 100k\Omega}\right) = 106\ M\Omega$$

15.129

$$V_{EQ} = -15V\frac{390k\Omega}{390k\Omega + 100k\Omega} = -11.9V \quad | \quad R_{EQ} = 390k\Omega\|100k\Omega = 79.6k\Omega$$

$$V_B = -11.9 - 0.7 - \frac{I_{E4} + I_{B1} + I_{B2} + I_{B3}}{\beta_o + 1}R_{TH} \quad | \quad I_{E4} = \frac{V_B - 0.7 - (-15)}{27k\Omega}$$

$$I_{B1} = \frac{V_B - 1.4 - (-15)}{126(100k\Omega)} \quad | \quad I_{B2} = \frac{V_B - 1.4 - (-15)}{126(330k\Omega)} \quad | \quad I_{B3} = \frac{V_B - 1.4 - (-15)}{126(100k\Omega)}$$

$$I_{B1} + I_{B2} + I_{B3} \ll I_{E4}$$

Then: $I_{E4} = 126\dfrac{-11.9 - 0.7 - (-15)}{79.6k\Omega + 126(27k\Omega)} = 86.9\mu A \quad | \quad V_{E4} = -15 + 86.9\mu A(27k\Omega) = -12.6V$

$$I_{C3} = I_{C1} = \alpha_F I_{E1} = \frac{125}{126}\left(\frac{-12.6 - 0.7 - (-15)}{100k\Omega}\right) = 16.9\ \mu A \quad | \quad V_{CE1} = V_{CE3} = 0 - (-12.6 - 0.7) = 13.3V$$

$$I_{C2} = \alpha_F I_{E2} = \frac{125}{126}\left(\frac{-12.6 - 0.7 - (-15)}{330k\Omega}\right) = 5.11\ \mu A \quad | \quad V_{CE2} = 0 - (-12.6 - 0.7) = 13.3V$$

Checking: $I_{B1} + I_{B2} + I_{B3} = \dfrac{16.9\mu A + 5.11\mu A + 16.9\mu A}{125} = 0.311\mu A \ll I_{E4}$ – Assumption is ok.

$$r_{o3} = r_{o1} = \frac{(50 + 13.3)V}{16.9\mu A} = 3.75M\Omega \quad | \quad r_{o2} = \frac{(50 + 13.3)V}{5.11\mu A} = 12.4M\Omega$$

$$r_{\pi 3} = r_{\pi 1} = \frac{125(0.025V)}{16.9\ \mu A} = 185k\Omega \quad | \quad r_{\pi 2} = \frac{125(0.025V)}{5.11\ \mu A} = 612k\Omega \quad | \quad r_{\pi 4} = \frac{125(0.025V)}{86.9\ \mu A} = 36.0k\Omega$$

$$R_{IN3} = R_{IN1} = r_{\pi 1} + (\beta_o + 1)(100k\Omega) = 185k\Omega + 126(100k\Omega) = 12.8M\Omega$$

$$R_{IN2} = r_{\pi 2} + (\beta_o + 1)(330k\Omega) = 612k\Omega + 126(330k\Omega) = 42.3M\Omega$$

$$R_{O4} = 27k\Omega\left\|\frac{R_{EQ} + r_{\pi 4}}{\beta_o + 1}\right. = 27k\Omega\left\|\frac{79.6k\Omega + 36.0k\Omega}{126}\right. = 887\Omega$$

$$R_{th1} = R_{O4}\|R_{IN2}\|R_{IN3} \cong 887\Omega \quad | \quad R_{th2} = R_{O4}\|R_{IN1}\|R_{IN3} \cong 887\Omega \quad | \quad R_{th3} = R_{O4}\|R_{IN1}\|R_{IN2} \cong 887\Omega$$

$$R_{OUT3} = R_{OUT1} = r_{o1}\left(1 + \frac{\beta_o R_E}{R_{th} + r_{\pi 1} + R_E}\right) = 3.75M\Omega\left(1 + \frac{125(100k\Omega)}{0.887k\Omega + 185k\Omega + 100k\Omega}\right) = 168\ M\Omega$$

$$R_{OUT2} = r_{o2}\left(1 + \frac{\beta_o R_E}{R_{th} + r_{\pi 1} + R_E}\right) = 12.4M\Omega\left(1 + \frac{125(330k\Omega)}{0.887k\Omega + 612k\Omega + 330k\Omega}\right) = 555\ M\Omega$$

15.130

$$V_{EQ} = -12V \frac{20k\Omega}{20k\Omega + 39k\Omega} = -4.07V \quad | \quad R_{EQ} = 20k\Omega\|39k\Omega = 13.2k\Omega$$

$$I_B = -\left(\frac{1}{76}\frac{V_B + 0.7}{33k\Omega} + \frac{1}{76}\frac{V_B + 0.7}{16k\Omega} + \frac{1}{76}\frac{V_B + 0.7}{8.2k\Omega}\right) \quad | \quad V_B = -4.07V + 13200I_B \rightarrow V_B = -3.95V$$

$$I_{C1} = \frac{75}{76}\left(\frac{0 - 0.7V - (-3.95V)}{33k\Omega}\right) = 97.2\mu A \quad | \quad R_{OUT1} = r_{o1}\left(1 + \frac{\beta_o(33k\Omega)}{R_{th1} + r_{\pi1} + 33k\Omega}\right)$$

$$R_{th1} = 13.2k\Omega\|\left[r_{\pi2} + (\beta_{o2}+1)16k\Omega\right]\|\left[r_{\pi3} + (\beta_{o3}+1)8.2k\Omega\right] \cong 13.2k\Omega$$

$$R_{OUT1} = \frac{60 + 8.75}{97.2\mu A}\left(1 + \frac{75(33k\Omega)}{13.2k\Omega + 19.3k\Omega + 33k\Omega}\right) = 27.4 \text{ M}\Omega$$

$$I_{C2} = \frac{75}{76}\left(\frac{0 - 0.7V - (-3.95V)}{16k\Omega}\right) = 201\mu A \quad | \quad R_{OUT} = r_{o2}\left(1 + \frac{\beta_o(16k\Omega)}{R_{th2} + r_{\pi2} + 16k\Omega}\right)$$

$$R_{th2} = 13.2k\Omega\|\left[r_{\pi1} + (\beta_{o1}+1)33k\Omega\right]\|\left[r_{\pi3} + (\beta_{o3}+1)8.2k\Omega\right] \cong 13.2k\Omega$$

$$R_{OUT2} = \frac{60 + 8.75}{201\mu A}\left(1 + \frac{75(16k\Omega)}{13.2k\Omega + 9.33k\Omega + 16k\Omega}\right) = 11.0 \text{ M}\Omega$$

$$I_{C3} = \frac{75}{76}\left(\frac{0 - 0.7V - (-3.95V)}{8.2k\Omega}\right) = 391\mu A \quad | \quad R_{OUT} = r_{o3}\left(1 + \frac{\beta_o(8.2k\Omega)}{R_{th2} + r_{\pi2} + 8.2k\Omega}\right)$$

$$R_{th3} = 13.2k\Omega\|\left[r_{\pi1} + (\beta_{o1}+1)33k\Omega\right]\|\left[r_{\pi2} + (\beta_{o2}+1)16k\Omega\right] \cong 13.2k\Omega$$

$$R_{OUT3} = \frac{60 + 8.75}{391\mu A}\left(1 + \frac{75(8.2k\Omega)}{13.2k\Omega \mid 4.80k\Omega \mid 8.2k\Omega}\right) = 4.30 \text{ M}\Omega$$

15.131

$$V_{EQ} = 12V \frac{2M\Omega}{2M\Omega + 2M\Omega} = 6.00V \quad | \quad R_{EQ} = 2M\Omega\|2M\Omega = 1.00M\Omega \quad | \quad \text{Assume saturation:}$$

$$12 - 10^5 I_{SD1} - V_{SG1} = 6 \quad | \quad V_{SG1} = 1 + \sqrt{\frac{2I_{SD1}}{2.5\text{x}10^{-4}}}$$

$$I_{SD1} = 44.1 \ \mu A, \ V_{SG1} = 1.59V, \ V_{SD1} = 6 + V_{SG1} = 7.59V$$

$$R_{OUT1} = r_{o1}(1 + g_{m1}R_1) = \frac{50V + 7.59V}{44.1\mu A}\left(1 + 100k\Omega\sqrt{2(250\mu A)(44.1\mu A)[1 + 0.02(7.69)]}\right) = 22.2 \text{ M}\Omega$$

$$12 - 4.7\text{x}10^5 I_{SD2} - V_{SG2} = 6 \quad | \quad V_{SG2} = 1 + \sqrt{\frac{2I_{SD2}}{2.5\text{x}10^{-4}}}$$

$$I_{SD2} = 10.0 \ \mu A, \ V_{SG2} = 1.28 \ V, \ V_{SD2} = 6 + V_{SG2} = 7.28V$$

$$R_{OUT2} = r_{o2}(1 + g_{m2}R_2) = \frac{50V + 7.28V}{10.0\mu A}\left(1 + 470k\Omega\sqrt{2(250\mu A)(10.0\mu A)[1 + 0.02(7.28)]}\right) = 210 \text{ M}\Omega$$

15.132

```
*Problem 15.132
VCC 1 0 DC 12
R1 1 2 100K
R4 1 3 2MEG
R3 3 0 2MEG
R2 1 4 470K
M1 5 3 2 2 PFET
M2 6 3 4 4 PFET
VD1 5 0 DC 0
```

Results: $I_{O1} = 44.4 \ \mu A$, $R_{OUT1} = 22.1 \ M\Omega$, $I_{O1} = 10.1 \ \mu A$, $R_{OUT1} = 209 \ M\Omega$

15.133

For large A, $\quad I_O \cong \dfrac{V_{REF}}{R} = \dfrac{5V}{50k\Omega} = 100\mu A$

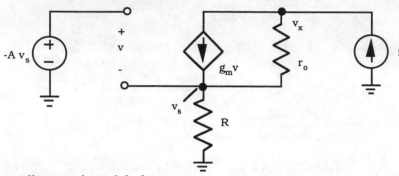

For the small - signal model above,

$\mathbf{v_x} = \mathbf{v_s} + (\mathbf{i_x} - g_m\mathbf{v})r_o \ | \ \mathbf{v} = (-A\mathbf{v_s}) - \mathbf{v_s} = -\mathbf{v_s}(1+A) \ | \ \mathbf{v_s} = \mathbf{i_x}R \ | \ $ Combining:

$R_{OUT} = \dfrac{\mathbf{v_x}}{\mathbf{i_x}} = R + r_o\big[1 + g_mR(1+A)\big] \ | \ r_o = \dfrac{50V + 10V}{100\mu A} = 600k\Omega$

$g_m = \sqrt{2\big(8x10^{-4}\big)\big(10^{-4}\big)\big[1 + 0.02(10)\big]} = 0.438mS$

$R_{OUT} = 50k\Omega + 600k\Omega\big[1 + 0.438mS(50k\Omega)(1 + 5x10^4)\big] = 6.57x10^{11}\Omega \ !!$

15.134

For large A, $\quad I_O \cong \alpha_F \dfrac{V_{REF}}{R} = \dfrac{120}{121}\dfrac{5V}{50k\Omega} = 99.2 \ \mu A$

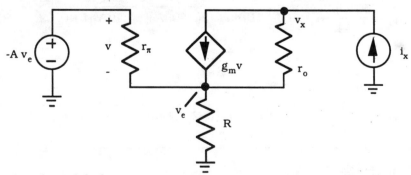

For the small - signal model above,

$\mathbf{v_x} = \mathbf{v_e} + (\mathbf{i_x} - g_m\mathbf{v})r_o \ | \ \mathbf{v} = (-A\mathbf{v_e}) - \mathbf{v_e} = -\mathbf{v_e}(1+A) \ | \ \mathbf{i_x} = G\mathbf{v_e} + g_\pi(1+A)\mathbf{v_e} \ | \ $ Combining:

$R_{OUT} = \dfrac{\mathbf{v_x}}{\mathbf{i_x}} = \dfrac{1 + \mu_f(1+A)}{G + g_\pi(1+A)} + \dfrac{1}{g_o} \cong r_o(1+\beta_o) \ $ for $g_\pi(1+A) >> G$ and $\mu_f(1+A) >> 1$

$$r_o = \frac{50V + 10V}{99.2\mu A} = 605k\Omega \quad | \quad R_{OUT} = 605k\Omega(121) = 73.2 \ M\Omega$$

R_{OUT} cannot exceed $\beta_o r_o$ because of the loss of base current through r_π.

15.135 R_{OUT} is limited to $\beta_o r_o$ of the BJT. We need to increase the effective current gain of the transistor which can be done by replacing Q_1 with a Darlington configuration of two transistors.

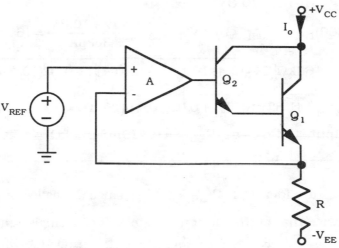

Now R_{OUT} can approach the $\beta_o r_o$ product of the Darlington which is $R_{OUT} \cong \frac{2}{3}\beta_o^2 r_{o2}$

15.136

$$V_{EQ} = 12V \frac{91k\Omega}{91k\Omega + 30k\Omega} = 9.03V \quad | \quad R_{EQ} = 91k\Omega \| 30k\Omega = 22.6k\Omega$$

$$I_{C3} = 85 I_{B3} = 85 \frac{12 - 0.7 - 9.03}{22.6k\Omega + 86(240k\Omega)} \frac{V}{\Omega} = 9.34 \ \mu A$$

$$V_{EC3} = 12 - I_E R_E - 0.7 = 12 - \frac{86}{85}(9.34\mu A)(240k\Omega) - 0.7 = 9.03V$$

$$I_{C1} = I_{C2} = \alpha_F \frac{I_{C3}}{2} = \frac{85}{86}\frac{9.34\mu A}{2} = 4.62\mu A \mid V_{EC1} = V_{EC2} = 0.7 - \left[-12 + 1.2M\Omega(4.62\mu A)\right] = 7.16V$$

Q – po int s: $(4.62\mu A, 7.62V) \ (4.62\mu A, 7.62V) \ (9.34\mu A, 9.03V)$

$$r_{\pi 3} = \frac{85(0.025V)}{9.34\mu A} = 228k\Omega \quad | \quad r_{o3} = \frac{(70 + 9.03)V}{9.34\mu A} = 8.46M\Omega$$

$$R_{OUT3} = r_{o3}\left(1 + \frac{\beta_o R_E}{R_{th} + r_{\pi 3} + R_E}\right) = 8.46M\Omega\left(1 + \frac{85(240k\Omega)}{22.6k\Omega + 228k\Omega + 240k\Omega}\right) = 360M\Omega$$

For a single - ended output, $A_V = \frac{g_m R_C}{2} = 20(4.62\mu A)(1.2M\Omega) = +111 \ (40.9dB)$

$$CMRR = g_{m1}R_{OUT3} = 40(4.62\mu A)(360M\Omega) = 6.65 \times 10^4 \ (96.5dB)$$

15.137

$$V_{EQ} = -15V \frac{100k\Omega}{100k\Omega + 51k\Omega} = -9.93V \quad | \quad R_{EQ} = 100k\Omega \| 51k\Omega = 33.8k\Omega \quad | \quad \text{Assume saturation:}$$

$$-9.93 = -15 + 7500 I_{DS3} + V_{GS3} \quad | \quad V_{GS3} = 1 + \sqrt{\frac{2 I_{DS3}}{4 \times 10^{-4}}} \quad | \quad I_{DS3} = 363 \, \mu A, \, V_{GS3} = 2.35V$$

$$I_{DS1} = I_{DS2} = \frac{I_{DS3}}{2} = 182\mu A \quad | \quad V_{GS1} = 1 + \sqrt{\frac{2(363\mu A)}{2(400\mu A)}} = 1.95V$$

$$V_{DS3} = -V_{GS1} - 7500 I_{DS3} - (-15) = 10.3V$$

$$V_{DS1} = V_{DS2} = 15 - 36000 I_{DS1} - V_{GS1} = 10.4V \quad | \quad r_{o3} = \frac{50V + 10.3V}{363\mu A} = 166k\Omega$$

$$R_{OUT3} = r_{o3}(1 + g_{m3}R_S) = 166k\Omega\left(1 + \sqrt{2(4 \times 10^{-4})(3.63 \times 10^{-4})[1 + 0.02(10.3)]}(7.5k\Omega)\right) = 903 \, k\Omega$$

$$A_{dd} = -g_m R_D = -\sqrt{2(4 \times 10^{-4})(1.82 \times 10^{-4})[1 + 0.02(10.4)]}(36k\Omega) = 0.419mS(36k\Omega) = -15.1$$

For a single-ended output, $CMRR = g_{m1}R_{OUT3} = 0.419mS(903k\Omega) = 378 \quad (51.6 \, dB)$

15.138

Assuming all devices are identical, $R_{OUT} = \beta_{o1}\frac{r_{o1}}{2}$ since the collector current of the current source is twice that of the input transistors. For a single-ended output,

$$A_{dd} = -\frac{g_{m1}R_C}{2} \quad | \quad A_{cc} = -\frac{R_C}{2\left(\beta_{o1}\frac{r_{o1}}{2}\right)} = -\frac{R_C}{\beta_{o1}r_{o1}} \quad | \quad CMRR = \frac{g_{m1}\beta_{o1}r_{o1}}{2} = \frac{\beta_{o1}\mu_{f1}}{2}$$

Using our default paramters: $CMRR \cong 20\beta_{o1}V_{A1} = 20(100)(70) = 140,000 \, (103dB)$
(Note that this analysis neglects the contribution of the output resistance r_o of the input pair. If this resistance is included, a theoretical cancellation occurs and $A_{cc} = 0$! Of course the output resistance expression $R_{OUT} = \frac{\beta_o r_o}{2}$ is not precise, but an improvement over the CMRR expression above is possible.)

15.139

$$R_{OUT} = r_o(1 + g_m R_S) \cong \mu_F R_S = g_m r_o R_S \cong \sqrt{2 K_n I_{DS}}\frac{1}{\lambda I_{DS}}R_S$$

$$V_{R_S} = I_{DS}R_S = \frac{\lambda I_{DS}^{1.5}R_{OUT}}{\sqrt{2K_n}} = \frac{0.02(10^{-4})^{1.5}(5 \times 10^6)}{\sqrt{2(5 \times 10^{-4})}} = 3.16 \, V$$

15.140

```
*Problem 15.140 - Fig. 15.72(a) - BJT Current Source Monte Carlo Analysis
*Generate a Voltage Source with 5% Tolerances
IEE 0 5 DC 1
REE 5 0 RTOL 15
EEE 1 0 5 0 -1
*

VO 4 0 AC 1
RE 1 2 RTOL 18.4K
R1 1 3 RTOL 113K
R2 3 0 RTOL 263K
```

```
Q1 4 3 2 NBJT
.OP
.DC VO 0 0 .01
.AC LIN 1 1000 1000
.PRINT AC IM(VO) IP(VO)
.MODEL NBJT NPN BF=150 VA=75
.MODEL RTOL RES (R=1 DEV 5%)
.MC 1000 DC I(VO) YMAX
*.MC 1000 AC IM(VO) YMAX
.END
```

Results - 3σ limits: I_o = 199 μA $\pm$ 32.5 μA, R_{OUT} = 11.8 MΩ $\pm$ 2.6 MΩ

```
*Problem 15.140 - Fig. 15.72(b) - MOSFET Current Source
*Generate a Voltage Source with 5% Tolerance
IEE 0 5 DC 1
REE 5 0 RTOL 15
EEE 1 0 5 0 -1
*
VO 4 0 AC 1
RS 1 2 RTOL 18K
R3 1 3 RTOL 240K
R4 3 0 RTOL 510K
M1 4 3 2 2 NFET
.OP
.DC VO 0 0 .01
.AC LIN 1 1000 1000
.PRINT AC IM(VO) IP(VO)
.MODEL NFET NMOS KP=9.95M VTO=1 LAMBDA=0.01
.MODEL RTOL RES (R=1 DEV 5%)
.MC 1000 DC I(VO) YMAX
*.MC 1000 AC IM(VO) YMAX
.END
```

Results - 3σ limits: I_o = 201 μA $\pm$ 34.7 μA, R_{OUT} = 21.7 MΩ $\pm$ 3.6 MΩ

CHAPTER 16

16.1

$$3.64k\Omega(1+0.15)(1-0.03) \le R \le 3.64k\Omega(1+0.15)(1+0.03) \quad | \quad 4.06k\Omega \le R \le 4.31k\Omega$$

16.2

$$I_{C1} = I_{S1} \exp\left(\frac{V_{BE1}}{V_T}\right) \mid I_{C2} = I_{S2} \exp\left(\frac{V_{BE2}}{V_T}\right) \mid \frac{I_{C2}}{I_{C1}} = \frac{I_{S2}}{I_{S1}} \exp\left(\frac{V_{BE2} - V_{BE1}}{V_T}\right) \mid \Delta V_{BE} = V_{BE2} - V_{BE1}$$

$$\Delta I_S = I_{S1} - I_{S2} \mid I_S = \frac{I_{S1} + I_{S2}}{2} \mid I_{S1} = I_S\left(1 + \frac{\Delta I_S}{2I_S}\right) \mid I_{S2} = I_S\left(1 - \frac{\Delta I_S}{2I_S}\right)$$

(a) $I_{C2} = I_{C1}$: $\quad \Delta V_{BE} = V_T \ln\left(\frac{I_{C2}}{I_{C1}} \frac{I_{S1}}{I_{S2}}\right) = 0.025 \ln\left[(1) \frac{I_S\left(1 + \frac{\Delta I_S}{2I_S}\right)}{I_S\left(1 - \frac{\Delta I_S}{2I_S}\right)}\right] = 0.025 \ln\left[\frac{(1.05)}{(0.95)}\right] = 2.50 \text{ mV}$

(b) $\Delta V_{BE} = 0.025 \ln\left[\frac{(1.10)}{(0.90)}\right] = 5.02 \text{ mV}$

(b) $\frac{I_{S1}}{I_{S2}} = \frac{\left(1 + \frac{\Delta I_S}{I_S}\right)}{\left(1 - \frac{\Delta I_S}{I_S}\right)} = \exp\left(\frac{V_{BE2} - V_{BE1}}{V_T}\right) = \exp\left(\frac{0.001}{0.025}\right) = 1.04 \rightarrow \frac{\Delta I_S}{I_S} = 0.02 \text{ or } 2\%$

16.3

(a) $I_{DS} = \frac{(250)(1 \pm 0.05)}{2} \frac{\mu A}{V^2}\left[2 - (1 \pm 0.025)\right]^2 \mid I_{DS}^{max} = \frac{(250)(1 + 0.05)}{2} \frac{\mu A}{V^2}\left[1 + 0.025\right]^2 = 138\mu A$

$I_{DS}^{min} = \frac{(250)(1 - 0.05)}{2} \frac{\mu A}{V^2}\left[1 - 0.025\right]^2 = 113\mu A$

$I_{DS} = \frac{138\mu A + 113\mu A}{2} = 125.5\mu A \mid \Delta I_{DS} = 138\mu A - 113\mu A = 25\mu A \mid \frac{\Delta I_{DS}}{I_{DS}} = 19.8\%$

(b) $I_{DS}^{max} = \frac{(250)(1 + 0.05)}{2} \frac{\mu A}{V^2}\left[3 + 0.025\right]^2 = 1.20mA$

$I_{DS}^{min} = \frac{(250)(1 - 0.05)}{2} \frac{\mu A}{V^2}\left[3 - 0.025\right]^2 = 1.05mA$

$I_{DS} = \frac{1.20mA + 1.05mA}{2} = 1.125mA \mid \Delta I_{DS} = 1.20mA - 1.05mA = 0.150mA \mid \frac{\Delta I_{DS}}{I_{DS}} = 13.3\%$

16.4

$$V_{GS1} = V_{TN} + \sqrt{\dfrac{2I_{DS1}}{K_n'\left(\dfrac{W}{L}\right)_1}} = V_{TN} + \sqrt{\dfrac{2I_{DS1}}{K_n'\left(\dfrac{W}{L}\right)}}\sqrt{\dfrac{1}{1+\dfrac{\Delta(W/L)}{2(W/L)}}} \cong V_{TN} + \sqrt{\dfrac{2I_{DS1}}{K_n'\left(\dfrac{W}{L}\right)}}\left(1-\dfrac{\Delta(W/L)}{4(W/L)}\right)$$

$$V_{GS2} = V_{TN} + \sqrt{\dfrac{2I_{DS2}}{K_n'\left(\dfrac{W}{L}\right)_2}} = V_{TN} + \sqrt{\dfrac{2I_{DS2}}{K_n'\left(\dfrac{W}{L}\right)}}\sqrt{\dfrac{1}{1-\dfrac{\Delta(W/L)}{2(W/L)}}} \cong V_{TN} + \sqrt{\dfrac{2I_{DS2}}{K_n'\left(\dfrac{W}{L}\right)}}\left(1+\dfrac{\Delta(W/L)}{4(W/L)}\right)$$

$$I_{DS2} = I_{DS1}: \quad V_{GS2} - V_{GS1} = \sqrt{\dfrac{2I_{DS2}}{K_n'\left(\dfrac{W}{L}\right)}}\left(\dfrac{\Delta(W/L)}{2(W/L)}\right) = (V_{GS} - V_{TN})\left(\dfrac{\Delta(W/L)}{2(W/L)}\right)$$

(a) $\Delta V_{GS} = (V_{GS} - V_{TN})\left(\dfrac{\Delta(W/L)}{2(W/L)}\right) = (0.5)\left(\dfrac{0.10}{2}\right) = 25$ mV

(b) $\dfrac{\Delta(W/L)}{(W/L)} = 2\dfrac{\Delta V_{GS}}{(V_{GS} - V_{TN})} = 2\dfrac{0.003}{0.5} = 1.2$ %

16.5

$$I_{S1}\exp\left(\dfrac{V_{BE1}}{V_T}\right) = I_{S2}\exp\left(\dfrac{V_{BE1}+0.002}{V_T}\right) \mid \dfrac{I_{S1}}{I_{S2}} = \exp\left(\dfrac{0.002}{0.025}\right) = 1.08 \mid I_{S1} = 1.08I_{S2}$$

$$\Delta I_S = I_{S1} - I_{S2} = 0.08I_{S2} \mid I_S = \dfrac{I_{S1}+I_{S2}}{2} = 1.04I_{S2} \mid \dfrac{\Delta I_S}{I_S} = \dfrac{0.08}{1.04} = 7.7\%$$

$$\beta_{F1} = 100(1+0.025)\left(1+\dfrac{10V}{50V}\right) = 123 \mid \beta_{F2} = 100(1-0.025)\left(1+\dfrac{10V}{50V}\right) = 117$$

$$I_{B1} = \dfrac{100\mu A}{123} = 0.813\ \mu A \mid I_{B2} = \dfrac{100\mu A}{117} = 0.855\ \mu A$$

16.6

$$I_{OX} = \dfrac{\left(\dfrac{W}{L}\right)_X}{\left(\dfrac{W}{L}\right)_1}I_{REF}\dfrac{1+\lambda V_{DSX}}{1+\lambda V_{DS1}} \mid R_{OX} = \dfrac{\dfrac{1}{\lambda}+V_{DSX}}{I_{OX}}$$

$$V_{DS1} = V_{GS1} = V_{TN} + \sqrt{\dfrac{2I_{D1}}{K_n}} = 0.75 + \sqrt{\dfrac{2(30\times10^{-6})}{4(25\times10^{-6})}} = 1.52V$$

$$I_{O2} = \dfrac{10}{4}(30\mu A)\dfrac{1+0.015(10)}{1+0.015(1.52)} = 84.3\mu A \mid R_{O2} = \dfrac{\dfrac{1}{0.015}+10}{84.3\mu A} = 909k\Omega$$

$$I_{O3} = \dfrac{20}{4}(30\mu A)\dfrac{1+0.0158}{1+0.015(1.52)} = 164\mu A \mid R_{O3} = \dfrac{\dfrac{1}{0.015}+8}{164\mu A} = 455k\Omega$$

$$I_{O4} = \dfrac{40}{4}(30\mu A)\dfrac{1+0.015(12)}{1+0.015(1.52)} = 346\mu A \mid R_{O4} = \dfrac{\dfrac{1}{0.015}+12}{346\mu A} = 227k\Omega$$

16.7

$$I_{SD1} = \frac{5 - V_{SG1}}{R} \quad | \quad \frac{15\times10^{-6}}{2}\left(\frac{2}{1}\right)(V_{SG1} - 0.9)^2(1 + 0.01V_{SG1}) = \frac{5 - V_{SG1}}{3\times10^4} \rightarrow V_{SG1} = 2.985V$$

$$I_{REF} = \frac{5 - 2.985}{3\times10^4} = 67.2\mu A$$

$$I_{O2} = \frac{15\times10^{-6}}{2}\left(\frac{8}{1}\right)(2.985 - 0.9)^2[1 + 0.01(5)] = 274\mu A \quad | \quad R_{OUT2} = \frac{\frac{1}{\lambda} + V_{SD2}}{I_{O2}} = \frac{100 + 5}{274\mu A} = 383k\Omega$$

$$I_{O3} = \frac{15\times10^{-6}}{2}\left(\frac{16}{1}\right)(2.985 - 0.9)^2[1 + 0.01(10)] = 574\mu A \quad | \quad R_{OUT3} = \frac{100 + 10}{574\mu A} = 192k\Omega$$

16.8

```
*Problem 16.8 - NMOS Current Source Array
IREF 0 1 DC 30U
VD2 2 0 DC 10 AC 1
VD3 3 0 DC 8 AC 1
VD4 4 0 DC 12 AC 1
M1 1 1 0 0 NFET W=4U L=1U
M2 2 1 0 0 NFET W=10U L=1U
M3 3 1 0 0 NFET W=20U L=1U
M4 4 1 0 0 NFET W=40U L=1U
.MODEL NFET NMOS KP=25U VTO=0.75 LAMBDA=0.015
.OP
.AC LIN 1 1000 1000
.PRINT AC IM(VD2) IM(VD3) IM(VD4) IP(VD2) IP(VD3) IP(VD4)
.END
```

The results are identical to the hand calculations.

16.9

```
*Problem 16.9 - PMOS Current Source Array
RREF 0 1 30K
VSS 4 0 DC 5
VD2 2 0 DC 0 AC 1
VD3 3 0 DC -5 AC 1
M1 1 1 4 4 PFET W=2U L=1U
M2 2 1 4 4 PFET W=8U L=1U
M3 3 1 4 4 PFET W=16U L=1U
.MODEL PFET PMOS KP=15U VTO=-0.9 LAMBDA=0.01
.OP
.AC LIN 1 1000 1000
.PRINT AC IM(VD2) IM(VD3) IP(VD2) IP(VD3)
.END
```

The results are identical to the hand calculations.

16.10

$$I_{SD2} = \frac{K_p'}{2}\left(\frac{W}{L}\right)(V_{SG2} + V_{TP})^2[1 + \lambda V_{SD2}] \quad | \quad 35\times10^{-6} = \frac{15\times10^{-6}}{2}\left(\frac{8}{1}\right)(V_{SG1} - 0.9)^2[1 + 0.01(5)]$$

$$V_{SG1} = 1.645V \quad | \quad \frac{I_{SD2}}{I_{REF}} = \frac{\left(\frac{W}{L}\right)_2[1 + \lambda V_{SD2}]}{\left(\frac{W}{L}\right)_1[1 + \lambda V_{SD1}]} \quad | \quad \frac{35\mu A}{I_{REF}} = \frac{\left(\frac{8}{1}\right)_2[1 + 0.01(5)]}{\left(\frac{2}{1}\right)_1[1 + 0.01(1.645)]} \rightarrow I_{REF} = 8.47\mu A$$

$$I_{REF} = \frac{5 - V_{SG1}}{R} \quad | \quad R = \frac{5 - 1.645}{8.47\mu A} = 396 \text{ k}\Omega$$

16.11 (a)

(a) $I_{REF} = \frac{12 - 0.7}{5 \times 10^4} = 226 \text{ }\mu A \quad | \quad I_{REF} = I_{C1} + (1 + 5 + 8.3)I_B \quad | \quad I_{REF} = I_S \exp\left(\frac{V_{BE}}{V_T}\right)\left(1 + \frac{14.3}{\beta_{FO}} + \frac{V_{BE}}{V_A}\right)$

$$I_{O2} = 5I_S \exp\left(\frac{V_{BE}}{V_T}\right)\left(1 + \frac{V_{CE2}}{V_A}\right) = 5I_{REF}\frac{1 + \frac{V_{CE2}}{V_A}}{1 + \frac{14.3}{\beta_{FO}} + \frac{V_{BE}}{V_A}} \quad | \quad I_{O2} = 5(226\mu A)\frac{1 + \frac{5}{60}}{1 + \frac{14.3}{50} + \frac{0.7}{60}} = 944 \text{ }\mu A$$

$$R_{OUT2} = r_{o2} = \frac{V_A + V_{CE2}}{I_{C2}} = \frac{60 + 5}{9.44 \times 10^{-4}} = 68.9 \text{ k}\Omega$$

$$I_{O3} = 8.3I_{REF}\frac{1 + \frac{V_{CE3}}{V_A}}{1 + \frac{14.3}{\beta_{FO}} + \frac{V_{BE}}{V_A}} = 8.3(226\mu A)\frac{1 + \frac{3}{60}}{1 + \frac{14.3}{50} + \frac{0.7}{60}} = 1.52 \text{ mA}$$

$$R_{OUT3} = r_{o3} = \frac{V_A + V_{CE3}}{I_{C3}} = \frac{60 + 3}{1.52 \times 10^{-3}} = 41.5 \text{ k}\Omega$$

(b) $I_{REF} = \frac{12 - 0.7 - 0.7}{5 \times 10^4} = 212 \text{ }\mu A \quad | \quad I_{REF} = I_{C1} + (1 + 5 + 8.3)\frac{I_B}{\beta_{FO} + 1}$

$$I_{REF} = I_S \exp\left(\frac{V_{BE}}{V_T}\right)\left(1 + \frac{14.3}{\beta_{FO}(\beta_{FO} + 1)} + \frac{2V_{BE}}{V_A}\right)$$

$$I_{O2} = 5I_S \exp\left(\frac{V_{BE}}{V_T}\right)\left(1 + \frac{V_{CE2}}{V_A}\right) = 5I_{REF}\frac{1 + \frac{V_{CE2}}{V_A}}{1 + \frac{14.3}{\beta_{FO}(\beta_{FO} + 1)} + \frac{2V_{BE}}{V_A}}$$

$$I_{O2} = 5(212\mu A)\frac{1 + \frac{5}{60}}{1 + \frac{14.3}{50(51)} + \frac{1.4}{60}} = 1.12\text{mA} \quad | \quad R_{OUT2} = r_{o2} = \frac{V_A + V_{CE2}}{I_{C2}} = \frac{60V + 5V}{1.12\text{mA}} = 58.0 \text{ k}\Omega$$

$$I_{O3} = 8.3I_{REF}\frac{1 + \frac{V_{CE3}}{V_A}}{1 + \frac{14.3}{\beta_{FO}(\beta_{FO} + 1)} + \frac{2V_{BE}}{V_A}} = 8.3(212\mu A)\frac{1 + \frac{3}{60}}{1 + \frac{14.3}{50(51)} + \frac{1.4}{60}} = 1.80 \text{ mA}$$

$$R_{OUT3} = r_{o3} = \frac{V_A + V_{CE3}}{I_{C3}} = \frac{60V + 3V}{1.80\text{mA}} = 35.0 \text{ k}\Omega$$

16.12

```
*Problem 16.12(a) - NPN Current Source Array
RREF 2 1 50K
VCC 2 0 DC 12
VC2 3 0 DC 5 AC 1
VC3 4 0 DC 3 AC 1
Q1 1 1 0 NBJT 1
Q2 3 1 0 NBJT 5
Q3 4 1 0 NBJT 8.3
.MODEL NBJT NPN BF=50 VA=60
```

```
.OP
.AC LIN 1 1000 1000
.PRINT AC IM(VC2) IM(VC3) IP(VC2) IP(VC3)
.END
*Problem 16.12(b) - Buffered NPN Current Source Array
RREF 2 5 50K
VCC 2 0 DC 12
VC2 3 0 DC 5 AC 1
VC3 4 0 DC 3 AC 1
Q1 5 1 0 NBJT 1
Q2 3 1 0 NBJT 5
Q3 4 1 0 NBJT 8.3
Q4 2 5 1 NBJT 1
.MODEL NBJT NPN BF=50 VA=60
.OP
.AC LIN 1 1000 1000
.PRINT AC IM(VC2) IM(VC3) IP(VC2) IP(VC3)
.END
```

The results are almost identical to the hand calculations.

16.13

$$I_{REF} = I_{C1} + (1 + 5 + 8.3)\frac{I_B}{\beta_{FO} + 1} = I_{C1} + \frac{14.3 I_B}{\beta_{FO} + 1} = I_S \exp\left(\frac{V_{BE}}{V_T}\right)\left(1 + \frac{14.3}{\beta_{FO}(\beta_{FO} + 1)} + \frac{2V_{BE}}{V_A}\right)$$

$$I_{REF} = I_S \exp\left(\frac{V_{BE}}{V_T}\right)\left(1 + \frac{14.3}{50(51)} + \frac{1.4}{60}\right) = 1.029 I_S \exp\left(\frac{V_{BE}}{V_T}\right)$$

$$I_{O3} = 8.3 I_S \exp\left(\frac{V_{BE}}{V_T}\right)\left(1 + \frac{V_{CE3}}{V_A}\right) = 8.3 I_{REF} \frac{1 + \frac{V_{CE2}}{V_A}}{1.029} \quad | \quad I_{REF} = \frac{166\mu A(1.029)}{8.3\left(1 + \frac{3}{60}\right)} = 19.6\mu A$$

$$I_{REF} = \frac{12 - 0.7 - 0.7}{5 \times 10^4} \quad | \quad R = \frac{12 - 1.4}{19.6\mu A} = 541 \text{ k}\Omega$$

$$I_{O2} = 5 I_{REF} \frac{1 + \frac{V_{CE2}}{V_A}}{1.029} = 5(19.6\mu A)\frac{1 + \frac{5}{60}}{1.029} = 103 \text{ }\mu A$$

16.14

$$I_{REF} = \frac{15 - 0.7}{6 \times 10^4} = 238\mu A \quad | \quad I_{REF} = 2I_{C1} + (2 + 1 + 6 + 9)I_B = 2\beta_{FO}\left(1 + \frac{V_{EC1}}{V_A}\right)I_B + 18 I_B$$

$$I_B = \frac{238\mu A}{18 + 2(50)\left(1 + \frac{0.7}{60}\right)} = 2.00\mu A$$

$$I_{O2} = \beta_{FO}\left(1 + \frac{V_{EC2}}{V_A}\right)I_B = 50\left(1 + \frac{15}{60}\right)(2.00\mu A) = 125\mu A \quad | \quad R_{OUT2} = r_{o2} = \frac{60 + 15}{1.25 \times 10^{-4}} = 600 \text{ k}\Omega$$

$$I_{O3} = 6\beta_{FO}\left(1 + \frac{V_{EC3}}{V_A}\right)I_B = 300\left(1 + \frac{9}{60}\right)(2.00\mu A) = 690\mu A \quad | \quad R_{OUT2} = r_{o2} = \frac{60 + 9}{6.90 \times 10^{-4}} = 100 \text{ k}\Omega$$

$$I_{O2} = 9\beta_{FO}\left(1 + \frac{V_{EC4}}{V_A}\right)I_B = 450\left(1 + \frac{27}{60}\right)(2.00\mu A) = 1.31mA \quad | \quad R_{OUT2} = r_{o2} = \frac{60 + 27}{1.31 \times 10^{-3}} = 66.4 \text{ k}\Omega$$

16.15

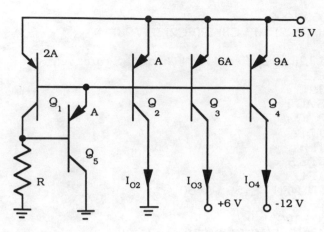

$$R_{REF} = \frac{15V - 0.7V - 0.7V}{25\mu A} = 544k\Omega \quad | \quad I_{REF} = I_{C1} + \frac{(2+1+6+9)I_B}{\beta_{FO}+1}$$

$$I_{REF} = 2\beta_{FO}\left(1 + \frac{V_{EC1}}{V_A}\right)I_B + \frac{18I_B}{\beta_{FO}+1} \quad | \quad I_B = \frac{25\mu A}{2(50)\left(1 + \frac{1.4}{60}\right) + \frac{18}{51}} = 0.2435\mu A$$

$$I_{O2} = \beta_{FO}\left(1 + \frac{V_{EC2}}{V_A}\right)I_B = 50\left(1 + \frac{15}{60}\right)I_B = 15.2 \ \mu A$$

$$I_{O3} = 6\beta_{FO}\left(1 + \frac{V_{EC3}}{V_A}\right)I_B = 300\left(1 + \frac{9}{60}\right)I_B = 84.0 \ \mu A$$

$$I_{O4} = 9\beta_{FO}\left(1 + \frac{V_{EC4}}{V_A}\right)I_B = 450\left(1 + \frac{27}{60}\right)I_B = 159 \ \mu A \quad | \quad I_{C5} = \alpha_F I_{E5} = \frac{50}{51}18I_B = 4.30 \ \mu A$$

16.16

$$V_{BE2} + I_{E2}R_2 = V_{BE3} + I_{E3}R_3 \rightarrow I_{E3} = \frac{R_2}{R_3}I_{E2} + \frac{V_{BE2} - V_{BE3}}{R_3}$$

In order to have equal base‑emitter voltages, the two transistors must operate at the

equal collector–current densities: $\dfrac{I_{E2}}{2A} = \dfrac{I_{E3}}{nA} = \dfrac{5I_{E2}}{nA} \rightarrow n = 10$

16.17 Note: The two **5-V** supplies should be **10 V**. With the large voltage drop across the emitter resistances, the output resistance of the current sources will be very high and the V_{CE} mismatch terms will be negligible.

$$I_{REF} = I_{C1} + 7I_B \quad | \quad I_{C1} \cong \frac{I_{REF}}{1 + \dfrac{7}{75}} = \frac{I_{REF}}{1.093} \quad | \quad I_{E1} = \frac{I_{C1}}{\alpha_F} = \frac{76}{75}\left(\frac{I_{REF}}{1.093}\right) = \frac{I_{REF}}{1.079}$$

$$12 = I_{REF}(10k\Omega) + 0.7V + \frac{I_{REF}}{1.079}(10k\Omega) \quad | \quad I_{REF} = \frac{12V - 0.7V}{10k\Omega(1.927)} = 586\mu A \quad | \quad I_{E1} = 543\mu A$$

$$I_{E2} = 2I_{E1} \quad | \quad I_{O2} = \alpha_F(2I_{E1}) = 2\frac{75}{76}(543\mu A) = 1.07mA$$

$$I_{E3} = 4I_{E1} \quad | \quad I_{O3} = \alpha_F(4I_{E1}) = 4\frac{75}{76}(543\mu A) = 2.14mA \quad | \quad \frac{1}{g_{m1}} = \frac{1}{40(536\mu A)} = 46.6\Omega$$

$$R_{th} = R \left\| \left(\frac{1}{g_{m1}} + R_1 \right) = 10k\Omega \| (46.6\Omega + 10k\Omega) = 5.01k\Omega \quad | \quad R_{th2} = R_{th} \| \left[r_{\pi3} + (\beta_{o3} + 1)(2.5k\Omega) \right]$$

$$r_{\pi2} = \frac{75(0.025V)}{1.07mA} = 1.75k\Omega \quad | \quad r_{\pi3} = \frac{75(0.025V)}{2.14mA} = 0.876k\Omega \quad | \quad r_{o2} = \frac{60 + (10 - 5.35)}{1.07mA} = 60.4k\Omega$$

$$R_{th2} = 5.01k\Omega \| \left[0.876k\Omega + (76)(2.5k\Omega) \right] = 4.88k\Omega$$

$$R_{OUT2} = r_{o2} \left(1 + \frac{\beta_o R_E}{R_{th2} + r_{\pi2} + R_E} \right) = 60.4k\Omega \left(1 + \frac{75(5k\Omega)}{4.88k\Omega + 1.75k\Omega + 5k\Omega} \right) = 2.01 \ M\Omega$$

$$r_{o3} = \frac{(60 + 10 - 5.35)V}{2.14mA} = 30.2k\Omega \quad | \quad R_{th2} = R_{th} \| \left[r_{\pi2} + (\beta_o + 1)(5k\Omega) \right]$$

$$R_{th3} = 5.01k\Omega \| \left[1.75k\Omega + (76)(5k\Omega) \right] = 4.95k\Omega$$

$$R_{OUT3} = r_{o3} \left(1 + \frac{\beta_o R_E}{R_{th} + r_{\pi3} + R_E} \right) = 30.2k\Omega \left(1 + \frac{75(2.5k\Omega)}{4.95k\Omega + 0.876k\Omega + 2.5k\Omega} \right) = 710 \ k\Omega$$

16.18

$$\text{For } V_{BE2} = V_{BE3}, \ I_{O3}R_3 = I_{O2}R_2 \quad | \quad R_3 = \frac{I_{O2}}{I_{O3}} R_2 = 3(5k\Omega) = 15 \ k\Omega \quad | \quad \frac{I_{O2}}{2A} = \frac{I_{O3}}{nA} \quad | \quad n = \frac{2}{3}$$

16.19

$$I_{REF} = \frac{10V - 0.7V - 0.7V}{10k\Omega} = 860\mu A \cong I_{C1} \quad | \quad I_{O2}R_2 = V_T \ln\left(\frac{I_{C1}}{I_{O2}} \frac{I_{S2}}{I_{S1}} \right)$$

$$10^4 I_{O2} = 0.025 \ln\left(\frac{860\mu A}{I_{O2}} \frac{2}{1} \right) \rightarrow I_{O2} = 12.4 \ \mu A \quad | \quad V_{E2} \cong 12.4 \ \mu A(10k\Omega) = 0.124V$$

$$r_{o2} = \frac{60 + 5 - 0.124}{12.4\mu A} = 5.23 \ M\Omega \quad | \quad R_{th} \text{ is small and the voltage across } R_E \text{ is also small.}$$

$$R_{OUT2} \cong r_{o2}(1 + g_{m2}R_{E2}) = 5.23M\Omega \left[1 + 40(12.4 \ \mu A)(10k\Omega) \right] = 31.2 \ M\Omega$$

$$5 \times 10^3 I_{O3} = 0.025 \ln\left(\frac{860\mu A}{I_{O2}} \frac{12}{1} \right) \rightarrow I_{O3} = 29.3 \ \mu A \quad | \quad V_{E3} \cong 29.3 \ \mu A(5k\Omega) = 0.147V$$

$$r_{o3} = \frac{60 + 5 - 0.147}{29.3\mu A} = 2.21 \ M\Omega \ | \ R_{OUT2} \cong r_{o3}(1 + g_{m3}R_{E3}) = 2.21M\Omega \left[1 + 40(0.147) \right] = 15.2 \ M\Omega$$

16.20

$$R = \frac{(10 - 0.7 - 0.7)V}{75\mu A} = 115k\Omega \quad | \quad R_2 = \frac{V_T}{I_{o2}} \ln\left(\frac{I_{REF}}{I_{o2}} \frac{I_{S2}}{I_{S1}} \right) = \frac{0.025V}{5\mu A} \ln\left(\frac{75\mu A}{5\mu A} \frac{2}{1} \right) = 17.0 \ k\Omega$$

$$I_{o3}R_3 = V_T \ln\left(\frac{I_{REF}}{I_{o3}} \frac{I_{S3}}{I_{S1}} \right) \quad | \quad (10\mu A)(2k\Omega) = 0.025V \ln\left(\frac{75\mu A}{10\mu A} \frac{n}{1} \right) \rightarrow n = 0.297$$

16.21

```
*Problem 16.21 - Buffered NPN Widlar Current Source Array
RREF 1 3 10K
VCC 1 0 DC 10
VC2 2 0 DC 5 AC 1
Q1 3 4 0 NBJT 1
Q2 2 4 5 NBJT 2
RE2 5 0 10K
Q3 2 4 6 NBJT 12
```

Results: $I_{C1} = 858$ μA, $I_{C2} = 12.7$ μA, $I_{C3} = 30.2$ μA, $R_{OUT2} = 28.8$ MΩ, $R_{OUT3} = 13.9$ MΩ

16.22 **Note:** Use $V_A = 70$ V

$$I_{REF} = \frac{5V - 0.7V - 0.7V - (-5V)}{40k\Omega} = 215\mu A \cong I_{C1} \quad | \quad I_{O2} = \frac{V_T}{R_2} \ln\left(\frac{I_{C1}}{I_{O2}} \frac{I_{S2}}{I_{S1}}\right)$$

$$I_{O2} = \frac{0.025V}{5k\Omega} \ln\left(\frac{215\mu A}{I_{O2}} \frac{10}{1}\right) \rightarrow I_{O2} = 22.7 \text{ μA} \quad | \quad V_{E2} \cong 22.7\mu A(5k\Omega) = 0.114V$$

$$r_{o2} = \frac{70 + 5 - 0.114}{22.7\mu A} = 3.30M\Omega \quad | \quad R_{th} \text{ is small and the voltage across } R_E \text{ is also small.}$$

$$R_{OUT2} \cong r_{o2}(1 + g_{m2}R_{E2}) = r_{o2}(1 + 40I_{C2}R_{E2}) = 3.30M\Omega[1 + 40(0.114)] = 18.3 \text{ MΩ}$$

$$I_{O3} = \frac{0.025V}{2.5k\Omega} \ln\left(\frac{215\mu A}{I_{O3}} \frac{20}{1}\right) \rightarrow I_{O3} = 45.5 \text{ μA} \quad | \quad V_{E3} \cong 45.4\mu A(2.5k\Omega) = 0.114V$$

$$r_{o3} = \frac{70 + 5 - 0.114}{45.5\mu A} = 1.65M\Omega \quad | \quad R_{OUT3} \cong r_{o3}(1 + g_{m3}R_{E3}) = 1.65M\Omega[1 + 40(0.114)] = 9.17 \text{ MΩ}$$

16.23

$$R = \frac{[5 - 0.7 - 0.7 - (-5)]V}{50\mu A} = 172 \text{ kΩ}$$

$$R_2 = \frac{V_T}{I_{o2}} \ln\left(\frac{I_{REF}}{I_{O2}} \frac{I_{S2}}{I_{S1}}\right) = \frac{0.025V}{10\mu A} \ln\left(\frac{50\mu A}{10\mu A} \frac{10}{1}\right) = 9.78 \text{ kΩ}$$

$$I_{o3}R_3 = V_T \ln\left(\frac{I_{REF}}{I_{O3}} \frac{I_{S3}}{I_{S1}}\right) \quad | \quad (10\mu A)(2k\Omega) = 0.025V \ln\left(\frac{50\mu A}{10\mu A} \frac{n}{1}\right) \rightarrow n = 0.445$$

16.24 Note: Use $-V_{EE} = -5$ V

For the current mirror at the bottom: $I_{C2} = \beta_F I_{B2} \quad | \quad I_{E3} = I_{C1} + I_{B1} + I_{B2} = n\beta_F I_{B2} + nI_{B2} + I_{B2}$

$$I_{C2} = \frac{\beta_F}{1 + n(\beta_F + 1)} I_{E3} \quad | \quad I_O = \alpha_F I_{E3} = \frac{\beta_F}{\beta_F + 1} \frac{1 + n(\beta_F + 1)}{\beta_F} I_{C2} \quad | \quad I_{C2} = I_{REF} - I_{B3} = I_{REF} - \frac{I_O}{\beta_F}$$

$$I_O = \frac{1 + n(\beta_F + 1)}{\beta_F + 1}\left(I_{REF} - \frac{I_O}{\beta_F}\right) \rightarrow I_O = \frac{n + \frac{1}{\beta_F(\beta_F + 1)}}{1 + \frac{n}{\beta_F} + \frac{1}{\beta_F(\beta_F + 1)}} I_{REF} \cong \frac{n}{1 + \frac{n}{\beta_F}} I_{REF} \cong nI_{REF} \text{ for } \beta_F \gg n$$

(a) $I_O \cong \dfrac{1}{1 + \dfrac{1}{125}} 50\mu A = 49.6 \text{ μA} \quad | \quad R_{OUT} \cong \dfrac{\beta_o r_o}{2} = \dfrac{125}{2} \dfrac{40 - 0.7 - (-5)}{49.6} \dfrac{V}{\mu A} = 55.8 \text{ MΩ}$

(b) $I_O \cong \dfrac{3}{1 + \dfrac{3}{125}} 50\mu A = 146 \text{ μA} \quad | \quad R_{OUT} \cong \dfrac{\beta_o r_o}{2} = \dfrac{125}{2} \dfrac{44.3}{146} \dfrac{V}{\mu A} = 19.0 \text{ MΩ}$

(c) $V_{CS} = I_O R_{OUT} = 146\mu A(19.0M\Omega) = 2770V$ (d) $V_{CB3} = V_{EE} - 0.7V - 0.7V \geq 0 \rightarrow V_{EE} \geq 1.40V$

16.25

$$R_{OUT} \cong \frac{\beta_o r_o}{2} \cong \frac{\beta_o V_A}{2I_O} = \frac{\beta_o V_A}{2nI_{REF}} \quad | \quad \text{For Prob. } 16.24, \ R_{OUT} \cong \frac{125(40)}{2n(50\mu A)} = \frac{50}{n} M\Omega$$

16.26

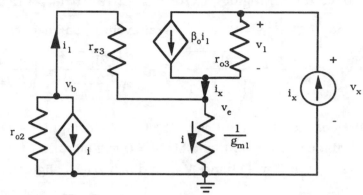

$$\begin{bmatrix} i_x \\ 0 \end{bmatrix} = \begin{bmatrix} g_{m1} + g_{\pi 3} & -g_{\pi 3} \\ g_{m1} - g_{\pi 3} & g_{\pi 3} + g_{o2} \end{bmatrix} \begin{bmatrix} v_e \\ v_b \end{bmatrix} \quad | \quad I_{C1} \cong I_{C2} \cong I_{C3} \text{ so small - signal parameters are the same}$$

$$\Delta = 2g_{m1}g_{\pi 3} + g_{m1}g_{o2} + g_{\pi 3}g_{o2} = g_{m1}g_{\pi 3}\left(2 + \frac{\beta_o}{\mu_f} + \frac{1}{\mu_f}\right) \cong 2g_{m1}g_{\pi 3} \quad \text{for} \quad \mu_f \gg \beta_o \gg 1$$

$$v_e = i_x \frac{g_{\pi 3} + g_{o2}}{\Delta} = \frac{i_x}{2g_{m1}}\left(1 + \frac{\beta_o}{\mu_f}\right) \cong \frac{i_x}{2g_{m1}} \quad | \quad v_b = -i_x \frac{g_{m1} - g_{\pi 3}}{\Delta}$$

$$v_b - v_e = -i_x \frac{g_{m1} + g_{o2}}{\Delta} = -\frac{i_x}{2g_{\pi 3}}\left(1 + \frac{1}{\mu_f}\right) \cong \frac{i_x}{2} r_{\pi 3} \quad | \quad i_1 = g_{\pi 3}(v_b - v_e) = \frac{i_x}{2}$$

$$v_x = v_e + (i_x - \beta_o i_1)r_{o3} = \frac{i_x}{2g_{m1}} + i_x r_{o3} + \beta_o r_{o3}\frac{i_x}{2} \quad | \quad R_{OUT} = \frac{1}{2g_{m1}} + r_{o3} + \frac{\beta_o r_{o3}}{2} \cong \frac{\beta_o r_{o3}}{2}$$

16.27

$$V_{CB3} = V_{C3} - V_{BE3} - V_{BE2} - (-V_{EE}) \geq 0 \rightarrow V_{C3} \geq -V_{EE} + V_{BE3} + V_{BE2}$$

$$V_{BE3} + V_{BE1} = V_T \ln\frac{I_{C3}}{I_{S3}} + V_T \ln\frac{I_{C1}}{I_{S1}} \quad | \quad I_{C1} + \frac{I_{C1}}{\beta_F} + \frac{I_{C1}}{n\beta_F} = \frac{I_{C3}}{\alpha_F} \cong \frac{\beta_F + 1}{\beta_F}I_{C3} \quad | \quad \text{From Prob.}$$

$$16.24: \ I_{C3} \cong \frac{n}{1 + \dfrac{n}{\beta_F}}I_{REF} = \frac{5}{1 + \dfrac{5}{125}}15\mu A = 72.1\mu A \quad | \quad I_{C1} = \frac{1}{1 + \dfrac{1}{\beta_F} + \dfrac{1}{n\beta_F}}\frac{\beta_F + 1}{\beta_F}I_{C3} = 72.0\mu A$$

$$V_{BE3} + V_{BE2} = 0.025V\left(\ln\frac{72.1\mu A}{3fA} + \ln\frac{72.0\mu A}{15fA}\right) = 1.16V \quad | \quad V_{C3} \geq -V_{EE} + 1.16 \ V$$

16.28 (a)

Assuming balanced drain voltages, $I_{DS3} = I_{DS1} = I_{REF}\dfrac{\left(\dfrac{W}{L}\right)_1}{\left(\dfrac{W}{L}\right)_2} = \dfrac{I_{REF}}{4} \quad | \quad I_{REF} = \dfrac{5 - V_{GS1} - V_{GS3}}{30k\Omega}$

$$V_{GS1} = V_{TN} + \sqrt{\frac{2I_{DS1}}{K_{n1}}} = 0.75 + \sqrt{\frac{2I_{REF}}{4(5K_n')}} \quad | \quad V_{GS3} = 0.75 + \sqrt{\frac{2I_{REF}}{4(20K_n')}}$$

$$I_{REF} = \frac{5 - 0.75 - \sqrt{\dfrac{2I_{REF}}{4(5K_n')}} - 0.75 - \sqrt{\dfrac{2I_{REF}}{4(20K_n')}}}{30k\Omega} \quad | \quad (30k\Omega)I_{REF} = 3.5 - 1.5\sqrt{\dfrac{I_{REF}}{10K_n'}}$$

Using $K_n' = 25 \times 10^{-6}$ and rearranging: $\quad 9 \times 10^{8} I_{REF}^{2} - 2.19 \times 10^{5} I_{REF} + 12.25 = 0$

$I_{REF} = 87.2 \, \mu A$ and $I_O = \dfrac{I_{REF}}{4} = 21.8 \, \mu A$. Drain voltage balance on M_1 and M_2

requires $V_{GS4} = V_{GS3} \quad | \quad V_{TN} + \sqrt{\dfrac{2I_{REF}}{\left(\dfrac{W}{L}\right)_4 K_n'}} = V_{TN} + \sqrt{\dfrac{2I_{REF}}{4(20K_n')}} \quad | \quad \left(\dfrac{W}{L}\right)_4 = \dfrac{80}{1}$

(b)

This part requires an iterative solution or the use of a computer solver.
Assuming V_{DS} balance between M_1 and M_2, $\lambda \neq 0$ will not affect the
current mirror ratio, but it will change V_{GS} and hence I_{REF} slightly.
One iterative approach:

Guess $V_{GS1} \quad |$ Then $I_{D1} = \dfrac{5K_n'}{2}(V_{GS1} - V_{TN})^2 (1 + \lambda V_{GS1})$

Since $I_{DS3} = I_{DS1}$, $V_{GS3} = V_{TN} + \sqrt{\dfrac{2I_{DS1}}{20K_n'[1 + \lambda(5 - V_{GS1})]}}$

$I_{REF} = \dfrac{5 - V_{GS1} - V_{GS3}}{30k\Omega}$ and $I_{DS1} = \dfrac{I_{REF}}{4}$.

If the second value of I_{DS1} does not agree with the first, then try a new V_{GS1}.
A spreadsheet yields: $V_{GS1} = 1.336V$, $V_{GS3} = 1.381V$, $I_{REF} = 87.5\mu A$, $I_O = 21.7\mu A$.

Note: There is essentially no change from the first answer!

(c)
```
*Problem 16.28 - NMOS Wilson Source
RREF 1 0 30K
VSS 4 0 DC -5
M1 3 3 4 4 NFET W=5U L=1U
M2 2 3 4 4 NFET W=20U L=1U
M3 0 1 3 3 NFET W=20U L=1U
M4 1 1 2 2 NFET W=80U L=1U
.MODEL NFET NMOS KP=25U VTO=0.75 LAMBDA=0.015
.OP
.END
```

16.29

$$I_O = I_{REF}\frac{\left(\dfrac{W}{L}\right)_1}{\left(\dfrac{W}{L}\right)_2} \quad | \quad R_{OUT} = \mu_{f2} r_{o3} = \mu_{f2}\frac{1}{\lambda_3 I_O} = \frac{1}{\lambda_2}\sqrt{\frac{2K_n}{I_{DS2}}}\frac{1}{\lambda_3 I_O}$$

$$R_{OUT} = \frac{1}{\lambda_2}\sqrt{\frac{2\left(\dfrac{W}{L}\right)_2 K_n'}{I_{REF}}}\frac{1}{\lambda_3 I_{REF}}\frac{\left(\dfrac{W}{L}\right)_2}{\left(\dfrac{W}{L}\right)_1} = \frac{1}{\lambda_2 \lambda_3}\left[\frac{\left(\dfrac{W}{L}\right)_2}{I_{REF}}\right]^{\frac{3}{2}}\frac{\sqrt{2K_n'}}{\left(\dfrac{W}{L}\right)_1}$$

16.30

Since $\lambda = 0$, $I_{DS3} = I_{DS1} = I_{REF} \dfrac{\left(\dfrac{W}{L}\right)_1}{\left(\dfrac{W}{L}\right)_2} = \dfrac{150\mu A}{4} = 37.5\mu A$

$V_{DS3} \geq V_{GS3} - V_{TN3} \ | \ V_{D3} - (-10 + V_{GS1}) \geq V_{GS3} - V_{TN3} \ | \ V_{D3} \geq -10 + V_{GS1} + V_{GS3} - V_{TN3}$

$V_{D3} \geq -10 + V_{TN1} + \sqrt{\dfrac{2I_{DS1}}{K_{n1}}} + V_{TN3} + \sqrt{\dfrac{2I_{DS3}}{K_{n3}}} - V_{TN3}$

$V_{D3} \geq -10V + 0.75V + \sqrt{\dfrac{2(37.5\mu A)V^2}{5(25\mu A)}} + \sqrt{\dfrac{2(37.5\mu A)V^2}{20(25\mu A)}} = -8.09 \ V$

16.31

$R_{OUT} \cong \mu_{f2}r_{o3} \ | \ \left(\dfrac{W}{L}\right)_2 = \left(\dfrac{W}{L}\right)_1 \Rightarrow I_O = I_{REF} = 50\mu A \ | \ r_{o3} \cong \dfrac{1}{\lambda I_{DS3}} = \dfrac{1}{0.0125(50\mu A)} = 1.60M\Omega$

$\mu_{f2} = \dfrac{R_{OUT}}{r_{o3}} = \dfrac{250M\Omega}{1.60M\Omega} = 156 \ | \ $ Using Eq. 13.71, $\mu_{f2} = \dfrac{1}{\lambda}\sqrt{\dfrac{2K_n}{I_{DS2}}}$

$\left(\dfrac{W}{L}\right)_2 = (\lambda\mu_{f2})^2 \dfrac{I_{DS2}}{2K_n} = [0.0125(156)]^2 \dfrac{5\times10^{-5}}{2(2.5\times10^{-5})} = \dfrac{3.80}{1}$

16.32 The circuit is the same as Fig. 16.20 with the addition of R_{REF} in parallel with r_{o2}. We require $R_{REF} >> r_{o2}$ in order not to reduce the gain of the feedback loop. A current source with a source resistor which achieves $R_{OUT} - r_o(1 + g_m R_s)$ should be sufficient. A cascode or Wilson source will also work.

16.33

(a) $R_O = \mu_{F4}r_{o2} \ | \ $ All K_n are the same: $I_O = I_{REF} = 17.5\mu A$

$V_{GS1} = 0.75 + \sqrt{\dfrac{2(17.5\times10^{-6})}{75\times10^{-6}}} = 1.43V \ | \ \Delta V_3 = V_{GS3} - V_{TN3} = 1.43V - 0.75V = 0.680$

$r_{o2} = \dfrac{\dfrac{1}{0.0125} + 1.43}{17.5\mu A} = 4.65M\Omega \ | \ r_{o4} = \dfrac{\dfrac{1}{0.0125} + (5 - 1.43)}{17.5\mu A} = 4.78M\Omega$

$g_{m4} = \sqrt{2(75\times10^{-6})(17.5\times10^{-6})(1 + 0.0125(5 - 1.43))} = 5.24\times10^{-5}S$

$\mu_{F4} = 5.24\times10^{-5}S(4.78M\Omega) = 250 \ | \ R_O = 1.16 \ G\Omega$

(b) $V_{CS} = I_O R_O = 20.3 \ kV!$ (c) $V_{DD}^{min} = V_{GS1} + \Delta V_4 = 1.43 + 0.680 = 2.11V$

16.34

```
*Problem 16.34 - NMOS Cascode Source
IREF 0 1 DC 17.5U
VDD 2 0 DC 5
M1 3 3 0 0 NFET W=3U L=1U
M2 4 3 0 0 NFET W=3U L=1U
M3 1 1 3 3 NFET W=3U L=1U
M4 2 1 4 4 NFET W=3U L=1U
.MODEL NFET NMOS KP=25U VTO=0.75 LAMBDA=0.0125
.OP
```

Results: $I_O = 17.5\ \mu A$ $R_{OUT} = 1.17\ G\Omega$ – The same as the hand analysis.

16.35

(a) $I_{REF} = I_{C3} + I_{B3} + I_{B4} = I_{E3} + I_{B4} = I_{C1} + \dfrac{2I_{C1}}{\beta_F} + \dfrac{I_{C2}}{\beta_F + 1} = I_{C1} + \dfrac{2I_{C1}}{\beta_F} + \dfrac{I_{C1}}{\beta_F + 1}$

$I_{C1} = \dfrac{I_{REF}}{1 + \dfrac{2}{\beta_F} + \dfrac{1}{\beta_F + 1}}$ | $I_O = I_{C4} = \alpha_F I_{C2} = \alpha_F I_{C1} = \dfrac{\beta_F}{\beta_F + 1}\dfrac{I_{REF}}{1 + \dfrac{2}{\beta_F} + \dfrac{1}{\beta_F + 1}}$

$I_O = \dfrac{110}{111}\left(\dfrac{17.5\mu A}{1 + \dfrac{2}{110} + \dfrac{1}{111}}\right) = 16.9\ \mu A$ | $R_{OUT} = \dfrac{\beta_o r_o}{2} \cong \dfrac{110(50)}{2(16.9\mu A)} = 163\ M\Omega$

(b) $V_{CS} = I_O R_{OUT} = 16.9\mu A(163M\Omega) = 2750$ (c) $V_{CC} \geq 2V_{BE} = 1.40\ V$

16.36

```
*Problem 16.36 - NPN Cascode Current Source
IREF 0 1 17.5U
VCC 2 0 DC 5
Q1 3 3 0 NBJT 1
Q2 4 3 0 NBJT 1
Q3 1 1 3 NBJT 1
Q4 2 1 4 NBJT 1
.MODEL NBJT NPN BF=110 VA=50
.OP
.TF I(VCC) VCC
.END
```

Results: $I_O = 16.9\ \mu A$ $R_{OUT} = 1.86\ M\Omega$ – The same as the hand analysis.

16.37

$R_{OUT} = \mu_{f4} r_{o2}$ | $\left(\dfrac{W}{L}\right)_2 = \left(\dfrac{W}{L}\right)_1 \Rightarrow I_O = I_{REF} = 50\mu A$ | $r_{o2} \cong \dfrac{1}{\lambda I_{DS2}} = \dfrac{1}{0.0125(50\mu A)} = 1.60M\Omega$

$\mu_{f4} = \dfrac{R_{OUT}}{r_{o2}} = \dfrac{250M\Omega}{1.60M\Omega} = 156$ | Using Eq. 13.71, $\mu_{f4} = \dfrac{1}{\lambda}\sqrt{\dfrac{2K_{n4}}{I_{DS4}}}$

$\left(\dfrac{W}{L}\right)_4 = \left(\lambda\mu_{f4}\right)^2 \dfrac{I_{DS4}}{2K_n} = \left[0.0125(156)\right]^2 \dfrac{5\times10^{-5}}{2\left(2.5\times10^{-5}\right)} = \dfrac{3.80}{1}$

16.38

```
*Problem 16.38 - NPN Widlar Current Source
IREF 2 1 50U
VCC 2 0 DC 10
Q1 1 1 0 NBJT 1
Q2 2 1 3 NBJT 20
R2 3 0 4K
.MODEL NBJT NPN BF=110
.OP
.DC IREF 50U 5M 50U
.PROBE IC(Q2)
.END
```

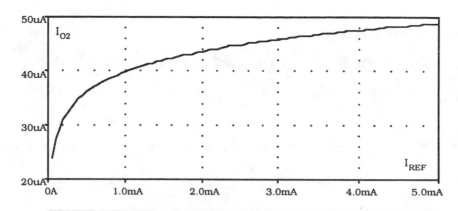

16.39

$$I_O = \alpha_F I_{E2} = \alpha_F \left(\frac{V_{BE1}}{R_2} + I_{B1} \right) \cong \frac{V_{BE1}}{R_2} = \frac{V_T}{R_2} \ln \frac{I_{C1}}{I_{S1}}$$

$$I_{C1} = \frac{V_{EE} - V_{BE2} - V_{BE1}}{R_1} - I_{B2} \cong \frac{V_{EE} - V_{BE2} - V_{BE1}}{R_1}$$

(a) $I_{C2} \cong \dfrac{0.025V}{2.2k\Omega} \ln \dfrac{15 - 1.4}{10^4 \left(10^{-15}\right)} = 318 \ \mu A$ | Note: $\dfrac{V_{BE1}}{R_2} \cong \dfrac{0.7V}{2.2k\Omega} = 318 \ \mu A$

(b) $I_{C2} \cong \dfrac{0.025V}{2.2k\Omega} \ln \dfrac{3.3 - 1.4}{10^4 \left(10^{-15}\right)} = 295 \ \mu A$ | Note: $\dfrac{V_{BE1}}{R_2} \cong \dfrac{0.7V}{2.2k\Omega} = 318 \ \mu A$

(c) $I_{C2} \cong \dfrac{V_T}{R_2} \ln \dfrac{V_{CC} - V_{EB1} - V_{EB2}}{I_{S1}R_1} = \dfrac{0.025V}{10k\Omega} \ln \dfrac{5 - 1.4}{10^4 \left(10^{-15}\right)} = 66.5 \ \mu A$ | $\dfrac{0.7V}{10k\Omega} = 70 \ \mu A$

16.40

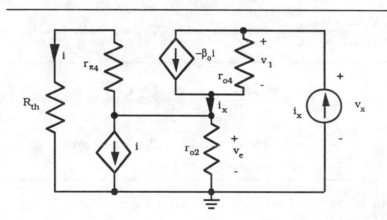

$$\mathbf{v_x} = \mathbf{v_1} + \mathbf{v_e} = \left(\mathbf{i_x} - \beta_o \mathbf{i_1}\right) r_{o4} + \left(\mathbf{i_x} - 2\mathbf{i}\right) r_{o2} \ \ | \ \ \mathbf{i_1} = -\mathbf{i} \ \ | \ \ \mathbf{v_x} = \left(\mathbf{i_x} + \beta_o \mathbf{i}\right) r_{o4} + \left(\mathbf{i_x} - 2\mathbf{i}\right) r_{o2}$$

$$\mathbf{i} = \frac{\left(\mathbf{i_x} - 2\mathbf{i}\right) r_{o2}}{r_{\pi4} + R_{th}} \ \text{ where } R_{th} = \frac{1}{g_{m3}} + \frac{1}{g_{m2}} << r_{\pi4} \ \ | \ \ \mathbf{i} \cong \frac{\left(\mathbf{i_x} - 2\mathbf{i}\right) r_{o2}}{r_{\pi4}} \ \ | \ \ \mathbf{i} = \mathbf{i_x} \frac{r_{o2}}{r_{\pi4} + 2r_{o2}}$$

$$\mathbf{i} = \mathbf{i_x} \frac{\mu_{f2}}{\beta_{o4} + 2\mu_{f2}} \cong \frac{\mathbf{i_x}}{2} \ \text{ for } 2\mu_{f2} >> \beta_o \ \ | \ \ \mathbf{v_x} = \mathbf{i_x}\left(r_{o2} + r_{o4} + \frac{\beta_o r_{o4}}{2} - r_{o2} \right)$$

$$R_{OUT} \cong r_{o4}\left(\frac{\beta_o}{2} + 1\right) \cong \frac{\beta_o r_{o4}}{2} \ \ \text{ for } R_{th} << r_{\pi4} \text{ and } 2\mu_{f2} >> \beta_o$$

16.41

An iterative solution is required:

1. Choose V_{GS2}. Then $I_{DS2} = \dfrac{K_{n2}}{2}\left(V_{GS2} - V_{TN2}\right)^2$ and $I_{DS1} = \dfrac{V_{GS2}}{R_2}$

2. $V_{GS1} = V_{TN1} + \sqrt{\dfrac{2I_{DS1}}{K_{n1}}}$

3. $I_{DS2} = \dfrac{V_{DD} - V_{GS1} - V_{GS2}}{R_1}$ Compare to I_{DS2} in step 1 and choose new V_{GS2}

$I_{DS2} = \dfrac{2.5 \times 10^{-4}}{2}\left(V_{GS2} - 0.75\right)^2$ | $I_{DS1} = \dfrac{V_{GS2}}{15k\Omega}$ | $V_{GS1} = 0.75 + \sqrt{\dfrac{2I_{DS1}}{2.5 \times 10^{-4}}}$

$I_{DS2} = \dfrac{10 - V_{GS1} - V_{GS2}}{10k\Omega}$ | Iteration yields $V_{GS2} = 2.8V$, $I_O = I_{DS2} = 187\ \mu A$

16.42

An iterative solution is required:

1. Choose V_{SG1}. Then $I_{SD1} = \dfrac{K_{p1}}{2}\left(V_{SG1} + V_{TP1}\right)^2$ and $I_{SD2} = \dfrac{V_{SG1}}{R_2}$

2. $V_{SG2} = -V_{TP2} + \sqrt{\dfrac{2I_{SD2}}{K_{p2}}}$

3. $I_{SD1} = \dfrac{V_{DD} - V_{SG1} - V_{SG2}}{R_1}$ Compare to I_{SD1} in step 1 and choose new V_{SG1}

$I_{SD1} = \dfrac{10^{-4}}{2}\left(V_{SG1} - 0.75\right)^2$ | $I_{SD2} = \dfrac{V_{GS2}}{18k\Omega}$ | $V_{SG2} = 0.75 + \sqrt{\dfrac{2I_{SD2}}{10^{-4}}}$

$I_{SD1} = \dfrac{V_{DD} - V_{SG1} - V_{SG2}}{10k\Omega}$ | Iteration yields $V_{GS2} = 2.24V$, $I_O = I_{DS2} = 111\ \mu A$

16.43

$I_{C1} = I_{C3} = 3I_{C4}$ | $I_{C4} = I_{C2} = \dfrac{V_{BE1} - V_{BE2}}{R} = \dfrac{V_T}{R}\left(\ln\dfrac{I_{C1}}{I_{S1}} - \ln\dfrac{I_{C2}}{I_{S2}}\right) = \dfrac{V_T}{R}\left(\ln\dfrac{I_{C1}}{I_{C2}}\dfrac{I_{S2}}{I_{S1}}\right)$

$I_{C2} = \dfrac{0.025V}{2.2k\Omega}\left(\ln\dfrac{3I_{C2}}{I_{C2}}\dfrac{20A}{A}\right) = 46.5\ \mu A$ | $I_{C1} = 3I_{C2} = 140\ \mu A$

16.44

```
*Problem 16.44 - BJT reference current cell
VCC 1 0 DC 1.5 AC 1
VEE 5 0 DC -1.5
Q4 2 2 1 PBJT 1
Q3 3 2 1 PBJT 3
Q1 3 3 5 NBJT 1
Q2 2 3 4 NBJT 20
R 4 5 2.2K
.MODEL NBJT NPN BF=100 VA=50
.MODEL PBJT PNP BF=100 VA=50
.OP
.AC LIN 1 1000 1000
.PRINT AC IC(Q1) IC(Q2)
.END
```

Results: $I_{C1} = 140\ \mu A$ $I_{C2} = 47.8\ \mu A$ $S_{V_{CC}}^{I_{C1}} = 2.92 \times 10^{-2}$ $S_{V_{CC}}^{I_{C2}} = 9.92 \times 10^{-3} S$

16.45

The M_3 - M_4 current mirror forces $I_{SD1} = I_{SD2}$.

$$V_{GS1} - V_{GS2} = I_{DS2}R \mid I_{DS2}R = V_{TN} + \sqrt{\frac{2I_{DS1}}{10K_n'}} - V_{TN} - \sqrt{\frac{2I_{DS2}}{20K_n'}} \mid I_{DS2}R = \sqrt{\frac{2I_{DS2}}{10K_n'}}\left(1 - \frac{1}{\sqrt{2}}\right)$$

$$\sqrt{I_{DS2}} = \frac{0.293}{R}\sqrt{\frac{1}{5K_n'}} = \frac{0.293}{5100}\sqrt{\frac{1}{5(25x10^{-6})}} \Rightarrow I_{DS2} = 26.4 \ \mu A$$

16.46

(a) The M_3 - M_4 current mirror forces $I_{SD1} = I_{SD2}$.

$$V_{GS1} - V_{GS2} = I_{DS2}R \mid I_{DS2}R = V_{TN1} + \sqrt{\frac{2I_{DS1}}{10K_n'}} - V_{TN2} - \sqrt{\frac{2I_{DS2}}{20K_n'}} \mid I_{DS2}R = \sqrt{\frac{2I_{DS2}}{10K_n'}}\left(1 - \frac{1}{\sqrt{2}}\right)$$

$$\sqrt{I_{DS2}} = \frac{0.293}{R}\sqrt{\frac{1}{5K_n'}} = \frac{0.293}{10^4}\sqrt{\frac{1}{5(25x10^{-6})}} \Rightarrow I_{DS2} = 6.86 \ \mu A$$

(b) $V_{TN1} = V_{TO} \mid V_{TN2} = V_{TO} + \gamma\left(\sqrt{2\phi_F + V_{SB}} - \sqrt{2\phi_F}\right) = V_{TO} + 0.5\left(\sqrt{0.6 + I_{DS2}R} - \sqrt{0.6}\right)$

$$I_{DS2}R = V_{TO} + \sqrt{\frac{2I_{DS1}}{10K_n'}} - V_{TO} - 0.5\left(\sqrt{0.6 + I_{DS2}R} - \sqrt{0.6}\right) - \sqrt{\frac{2I_{DS2}}{20K_n'}}$$

$$I_{DS2} = \frac{0.293}{10^4}\sqrt{\frac{2I_{DS2}}{10K_n'}} - \frac{0.5}{10^4}\left(\sqrt{0.6 + 10^4 I_{DS2}} - \sqrt{0.6}\right) \rightarrow I_{DS2} = 3.96 \ \mu A$$

16.47

```
*Problem 16.47(a)  MOS reference current cell
VDD 1 0 DC 5 AC 1
VSS 5 0 DC -5
M1 3 3 5 5 NFET W=10U L=1U
M2 2 3 4 5 NFET W=20U L=1U
M3 3 2 1 1 PFET W=10U L=1U
M4 2 2 1 1 PFET W=10U L=1U
R 4 5 10K
.MODEL NFET NMOS KP=25U VTO=0.75 PHI=0.6 GAMMA=0 LAMBDA=0.017
.MODEL PFET PMOS KP=10U VTO=-0.75 PHI=0.6 GAMMA=0 LAMBDA=0.017
*.MODEL NFET NMOS KP=25U VTO=0.75 PHI=0.6 GAMMA=0 LAMBDA=0
*.MODEL PFET PMOS KP=10U VTO=-0.75 PHI=0.6 GAMMA=0 LAMBDA=0
*Problem 16.47(b) - MOS reference current cell
*.MODEL NFET NMOS KP=25U VTO=0.75 PHI=0.6 GAMMA=0.5 LAMBDA=0.017
*.MODEL PFET PMOS KP=10U VTO=-0.75 PHI=0.6 GAMMA=0.75 LAMBDA=0.017
.OP
.AC LIN 1 1000 1000
.PRINT AC ID(M1) ID(M2)
.END
```

Results: (a) $I_{D2} = 13.9 \ \mu A$ $I_{D2} = 12.3 \ \mu A$ $\quad S_{V_{DD}}^{I_{DS1}} = 7.64x10^{-2}$ $\quad S_{V_{DD}}^{I_{DS2}} = 6.23x10^{-2}$

The currents differ considerably from the hand calculations.

Results: (b) $I_{D1} = 8.19 \ \mu A$ $I_{D2} = 7.24 \ \mu A$ $\quad S_{V_{DD}}^{I_{DS1}} = 7.75x10^{-2}$ $\quad S_{V_{DD}}^{I_{DS2}} = 6.31x10^{-2}$

The currents differ considerably from the hand calculations.

The currents are quite sensitive to the value of λ. The hand calculations used $\lambda = 0$. If the simulations are run with $\lambda = 0$, then the results are identical to the hand calculations.

16.48

$$I_{C2} = \frac{V_T}{R} \ln\left(\frac{I_{C1}}{A} \frac{5A}{I_{C2}}\right) \;\Big|\; I_{C1} = I_{C3} = 2I_{C4} = 2I_{C2} \;\Big|\; I_{C2} = \frac{0.025V}{11k\Omega} \ln\left(\frac{2I_{C2}}{A} \frac{5A}{I_{C2}}\right) = 5.23 \;\mu A$$

$$I_{C7} = 5I_{C4} = 5(5.23\mu A) = 26.2 \;\mu A \;\Big|\; I_{C8} = \frac{V_T}{R_8} \ln\left(\frac{I_{C4}}{A} \frac{3A}{I_{C8}}\right) = \frac{0.025V}{4k\Omega} \ln\left(\frac{15.7\mu A}{I_{C8}}\right) \rightarrow I_{C8} = 6.00 \;\mu A$$

$$I_{C5} = 2.5I_{C1} = 5I_{C2} = 26.2 \;\mu A \;\Big|\; I_{C6} = \frac{V_T}{R_6} \ln\left(\frac{I_{C1}}{A} \frac{A}{I_{C6}}\right) = \frac{0.025V}{3k\Omega} \ln\left(\frac{10.4\mu A}{I_{C6}}\right) \rightarrow I_{C8} = 5.42 \;\mu A$$

16.49

$$I_{C1} = 2I_{C2} \;\Big|\; I_{C2} = \frac{V_T}{R}\left(\ln \frac{I_{C1}}{I_{C2}} \frac{I_{S2}}{I_{S1}}\right) = \frac{0.025V}{4.3k\Omega}\left(\ln \frac{2I_{C2}}{I_{C2}} \frac{7I_{S1}}{I_{S1}}\right) = 15.3 \;\mu A \;\Big|\; I_{C1} = 2I_{C2} = 30.6 \;\mu A$$

$$I_{C4} = I_{C5} = I_{C6} = I_{C1} = 30.6 \;\mu A \;\Big|\; I_{C3} = I_{C7} = I_{C2} = 15.3 \;\mu A$$

16.50

```
*Problem 16.50 - NPN Cascode Current Source
VCC 1 0 DC 5 AC 1
Q4 2 2 1 PBJT 2
Q3 3 2 1 PBJT 1
Q5 4 3 2 PBJT 1
Q1 6 6 0 NBJT 1
Q2 5 6 7 NBJT 7
Q6 4 4 6 NBJT 1
Q7 3 4 5 NBJT 1
R 7 0 4.3K
.MODEL NBJT NPN BF=100 VA=50
.MODEL PBJT PNP BF=50 VA=50
.OP
.AC LIN 1 1000 1000
.PRINT AC IC(Q7) IC(Q5)
.END
```

Results: $I_{C2} = 15.2 \;\mu A$ $I_{C1} = 28.5 \;\mu A$ Similar to hand calculations.

$$S_{V_{CC}}^{I_{C2}} = 1.81 \times 10^{-3} \quad S_{V_{CC}}^{I_{C2}} = 7.07 \times 10^{-4}$$

16.51 Note: $V_{DD} = 10$ V is not large enough to saturate all the transistors. Use $V_{DD} = 15$ V to ensure saturation.

The M_3 - M_4 current mirror forces $I_{DS1} = 1.5 I_{DS2}$.

$$V_{GS1} - V_{GS2} = I_{DS2}R \;\Big|\; I_{DS2}R = V_{TN} + \sqrt{\frac{2I_{DS1}}{10K_n'}} - V_{TN} - \sqrt{\frac{2I_{DS2}}{30K_n'}}$$

$$I_{DS2} = \frac{1}{R}\left(\sqrt{\frac{3I_{DS2}}{10K_n'}} - \sqrt{\frac{2I_{DS2}}{30K_n'}}\right) = \frac{1}{3300}\left(\sqrt{\frac{3I_{DS2}}{10(25 \times 10^{-6})}} - \sqrt{\frac{2I_{DS2}}{30(25 \times 10^{-6})}}\right)$$

$$\sqrt{I_{DS2}} = \frac{57.9}{3300} \Rightarrow I_{DS2} = 308 \;\mu A \quad I_{DS1} = 462 \;\mu A$$

$$I_{SD4} = I_{SD5} = I_{SD6} = I_{DS1} = 462 \;\mu A \;\Big|\; I_{SD3} = I_{SD7} = I_{DS2} = 308 \;\mu A$$

16.52 Note: $V_{DD} = 10$ V is not large enough to saturate all the transistors.

```
*Problem 16.52 - MOS reference current cell
VDD 1 0 DC 15 AC 1
M3 3 2 1 1 PFET W=10U L=1U
M4 2 2 1 1 PFET W=15U L=1U
M5 4 3 2 2 PFET W=10U L=1U
M6 4 4 6 6 NFET W=10U L=1U
M7 3 4 5 5 NFET W=10U L=1U
M1 6 6 0 0 NFET W=10U L=1U
M2 5 6 7 7 NFET W=30U L=1U
R 7 0 3.3K
*.MODEL NFET NMOS KP=25U VTO=0.75 LAMBDA=0
*.MODEL PFET PMOS KP=10U VTO=-0.75 LAMBDA=0
.MODEL NFET NMOS KP=25U VTO=0.75 LAMBDA=0.017
.MODEL PFET PMOS KP=10U VTO=-0.75 LAMBDA=0.017
.OP
.AC LIN 1 1000 1000
.PRINT AC ID(M1) ID(M2)
.END
```

Results: $I_{DS2} = 265$ µA $I_{DS1} = 377$ µA These differ from the hand calculations due to the non-zero value of λ. Simulation with $\lambda = 0$ (and $V_{DD} = 15$ V) gives results very close to the hand calculations.

$$S_{V_{DD}}^{I_{DS2}} = 9.82 \times 10^{-4} \quad S_{V_{CC}}^{I_{c2}} = 6.99 \times 10^{-4}$$

16.53

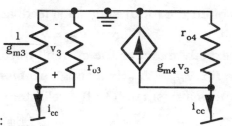

Current mirror model:

Assuming $V_{DS} \ll \dfrac{1}{\lambda}$ since it is unknown:

$$A_{dd} = g_{m1}(r_{o2} \| r_{o4}) \cong g_{m1} \frac{r_{o4}}{2} \cong \sqrt{2(5 \times 10^{-4})(10^{-4})} \left(\frac{50}{10^{-4}} \left\| \frac{50}{10^{-4}} \right. \right) = 0.316 \text{mS}(250\text{k}\Omega) = 79.1$$

A_{cd} is determined by the mirror ratio error:

$$i_{cc} + g_{m4}\mathbf{v_3} = i_{cc} - g_{m4} \frac{i_{cc}}{g_{m3} + g_{o3}} = i_{cc} \frac{g_{m3} - g_{m4} + g_{o3}}{g_{m3} + g_{o3}} = i_{cc} \frac{1}{\mu_{f3} + 1} \quad \text{for } g_{m3} = g_{m4}$$

This error current goes through r_{o4} to produce the output voltage since the

common - mode output resistance at the drain of M_2 is very large: $\mathbf{v_{od}} = i_{cc} \dfrac{r_{o4}}{\mu_{f3} + 1}$

$$\mathbf{i_{cc}} = \mathbf{v_{ic}} \frac{g_{m1}}{1 + 2g_{m1}R_{SS}} \cong \mathbf{v_{ic}} \frac{1}{2R_{SS}} \quad \Big| \quad A_{cd} = \frac{1}{\mu_{f3} + 1}\left(\frac{r_{o4}}{2R_{SS}} \right) = \left[\frac{1}{2(79.1) + 1} \right] \frac{500\text{k}\Omega}{50\text{M}\Omega} = 6.28 \times 10^{-5}$$

$$\text{CMRR} = \frac{79.1}{6.28 \times 10^{-5}} = 1.26 \times 10^6 \quad (122 \text{ dB})$$

16.54

```
*Problem 16.54 - MOS Amplifier with Active Load
VDD 1 0 DC 10
```

```
VSS 5 0 DC -10
V1 6 8 DC 0 AC 0.5
V2 7 8 DC 0 AC -0.5
VIC 8 0 DC 0
M3 2 2 1 1 PFET W=50U L=1U
M4 3 2 1 1 PFET W=50U L=1U
M1 2 6 4 4 NFET W=20U L=1U
M2 3 7 4 4 NFET W=20U L=1U
ISS 4 5 DC 199.7U
RSS 4 5 25MEG
.MODEL NFET NMOS KP=25U VTO=1 LAMBDA=0.02
.MODEL PFET PMOS KP=10U VTO=-1 LAMBDA=0.02
.OP
.AC LIN 1 1000 1000
.PRINT AC VM(3) VP(3)
.TF V(3) VIC
.END
```

Results: $A_{dm} = 95.8$ $A_{cd} = 6.16 \times 10^{-5}$. The results are similar to hand calculations. The discrepancies result from not including V_{DS} in the hand calculations for g_m and r_o.

16.55
Assuming $V_{CE} \ll V_A$ since it is unknown:

$$A_{dd} = g_{m2}(r_{o2} \| r_{o4}) \cong g_{m2} \frac{r_{o4}}{2} \cong 40(10^{-4})\left(\frac{60}{10^{-4}} \Big\| \frac{60}{10^{-4}}\right) = 4.00 \text{mS}(300 \text{k}\Omega) = 1200$$

A_{cd}: This circuit is often the input stage of a feedback amplifier and the feedback applies an offset voltage V_{os} that forces $V_{C1} = V_{C2}$. In this case, the induced collector current imbalance exactly matches the current mirror imbalance and $A_{cd} = 0$.

Note that the case for $V_{C1} \neq V_{C2}$ is a tough problem!

The mirror ratio causes a mismatch in the collector currents and therefore

a mismatch in g_m: $g_{m1} = g_m + \dfrac{\Delta g_m}{2}$ $g_{m2} = g_m - \dfrac{\Delta g_m}{2}$ | The common-mode voltage that is

developed across $r_{\pi 1}$ and $r_{\pi 2}$ $\left(v_\pi^{cm}\right)$ is multiplied by g_{m1} and g_{m2}. The common $g_m v_\pi^{cm}$ term is canceled out by the current mirror, but the mismatch terms add at the output of the current mirror. The output voltage is given approximately by

$$\mathbf{v_o} = \Delta g_{m2} \mathbf{v}_\pi^{cm}\left(r_{o4} \| r_{o2}\right) = \Delta g_{m2} \mathbf{v}_\pi^{cm} \frac{r_{o2}}{2} = \frac{\Delta g_{m2}}{g_{m2}} \mathbf{v}_\pi^{cm} \frac{\mu_{f2}}{2}$$

$$\mathbf{v}_\pi^{cm} = \mathbf{v_{ic}} \frac{r_{\pi 2}}{r_{\pi 2} + (\beta_o + 1)(2R_1 \| r_{o2})} \cong \mathbf{v_{ic}} \frac{1}{g_{m2}(2R_1 \| r_{o2})} \cong \frac{\mathbf{v_{ic}}}{g_{m2} r_{o2}} = \frac{\mathbf{v_{ic}}}{\mu_{f2}} \text{ for } 2R_1 \gg r_{o2}$$

$$A_{cd} = \frac{\mathbf{v_o}}{\mathbf{v_{ic}}} \cong \frac{1}{2} \frac{\Delta g_{m2}}{g_{m2}}$$

The collector current imbalance can be found as follows: Assume that $V_{EC4} = V_{EC3} + \Delta V$

and equal Early voltages: $I_{C4} = I_{C2} \Rightarrow I_{C1} \dfrac{1 + \dfrac{0.7 + \Delta V}{V_A}}{1 + \dfrac{2}{\beta_F} + \dfrac{0.7}{V_A}} = I_{C1}\left(1 - \dfrac{\Delta V}{V_A}\right)$ | $\Delta V \cong \dfrac{V_A}{\beta_F} = \dfrac{60V}{125} = 0.48V$

$$\Delta I_C = I_{C1} - I_{C2} = I_{C0}\left(1 + \frac{V_{C1}}{V_A}\right) - I_{C0}\left(1 + \frac{V_{C1} - \Delta V}{V_A}\right) = I_{C0}\frac{\Delta V}{V_A} \quad | \quad I_{C0} = I_S \exp\frac{V_{BE}}{V_T} \cong I_C$$

$$\Delta I_C = I_{C0}\frac{\Delta V}{V_A} \cong I_C\frac{\Delta V}{V_A} \quad | \quad \frac{\Delta I_C}{I_C} \cong \frac{\Delta V}{V_A} = \frac{1}{\beta_F} \quad | \quad \frac{\Delta g_{m2}}{g_{m2}} = \frac{\Delta I_C}{I_C} = \frac{1}{\beta_F} \quad | \quad A_{cd} = \frac{1}{2\beta_F}$$

$$A_{cd} = \frac{1}{2(125)} = 4\times10^{-3} \quad | \quad CMRR = \frac{1200}{4\times10^{-3}} = 3\times10^5 \quad (110 \text{ dB})$$

Note that $V_{os} \cong \frac{\Delta V}{A_{dd}} \quad | \quad \Delta V \cong \frac{60}{125} = 0.48V \quad | \quad V_{os} \cong \frac{0.48}{1200} = 0.400mV$

These results can be easily checked with SPICE - See Problem 16.56.

16.56

```
*Problem 16.56 - BJT Differential Amplifier with Active Load
VCC 1 0 DC 5
VEE 5 0 DC -5
Q4 3 2 1 PBJT 1
Q3 2 2 1 PBJT 1
Q1 2 6 4 NBJT 1
Q2 3 7 4 NBJT 1
*Apply offset voltage to balance collector voltages
V1 6 8 DC 0.4107M AC 0.5
*V1 6 8 DC 0 AC 0.5
V2 7 8 DC 0 AC -0.5
VIC 8 0 DC 0
I1 4 5 199.8U
R1 4 5 25MEG
.MODEL NBJT NPN BF=125 VA=60
.MODEL PBJT PNP BF=125 VA=60
.OP
.AC LIN 1 1000 1000
.PRINT AC VM(3) VP(3) VM(4) VP(4)
.TF V(3) VIC
.END
```

Results: $A_{dm} = 1200$ $A_{cd} = 5.11\times10^{-6}$. CMRR = 167 dB. The results are similar to hand calculations. Note that a very high CMRR is achieved when the circuit is brought back to balance, as is the case in operational amplifier input stages with feedback applied. For the case with no offset voltage applied, $A_{cd} = 3.73\times10^{-3}$, and $\Delta V = 0.49$ V. These agree well with the analysis in Prob. 16.55. The value of the required offset voltage is also very similar to the hand calculations.

16.57

(a) $I_{SD5} = I_{SD4} = I_{SD3} = I_{DS2} = I_{DS1} = \frac{I_{SS}}{2} = 100 \ \mu A$

$$V_{GS2} = V_{GS1} = V_{TN} + \sqrt{\frac{2I_{DS1}}{K_{n1}}} = 0.75 + \sqrt{\frac{2(10^{-4})}{40(2.5\times10^{-5})}} = 1.20V$$

$$V_{SG5} = V_{SG4} = V_{SG3} = -V_{TP} + \sqrt{\frac{2I_{SD4}}{K_{p4}}} = 0.75 + \sqrt{\frac{2(10^{-4})}{80(10^{-5})}} = 1.25V \quad | \quad V_{SD3} = V_{SG4} + V_{SG5} = 2.50V$$

$$V_{DS1} = V_{DS2} = 10 - V_{SG4} - V_{SG5} - (-V_{GS1}) = 8.70V \quad | \quad V_{SD5} = V_{SD4} = V_{SG4} = 1.25V$$

Q – Pts: $(100\mu A, 8.70V)$ $(100\mu A, 8.70V)$ $(100\mu A, 2.50V)$ $(100\mu A, 1.25V)$ $(100\mu A, 1.25V)$

(b) $A_{dd} = g_{m2}\left(r_{o2}\left\|\dfrac{2}{3}\mu_{f3}r_{o5}\right.\right) \cong g_{m2}r_{o2}$

$$A_{dd} = \sqrt{2(40)(2.5x10^{-5})(10^{-4})[1+0.017(8.7)]}\left(\dfrac{\dfrac{1}{0.017}+8.7}{10^{-4}}\right) = 0.479mS(675k\Omega) = 323$$

(Note that the loop - gain of the Wilson source is reduced by the presence of $R_{OUT1} \cong 2r_{o1}$.)

(c) $A_{dd} = g_{m1}(r_{o1}\|r_{o3}) \quad | \quad r_{o3} = \left(\dfrac{\dfrac{1}{0.017}+1.25}{10^{-4}}\right) = 601k\Omega$

$A_{dd} = 0.479mS(675k\Omega\|601k\Omega) = 152$ - The Wilson source yields a 2X improvement

___

16.58

$I_{DS2} = I_{DS1} = \dfrac{I_1}{2} = 125 \ \mu A \quad | \quad I_{SD3} = I_{SD4} = I_{DS5} = I_{DS6} = I_{DS7} = I_2 - \dfrac{I_1}{2} = 125 \ \mu A$

For the NMOS transistors $V_{GS} = V_{TN} + \sqrt{\dfrac{2I_{DS}}{K_n}} = 0.75 + \sqrt{\dfrac{2(1.25x10^{-4})}{40(2.5x10^{-5})}} = 1.25V$

For the PMOS transistors $V_{SG} = -V_{TP} + \sqrt{\dfrac{2I_{SD}}{K_p}} = 0.75 + \sqrt{\dfrac{2(1.25x10^{-4})}{40(10^{-5})}} = 1.54V$

$V_{DS1} = V_{DS2} = V_{SG3} = 1.54V \quad | \quad V_{DS7} = V_{DS6} = V_{GS6} = 1.25V \quad | \quad V_{DS5} = V_{GS6} + V_{GS7} = 2.50V$

$V_{SD4} = V_{SD3} = -V_{GS1} + V_{SG3} - (-5 + V_{DS5}) = -1.25 + 1.54 + 5 - 2.50 = 2.79V$

Q – Pts: (125μA, 1.54V) (125μA, 1.54V) (125μA, 2.79V) (125μA, 2.79V)

(125μA, 2.50V) (125μA, 1.25V) (125μA, 1.25V)

(b) $A_{dd} = g_{m2}(\mu_{f4}r_{o2}\|\mu_{f5}r_{o7}) \cong \dfrac{\mu_{f2}\mu_{f4}}{2}$

$g_{m2} = \sqrt{2(40)(2.5x10^{-5})(1.25x10^{-4})[1+0.017(1.54)]} = 0.507mS \quad | \quad r_{o3} = \left(\dfrac{\dfrac{1}{0.017}+1.54}{1.25x10^{-4}}\right) = 483k\Omega$

$g_{m4} = \sqrt{2(40)(10^{-5})(1.25x10^{-4})[1+0.017(2.79)]} = 0.324mS \quad | \quad r_{o4} = \left(\dfrac{\dfrac{1}{0.017}+2.79}{1.25x10^{-4}}\right) = 493k\Omega$

$A_{dd} \cong \dfrac{\mu_{f2}\mu_{f4}}{2} = \dfrac{(0.507mS)(483k\Omega)(0.324mS)(493k\Omega)}{2} = 19600$

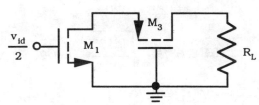

16.59

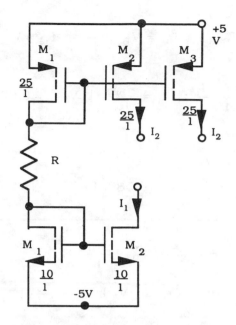

$$V_{SG} = V_{GS} = V_{TN} + \sqrt{\frac{2I_{DS}}{K_n}} = 0.75 + \sqrt{\frac{2\left(2.5\text{x}10^{-4}\right)}{10\left(25\text{x}10^{-6}\right)}} = 2.16V \quad | \quad R = \frac{10 - 2.16 - 2.16}{2.5\text{x}10^{-4}} \frac{V}{A} = 22.7k\Omega$$

16.60

```
*Problem 16.60 - CMOS Folded Cascode Amplifier with Active Load
VDD 1 0 DC 5
VSS 10 0 DC -5
*an offset voltage must be applied to bring output to -2.5V
V1 4 11 DC -5.085M AC 0.5
V2 5 11 DC 0 AC -0.5
VIC 11 0 DC 0
M1 2 4 6 6 NFET W=40U L=1U
M2 3 5 6 6 NFET W=40U L=1U
M3 8 6 2 2 PFET W=40U L=1U
M4 7 6 3 3 PFET W=40U L=1U
M5 8 9 10 10 NFET W=40U L=1U
M6 9 9 10 10 NFET W=40U L=1U
M7 7 8 9 9 NFET W=40U L=1U
I2A 1 2 DC 250U
I2B 1 3 DC 250U
I1 6 10 DC 250U
.MODEL NFET NMOS KP=25U VTO=0.75 LAMBDA=0.017
.MODEL PFET PMOS KP=10U VTO=-0.75 LAMBDA=0.017
.OP
.AC LIN 1 1000 1000
.PRINT AC VM(7) VP(7) VM(6) VP(6) VM(8) VP(8)
.TF V(7) VIC
.END
```

Results: $A_{dd} = 23700$, $A_{cd} = 1.81\text{x}10^{-4}$. $R_{OUT} = 47.7$ MΩ, CMRR $= 1.31 \times 10^8$. The values of A_{dd} and R_{OUT} are similar to hand calculations. A_{cd} and the CMRR are limited by the small residual mismatches in device parameters.

16.61

For $\beta_F = \infty$, $I_B = 0$. $V_{BE3} + V_{EB4} = V_{BE2} + \dfrac{V_{BE2}}{R_1}R_2 = V_{BE2}\left(1 + \dfrac{R_2}{R_1}\right)$

$V_{BE2} = 0.025\ln\dfrac{200\mu A - I_1}{10fA}$ | $I_1 = \dfrac{V_{BE2}}{R_1}$ | $V_{BE2} = 0.025\ln\dfrac{200\mu A - \dfrac{V_{BE2}}{R_1}}{10fA}$

$V_{BE2} = 0.025\ln\dfrac{200\mu A - \dfrac{V_{BE2}}{20k\Omega}}{10fA} \rightarrow V_{BE2} = 0.589V$ | $I_{C2} = 00\mu A - \dfrac{0.589}{20k\Omega} = 171\mu A$

Since $I_{S4} = I_{S3}$, $V_{BE3} = V_{BE4} = \dfrac{1}{2}(0.589)\left(1 + \dfrac{20k\Omega}{20k\Omega}\right) = 0.589V$ and $I_{C4} = I_{C3} = 171\ \mu A$

16.62

$\beta_F = \infty$: $V_{BE3} + V_{EB4} = V_{BE1} + V_{EB2} + \dfrac{V_{BE2}}{R_1}R_2$

$V_T\ln\dfrac{I_O}{I_{SON}\dfrac{A_{E3}}{A_{EO}}} + V_T\ln\dfrac{I_O}{I_{SOP}\dfrac{A_{E4}}{A_{EO}}} - V_T\ln\dfrac{I_2}{I_{SON}\dfrac{A_{E1}}{A_{EO}}} - V_T\ln\dfrac{I_2}{I_{SOP}\dfrac{A_{E2}}{A_{EO}}} = 0$

$V_T\ln\left[\dfrac{I_O^2 A_{EO}^2}{I_{SON}I_{SOP}A_{E3}A_{E4}}\dfrac{I_{SON}I_{SOP}A_{E1}A_{E2}}{I_2^2 A_{EO}^2}\right] = 0 \rightarrow \dfrac{I_O^2 A_{E1}A_{E2}}{I_2^2 A_{E3}A_{E4}} = 1$ | $I_O = I_2\sqrt{\dfrac{A_{E3}A_{E4}}{A_{E1}A_{E2}}}$

16.63

Using the results from Prob. 16.62, $I_O = 300\mu A\sqrt{\dfrac{A_{E3}A_{E4}}{3A_{E3}3A_{E4}}} = 100\ \mu A$

16.64 **Note:** The W/L of M_7 should be 15/1.

$I_{DS9} = I_{DS10} = I_{DS12} = I_{DS11} = I_{REF} = 250\mu A$ | $I_{SD6} = I_{DS7} = I_{DS8} = 3I_{DS12} = 750\mu A$

$I_{DS1} = I_{DS2} = I_{SD13} = I_{SD5} = I_{SD3} = I_{SD4} = \dfrac{I_{DS9}}{2} = 125\mu A$

$V_{DS10} = V_{DS12} = V_{DS11} = V_{GS12} = V_{TN} + \sqrt{\dfrac{2I_{DS12}}{K_{n12}}} = 0.75 + \sqrt{\dfrac{2(250\mu A)}{5(25x10^{-6})}} = 2.75V$

$V_{GS1} = 0.75 + \sqrt{\dfrac{2(125\mu A)}{40(25x10^{-6})}} = 1.25V$ | $V_{DS9} = -V_{GS1} - (-10 + V_{GS12}) = 6V$

$V_{DS7} = V_O - (-10 + V_{GS12} + V_{GS11} - V_{GS7}) = 0 + 10 - 2.75 - 2.75 + 0.75 + \sqrt{\dfrac{2(750\mu A)}{15(25x10^{-6})}} = 7.25V$

$V_{DS8} = 10 - V_{DS7} = 2.75V$

$V_{SD6} = 10 - V_O = 10V - 0 = 10V$ | $V_{SD5} = V_{SD13} = V_{SD3} = V_{SD4} = 0.75 + \sqrt{\dfrac{2(125\mu A)}{80(10x10^{-6})}} = 1.31V$

	1	2	3	4	5	6	7	8	9	10	11	12	13
I_{DS} (μA)	125	125	-125	-125	-125	-750	750	750	250	250	250	250	-125
V_{DS} (V)	8.63	8.63	-1.31	-1.31	-1.31	-10	8.71	1.29	6.00	2.75	2.75	2.75	-1.31

(b) $\dfrac{K_n'}{2}\left(\dfrac{W}{L}\right)_6\left(V_{SG6} + V_{TP}\right)^2 = \dfrac{10^{-5}}{2}\left(\dfrac{W}{L}\right)_6\left(V_{SD4} + V_{SD5} - 0.75\right)^2 = 750\mu A$

$\dfrac{10^{-5}}{2}\left(\dfrac{W}{L}\right)_6(2.62 - 0.75)^2 = 750\mu A \rightarrow \left(\dfrac{W}{L}\right)_6 = 42.9$

$A_{dd} = A_{V1}A_{V2} = (g_{m2}r_{o2})(g_{m6}r_{o6}) = \mu_{f2}\mu_{f6} \ \mid \ \mu_{f2} \cong \dfrac{1}{\lambda_n}\sqrt{\dfrac{2K_{n2}}{I_{DS2}}} = \dfrac{1}{0.017}\sqrt{\dfrac{2(40)(25\text{x}10^{-6})}{125\text{x}10^{-6}}} = 235$

$\mu_{f6} \cong \dfrac{1}{\lambda_p}\sqrt{\dfrac{2K_{p6}}{I_{SD6}}} = \dfrac{1}{0.017}\sqrt{\dfrac{2(42.9)(10\text{x}10^{-6})}{750\text{x}10^{-6}}} = 62.9 \ \mid \ A_{dd} = 235(62.9) = 14800$

16.65

```
*Problem 16.65 - CMOS Amplifier with Active Load
VDD 8 0 DC 10
VSS 14 0 DC -10
*Connect feedback to deterimine Vos
*V1 1 13 DC 0
*The offset voltage must be used to set Vo to approximately zero voltages.
V1 1 15 DC 0.4423M AC 0.5
V2 2 15 DC 0 AC -0.5
VIC 15 0 DC 0
M1 3 1 5 5 NFET W=40U L=1U
M2 4 2 5 5 NFET W=40U L=1U
M3 6 7 8 8 PFET W=80U L=1U
M4 7 7 8 8 PFET W=80U L=1U
M5 4 3 7 7 PFET W=80U L=1U
M6 13 4 8 8 PFET W=42.9U L=1U
*The offset can be adjusted to zero by correcting the value of W/L
*M6 13 4 8 8 PFET W=37.25U L=1U
M7 13 9 12 12 NFET W=15U L=1U
M8 12 10 14 14 NFET W=15U L=1U
M9 5 9 11 11 NFET W=5U L=1U
M10 11 10 14 14 NFET W=5U L=1U
M11 9 9 10 10 NFET W=5U L=1U
M12 10 10 14 14 NFET W=5U L=1U
M13 3 3 6 6 PFET W=80U L=1U
IREF 0 9 DC 250U
.MODEL NFET NMOS KP=25U VTO=0.75 LAMBDA=0.017
.MODEL PFET PMOS KP=10U VTO=-0.75 LAMBDA=0.017
.OP
.AC LIN 1 1000 1000
.PRINT AC VM(13) VP(13) VM(4) VP(4)
.TF V(13) VIC
.END
```

Results: $V_{os} = 0.4423$ mV, $A_{dm} = 22500$, $A_{cm} = 0.2305$, CMRR = 99.9 dB, $R_{OUT} = 90.3$ MΩ. The values of A_{dd} and R_{OUT} are similar to hand calculations. A_{cd} and the CMRR are limited by the offset induced mismatches in the devices. With the W/L of M_6 corected, $V_{os} \approx 0$, $A_{dm} = 20800$, $A_{cm} = 9.28 \times 10^{-3}$. $R_{OUT} = 90.3$ MΩ, CMRR = 127 dB.

16.66

$$A_{dm} = A_{V1}A_{V2}A_{V3} = \left[g_{m2}\left(r_{o2}\|r_{o4}\right)\right]\left[g_{m5}\left(r_{o5}\|r_{o12}\right)\right] [1]$$

$$I_{DS10} = I_{REF} = 100\mu A \mid I_{DS12} = I_{DS11} = 2I_{DS10} = 200\mu A \mid I_{DS1} = I_{DS2} = I_{SD3} = I_{SD4} = \frac{I_{DS11}}{2} = 100\mu A$$

$$I_{SD5} = I_{DS12} = 200\mu A \mid V_{SD4} = V_{SG3} = V_{GS2} = V_{TN} + \sqrt{\frac{2I_{DS2}}{K_{n2}}} = 0.75 + \sqrt{\frac{2(100\mu A)}{20\left(25x10^{-6}\right)}} = 1.38V$$

$$V_{DS2} = 10 - V_{SD4} - \left(-V_{GS2}\right) = 10.0V \mid g_{m2} = \sqrt{2(20)\left(25x10^{-6}\right)(100\mu A)\left[1 + 0.017(10)\right]} = 0.342mS$$

$$\frac{1}{\lambda} = \frac{1}{0.017} = 58.8V \mid r_{o2} = \frac{58.8 + 10}{10^{-4}}\frac{V}{A} = 688k\Omega \mid r_{o4} = \frac{58.8 + 1.38}{10^{-4}}\frac{V}{A} = 602k\Omega \mid A_{V1} = 110$$

$$V_{SD12} = V_{SD5} = 10 - \frac{V_{GSGG}}{2} \mid V_{GSGG} = 0.75 + \sqrt{\frac{2(200\mu A)}{5\left(25x10^{-6}\right)}} = 2.54V \mid V_{SD12} = V_{SD5} = 8.73V$$

$$g_{m5} = \sqrt{2(100)\left(10^{-5}\right)\left(2x10^{-4}\right)\left[1 + 0.017(8.73)\right]} = 0.678mS \mid r_{o12} = r_{o5} = \frac{58.8 + 8.73}{2x10^{-4}}\frac{V}{A} = 338k\Omega$$

$$A_{V2} = 115 \mid A_{dm} = A_{V1}A_{V2}A_{V3} = [110][115][1] = 12600$$

$A_{dm} = 10900$ if $\left(1 + \lambda V_{DS}\right)$ is neglected in g_m.

16.67

```
*Problem 16.67 - CMOS Amplifier with Active Load
VDD 8 0 DC 10
VSS 14 0 DC -10
*An offset voltage is used to set Vo to approximately zero volts.
V2 1 15 DC 0.3506M AC 0.5
V1 2 15 DC 0 AC -0.5
VIC 15 0 DC 0
M1 3 1 5 14 NFET W=20U L=1U
M2 4 2 5 14 NFET W=20U L=1U
M3 3 3 8 8 PFET W=50U L=1U
M4 4 3 8 8 PFET W=50U L=1U
M5 6 4 8 8 PFET W=100U L=1U
*The offset can be adjusted to zero by correcting the value of W/L
*M5 6 4 8 8 PFET W=89.5U L=1U
M6 8 6 13 14 NFET W=10U L=1U
M7 14 7 13 8 PFET W=25U L=1U
MGG 6 6 7 14 NFET W=5U L=1U
M10 9 9 14 14 NFET W=10U L=1U
M11 5 9 14 14 NFET W=20U L=1U
M12 7 9 14 14 NFET W=20U L=1U
IREF 0 9 DC 100U
.MODEL NFET NMOS KP=25U VTO=0.75 LAMBDA=0.017
.MODEL PFET PMOS KP=10U VTO=-0.75 LAMBDA=0.017
*.MODEL NFET NMOS KP=25U VTO=0.75 GAMMA=0.6 LAMBDA=0.017
*.MODEL PFET PMOS KP=10U VTO=-0.75 GAMMA=0.75 LAMBDA=0.017
.OP
.AC LIN 1 1000 1000
.PRINT AC VM(13) VP(13) VM(4) VP(4)
.TF V(13) VIC
.END
```

Results: $A_{dm} = 11200$, $A_{cm} = 0.604$, $R_{OUT} = 3.10 k\Omega$.

(a)	1	2	3	4	5	6	7	GG	10	11	12
I_{DS} (µA)	112	112	-112	-112	-223	44.2	-44.2	223	100	223	223
V_{DS} (V)	9.96	9.99	-1.41	-1.37	-8.70	10.0	-10.0	2.60	1.63	8.63	8.70
(b)											
I_{DS} (µA)	110	110	-110	-110	-219	0	0	219	100	219	219
V_{DS} (V)	11.2	11.2	-1.40	-1.37	-8.85	10.0	-9.97	3.79	1.63	7.41	7.35

Note that the body effect has increased the threshold voltages of M_6 and M_7 to the point that they are no longer conducting. $V_{TN6} = 2.24$ V $V_{TP7} = -2.61$V. The W/L ratio of M_{GG} needs to be redesigned to solve this problem.

16.68

$$I_{DS10} = I_{REF} = 250µA \mid I_{DS11} = 2I_{DS10} = 500µA \mid I_{DS12} = 4I_{DS10} = 1000µA$$

$$I_{DS1} = I_{DS2} = I_{SD3} = I_{SD4} = \frac{I_{DS11}}{2} = 250µA \mid V_{DS10} = V_{GS10} = 0.75 + \sqrt{\frac{2(250µA)}{10(25x10^{-6})}} = 2.16V$$

$$I_{SD5} = I_{DSGG} = I_{DS12} = 1000µA \mid V_{GSGG} = 0.75 + \sqrt{\frac{2(1000µA)}{5(25x10^{-6})}} = 4.75V$$

$$V_{GS6} = V_{SG7} = \frac{V_{GSGG}}{2} = 2.375V \mid I_{SD7} = I_{DS6} = \frac{10(25x10^{-6})}{2}(2.375 - 0.75)^2 = 330µA$$

$$V_{SD4} = V_{SD3} = V_{SG3} = V_{GS2} = V_{TN} + \sqrt{\frac{2I_{DS2}}{K_{n2}}} = 0.75 + \sqrt{\frac{2(250µA)}{20(25x10^{-6})}} = 1.75V$$

$$V_{DS1} = V_{DS2} = 7.5 - V_{SD4} - (-V_{GS2}) = 7.50V \mid V_{SD12} = V_{SD5} = 7.5 - \frac{V_{GSGG}}{2} = 5.13V$$

$$V_{DS6} = V_{SD7} = 7.5V \mid V_{DS11} = 7.5 - V_{GS2} = 7.5 - 1.75 = 5.75V$$

	1	2	3	4	5	6	7	GG	10	11	12
I_{DS} (µA)	250	250	-250	-250	-1000	330	-330	1000	250	500	1000
V_{DS} (V)	7.50	7.50	-1.75	-1.75	-5.13	7.50	-7.50	4.75	2.16	5.75	5.13
SPICE											
I_{DS} (µA)	264	266	-264	-266	219	359	-359	1050	250	530	1050
V_{DS} (V)	7.46	7.09	-1.76	-2.14	-5.20	7.54	-7.46	4.69	2.14	5.78	5.11

$$A_{dm} = A_{V1}A_{V2}A_{V3} = \left[g_{m2}(r_{o2}\|r_{o4})\right]\left[g_{m5}(r_{o5}\|r_{o12})\right] [1]$$

$$g_{m2} = \sqrt{2(20)(25x10^{-6})(250µA)[1 + 0.017(7.50)]} = 0.531mS$$

$$\frac{1}{\lambda} = \frac{1}{0.017} = 58.8V \mid r_{o2} = \frac{58.8 + 7.50}{2.5x10^{-4}} \frac{V}{A} = 265k\Omega \mid r_{o4} = \frac{58.8 + 1.75}{2.5x10^{-4}} \frac{V}{A} = 242k\Omega \mid A_{V1} = 67.2$$

$$g_{m5} = \sqrt{2(100)(10^{-5})(10^{-3})[1 + 0.017(5.13)]} = 1.48mS \mid r_{o12} = r_{o5} = \frac{58.8 + 5.13}{10^{-3}} \frac{V}{A} = 63.9k\Omega$$

$$A_{V2} = 47.3 \mid A_{dm} = A_{V1}A_{V2}A_{V3} = [67.2][47.3][1] = 3180$$

SPICE Results: $A_{dm} = 2950$, $A_{cm} = 0.03$, $R_{OUT} = 1.10$ kΩ.

16.69

(a) For saturation of M_{11}:

$$V_{DS11} = 0 - V_{GS2} - (-V_{SS}) = V_{SS} - V_{GS2} \geq \sqrt{\frac{2I_{DS11}}{K_{n11}}} = \sqrt{\frac{2(200\mu A)}{20(25 \times 10^{-6})}} = 0.894$$

$$V_{GS2} = V_{TN} + \sqrt{\frac{2I_{DS2}}{K_{n2}}} = 0.75 + \sqrt{\frac{2(100\mu A)}{20(25 \times 10^{-6})}} = 1.38V \ | \ V_{SS} - 1.38 \geq 0.894 \rightarrow V_{SS} \geq 2.27V$$

For saturation of M_{12}:

$$V_{DS11} = 0 - \frac{V_{GSGG}}{2} - (-V_{SS}) = V_{SS} - \frac{V_{GSGG}}{2} \geq \sqrt{\frac{2I_{DS12}}{K_{n12}}} = \sqrt{\frac{2(200\mu A)}{20(25 \times 10^{-6})}} = 0.894$$

$$V_{GSGG} = 0.75 + \sqrt{\frac{2(200\mu A)}{5(25 \times 10^{-6})}} = 2.54V \ | \ V_{SS} - \frac{2.54}{2} \geq 0.894 \rightarrow V_{SS} \geq 2.16V$$

For saturation of M_1 and M_2:

$$V_{DS1} = V_{DD} - V_{SG3} - (-V_{GS1}) = V_{DD} - V_{SG3} + V_{GS1} \geq \sqrt{\frac{2I_{DS1}}{K_{n1}}} = \sqrt{\frac{2(100\mu A)}{20(25 \times 10^{-6})}} = 0.633$$

$V_{SG3} = V_{GS1}$: $V_{DD} \geq 0.633V$

For saturation of M_5:

$$V_{SD5} = V_{DD} - \frac{2.54}{2} \geq \sqrt{\frac{2I_{SD5}}{K_{p5}}} = \sqrt{\frac{2(200\mu A)}{100(10 \times 10^{-6})}} = 0.633V \rightarrow V_{DD} \geq 1.90V$$

M_6 and M_7 are always saturated: e.g. $V_{DS6} \geq V_{GS6}$

The minimum supply voltages are: $V_{DD} \geq 1.90V$ $V_{SS} \geq 2.27V$

For the symmetrical supply case, $V_{DD} = V_{SS} \geq 2.27V$

(b) The values of V_{DD} and V_{SS} in part (a) do not permit any significant common-mode input voltage range. For saturation of M_{11} with $V_{IC} = -5V$,

$$V_{DS11} = V_{IC} - V_{GS2} - (-V_{SS}) = V_{SS} - 1.38 - 5 \geq 0.894 \rightarrow V_{SS} \geq 7.27V$$

For saturation of M_1 and M_2:

$$V_{DS1} = V_{DD} - V_{SG3} - (V_{IC} - V_{GS1}) = V_{DD} - 5 - 1.38 + 1.38 \geq 0.633 \rightarrow V_{DD} \geq 5.63V$$

For an output range of 5V, saturation of M_{12} requires

$$V_{DS12} = -5 - \frac{V_{GSGG}}{2} - (-V_{SS}) = V_{SS} - 5 - \frac{2.54}{2} \geq 0.894 \rightarrow V_{SS} \geq 7.25V$$

For Saturation of M_5:

$$V_{SD5} = V_{DD} - \frac{2.54}{2} - 5 \geq 0.633V \rightarrow V_{DD} \geq 6.90V$$

The minimum supply voltages are: $V_{DD} \geq 6.90V$ $V_{SS} \geq 7.25V$

For the symmetrical supply case, $V_{DD} = V_{SS} \geq 7.25V$

16.70

$$I_{DS8} = I_{REF} = 250\mu A \mid I_{DS10} = I_{DS9} = 2I_{DS8} = 500\mu A$$

$$I_{DS1} = I_{DS2} = I_{SD3} = I_{SD4} = \frac{I_{DS9}}{2} = 250\mu A \mid V_{DS8} = V_{GS8} = 0.75 + \sqrt{\frac{2(250\mu A)}{10(25x10^{-6})}} = 2.16V$$

$$I_{SD5} = I_{DS11} = I_{DS10} = 500\mu A \mid V_{GS11} = 0.75 + \sqrt{\frac{2(500\mu A)}{5(25x10^{-6})}} = 3.58V$$

$$V_{GS6} = V_{SG7} = \frac{V_{GS11}}{2} = 1.789V \mid I_{SD7} = I_{DS6} = \frac{10(25x10^{-6})}{2}(1.789 - 0.75)^2 = 135\mu A$$

$$V_{SD4} = V_{SD3} = V_{SG3} = V_{GS2} = V_{TN} + \sqrt{\frac{2I_{DS2}}{K_{n2}}} = 0.75 + \sqrt{\frac{2(250\mu A)}{20(25x10^{-6})}} = 1.75V$$

$$V_{DS1} = V_{DS2} = 5 - V_{SD4} - (-V_{GS2}) = 5.00V \mid V_{SD10} = V_{SD5} = 5 - \frac{V_{GS11}}{2} = 3.21V$$

$$V_{DS6} = V_{SD7} = 5.00V \mid V_{DS9} = 5 - V_{GS2} = 5 - 1.75 = 3.25V$$

	1	2	3	4	5	6	7	8	9	10	11
I_{DS} (μA)	250	250	-250	-250	-500	135	-135	250	500	500	500
V_{DS} (V)	5.00	5.00	-1.75	-1.75	-3.21	5.00	-5.00	2.16	3.25	3.21	3.58
SPICE											
I_{DS} (μA)	255	255	-255	-255	-509	139	-139	250	509	509	509
V_{DS} (V)	4.97	4.99	-1.74	-1.73	-3.24	5.01	-5.00	2.14	3.28	3.23	3.52

$$A_{dm} = A_{V1}A_{V2}A_{V3} = \left[g_{m2}(r_{o2}\|r_{o4})\right]\left[g_{m5}(r_{o5}\|r_{o12})\right][1]$$

$$g_{m2} = \sqrt{2(20)(25x10^{-6})(2.50x10^{-4})[1 + 0.017(5.00)]} = 0.521mS$$

$$\frac{1}{\lambda} = \frac{1}{0.017} = 58.8V \mid r_{o2} = \frac{58.8 + 5.00}{2.5x10^{-4}}\frac{V}{A} = 255k\Omega \mid r_{o4} = \frac{58.8 + 1.75}{2.5x10^{-4}}\frac{V}{A} = 242k\Omega \mid A_{V1} = 64.7$$

$$g_{m5} = \sqrt{2(100)(10^{-5})(5.00x10^{-4})[1 + 0.017(3.21)]} = 1.03mS \mid r_{o12} = r_{o5} = \frac{58.8 + 3.21}{5.00x10^{-4}}\frac{V}{A} = 124k\Omega$$

$$A_{V2} = 63.9 \mid A_{dm} = A_{V1}A_{V2}A_{V3} = [64.7][63.9][1] = 4130$$

SPICE Results: $A_{dm} = 4000$, $A_{cm} = 0.509$, $R_{OUT} = 1.81$ kΩ.

16.71

$$A_{dm} \cong \frac{\mu_{f2}\mu_{f5}}{2} \mid \text{For the MOSFET, } \mu_{f2} \propto \frac{1}{\sqrt{I_{DS}}} \quad \therefore \quad A_{dm} \propto \frac{1}{\sqrt{I_{DS2}}}\frac{1}{\sqrt{I_{SD5}}}$$

But, $I_{DS2} \propto I_{REF}$ and $I_{SD5} \propto I_{REF} \rightarrow A_{dm} \propto \frac{1}{I_{REF}}$

(a) $A_{dm} = 16000\frac{100\mu A}{250\mu A} = 6400$ (b) $A_{dm} = 16000\frac{100\mu A}{20\mu A} = 80000$

16.72

$$A_{dm} \cong \frac{I_{C2}}{I_{C5}}\beta_{o5}\frac{\mu_{f5}}{2} \mid \text{For our BJT models, } \mu_f \text{ and } \beta_o \text{ are independent of current}$$

We have $I_{C2} \propto I_{REF}$ and $I_{C5} \propto I_{REF} \Rightarrow A_{dm}$ is constant (a) $A_{dm} = 7500$ (b) $A_{dm} = 7500$

16.73

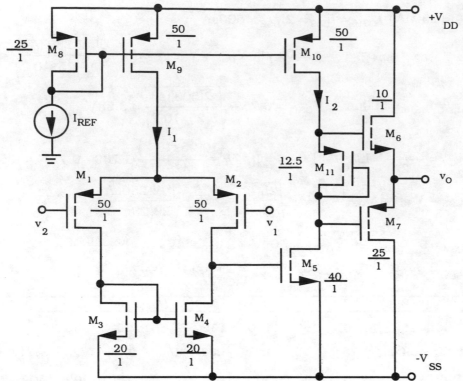

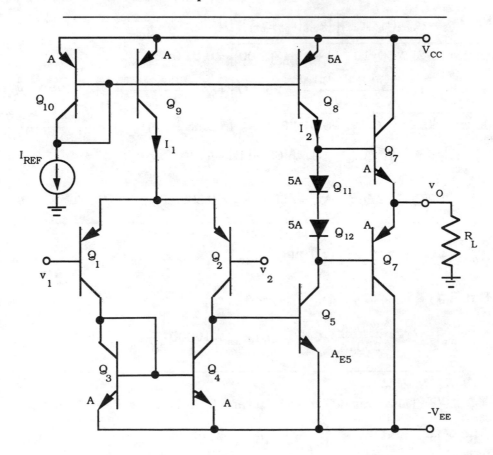

The W/L ratios have been scaled to keep the Q-points and gain the same. Note that the output stage should remain a source follower pair and is not mirrored.

16.74

Note that the output stage should remain complementary emitter – followers.

The gain of the first stage is approximately $A_{V1} = g_{m1}r_{\pi5} = \dfrac{I_{C1}}{I_{C5}}\beta_{o5}$, the mirror

image amplifier with an npn transistor for Q_5 will have the highest gain. The
voltage gain of the rest of the amplifier is the same.

16.75

$$V_{EB7} + V_{EB8} = V_{EB6} + V_{EB4} = 2V_T \ln\frac{I_{C4}}{I_{S4}} = 2V_T \ln\frac{I_{C44}}{2I_{S4}} = 0.05\ln\left[\frac{250\mu A}{2(15fA)}\right] = 1.142V$$

$$V_{EB7} + V_{EB8} = V_T \ln\frac{I_{C7}}{I_{S7}} + V_T \ln\frac{I_{C8}}{I_{S8}} \quad I_{C7} = \alpha_F I_{B8} = \alpha_F\frac{I_{C8}}{\beta_F} = \frac{60}{61}\frac{I_{C8}}{60} = \frac{I_{C8}}{61}$$

$$V_{EB7} + V_{EB8} = V_T \ln\frac{I_{C8}}{61(15fA)} + V_T \ln\frac{I_{C8}}{4(15fA)} \rightarrow 0.025\ln\frac{I_{C8}^2}{61(15fA)(4)(15fA)} = 1.142$$

$$I_{C8} = 1.946 \text{ mA} \mid I_{C16} \cong I_{C8} \mid A_{E16} = \frac{I_{C16}}{I_{C12}} A_{E12} = \frac{1946\mu A}{250\mu A}(1) = 7.78$$

$$V_{BE6} = V_{EB10} = 0.025\ln\left(\frac{75\mu A}{15fA}\right) = 0.558V \mid R_{BB} = \frac{2(0.5583V)}{1.946 \text{ mA}} = 574 \ \Omega$$

$$A_{dm} = A_{V1}A_{V2}A_{V3} \cong \left[g_{m2}\left\{r_{o2}\|\left[r_{\pi7} + (\beta_o+1)r_{\pi8}\right]\right\}\right]\left[\frac{(\beta_o+1)r_{\pi8}}{r_{\pi7} + (\beta_o+1)r_{\pi8}}g_{m8}(r_{o8}\|r_{o16})\right][1]$$

$$A_{dm} = A_{V1}A_{V2}A_{V3} \cong \left[g_{m2}(r_{o2}\|r_{\pi7} + (\beta_o+1)r_{\pi8})\right]\left[\frac{(\beta_o+1)r_{\pi8}}{r_{\pi7} + (\beta_o+1)r_{\pi8}}\frac{\mu_{f8}}{2}\right][1]$$

$$A_{dm} \cong \left[g_{m2}(r_{o2}\|2r_{\pi7})\right]\frac{\mu_{f8}}{4} \cong \frac{I_{C2}}{I_{C7}}\beta_{o7}\frac{\mu_{f8}}{2} = \frac{125\mu A}{31,8\mu A}60\frac{(40)(60+4.3)}{2} = 3.03 \times 10^5$$

$$R_{ID} = 2r_{\pi1} = 2\frac{150(0.025V)}{125\mu A} = 60 \text{ k}\Omega$$

16.76

```
*Problem 16.76 - Bipolar Op-Amp
VCC 1 0 DC 5
VEE 14 0 DC -5
V1 6 15 DC -74.17U AC 0.5
V2 7 15 DC 0 AC -0.5
VIC 15 0 DC 0
Q1 4 6 8 NBJT 1
Q2 5 7 8 NBJT 1
Q3 4 4 2 PBJT 1
Q4 5 4 3 PBJT 1
Q5 2 3 1 PBJT 1
Q6 3 3 1 PBJT 1
Q7 14 5 10 PBJT 1
Q8 11 10 1 PBJT 4
Q9 1 11 12 NBJT 1
Q10 14 13 12 PBJT 1
Q12 9 9 14 NBJT 1
Q14 8 9 14 NBJT 1
Q16 13 9 14 NBJT 7.78
IB 0 9 250U
RBB 11 13 574
.MODEL NBJT NPN BF=150 VA=60 IS=15F
```

```
.MODEL PBJT PNP BF=60 VA=60 IS=15F
.OP
.AC LIN 1 1000 1000
.PRINT AC VM(12) VP(12)
.TF V(12) VIC
.END
```

SPICE Results: $V_{os} = -74.17\mu V$, $A_{dm} = 2.83 \times 10^5$, $A_{cm} = 0.507$, CMRR $= 115$ dB,

$$R_{ID} = 81.6 \text{ k}\Omega, \quad R_{OUT} = 523 \ \Omega.$$

16.77

(a) We require forward - active region operation of all transistors.

For Q_{14}: $V_{CB14} = 0 - V_{BE1} - (-V_{EE} + V_{BE14}) \geq 0 \to V_{EE} \geq 1.4V$

For Q_1: $V_{CB1} = V_{CC} - V_{EB6} - V_{EB4} \geq 0 \to V_{CC} \geq 1.4V$

For Q_{16}: $V_{CB16} = 0 - V_{EB10} - (-V_{EE} + V_{BE14}) \geq 0 \to V_{EE} \geq 1.4V$

For Q_8: $V_{BC8} = V_{CC} - V_{EB8} - V_{BE6} \geq 0 \to V_{CC} \geq 1.4V$

So $V_{CC} \geq 1.4V$ and $V_{EE} \geq 1.4V$

(b) We require forward - active region operation of all transistors with V_{IC} present.

For Q_{14}: $V_{CB14} = V_{IC} - V_{BE1} - (-V_{EE} + V_{BE14}) = -1 - 0.7 - (-V_{EE} + 0.7) = \geq 0 \to V_{EE} \geq 2.4V$

For Q_1: $V_{CB1} = V_{CC} - V_{EB6} - V_{EB4} - V_{IC} = V_{CC} - 0.7 - 0.7 - 1 \geq 0 \to V_{CC} \geq 2.4V$

For an output range of $\pm 1V$,

For Q_{16}: $V_{CB16} = V_0 - V_{EB10} - (-V_{EE} + V_{BE14}) = -1 \geq 0 \to V_{EE} \geq 1.4V$

For Q_8: $V_{BC8} = V_{CC} - V_{EB8} - (V_0 + V_{BE6}) = V_{CC} - 0.7 - (1 + 0.7) \geq 0 \to V_{CC} \geq 2.4V$

So $V_{CC} \geq 2.4V$ and $V_{EE} \geq 2.4V$

16.78

(a) $I_{C22} = I_{C20} = \dfrac{V_{CC} - V_{EB22} - V_{BE20} - (-V_{EE})}{R_1} = \dfrac{3V - 0.7 - 0.7 - (-3V)}{100k\Omega} = 46.0\mu A$

$I_{C23} = 3I_{C22} = 138 \ \mu A \ | \ I_{C24} = I_{C22} = 46.0 \ \mu A \ |$

$I_1 = \dfrac{V_T}{R} \ln \dfrac{I_{C20}}{I_1} = \dfrac{0.025V}{4k\Omega} \ln \dfrac{46.0\mu A}{I_1} = 6.25\mu A \ln \dfrac{46.0\mu A}{I_1} = \to I_1 = 9.72\mu A$

(b) $I_{C22} = I_{C20} = \dfrac{22V - 0.7 - 0.7 - (-22V)}{100k\Omega} = 426\mu A$

$I_{C23} = 3I_{C22} = 128 \ mA \ | \ I_{C24} = I_{C22} = 426 \ \mu A \ |$

$I_1 = \dfrac{V_T}{R} \ln \dfrac{I_{C20}}{I_1} = 6.25\mu A \ln \dfrac{426\mu A}{I_1} \to I_1 = 19.3\mu A$

(c) The input bias current and input resistance of the amplifier are directly dependent upon I_1 whereas the gain of the interior amplifier stages is approximatley independent of bias current.

16.79

$$I_2 = 3I_{REF} \rightarrow I_{REF} = \frac{250\mu A}{3} = 83.3 \ \mu A \ | \ I_3 = I_{REF} = 83.3 \ \mu A$$

$$I_{REF} = \frac{V_{CC} - V_{EB22} - V_{BE20} - (-V_{EE})}{R_1} \ | \ R_1 = \frac{12 - 0.7V - 0.7 - (-12)}{83.3} \frac{V}{\mu A} = 271 \ k\Omega$$

$$R_2 = \frac{V_T}{I_1} \ln \frac{I_{REF}}{I_1} = \frac{0.025V}{50\mu A} \ln \frac{83.3\mu A}{50\mu A} = 255 \ \Omega$$

16.80

$$I_{REF} = I_3 = 300 \ \mu A \ | \ I_2 = 3I_{REF} = 900 \ \mu A$$

$$I_{REF} = \frac{V_{CC} - V_{EB22} - V_{BE20} - (-V_{EE})}{R_1} \ | \ R_1 = \frac{15 - 0.7V - 0.7 - (-15)}{300} \frac{V}{\mu A} = 95.3 \ k\Omega$$

$$R_2 = \frac{V_T}{I_1} \ln \frac{I_{REF}}{I_1} = \frac{0.025V}{75\mu A} \ln \frac{300\mu A}{75\mu A} = 462 \ \Omega$$

16.81

For forward - active region operation of Q_3, $V_{BC3} \geq 0$

$V_{EE} \geq V_{IC} + V_{BE1} + V_{BE3} + V_{BE7} + V_{BE5} + V_{R_1}$

For forward - active region operation of Q_1, $V_{CB1} \geq 0$

$V_{CC} - V_{EB9} \geq V_{IC}$

For the output stage, $V_{CC} \geq V_{BE15} + V_{I3} = 0.7 + 0.7 = 1.4 \ V$

$-V_{EB16} - V_{EB12} \geq V_{BE11} + V_{R_5} - (-V_{EE}) \rightarrow V_{EE} \geq 3V_{BE} + V_{R_1} \cong 2.1V$

(a) $V_{IC} = 0$, $V_{EE} \geq 4V_{BE} + V_{R_1} \cong 2.8V \ | \ V_{CC} - V_{EB9} \geq 0 \rightarrow V_{CC} \geq 0.7V$

Combining these results yields: $V_{CC} \geq 1.4V$ and $V_{EE} \geq 2.8V$

(b) $V_{IC} = \pm 1$, $V_{EE} \geq 1 + 4V_{BE} + V_{R_1} \cong 3.8V \ | \ V_{CC} - V_{EB9} \geq 1 \rightarrow V_{CC} \geq 1.7V$

If also account for the output stage, $V_{CC} \geq V_O + V_{BE15} + V_{I3} = 1 + 0.7 + 0.7 = 2.4 \ V$

Combining these results yields: $V_{CC} \geq 2.4V$ and $V_{EE} \geq 3.8V$

16.82

The input stage current is proportional to I_1: $I_{C2} = \frac{50\mu A}{18\mu A}(7.32\mu A) = 20.3\mu A$

Using Eq. 16.12: $i_o = -20(20.3\mu A)\mathbf{v_{id}} = (-0.406 \ mS)\mathbf{v_{id}} \ | \ I_{C4} = \frac{50\mu A}{18\mu A}(7.25\mu A) = 20.1\mu A$

$$R_{OUT6} = r_{o6}\left(1 + \frac{20.3\mu A(1k\Omega)}{0.,025V}\right) = 1.81r_{o6} \ | \ 1.81r_{o6}\|2r_{o4} = 0.952r_{o4} = 0.95\frac{60V}{20.1\mu A} = 283 \ M\Omega$$

$i_o = \left(-4.06 \ x \ 10^{-4}\right)\mathbf{v_{id}} \ | \ R = 283 \ M\Omega$

16.83

(a) $R_2 = \frac{\beta_{o2}r_{o2}}{2} = \frac{50}{2}\frac{60 + 15.7}{0.666mA} = 2.84M\Omega \ | $ The cascode source uses up an extra V_{EB}

(b) $[y_{22}]^{-1} = R_{OUT11}\|R_2 = 407k\Omega\|2.84M\Omega = 356k\Omega \ | $ Other y - paramters are unchanged.

(c) $A_{dm} = 256(6.70mS)(356k\Omega) = 6.11 \ x \ 10^5$

16.84

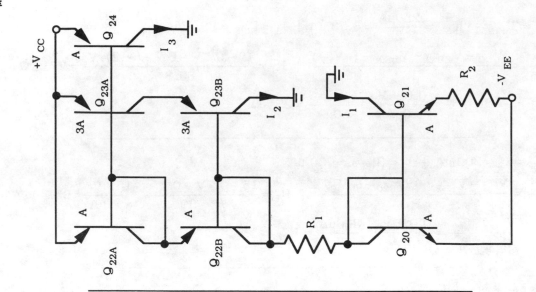

16.85

$$g_{m10} = 40(19.8\mu A) = 0.792mS \quad | \quad r_{\pi10} = \frac{150(0.025V)}{19.8\mu A} = 189k\Omega \quad | \quad r_{o10} = \frac{60V}{19.8\mu A} = 3.03M\Omega$$

$$g_{m11} = 40(0.666mA) = 26.6mS \quad | \quad r_{\pi11} = \frac{150(0.025V)}{0.666mA} = 5.63k\Omega \quad | \quad r_{o11} = \frac{60V}{0.666mA} = 90.1k\Omega$$

```
*Problem 16.85 - Small Signal Parameters.
V1 1 0 DC 0
V2 4 0 AC 1
RPI10 1 2 189K
RO10 2 0 3.03MEG
GM10 0 2 1 2 0.792M
RE10 2 0 50K
RPI11 2 3 5.63K
RO11 4 3 90.1K
GM11 4 3 2 3 26.6M
RE11 3 0 100
R2 4 0 115K
.TF I(V2) V1
.AC LIN 1 1000 1000
.PRINT AC IM(V2) IP(V2) IM(V1) IP(V1)
.END
```

Results: $y_{11}^{-1} = 2.38 \, M\Omega \quad | \quad y_{12} = 3.27 \times 10^{-10} S \cong 0 \quad | \quad y_{21} = 6.66 \, mS \quad | \quad y_{22}^{-1} = 81.9 \, k\Omega$

16.86

(a) Assume large β_F: $\quad I_{C11} = I_{REF} = 100\mu A \quad | \quad I_{C4} = I_{C5} = \dfrac{I_{C11}}{2} = 50\mu A \quad | \quad I_{C3} = I_{C6} = I_{C4} = 50\mu A$

$$I_{C1} = I_{C3} = I_{C7} = 50\mu A \quad | \quad I_{C2} = I_{C6} = I_{C8} = 50\mu A \quad | \quad I_{C9} = 2\frac{I_{C8}}{\beta_F}$$

$$V_{CE1} = V_{CE2} = 15 - (-0.7) = 15.7V \quad | \quad V_{EC4} = V_{EC5} = 0.7V$$

$$V_{CE7} = V_{CE8} = 0.7 + 0.7 = 1.4V \quad | \quad V_{CE9} = 15 - (-15 + 0.7) = 29.3V \quad | \quad V_{CE10} = 0.7V$$

$$V_{EC3} = V_{EC2} = (0 - 0.7) - (-15 + 1.4) = 12.9 \quad | \quad V_{CE11} = 0 - 0.7 - 0.7 - (-15) = 13.6V$$

	1	2	3	4	5	6	7	8	9	10	11
I_C (µA)	100	100	-50	-50	-50	-50	50	50	---	100	100
V_{CE} (V)	15.7	15.7	-12.9	-0.7	-0.7	-12.9	1.4	1.4	29.3	0.7	13.6

(b) Transistor Q_{11} replicates the reference current. This current divides in two and controls two matched current mirrors formed of Q_4-Q_3 and Q_5-Q_6. The currents of Q_1 and Q_7, and Q_2 and Q_8 are equal to the output current of Q_3 and Q_4.

(c) v_1 is the inverting input; v_2 is the non-inverting input.

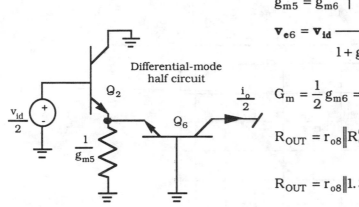

$$g_{m5} = g_{m6} \mid g_{m2} = 2g_{m6} \mid r_{o8} = r_{o6} \mid i_o = g_{m6}v_{e6}$$

$$v_{e6} = v_{id}\frac{g_{m2}}{1 + g_{m2}\left(\dfrac{1}{g_{m5}}\middle\|\dfrac{1}{g_{m6}}\right)} = \frac{1}{2}v_{id} \mid i_o = g_{m6}\frac{1}{2}v_{id}$$

Differential-mode half circuit

$$G_m = \frac{1}{2}g_{m6} = \frac{1}{4}g_{m2} = \frac{1}{4}(40)(100\mu A) = 1.00 \text{ mS}$$

$$R_{OUT} = r_{o8}\|R_{OUT}^6 = r_{o8}\|r_{o6}\left[1 + g_{m6}\left(\frac{1}{g_{m5} + g_{m2}}\right)\right]$$

$$R_{OUT} = r_{o8}\|1.33r_{o6} = \frac{61.4V}{50\mu A}\|1.33\frac{72.9V}{50\mu A} = 752 \text{ k}\Omega$$

16.87

(a) Assume large β_F: $I_{C8} = I_{REF} = 100\mu A \mid I_{C10} = I_{C9} = I_{B8} = \dfrac{I_{C8}}{\beta_F}$

$$I_{C3} = I_{C4} = \beta_F\frac{I_{C10}}{2} = \frac{I_{C8}}{2} = 50\mu A \quad I_{C1} = I_{C3} = I_{C5} = 50\mu A \mid I_{C2} = I_{C4} = I_{C6} = 50\mu A \mid I_{C7} = 2\frac{I_{C5}}{\beta_F}$$

$$V_{CE1} = V_{CE2} = 15 - (-0.7) = 15.7V \mid V_{CE5} = V_{CE6} = 0.7 + 0.7 = 1.4V$$

$$V_{EC3} = V_{EC4} = 0 - 0.7 - (-15 + 1.4) = 12.9V \mid V_{CE7} = 15 - (-15 + 0.7) = 29.3V$$

$$V_{EC8} = 0.7 + 0.7 = 1.4V \mid V_{CE9} = 0.7V \mid V_{CE10} = 0 - 0.7 - 0.7 - (-15) = 13.6V$$

	1	2	3	4	5	6	7	8	9	10
I_C (µA)	50	50	-50	-50	50	50	---	-100	---	---
V_{CE} (V)	15.7	15.7	-12.9	-12.9	1.4	1.4	29.3	1.4	0.7	13.6

(b) Transistors Q_9 and Q_{10} form a current mirror that replicates the base current of transistor Q_8. The output current divides in two and forms the base currents of Q_3 and Q_4. Since Q_3 and Q_4 match Q_8, the collector currents of Q_1-Q_6 will all be equal to $I_{REF}/2$.

(c) v_1 is the inverting input; v_2 is the non-inverting input.

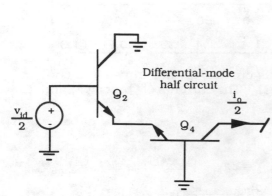

Differential-mode half circuit

$$g_{m2} = g_{m4} \mid r_{o6} = r_{o4} \mid \frac{i_o}{2} = g_{m4}\mathbf{v_{e4}} \mid i_o = 2g_{m4}\mathbf{v_{e4}}$$

$$\mathbf{v_{e4}} = \frac{\mathbf{v_{id}}}{2}\frac{g_{m2}}{1 + g_{m2}\left(\dfrac{1}{g_{m4}}\right)} = \frac{1}{4}\mathbf{v_{id}} \mid i_o = g_{m4}\frac{\mathbf{v_{id}}}{2}$$

$$G_m = \frac{1}{2}g_{m4} = \frac{1}{2}g_{m2} = \frac{1}{2}(40)(50\mu A) = 1.00 \text{ mS}$$

$$R_{OUT} = r_{o6}\|R_{OUT}^4 = r_{o6}\left\|r_{o4}\left[1 + g_{m4}\left(\frac{1}{g_{m2}}\right)\right]\right.$$

$$R_{OUT} = r_{o6}\|2r_{o4} = \frac{61.4V}{50\mu A}\left\|2\frac{72.9V}{50\mu A}\right. = 864 \text{ k}\Omega$$

16.88

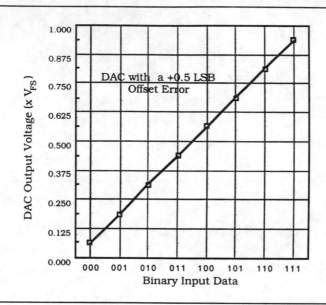

DAC with a +0.5 LSB Offset Error

y-axis: DAC Output Voltage (x V_{FS})

x-axis: Binary Input Data

000 001 010 011 100 101 110 111

16.89

(a) $v_O = (0)\left[-\dfrac{R}{2R}V_{REF}\right] + (1)\left[-\dfrac{R}{4R}V_{REF}\right] + (1)\left[-\dfrac{R}{8R}V_{REF}\right] + (0)\left[-\dfrac{R}{16R}V_{REF}\right] = -1.125V$

(b) $v_O = (1)\left[-\dfrac{R}{2R}V_{REF}\right] + (0)\left[-\dfrac{R}{4R}V_{REF}\right] + (0)\left[-\dfrac{R}{8R}V_{REF}\right] + (1)\left[-\dfrac{R}{16R}V_{REF}\right] = -1.688V$

0000	0	0100	-0.750 V	1000	-1.500 V	1100	-2.250 V
0001	-0.188 V	0101	-0.938 V	1001	-1.688 V	1101	-2.438 V
0010	-0.375 V	0110	-1.125 V	1010	-1.875 V	1110	-2.625 V
0011	-0.563 V	0111	-1.313 V	1011	-2.063 V	1111	2.813 V

16.90

For an input code of 0000, $v_O = V_{OS}\left(1 + \dfrac{1.05R}{R_{EQ}}\right)$ | $R_{EQ} = 16R\|8R\|4R\|2R = 0.9375R$

$v_O = 0.005V\left(1 + \dfrac{1.05R}{0.9375R}\right) = 10.6$ mV | The DAC offset voltage is $+10.6$ mV

1 LSB is now equal to $V_{REF}\left(\dfrac{1.05R}{16R}\right) = 0.06563V_{REF}$ instead of $V_{REF}\left(\dfrac{1R}{16R}\right) = 0.0625V_{REF}$

The DAC has a gain error of 5%.

16.91

Code	Output Voltage	Step Size (LSB)	DLE (LSB)	ILE (LSB)
000	0.0000			0.0000
001	0.1000	0.8000	-0.2000	-0.2000
010	0.3000	1.6000	0.6000	0.4000
011	0.3500	0.4000	-0.6000	-0.2000
100	0.4750	1.0000	0.0000	-0.2000
101	0.6300	1.2400	0.2400	0.0400
110	0.7250	0.7600	-0.2400	-0.2000
111	0.8750	1.2000	0.2000	0.0000
LSB Size:	0.125			

16.92

	Nominal Case			
Code	Output Voltage	Step Size (LSB)	DLE (LSB)	ILE (LSB)
000	0.0000			0.0000
001	0.1220	0.9719	-0.0281	-0.0281
010	0.2564	1.0716	0.0716	0.0434
011	0.3784	0.9719	-0.0281	0.0153
100	0.5000	0.9694	-0.0306	-0.0153
101	0.6220	0.9719	-0.0281	-0.0434
110	0.7564	1.0716	0.0716	0.0281
111	0.8784	0.9719	-0.0281	0.0000
LSB Size:	0.12548021			

Test Case -1	1	4R & 8R 5% Low, 2R 5% High		
Code	Output Voltage	Step Size (LSB)	DLE	ILE
000	0.0000			
001	0.1161	0.9169	-0.0831	-0.0831
010	0.2442	1.0110	0.0110	-0.0721
011	0.3603	0.9169	-0.0831	-0.1552
100	0.5263	1.3103	0.3103	0.1552
101	0.6425	0.9169	-0.0831	0.0721
110	0.7705	1.0110	0.0110	0.0831
111	0.8867	0.9169	-0.0831	0.0000
LSB Size:	0.12666572			

Test Case - 2	1	4R & 8R 5% High, 2R 5% Low		
Code	Output Voltage	Step Size (LSB)	DLE (LSB)	ILE(LSB)
000	0.0000			0.0000
001	0.1284	1.0276	0.0276	0.0276
010	0.2699	1.1330	0.1330	0.1606
011	0.3983	1.0276	0.0276	0.1881
100	0.4762	0.6237	-0.3763	-0.1881
101	0.6046	1.0276	0.0276	-0.1606
110	0.7461	1.1330	0.1330	-0.0276
111	0.8745	1.0276	0.0276	0.0000
LSB Size:	0.12492367			

16.93 The five resistors are each assigned a random value, and the 16 output voltages are calculated using these values. Then the step sizes, differential linearity error and integral linearity error are found. This is repeated for 200 test cases using a spreadsheet.

$$R = 1 + 0.1 * (RAND() - 0.5)$$
$$R2 = 2 * (1 + 0.1 * (RAND - 0.5))$$
$$R4 = 4 * (1 + 0.1 * (RAND - 0.5))$$
$$R8 = 8 * (1 + 0.1 * (RAND - 0.5))$$
$$R16 = 16 * (1 + 0.1 * (RAND - 0.5))$$

Results: The worst case results observed in a number of trials - DLE = 0.66 LSB, ILE = 0.33 LSB

16.94 Note that the two switches should be driven with complementary signals.

$$R_{on} = \cfrac{1}{K_n'\left(\cfrac{W}{L}\right)(V_{GS} - V_{TN} - V_{DS})} \quad | \quad \text{The worst-case condition for the switches occurs}$$

for the one with $V_{DS} \neq 0$ and $V_{SB} = 0$. If $V_{REF} = 3V$ and $R_{ON} = 0.01(10k\Omega) = 100\Omega$

$$V_D = 3V \quad \text{and} \quad V_S = 3V \frac{10k\Omega}{10k\Omega + 100\Omega} = 2.97V \quad | \quad V_{DS} = 0.03V$$

$$V_{TN} = 1 + 0.5\left(\sqrt{2.97 + 0.6} - \sqrt{.6}\right) = 1.56V$$

$$\left(\frac{W}{L}\right) = \frac{1}{5\times10^{-5}(100)[(5 - 2.97) - 1.56 - 0.03]} = \left(\frac{455}{1}\right)$$

When the grounded transistor is on, $V_{DS} = 0$ | $\left(\dfrac{W}{L}\right) = \dfrac{1}{5\times10^{-5}(100)[5 - 1 - 0]} = \left(\dfrac{50}{1}\right)$

16.95 Consider each bit acting by itself:

$$V_{REF}\left[\frac{R(1 + \varepsilon_0)}{2R(1 - \varepsilon_1)}\right] - \frac{V_{REF}}{2} \approx V_{REF}\left[\frac{(1 + \varepsilon_0 + \varepsilon_1)}{2} - \frac{1}{2}\right] = V_{REF}\frac{(\varepsilon_0 + \varepsilon_1)}{2}$$

$$V_{REF}\left[\frac{R(1 + \varepsilon_0)}{4R(1 - \varepsilon_2)}\right] - \frac{V_{REF}}{4} \approx V_{REF}\frac{(\varepsilon_0 + \varepsilon_2)}{4}$$

$$V_{REF}\left[\frac{R(1 + \varepsilon_0)}{8R(1 - \varepsilon_3)}\right] - \frac{V_{REF}}{8} \approx V_{REF}\frac{(\varepsilon_0 + \varepsilon_3)}{8}$$

Adding these together yields

$$V_{REF}\frac{(\varepsilon_0 + \varepsilon_1)}{2} + V_{REF}\frac{(\varepsilon_0 + \varepsilon_2)}{4} + V_{REF}\frac{(\varepsilon_0 + \varepsilon_3)}{8} = 0.05 V_{REF}$$

$$\frac{7}{8}\varepsilon_0 + \frac{\varepsilon_1}{2} + \frac{\varepsilon_2}{4} + \frac{\varepsilon_3}{8} = 0.05$$

Giving each term the same weight:

$$\frac{7}{8}\varepsilon_0 = 1.25\% \quad \text{and} \quad \varepsilon_0 = 1.43\% \quad | \quad \frac{\varepsilon_1}{2} = 1.25\% \quad \text{and} \quad \varepsilon_1 = 2.5\% \quad \varepsilon_2 = 5\% \quad \varepsilon_3 = 10\%$$

16.96   An n-bit DAC requires (n+1) resistors. Ten bits requires 11 resistors.

$$\frac{2^{10}R}{R} = \frac{2^{10}}{1} \quad \text{or} \quad 1024:1$$

A wide range of resistor values is required but it could be done. For R = 1 kΩ, 1024R = 1.024 MΩ.

16.97 Taking successive Thévenin equivalent circuits at each ladder node yields:

	V_{TH}	R_{TH}	v_O
0001	$V_{REF}/16$	R	-0.3125 V
0010	$V_{REF}/8$	R	-0.6250V
0100	$V_{REF}/4$	R	-1.250 V
1000	$V_{REF}/2$	R	-2.500 V

16.98 **Note**: The feedback resistor should be **1.2188kΩ** to give the ideal step size.

Code	Output Voltage	Step Size (LSB)	DLE (LSB)	ILE (LSB)
000	0.000			0.000
001	-0.739	1.182	**0.182**	0.182
010	-1.434	1.112	0.112	0.294
011	-2.089	1.048	0.048	**0.342**
100	-2.708	0.990	-0.010	0.333
101	-3.294	0.938	-0.062	0.270
110	-3.849	0.888	-0.112	0.158
111	-4.375	0.842	-0.158	0.000
LSB Size:	-0.625			

16.99

$R_{REF} = 0$		$R_1 = 2.2kΩ$ $R_2 = 4.2kΩ$ $R_3 = 8.2kΩ$		
R	1.0742 kΩ			
Code	Output Voltage	Step Size (LSB)	DLE (LSB)	ILE (LSB)
000	0.0000			0.0000
001	-0.6550	1.0480	0.0480	0.0480
010	-1.2788	0.9981	-0.0019	0.0460
011	-1.9337	1.0480	0.0480	**0.0940**
100	-2.4413	0.8121	**-0.1879**	-0.0940
101	-3.0962	1.0480	0.0480	-0.0460
110	-3.7200	0.9981	-0.0019	-0.0480
111	-4.3750	1.0480	0.0480	0.0000
LSB Size:	-0.6250	1.0000		

R	1.2929 kΩ		RREF = 250 Ω	
Code	Output Voltage	Step Size (LSB)	DLE (LSB)	ILE (LSB)
000	0.0000			0.0000
001	-0.7650	1.2241	**0.2241**	0.2241
010	-1.4527	1.1003	0.1003	0.3243
011	-2.1353	1.0922	0.0922	**0.4165**
100	-2.6386	0.8052	-0.1948	0.2217
101	-3.2573	0.9900	-0.0100	0.2117
110	-3.8167	0.8950	-0.1050	0.1067
111	-4.3750	0.8933	-0.1067	0.0000
LSB Size:	-0.6250	1.0000		

16.100 Note: The areas of the left four transistors should be **128A, 64A, 32A, 16A**.

Let R_1 be the scaling resistor to be found. The total current through R_1 is $\frac{I_R}{8}$.

For the $\frac{I_R}{16}$ transistor: $I_{E16} = \frac{1}{\alpha_F}\frac{I_R}{16} = \frac{V_{REF} - V_{BE} - \frac{1}{\alpha_F}\frac{I_R}{8}R_1}{R} = \frac{V_{REF} - V_{BE}}{R} - \frac{1}{\alpha_F}\frac{I_R}{8}\frac{R_1}{R}$

However, for the I_R transistor: $I_{E1} = \frac{V_{REF} - V_{BE}}{R} = \frac{I_R}{\alpha_F}$

$$\frac{1}{\alpha_F}\frac{I_R}{16} = \frac{I_R}{\alpha_F} - \frac{1}{\alpha_F}\frac{I_R}{8}\frac{R_1}{R} \rightarrow R_1 = \frac{15}{2}R$$

16.101

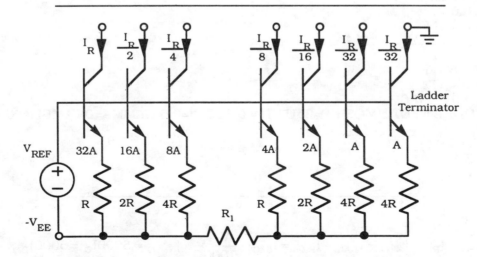

For this design, two three-bit sections are connected through a scaling resistor R_1.

Let R_1 be the scaling resistor. The total current through R_1 is $\frac{I_R}{4}$.

If I_R is the current in the MSB, then the first transistor in the second section has $I_C = \dfrac{I_R}{8}$

For the $\dfrac{I_R}{8}$ transistor: $I_{E8} = \dfrac{1}{\alpha_F}\dfrac{I_R}{8} = \dfrac{V_{REF} - V_{BE} - \dfrac{1}{\alpha_F}\dfrac{I_R}{4}R_1}{R} = \dfrac{V_{REF} - V_{BE}}{R} - \dfrac{1}{\alpha_F}\dfrac{I_R}{4}\dfrac{R_1}{R}$

However, for the I_R transistor: $I_{E1} = \dfrac{V_{REF} - V_{BE}}{R} = \dfrac{I_R}{\alpha_F} \mid \dfrac{1}{\alpha_F}\dfrac{I_R}{8} = \dfrac{I_R}{\alpha_F} - \dfrac{1}{\alpha_F}\dfrac{I_R}{4}\dfrac{R_1}{R} \rightarrow R_1 = \dfrac{7}{2}R$

$R = \dfrac{V_{REF} - V_{BE}}{I_{MSB}} = \dfrac{3 - 0.7}{2^6(25\mu A)} = 1.438\ k\Omega \mid \dfrac{7}{2}R = 5.031\ k\Omega \mid 2R = 2.875\ k\Omega \mid 4R = 5.750\ k\Omega$

16.102

(a) The n‑th bit requires $2^n C$, and the feedback capcitor = C: $C_{TOTAL} = \sum_{i=0}^{n} 2^i C = \left(2^{n+1} - 1\right)C$

(b) Each bit requires $(C + 2C)$, and a single terminator is required: $C_{TOTAL} = (3n + 1)C$

16.103

```
*Problem 16.103 - C-2C Ladder
VREF 9 0 DC 5
VB3 8 0 PWL (0 0 5N 0 10N 10 50N 10 55N 0 100N 0)
VB3B 7 0 PWL (0 10 5N 10 10N 0 50N 0 55N 10 100N 10)
M1 6 7 0 0 NFET W=10U L=1U
M2 9 8 6 6 NFET W=10U L=1U
C1 1 0 0.5PF
C2 1 0 0.5PF
R1 1 0 1T
C3 1 2 1PF
C4 2 6 0.5PF
R2 2 0 1T
C5 2 3 1PF
C6 3 0 0.5PF
R3 3 0 1T
C7 3 4 1PF
C8 4 0 0.5PF
R4 4 0 1T
CF 4 5 1PF
RF 5 4 1T
E1 5 0 0 4 1E6
.MODEL NFET NMOS KP=25U VTO=0.75 PHI=0.6 GAMMA=0 LAMBDA=0.017
.OP
.TRAN 0.5N 60N
.PROBE
.END
```

16.104

(a) $I_{DAC} = I_O + I_{REF} \mid I_O = I_{DAC} - I_{REF} = I_{DAC} - \dfrac{V_{REF}}{1000\Omega} \mid V_O = 5000 I_O = 5000 I_{DAC} - 5$

(b) $I_{OS} = \dfrac{5mV}{1k\Omega} = 5\mu A \mid 1\ LSB = \dfrac{2mA}{2^4} = 125\mu A \mid I_{OS}$ is negligible.

0000	-5.000
0001	-4.375
0010	-3.750
0011	-3.125
0100	-2.500
0101	-1.875
0110	-1.250
0111	-0.625
1000	0.000
1001	0.625
1010	1.250
1011	1.875
1100	2.500
1101	3.125
1110	3.750
1111	4.375

16.105

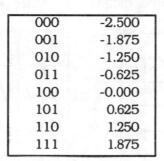

000	-2.500
001	-1.875
010	-1.250
011	-0.625
100	-0.000
101	0.625
110	1.250
111	1.875

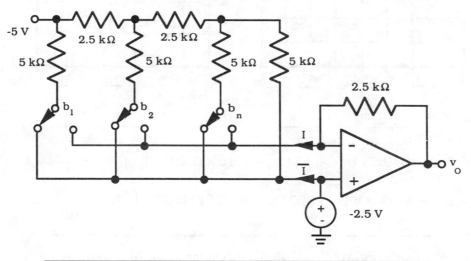

16.106 **Note** that the resistor width should be **5 μm**. The DAC will require 1024 resistors of equal value. Suppose R = 500 Ω. This requires 10 squares per resistor or 10240 squares. For a 5 μm width, the total length would be 0.0512 m or 5.12 cm. 5.12 cm/2.54 cm/in = 2.02 in! Note that contacts have been neglected in this estimate.

16.107

ADC code is equivalent to $\left(2^{-1} + 2^{-3} + 2^{-5} + 2^{-7} + 2^{-9} + 2^{-10} + 2^{-13}\right) \times V_{FS} = 0.66711426 \times V_{FS}$

The ADC input may be anywhere in the range:

$$\left(0.66711426 \pm \frac{1}{2} \text{LSB}\right) \times V_{FS} = 3.4154625V \pm 0.15625mV \quad | \quad 3.415469V \leq V_X \leq 3.415781V$$

16.108

(a) $1 \text{ LSB} = \dfrac{2V}{2^{20} \text{bits}} = 1.90735 \ \mu V$

(b) $\dfrac{1.63V}{2V} 2^{20} = 854589.4 \text{ bits} \rightarrow 854589_{10} = 11010000101000111101_2$

(c) $\dfrac{0.997003V}{2V} 2^{20} = 522716.7 \text{ bits} \rightarrow 522717_{10} = 01111111100111011101_2$

16.109

The quantization error is always positive and can be as large as 1 LSB. Both these characteristics are undesirable. Note, however, that the properly offset ADC does have a large quantization error for inputs approaching the full scale range of the converter.

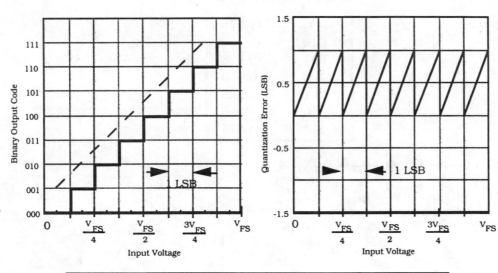

16.110 Use $f_c = 1\text{MHz.}$

(a) $\dfrac{3.760V}{10V} 2^{12} = 1540.01 \text{ bits} \rightarrow 1541_{10} = 011000000101 1_2 \quad | \quad T_T = \dfrac{1541}{f_C} = 1.541 \text{ ms}$

(b) $\dfrac{7.333V}{10V} 2^{12} = 3003.6 \text{ bits} \rightarrow 3004_{10} = 101110111100_2 \quad | \quad T_T = \dfrac{3004}{f_C} = 3.004 \text{ ms}$

16.111

$1 \text{ LSB} = \dfrac{5.12V}{2^{10} \text{bits}} = \dfrac{5.000 \text{ mV}}{\text{bit}} \quad | \quad t = \dfrac{n}{f_C} = 10^{-6} n \quad | \quad$ The conversion is complete when

the counter ramp first exceeds the input voltage: $0.005n \geq 5\cos\left[5000\pi\left(10^{-6} n\right)\right]$

Using MATLAB, $n = 94.0065 \rightarrow n = 95_{10} = 0001011111_2 \quad | \quad T_T = 95 \ \mu s$

16.112

(a) $0.1 \text{ LSB} = 0.1 \dfrac{2V}{2^{12} \text{bits}} = 48.8 \ \mu V$ (b) $0.1 \text{ LSB} = 0.1 \dfrac{2V}{2^{20} \text{bits}} = 0.191 \ \mu V$

16.113

The total conversion time is $T_T = \dfrac{1}{5 \times 10^4} = 20.0$ µs.

Twelve decisions must be made during this time (ignoring the final logic decision).

The time for each decision is $\dfrac{20.0 \mu s}{12} = \dfrac{1.67 \mu s}{bit} \;\mid\; f_C = 600 kHz \;\mid\; (0.1\ bit)\dfrac{1.67 \mu s}{bit} = 167$ ns

---

16.114 Note: Part (b) should refer to a **single-ramp** converter

(a) $V'_{REF} = 3.00 - 0.01 = 2.99$ V

(b) $\dfrac{1}{RC}\displaystyle\int_0^{T_T} 3\,dt = 5.12V \;\mid\; \dfrac{3}{RC}\dfrac{1}{30} = 5.12 \to RC = 19.53$ mS $\;\mid\; C = \dfrac{19.53 mS}{50 k\Omega} = 0.391$ µF

16.115

$$A(s) = -\frac{1}{sRC}\frac{A_o\beta(s)}{1+A_o\beta(s)} \;\mid\; \beta(s) = \frac{R}{R+\dfrac{1}{sC}} = \frac{sCR}{sCR+1} \;\mid\; V_S(s) = \frac{5}{s}$$

$$A(s) = -\frac{1}{sRC}\left(\frac{A_o\dfrac{sCR}{sCR+1}}{1+A_o\dfrac{sCR}{sCR+1}}\right) = -\frac{A_o}{sCR(A_o+1)+1} = -\frac{1}{RC}\frac{A_o}{1+A_o}\frac{1}{s+\dfrac{1}{RC(A_o+1)}}$$

$$V_O(s) = -\frac{1}{RC}\frac{A_o}{1+A_o}\frac{5}{s}\frac{1}{s+\dfrac{1}{RC(A_o+1)}} = \frac{A}{s}+\frac{B}{s+\dfrac{1}{RC(A_o+1)}}$$

$$A = -\frac{5}{RC}\frac{A_o}{1+A_o}RC(A_o+1) = 5A_o = 2.5 \times 10^5 \;\mid\; B = -\frac{5}{RC}\frac{A_o}{1+A_o}RC(A_o+1) = -5A_o = -2.5 \times 10^5$$

$$V_O(s) = 2.5 \times 10^5\left[\frac{1}{s}-\frac{1}{s+\dfrac{1}{RC(A_o+1)}}\right] \;\mid\; v_O(t) = 2.5\times 10^5\left(1-\exp\frac{-t}{5\times 10^4 RC}\right) \text{ for } t \geq 0$$

The output of an ideal integrator at t = 200ms would be $v_O(200ms) = \dfrac{5}{RC}(0.2s) = \dfrac{1}{RC}$

Desire: $\dfrac{1}{RC} - 2.5\times 10^5\left(1-\exp\dfrac{-0.2}{5\times 10^4 RC}\right) \leq 0.001 \to RC \geq 0.0447$ using MATLAB

Note however, for the minimum RC = 0.0447, $v_O(0.2s) = 22.4V$.

16.116

The time corresponding to 1 LSB is $T_{LSB} = \dfrac{0.2s}{2^{20} bits} = 190.7$ ns $\;\mid\; 0.1T_{LSB} = 19.1$ ns

---

16.117

$$V_O(\omega) = \frac{1}{RC}\int_0^{T_T} v(t)dt = \frac{1}{RC}\int_0^{T_T} V_M\cos(\omega t + \theta)dt = \frac{V_M}{\omega RC}\int_\theta^{\omega t+\theta}\cos x\, dx = \frac{V_M}{\omega RC}[\sin(\omega T_T + \theta)-\sin\theta]$$

For $\theta = 0$, $V_O(\omega) = \dfrac{V_M}{RC}\dfrac{\sin\omega T_T}{\omega} = \dfrac{V_M T_T}{RC}\left(\dfrac{\sin\omega T_T}{\omega T_T}\right)$

16.118
$$N_R = 2^n \quad \text{and} \quad N_C = 2^n - 1$$

16.119

$$[y_{11}]^{-1} = r_\pi + (\beta_o + 1)R_E \cong r_\pi + \beta_o R_E = r_\pi(1 + g_m R_E) \mid r_\pi' = r_\pi(1 + g_m R_E)$$

$$y_{21} = \frac{\beta_o}{r_\pi + (\beta_o + 1)R_E} \cong \frac{\beta_o}{r_\pi(1 + g_m R_E)} = \frac{g_m}{1 + g_m R_E} \mid g_m' = \frac{g_m}{1 + g_m R_E}$$

$$[y_{22}]^{-1} = r_o\left(1 + \frac{g_m R_E}{1 + \frac{R_E}{r_\pi}}\right) \cong r_o(1 + g_m R_E) \text{ for } R_E \ll r_\pi \text{ or } I_C R_E \ll \beta_o V_T \approx 2.5V$$

$$r_o' = r_o(1 + g_m R_E) \mid \text{Note: } \beta_o' = g_m' r_\pi' = \beta_o \text{ and } \mu_f' = g_m' r_o' = \mu_f \text{ are both conserved.}$$

16.120

$$\text{For } R_{th} = 0, \ R_{OUT} = r_o\left(1 + \frac{\beta_o R_E}{R_{th} + r_\pi + R_E}\right) = r_o\left(1 + \frac{g_m R_E}{1 + \frac{R_{th} + R_E}{r_\pi}}\right) = r_o\left(1 + \frac{g_m R_E}{1 + \frac{R_E}{r_\pi}}\right)$$

$$R_{OUT} = r_o\left(1 + \frac{g_m R_E}{1 + \frac{I_C R_E}{\beta_o V_T}}\right) \cong r_o(1 + g_m R_E) \text{ for } I_C R_E \ll \beta_o V_T \mid \text{ For common values,}$$

$$\beta_o V_T \approx 100(0.025V) = 2.5V, \text{ and the approximation holds for } I_C R_E \ll 2.5V$$

450

CHAPTER 17

17.1

$A_V(s) = 25\dfrac{s^2}{(s+1)(s+20)}$ | $A_{mid} = 25$ | $F_L(s) = \dfrac{s^2}{(s+1)(s+20)}$ | Poles: -1,-20 | Zeros: 0,0

yes, $s = -20$ | $A_V(s) \approx 25\dfrac{s}{(s+20)}$ | $\omega_L = 20\dfrac{rad}{s}$ | $f_L = \dfrac{\omega_L}{2\pi} \cong \dfrac{20}{2\pi} = 3.18Hz$

$f_L = \dfrac{1}{2\pi}\sqrt{20^2 + 1^2 - 2(0)^2 - 2(0)^2} = 3.19Hz$

$\left|A_V(j\omega)\right| = \dfrac{25\omega^2}{\sqrt{\omega^2 + 1^2}\sqrt{\omega^2 + 20^2}}$ | MATLAB: -3.19 Hz

17.2

$A_V(s) = 250\dfrac{s^2}{(s+100)(s+500)}$ | $A_{mid} = 250$ | $F_L(s) = \dfrac{s^2}{(s+100)(s+500)}$

Poles: -100,-500 $\dfrac{rad}{s}$ | Zeros: 0, 0 | Yes, a 5:1 split is sufficient | $s = -500$

$A_V(s) \approx 250\dfrac{s}{(s+500)}$ | $\omega_L \cong 500\dfrac{rad}{s}$ | $f_L \cong \dfrac{500}{2\pi} = 79.6$ Hz

$f_L \cong \dfrac{1}{2\pi}\sqrt{100^2 + 500^2 - 2(0)^2 - 2(0)^2} = 81.2$ Hz

$\left|A_V(j\omega)\right| = \dfrac{250\omega^2}{\sqrt{\omega^2 + 100^2}\sqrt{\omega^2 + 500^2}}$ | MATLAB: 82.6 Hz

17.3

$A_V(s) = -150\dfrac{s(s+15)}{(s+12)(s+20)}$ | $A_{mid} = -150$ | $F_L(s) = \dfrac{s(s+15)}{(s+12)(s+20)}$

Poles: -12, -20 $\dfrac{rad}{s}$ | Zeros: 0, -15 $\dfrac{rad}{s}$ | No, the poles and zeros are closely spaced.

$f_L \cong \dfrac{1}{2\pi}\sqrt{12^2 + 20^2 - 2(0)^2 - 2(15)^2} = 1.54$ Hz

$\left|A_V(j\omega)\right| = \dfrac{150\omega\sqrt{\omega^2 + 15^2}}{\sqrt{\omega^2 + 12^2}\sqrt{\omega^2 + 20^2}}$ | MATLAB: $f_L = 2.72$ Hz | $\omega_L = 17.1\dfrac{rad}{s}$

Note that $\omega_L = 17.1$ rad/s does not satisfy the assumption used to obtain Eq. (17.15), and the estimate using Eq. (17.15) is rather poor.

17.4

$A_V(s) = \dfrac{(2x10^{11})(10^{-4})(10^{-5})}{\left(\dfrac{s}{10^4}+1\right)\left(\dfrac{s}{10^5}+1\right)} = \dfrac{200}{\left(\dfrac{s}{10^4}+1\right)\left(\dfrac{s}{10^5}+1\right)}$ | $A_{mid} = 200$ | $F_H(s) = \dfrac{1}{\left(\dfrac{s}{10^4}+1\right)\left(\dfrac{s}{10^5}+1\right)}$

Poles: $-10^4, -10^5$ $\dfrac{rad}{s}$ | Yes: $A_V(s) \approx \dfrac{200}{\dfrac{s}{10^4}+1}$ | $\omega_H \approx 10^4\dfrac{rad}{s}$ | $f_H \approx \dfrac{10^4}{2\pi} = 1.59kHz$

$$f_H \cong \frac{1}{2\pi}\left(\sqrt{\left(\frac{1}{10^4}\right)^2 + \left(\frac{1}{10^5}\right)^2 - 2\left(\frac{1}{\infty}\right)^2 - 2\left(\frac{1}{\infty}\right)^2}\right)^{-1} = 1.58 \text{ kHz}$$

$$\left|A_V(j\omega)\right| = \frac{2\times10^{11}}{\sqrt{\omega^2 + \left(10^4\right)^2}\sqrt{\omega^2 + \left(10^5\right)^2}} \quad | \quad \text{MATLAB: 1.58 kHz}$$

17.5

$$A_V(s) = \frac{\left(2\times10^9\right)\left(1+\dfrac{s}{2\times10^9}\right)}{10^7\left(1+\dfrac{s}{10^7}\right)\left(1+\dfrac{s}{10^9}\right)} = 200\frac{\left(1+\dfrac{s}{2\times10^9}\right)}{\left(1+\dfrac{s}{10^7}\right)\left(1+\dfrac{s}{10^9}\right)}$$

$$A_{mid} = 200 \quad | \quad F_H(s) = \frac{\left(1+\dfrac{s}{2\times10^9}\right)}{\left(1+\dfrac{s}{10^7}\right)\left(1+\dfrac{s}{10^9}\right)} \quad | \quad \text{Poles: } -10^7, \ -10^9 \quad \text{Zeros: } -2\times10^9, \ \infty$$

$$\text{Yes: } A_V(s) \approx \frac{200}{\left(1+\dfrac{s}{10^7}\right)} \quad | \quad \omega_H \approx 10^7\frac{\text{rad}}{\text{s}} \quad | \quad f_H \approx \frac{10^4}{2\pi} = 1.59 \text{ MHz}$$

$$f_H = \frac{1}{2\pi}\left(\sqrt{\left(\frac{1}{10^7}\right)^2 + \left(\frac{1}{10^9}\right)^2 - 2\left(\frac{1}{2\times10^9}\right)^2 - 2\left(\frac{1}{\infty}\right)^2}\right)^{-1} = 1.59 \text{ MHz}$$

$$\left|A_V(j\omega)\right| = \frac{2\times10^9\sqrt{\omega^2 + \left(2\times10^9\right)^2}}{\sqrt{\omega^2 + \left(10^7\right)^2}\sqrt{\omega^2 + \left(10^9\right)^2}} \quad | \quad \text{MATLAB: 1.59 MHz}$$

17.6

$$A_V(s) = \frac{\left(4\times10^9\right)\left(5\times10^5\right)\left(1+\dfrac{s}{5\times10^5}\right)}{\left(1.3\times10^5\right)\left(2\times10^6\right)\left(1+\dfrac{s}{1.3\times10^5}\right)\left(1+\dfrac{s}{2\times10^6}\right)} = 7692\frac{\left(1+\dfrac{s}{5\times10^5}\right)}{\left(1+\dfrac{s}{1.3\times10^5}\right)\left(1+\dfrac{s}{2\times10^6}\right)}$$

$$A_{mid} = 7692 \quad | \quad F_H(s) = \frac{\left(1+\dfrac{s}{5\times10^5}\right)}{\left(1+\dfrac{s}{1.3\times10^5}\right)\left(1+\dfrac{s}{2\times10^6}\right)} \quad | \quad \text{Poles: } -1.3\times10^5, \ -2\times10^6 \ \frac{\text{rad}}{\text{s}}$$

Zeros: $-5\times10^5 \ \dfrac{\text{rad}}{\text{s}}, \ \infty$ | No, the poles and zeros are closely spaced and will interact.

$$f_H \cong \frac{1}{2\pi}\left(\sqrt{\left(\frac{1}{1.3\,10^5}\right)^2 + \left(\frac{1}{2\times10^6}\right)^2 - 2\left(\frac{1}{5\times10^5}\right)^2 - 2\left(\frac{1}{\infty}\right)^2}\right)^{-1} = 22.2 \text{ kHz}$$

$$\left|A_V(j\omega)\right| = \frac{4\times10^9\sqrt{\omega^2 + \left(5\times10^5\right)^2}}{\sqrt{\omega^2 + \left(1.3\times10^5\right)^2}\sqrt{\omega^2 + \left(2\times10^6\right)^2}} \quad | \quad \text{MATLAB: 22.1 kHz}$$

$$A_V(s) = \frac{10^8}{500(1000)} \frac{s^2}{(s+1)(s+2)} \frac{1}{\left(1+\dfrac{s}{500}\right)\left(1+\dfrac{s}{1000}\right)}$$

$$A_V(s) = 200\left[\frac{s^2}{(s+1)(s+2)}\right]\left[\frac{1}{\left(1+\dfrac{s}{500}\right)\left(1+\dfrac{s}{1000}\right)}\right] = 200F_L(s)F_H(s)$$

Poles; -1, -2, -500, -1000 $\dfrac{rad}{s}$ | Zeros: 0, 0, ∞, ∞ | No. | No.

$$|A_V(j\omega)| = \frac{10^8\omega^2}{\sqrt{1^2+\omega^2}\sqrt{2^2+\omega^2}\sqrt{500^2+\omega^2}\sqrt{1000^2+\omega^2}}$$

$$f_L = \frac{1}{2\pi}\sqrt{(1)^2+(2)^2-2(0)^2-2(0)^2} = 0.356 \text{ Hz} \mid \text{MATLAB: } 0.380 \text{ Hz}$$

$$f_H = \frac{1}{2\pi}\sqrt{\left(\frac{1}{500}\right)^2+\left(\frac{1}{1000}\right)^2-2\left(\frac{1}{\infty}\right)^2-2\left(\frac{1}{\infty}\right)^2} = 71.2 \text{ kHz} \mid \text{MATLAB: } 66.7 \text{ Hz}$$

17.8

$$A_V(s) = \frac{10^{10}(200)}{(100)^2(300)} \frac{s^2(s+1)}{(s+3)(s+5)(s+7)} \frac{\left(1+\dfrac{s}{200}\right)}{\left(1+\dfrac{s}{100}\right)^2\left(1+\dfrac{s}{300}\right)}$$

$$A_V(s) = 6.67x10^5\left[\frac{s^2(s+1)}{(s+3)(s+5)(s+7)}\right]\left[\frac{\left(1+\dfrac{s}{200}\right)}{\left(1+\dfrac{s}{100}\right)^2\left(1+\dfrac{s}{300}\right)}\right] = 6.67x10^5 F_L(s)F_H(s)$$

No dominant pole at either low or high frequencies.

$$|A_V(j\omega)| = \frac{10^{10}\omega^2\sqrt{\omega^2+1^2}\sqrt{\omega^2+200^2}}{\sqrt{\omega^2+3^2}\sqrt{\omega^2+5^2}\sqrt{\omega^2+7^2}\left(\omega^2+100^2\right)\sqrt{\omega^2+300^2}}$$

$$f_L = \frac{1}{2\pi}\sqrt{(3)^2+(5)^2+(7)^2-2(1)^2-2(0)^2} = 1.43 \text{ Hz} \mid \text{MATLAB: } 1.62 \text{ Hz}$$

$$f_H = \frac{1}{2\pi}\left(\sqrt{\left(\frac{1}{100}\right)^2+\left(\frac{1}{100}\right)^2+\left(\frac{1}{300}\right)^2-2\left(\frac{1}{200}\right)^2-2\left(\frac{1}{\infty}\right)^2}\right)^{-1} = 12.5 \text{ Hz} \mid \text{MATLAB: } 10.6 \text{ Hz}$$

17.9

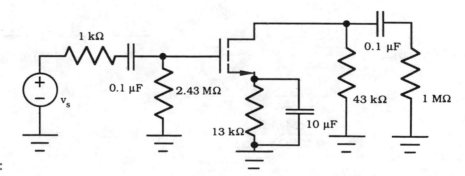

Low frequency:

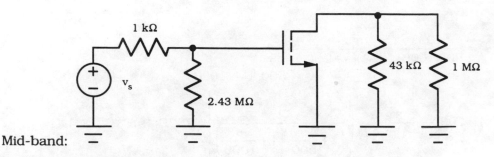

Mid-band:

$$g_m = \frac{2I_{DS}}{V_{GS} - V_{TN}} = \frac{2(0.2\text{mA})}{1\text{V}} = 0.400\text{mS}$$

$$A_{mid} = -\frac{2.43\text{M}\Omega}{2.43\text{M}\Omega + 1\text{k}\Omega}(0.400\text{mS})(43\text{k}\Omega\|1\text{M}\Omega) = -16.5$$

$$\omega_1 = \frac{1}{(10^{-7}\text{F})(2.43\text{M}\Omega + 1\text{k}\Omega)} = 4.11\frac{\text{rad}}{\text{s}} \quad | \quad \omega_2 = \frac{1}{(10^{-7}\text{F})(43\text{k}\Omega + 1\text{M}\Omega)} = 9.59\frac{\text{rad}}{\text{s}}$$

$$\omega_3 = \frac{1}{(10^{-5}\text{F})\left(13\text{k}\Omega\left\|\frac{1}{g_m}\right.\right)} = \frac{1}{(10^{-5}\text{F})(13\text{k}\Omega\|2.5\text{k}\Omega)} = 47.7\frac{\text{rad}}{\text{s}} \quad | \quad \omega_Z = \frac{1}{(10^{-5}\text{F})(13\text{k}\Omega)} = 7.69\frac{\text{rad}}{\text{s}}$$

ω_3 is dominant: $f_L \cong \dfrac{\omega_3}{2\pi} = 7.59$ Hz

Using Eq. (17.16) yields: $f_L \cong \dfrac{1}{2\pi}\sqrt{(4.11)^2 + (9.59)^2 + (47.7)^2 - 2(7.69)^2} = 7.58$ Hz

_____

17.10

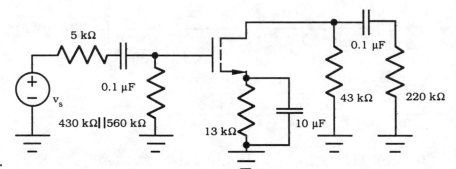

Low frequency:

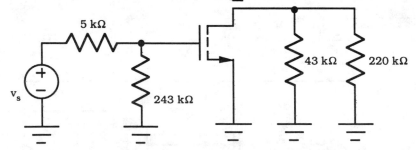

Mid-band:

$$g_m = \frac{2I_{DS}}{V_{GS} - V_{TN}} = \frac{2(0.2\text{mA})}{1\text{V}} = 0.400\text{mS}$$

$$A_{mid} = -\frac{243\text{k}\Omega}{243\text{k}\Omega + 5\text{k}\Omega}(0.400\text{mS})(43\text{k}\Omega\|220\text{k}\Omega) = -14.1$$

$$\omega_1 = \frac{1}{\left(10^{-7}\text{F}\right)\left(243\text{k}\Omega + 5\text{k}\Omega\right)} = 40.3\frac{\text{rad}}{\text{s}} \quad | \quad \omega_2 = \frac{1}{\left(10^{-7}\text{F}\right)\left(43\text{k}\Omega + 220\text{k}\Omega\right)} = 38.0\frac{\text{rad}}{\text{s}}$$

$$\omega_3 = \frac{1}{\left(10^{-5}\text{F}\right)\left(13\text{k}\Omega\left\|\frac{1}{g_m}\right.\right)} = \frac{1}{\left(10^{-5}\text{F}\right)\left(13\text{k}\Omega\|2.5\text{k}\Omega\right)} = 47.7\frac{\text{rad}}{\text{s}} \quad | \quad \omega_Z = \frac{1}{\left(10^{-5}\text{F}\right)\left(13\text{k}\Omega\right)} = 7.69\frac{\text{rad}}{\text{s}}$$

Using Eq. (17.16): $f_L \cong \frac{1}{2\pi}\sqrt{(40.3)^2 + (38.0)^2 + (47.7)^2 - 2(7.69)^2} = 11.5$ Hz

17.11

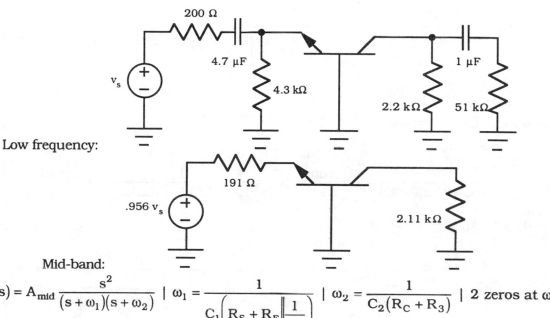

Low frequency:

Mid-band:

(b) $A_V(s) = A_{mid}\dfrac{s^2}{(s+\omega_1)(s+\omega_2)} \quad | \quad \omega_1 = \dfrac{1}{C_1\left(R_S + R_E\left\|\frac{1}{g_m}\right.\right)} \quad | \quad \omega_2 = \dfrac{1}{C_2(R_C + R_3)} \quad | \quad 2$ zeros at $\omega = 0$

$\mathbf{v_{th}} = \mathbf{v_s}\dfrac{4300\Omega}{4300\Omega + 200\Omega} = 0.956\mathbf{v_s} \quad | \quad R_{th} = 4.3\text{k}\Omega\|200\Omega = 191\Omega \quad | \quad R_L = 2.2\text{k}\Omega\|51\text{k}\Omega = 2.11\text{k}\Omega$

(c) $A_{mid} = 0.956(\alpha_o)\dfrac{R_L}{R_{th} + \frac{1}{g_m}} = 0.956\left(\dfrac{100}{101}\right)\dfrac{2.11\text{k}\Omega}{191\Omega + \frac{1\text{V}}{40(10^{-3}\text{A})}} = +9.25 \rightarrow 19.3$ dB

$\omega_1 = \dfrac{1}{4.7\text{x}10^{-6}(200 + 4300\|25)} = 946\dfrac{\text{rad}}{\text{s}} \quad | \quad \omega_2 = \dfrac{1}{10^{-6}(2.2\text{k}\Omega + 51\text{k}\Omega)} = 18.8\dfrac{\text{rad}}{\text{s}}$

ω_1 is dominant: $f_L \cong \dfrac{\omega_1}{2\pi} = 151$ Hz

(d) $\mathbf{v_{th}} = \mathbf{v_s}\dfrac{430\text{k}\Omega}{430\text{k}\Omega + 200\Omega} = 1.00\mathbf{v_s} \quad | \quad R_{th} = 430\text{k}\Omega\|200\Omega = 200\Omega \quad | \quad R_L = 220\text{k}\Omega\|510\text{k}\Omega = 154\text{k}\Omega$

$A_{mid} = \alpha_o\dfrac{R_L}{R_{th} + \frac{1}{g_m}} = \left(\dfrac{100}{101}\right)\dfrac{154\text{k}\Omega}{200\Omega + \frac{1\text{V}}{40(10^{-5}\text{A})}} = +56.5 \rightarrow 35.0$ dB

$\omega_1 = \dfrac{1}{4.7\text{x}10^{-6}(200 + 430\text{k}\Omega\|2.5\text{k}\Omega)} = 79.2\dfrac{\text{rad}}{\text{s}} \quad | \quad \omega_2 = \dfrac{1}{10^{-6}(220\text{k}\Omega + 510\text{k}\Omega)} = 1.37\dfrac{\text{rad}}{\text{s}}$

ω_1 is dominant: $f_L \cong \dfrac{\omega_1}{2\pi} = 12.6$ Hz

17.12

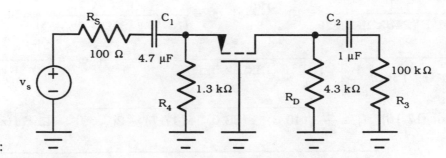

Low Frequency:

(b) $A_V(s) = A_{mid} \dfrac{s^2}{(s+\omega_1)(s+\omega_2)}$ | $\omega_1 = \dfrac{1}{C_1\left(R_S + R_4 \left\| \dfrac{1}{g_m}\right.\right)}$ | $\omega_2 = \dfrac{1}{C_2(R_D + R_3)}$ | 2 zeros at $\omega = 0$

(c) $\mathbf{v_{th}} = \mathbf{v_s} \dfrac{1.3k\Omega}{1.3k\Omega + 100\Omega} = 0.929\mathbf{v_s}$ | $R_{th} = 1.3k\Omega \| 100\Omega = 92.9\Omega$ | $R_L = 4.3k\Omega \| 100k\Omega = 4.12k\Omega$

$A_{mid} = 0.929 \dfrac{R_L}{R_{th} + \dfrac{1}{g_m}} = 0.929 \dfrac{4.12k\Omega}{92.9\Omega + \dfrac{1}{5mS}} = 13.1 \rightarrow 22.3$ dB

$\omega_1 = \dfrac{1}{4.7\text{x}10^{-6}(100 + 1300\|200)} = 778 \dfrac{rad}{s}$ | $\omega_2 = \dfrac{1}{10^{-6}(4.3k\Omega + 100k\Omega)} = 9.59 \dfrac{rad}{s}$

ω_1 is dominant: $f_L \cong \dfrac{\omega_1}{2\pi} = 124$ Hz

17.13

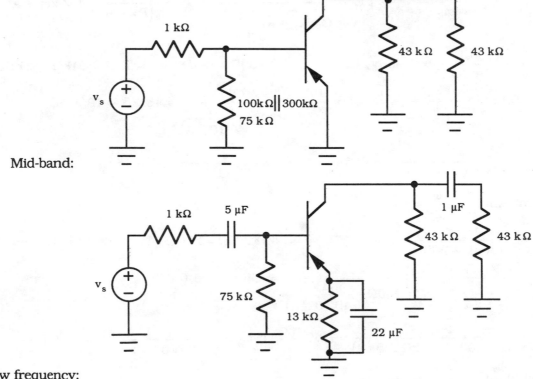

Mid-band:

Low frequency:

(b) $g_m = 40I_C = 40(0.164\text{mA}) = 6.56\text{mS} \mid r_\pi = \dfrac{\beta_o}{g_m} = \dfrac{100}{6.56\text{mS}} = 15.2\text{k}\Omega \mid r_o = \infty$ (V_A not given)

$\mathbf{v_{th}} = \mathbf{v_s}\dfrac{75\text{k}\Omega}{1\text{k}\Omega + 75\text{k}\Omega} = 0.987\mathbf{v_s} \mid R_{th} = 75\text{k}\Omega\|1\text{k}\Omega = 987\Omega \mid R_L = 43\text{k}\Omega\|43\text{k}\Omega = 21.5\text{k}\Omega$

$A_{mid} = -0.987\dfrac{\beta_o R_L}{R_{th} + r_\pi} = -0.987\dfrac{100(21.5\text{k}\Omega)}{987\Omega + 15.2\text{k}\Omega} = -131$

SCTC: $R_{1S} = R_s + R_B\|r_\pi = 1\text{k}\Omega + 75\text{k}\Omega\|15.2\text{k}\Omega = 13.6\text{k}\Omega$

$R_{2S} = R_E\left\|\dfrac{R_{th} + r_\pi}{\beta_o + 1}\right. = 13\text{k}\Omega\left\|\dfrac{987\Omega + 15.2\text{k}\Omega}{101}\right. = 158\Omega \mid R_{3S} = R_C + R_3 = 43\text{k}\Omega + 43\text{k}\Omega = 86\text{k}\Omega$

$f_L \cong \dfrac{1}{2\pi}\left[\dfrac{1}{5\text{x}10^{-6}(13.6\text{k}\Omega)} + \dfrac{1}{22\text{x}10^{-6}(158\Omega)} + \dfrac{1}{1\text{x}10^{-6}(86\text{k}\Omega)}\right] = \dfrac{(14.7 + 288 + 11.6)}{2\pi} = 50.0\text{ Hz}$

17.14

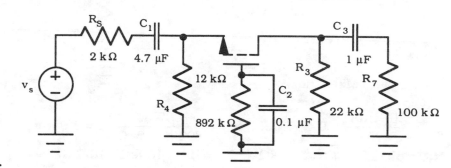

Low Frequency:

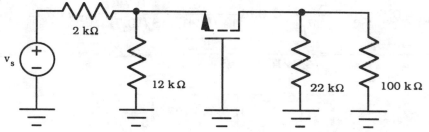

Mid-band:

$g_m = \dfrac{2(0.1\text{mA})}{1\text{V}} = 0.200\text{mS} \mid \dfrac{1}{g_m} = 5000\Omega \mid \mathbf{v_{th}} = \dfrac{12\text{k}\Omega}{12\text{k}\Omega + 2\text{k}\Omega}\mathbf{v_s} = 0.857\mathbf{v_s}$

$R_{th} = 12\text{k}\Omega\|2\text{k}\Omega = 1.71\text{k}\Omega \mid R_L = 22\text{k}\Omega\|100\text{k}\Omega = 18.0\text{k}\Omega$

$A_{mid} = 0.857\dfrac{R_L}{R_{th} + \dfrac{1}{g_m}} = 0.857\dfrac{18.0\text{k}\Omega}{1.71\text{k}\Omega + 5\text{k}\Omega} = 2.30$ (7.24dB)

$\omega_1 = \dfrac{1}{4.7\text{x}10^{-6}(2\text{k}\Omega + 12\text{k}\Omega\|5\text{k}\Omega)} = 38.5\dfrac{\text{rad}}{\text{s}} \mid \omega_2 = $ doesn't matter since $i_g = 0$!

$\omega_3 = \dfrac{1}{10^{-7}(100\text{k}\Omega + 22\text{k}\Omega)} = 82.0\dfrac{\text{rad}}{\text{s}} \mid f_L \approx \dfrac{1}{2\pi}(38.5 + 82.0) = 19.2\text{Hz}$

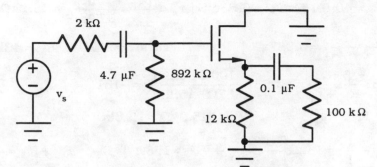

Low Frequency:

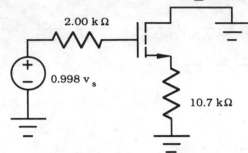

Mid-band:

$$g_m = \frac{2(0.1mA)}{0.75V} = 0.267mS \quad | \quad \mathbf{v}_{th} = \frac{892k\Omega}{892k\Omega + 2k\Omega}\mathbf{v_s} = 0.998\mathbf{v_s}$$

$$R_{th} = 892k\Omega\|2k\Omega = 2.00k\Omega \quad | \quad R_L = 12k\Omega\|100k\Omega = 10.7k\Omega$$

$$A_{mid} = 0.998\frac{g_m R_L}{1 + g_m R_L} = 0.998\frac{(0.267mS)(10.7k\Omega)}{1 + (0.267mS)(10.7k\Omega)} = +0.739 \quad (-2.62 \text{ dB})$$

$$\omega_1 = \frac{1}{C_1(R_S + R_G)} = \frac{1}{4.7 \times 10^{-6}(2k\Omega + 892k\Omega)} = 0.238\frac{rad}{s}$$

$$\omega_3 = \frac{1}{C_3\left(R_7 + R_4\left\|\dfrac{1}{g_m}\right.\right)} = \frac{1}{10^{-7}\left(100k\Omega + 12k\Omega\left\|\dfrac{1}{0.267mS}\right.\right)} = 97.2\frac{rad}{s}$$

$$f_L \approx \frac{1}{2\pi}(0.238 + 97.2) = 15.5 \text{ Hz}$$

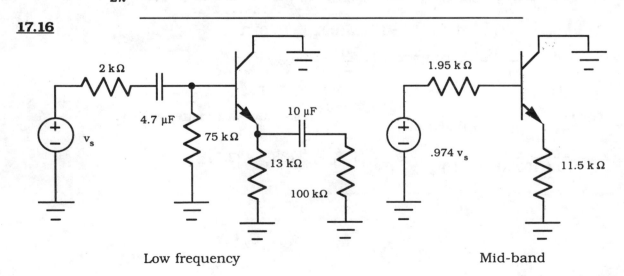

Low frequency   Mid-band

(b) $v_{th} = \dfrac{75k\Omega}{75k\Omega + 2k\Omega} v_s = 0.974 v_s$ | $R_{th} = 75k\Omega \| 2k\Omega = 1.95k\Omega$ | $R_L = 13k\Omega \| 100k\Omega = 11.5k\Omega$

$r_\pi = \dfrac{100}{40(0.25mA)} = 10.0k\Omega$ | $A_{mid} = 0.974 \dfrac{101(11.5k\Omega)}{[1.95 + 10.0 + 101(11.5)]k\Omega} = 0.964$

$R_{1S} = R_S + R_B \| [r_\pi + (\beta_o + 1)R_L] = 2k\Omega + 75k\Omega \| [10.0k\Omega + (101)11.5k\Omega] = 72.5k\Omega$

$\omega_1 = \dfrac{1}{(72.5k\Omega)4.7 \times 10^{-6}} = 2.94 \dfrac{rad}{s}$

$R_{3S} = R_7 + R_4 \left\| \dfrac{R_{th} + r_\pi}{(\beta_o + 1)} = 100k\Omega + 13k\Omega \right\| \dfrac{1.95k\Omega + 10.0k\Omega}{101} = 100k\Omega$

$\omega_3 = \dfrac{1}{10^{-5}(10^5)} = 1 \dfrac{rad}{s}$ $f_L \approx \dfrac{(2.94 + 1)}{2\pi} = 0.627 Hz$

17.17

SCTC requires: $\omega_L \cong \displaystyle\sum_{i=1}^{3} \dfrac{1}{R_{is}C_i} = 2\pi(500) = 3140 \dfrac{rad}{s}$

$\omega_1 = \dfrac{1}{(10^{-7}F)(2.43M\Omega + 1k\Omega)} = 4.11 \dfrac{rad}{s}$ | $\omega_2 = \dfrac{1}{(10^{-7}F)(43k\Omega + 1M\Omega)} = 9.59 \dfrac{rad}{s}$

$\omega_1 + \omega_2 << \omega_L$ | ω_3 will be dominant $\rightarrow \omega_3 \cong \omega_L$

$\omega_3 = \dfrac{1}{C_3\left(R_4 \left\| \dfrac{1}{g_m}\right.\right)}$ | $g_m = \dfrac{2I_{DS}}{V_{GS} - V_{TN}} = \dfrac{2(0.2mA)}{1V} = 0.400mS$ | $\dfrac{1}{g_m} = 2.50k\Omega$

$C_3 = \dfrac{1}{3140(13k\Omega \| 2.5k\Omega)} = 0.152\ \mu F \rightarrow 0.15\ \mu F$ from Appendix C

17.18

(a) SCTC requires: $\omega_L \cong \displaystyle\sum_{i=1}^{3} \dfrac{1}{R_{is}C_i} = 2\pi(100) = 628 \dfrac{rad}{s}$

$\omega_2 = \dfrac{1}{(10^{-6}F)(2.2k\Omega + 51k\Omega)} = 18.8 \dfrac{rad}{s} << \omega_L$ | ω_1 will be dominant $\rightarrow \omega_L \cong \omega_1$

$\omega_1 = \dfrac{1}{C_1\left(R_S + R_E \left\| \dfrac{1}{g_m}\right.\right)}$ | $\dfrac{1}{g_m} = \dfrac{1}{40(10^{-53})} = 25\Omega$

$C_1 = \dfrac{1}{628(200\Omega + 4.3k\Omega \| 25\Omega)} = 7.08\ \mu F \rightarrow 6.8\ \mu F$ nearest value in Appendix C

Note: We might want to choose 8.2 μF to insure that $f_L \leq 100$ Hz

(b) SCTC requires: $\omega_L \cong \displaystyle\sum_{i=1}^{3} \dfrac{1}{R_{is}C_i} = 2\pi(100) = 628 \dfrac{rad}{s}$

$\omega_2 = \dfrac{1}{(10^{-6}F)(220k\Omega + 510k\Omega)} = 1.37 \dfrac{rad}{s}$ | ω_1 will be dominant $\rightarrow \omega_L \cong \omega_1$

$\omega_1 = \dfrac{1}{C_1\left(R_S + R_E \left\| \dfrac{1}{g_m}\right.\right)}$ | $\dfrac{1}{g_m} = \dfrac{1}{40(10^{-5})} = 2.5k\Omega$

$$C_1 = \frac{1}{628(200\Omega + 430k\Omega \| 2.5k\Omega)} = 0.592 \ \mu F \rightarrow 0.56 \ \mu F \text{ nearest value in Appendix C}$$

Note: We might want to use $0.68 \ \mu F$ to insure that $f_L \le 100$ Hz

---

17.19

(b) $g_m = 40I_C = 40(0.164mA) = 6.56mS \mid r_\pi = \dfrac{\beta_o}{g_m} = \dfrac{100}{6.56mS} = 15.2k\Omega \mid r_o = \infty \ (V_A \text{ not given})$

SCTC requires: $\displaystyle\sum_{i=1}^{3} \frac{1}{R_{is}C_i} = 2\pi(20) = 126 \ \frac{rad}{s}$

$R_{1S} = R_s + R_B \| r_\pi = 1k\Omega + 75k\Omega \| 15.2k\Omega = 13.6k\Omega \mid \omega_1 = \dfrac{1}{5x10^{-6}(13.6k\Omega)} = 14.7$

$R_{3S} = R_C + R_3 = 43k\Omega + 43k\Omega = 86k\Omega \mid \omega_3 = \dfrac{1}{1x10^{-6}(86k\Omega)} = 11.6$

$\omega_2 = 126 - 14.7 - 11.6 = 99.7 \ \dfrac{rad}{s} \mid R_{2S} = R_E \left\| \dfrac{R_{th} + r_\pi}{\beta_o + 1} = 13k\Omega \right\| \dfrac{987\Omega + 15.2k\Omega}{101} = 158\Omega$

$C_2 \cong \dfrac{1}{99.7(158)} = 63.5 \ \mu F \rightarrow 68 \ \mu F \text{ from Appendix C}$

17.20

SCTC requires: $\displaystyle\sum_{i=1}^{3} \frac{1}{R_{is}C_i} = 2\pi(1) = 6.28 \ \frac{rad}{s}$

However, $R_{3S} = R_3 + R_7 = 22k\Omega + 100k\Omega = 122k\Omega$

$\omega_3 = \dfrac{1}{1x10^{-7}(122k\Omega)} = 82.0 \ \dfrac{rad}{s} > 6.28 \ \dfrac{rad}{s} \mid \text{The design goal cannot be met.}$

It is not possible to force f_L below the limit set by C_3

17.21

SCTC requires: $\omega_L \cong \displaystyle\sum_{i=1}^{3} \frac{1}{R_{is}C_i} = 2\pi(10) = 62.8 \ \frac{rad}{s}$

$\omega_1 = \dfrac{1}{C_1(R_S + R_G)} = \dfrac{1}{4.7x10^{-6}(2k\Omega + 892k\Omega)} = 0.238 \ \dfrac{rad}{s} \mid \omega_L \gg \omega_1 \rightarrow \omega_3 \text{ is dominant}$

$\omega_L \cong \omega_3 = \dfrac{1}{C_3\left(R_7 + R_4 \left\| \dfrac{1}{g_m}\right)\right)} \mid \dfrac{1}{g_m} = \dfrac{0.75V}{2(0.1mA)} = 3.75k\Omega$

$C_3 = \dfrac{1}{62.8(100k\Omega + 12k\Omega \| 3.75k\Omega)} = 0.155 \ \dfrac{rad}{s} \rightarrow 0.15 \ \mu F \text{ using Appendix C}$

17.22

SCTC requires: $\omega_L \cong \displaystyle\sum_{i=1}^{3} \frac{1}{R_{is}C_i} = 2\pi(5) = 31.4 \ \frac{rad}{s}$

$R_{th} = 75k\Omega \| 2k\Omega = 1.95k\Omega \mid R_L = 13k\Omega \| 100k\Omega = 11.5k\Omega \mid r_\pi = \dfrac{100}{40(0.25mA)} = 10.0k\Omega$

$R_{1S} = R_S + R_B \| [r_\pi + (\beta_o + 1)R_L] = 2k\Omega + 75k\Omega \| [10.0k\Omega + (101)11.5k\Omega] = 72.5k\Omega$

$$\omega_1 = \frac{1}{(72.5k\Omega)4.7x10^{-6}} = 2.94 \frac{rad}{s} \quad | \quad \omega_3 = 31.4 - 2.94 = 28.5 \frac{rad}{s}$$

$$R_{3S} = R_7 + R_4 \left\| \frac{R_{th} + r_\pi}{(\beta_o + 1)} = 100k\Omega + 13k\Omega \right\| \frac{1.95k\Omega + 10.0k\Omega}{101} = 100k\Omega$$

$$C_3 = \frac{1}{28.5(100k\Omega)} = 0.351 \, \mu F \rightarrow 0.39 \, \mu F \text{ using the values from Appendix C}$$

17.23

$$f_T = \frac{1}{2\pi}\left(\frac{g_m}{C_\pi + C_\mu}\right) \quad | \quad C_\pi = \frac{g_m}{2\pi f_T} - C_\mu \quad | \quad g_m = 40I_C$$

I_C	f_T	C_π	C_μ	$1/2\pi r_x C_\mu$
10 µA	50 MHz	**0.733 pF**	0.5 pF	**1.27 GHz**
100 µA	300 MHz	0.75 pF	**1.37 pF**	**465 MHz**
50 µA	1 GHz	**2.93 pF**	0.25 pF	**2.55 GHz**
10 mA	**6.12 GHz**	10 pF	**0.400 pF**	1.59 GHz
1 µA	**3.18 MHz**	1 pF	1 pF	**636 MHz**
1.18 mA	5 GHz	1 pF	0.5 pF	**1.27 GHz**

17.24

$$f_T = \frac{1}{2\pi}\left(\frac{g_m}{C_{GS} + C_{GD}}\right) \quad | \quad g_m = \sqrt{2K_n I_{DS}}$$

I_{DS}	f_T	C_{GS}	C_{GD}
10 µA	**11.3 MHz**	1.5 pF	0.5 pF
250 µA	**56.3 MHz**	1.5 pF	0.5 pF
4.93 mA	250 MHz	1.5 pF	0.5 pF

17.25

$$C_\pi = g_m \tau_F \quad | \quad C_\pi = \frac{g_m}{\omega_T} - C_\mu \quad | \quad V_{CB} = 5 - 0.7 = 4.3V \quad | \quad C_\mu = \frac{C_{\mu o}}{\sqrt{1 + \frac{V_{CB}}{\phi_{jc}}}} = \frac{2pF}{\sqrt{1 + \frac{4.3V}{0.9V}}} = 0.832pF$$

$$C_\pi = \frac{40(2x10^{-3})}{2\pi(5x10^8)} - 0.832pF = 24.6 \, pF \quad | \quad \tau_F = \frac{C_\pi}{g_m} = \frac{24.6x10^{-12}}{40(2x10^{-3})} = 0.308ns = 308 \, ps$$

17.26

(a) $\mathbf{v_{th}} = \frac{7.5k\Omega}{7.5k\Omega + 1k\Omega}\mathbf{v_s} = 0.882\mathbf{v_s} \quad | \quad R_{th} = 7.5k\Omega \| 1k\Omega = 882\Omega \quad | \quad R_L = 4.3k\Omega \| 100k\Omega = 4.12k\Omega$

$r_\pi = \frac{100(0.025V)}{1mA} = 2.5k\Omega \quad | \quad A_{mid} = -0.882\frac{\beta_o R_L}{R_{th} + r_x + r_\pi} = -0.882\frac{100(4120)}{882 + 250 + 2500} = -100$

(b) $A_{mid} = -0.882 \dfrac{\beta_o R_L}{R_{th} + r_\pi} = -0.882 \dfrac{100(4120\Omega)}{882\Omega + 2500\Omega} = -107$

17.27

$\mathbf{v_{th}} = \dfrac{43k\Omega}{43k\Omega + 100\Omega}\mathbf{v_s} = 0.998\mathbf{v_s} \mid R_{th} = 43k\Omega\|100\Omega = 998\Omega \mid R_L = 22k\Omega\|75k\Omega = 17.0k\Omega$

$r_\pi = \dfrac{100(0.025V)}{0.1mA} = 25k\Omega \mid g_m' = \dfrac{\beta_o}{r_x + r_\pi} = \dfrac{100}{250\Omega + 25k\Omega} = 3.96mS$

(a) $A_{mid} = 0.882\dfrac{g_m' R_L}{1 + g_m' R_{th}} = -0.882\dfrac{3.96mS(17.0k\Omega)}{1 + 3.96mS(998\Omega)} = 12.0$

(b) $A_{mid} = 0.882\dfrac{g_m R_L}{1 + g_m R_{th}} = -0.882\dfrac{4.00mS(17.0k\Omega)}{1 + 4.00mS(998\Omega)} = 12.0$

17.28

$\mathbf{v_{th}} = \dfrac{100k\Omega}{100k\Omega + 1k\Omega}\mathbf{v_s} = 0.990\mathbf{v_s} \mid R_{th} = 100k\Omega\|1k\Omega = 990\Omega$

$R_L = 3k\Omega\|47k\Omega = 2.82k\Omega \mid r_\pi = \dfrac{100(0.025V)}{1mA} = 2.50k\Omega$

(a) $A_{mid} = 0.990\dfrac{(\beta_o + 1)R_L}{R_{th} + r_x + r_\pi + (\beta_o + 1)R_L} = 0.990\dfrac{101(2820)}{990 + 250 + 2500 + 101(2820)} = 0.977$

(b) $A_{mid} = 0.990\dfrac{(\beta_o + 1)R_L}{R_{th} + r_\pi + (\beta_o + 1)R_L} = 0.990\dfrac{101(2820)}{990 + 2500 + 101(2820)} = 0.978$

17.29

(a) $s^2 + 5100s + 500000 \mid s_1 \approx -\dfrac{5100}{1} = -5100 \mid s_2 \approx -\dfrac{5x10^5}{5100} = -98.0$

$s = \dfrac{-5100 \pm \sqrt{5100^2 - 4(5x10^5)}}{2} = \dfrac{-5100 \pm 4900}{2} \rightarrow -100, \; -5000 \mid 2\% \text{ error}$

(b) $2s^2 + 700s + 30000 = 2(s^2 + 350s + 15000)$

$s_1 \approx -\dfrac{350}{1} = -350 \mid s_2 \approx -\dfrac{15000}{350} = -42.9$

$s = \dfrac{-350 \pm \sqrt{350^2 - 4(15000)}}{2} = \dfrac{-350 \pm 250}{2} \rightarrow -50, \; -300 \mid 14\% \text{ error}$

17.30

$s^3 + 1110s^2 + 111000s + 1000000$

$s_1 \approx -\dfrac{1110}{1} = -1110 \mid s_2 \approx -\dfrac{111000}{1110} = -100 \mid s_3 \approx -\dfrac{1000000}{111000} = -9.01$

Factoring the polynomial: $s^3 + 1110s^2 + 111000s + 1000000 = (s + 10)(s + 100)(s + 1000)$

$s = -1000, \; -100, \; -10 \mid 11\% \text{ error in } s_1, \; 10\% \text{ error in } s_3$

MATLAB: roots([1 1110 111000 1000000])

17.31

$$f(s) = s^6 + 138s^5 + 4263s^4 + 4760s^3 + 235550s^2 + 94000s + 300000$$

$$f'(s) = 6s^5 + 690s^4 + 17052s^3 + 14280s^2 + 471100s + 94000$$

$$s^{i+1} = s^i - \frac{f(s^i)}{f'(s^i)} \quad | \quad \text{Using a spreadsheet, two real roots are found: } -46.7962, \ -91.8478$$

Using MATLAB: roots([1 138 4263 4760 235550 94000 300000])

ans = -91.8478, -46.7962, 0.5189 + 7.2789i, 0.5189 - 7.2789i, -0.1970 + 1.1278i, -0.1970 -

1.1278i

A better polymonial: $f(s) = s^6 + 142s^5 + 4757s^4 + 58230s^3 + 256950s^2 + 398000s + 300000$

Roots: -100, -20, -15, -5, -1+i, -1-i

17.32 Note: Use $C_{GS} = C_{GD} = 2.5$ pF for the MOSFET

$$\mathbf{v_{th}} = \frac{2.43M\Omega}{2.43M\Omega + 1k\Omega}\mathbf{v_s} = 1.00\mathbf{v_s} \quad | \quad R_{th} = 2.43M\Omega \| 1k\Omega = 1.00k\Omega \quad | \quad R_L = 43k\Omega \| 1M\Omega = 41.2k\Omega$$

$$g_m = \frac{2I_{DS}}{V_{GS} - V_{TN}} = \frac{2(0.2mA)}{1} = 0.400mS \quad | \quad A_{mid} = -1.00g_m R_L = -0.400mS(41.2k\Omega) = -16.5$$

$$f_H = \frac{1}{2\pi r_{\pi o} C_T} \quad | \quad r_{\pi o} = R_{th} = 1.00k\Omega$$

$$C_T = 2.5pF + 2.5pF\left[1 + (0.400ms)(41.2k\Omega) + \frac{4.12k\Omega}{1k\Omega}\right] = 149pF$$

$$f_H = \frac{1}{2\pi(1k\Omega)(1.49x10^{-10})} = 1.07 \text{ MHz}$$

17.33

```
*Problem 17.33 - Common-Source Amplifier
VDD 7 0 DC 0
VS 1 0 AC 1
RS 1 2 1K
C1 2 3 0.1UF
R1 3 0 4.3MEG
R2 3 7 5.6MEG
RD 7 5 43K
R4 4 0 13K
C3 4 0 10UF
C2 5 6 0.1UF
R3 6 0 1MEG
*Small-Signal FET Model
GM 5 4 3 4 0.4MS
CGS 3 4 2.5PF
CGD 3 5 2.5PF
*
.AC DEC 20 1 10MEG
.PRINT AC VM(6)
.PROBE
.END
```

Results: $A_{mid} = -16.5$, $f_L = 7.9$ Hz, $f_H = 1.06$ MHz

17.34

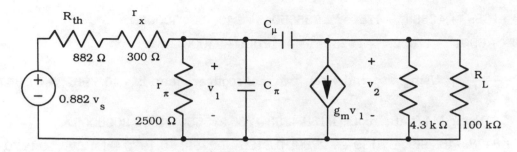

$$r_\pi = \frac{100(0.025)}{0.001} = 2500\Omega \mid C_\mu = 0.75 \text{ pF} \mid C_\pi = \frac{40(10^{-3})}{2\pi(5 \times 10^8)} - 0.75 = 12.0 \text{ pF}$$

$$\mathbf{v_{th}} = \frac{7.5k\Omega}{7.5k\Omega + 1k\Omega} \mathbf{v_s} = 0.882\mathbf{v_s} \mid R_{th} = 7.5k\Omega \| 1k\Omega = 882\Omega \mid R_L = 4.3k\Omega \| 100k\Omega = 4.12k\Omega$$

$$A_{mid} = -0.882 \frac{100(4120)}{882 + 300 + 2500} = -98.7 \mid \omega_H = \frac{1}{r_{\pi o}C_T} \mid r_{\pi o} = 2500 \| (882 + 300) = 803 \ \Omega$$

$$C_T = 12.0 + 0.75\left[1 + 40(10^{-3})(4120) + \frac{4120}{803}\right] = 140pF \mid f_H = \frac{1}{2\pi(803)(1.4 \times 10^{-10})} = 1.42 \text{ MHz}$$

17.35

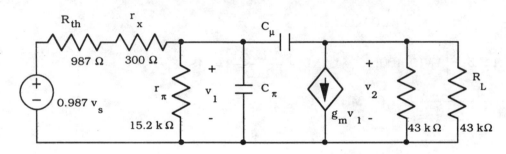

$$g_m = 40I_C = 40(0.164mA) = 6.56mS \mid r_\pi = \frac{\beta_o}{g_m} = \frac{100}{6.56mS} = 15.2k\Omega \mid r_o = \infty \ (V_A \text{ not given})$$

$$\mathbf{v_{th}} = \mathbf{v_s} \frac{75k\Omega}{1k\Omega + 75k\Omega} = 0.987\mathbf{v_s} \mid R_{th} = 75k\Omega \| 1k\Omega = 987\Omega \mid R_L = 43k\Omega \| 43k\Omega = 21.5k\Omega$$

$$C_\pi = \frac{g_m}{\omega_T} - C_\mu = \frac{6.56mS}{2\pi(5 \times 10^8 Hz)} - 0.75 = 1.34 \text{ pF}$$

$$A_{mid} = -0.987 \frac{\beta_o R_L}{R_{th} + r_x + r_\pi} = 0.987 \frac{-100(21.5 \times 10^3)}{987 + 300 + 15.2 \times 10^3} = -129$$

$$\omega_H = \frac{1}{r_{\pi o}C_T} \mid r_{\pi o} = r_\pi \| (R_{th} + r_x) = 15.2 \ k\Omega \| (987 + 300) = 1.19 \ k\Omega$$

$$C_T = C_\pi + C_\mu\left(1 + g_m R_L + \frac{R_L}{r_{\pi o}}\right) = 1.34pF + 0.75pF\left[1 + 6.56mS(21.5k\Omega) + \frac{21.5k\Omega}{1.19k\Omega}\right] = 121pF$$

$$f_H \cong \frac{1}{2\pi(1.19k\Omega)(1.21 \times 10^{-10})} = 1.10 \text{ MHz}$$

17.36

```
*Problem 17.36 - Common-Emitter Amplifier
VCC 7 0 DC 0
VS 1 0 AC 1
RS 1 2 1K
C1 2 3 5UF
R1 3 0 300K
R2 3 7 100K
RC 5 0 43K
R4 7 4 13K
C2 7 4 22UF
C3 5 6 1UF
R3 6 0 43K
*Small-signal Model for the BJT
GM 5 4 8 4 6.56MS
RX 3 8 0.3K
RPI 8 4 15.24K
CPI 8 4 1.34PF
CU 8 5 0.75PF
*
.AC DEC 100 1 10MEG
.PRINT AC VM(6)
.PROBE
.END
```

Results: $A_{mid} = -128$, $f_L = 47$ Hz, $f_H = 1.10$ MHz

17.37 Using Eq. (17.98),

$$A_V(s) = \frac{\left(\dfrac{1}{RC}\right)\dfrac{A(s)}{1+A(s)}}{s+\dfrac{1}{RC[1+A(s)]}} \quad \Bigg| \quad A(s) = \frac{10A_o}{s+10} \quad \Bigg| \quad A_V(s) = \left(\frac{1}{RC}\right)\frac{\dfrac{\frac{10A_o}{s+10}}{1+\frac{10A_o}{s+10}}}{s+\dfrac{1}{RC\left(1+\frac{10A_o}{s+10}\right)}}$$

$$A_V(s) = \left(\frac{1}{RC}\right)\frac{10A_o}{s^2+s(1+A_o)10+\dfrac{s+10}{RC}} = \frac{\left(\dfrac{10A_o}{RC}\right)}{s^2+s\left[\dfrac{1}{RC}+10(1+A_o)\right]+\dfrac{10}{RC}}$$

(a) $$A_V(s) = \frac{\left(\dfrac{10^6}{RC}\right)}{s^2+s\left[\dfrac{1}{RC}+10^6\right]+\dfrac{10}{RC}} \cong \frac{\left(\dfrac{10^6}{RC}\right)}{\left(s+10^6\right)\left(s+\dfrac{1}{10^5RC}\right)}; \quad \omega_L = \frac{1}{10^5 RC}$$

(b) $$A_V(s) = \frac{\left(\dfrac{10^7}{RC}\right)}{s^2+s\left[\dfrac{1}{RC}+10^7\right]+\dfrac{10}{RC}} \cong \frac{\left(\dfrac{10^6}{RC}\right)}{\left(s+10^7\right)\left(s+\dfrac{1}{10^6RC}\right)}; \quad \omega_L = \frac{1}{10^6 RC}$$

(c) $$\lim_{A_o \to \infty} A_V(s) = \frac{\left(\dfrac{10A_o}{RC}\right)}{10A_o s} = \frac{1}{sRC}$$

465

(a) $Y_{in} = \dfrac{1+A}{Z(s)} = \dfrac{1+A}{\dfrac{1}{sC}} = sC(1+A) \quad | \quad C_{in} = C(1+A) = 10^{-10}\,F(1+10^5) = 10\ \mu F$

(b) $Z_{in} = \dfrac{1}{Y_{in}} = \dfrac{Z(s)}{1+A(s)} = \dfrac{10^5}{1+\dfrac{10^6}{s+10}} = 10^5\,\dfrac{s+10}{s+10+10^6} \cong 10^5\,\dfrac{s+10}{s+10^6}$

Using MATLAB: $Z_{in}(j2000\pi) = (4.95 + j6.28)\ \Omega$

$Z_{in}(j10^5\pi) = (8.98 + j28.6)\ k\Omega \quad | \quad Z_{in}(j2\pi\times10^6) = (97.5 + j15.5)\ k\Omega$

17.39

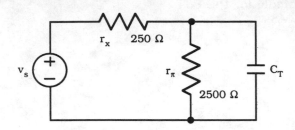

$r_{\pi o} = 2500\Omega \| 250\Omega = 227\Omega \quad | \quad C_T = 15 + 1\left[1 + 0.04(2500) + \dfrac{2500}{227}\right] = 127\ pF$

(a) $Z_C = \dfrac{1}{j(2\pi)(10^3)(127\,pF)} = -j(1.25\times10^6)$

Using MATLAB: $Z = 250 + \dfrac{2500 Z_C}{2500 + Z_C} = (2750 - j4.99)\ \Omega \quad | \quad$ SPICE: $(2750 - j4.56)\ \Omega$

(b) $Z_C = \dfrac{1}{j(2\pi)(5\times10^4)(127\,pF)} = -j2.51\times10^4\ \Omega$

Using MATLAB: $Z = 250 + \dfrac{2500 Z_C}{2500 + Z_C} = (2730 - j247)\ \Omega \quad | \quad$ SPICE: $(2730 - j226)\ \Omega$

(c) $Z_C = \dfrac{1}{j(2\pi)(10^6)(127\,pF)} = -j(12.53)$

Using MATLAB: $Z = 250 + \dfrac{2500 Z_C}{2500 + Z_C} = (752 - j1000)\ \Omega \quad | \quad$ SPICE: $(836 - j1040)\ \Omega$

```
*Problem 17.39 - Common-Emitter Amplifier
IS 0 1 AC 1
RX 1 2 0.25K
RPI 2 0 2.5K
CPI 2 0 15PF
CU 2 3 1PF
GM 3 0 2 0 40MS
RL 3 0 2.5K
.AC LIN 1 1KHZ 1KHZ
*.AC LIN 1 50KHZ 50KHZ
*.AC LIN 1 1MEG 1MEG
.PRINT AC VR(1) VI(1) VM(1) VP(1)
.END
```

Note that the C_T approximation does provide give a good estimate of Z_{in} at high frequencies (note the discrepancy at 1 MHz). See the analysis following Prob. 17.78.

17.40

$$f_H = \frac{1}{2\pi r_{\pi o}C_T} = \frac{1}{2\pi(656\Omega)C_T} \quad | \quad C_T = \frac{1}{2\pi(656\Omega)(5\text{MHz})} = 48.5\text{pF}$$

$$C_T = C_\pi + C_\mu\left[1 + g_m R_L + \frac{R_L}{r_{\pi o}}\right] \quad | \quad R_L\left(g_m + \frac{1}{r_{\pi o}}\right) = \frac{C_T - C_\pi}{C_\mu} - 1 = \frac{48.5\text{pF} - 19.9\text{pF}}{0.5\text{pF}} - 1 = 56.2$$

$$R_L = \frac{56.2}{\left(.064\text{S} + \frac{1}{656\Omega}\right)} = 858\Omega \quad | \quad R_L = R_C\|100\text{k}\Omega \rightarrow R_C = 865\Omega$$

$$A_{mid} = -\frac{100(858\Omega)}{882\Omega + 250\Omega + 1560\Omega} = -31.9 \quad | \quad GBW = 31.9(5\text{MHz}) = 160\text{ MHz}$$

Nearest 5% value is $R_C = 820\ \Omega$ | $R_L = 820\Omega\|100\text{k}\Omega = 813\Omega$

$$A_{mid} = -\frac{100(813\Omega)}{882\Omega + 250\Omega + 1560\Omega} = -30.2 \quad | \quad C_T = 19.9 + 0.5\left[1 + 0.064(813) + \frac{813}{656}\right] = 47.0\text{pF}$$

$$f_H = \frac{1}{2\pi r_{\pi o}C_T} = \frac{1}{2\pi(656\Omega)(47.0\text{pF})} = 5.16\text{ MHz} \quad | \quad GBW = 156\text{ MHz}$$

17.41

$$I_B = \frac{3 - 0.7}{75\text{k}\Omega + 101(13\text{k}\Omega)} = 1.657\mu\text{A} \quad | \quad I_C = 166\mu\text{A} \quad | \quad V_{CE} = 12 - 43\text{k}\Omega(I_C) - 13\text{k}\Omega\left(\frac{I_C}{\alpha_F}\right) = 2.70\text{V}$$

$2.70\text{V} \geq 0.7\text{V}$ Forward-active region is correct. | $r_\pi = \dfrac{100(0.025)}{0.166\text{ mA}} = 15.1\text{ k}\Omega$

$$g_m = 40(0.166\text{ mA}) = 6.63\text{mS} \quad | \quad C_\pi = \frac{6.63\text{mS}}{2\pi(3\times10^8)} - 0.5 = 3.02\text{ pF} \quad | \quad r_x = 300\Omega \quad | \quad C_\mu = 0.5\text{pF}$$

$$\mathbf{v_{th}} = \frac{75\text{k}\Omega}{75\text{k}\Omega + 100\Omega}\mathbf{v_s} = 0.999\mathbf{v_s} \quad | \quad R_{th} = 75\text{k}\Omega\|100\Omega = 99.9\Omega \quad | \quad R_L = 43\text{k}\Omega\|100\text{k}\Omega = 30.1\text{k}\Omega$$

$$A_{mid} = 0.999\frac{-100(30.1\text{k}\Omega)}{99.9\Omega + 300\Omega + 15.1\text{k}\Omega + 101(3\text{k}\Omega)} = -9.44$$

Short-Circuit Time Constants

$$R_{1S} = 100\Omega + 75k\Omega \| [300\Omega + 15.1k\Omega + 101(3k\Omega)] = 60.8k\Omega$$

$$R_{2S} = 43k\Omega + 100k\Omega = 143k\Omega$$

$$R_{3S} = 10k\Omega \| \left(3k\Omega + \frac{15.1k\Omega + 99.9\Omega}{101}\right) = 2.40k\Omega$$

$$f_L \approx \frac{1}{2\pi}\left[\frac{1}{(60.8k\Omega)(1\mu F)} + \frac{1}{(143k\Omega)(0.1\mu F)} + \frac{1}{(2.40k\Omega)(2.2\mu F)}\right] = 43.9Hz$$

Open-Circuit Time Constants

Using the result in Table 17.2 on page 944: $R_{th} + r_x = 99.9\Omega + 300\Omega = 400\Omega$

$$C_{TB} = \frac{3.02pF}{1 + (6.63mS)(3k\Omega)}\left(1 + \frac{3k\Omega}{400\Omega}\right) + 0.5pF\left[1 + \frac{(6.63mS)(30.1k\Omega)}{1 + (6.63mS)(3k\Omega)} + \frac{30.1k\Omega}{400\Omega}\right]$$

$$C_{TB} = 44.1pF \qquad f_H = \frac{1}{2\pi(400\Omega)(44.1pF)} = 9.02 \text{ MHz}$$

17.42

Using the result in Table 17.2 on page 944: $R_{th} + r_x = 99.9\Omega + 300\Omega = 400\Omega$

$$C_{TB} = \frac{1}{2\pi(400\Omega)(7.5MHz)} = 53.1 \text{ pF}$$

$$C_{TB} = \frac{3.02pF}{1 + (6.63mS)R_E}\left(1 + \frac{R_E}{400\Omega}\right) + 0.5pF\left[1 + \frac{(6.63mS)(30.1k\Omega)}{1 + (6.63mS)R_E} + \frac{30.1k\Omega}{400\Omega}\right] = 53.1 \text{ pF}$$

Using MATLAB: $R_E = 957 \ \Omega$

$$A_{mid} = 0.999 \frac{-100(30.1k\Omega)}{99.9\Omega + 300\Omega + 15.1k\Omega + 101(957\Omega)} = -26.8 \quad | \quad GBW = 201 \text{ MHz}$$

Closest 5% resistor values are $R_E = 1 \ k\Omega$ and $R_6 = 12 \ k\Omega$

$$C_{TB} = \frac{3.02pF}{1 + (6.63mS)1k\Omega}\left(1 + \frac{1k\Omega}{400\Omega}\right) + 0.5pF\left[1 + \frac{(6.63mS)(30.1k\Omega)}{1 + (6.63mS)1k\Omega} + \frac{30.1k\Omega}{400\Omega}\right] = 52.6 \text{ pF}$$

$$f_H = \frac{1}{2\pi(400\Omega)(52.6 \text{ pF})} = 7.56MHz$$

$$A_{mid} = 0.999 \frac{-100(30.1k\Omega)}{99.9\Omega + 300\Omega + 15.1k\Omega + 101(1k\Omega)} = -25.8 \quad | \quad GBW = 195 \text{ MHz}$$

17.43   **Use $r_x = 300 \ \Omega$**

$$I_B = \frac{3 - 0.7}{7.5k\Omega + 101(1.3k\Omega)} = 16.6\mu A \ | \ I_C = 1.66mA \ | \ V_{CE} = 12 - 4.3k\Omega(I_C) - 1.3k\Omega\left(\frac{I_C}{\alpha_F}\right) = 2.69V$$

$2.69V \geq 0.7V$ Forward-active region is correct. $\ | \ r_\pi = \dfrac{100(0.025)}{1.66 \text{ mA}} = 1.51 \ k\Omega$

$$g_m = 40(1.66 \text{ mA}) = 66.4mS \ | \ C_\pi = \frac{66.4mS}{2\pi(2 \times 10^8)} - 1 = 51.8 \text{ pF} \ | \ r_x = 300\Omega \ | \ C_\mu = 1.0pF$$

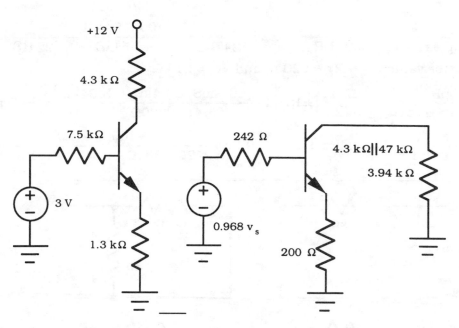

$$\mathbf{v}_{th} = \frac{7.5k\Omega}{7.5k\Omega + 250\Omega}\mathbf{v_s} = 0.968\mathbf{v_s} \quad | \quad R_{th} = 7.5k\Omega\|250\Omega = 242\Omega \quad | \quad R_L = 4.3k\Omega\|47k\Omega = 3.94k\Omega$$

$$A_{mid} = 0.968\frac{\beta_o R_L}{R_{th} + r_x + r_\pi + (\beta_o + 1)R_{E1}} = 0.968\frac{-100(3.94k\Omega)}{242\Omega + 300\Omega + 1.51k\Omega + 101(200\Omega)} = -17.1$$

Short-Circuit Time Constants

$$R_{1S} = 250\Omega + 7.5k\Omega\|[300\Omega + 1.51k\Omega + 101(200\Omega)] = 5.84k\Omega$$

$$R_{2S} = 4.3k\Omega + 43k\Omega = 47.3k\Omega$$

$$R_{3S} = 1.1k\Omega\left\|\left(200\Omega + \frac{1.51k\Omega + 300 + 242\Omega}{101}\right) = 184\Omega\right.$$

$$f_L \approx \frac{1}{2\pi}\left[\frac{1}{(5.84k\Omega)(5\mu F)} + \frac{1}{(47.3k\Omega)(1\mu F)} + \frac{1}{(184\Omega)(4.7\mu F)}\right] = 193Hz$$

Open-Circuit Time Constants

Using the result in Table 17.2 on page 944: $R_{th} + r_x = 242\Omega + 300\Omega = 542\Omega$

$$C_{TB} = \frac{51.8pF}{1 + (66.4mS)(200\Omega)}\left(1 + \frac{200\Omega}{542\Omega}\right) + 1pF\left[1 + \frac{(66.4mS)(3.94k\Omega)}{1 + (66.4mS)(200\Omega)} + \frac{3.94k\Omega}{542\Omega}\right]$$

$$C_{TB} = 31.6pF \quad f_L = \frac{1}{2\pi(542\Omega)(31.6pF)} = 9.29 \text{ MHz}$$

17.44

Using the result in Table 17.2 on page 944 and the values from Prob. 17.43:

$$R_{th} + r_x = 242\Omega + 300\Omega = 542\Omega \quad | \quad C_{TB} = \frac{1}{2\pi(542\Omega)(10MHz)} = 29.4 \text{ pF}$$

$$C_{TB} = \frac{51.8}{1 + (66.4mS)R_E}\left(1 + \frac{R_E}{542\Omega}\right) + 1pF\left[1 + \frac{(66.4mS)(3.94k\Omega)}{1 + (66.4mS)R_E} + \frac{3.94k\Omega}{542\Omega}\right] = 29.4 \text{ pF}$$

Using MATLAB: $R_E = 224 \ \Omega$

$$A_{mid} = 0.968 \frac{\beta_o R_L}{R_{th} + r_x + r_\pi + (\beta_o + 1)R_{E1}} = 0.968 \frac{-100(3.94k\Omega)}{242\Omega + 300\Omega + 1.51k\Omega + 101(224\Omega)} = -15.5$$

Closest 5% resistor values are $R_E = 220\ \Omega$ and $R_6 = 1.1\ k\Omega$

$$C_{TB} = \frac{51.8pF}{1 + (66.4mS)220\Omega}\left(1 + \frac{220\Omega}{542\Omega}\right) + 1pF\left[1 + \frac{(66.4mS)(3.94k\Omega)}{1 + (66.4mS)220\Omega} + \frac{3.94k\Omega}{542\Omega}\right] = 29.7\ pF$$

$$f_H = \frac{1}{2\pi(542\Omega)(29.7pF)} = 9.89MHz \quad | \quad A_{mid} = 0.968 \frac{-100(3.94k\Omega)}{242\Omega + 300\Omega + 1.51k\Omega + 101(220\Omega)} = -15.7$$

17.45

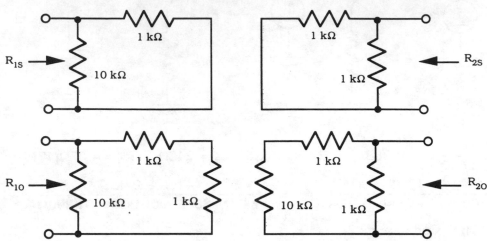

(a) SCTC:

$$R_{1S} = 10k\Omega\|1k\Omega = 909\Omega \quad | \quad R_{2S} = 1k\Omega\|1k\Omega = 500\Omega \quad | \quad \omega_L = \frac{1}{909(10^{-6})} + \frac{1}{500(10^{-5})} = 1300\ \frac{rad}{s}$$

(b) OCTC:

$$R_{1O} = 10k\Omega\|2k\Omega = 1.67k\Omega \quad | \quad R_{2O} = 1k\Omega\|1\ 1k\Omega = 917\Omega \quad | \quad \omega_L = \frac{1}{1670(10^{-6}) + 917(10^{-5})} = 92.3\ \frac{rad}{s}$$

There are two poles. The SCTC technique assumes both are at low frequency and yields the largest one. The OCTC assumes both are at high frequency and yields the smallest one.

$$\begin{bmatrix} (sC_1 + G_1 + G_2) & -G_2 \\ -G_2 & (sC_2 + G_2 + G_3) \end{bmatrix}\begin{bmatrix} V_1 \\ V_2 \end{bmatrix} = 0$$

$$\Delta = s^2 C_1 C_2 + s[C_2(G_1 + G_2) + C_1(G_2 + G_3)] + G_1 G_2 + G_2 G_3 + G_1 G_3$$

$$\Delta = s^2 10^{-11} + s(1.30 \times 10^{-8}) + 1.20 \times 10^{-6}$$

$$\Delta = s^2 + 1300s + 1.20 \times 10^5 \rightarrow s = -1200, -100\ \frac{rad}{s}$$

17.46

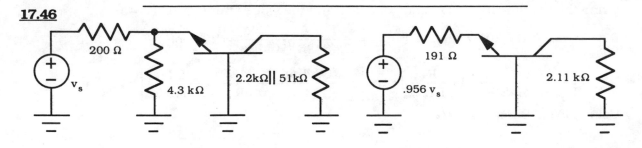

$$g_m = 40(1\text{ mA}) = 0.04\text{S} \quad | \quad r_x = 300\Omega \quad | \quad r_\pi = \frac{100(0.025)}{1\text{ mA}} = 2.50\text{k}\Omega$$

$$C_\mu = 0.6\text{pF} \quad | \quad C_\pi = \frac{40(10^{-3})}{2\pi(5\times10^8)} - 0.6 = 12.1\text{ pF}$$

$$\mathbf{v_{th}} = \frac{4.3\text{k}\Omega}{4.3\text{k}\Omega + 200\Omega}\mathbf{v_s} = 0.956\mathbf{v_s} \quad | \quad R_{th} = 4.3\text{k}\Omega\|200\Omega = 191\Omega \quad | \quad R_L = 2.2\text{k}\Omega\|51\text{k}\Omega = 2.11\text{k}\Omega$$

$$A_{mid} = 0.956\alpha_o\frac{R_L}{R_{th} + \frac{r_\pi + r_x}{\beta_o + 1}} = 0.956\left(\frac{100}{101}\right)\frac{2110}{191 + \frac{2500 + 300}{101}} = +9.13$$

$$\omega_H = \frac{1}{191\frac{12.1\text{pF}}{1 + 0.04(191)}\left(1 + \frac{300}{191}\right) + 0.6\text{pF}(300\Omega)\left[1 + \frac{0.04(2110)}{1 + 0.04(191)} + \frac{30.1\text{k}\Omega}{1.3\text{k}\Omega}\right] + 0.6\text{pF}(2110\Omega)}$$

$$f_H = \frac{1}{2\pi}\left(\frac{1}{6.876\times10^{-10} + 1.938\times10^{-9} + 1.266\times10^{-9}}\right) = 40.9\text{MHz}$$

17.47   Estimating the required SPICE parameters:

$$C_\mu = \frac{CJC}{\sqrt{1 + \frac{V_{CB}}{\phi_{jc}}}} \quad | \quad CJC = 0.5\text{pF}\sqrt{1 + \frac{V_{CB}}{\phi_{jc}}} \cong 0.5\text{pF}\sqrt{1 + \frac{2.8}{0.9}} \cong 1\text{pF}$$

$$\tau_F = \frac{C_\pi}{g_m} = \frac{1}{\omega_T} - \frac{C_\mu}{g_m} = \frac{1}{10^9\pi} - \frac{0.5\text{pF}}{40(1\text{mA})} = 306\text{ ps}$$

```
*Problem 17.47 - Common-Base Amplifier
VCC 6 0 DC 5
VEE 7 0 DC -5
VS 1 0 AC 1
RS 1 2 200
C1 2 3 4.7UF
RE 3 7 4.3K
Q1 4 0 3 NBJT
RC 4 6 2.2K
C2 4 5 1UF
R3 5 0 51K
.MODEL NBJT NPN BF=100 RB=300 CJC=1PF TF=306PS
.OP
.AC DEC 50 1 50MEG
.PRINT AC VM(5)
.PROBE
.END
```

Results: $A_{mid} = 9.05$, $f_L = 150$ Hz, $f_H = 44$ MHz

17.48

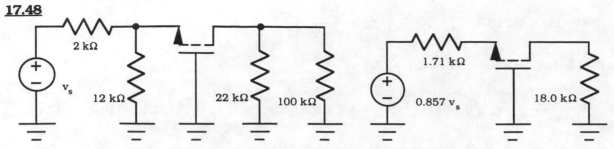

$$\mathbf{v_{th}} = \frac{12k\Omega}{12k\Omega + 2k\Omega}\mathbf{v_s} = 0.857\mathbf{v_s} \quad | \quad R_{th} = 12k\Omega\|2k\Omega = 1.71k\Omega \quad | \quad R_L = 22k\Omega\|100k\Omega = 18.0k\Omega$$

$$g_m = \frac{2(0.1mA)}{1V} = 0.2mS \quad | \quad C_{GS} = 3.0pF \quad | \quad C_{GD} = 0.6pF$$

$$A_{mid} = 0.857\frac{R_L}{R_{th} + \dfrac{1}{g_m}} = 0.857\frac{18.0k\Omega}{1.71k\Omega + \dfrac{1}{0.2mS}} = +2.30$$

$$f_H = \frac{1}{2\pi}\left(\frac{1}{\dfrac{C_{GS}}{G_{th} + g_m} + C_{GD}R_L}\right) = \frac{1}{2\pi}\left(\frac{1}{\dfrac{3.0pF}{(0.5848 + 0.2)mS} + 0.6pF(18.0k\Omega)}\right) = 10.9 \text{ MHz}$$

17.49 Calculating the SPICE parameters require to achieve $I_{DS} = 0.1mA$:

$$V_{GG} = \frac{1.5M\Omega}{1.5M\Omega + 2.2M\Omega}12V = 4.87V \quad | \quad V_{GG} - V_{GS} = 0.1mA(12k\Omega) \rightarrow V_{GS} = 3.67V$$

$$V_{GS} - V_{TN} = 1V \rightarrow V_{TN} = 2.67V \quad | \quad K_n = \frac{2I_{DS}}{(V_{GS} - V_{TN})^2} = \frac{2(0.1mA)}{1^2} = 0.2mS$$

```
*Problem 17.49 - Common-Source Amplifier
VDD 7 0 DC 12
VS 1 0 AC 1
RS 1 2 2K
C1 2 3 4.7UF
R4 3 0 12K
R1 4 0 1.5MEG
R2 7 4 2.2MEG
C2 4 0 0.1UF
R3 7 5 22K
C3 5 6 0.1UF
R7 6 0 100K
M1 5 4 3 3 NFET
.MODEL NFET NMOS VTO=2.67 KP=0.200M CGSO=30NF CGDO=6NF
.OP
.AC DEC 100 1 50MEG
.PRINT AC VM(6) VP(6)
.END
```

Results: $A_{mid} = 2.30, \quad f_L = 15.5 \text{ Hz}, \quad f_H = 13.2 \text{ MHz}$

17.50 Calculating the SPICE parameters required to achieve $I_{DS} = 0.1mA$:

$$V_{GG} = \frac{1.5M\Omega}{1.5M\Omega + 2.2M\Omega} 10V = 4.05V \mid V_{GG} - V_{GS} = 0.1mA(12k\Omega) \rightarrow V_{GS} = 2.85V$$

$$V_{GS} - V_{TN} = 0.75V \rightarrow V_{TN} = 2.10V \mid K_n = \frac{2I_{DS}}{(V_{GS} - V_{TN})^2} = \frac{2(0.1mA)}{(0.75)^2} = 0.356 \frac{mA}{V^2}$$

From Prob. 14.15: $A_{mid} = 0.739 \mid f_H = \{2\pi(2k\Omega)[3pF(1-0.739) + 0.6pF]\}^{-1} = 57.5$ MHz

Note that a low frequency RHP zero makes this a very poor estimate for the FET case. See the anlaysis in Prob. 16.52 which shows $\omega_z = -g_m/C_{GS}$.

```
*Problem 17.50 - Common-Drain Amplifier
VDD 6 0 DC 10
VS 1 0 AC 1
RS 1 2 2K
C1 2 3 4.7UF
R1 3 0 1.5MEG
R2 6 3 2.2MEG
M1 6 3 4 4 NFET
R4 4 0 12K
C3 4 5 0.1UF
R7 5 0 100K
.MODEL NFET NMOS VTO=2.10 KP=0.356MS CGSO=30NF CGDO=6NF
.OP
.AC DEC 100 1 500MEG
.PRINT AC VM(5) VP(5)
.END
```

Results: $A_{mid} = 0.740$, $f_L = 15.5$ Hz, $f_H = 195$MHz - Note that there is peaking in the response.

17.51

$$g_m = 40(0.25 \text{ mA}) = 0.01S \mid r_x = 300\Omega \mid r_\pi = \frac{100(0.025)}{0.25 \text{ mA}} = 10.0k\Omega$$

$$C_\mu = 0.6pF \mid C_\pi = \frac{0.01}{2\pi(5 \times 10^8)} - 0.6 = 2.58 \text{ pF} \mid R_B = 100k\Omega \| 300k\Omega = 75.0k\Omega$$

$$\mathbf{v}_{th} = \frac{75k\Omega}{75k\Omega + 2k\Omega} \mathbf{v}_s = 0.974\mathbf{v}_s \mid R_{th} = 75k\Omega \| 2k\Omega = 1.95k\Omega \mid R_L = 13k\Omega \| 100k\Omega = 11.5k\Omega$$

$$A_{mid} = 0.974 \frac{(\beta_o + 1)R_L}{R_{th} + r_x + r_\pi + (\beta_o + 1)R_L} = 0.974 \frac{101(11.5k\Omega)}{[1.95 + 0.300 + 10.0 + 101(11.5)]k\Omega} = 0.964$$

$$f_H \cong \frac{1}{2\pi} \frac{1}{(1950 + 300)\left[\dfrac{2.58pF}{1 + 10mS(11.5k\Omega)} + 0.6pF\right]} = \frac{1}{2\pi} \frac{1}{(2250)(0.622pF)} = 114 \text{ MHz}$$

(b) Calculating the required SPICE parameters:

$$C_\mu = \frac{CJC}{\left(1 + \dfrac{V_{CB}}{PHIE}\right)^{ME}} \mid CJC = 0.6pF\left(1 + \frac{11.8}{0.75}\right)^{0.333} \cong 1.54 \text{ pF}$$

$$\tau_F = \frac{C_\pi}{g_m} = \frac{1}{\omega_T} - \frac{C_\mu}{g_m} = \frac{1}{10^9\pi} - \frac{0.6pF}{40(0.25mA)} = 260 \text{ ps} \mid TF = 260 \text{ ps}$$

VCC 6 0 DC 15
VS 1 0 AC 1
RS 1 2 2K
C1 2 3 4.7UF
R1 3 0 100K
R2 6 3 300K
Q1 6 3 4 NBJT
R4 4 0 13K
C3 4 5 10UF
R7 5 0 100K
.MODEL NBJT NPN BF=100 TF=260PS CJC=1.54PF RB=300
.OP
.AC DEC 100 0.1 200MEG
.PRINT AC VM(5) VP(5)
.END

Results: $A_{mid} = 0.962$, $f_L = 0.52$ Hz, $f_H = 110$ MHz

17.52

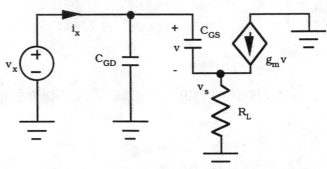

$$I_x = sC_{GD}V_x + sC_{GS}(V_x - V_s) \quad | \quad V_x = V + (sC_{GS}V + g_mV)R_L \quad | \quad V = \frac{V_x}{(1 + g_mR_L + sC_{GS}R_L)}$$

$$I_x = sC_{GD}V_x + sC_{GS}\frac{V_x}{(1 + g_mR_L + sC_{GS}R_L)} \quad | \quad \text{Note: } V_s = \frac{(sC_{GS} + g_m)R_L}{(1 + g_mR_L + sC_{GS}R_L)}V_x$$

$$\frac{I_x}{V_x} = s\left[C_{GD} + \frac{C_{GS}}{1 + g_mR_L}\frac{1}{1 + s\frac{C_{GS}R_L}{1 + g_mR_L}}\right] \quad | \quad \frac{C_{GS}R_L}{1 + g_mR_L} \approx \frac{C_{GS}R_L}{g_mR_L} = \frac{C_{GS}}{g_m} \quad \& \quad \frac{g_m}{C_{GS}} > \omega_T$$

Assuming $\omega << \omega_T$: $\quad C_{IN} \approx C_{GD} + \dfrac{C_{GS}}{1 + g_mR_L}$ $\quad | \quad$ Note the zero in V_s at $\omega_z = -\dfrac{g_m}{C_{GS}}$

17.53

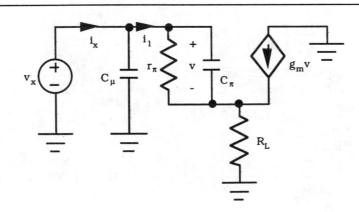

$$I_x = sC_\mu V_x + I_1 \quad | \quad V_x = \frac{I_1}{(sC_\pi + g_\pi)} + \left(I_1 + g_m \frac{I_1}{(sC_\pi + g_\pi)}\right)R_L$$

$$Z_1 = \frac{V_x}{I_1} = \frac{sC_\pi r_\pi R_L + R_L + r_\pi + \beta_o R_L}{sC_\pi r_\pi + 1} = \frac{sC_\pi r_\pi R_L + r_\pi + (\beta_o + 1)R_L}{sC_\pi r_\pi + 1}$$

$$Y_1 = \frac{1}{Z_1} = \frac{\dfrac{sC_\pi r_\pi}{r_\pi + (\beta_o + 1)R_L} + \dfrac{1}{r_\pi + (\beta_o + 1)R_L}}{s\dfrac{C_\pi r_\pi R_L}{r_\pi + (\beta_o + 1)R_L} + 1} \cong \frac{\dfrac{sC_\pi}{(1 + g_m R_L)} + \dfrac{1}{r_\pi + (\beta_o + 1)R_L}}{s\dfrac{C_\pi R_L}{(1 + g_m R_L)} + 1} \quad \text{for } \beta_o \gg 1$$

$$\omega \frac{C_\pi R_L}{(1 + g_m R_L)} \ll 1 \rightarrow \omega \ll \frac{1}{C_\pi}\left(\frac{1}{R_L} + g_m\right) \text{ but } \frac{1}{C_\pi}\left(\frac{1}{R_L} + g_m\right) > \omega_T$$

So, for $\omega \ll \omega_T$, $Y_1 \cong s\dfrac{C_\pi}{(1 + g_m R_L)} + \dfrac{1}{r_\pi + (\beta_o + 1)R_L}$

$$C_{in} = C_\mu + \frac{C_\pi}{(1 + g_m R_L)} \quad \text{and} \quad R_{in} = r_\pi + (\beta_o + 1)R_L$$

ω_H is determined by the input capacitance C_{in} and the source resistance $R_{th} + r_x$.

17.54

$$\omega_H = \frac{g_{m1}}{C_{GS1} + C_{GS2} + C_{GD2}(1 + g_{m1}r_{o2} + g_{m2}r_{o2})}$$

$$g_{m1} = g_{m2} = \sqrt{2(25 \times 10^{-6})\left(\frac{5}{1}\right)(10^{-4})} = 158 \ \mu S \quad | \quad r_{o2} \cong \frac{50V}{0.1mA} = 500k\Omega$$

$$C_{GS1} = 3pF \quad | \quad C_{GS2} = 3pF \quad | \quad C_{GD1} = 0.5pF \quad | \quad C_{GD2} = 0.5pF$$

$$f_H = \frac{1}{2\pi} \frac{158\mu S}{3pF + 3pF + 0.5pF[1 + 2(0.158mS)500k\Omega]} = 294 \ kHz$$

17.55

$$\omega_H = \frac{g_{m1}}{C_{GS1} + C_{GS2} + C_{GD2}(1 + g_{m1}r_{o2} + g_{m2}r_{o2})} \quad | \quad I_{DS2} = 5I_{DS1} = 1.00mA \quad | \quad r_{o2} = \frac{50V}{1mA} = 50k\Omega$$

$$g_{m1} = \sqrt{2(25 \times 10^{-6})\left(\frac{5}{1}\right)(2 \times 10^{-4})} = 224\mu S \quad | \quad g_{m2} = \sqrt{2(25 \times 10^{-6})\left(\frac{25}{1}\right)(1 \times 10^{-3})} = 1.12mS$$

C_{GS} & $C_{GD} \propto W$: $C_{GS1} = 3pF \quad | \quad C_{GS2} = 15pF \quad | \quad C_{GD1} = 1pF \quad | \quad C_{GD2} = 5pF$

$$f_H = \frac{1}{2\pi} \frac{0.224mS}{3pF + 15pF + 5pF[1 + (1.12mS + 0.224mS)50k\Omega]} = 99.3 \ kHz$$

17.56

$$\omega_H = \frac{g_{m1}}{C_{\pi 1} + C_{\pi 2} + C_{\mu 2}[1 + (g_{m1} + g_{m2})r_{o2}]} \quad | \quad I_{C2} \cong I_{C1} = 100\mu A$$

$$r_{o2} = \frac{60V}{100\mu A} = 600k\Omega \quad | \quad C_{\pi 2} = C_{\pi 1} = \frac{40(10^{-4})}{10^8 \pi} - 2pF = 10.7pF$$

$$f_H = \frac{1}{2\pi}\left[\frac{40(10^{-4})}{10.7pF + 10.7pF + 2pF(1 + 2(40)(0.100mA)600k\Omega)}\right] = 66.2 \ kHz$$

17.57 The most probable answer that will be produced is

$$\omega_H = \frac{g_{m1}}{C_{\pi 1} + C_{\pi 2} + C_{\mu 2}\left[1 + (g_{m1} + g_{m2})r_{o2}\right]} \quad | \quad I_{C2} \cong 10I_{C1} = 1.00\text{mA} \quad | \quad r_{o2} = \frac{60\text{V}}{1.00\text{mA}} = 60\text{k}\Omega$$

$$C_{\pi 1} = \frac{40\left(10^{-4}\right)}{1.2\text{x}10^9\,\pi} - 0.5\text{pF} = 0.561\text{pF} \quad | \quad C_{\pi 2} = \frac{40\left(10^{-3}\right)}{1.2\text{x}10^9\,\pi} - 0.5\text{pF} = 10.1\text{pF}$$

$$f_H = \frac{1}{2\pi}\frac{40\left(10^{-4}\right)}{0.561\text{pF} + 10.1\text{pF} + 0.5\text{pF}\left[1 + 40(1.1\text{mA})60\text{k}\Omega\right]} = 478 \text{ kHz}$$

However, C_μ should be approximately proportional to emitter area:

$$C_{\mu 2} = 10C_{\mu 1} = 5.00\text{pF} \quad | \quad C_{\pi 2} = \frac{40\left(10^{-3}\right)}{1.2\text{x}10^9\,\pi} - 5.00\text{pF} = 5.10\text{pF}$$

$$f_H = \frac{1}{2\pi}\frac{40\left(10^{-4}\right)}{0.561\text{pF} + 5.10\text{pF} + 5.00\text{pF}\left[1 + 40(1.1\text{mA})60\text{k}\Omega\right]} = 48.2 \text{ kHz}$$

17.58 With the addition of r_x, we must re-evaluate the open-circuit time constants.

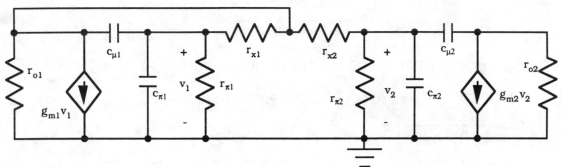

Assume: $r_x \ll r_o$

$C_{\pi 2}$ & $C_{\mu 2}$ are part of a common - emitter stage with $r_{\pi o2} = r_{\pi 2}\left\|\left(r_{x2} + \dfrac{1}{g_{m1}}\right)\right. \cong \dfrac{1 + g_{m1}r_{x2}}{g_{m1}}$

$$C_{\pi 1}: \quad R_{\pi 1o}^{-1} = g_{\pi 1} + g_{x1}\left(1 + \frac{g_{m1}}{g_{x1} + g_{o1} + \dfrac{1}{r_{x2} + r_{\pi 2}}}\right) \quad | \quad R_{\pi 1o} \cong \frac{r_{x1}}{1 + g_{m1}r_{x1}} \cong \frac{1}{g_{m1}}$$

$$C_{\mu 1}: \quad R_{\mu 1o} = \frac{r_{x1}}{1 + \dfrac{1}{\beta_o} + \dfrac{1}{g_m R}} \quad \text{with } R = r_{o1}\|\left(r_{x2} + r_{\pi 2}\right) \quad | \quad R_{\mu 1o} \cong r_{x1}$$

$$\omega_H = \left\{C_{\pi 1}\frac{r_{x1}}{1 + g_{m1}r_{x1}} + C_{\mu 1}r_{x1} + \frac{1 + g_{m1}r_{x2}}{g_{m1}}\left[C_{\pi 2} + C_{\mu 2}\left(1 + g_{m2}r_{o2}\right)\right]\right\}^{-1}$$

The last term will be dominant: $\omega_H \cong \dfrac{1}{\dfrac{1 + g_{m1}r_{x2}}{g_{m1}}C_{\mu 2}\left(1 + g_{m2}r_{o2}\right)}$

The most probable answer that will be generated is

$$I_{C2} \cong 4I_{C1} = 1.00\text{mA} \mid r_{o2} = \frac{50\text{V}}{1.00\text{mA}} = 50\text{k}\Omega \mid g_{m2} = 40(0.001) = 40\text{mS}$$

$$C_{\pi 1} = \frac{40(2.5\text{x}10^{-4})}{10^9\pi} - 0.3\text{pF} = 2.88\text{pF} \mid C_{\pi 2} = \frac{40(10^{-3})}{10^9\pi} - 0.3\text{pF} = 9.73\text{pF}$$

$$f_H \cong \frac{1}{2\pi} \frac{1}{\dfrac{1+0.01\text{S}(175\Omega)}{0.01\text{S}}0.3\text{pF}[1+40\text{mS}(50\text{k}\Omega)]} = 964 \text{ kHz}$$

However, C_μ should be approximately proportional to emitter area:

$$C_{\mu 2} = 4C_{\mu 1} = 1.2\text{pF} \mid f_H \cong \frac{1}{2\pi} \frac{1}{\dfrac{1+0.01\text{S}(175\Omega)}{0.01\text{S}}1.2\text{pF}[1+40\text{mS}(50\text{k}\Omega)]} = 241 \text{ kHz}$$

17.59

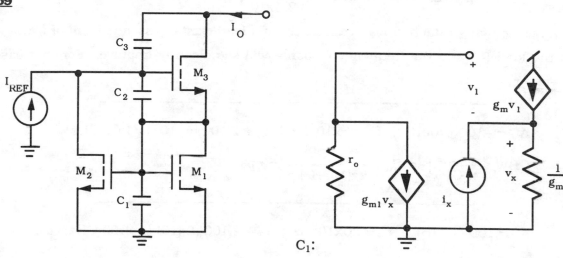

C_1:

$$C_1 = C_{GS1} + C_{GS2} \mid C_2 = C_{GD2} + C_{GS3} \mid C_1 = C_{GD3}$$

$$R_{1O}: \mathbf{v_x} = (\mathbf{i_x} + g_m\mathbf{v_1})\frac{1}{g_m} \mid \mathbf{v_1} = -\mu_f\mathbf{v_x} - \mathbf{v_x} \mid R_{1O} = \frac{\mathbf{v_x}}{\mathbf{i_x}} = \frac{1}{g_m(\mu_f + 2)}$$

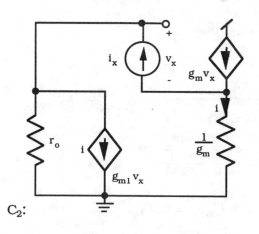

C_2:

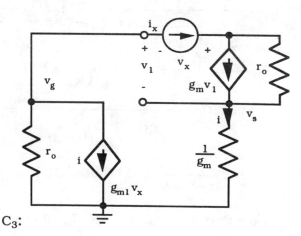

C_3:

477

R_{2O}: $\mathbf{v_x} = (\mathbf{i_x} - \mathbf{i})r_o - (g_m\mathbf{v_x} - \mathbf{i_x})\dfrac{1}{g_m}$ | $\mathbf{i} = g_m\mathbf{v_x} - \mathbf{i_x}$

$$2\mathbf{v_x} = \mathbf{i_x}\left(r_o + \frac{1}{g_m}\right) - r_o(g_m\mathbf{v_x} - \mathbf{i_x}) \;\;|\;\; R_{2O} = \frac{\mathbf{v_x}}{\mathbf{i_x}} = \frac{2r_o + \dfrac{1}{g_m}}{\mu_f + 2} \cong \frac{2}{g_m}$$

R_{3O}: $\mathbf{v_x} = (\mathbf{i_x} - g_m\mathbf{v_1})r_o + \dfrac{\mathbf{i_x}}{g_m} - (\mathbf{i_x} + \mathbf{i})r_o$ | $\mathbf{i} = \mathbf{i_x}$ | $\mathbf{v_1} = -2\mathbf{i_x}r_o - \dfrac{\mathbf{i_x}}{g_m}$

$$R_{3O} = \frac{\mathbf{v_x}}{\mathbf{i_x}} = 2\mu_f r_o + 4r_o + \frac{1}{g_m} \cong 2(\mu_f + 2)r_o \cong 2\mu_f r_o$$

$$\omega_H \cong \frac{1}{\dfrac{2C_{GS}}{g_m\mu_f} + 2\dfrac{C_{GS} + C_{GD}}{g_m} + 2\mu_f r_o C_{GD}} \cong \frac{1}{2\mu_f r_o C_{GD}} = \frac{1}{2g_m r_o^2 C_{GD}}$$

$$f_H \cong \frac{1}{2\pi}\frac{1}{2\sqrt{2(2.5\text{x}10^{-4})(2.5\text{x}10^{-4})\left(\dfrac{50}{2.5\text{x}10^{-4}}\right)^2(10^{-12})}} = 5.63 \text{ kHz}$$

Note: R_{3O} neglects any attached load resistance. If a load exists, essentially all of $\mathbf{i_x}$ will go through the load R_L, and the frequency response will significantly improve. For that case, $R_{3O} \approx R_L + r_o \approx r_o$.

17.60

$$A_V = -100 \text{ (40dB)} \;|\; f_H = 5\text{x}10^6\,\text{Hz} \;|\; f_T \geq 2(100)(5\text{x}10^6) = 1.00 \text{ GHz}$$

$$\text{GBW} \leq \frac{1}{r_x C_\mu} \;|\; r_x C_\mu \leq \frac{1}{2\pi(10^9\,\text{Hz})} = 159 \text{ ps}$$

17.61

$$A_V = 100 \text{ (40dB)} \;|\; f_H = 20\text{x}10^6\,\text{Hz} \;|\; f_T \geq 2(100)(2\text{x}10^7) = 4.00 \text{ GHz}$$

$$\text{GBW} \leq \frac{1}{r_x C_\mu} \;|\; r_x C_\mu \leq \frac{1}{2\pi(4\text{x}10^9\,\text{Hz})} = 39.8 \text{ ps}$$

17.62

$$\omega_H = \frac{1}{R_{th}\dfrac{C_{GS}}{1 + g_m R_{th}} + R_L C_{GD}} \;|\; A_{mid} = \frac{g_m R_L}{1 + g_m R_{th}} = \frac{R_L}{\dfrac{1}{g_m} + R_{th}}$$

$$R_L = A_{mid}\left(\frac{1}{g_m} + R_{th}\right) = 20\left(\frac{1}{g_m} + 100\right)$$

$$2\pi(25\text{x}10^6) = \frac{1}{100\Omega\dfrac{10^{-12}\,\text{F}}{1 + g_m(100\Omega)} + 20\left(\dfrac{1}{g_m} + 100\Omega\right)3\text{x}10^{-12}\,\text{F}} \rightarrow g_m = 56.9\text{mS}$$

$$R_L = 20\left(\frac{1}{.0569} + 100\right) = 2.35 \text{ k}\Omega \;|\; I_{DS} = \frac{g_m^2}{2K_n} = \frac{(56.9\text{mS})^2}{2\left(25\dfrac{\text{mS}}{\text{V}}\right)} = 64.8 \text{ mA}$$

Note that we cannot supply I_{DS} through R_L since $I_{DS}R_L = 152\text{V} > V_{DD}$.

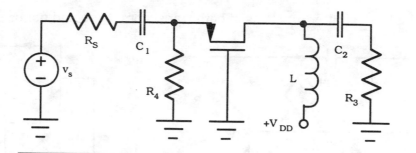

17.63

$$A_{mid} = g_m R_L \quad | \quad g_m = \frac{100}{100k\Omega} = 1.00mS \quad | \quad r_\pi = \frac{\beta_o}{g_m} \cong \frac{100}{1.00mS} = 100k\Omega$$

Assume $r_\pi \gg r_x \quad | \quad r_{\pi o} = r_\pi \| r_x \cong r_x$

$$\omega_H = \frac{1}{r_x\left[C_\pi + C_\mu\left(1 + g_m R_L + \frac{R_L}{r_x}\right)\right]} \cong \frac{1}{r_x C_\mu\left(1 + g_m R_L + \frac{R_L}{r_x}\right)} = \frac{1}{r_x C_\mu(1 + g_m R_L) + R_L C_\mu}$$

$$r_x C_\mu(1 + g_m R_L) + R_L C_\mu = \frac{1}{\omega_H} \quad | \quad r_x C_\mu(1 + 100) + 10^5 C_\mu = \frac{1}{2\pi(10^6)} = 1.59 \times 10^{-7}$$

$$C_\mu = \frac{1.59\ pF}{1 + 1.01 \times 10^{-3} r_x} \quad | \quad C_\mu \text{ cannot exceed } 1.59\ pF \text{ for an ideal transistor with } r_x = 0.$$

Other more realistic possibilities (C_u, r_x): $(1pF, 584\Omega)$ $(0.75pF, 1.11k\Omega)$ $(0.5pF, 2.16k\Omega)$

17.64

$$\omega_H = \frac{1}{R_{th}\left[C_{GS} + C_{GD}\left[1 + g_m R_L + \frac{R_L}{R_{th}}\right]\right]} = \frac{1}{100\left[15pF + 5pF\left[1 + g_m R_L + \frac{R_L}{100}\right]\right]}$$

$$2\pi(25 \times 10^6) = \frac{1}{100\left[20pF + 5pF\left[g_m R_L + \frac{R_L}{100}\right]\right]} \quad | \quad g_m R_L + \frac{R_L}{100} = \left[\frac{1}{2\pi(25 \times 10^6)(100)10^{-12}} - 20\right]\frac{1}{5}$$

$$g_m = \frac{8.73}{R_L} - 0.01 \rightarrow R_L \leq 873\Omega \quad | \quad I_{DS} = \frac{g_m^2}{2K_n} = \frac{g_m^2}{0.05} = 20g_m^2$$

For strong inversion (for the square-law model to be valid), we desire

$$(V_{GS} - V_{TN}) \geq 0.25V \rightarrow I_{DS} \geq \frac{0.025}{2}(0.25)^2 = 781\ \mu A.$$

We normally would like $g_m R_L$ to be as large as possible, so set $I_{DS} = 781\ \mu A$.

$$g_m = \sqrt{2K_n I_{DS}} = \sqrt{2(0.025)(7.81 \times 10^{-4})} = 6.25mS \quad | \quad R_L = \frac{8.73}{g_m - .01} = 537\Omega \quad | \quad g_m R_L = 3.36$$

17.65

$$f_H \leq \frac{1}{2\pi R_L C_\mu} = \frac{1}{2\pi(12k\Omega\|47k\Omega)(2pF)} \rightarrow f_H \leq 8.33\ MHz$$

17.66 Note that the base-emitter junctions of both transistors Q_2 should not be shorted.

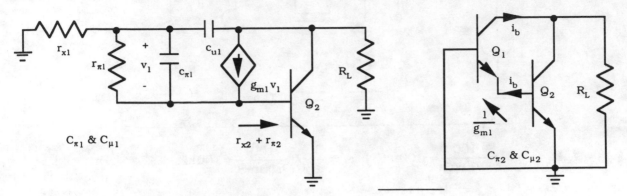

$C_{\pi 1}$ & $C_{\mu 1}$
$r_{x2} + r_{\pi 2}$
$C_{\pi 2}$ & $C_{\mu 2}$

(a) $R_{\mu 1O}$: $\mathbf{v_x} \cong \mathbf{i_x} r_{x1} - \mathbf{i_x} r_{x1} \left[\dfrac{(\beta_o + 1)(r_{x2} + r_{\pi 2})}{r_{\pi 1} + (\beta_o + 1)(r_{x2} + r_{\pi 2})} \right] \left(-\dfrac{\beta_o}{r_{x2} + r_{\pi 2}} R_L \right) - (-\mathbf{i_x} R_L)$

$R_{\mu 1O} \cong \mathbf{i_x} \left[R_L + r_{x1} \left(1 + \dfrac{\beta_o r_{\pi 2}}{r_{\pi 1} + \beta_o r_{\pi 2}} g_{m2} R_L \right) \right]$ assuming $r_{x2} \ll r_{\pi 2}$.

$r_{\pi 1} \cong 10 r_{\pi 2}$ | $\beta_o = 100$ | $g_{m1} \cong \dfrac{\beta_o}{r_{\pi 1}} = \dfrac{10}{r_{\pi 2}}$ | $R_{\mu 1O} = \dfrac{\mathbf{v_x}}{\mathbf{i_x}} = R_L + r_{x1} \left(1 + \dfrac{10}{11} g_{m2} R_L \right)$

$R_{\pi 1O}$: Split i_x and use superposition with $r_{x2} \ll r_{\pi 2}$:

$\mathbf{v_x} \cong \mathbf{i_x} r_{x1} \left[1 - \dfrac{(\beta_o + 1)(r_{x2} + r_{\pi 2})}{r_{\pi 1} + (\beta_o + 1)(r_{x2} + r_{\pi 2})} \right] + \dfrac{\mathbf{i_x}}{g_{\pi 2} + g_{m1}} \cong \mathbf{i_x} r_{x1} \dfrac{r_{\pi 1}}{r_{\pi 1} + \beta_o r_{\pi 2}} + \dfrac{\mathbf{i_x}}{g_{\pi 2} + 10 g_{\pi 2}}$

$R_{\pi 1O} = \dfrac{\mathbf{v_x}}{\mathbf{i_x}} \cong \dfrac{10 r_{x1} + r_{\pi 2}}{11}$

$R_{\pi 2O}$: The circuit is the same as that used for the C_T calculation.

$R_{\pi 2O} = r_{\pi 2} \left\| \left(r_{x2} + \dfrac{1}{g_{m1}} \right) = r_{\pi 2} \right\| \left(r_{x2} + \dfrac{r_{\pi 2}}{10} \right)$

$R_{\mu 2O}$: The circuit is the same as that used for the C_T calculation except the additional $i_b = i_x / 2$ is returned back to the output:

$R_{\mu 2O} = R_{\pi 2O} + R_{\pi 2O} g_{m2} R_L + \dfrac{R_L}{2} = R_{\pi 2O} \left(1 + g_{m2} R_L + \dfrac{R_L}{2 R_{\pi 2O}} \right)$

$$\omega_H = \dfrac{1}{C_{\pi 1} \left(\dfrac{10 r_{x1} + r_{\pi 2}}{11} \right) + C_{\mu 1} r_{x1} \left(1 + \dfrac{10}{11} g_{m2} R_L + \dfrac{R_L}{r_{x1}} \right) + R_{\pi 2O} \left[C_{\pi 2} + C_{\mu 2} \left(1 + g_{m2} R_L + \dfrac{R_L}{2 R_{\pi 2O}} \right) \right]}$$

$r_{\pi 2} = \dfrac{100(0.025V)}{1mA} = 2.50k\Omega$ | Use $R_L = \dfrac{r_{o2}}{2} = \dfrac{50V}{2mA} = 25.0k\Omega$

$C_{\pi 1} = \dfrac{40(10^{-4})}{6 \times 10^8 \pi} - 0.5pF = 1.62pF$ | $C_{\pi 2} = \dfrac{40(10^{-3})}{6 \times 10^8 \pi} - 0.5pF = 20.7pF$

$R_{\pi 2O} = r_{\pi 2} \left\| \left(r_{x2} + \dfrac{r_{\pi 2}}{10} \right) = 2.50k\Omega \right\| \left(300 + \dfrac{2.50k\Omega}{10} \right) = 451\Omega$

$$f_H = \frac{1}{2\pi}\left\{ \begin{array}{l} 1.62\text{pF}\left(\dfrac{3\text{k}\Omega+2.5\text{k}\Omega}{11}\right)+0.5\text{pF}(300\Omega)\left[1+40\text{mS}(25\text{k}\Omega)+\dfrac{25\text{k}\Omega}{300\Omega}\right] \\[3mm] +451\Omega\left[20.7\text{pF}+0.5\text{pF}\left(1+40\text{mS}(25\text{k}\Omega)+\dfrac{25\text{k}\Omega}{902\Omega}\right)\right] \end{array}\right\}^{-1} = 393\ \text{kHz}$$

(b) The circuit is almost the same except for two important changes: $C_{\mu 1}$ sees only r_{x1}, and the $i_b = i_x/2$ is not returned to the output for $C_{\mu 2}$.

$$\omega_H = \frac{1}{C_{\pi 1}\dfrac{10r_{x1}+r_{\pi 2}}{11}+C_{\mu 1}r_{x1}+R_{\pi 2O}\left[C_{\pi 2}+C_{\mu 2}\left(1+g_{m2}R_L+\dfrac{R_L}{R_{\pi 2O}}\right)\right]}$$

$$f_H = \frac{1}{2\pi}\left\{ \begin{array}{l} 1.62\text{pF}\left(\dfrac{3\text{k}\Omega+2.5\text{k}\Omega}{11}\right)+0.5\text{pF}(300\Omega) \\[3mm] +451\Omega\left[20.7\text{pF}+0.5\text{pF}\left(1+40\text{mS}(25\text{k}\Omega)+\dfrac{25\text{k}\Omega}{451\Omega}\right)\right] \end{array}\right\}^{-1} = 640\text{kHz}$$

(c) The C-C / C-E cascade offers significantly better bandwidth than the Darlington configuration because $C_{\mu 1}$ is not subject to Miller multiplication.

(d) Improved bandwidth is one reason for the use of the C-C / C-E cascade in the 741 op-amp.

17.67 Use $R_C = 100\ \text{k}\Omega$

$$f_Z = \frac{1}{2\pi R_{EE}C_{EE}} = \frac{1}{2\pi(10^7\,\Omega)(1\text{pF})} = 15.9\text{kHz}$$

$$f_p \cong \frac{1}{2\pi(r_x+R_C)C_\mu} = \frac{1}{2\pi(175\Omega+10^5\,\Omega)(0.3\text{pF})} = 5.30\ \text{MHz}$$

15.9 kHz   5.30 MHz

17.68

```
*Problem 17.68 - Bipolar Differential Amplifier CMRR
VIC 1 0 AC 5M
RX 1 2 175
RPI 2 3 25K
CPI 2 3 2.88PF
CU 2 4 0.3PF
GM 4 3 2 3 4MS
RO 4 3 500K
REE 3 0 10MEG
CEE 3 0 1PF
RL 4 0 100K
```

481

```
.AC DEC 100 10 20MEG
.PRINT AC VM(4) VP(4)
.PROBE
.END
```
Results agree with the drawing in Problem 17.67

17.69

$$f_T = \frac{g_m}{2\pi C_C} = \frac{\sqrt{2(0.001)(125 \times 10^{-6})}}{2\pi \times 10^{-11}} = 7.96 \text{ MHz} \quad | \quad SR = \frac{I_1}{C_C} \text{ since } I_2 > I_1, \text{ and the slew rate}$$

is symmetrical. $\quad | \quad SR = \dfrac{250 \times 10^{-6}}{10^{-11}} = 25 \times 10^6 \dfrac{V}{s} = 25 \dfrac{V}{\mu s}$

17.70

```
*Problem 17.70 - CMOS Op-amp
VDD 8 0 DC 10
VSS 9 0 -10
I1 1 9 250U
I2 6 9 500U
I3 7 9 2M
V1 4 0 DC -2.23M AC 0.5
V2 2 0 AC -0.5
M1 3 2 1 1 NFET W=20U L=1U
M2 5 4 1 1 NFET W=20U L=1U
M3 3 3 8 8 PFET W=40U L=1U
M4 5 3 8 8 PFET W=40U L=1U
M5 6 5 8 8 PFET W=160U L=1U
M6 8 6 7 7 NFET W=60U L=1U
CC 5 6 7.5PF
*CC 5 10 7.5PF
*RZ 10 6 1K
.MODEL NFET NMOS KP=2.5E-5 VTO=0.70 GAMMA=0.5
+LAMBDA=0.05 TOX=20N
+CGSO=4E-9 CGDO=4E-9 CJ=2.0E-4 CJSW=5.0E-10
.MODEL PFET PMOS  KP=1.0E-5 VTO=-0.70 GAMMA=0.75
+LAMBDA=0.05 TOX=20N
+CGSO=4E-9 CGDO=4E-9 CJ=2.0E-4 CJSW=5.0E-10
.OP
.TF V(7) V1
.AC DEC 100 1 20MEG
.PRINT AC VM(7) VP(7)
.PROBE
.END
```
Results: 8.1 MHz, -110 degrees; 8.0 MHz, -92 degrees

17.71

(a) $f_T = \dfrac{g_m}{2\pi C_C} = \dfrac{40 I_{C1}}{2\pi C_C} \quad | \quad I_{C1} = \dfrac{I_1}{2} \quad | \quad f_T = \dfrac{40(25\mu A)}{2\pi(12pF)} = 13.3 \text{ MHz}$

$SR = \dfrac{I_1}{C_C} = \dfrac{25\mu A}{12pF} = 2.09 \dfrac{MV}{s} = 2.09 \dfrac{V}{\mu s}$ since $I_2 > I_1$. The slew rate is symmetrical.

(b) $f_T = \dfrac{40(100\mu A)}{2\pi(12pF)} = 53.1 \text{ MHz} \quad | \quad SR = \dfrac{I_1}{C_C} = \dfrac{100\mu A}{12pF} = 8.33 \dfrac{MV}{s} = 8.33 \dfrac{V}{\mu s}$

17.72

$$SR = \frac{I_1}{C_C} = \frac{40\mu A}{5pF} = 8 \times 10^6 \, \frac{V}{s} = 8V \, \frac{V}{\mu s}$$

```
*Problems 17.72 - Bipolar Op-amp
VCC 8 0 DC 10
VEE 9 0 -10
I1 1 9 40U
I2 6 9 400U
I3 7 9 500U
V1 4 0 DC 0 PWL (0 0 5U 0 5.1U 5 10U 5 10.2U -5 15U -5 15.2U 5 20U 5)
VF 2 7 DC -0.0045
Q1 3 2 1 NBJT
Q2 5 4 1 NBJT
Q3 3 10 8 PBJT
Q4 5 10 8 PBJT
Q11 0 3 10 PBJT
Q5 6 5 8 PBJT
Q6 8 6 7 NBJT
CC 5 6 5PF
.MODEL NBJT NPN BF=100 IS=1FA VAF=80 RB=250 TF=0.65NS CJC=2PF
.MODEL PBJT PNP  BF=100 IS=1FA VAF=80 RB=250 TF=0.65NS CJC=2PF
.OP
.TRAN .05U 20U
.PROBE V(4) V(5) V(6) V(7)
.END
```

Results: -8V/μs, +6V/μs

17.73

$$f_T = \frac{g_m}{2\pi C_C} = \frac{40 I_{C1}}{2\pi C_C} \quad | \quad I_{C1} = \frac{I_1}{2} \quad | \quad f_T = \frac{40(50\mu A)}{2\pi(15pF)} = 21.2 \text{ MHz}$$

```
*Problem 17.73 - Bipolar Op-amp
VCC 8 0 DC 10
VEE 9 0 -10
I1 1 9 100U
I2 6 9 500U
I3 7 9 500U
V1 4 0 DC 2.10M AC 0.5
V2 2 0 DC 0 AC -0.5
Q1 3 2 1 NBJT
Q2 5 4 1 NBJT
Q3 3 10 8 PBJT
Q4 5 10 8 PBJT
Q11 0 3 10 PBJT
Q5 6 5 8 PBJT
Q6 8 6 7 NBJT
CC 5 6 15PF
.MODEL NBJT NPN BF=100 IS=1FA VAF=80 RB=250 TF=0.65NS CJC=2PF
.MODEL PBJT PNP  BF=100 IS=1FA VAF=80 RB=250 TF=0.65NS CJC=2PF
.OP
.TF V(7) V1
.AC DEC 100 1 20MEG
.PRINT AC VM(7) VP(7)
.PROBE
.END
```

Spice Results: (a) 16.2MHz (b) 16.3 MHz - 15 pF does not represent the effective value of C_C.

17.74

Zero output voltage occurs when the current through the base-collector admittance is exactly equal to the current in the controlled source:

$$g_m\mathbf{v} = sC_{GD}\mathbf{v} + \frac{\mathbf{v}}{R_Z + \dfrac{1}{sC_C}} \quad | \quad sC_{GD} - g_m + \frac{sC_C}{sC_CR_Z + 1} = 0$$

The numerator polynomial becomes: $s^2C_{GD}C_CR_Z + s(C_{GD} + C_C - C_CR_Zg_m) - g_m = 0$

For widely spaced roots, $z_1 \cong \dfrac{g_m}{C_{GD} + C_C - C_CR_Zg_m}$

z_1 can be eliminated by setting: $R_Z = \dfrac{1}{g_m}\left(1 + \dfrac{C_{GD}}{C_C}\right)$

17.75

$$f_o = \frac{1}{2\pi\sqrt{LC_{GD}}} = \frac{1}{2\pi\sqrt{10^{-5}\left(5\times10^{-12}\right)}} = 22.5 \text{ MHz}$$

$$g_m = \frac{2I_{DS}}{V_{GS} - V_{TN}} = \frac{0.02}{2} = 0.01S \qquad r_o = \frac{\dfrac{1}{0.0167} + 10}{0.01} = 59.9\text{k}\Omega$$

$$A_V = -g_m\left(r_o\|R_L\right) = -0.01S(59.9\text{k}\Omega\|10\text{k}\Omega) = -85.7$$

$$BW = \frac{1}{2\pi R_PC_{GD}} = \frac{1}{2\pi(8.57\text{k}\Omega)(5\text{pF})} = 3.71 \text{ MHz} \qquad Q = \frac{22.5}{3.71} = 6.06$$

17.76

(a) $f_o = \dfrac{1}{2\pi\sqrt{(C + C_\mu)L}} \rightarrow C = \dfrac{1}{(2\pi f_o)^2L} - C_\mu = \dfrac{1}{\left[2\pi(10.7\times10^6\text{Hz})\right]^2 10^{-5}\text{H}} - 2\text{pF} = 20.1\text{pF}$

(b) $r_o = \dfrac{75V + 10V}{10\text{mA}} = 8.50\text{k}\Omega \quad | \quad BW = \dfrac{1}{2\pi(8.5\text{k}\Omega)(22.1\text{pF})} = 847\text{kHz} \quad | \quad Q = \dfrac{10.7}{0.847} = 12.6$

(c) $Q = 100 \quad | \quad BW = \dfrac{f_o}{Q} = 107\text{kHz} \quad | \quad r_o = \dfrac{1}{\omega_o\left(C + C_\mu\right)} = \dfrac{1}{2\pi(107\text{kHz})(22.1\text{pF})} = 67.3\text{k}\Omega$

$n^2 = \dfrac{67.3\text{k}\Omega}{8.50\text{k}\Omega} = 7.918 \quad | \quad n = 2.81$

(d) $C'_\mu = \dfrac{C_\mu}{n^2} = \dfrac{2\text{pF}}{7.918} = 0.253\text{pF} \quad | \quad C = 22.1 - 0.253 = 21.9\text{pF}$

17.77

```
*Problem 17.77(a) - Double-Tuned Common-Source Amplifier
VDD 4 0 DC 15
VS 1 0 AC 12.65M
C1 1 2 25PF
L1 2 0 20UH
RG 2 0 100K
M1 3 2 0 0 NFET
CGS 2 0 25PF
L2 3 4 20UH
C2 3 4 50PF
RD 3 4 100K
.MODEL NFET NMOS VTO=-1 KP=20M LAMBDA=0.02
```

```
.OP
.AC LIN 500 4.5MEG 5.5MEG
.PRINT AC VM(2) VP(2) VM(3) VP(3)
.PROBE
.END
```

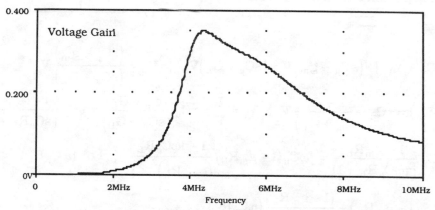

*Problem 17.77(b) - Double-Tuned Common-Source Amplifier

```
VDD 4 0 DC 15
VS 1 0 AC 12.65M
C1 1 2 25PF
L1 2 0 20UH
RG 2 0 100K
M1 3 2 0 0 NFET
CGS 2 0 25PF
CGD 2 3 1PF
L2 3 4 20UH
C2 3 4 50PF
RD 3 4 100K
.MODEL NFET NMOS VTO=-1 KP=20M LAMBDA=0.02
.OP
.AC LIN 500 1MEG 10MEG
.PRINT AC VM(2) VP(2) VM(3) VP(3)
.PROBE
.END
```

Note that the synchronous tuning and gain are ruined by the Miller multiplication of C_{GD}.

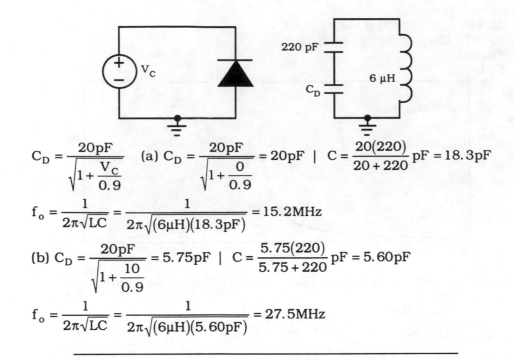

$$C_D = \frac{20pF}{\sqrt{1+\dfrac{V_C}{0.9}}} \quad \text{(a)} \ C_D = \frac{20pF}{\sqrt{1+\dfrac{0}{0.9}}} = 20pF \ | \ C = \frac{20(220)}{20+220}pF = 18.3pF$$

$$f_o = \frac{1}{2\pi\sqrt{LC}} = \frac{1}{2\pi\sqrt{(6\mu H)(18.3pF)}} = 15.2MHz$$

$$\text{(b)} \ C_D = \frac{20pF}{\sqrt{1+\dfrac{10}{0.9}}} = 5.75pF \ | \ C = \frac{5.75(220)}{5.75+220}pF = 5.60pF$$

$$f_o = \frac{1}{2\pi\sqrt{LC}} = \frac{1}{2\pi\sqrt{(6\mu H)(5.60pF)}} = 27.5MHz$$

Although the C_T approximation gives an excellent estimate for the dominant pole of the common-emitter amplifier, it does not do a good job of representing the input admittance at high frequencies. An improved estimate is needed for several of the problems to come.

$$Y_{in} = g_\pi + sC_\pi + Y_1 \ | \ (sC_\mu - g_m)\mathbf{V} = (sC_\mu + G_L)\mathbf{V_o} \ | \ \mathbf{V_o} = \frac{(sC_\mu - g_m)}{(sC_\mu + G_L)}\mathbf{V}$$

$$\mathbf{I} = sC_\mu(\mathbf{V} - \mathbf{V_o}) = sC_\mu\frac{g_m + G_L}{(sC_\mu + G_L)}\mathbf{V} \ | \ Y_1 = \frac{\mathbf{I}}{\mathbf{V}} = sC_\mu\frac{g_m + G_L}{(sC_\mu + G_L)} = sC_\mu\frac{1 + g_mR_L}{(sC_\mu R_L + 1)}$$

$$Y_1(j\omega) = j\omega C_\mu\frac{1 + g_mR_L}{(j\omega C_\mu R_L + 1)} = j\omega C_\mu(1 + g_mR_L)\frac{1 - j\omega C_\mu R_L}{(\omega C_\mu R_L)^2 + 1} \ | \ \text{For} \ (\omega C_\mu R_L)^2 \ll 1,$$

$$Y_1(j\omega) \cong j\omega C_\mu(1 + g_mR_L) + \frac{(1 + g_mR_L)}{R_L}(\omega C_\mu R_L)^2$$

From the results we see that the input capacitance is correctly modeled by the total Miller input capacitance, but the input resistance is not correctly modeled by just r_π:

$$C_{in} = C_{\pi} + C_{\mu}(1 + g_m R_L) \ | \ R_{in} = r_{\pi} \left\| \frac{R_L}{(1 + g_m R_L)(\omega C_{\mu} R_L)^2} \right.$$

17.79 (a)

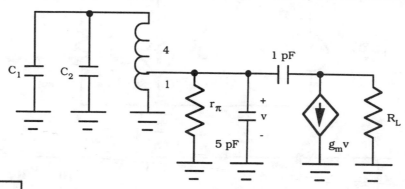

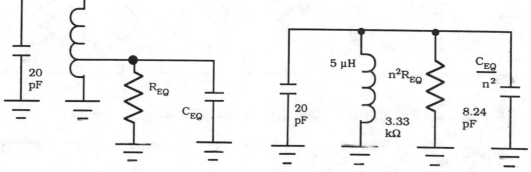

$$C_{EQ} = C_{\pi} + C_{\mu}[1 + g_m R_L] = 5pF + 1pF[1 + 40(1mA)(5k\Omega)] = 206 \text{ pF}$$

$$C_P = 20pF + \frac{C_{EQ}}{n^2} = 20pF + \frac{206pF}{5^2} = 28.2pF \ | \ f_o = \frac{1}{2\pi\sqrt{(5\mu H)(28.2pF)}} = 13.4 \text{ MHz}$$

$$R_{EQ} = r_{\pi} \left\| \frac{R_L}{(1 + g_m R_L)(\omega R_L C_{\mu})^2} \right. = 2.5k\Omega \left\| \frac{5000}{(1 + 200)\left[2\pi(13.4MHz)(5k\Omega)(1pF)\right]^2} \right. = 2.5k\Omega \| 140\Omega = 133\Omega$$

$$R_P = n^2 R_{EQ} = 25(133\Omega) = 3.33k\Omega \ | \ BW = \frac{1}{2\pi(3.33k\Omega)(28.2pF)} = 1.70 \text{ MHz} \ | \ Q = \frac{13.4}{1.70} = 7.88$$

Note the huge error that would be caused by using only r_{π} as the input resistance term.

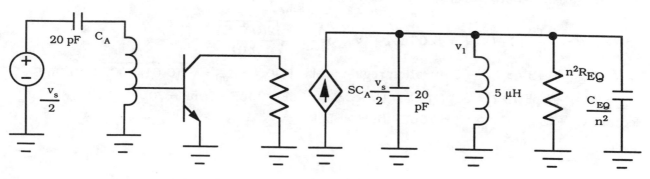

487

$$\mathbf{v_1} = j2\pi(13.4\text{MHz})(20\text{pF})\left(\frac{1}{2}\right)(3.33\text{k}\Omega)\mathbf{v_s} = j2.80\mathbf{v_s}$$

$$\mathbf{v_o} = (-g_mR_L)\frac{j2.80\mathbf{v_s}}{5} = -40\left(10^{-3}\right)(5\text{k}\Omega)j0.560\mathbf{v_s} \quad | \quad A_V = 112\angle - 90°$$

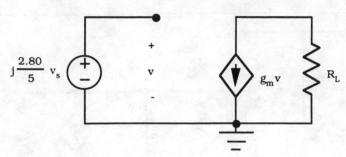

17.79 (b)

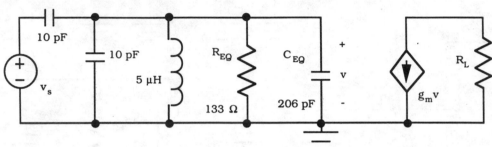

$$C_T = 5\text{pF} + 1\text{pF}\big[1 + 40(1\text{mA})(5\text{k}\Omega)\big] = 206 \text{ pF} \quad | \quad C_P = 20\text{pF} + 206\text{pF} = 226\text{pF}$$

$$f_o = \frac{1}{2\pi\sqrt{(5\mu\text{H})(226\text{pF})}} = 4.74\text{MHz}$$

$$R_{EQ} = r_\pi \left\Vert \frac{R_L}{(1 + g_mR_L)(\omega R_L C_\mu)^2} = 2.5\text{k}\Omega \right\Vert \frac{5000}{(1 + 200)\big[2\pi(4.74\text{MHz})(5\text{k}\Omega)(1\text{pF})\big]^2}$$

$$R_{EQ} = 2.5\text{k}\Omega\Vert1.12\text{k}\Omega = 774\Omega \quad | \quad BW = \frac{1}{2\pi(774\Omega)(226\text{pF})} = 910 \text{ kHz} \quad | \quad Q = \frac{4.74}{0.910} = 5.21$$

$$\mathbf{v_o} = j2\pi(4.74\text{MHz})(10\text{pF})(774\Omega)(-g_mR_L)\mathbf{v_s}$$

$$\mathbf{v_o} = j2\pi(4.74\text{MHz})(10\text{pF})(774\Omega)\big[-0.04\text{mS}(5\text{k}\Omega)\big]\mathbf{v_s} \quad | \quad A_V = 46.1\angle - 90°$$

17.80

(a) $C_{EQ} = C_{GS1} + C_{GD1}(1 + g_{m1}R_L) = C_{GS1} + C_{GD1}\left(1 + \frac{g_{m1}}{g_{m2}}\right)$

$$I_{DS2} = I_{DS1} = \frac{0.01}{2}\big[0 - (-1)\big]^2 = 5.00\text{mA} \quad | \quad V_{GS2} = -4 + \sqrt{\frac{2(0.005)}{0.01}} = -3\text{V}$$

$V_{DS1} = V_{SG2} = +3\text{V} > 1\text{V} \rightarrow$ Saturation region is ok. $\quad | \quad g_{m2} = g_{m1} = \sqrt{2(0.01)0.005} = 10.0\text{mS}$

$C_{EQ} = 20\text{pF} + 5\text{pF}[1 + 1] = 30\text{pF} \quad | \quad C_P = C_1 + C_{EQ} = 30\text{pF} + 20\text{pF} + 20\text{pF} = 70\text{pF}$

Require $C_2 + C_{GD} = C_P \rightarrow C_2 = 70\text{pF} - 5\text{pF} = 65\text{pF}$

(b) $f_o = \dfrac{1}{2\pi\sqrt{LC_P}} = \dfrac{1}{2\pi\sqrt{(10\mu H)(70pF)}} = 6.02$ MHz $\mid R_{L1} = \dfrac{1}{g_{m2}}$

$R_P = R_G \left\| \dfrac{R_{L1}}{(1+g_{m1}R_{L1})(\omega R_{L1}C_{GD1})^2} = 100k\Omega \right\| \dfrac{100}{(1+1)[2\pi(6.02MHz)(100)(5pF)]^2}$

$R_P = 100k\Omega \| 140k\Omega = 58.3k\Omega \mid BW_1 = \dfrac{1}{2\pi R_P C_P} = \dfrac{1}{2\pi(58.3k\Omega)(70pF)} = 39.0$ kHz

$BW_2 \cong BW_1\sqrt{2^{\frac{1}{2}}-1} = 25.1$ kHz $\mid$ Note that this is an approximation since $R_P = 100k\Omega$

at the output and 58.3 kΩ at the input. $\mid Q = \dfrac{6.02\ MHz}{25.1kHz} = 240 \mid \mathbf{v_o} = (\omega C_3 \mathbf{v_s})(R_P)(-g_m R_D)$

$A_{mid} = 2\pi(6.02MHz)(20pF)(58.3k\Omega)(-10.0mS)(100k\Omega) = 4.41x10^4$

17.81

```
*Problem 17.81 - Synchronously-Tuned Cascode Amplifier
VDD 5 0 DC 12
VS 1 0 AC 1
C3 1 2 20PF
L1 2 0 10UH
C1 2 0 20PF
RG 2 0 100K
M1 3 2 0 0 NFET1
CGS1 2 0 20PF
CGD1 2 3 5PF
M2 4 0 3 3 NFET2
CGS2 3 0 20PF
CGD2 4 3 5PF
L2 4 5 10UH
C2 4 5 65PF
RD 4 5 100K
.MODEL NFET1 NMOS VTO=-1 KP=10M
.MODEL NFET2 NMOS VTO=-4 KP=10M
.OP
.AC LIN 200 5.5MEG 6.5MEG
.PRINT AC VM(2) VP(2) VM(3) VP(3) VM(4) VP(4)
.PROBE
.END
```
Results: $A_{mid} = 279$, $f_o = 6.10$ MHz, $Q = 24$

The amplifier is actually stagger-tuned. Note that the loop of capacitors around M_1 messes up the hand results based upon the C_{EQ} approximation. The C_{EQ} approximation itself may not be accurate enough for precise synchronous tuning. Plot a graph of V(2) and V(3) to show the problem. Evidence of the problem is also provided by the huge error in the mid-band gain.

From Prob. 17.80: $C_{P2} = \dfrac{1}{(2\pi f_o)^2 L} = \dfrac{1}{\left(2\pi \dfrac{1.02}{\sqrt{LC_{P1}}}\right)^2 L} = \dfrac{C_{P1}}{(1.02)^2} = \dfrac{70pF}{(1.02)^2} = 67.3 \text{ pF}$

$C_2 = C_{P2} - C_{GD2} = 67.3pF - 5pF = 62.3pF \mid R_{p2} = 100k\Omega \mid$ From Prob. 14.81:

$BW_1 = \dfrac{1}{2\pi(58.3k\Omega)(70pF)} = 39.0kHz \mid BW_2 = \dfrac{1}{2\pi(10^5\Omega)(67.3pF)} = 23.7kHz$

$BW \cong \dfrac{BW_1}{2} + 0.02f_{o1} + \dfrac{BW_2}{2} = \dfrac{39.0kHz}{2} + 0.02(6.02MHz) + \dfrac{23.7kHz}{2} = 152kHz$

The new $f_o \cong \dfrac{f_{o1} + 1.02f_o}{2} = 6.08 \text{ MHz} \mid Q = \dfrac{6.08 \text{ MHz}}{152kHz} = 40$

17.83

```
*Problem 17.83 - Stagger-Tuned Cascode Amplifier
VDD 5 0 DC 12
VS 1 0 AC 1
C3 1 2 20PF
L1 2 0 10UH
C1 2 0 20PF
RG 2 0 100K
M1 3 2 0 0 NFET1
CGS1 2 0 20PF
CGD1 2 3 5PF
M2 4 0 3 3 NFET2
CGS2 3 0 20PF
CGD2 4 3 5PF
L2 4 5 10UH
C2 4 5 62.3PF
RD 4 5 100K
.MODEL NFET1 NMOS VTO=-1 KP=10M
.MODEL NFET2 NMOS VTO=-4 KP=10M
.OP
.AC LIN 200 5.5MEG 6.5MEG
.PRINT AC VM(2) VP(2) VM(3) VP(3) VM(4) VP(4)
.PROBE
.END
```
        Results: $A_{mid} = 512$, $f_o = 6.19 \text{ MHz}$, BW = 0.19 MHz, Q = 33

17.84 **Note**: The output should be taken across the inductor in both circuits.

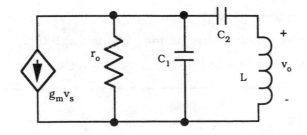

(a) $\begin{bmatrix} -g_m\mathbf{V_s} \\ 0 \end{bmatrix} = \begin{bmatrix} s(C_1+C_2)+g_o & -sC_2 \\ -sC_2 & sC_2+\dfrac{1}{sL} \end{bmatrix}\begin{bmatrix} \mathbf{V_1} \\ \mathbf{V_o} \end{bmatrix}$ | $A_V(j\omega) = \dfrac{\mathbf{V_o}}{\mathbf{V_s}} = -\dfrac{j\omega C_2 g_m}{\Delta}$

$$\Delta(s) = C_1C_2\left[s^2 + s\frac{g_o}{C_1} + \frac{g_o}{sC_1C_2L} + \frac{C_1+C_2}{C_1C_2}\frac{1}{L}\right]$$

$$\Delta(j\omega) = C_1C_2\left[\frac{C_1+C_2}{C_1C_2}\frac{1}{L} - \omega^2 + j\omega\frac{g_o}{C_1} + \frac{g_o}{j\omega C_1C_2L}\right] \quad | \quad \omega_o^2 = \frac{C_1+C_2}{C_1C_2}\frac{1}{L}$$

$$A_V(j\omega_o) = -\frac{\omega_o\dfrac{g_m}{C_1}}{\omega_o\dfrac{g_o}{C_1} - \dfrac{g_o}{\omega_o C_1C_2L}} = -\frac{g_m r_o}{1 - \dfrac{1}{\omega_o^2 LC_2}} = -\frac{\mu_f}{1 - \dfrac{C_1}{C_1+C_2}} = -\mu_f\left(1 + \frac{C_1}{C_2}\right)$$

Referring to Eq. (12.153): $BW = \dfrac{\omega_o}{Q} = \dfrac{g_o}{C_1} - \dfrac{g_o}{\omega_o^2 C_1C_2L} = \dfrac{1}{r_oC_1}\left(1 - \dfrac{1}{\omega_o^2 LC_2}\right) = \dfrac{1}{r_oC_1\left(1+\dfrac{C_1}{C_2}\right)}$

$C_{EQ} = \dfrac{45(40)}{45+40}\,\text{pF} = 21.2\,\text{pF}$ | $f_o = \dfrac{1}{2\pi\sqrt{(10\mu H)(21.2 pF)}} = 10.9\,\text{MHz}$

$r_o = \dfrac{1}{0.02(20mA)} = 2.50\,\text{k}\Omega$ | $BW = \dfrac{1}{2\pi(2.50k\Omega)(45pF)\left(1+\dfrac{45}{40}\right)} = 666\,\text{kHz}$

$Q = \dfrac{10.9}{0.666} = 16.4$ | $A_{mid} = -\mu_f\left(1+\dfrac{C_1}{C_2}\right) = -\sqrt{2(0.005)(0.02)}(2500)\left(1+\dfrac{45pF}{40pF}\right) = -75.1$

(b) $f_o = \dfrac{1}{2\pi\sqrt{(10\mu H)(25pF)}} = 10.1\,\text{MHz}$ | $BW = \dfrac{1}{2\pi(2.5k\Omega)(25pF)} = 2.55\,\text{MHz}$

$Q = \dfrac{10.1}{2.55} = 3.96$ | $A_{mid} = -g_m r_o = -\mu_f = -35.4$

17.85

$C_{EQ} = \dfrac{(C_1+5pF)C_2}{C_1+5pF+C_2} = 25\,\text{pF}$ | $C_2 = 50\,\text{pF}$ | $C_1 = 45\,\text{pF}$

$f_o = \dfrac{1}{2\pi\sqrt{(10\mu H)(25pF)}} = 10.1\,\text{MHz}$ | $r_o = \dfrac{1}{0.02(20mA)} = 2.50\,\text{k}\Omega$

Using the results from Prob. 17.84: $BW = \dfrac{1}{2\pi(2.50k\Omega)(50pF)\left(1+\dfrac{50pF}{50pF}\right)} = 635\,\text{kHz}$

$Q = \dfrac{10.1}{0.635} = 15.9$ | $A_{mid} = -\mu_f\left(1+\dfrac{C_1}{C_2}\right) = -\sqrt{2(0.005)(0.02)}(2500)\left(1+\dfrac{50pF}{50pF}\right) = -70.7$

17.86

```
*Problem 17.86(a) - Fig. P17.84(a)
VS 1 0 AC 1
CGD 1 2 5PF
GM 2 0 1 0 14.1MS
RO 2 0 2.5K
C1 2 0 40PF
C2 2 3 40PF
```

```
L1 3 0 10UH
.AC LIN 400 8MEG 12MEG
.PRINT AC VM(2) VP(2) VM(3) VP(3)
.PROBE V(2) V(3)
.END
```

Results: $A_{mid} = 75.1$, $f_o = 10.1$ MHz, BW = 670 kHz

```
*Problem 17.86(a) - Fig. P17.84(b)
VS 1 0 AC 1
CGD 1 2 5PF
GM 2 0 1 0 14.1MS
RO 2 0 2.5K
C1 2 0 20PF
L1 2 0 10UH
.AC LIN 400 8MEG 12MEG
.PRINT AC VM(2) VP(2)
.PROBE V(2)
.END
```

Results: $A_{mid} = 35.3$, $f_o = 10.1$ MHz, BW = 2.50 MHz

```
*Problem 17.86(b) - Problem 17.85
VS 1 0 AC 1
CGD 1 2 5PF
GM 2 0 1 0 14.1MS
RO 2 0 2.5K
C1 2 0 45PF
C2 2 3 50PF
L1 3 0 10UH
.AC LIN 400 8MEG 12MEG
.PRINT AC VM(2) VP(2) VM(3) VP(3)
.PROBE V(2) V(3)
.END
```

Results: $A_{mid} = 70.7$, $f_o = 10.1$ MHz, BW = 640 kHz

17.87

$$Y_{in} = g_\pi + sC_\pi + Y_1 \quad | \quad (sC_\mu - g_m)\mathbf{V} = (sC_\mu + G_L)\mathbf{V_o} \quad | \quad \mathbf{V_o} = \frac{(sC_\mu - g_m)}{(sC_\mu + G_L)}\mathbf{V}$$

$$\mathbf{I} = sC_\mu(\mathbf{V} - \mathbf{V_o}) = sC_\mu\frac{g_m + G_L}{(sC_\mu + G_L)}\mathbf{V} \quad | \quad Y_1 = \frac{\mathbf{I}}{\mathbf{V}} = sC_\mu\frac{g_m + G_L}{(sC_\mu + G_L)} = sC_\mu\frac{1 + g_mR_L}{(sC_\mu R_L + 1)}$$

$$Y_1(j\omega) = j\omega C_\mu\frac{1 + g_mR_L}{(j\omega C_\mu R_L + 1)} = j\omega C_\mu(1 + g_mR_L)\frac{1 - j\omega C_\mu R_L}{(\omega C_\mu R_L)^2 + 1} \quad | \quad \text{For } (\omega C_\mu R_L)^2 \ll 1,$$

$$Y_1(j\omega) \cong j\omega C_\mu(1 + g_mR_L) + \frac{(1 + g_mR_L)}{R_L}(\omega C_\mu R_L)^2$$

From the results we see that the input capacitance is correctly modeled by the total Miller input capacitance, but the input resistance is not correctly modeled by just r_π:

$$C_{in} = C_\pi + C_\mu(1 + g_m R_L) \quad | \quad R_{in} = r_\pi \left\| \frac{R_L}{(1 + g_m R_L)(\omega C_\mu R_L)^2} \right.$$

(b) $C_{in} = C_{GS} + C_{GD}(1 + g_m R_L) = 6pF + 2pF[1 + 5mS(10k\Omega)] = 108pF$

$$R_{in} = \frac{R_L}{(1 + g_m R_L)(\omega C_{GD} R_L)^2} = \frac{10k\Omega}{[1 + 5mS(10k\Omega)][2\pi(5x10^6)(2pF)(10k\Omega)]^2} = 497\Omega \text{ !}$$

Note also that $X_{C_{in}} = \dfrac{1}{2\pi(5x10^6)(108pF)} = 295 \ \Omega \quad | \quad$ Both values are far less than infinity.

CHAPTER 18

18.1

$$S_A^{A_V} = \frac{A}{A_V}\frac{\partial A_V}{\partial A} \qquad A_V = \frac{A}{1+A\beta}$$

$$\frac{\partial A_V}{\partial A} = \frac{(1+A\beta)1 - A\beta}{(1+A\beta)^2} = \frac{1}{(1+A\beta)^2} \qquad S_A^{A_V} = \frac{A}{\frac{A}{1+A\beta}}\frac{1}{(1+A\beta)^2} = \frac{1}{1+A\beta} \approx \frac{1}{A\beta}$$

$$S_A^{A_V} = \frac{1}{1+10^5(0.01)} = \frac{1}{1001}$$

$$\frac{\partial A_V}{A_V} = S_A^{A_V}\frac{\partial A}{A} = \frac{1}{1001}10\% = 9.99\text{x}10^{-3}\%$$

18.2

$$A_V = \frac{A}{1+A\beta} = \frac{A}{1+A} \quad | \quad \text{From Chapter 12, } GE = \frac{1}{1+A\beta} = \frac{1}{1+A}$$

$$\frac{1}{1+A} \le 10^{-4} \to A \ge 9999 \quad | \quad A \ge 80 \text{ dB}$$

18.3

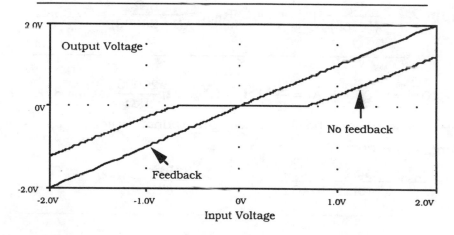

```
*Problem 18.3 - Class-B Amplifiers
VCC 3 0 DC 10
VEE 4 0 DC -10
VS 1 0 DC 0
Q1 3 1 2 NBJT
Q2 4 1 2 PBJT
RL1 2 0 2K
RID 1 7 100K
E1 5 0 1 7 5000
RO 5 6 100
Q3 3 6 7 NBJT
Q4 4 6 7 PBJT
RL2 7 0 2K
.MODEL NBJT NPN
.MODEL PBJT PNP
.OP
.DC VS -10 10 .01
```

18.4

$$A_V = \frac{A}{1 + A\beta} \quad \Big| \quad \text{From Chapter 12, } GE = \frac{1}{1 + A\beta} \approx \frac{1}{A\beta}$$

$$\frac{1}{\beta} = 200 \quad | \quad GE \approx \frac{200}{A} \leq 0.002 \rightarrow A \geq \frac{200}{0.002} = 10^5 \quad | \quad A \geq 100 \text{ dB}$$

18.5   (a) Series-series (b) Shunt-series (c) Shunt-shunt (d) Series-shunt

18.6   (a) Series-shunt (b) Shunt-series (c) Series-series (d) Shunt-shunt

18.7

$$A = 10^{\frac{86}{20}} = 20000$$

(a) $R_{IN} = R_{ID}(1 + A\beta) \quad | \quad$ For $\beta = 1$, $\ R_{IN} = 40k\Omega(1 + 20000) = 800 \text{ M}\Omega$

(b) $R_{IN} = \dfrac{R_{ID}}{(1 + A\beta)} \quad | \quad$ For $\beta = 1$, $\ R_{IN} = \dfrac{40k\Omega}{(1 + 20000)} = 2.00 \ \Omega$

(c) $R_{OUT} = R_O(1 + A\beta) \quad | \quad$ For $\beta = 1$, $\ R_{OUT} = 1k\Omega(1 + 20000) = 20 \text{ M}\Omega$

(d) $R_{OUT} = \dfrac{R_O}{(1 + A\beta)} \quad | \quad$ For $\beta = 1$, $\ R_{OUT} = \dfrac{1k\Omega}{(1 + 20000)} = 50.0 \text{ m}\Omega$

18.8

(a) $A_V = 10^{\frac{86}{20}} = 20000 \quad | \quad A_I = \dfrac{i_o}{i_s} \quad | \quad i_o = i_s(40k\Omega)\dfrac{20000}{1k\Omega} \rightarrow A_I = 8.00 \text{ x } 10^5$

With resistive feedback, the closed-loop gain cannot exceed the open-loop gain.
Therefore, $A_I \leq 8.00 \text{ x } 10^5$.

(b) $A_{TR} = \dfrac{i_o}{v_s} = \dfrac{i_o}{i_s(40k\Omega)} = \dfrac{A_I}{(40k\Omega)} \quad | \quad A_{TR} \leq \dfrac{8 \text{x} 10^5}{4 \text{x} 10^4 \Omega} = 20 \text{ S}$

18.9 (a)

$$h_{11}^A = \frac{v_1}{i_1}\bigg|_{v_2 = 0} = 15k\Omega \quad | \quad h_{11}^F = 4.3k\Omega \| 39k\Omega = 3.87k\Omega \quad | \quad h_{11}^T = 18.9k\Omega$$

$$h_{22}^A = \frac{i_2}{v_2}\bigg|_{i_1 = 0} = (1k\Omega)^{-1} = (1k\Omega)^{-1} \quad | \quad h_{22}^F = (39k\Omega + 4.3k\Omega)^{-1} = (43.3k\Omega)^{-1} \quad | \quad h_{22}^T = 1.02mS$$

$$h_{21}^A = \frac{i_2}{i_1}\bigg|_{v_2 = 0} = -\frac{15k\Omega(5000)}{1k\Omega} = -75,000 \quad | \quad h_{21}^F = \frac{i_2}{i_1}\bigg|_{v_2 = 0} = -\frac{4.3k\Omega}{39k\Omega + 4.3k\Omega} = -0.0993$$

$$h_{12}^A = \frac{v_1}{v_2}\bigg|_{i_1 = 0} = 0 \quad | \quad h_{12}^F = \frac{v_1}{v_2}\bigg|_{i_2 = 0} = \frac{4.3k\Omega}{39k\Omega + 4.3k\Omega} = 0.0993$$

(b) $A = \dfrac{-h_{21}^A}{\left(R_S + h_{11}^T\right)\left(h_{22}^T + G_L\right)} = \dfrac{-(-75000)}{(1k\Omega + 15k\Omega + 3.87k\Omega)\left(\dfrac{1}{5.6k\Omega} + \dfrac{1}{1k\Omega} + \dfrac{1}{43.3k\Omega}\right)} = 3140$

$\beta = 0.0993$

(c) $A_V = \dfrac{3140}{1 + 3140(0.0993)} = 10.0$ | $h_{21}^A \gg h_{21}^F$ | $h_{12}^F \gg h_{12}^A$ | $(R_{IN} = 6.22\ M\Omega, R_{OUT} = 2.66\ \Omega)$

18.10 The circuit topology is identical to Fig. 18.8.

$$h_{11}^F = 5k\Omega \| 45k\Omega = 4.50 k\Omega \quad | \quad h_{22}^F = (45k\Omega + 5k\Omega)^{-1} = (50.0 k\Omega)^{-1}$$

$$\beta = h_{12}^F = \left.\frac{v_1}{v_2}\right|_{i_2=0} = \frac{5k\Omega}{5k\Omega + 45k\Omega} = \frac{1}{10} \quad | \quad R_L \left\| \frac{1}{h_{22}^F} = 5k\Omega\|50k\Omega = 4.55k\Omega\right.$$

$$A = \frac{15k\Omega}{1k\Omega + 15k\Omega + 4.5k\Omega}(5000)\frac{4.55k\Omega}{1k\Omega + 4.55k\Omega} = 3000$$

$$A_V = \frac{A}{1 + A\beta} = \frac{3000}{1 + 3000\left(\dfrac{1}{10}\right)} = \frac{3000}{301} = 9.97$$

$$R_{IN} = R_{IN}^A(1 + A\beta) = (1k\Omega + 15k\Omega + 4.5k\Omega)(301) = 6.17\ M\Omega$$

$$R_{OUT} = \frac{R_{OUT}^A}{1 + A\beta} = \frac{5k\Omega\|50k\Omega\|1k\Omega}{301} = 2.72\ \Omega$$

18.11

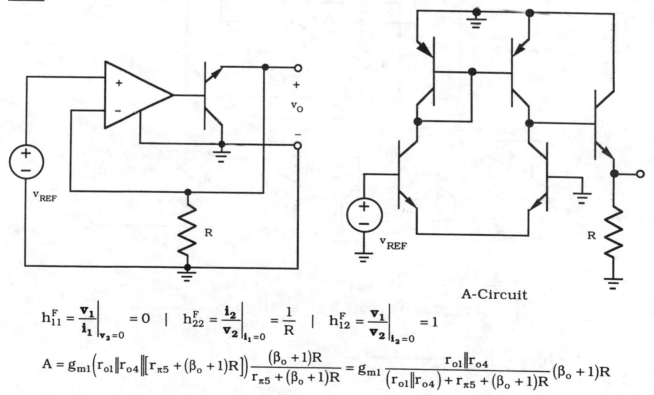

A-Circuit

$$h_{11}^F = \left.\frac{v_1}{i_1}\right|_{v_2=0} = 0 \quad | \quad h_{22}^F = \left.\frac{i_2}{v_2}\right|_{i_1=0} = \frac{1}{R} \quad | \quad h_{12}^F = \left.\frac{v_1}{v_2}\right|_{i_2=0} = 1$$

$$A = g_{m1}\left(r_{o1}\|r_{o4}\|\left[r_{\pi5} + (\beta_o + 1)R\right]\right)\frac{(\beta_o + 1)R}{r_{\pi5} + (\beta_o + 1)R} = g_{m1}\frac{r_{o1}\|r_{o4}}{(r_{o1}\|r_{o4}) + r_{\pi5} + (\beta_o + 1)R}(\beta_o + 1)R$$

$$r_{o1} = \frac{50 + 1.4}{10^{-4}} = 514k\Omega \quad | \quad r_{o4} = \frac{50 + 11.3}{10^{-4}} = 613k\Omega \quad | \quad r_{o1}\|r_{o4} = 280k\Omega$$

$$I_{C5} = \frac{12}{10^4} = 1.2mA \quad | \quad r_{\pi5} = \frac{100(.025)}{1.2mA} = 2.08k\Omega$$

$$A = 40(10^{-4})(280k\Omega)\frac{(101)10k\Omega}{280k\Omega + 2.08k\Omega + (101)10k\Omega} = 876$$

$$A_V = \frac{A}{1+T} = \frac{876}{1 + 876(1)} = \frac{109}{110} = 0.999$$

$$R_{IN} = R_{ID}(1+T) = 2r_{\pi1}(1+T) = 2\frac{100(0.025)}{10^{-4}}(877) = 43.9\ M\Omega$$

$$R_{OUT} = \frac{R\left\|\dfrac{r_{\pi5} + r_{o2}\|r_{o4}}{\beta_o + 1}\right.}{1+T} = \frac{10k\Omega\left\|\dfrac{2.08k\Omega + 280k\Omega}{101}\right.}{877} = 2.49\ \Omega$$

$$i_o = \alpha_o i_e = \alpha_o\frac{v_o}{R} \quad | \quad \frac{i_o}{v_{ref}} = \frac{\alpha_o}{R}\frac{v_o}{v_{ref}} = \frac{100}{101}\left(\frac{1}{10^4}\right)(0.999) = 98.9\ \mu S$$

18.12

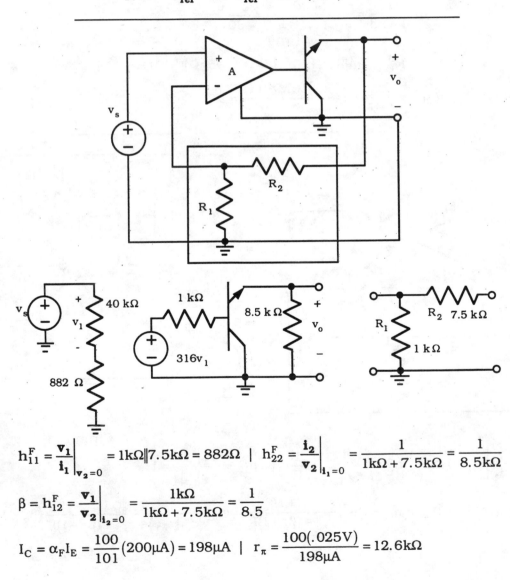

$$h_{11}^F = \left.\frac{v_1}{i_1}\right|_{v_2 = 0} = 1k\Omega\|7.5k\Omega = 882\Omega \quad | \quad h_{22}^F = \left.\frac{i_2}{v_2}\right|_{i_1 = 0} = \frac{1}{1k\Omega + 7.5k\Omega} = \frac{1}{8.5k\Omega}$$

$$\beta = h_{12}^F = \left.\frac{v_1}{v_2}\right|_{i_2 = 0} = \frac{1k\Omega}{1k\Omega + 7.5k\Omega} = \frac{1}{8.5}$$

$$I_C = \alpha_F I_E = \frac{100}{101}(200\mu A) = 198\mu A \quad | \quad r_\pi = \frac{100(.025V)}{198\mu A} = 12.6k\Omega$$

$$A = \frac{v_o}{v_s} = \frac{40k\Omega}{40k\Omega + 0.882k\Omega}(316)\frac{(\beta_o+1)8.5k\Omega}{R_O + r_\pi + (\beta_o+1)8.5k\Omega} = 309\frac{(101)8.5k\Omega}{1k\Omega + 12.6k\Omega + (101)8.5k\Omega} = 304$$

$$A_V = \frac{A}{1+T} = \frac{304}{1+304\left(\dfrac{1}{8.5}\right)} = \frac{304}{36.8} = 8.27$$

$$R_{IN} = R_{IN}^A(1+T) = 40.9k\Omega(36.8) = 1.51\ M\Omega$$

$$R_{OUT} = \frac{R_{OUT}^A}{1+T} = \frac{8.5k\Omega \left\| \dfrac{12.6k\Omega + 1k\Omega}{101}\right.}{36.8} = 3.60\ \Omega$$

18.13

$$S_A^{R_{IN}} = \frac{A}{R_{IN}}\frac{\partial R_{IN}}{\partial A} \quad | \quad R_{IN} = R_{IN}^A(1+A\beta) \quad | \quad S_A^{R_{IN}} = \frac{A}{R_{IN}^A(1+A\beta)}R_{IN}^A\beta = \frac{A\beta}{(1+A\beta)} \approx 1$$

$$\frac{\partial R_{IN}}{R_{IN}} = S_A^{R_{IN}}\frac{\partial A}{A} = \frac{10^5(0.01)}{1+10^5(0.01)}10\% = 9.99\%$$

18.14

$$S_A^{R_{OUT}} = \frac{A}{R_{OUT}}\frac{\partial R_{OUT}}{\partial A} \quad | \quad R_{OUT} = \frac{R_{OUT}^A}{(1+A\beta)} \quad | \quad \frac{\partial R_{OUT}}{\partial A} = -\frac{\beta R_{OUT}^A}{(1+A\beta)^2}$$

$$S_A^{R_{OUT}} = -\frac{A(1+A\beta)}{R_{OUT}^A}\frac{\beta R_{OUT}^A}{(1+A\beta)^2} = -\frac{A\beta}{(1+A\beta)} \approx -1 \quad | \quad \frac{\partial R_{IN}}{R_{IN}} = S_\Lambda^{R_{IN}}\frac{\partial A}{A} = -\frac{10^5(0.01)}{1+10^5(0.01)}10\% = -9.99\%$$

18.15

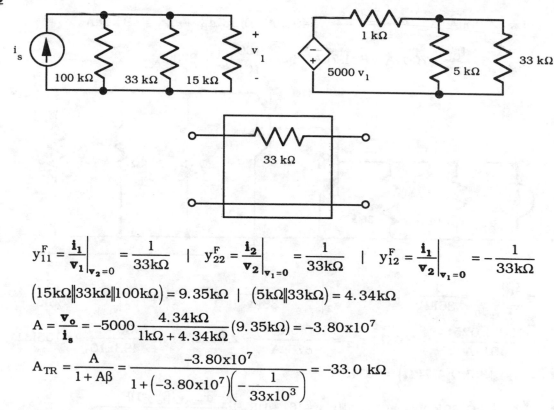

$$y_{11}^F = \frac{i_1}{v_1}\bigg|_{v_2=0} = \frac{1}{33k\Omega} \quad | \quad y_{22}^F = \frac{i_2}{v_2}\bigg|_{v_1=0} = \frac{1}{33k\Omega} \quad | \quad y_{12}^F = \frac{i_1}{v_2}\bigg|_{v_1=0} = -\frac{1}{33k\Omega}$$

$$(15k\Omega\|33k\Omega\|100k\Omega) = 9.35k\Omega \quad | \quad (5k\Omega\|33k\Omega) = 4.34k\Omega$$

$$A = \frac{v_o}{i_s} = -5000\frac{4.34k\Omega}{1k\Omega + 4.34k\Omega}(9.35k\Omega) = -3.80\text{x}10^7$$

$$A_{TR} = \frac{A}{1+A\beta} = \frac{-3.80\text{x}10^7}{1+\left(-3.80\text{x}10^7\right)\left(-\dfrac{1}{33\text{x}10^3}\right)} = -33.0\ k\Omega$$

$$R_{IN} = \frac{(15k\Omega\|33k\Omega\|100k\Omega)}{1+(-3.80 \times 10^7)\left(-\dfrac{1}{33 \times 10^3}\right)} = 8.11\ \Omega \quad | \quad R_{OUT} = \frac{(33k\Omega\|5k\Omega\|1k\Omega)}{1+(-3.80 \times 10^7)\left(-\dfrac{1}{33 \times 10^3}\right)} = 0.705\ \Omega$$

18.16

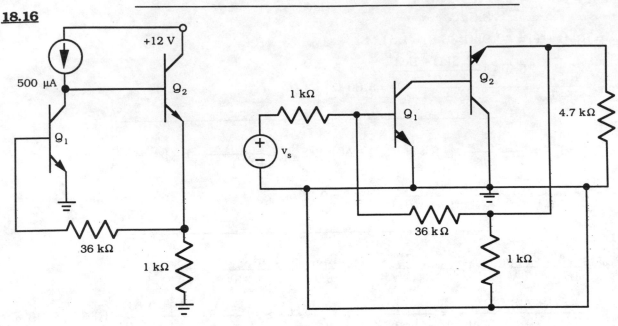

$$I_{C1} = 500\mu A - I_{B2} \quad I_{E2} = I_{B1} + \frac{36000 I_{B1} + 0.7}{1000} = 37 I_{B1} + 700\mu A \quad I_{B2} = \frac{I_{E2}}{101}$$

$$I_{C1} = 500\mu A - \frac{37 I_{B1} + 700\mu A}{101} = 493\mu A - 0.366 I_{B1} \rightarrow I_{C1} = 491.2\mu A$$

$$I_{E2} = 37\frac{I_{C1}}{100} + 700\mu A = 881.7\mu A \quad I_{C2} = \frac{100}{101} I_{E2} = 873\mu A$$

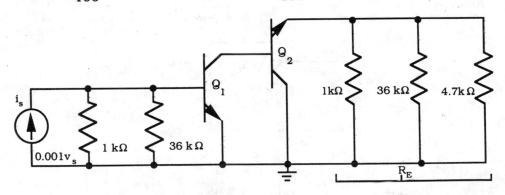

$$y_{11}^F = \left.\frac{i_1}{v_1}\right|_{v_2=0} = \frac{1}{36k\Omega} \quad | \quad y_{22}^F = \left.\frac{i_2}{v_2}\right|_{v_1=0} = \frac{1}{36k\Omega\|1k\Omega} \quad | \quad y_{12}^F = \left.\frac{i_1}{v_2}\right|_{v_1=0} = -\frac{1}{36k\Omega}$$

$$r_{\pi 1} = \frac{100(0.025)}{491\mu A} = 5.09k\Omega \mid r_{\pi 2} = \frac{100(0.025)}{873\mu A} = 2.86k\Omega \mid r_{o1} = \frac{50+1.6}{493 \times 10^{-6}} = 105k\Omega$$

$$R_E = (1k\Omega\|36k\Omega\|4.7k\Omega) = 807\Omega$$

$$A = \frac{v_o}{i_s} = (1k\Omega\|36k\Omega\|r_{\pi 1})g_{m1}\left[r_{o1}\|(r_{\pi 2}+(\beta_o+1)R_E)\right]\frac{r_{\pi 2}+(\beta_o+1)R_E}{r_{o1}+r_{\pi 2}+(\beta_o+1)R_E}$$

$$A = \frac{v_o}{i_s} = -\left(1k\Omega\|36k\Omega\|5.09k\Omega\right)g_{m1}\left[r_{o1}\|\left(r_{\pi2} + (\beta_o + 1)R_E\right)\right]\frac{r_{\pi2} + (\beta_o + 1)R_E}{r_{o1} + r_{\pi2} + (\beta_o + 1)R_E}$$

$$\left(1k\Omega\|36k\Omega\|r_{\pi1}\right) = \left(1k\Omega\|36k\Omega\|5.09k\Omega\right) = 817\Omega \quad | \quad g_m = 40(491\mu A) = 19.6mS$$

$$\left[r_{o1}\|\left(r_{\pi2} + (\beta_o + 1)R_E\right)\right] = \left[105k\Omega\|(2.86k\Omega + (101)806\Omega)\right] = 46.8k\Omega$$

$$\frac{r_{\pi2} + (\beta_o + 1)R_E}{r_{o1} + r_{\pi2} + (\beta_o + 1)R_E} = \frac{2.86k\Omega + (101)806\Omega}{105k\Omega + 2.86k\Omega + (101)806\Omega} = 0.430$$

$$A = -(817\Omega)(19.6mS)(46.8k\Omega)(0.430) = -322\ k\Omega$$

$$A_{TR} = \frac{A}{1 + A\beta} = \frac{-322k\Omega}{1 + (-322k\Omega)\left(-\frac{1}{36k\Omega}\right)} = -\frac{322k\Omega}{9.94} = -32.4\ k\Omega$$

$$R_{IN} = \frac{\left(1k\Omega\|36k\Omega\|5.09k\Omega\right)}{1 + A\beta} = \frac{817\Omega}{9.94} = 82.2\ \Omega$$

$$R_{OUT} = \frac{\left(1k\Omega\|36k\Omega\|4.7k\Omega\left\|\frac{r_{\pi2} + r_{o1}}{101}\right.\right)}{1 + A\beta} = \frac{\left(806\Omega\left\|\frac{2.86k\Omega + 105k\Omega}{101}\right.\right)}{9.94} = 46.2\ \Omega$$

$$i_s = 10^{-3}v_s \rightarrow A_V = \frac{v_o}{v_s} = \frac{v_o}{1000i_s} = -32.4$$

Note that this amplifier can be analyzed as a shunt-shunt feedback amplifier. This is good for student practice - See Problem 18.25.

18.17

```
*Problem 18.17
VCC 5 0 DC 12
IDC 5 4 DC 500UA
IS 0 2 AC 1
*IX 0 7 AC 1
RS 2 0 1K
C1 2 3 82UF
Q1 4 3 0 NBJT
Q2 5 4 6 NBJT
RF 3 6 36K
RE 6 0 1K
C2 6 7 47UF
RL 7 0 4.7K
.MODEL NBJT NPN BF=100 VA=50 IS=1E-15
.OP
.AC DEC 100 1E2 1E7
.PRINT AC VM(7) VP(7) VM(2) VP(2)
.END
```

Results: $A_{TR} = $ -34.4 kΩ, $R_{IN} = $ 36.8 Ω, $R_{OUT} = $ 18.6 Ω -- Note that these values are highly sensitive to the precise value of $r_{\pi1}$.

18.18

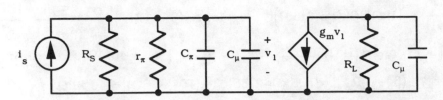

$$y_{12}^F = -sC_\mu \quad | \quad A = \frac{v_o}{i_s} = -\frac{r_{\pi o}}{s(C_\pi + C_\mu)r_{\pi o} + 1}(g_m)\frac{R_L}{sC_\mu R_L + 1} = -\frac{g_m r_{\pi o} R_L}{\left[s(C_\pi + C_\mu)r_{\pi o} + 1\right]\left[sC_\mu R_L + 1\right]}$$

$$Z_{IN}^A = \frac{r_{\pi o}}{s(C_\pi + C_\mu)r_{\pi o} + 1} \quad | \quad Z_{IN} = \frac{Z_{IN}^A}{1 + A\beta} = \frac{\dfrac{r_{\pi o}}{s(C_\pi + C_\mu)r_{\pi o} + 1}}{1 - \dfrac{g_m r_{\pi o} R_L}{\left[s(C_\pi + C_\mu)r_{\pi o} + 1\right]\left[sC_\mu R_L + 1\right]}(-sC_\mu)} \quad \text{(More)}$$

$$Z_{IN} = \frac{r_{\pi o}(sC_\mu R_L + 1)}{\left[s(C_\pi + C_\mu)r_{\pi o} + 1\right]\left[sC_\mu R_L + 1\right] + sC_\mu g_m r_{\pi o} R_L}$$

$$Z_{IN} = \frac{r_{\pi o}(sC_\mu R_L + 1)}{s^2(C_\pi + C_\mu)C_\mu r_{\pi o} R_L + sr_{\pi o}\left[C_\pi + C_\mu(1 + g_m R_L) + \dfrac{R_L}{r_{\pi o}}\right] + 1} = \frac{r_{\pi o}(sC_\mu R_L + 1)}{s^2(C_\pi + C_\mu)C_\mu r_{\pi o} R_L + sr_{\pi o}C_T + 1}$$

$$Z_{IN} \cong \frac{r_{\pi o}(sC_\mu R_L + 1)}{sr_{\pi o}\left[C_\pi + C_\mu(1 + g_m R_L) + \dfrac{R_L}{r_{\pi o}}\right] + 1} = \frac{r_{\pi o}(sC_\mu R_L + 1)}{sr_{\pi o}C_T + 1} \quad \text{for} \quad \omega \ll \omega_T$$

18.19

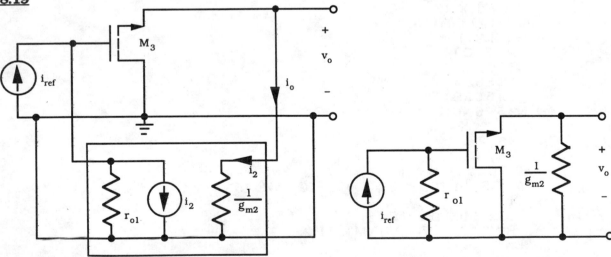

$$y_{11}^F = \frac{i_1}{v_1}\bigg|_{v_2=0} = g_{o1} \quad | \quad y_{22}^F = \frac{i_2}{v_2}\bigg|_{v_1=0} = g_{m2} \quad | \quad y_{12}^F = \frac{i_1}{v_2}\bigg|_{v_1=0} = g_{m2}$$

$$A = \frac{v_o}{i_{ref}} = r_{o1}\frac{g_{m3}\dfrac{1}{g_{m2}}}{1 + g_{m3}\dfrac{1}{g_{m2}}} = \frac{r_{o1}}{2} \quad | \quad A_{TR} = \frac{A}{1 + A\beta} = \frac{\dfrac{r_{o1}}{2}}{1 + \dfrac{r_{o1}}{2}(g_{m2})} = \frac{r_{o1}}{2 + \mu_{f1}}$$

$$R_{IN} = \frac{r_{o1}}{1 + A\beta} = \frac{r_{o1}}{1 + \dfrac{\mu_{f2}}{2}} = \frac{36k\Omega}{1 + \dfrac{72}{2}} = 973\Omega \quad | \quad \text{Note:} \quad R_{IN} \cong \frac{2}{g_m}$$

$$i_o = i_2 = g_{m2}v_o = g_{m2}\frac{r_{o1}}{\mu_{f1} + 2}i_{ref} \quad | \quad \frac{i_o}{i_{ref}} = \frac{\mu_{f1}}{\mu_{f1} + 2} = 0.973$$

18.20

$$y_{11}^F = \frac{i_1}{v_1}\bigg|_{v_2=0} = g_{o1} \quad | \quad y_{22}^F = \frac{i_2}{v_2}\bigg|_{v_1=0} = g_{m2} \quad | \quad y_{12}^F = \frac{i_1}{v_2}\bigg|_{v_1=0} = \frac{\beta}{\beta+2}g_{m2} \cong g_{m2}$$

$$i_o = \alpha_o i_2 = \alpha_o g_{m2}v_o \quad | \quad A = \frac{v_o}{i_{ref}} = r_{o1}\frac{(\beta_o + 1)\dfrac{1}{g_{m2}}}{r_{o1} + r_{\pi3} + (\beta_o + 1)\dfrac{1}{g_{m2}}} \cong r_{o1}\frac{(\beta_o + 1)}{\mu_f + 2\beta_o + 1} \cong \frac{\beta_o}{\mu_f}r_{o1} = r_{\pi1}$$

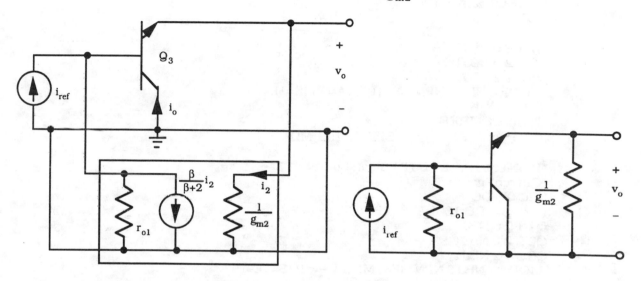

$$A_{TR} = \frac{A}{1 + A\beta} = \frac{r_{o1}\dfrac{(\beta_o + 1)}{\mu_f + 2\beta_o + 1}}{1 + r_{o1}\dfrac{(\beta_o + 1)}{\mu_f + 2\beta_o + 1}(g_{m2})} \cong r_{o1}\frac{\beta_o + 1}{\mu_f\beta_o + 2\mu_f + 2\beta_o + 2} \cong \frac{r_{o1}}{\mu_f} = \frac{1}{g_{m1}}$$

$$A_{TR} = \frac{1}{50mS} = 20.0\ \Omega \quad | \quad A_I = \frac{i_o}{i_{ref}} = \alpha_o g_{m2}\frac{v_o}{i_{ref}} = \alpha_o\frac{g_{m2}}{g_{m1}} \cong 1$$

$$R_{IN}^A = r_{o1}\left\|\left[r_{\pi3} + (\beta_o + 1)\frac{1}{g_{m2}}\right]\right. \cong r_{o1}\|2r_{\pi3} \cong 2r_{\pi3}$$

$$R_{IN} = \frac{R_{IN}^A}{1 + A\beta} = \frac{r_{o1}\|2r_{\pi3}}{1 + r_{o1}\dfrac{(\beta_o + 1)}{\mu_f + 2\beta_o + 1}(g_{m2})} \cong \frac{r_{o1}\|2r_{\pi3}}{1 + \dfrac{\mu_f(\beta_o + 1)}{\mu_f + 2\beta_o + 1}} \cong \frac{r_{o1}\|2r_{\pi3}}{\beta_o + 1} \cong \frac{2r_{\pi3}}{\beta_o + 1} \cong \frac{2}{g_{m3}}$$

$$R_{IN} = \frac{r_{o1}\|2r_{\pi3}}{\beta_o + 1} = \frac{40k\Omega\|4k\Omega}{101} = 36.0\ \Omega$$

```
*Problem 18.21 - BJT Wilson Source
*Current gain = 100
VCC 0 3 DC -6
IREF 0 1 DC 100UA
Q1 1 2 0 NBJT
Q2 2 2 0 NBJT
Q3 3 1 2 NBJT
.MODEL NBJT NPN BF=100 VA=50 IS=1E-15
.OP
.TF I(VCC) IREF
.END
```

$$\frac{\beta r_{o3}}{2} = \frac{100(55.3V)}{2(100\mu A)} = 27.7 \text{ M}\Omega \quad | \quad \text{SPICE: } 29.9 \text{ M}\Omega$$

```
*Problem 18.21 - BJT Wilson Source
*Current gain = 10K
VCC 0 3 DC -6
IREF 0 1 DC 100UA
Q1 1 2 0 NBJT
Q2 2 2 0 NBJT
Q3 3 1 2 NBJT
.MODEL NBJT NPN BF=10K VA=50 IS=1E-15
.OP
.TF I(VCC) IREF
.END                    SPICE:  799 MΩ
```

```
*Problem 18.21 - BJT Wilson Source
*Current gain = 1MEG
VCC 0 3 DC -6
IREF 0 1 DC 100UA
Q1 1 2 0 NBJT
Q2 2 2 0 NBJT
Q3 3 1 2 NBJT
.MODEL NBJT NPN BF=1MEG VA=50 IS=1E-15
.OP
.TF I(VCC) IREF
.END
```

$$\mu_{f1} r_{o3} = 40(51.4)\frac{55.3V}{100\mu A} = 1.14 \text{ G}\Omega \quad | \quad \text{SPICE: } 1.08 \text{ G}\Omega$$

18.22

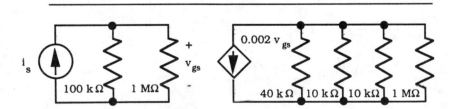

$$y_{11}^F = \frac{i_1}{v_1}\bigg|_{v_2=0} = 10^{-6}\text{S} \quad | \quad y_{22}^F = \frac{i_2}{v_2}\bigg|_{v_1=0} = 10^{-6}\text{S} \quad | \quad y_{12}^F = \frac{i_1}{v_2}\bigg|_{v_1=0} = -10^{-6}\text{S}$$

$$v_{gs} = i_s(100k\Omega\|1M\Omega) = (90.9k\Omega)i_s \quad | \quad v_o = -(2\times10^{-3})v_{gs}(40k\Omega\|10k\Omega\|10k\Omega\|1M\Omega)$$

$$A = \frac{v_o}{i_s} = -(2mS)(4.44k\Omega)(90.9k\Omega) = -8.08\times10^5$$

$$A_{TR} = \frac{A}{1+A\beta} = \frac{-8.08 \times 10^5}{1 + (-8.08 \times 10^5)(-10^{-6})} = \frac{-8.08 \times 10^5}{1.81} = -446 \text{ k}\Omega$$

$$R_{IN} = \frac{(100\text{k}\Omega \| 1\text{M}\Omega)}{(1+A\beta)} = \frac{90.9\text{k}\Omega}{1.81} = 50.2 \text{ k}\Omega$$

$$R_{OUT} = \frac{(40\text{k}\Omega \| 10\text{k}\Omega \| 10\text{k}\Omega \| 1\text{M}\Omega)}{(1+A\beta)} = \frac{4.44\text{k}\Omega}{1.81} = 2.45\text{k}\Omega$$

18.23

$$g_{11}^F = \left.\frac{i_1}{v_1}\right|_{i_2=0} = \frac{1}{11\text{k}\Omega} \quad | \quad g_{22}^F = \left.\frac{v_2}{i_2}\right|_{v_1=0} = 1\text{k}\Omega \| 10\text{k}\Omega = 909\Omega \quad | \quad g_{12}^F = \left.\frac{i_1}{i_2}\right|_{v_1=0} = -\frac{1\text{k}\Omega}{10\text{k}\Omega + 1\text{k}\Omega} = -\frac{1}{11}$$

$$A = \frac{i_2}{i_s} = -(100\text{k}\Omega \| 11\text{k}\Omega \| 15\text{k}\Omega)\frac{5\text{k}\Omega}{(5+1+0.909)\text{k}\Omega} = -4.32 \times 10^3$$

$$A_I = \frac{A}{1+A\beta} = \frac{-4.32 \times 10^3}{1 + (-4.32 \times 10^3)\left(-\frac{1}{11}\right)} = -11.0$$

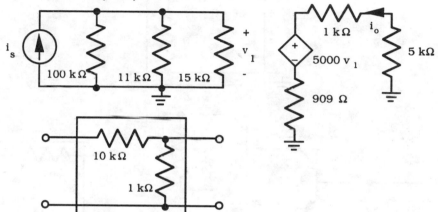

$$R_{IN} = \frac{(100\text{k}\Omega \| 11\text{k}\Omega \| 15\text{k}\Omega)}{(1+A\beta)} = \frac{5.97\text{k}\Omega}{394} = 15.2 \ \Omega$$

$$R_{OUT} = (5\text{k}\Omega + 1\text{k}\Omega + 0.909\text{k}\Omega)(1+A\beta) = (6.91\text{k}\Omega)(394) = 2.72\text{M}\Omega$$

18.24 See Problem 18.16 for the Q-point calculation.

$$g_{11}^F = \left.\frac{i_1}{v_1}\right|_{i_2=0} = \frac{1}{37 \text{ k}\Omega} \quad | \quad g_{22}^F = \left.\frac{v_2}{i_2}\right|_{v_1=0} = 36\text{k}\Omega \| 1\text{k}\Omega = 973 \ \Omega \quad | \quad g_{12}^F = \left.\frac{i_1}{i_2}\right|_{v_1=0} = -\frac{1\text{k}\Omega}{1\text{k}\Omega + 36\text{k}\Omega} = -\frac{1}{37}$$

$$1\text{k}\Omega \| 37\text{k}\Omega = 974 \ \Omega \quad | \quad r_{\pi 1} = \frac{100(0.025)}{491\mu\text{A}} = 5.09 \text{ k}\Omega \quad | \quad r_{\pi 2} = \frac{100(0.025)}{873\mu\text{A}} = 2.86 \text{ k}\Omega$$

$$A = \frac{i_o}{i_s} = -\frac{974\Omega}{974\Omega + 5090\Omega}(-100)(101)\left(\frac{4700\Omega}{973\Omega + 4700\Omega}\right) = -1340$$

$$A_I = \frac{A}{1+A\beta} = \frac{-1340}{1 + (-1340)\left(-\frac{1}{37}\right)} = \frac{-1340}{37.2} = -36.0 \quad | \quad 1+A\beta = 37.2$$

$$A_V = \frac{\mathbf{v_o}}{\mathbf{v_s}} = \frac{973 i_o}{1000 i_s} = 0.973 \frac{i_o}{i_s} = -35.0$$

$$R_{IN} = \frac{\left(1k\Omega \| 37k\Omega \| r_{\pi 1}\right)}{1 + A\beta} = \frac{\left(1k\Omega \| 37k\Omega \| 5.09k\Omega\right)}{37.2} = 22.0 \ \Omega \ \bigg| \ r_{ol} = \frac{50 + 1.6}{493 \times 10^{-6}} = 105k\Omega$$

$$R_{OUT} = \frac{\left(1k\Omega \| 36k\Omega \| 4.7k\Omega \left\| \dfrac{r_{\pi 2} + r_{ol}}{101} \right. \right)}{1 + A\beta} = \frac{\left(1k\Omega \| 36k\Omega \| 4.7k\Omega \left\| \dfrac{5.09k\Omega + 105k\Omega}{101} \right. \right)}{37.2} = 12.5 \ \Omega$$

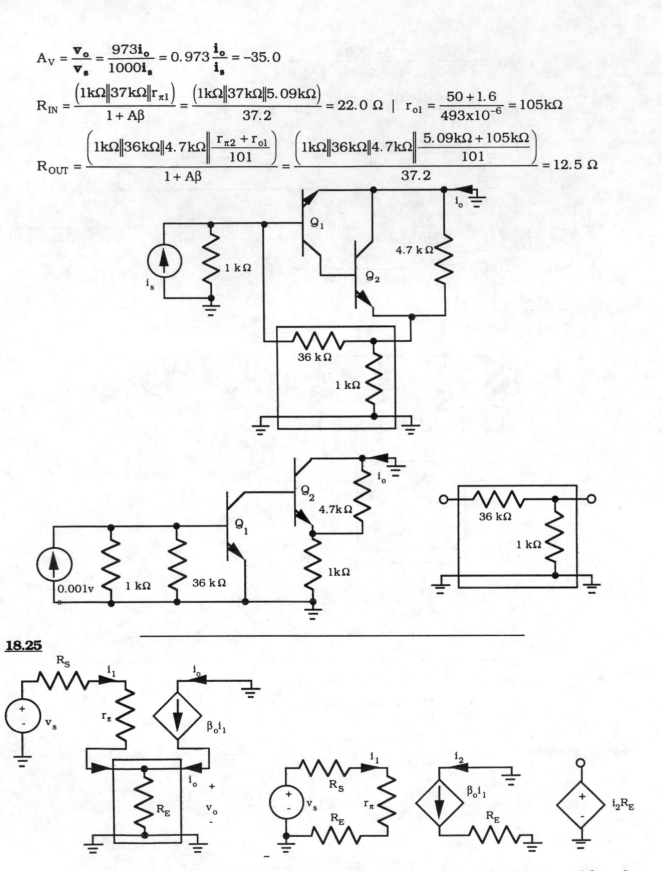

By carefully drawing the circuit, it can be represented as a series-series feedback amplifier. In particular, r_π and the current generator are connected within the feedback network.

$$A = \frac{i_2}{v_s} = \frac{\beta_o}{R_S + r_\pi + R_E} \quad | \quad \beta = z_{12}^F = R_E$$

$$A_{TC} = \frac{i_o}{v_s} = \frac{A}{1 + A\beta} = \frac{\dfrac{\beta_o}{R_S + r_\pi + R_E}}{1 + \dfrac{\beta_o}{R_S + r_\pi + R_E}R_E} = \frac{\beta_o}{R_S + r_\pi + (\beta_o + 1)R_E}$$

$$A_V = \frac{v_o}{v_s} = \frac{i_o}{v_s}\frac{R_E}{\alpha_o} = \frac{\beta_o}{R_S + r_\pi + (\beta_o + 1)R_E}\frac{(\beta_o + 1)R_E}{\beta_o} = \frac{(\beta_o + 1)R_E}{R_S + r_\pi + (\beta_o + 1)R_E}$$

$$R_{IN} = R_{IN}^A(1 + A\beta) = (R_S + r_\pi + R_E)\left(1 + \frac{\beta_o}{R_S + r_\pi + R_E}R_E\right) = R_S + r_\pi + (\beta_o + 1)R_E$$

Both answers agree with our previous direct derivations.

18.26

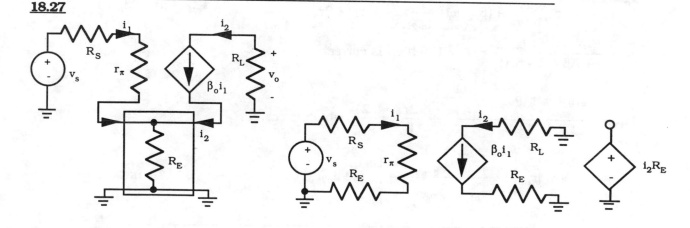

$$z_{11}^F = \frac{v_1}{i_1}\bigg|_{i_2=0} = 5\ k\Omega \quad | \quad z_{22}^F = \frac{v_2}{i_2}\bigg|_{i_1=0} = 5\ k\Omega \quad | \quad \beta = z_{12}^F = \frac{v_1}{i_2}\bigg|_{i_1=0} = 5\ k\Omega$$

$$A = \frac{i_o}{v_s} = \frac{15k\Omega}{2k\Omega + 15k\Omega + 5k\Omega}\left(\frac{5000}{5k\Omega + 1k\Omega + 5k\Omega}\right) = 0.310$$

$$A_{TR} = \frac{i_o}{v_s} = \frac{A}{1 + A\beta} = \frac{0.310}{1 + 0.310(5000)} = 0.200\ mS \quad | \quad \frac{v_o}{v_s} = 5000\frac{i_o}{v_s} = 1.00 \quad | \quad 1 + A\beta = 1550$$

$$R_{IN} = (2k\Omega + 15k\Omega + 5k\Omega)(1 + A\beta) = (22k\Omega)(1550) = 34.1\ M\Omega$$

$$R_{OUT} = (5k\Omega + 1k\Omega + 5k\Omega)(1 + A\beta) = (11k\Omega)(1550) = 17.1\ M\Omega$$

18.27

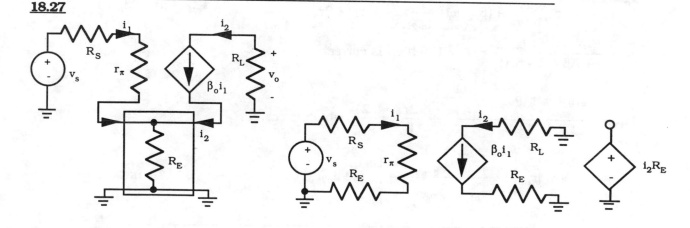

By carefully drawing the circuit, it can be represented as a series-series feedback amplifier. In particular, r_π and the current generator are connected within the feedback network.

$$A = \frac{i_2}{v_s} = \frac{\beta_o}{R_S + r_\pi + R_E} \quad | \quad \beta = z_{12}^F = R_E$$

$$A_{TC} = \frac{i_o}{v_s} = \frac{A}{1 + A\beta} = \frac{\dfrac{\beta_o}{R_S + r_\pi + R_E}}{1 + \dfrac{\beta_o}{R_S + r_\pi + R_E}R_E} = \frac{\beta_o}{R_S + r_\pi + (\beta_o + 1)R_E}$$

$$A_V = \frac{v_o}{v_s} = -\frac{i_o}{v_s}R_L = -\frac{\beta_o R_L}{R_S + r_\pi + (\beta_o + 1)R_E}$$

$$R_{IN} = R_{IN}^A(1 + A\beta) = (R_S + r_\pi + R_E)\left(1 + \frac{\beta_o}{R_S + r_\pi + R_E}R_E\right) = R_S + r_\pi + (\beta_o + 1)R_E$$

Both answers agree with our previous direct derivations.

18.28

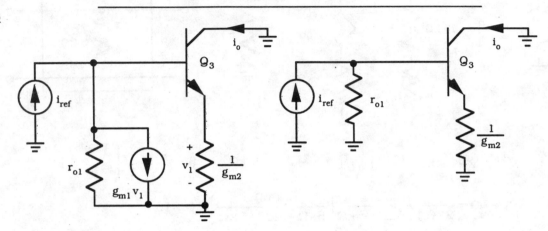

$$g_{11}^F = \left.\frac{i_1}{v_1}\right|_{i_2=0} = \frac{1}{r_{o1}} \quad | \quad g_{22}^F = \left.\frac{v_2}{i_2}\right|_{v_1=0} = \frac{1}{g_{m2}} \quad | \quad g_{12}^F = \left.\frac{i_1}{i_2}\right|_{v_1=0} = \frac{g_{m1}}{g_{m2}} \cong 1$$

$$i_o = i_{ref}r_{o1}\frac{\beta_o}{r_{o1} + r_{\pi3} + (\beta_{o3} + 1)\dfrac{1}{g_{m2}}} \approx i_{ref}\frac{\beta_o r_{o1}}{r_{o1} + 2r_{\pi3} + \dfrac{1}{g_{m2}}} \quad | \quad A = \frac{i_o}{i_{ref}} = \frac{\beta_o \mu_f}{\mu_f + 2\beta_o + 1} \approx \beta_o$$

$$A_I = \frac{A}{1 + A\beta} = \frac{\beta_o}{1 + \beta_o(1)} = \alpha_o \approx 1 \quad \text{which is correct.}$$

$$R_{IN} = \frac{r_{o1} \left\| \left(r_{\pi3} + (\beta_{o3} + 1)\dfrac{1}{g_{m2}}\right)\right.}{1 + \beta_o} \approx \frac{2r_\pi}{\beta_o} = \frac{2}{g_m} \quad \text{which is correct.}$$

$$R_{OUT} = (1 + \beta_o)r_{o3}\left(1 + \frac{\beta_{o3}\dfrac{1}{g_{m2}}}{r_{o1} + r_{\pi3} + \dfrac{1}{g_{m2}}}\right) = (1 + \beta_o)r_o\left(1 + \frac{\beta_o}{\mu_f + \beta_o + 1}\right) \approx \beta_o r_o \quad - \text{ not correct!}$$

18.29

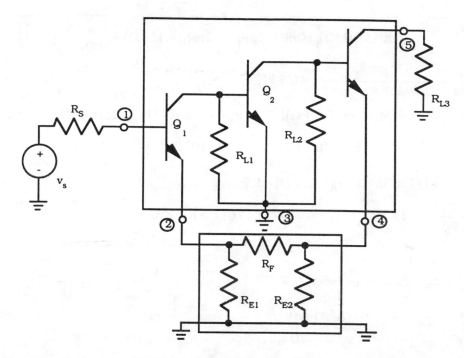

The amplifier is not a two-port. It has five separate terminals. It can be analyzed correctly as a series-shunt configuration with the output defined at terminal 4. In the series-shunt configuration, R_L is absorbed into the amplifier thereby making it a two-port.

18.30

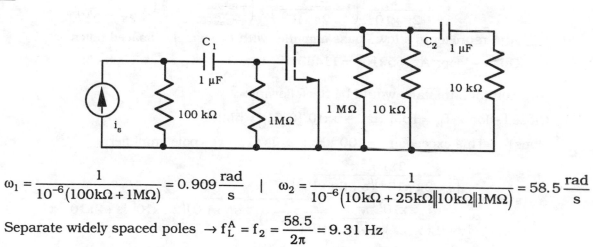

$$\omega_1 = \frac{1}{10^{-6}(100k\Omega + 1M\Omega)} = 0.909 \frac{rad}{s} \quad | \quad \omega_2 = \frac{1}{10^{-6}(10k\Omega + 25k\Omega\|10k\Omega\|1M\Omega)} = 58.5 \frac{rad}{s}$$

Separate widely spaced poles $\rightarrow f_L^A = f_2 = \frac{58.5}{2\pi} = 9.31$ Hz

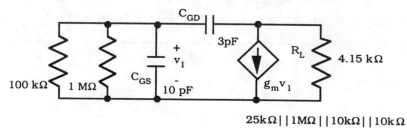

$25k\Omega\,||\,1M\Omega\,||\,10k\Omega\,||\,10k\Omega$

$$\omega_H^A = \frac{1}{r_{\pi o}C_T} = \frac{1}{(100k\Omega\|1M\Omega)\left[10pF + 3pF\left(1 + 2mS(4.15k\Omega) + \frac{4.15k\Omega}{100k\Omega\|1M\Omega}\right)\right]}$$

$$f_H^A = \frac{1}{2\pi}\frac{1}{(90.9k\Omega)(38.0pF)} = 46.1 \text{ kHz}$$

$$\mathbf{v_{gs}} = \mathbf{i_s}(100k\Omega\|1M\Omega) = (90.9k\Omega)\mathbf{i_s} \quad | \quad \mathbf{v_o} = -(2\times10^{-3})\mathbf{v_{gs}}(25k\Omega\|10k\Omega\|10k\Omega\|1M\Omega)$$

$$A = \frac{\mathbf{v_o}}{\mathbf{i_s}} = -(2mS)(4.15k\Omega)(90.9k\Omega) = -7.55\times10^5\Omega \quad | \quad y_{12}^F = -10^{-5}S$$

$$1 + A\beta = 1 + (-7.55\times10^5\Omega)(-10^{-6}S) = 1.76$$

$$f_L = \frac{9.31}{1.76} = 5.29 \text{ Hz} \qquad f_H = 46.1kHz(1.76) = 81.0 \text{ kHz}$$

18.31

$$S_{A_o}^{\omega_H^F} = \frac{A_o}{\omega_H^F}\frac{\partial\omega_H^F}{\partial A_o} \quad | \quad \omega_H^F = \omega_H^A(1 + A\beta) \quad | \quad S_{A_o}^{\omega_H^F} = \frac{A_o}{\omega_H^A(1 + A_o\beta)}\omega_H^A\beta = \frac{A_o\beta}{(1 + A_o\beta)} \cong +1$$

$$\frac{\partial\omega_H^F}{\omega_H^F} = S_{A_o}^{\omega_H^F}\frac{\partial A_o}{A_o} = \frac{10^5(0.01)}{1 + 10^5(0.01)}10\% = 9.99\%$$

18.32

(a) $\quad A(s) = \dfrac{\dfrac{2\times10^{14}\pi^2}{(2\pi\times10^3)(2\pi\times10^5)}}{\left(1 + \dfrac{s}{2\pi\times10^3}\right)\left(1 + \dfrac{s}{2\pi\times10^5}\right)} = \dfrac{5\times10^5}{\left(1 + \dfrac{s}{2\pi\times10^3}\right)\left(1 + \dfrac{s}{2\pi\times10^5}\right)}$

A(s) represents a low - pass amplifier with two widely - spaced poles

Open – loop: $A_o = 5\times10^5 = 114dB \quad | \quad f_L = 0 \quad | \quad f_H \approx f_1 = 1000 \text{ Hz}$

(b)A common mistake would be the following:

Closed – loop: $f_H = 1000Hz[1 + 5\times10^5(0.01)] = 5MHz$

Oops! - This exceeds $f_2 = 100$ kHz! This is a two - pole amplifier.

$$A_V(s) = \frac{\dfrac{2\times10^{14}\pi^2}{(s + 2\pi\times10^3)(s + 2\pi\times10^5)}}{1 + \dfrac{2\times10^{14}\pi^2}{(s + 2\pi\times10^3)(s + 2\pi\times10^5)}(0.01)} = \frac{2\times10^{14}\pi^2}{s^2 + 1.01(2\pi\times10^5)s + 2\times10^{12}\pi^2}$$

Using dominant - root factorization: $f_1 = 101$ kHz, $f_2 = 4.95$ MHz

So the closed - loop values are $f_H = 101$ kHz and $f_L = 0$.

18.33

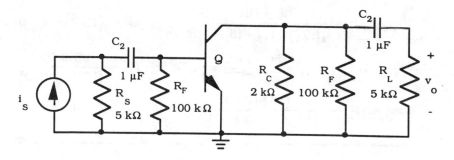

From the Exercise: $g_m = 40.3$ mS | $r_\pi = 3.72$ kΩ | $r_o = 50.8$ kΩ | $1 + A\beta = 2.19$

$$r_{o2} = \frac{50 + 1.4}{10^{-4}} = 514k\Omega \quad | \quad r_{o4} = \frac{50 + 11.3}{10^{-4}} = 613k\Omega \quad | \quad r_{\pi5} = \frac{100(0.025)}{0.0012} = 2.08k\Omega$$

$$C_{\pi1} = \frac{40.3mS}{2\pi(500MHz)} - 0.75pF = 12.1pF$$

Using the open-circuit time constant approach with $C_1 = C_2 = 1$ μF:

$R_{1O} = 5k\Omega + 100k\Omega\|r_\pi 5k\Omega + 100k\Omega\|3.72k\Omega = 8.59k\Omega$

$R_{2O} = 5k\Omega + 50.8k\Omega\|2k\Omega\|100k\Omega = 6,89k\Omega$

$$f_L = \frac{1}{2\pi}\left[\frac{1}{1\mu F(8.59k\Omega)} + \frac{1}{1\mu F(6.89k\Omega)}\right] = 41.6 \text{ Hz} \quad | \quad f_L^F = \frac{f_L}{1 + A\beta} = 19.0 \text{ Hz}$$

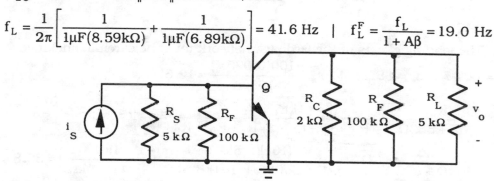

$$r_{\pi o} = 3.72k\Omega\|100k\Omega\|5k\Omega = 2.09k\Omega \quad | \quad R_L = 50.8k\Omega\|2k\Omega\|100k\Omega\|5k\Omega = 1.37k\Omega$$

$$C_T = 12.1pF + 0.75pf\left[1 + 40.3mS(1.37k\Omega) + \frac{1.37k\Omega}{2.09k\Omega}\right] = 54.8pF$$

$$f_H = \frac{1}{2\pi r_{\pi o}C_T} = \frac{1}{2\pi(1.37k\Omega)(54.8pF)} = 1.39 \text{ MHz} \quad | \quad f_H^F = f_H(1 + A\beta) = 3.04 \text{ MHz}$$

18.34

$$A(s) = \frac{2\pi \times 10^7}{s + 2000\pi} \quad | \quad A = \frac{25k\Omega}{1k\Omega + 25k\Omega + 9.01k\Omega}\left(\frac{2\pi \times 10^7}{s + 2000\pi}\right)\frac{1.96k\Omega}{1.96k\Omega + 1k\Omega} = \frac{2.97 \times 10^7}{s + 2000\pi}$$

$$A_V(s) = \frac{\dfrac{2.97 \times 10^7}{s + 2000\pi}}{1 + \dfrac{2.97 \times 10^7}{s + 2000\pi}(0.0990)} = \frac{2.97 \times 10^7}{s + 2.95 \times 10^6} = \frac{10.1}{1 + \dfrac{s}{2.95 \times 10^6}} \quad | \quad f_H = \frac{2.95 \times 10^6}{2\pi} = 470 \text{ kHz}$$

511

18.35

$$T = \frac{\mathbf{v_o}}{\mathbf{v_x}} = g_{m2}\left(r_{o2}\|r_{o4}\right)\frac{(\beta_o+1)R}{(r_{o2}\|r_{o4})+r_{\pi3}+(\beta_o+1)R} \quad | \quad g_{m1} = 40\left(10^{-4}\right) = 4.00\text{mS}$$

$$r_{o2} = \frac{50+1.4}{10^{-4}} = 514\text{k}\Omega \quad | \quad r_{o4} = \frac{50+11.3}{10^{-4}} = 613\text{k}\Omega \quad | \quad r_{\pi3} = \frac{100(0.025)}{(12V/10\text{k}\Omega)} = 2.08\text{k}\Omega$$

$$T = \left(4\text{x}10^{-3}\right)(280\text{k}\Omega)\frac{(101)10\text{k}\Omega}{280\text{k}\Omega+2.08\text{k}\Omega+101(10\text{k}\Omega)} = 876 \quad (58.9 \text{ dB})$$

18.36

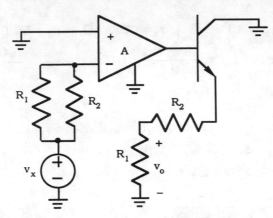

Note: The loading effects of the feedback network must be carefully included.

$$R_1\|R_2 = 1\text{k}\Omega\|7.5\text{k}\Omega = 882\Omega \quad | \quad r_\pi = \frac{100(0.025V)}{198\mu A} = 12.6\text{k}\Omega$$

$$T = \frac{\mathbf{v_o}}{\mathbf{v_x}} = \frac{R_{ID}}{R_{ID}+882\Omega}(A)\frac{(\beta_o+1)(R_1+R_2)}{R_O+r_\pi+(\beta_o+1)(R_1+R_2)}\left(\frac{R_1}{R_1+R_2}\right)$$

$$T = \frac{\mathbf{v_o}}{\mathbf{v_x}} = \frac{40\text{k}\Omega}{40\text{k}\Omega+882\Omega}(316)\frac{(101)(8.5\text{k}\Omega)}{1\text{k}\Omega+12.6\text{k}\Omega+(101)(8.5\text{k}\Omega)}\left(\frac{1\text{k}\Omega}{1\text{k}\Omega+7.5\text{k}\Omega}\right) = 35.8$$

which agrees with the result in Prob. 18.12.

18.37

$$y_{11}^F = \frac{\mathbf{i_1}}{\mathbf{v_1}}\bigg|_{\mathbf{v_2}=0} = \frac{1}{36\text{k}\Omega} \quad | \quad y_{22}^F = \frac{\mathbf{i_2}}{\mathbf{v_2}}\bigg|_{\mathbf{v_1}=0} = \frac{1}{36\text{k}\Omega\|1\text{k}\Omega} \quad | \quad y_{12}^F = \frac{\mathbf{i_1}}{\mathbf{v_2}}\bigg|_{\mathbf{v_1}=0} = -\frac{1}{36\text{k}\Omega}$$

$$r_{\pi1} = \frac{100(0.025)}{491\mu A} = 5.09\text{k}\Omega \quad | \quad r_{\pi2} = \frac{100(0.025)}{873\mu A} = 2.86\text{k}\Omega \quad | \quad r_{o1} = \frac{50+1.6}{493\text{x}10^{-6}} = 105\text{k}\Omega$$

$$T = \frac{\mathbf{v_o}}{\mathbf{v_s}} = \frac{1}{36\text{k}\Omega}\left(1\text{k}\Omega\|36\text{k}\Omega\|r_{\pi1}\right)g_{m1}\left[r_{o1}\|\left(r_{\pi2}+(\beta_o+1)R_E\right)\right]\frac{r_{\pi2}+(\beta_o+1)R_E}{r_{o1}+r_{\pi2}+(\beta_o+1)R_E}$$

$$\frac{\left(1k\Omega\|36k\Omega\|r_{\pi1}\right)}{36k\Omega} = \frac{\left(1k\Omega\|36k\Omega\|5.09k\Omega\right)}{36k\Omega} = 0.0227 \quad | \quad g_m = 40(491\mu A) = 19.6mS$$

$$\left[r_{o1}\|\left(r_{\pi2} + (\beta_o + 1)R_E\right)\right] = \left[105k\Omega\|\left(2.86k\Omega + (101)806\Omega\right)\right] = 46.8k\Omega$$

$$\frac{r_{\pi2} + (\beta_o + 1)R_E}{r_{o1} + r_{\pi2} + (\beta_o + 1)R_E} = \frac{2.86k\Omega + (101)806\Omega}{105k\Omega + 2.86k\Omega + (101)806\Omega} = 0.430$$

$$T = (0.0227)(19.6mS)(46.8k\Omega)(0.430) = 8.95$$

These results agree with those of Prob. 18.16

18.38

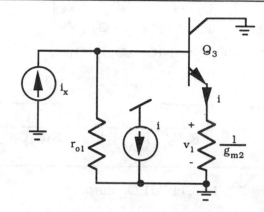

$$T = \frac{i_o}{i_x} = (\beta_o + 1)\frac{r_o}{r_o + r_\pi + (\beta_o + 1)\dfrac{1}{g_m}} = \frac{(\beta_o + 1)\mu_f}{\mu_f + 2\beta_o + 1} = \frac{(101)(2000)}{2000 + 200 + 1} = 91.8$$

These results agree with those of Prob. 18.20

18.39

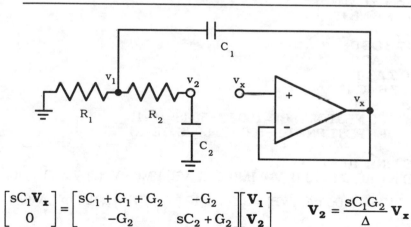

$$\begin{bmatrix} sC_1 \mathbf{V_x} \\ 0 \end{bmatrix} = \begin{bmatrix} sC_1 + G_1 + G_2 & -G_2 \\ -G_2 & sC_2 + G_2 \end{bmatrix} \begin{bmatrix} \mathbf{V_1} \\ \mathbf{V_2} \end{bmatrix} \qquad \mathbf{V_2} = \frac{sC_1 G_2}{\Delta}\mathbf{V_x}$$

$$\Delta = s^2 C_1 C_2 + s\left[C_1 G_2 + C_2(G_1 + G_2)\right] + G_1 G_2$$

$$T = \frac{\mathbf{V_2}}{\mathbf{V_x}} = \frac{\dfrac{s}{R_2 C_2}}{s^2 + s\left[\dfrac{1}{R_2 C_2} + \dfrac{1}{(R_1\|R_2)C_1}\right] + \dfrac{1}{R_1 R_2 C_1 C_2}}$$

18.40

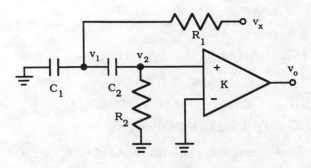

$$\begin{bmatrix} G_1\mathbf{V_x} \\ 0 \end{bmatrix} = \begin{bmatrix} s(C_1+C_2)+G_1 & -sC_2 \\ -sC_2 & sC_2+G_2 \end{bmatrix}\begin{bmatrix} \mathbf{V_1} \\ \mathbf{V_2} \end{bmatrix} \qquad \mathbf{V_o} = K\mathbf{V_2}$$

$$\Delta = s^2C_1C_2 + s\left[C_1G_2 + C_2(G_1+G_2)\right] + G_1G_2$$

$$T = \frac{\mathbf{V_o}}{\mathbf{V_x}} = K\frac{s\dfrac{1}{R_1C_1}}{s^2 + s\left[\dfrac{1}{R_2C_2} + \dfrac{1}{(R_1\|R_2)C_1}\right] + \dfrac{1}{R_1R_2C_1C_2}}$$

18.41

```
*Problem 18.41 - Fig. P18.11 BJT Op-amp
VCC 8 0 DC 12
VEE 9 0 DC -12
IS 2 9 DC 200U
VS 1 0 DC 0
Q1 4 1 2 NBJT
Q2 5 3 2 NBJT
Q3 4 4 8 PBJT
Q4 5 4 8 PBJT
Q5 8 5 6 NBJT
R 6 9 10K
VB 7 3 DC 0
VX 7 6 AC 0
IX 0 7 AC 1
*VX 7 6 AC 1
*IX 0 7 AC 0
.MODEL NBJT NPN BF=100 VA=50 IS=1E-15
.MODEL PBJT PNP BF=100 VA=50 IS=1E-15
.OP
.AC LIN 1 10 10
.PRINT AC IM(VX) IP(VX) IM(VB) IP(VB) VM(7) VP(7) VM(6) VP(6)
```

Results: I(VX) = 1.000 A, I(VB) = 3.703 x 10⁻⁵ A, V(7) = 1.188 mV, V(6) = -1.000 V

$$T_V = -\frac{-.9988V}{1.188mV} = 841 \quad | \quad T_I = \frac{1.000A}{37.03\mu A} = 2.70\times10^4$$

$$T = \frac{T_VT_I - 1}{2 + T_V + T_I} = \frac{841(2.70\times10^4)-1}{2+841+2.70\times10^4} = 816 \quad | \quad \frac{R_2}{R_1} = \frac{1+T_V}{1+T_I} = \frac{1+841}{2.70\times10^4} = 0.0312$$

18.42

```
*Problem 18.42 - Fig. P18.12
VCC 4 0 DC 10
```

514

```
    IS 5 0 DC 200U
    VS 1 0 DC 0
    Q1 4 3 5 NBJT
    RID 1 8 40K
    RO 2 3 1K
    E1 2 0 1 8 316.2
    R2 6 5 7.5K
    R1 8 0 1K
    VB 7 8 DC 0
    VX 7 6 AC 0
    IX 0 7 AC 1
    *VX 7 6 AC 1
    *IX 0 7 AC 0
    .MODEL NBJT NPN BF=100 VA=50 IS=1E-15
    .OP
    .AC LIN 1 10 10
    .PRINT AC IM(VX) IP(VX) IM(VB) IP(VB) VM(7) VP(7) VM(6) VP(6)
    .END
```

Results: I(VX) = 0.9759 A, I(VB) = 0.0241 A, V(7) = 3.078 mV, V(6) = -0.9969 V

$$T_V = -\frac{-.9969V}{3.078mV} = 324 \quad | \quad T_I = \frac{0.9759A}{0.0241A} = 40.5 \times 10^4$$

$$T = \frac{T_V T_I - 1}{2 + T_V + T_I} = \frac{324(40.5) - 1}{2 + 324 + 40.5} = 35.8 \quad | \quad \frac{R_2}{R_1} = \frac{1 + T_V}{1 + T_I} = \frac{1 + 324}{1 + 40.5} = 7.83$$

18.43 The circuit description is the same as Problem 18.42 except for the change in the values of R_1 and R_2.

```
    R2 6 5 300K
    R1 8 0 40K
```

Results: I(VX) = 0.9548 A, I(VB) = 45.19 mA, V(7) = 3.011 mV, V(6) = -0.9970 V

$$T_V = -\frac{-.9970V}{3.011mV} = 331 \quad | \quad T_I = \frac{0.9548A}{45.19mA} = 21.1$$

$$T = \frac{T_V T_I - 1}{2 + T_V + T_I} = \frac{331(21.1) - 1}{2 + 331 + 21.1} = 19.7 \quad | \quad \frac{R_2}{R_1} = \frac{1 + T_V}{1 + T_I} = \frac{1 + 331}{1 + 21.1} = 15.0$$

18.44

```
    *Problem 18.44 - Fig. P18.6(b)
    IS 0 1 DC 0
    RS 1 0 1K
    RID 1 0 15K
    RO 2 3 1K
    E1 3 4 1 0 5000
    RL 2 0 4.7K
    R2 4 0 1K
    R1 4 6 36K
    VB 7 1 DC 0
    VX 7 6 AC 0
    IX 0 7 AC 1
    *VX 7 6 AC 1
    *IX 0 7 AC 0
    .OP
    .AC LIN 1 10 10
    .PRINT AC IM(VX) IP(VX) IM(VB) IP(VB) VM(7) VP(7) VM(6) VP(6)
```

.END

Results: $I(VX) = 0.9500$ A, $I(VB) = 49.97$ mA, $V(7) = 1.271$ mV, $V(6) = -0.9987$ V

$$T_V = -\frac{-.9987V}{1.271mV} = 786 \quad | \quad T_I = \frac{0.9500A}{49.97mA} = 19.0$$

$$T = \frac{T_V T_I - 1}{2 + T_V + T_I} = \frac{786(19.0) - 1}{2 + 786 + 19.0} = 18.5 \quad | \quad \frac{R_2}{R_1} = \frac{1 + T_V}{1 + T_I} = \frac{1 + 786}{1 + 19.0} = 39.4$$

18.45

```
*Problem 18.45
VCC 5 0 DC 6
IREF 0 1 DC 100UA
Q1 1 4 0 NBJT
Q2 4 4 0 NBJT
Q3 5 3 4 NBJT
IX 0 2 DC 0
VX1 2 1 DC 0
VX2 2 3 DC 0
.MODEL NBJT NPN BF=100 VA=50 IS=1E-15
.OP
.TF I(VX1) IX                          --->  0.9910
*.TF I(VX2) IX                         --->  9.043 x 10⁻³
.END
*Problem 18.45
VCC 5 0 DC 6
IREF 0 1 DC 100UA
Q1 1 4 0 NBJT
Q2 4 4 0 NBJT
Q3 5 3 4 NBJT
IX 0 2 DC 0
VX1 2 1 DC 0
VX2 2 3 DC 0
.MODEL NBJT NPN BF=100 VA=50 IS=1E-15
.OP
.TF V(1) VX1                           --->  -0.9990
*.TF V(2) VX1                          --->  1.012 x 10⁻³
.END
```

$$T_V = -\frac{-0.9990}{1.012 \times 10^{-3}} = 987 \quad | \quad T_I = \frac{0.9910}{9.043 \times 10^{-3}} = 110$$

$$T = \frac{987(110) - 1}{2 + 987 + 110} = 98.8 \quad | \quad \frac{R_2}{R_1} = \frac{1 + 987}{1 + 110} = 8.90$$

18.46 Since the output resistance of the amplifier is zero ($R_2 = 0$), the simplified method can be used: $T = T_V$.

```
*Problem 18.46
VS 1 0 DC 0
C1 1 2 0.005UF
C2 2 3 0.005UF
R1 2 7 2K
R2 3 0 2K
E1 4 0 3 0 1
R 4 5 31.83
C 5 0 1NF
E2 6 0 5 0 2
VX 7 6 AC 1
```

```
.OP
.AC DEC 100 1 1E6
.PROBE V(6) V(7)
.END
```

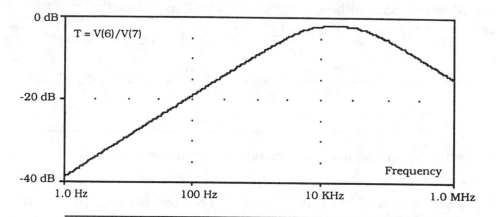

18.47

(a) $T(s) = \dfrac{4 \times 10^{19}\pi^3}{\left(s + 2\pi \times 10^4\right)\left(s + 2\pi \times 10^5\right)^2}\beta \quad | \quad \angle T(j\omega) = -\tan^{-1}\dfrac{f}{10^4} - 2\tan^{-1}\dfrac{f}{10^5} = -180°$

For $f \gg 10^4$, $-2\tan^{-1}\dfrac{f}{10^5} = -90° \rightarrow f = 10^5\,\text{Hz}$. Using this as a starting point

for iteration, we find $f = 110\,\text{kHz}$ or $\omega = 2.2 \times 10^5\pi$

(b) $\left|A\left(j2.2\times10^5\pi\right)\right| = \dfrac{4 \times 10^{19}\pi^3}{\sqrt{\left(2.2\times10^5\pi\right)^2 + \left(2\pi \times 10^4\right)^2}\left[\left(2.2\times10^5\pi\right)^2 + \left(2\pi \times 10^5\right)^2\right]} = 2048$

The amplifier will oscillate for closed-loop gains ≤ 2048 (66.2 dB).

18.48

$T(s) = A\beta = \left(\dfrac{10^7}{s+50}\right)\dfrac{\dfrac{1}{sC_L}}{R_O + \dfrac{1}{sC_L}} = \left(\dfrac{10^7}{s+50}\right)\dfrac{1}{sC_LR_O + 1} = \left(\dfrac{10^7}{s+50}\right)\dfrac{1}{500sC_L + 1}$

Assume that the unity-gain occurs at $\omega_1 \gg 50$: $\angle T(j\omega_1) = \angle A + \angle\beta = -90° - \tan^{-1}(500\omega_1C_L)$

$-90° - \tan^{-1}(500\omega_1C_L) = -180° + 60° \quad | \quad \tan^{-1}(500\omega_1C_L) = 30° \quad | \quad 500\omega_1C_L = 0.5774$

$\left|T(j\omega_1)\right| = 1 \quad | \quad \dfrac{10^7}{\omega_1\sqrt{1 + (500\omega_1C_L)^2}} = \dfrac{10^7}{\omega_1\sqrt{1 + \left[\tan(30°)\right]^2}} = 1 \rightarrow \omega_1 = 8.66 \times 10^6$

$C_L = \dfrac{\tan(30°)}{500\left(8.66\times10^6\right)} = 133\,\text{pF}$

18.49

(a) $T = A\beta = \dfrac{2x10^{14}\pi^2}{\left(s + 2x10^3\pi\right)\left(s + 2x10^5\pi\right)}\left(\dfrac{1}{5}\right)$ | Yes, it is a second-order system and will

have some phase margin, although Φ_M may be vanishingly small.

(b) For $\omega \gg 2\pi \text{ x } 10^5$, $\ |T(j\omega)| \approx \dfrac{4x10^{13}\pi^2}{\omega^2}$ and $|T(j\omega)| = 1$ for $\omega = 1.987x10^7\,\dfrac{\text{rad}}{\text{s}}$

$\angle T\left(j1.987x10^7\right) = -\tan^{-1}\dfrac{1.987x10^7}{2000\pi} - \tan^{-1}\dfrac{1.987x10^7}{2x10^5\pi} = 178.2° \rightarrow \Phi_M = 1.83°$ | A very

small phase margin.

18.50 (a)

The following command line will generate the complete bode plot:

w=logspace(3,8,400); bode((2e14*pi^2/5),conv([1 2000*pi],[1 2e5*pi]),w)

The following command line will generate the bode plot between 10^7 and 10^8rad/s:

w=logspace(7,8,100); bode((2e14*pi^2/5),conv([1 2000*pi],[1 2e5*pi]),w)

The second plot agrees with the results calculated in the previous problem.

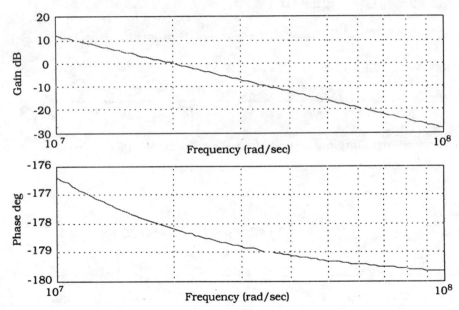

(b) w=logspace(7,8,100); bode((2e14*pi^2),conv([1 2000*pi],[1 2e5*pi]),w)

yields a phase margin of only 0.75 degrees

18.51

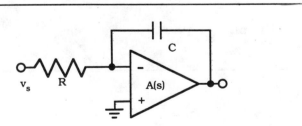

$$\beta = \frac{R}{R + \frac{1}{sC}} = \frac{sRC}{sRC + 1} \quad \Big| \quad T = \frac{2\pi \times 10^6}{s + 20\pi} \frac{sRC}{(sRC + 1)} \quad \Big| \quad \text{For } \omega RC \gg 1, \quad T \approx \frac{2\pi \times 10^6}{s + 20\pi}$$

and $|T| = 1$ for $\omega = 2\pi \times 10^6$. Given $RC = 10^{-8}(10^5) = 10^{-3}$, $\beta = \dfrac{s}{s + 1000}$

$$\angle T = 90° - \tan^{-1} \frac{2\pi \times 10^6}{20\pi} - \tan^{-1} \frac{2\pi \times 10^6}{1000} = -90.0° \quad \Big| \quad \Phi_M = 90.0°$$

18.52

$$\beta = \frac{R}{R + \frac{1}{sC}} = \frac{sRC}{sRC + 1} = \frac{s10^5(10^{-8})}{s10^5(10^{-8}) + 1} = \frac{s}{s + 1000}$$

$$A(s) = \frac{10^5}{\left(1 + \frac{s}{2000\pi}\right)\left(1 + \frac{s}{200000\pi}\right)} = \frac{4\pi^2 \times 10^{13}}{(s + 2000\pi)(s + 200000\pi)}$$

$$T = \frac{4\pi^2 \times 10^{13}}{(s + 2000\pi)(s + 200000\pi)} \frac{s}{(s + 1000)} \quad \Big| \quad \text{At high frequencies, } T \approx \frac{4\pi^2 \times 10^{13}}{s^2}$$

and the integrator will have a positive phase margin, although Φ_M may be very small.

For $\omega \gg 2\pi \times 10^5$, $\quad |T(j\omega_1)| \approx \dfrac{4\pi^2 \times 10^{13}}{\omega_1^2} = 1 \Rightarrow \omega = 1.987 \times 10^7 \dfrac{\text{rad}}{\text{s}} \gg 2\pi \times 10^5$

$$\angle T = 90° - \tan^{-1} \frac{1.987 \times 10^7}{2000\pi} - \tan^{-1} \frac{1.987 \times 10^7}{200000\pi} - \tan^{-1} \frac{1.987 \times 10^7}{1000} \quad \Big| \quad \Phi_M = 1.83°$$

18.53

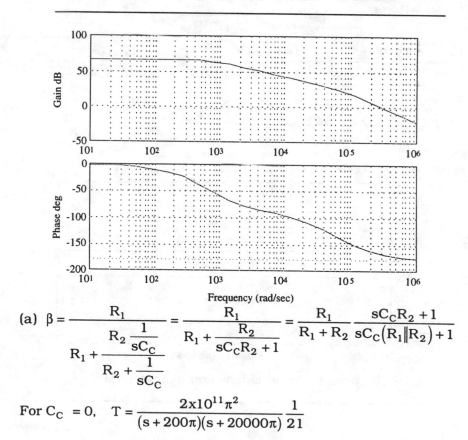

(a) $\beta = \dfrac{R_1}{R_1 + \dfrac{R_2 \frac{1}{sC_C}}{R_2 + \frac{1}{sC_C}}} = \dfrac{R_1}{R_1 + \dfrac{R_2}{sC_C R_2 + 1}} = \dfrac{R_1}{R_1 + R_2} \dfrac{sC_C R_2 + 1}{sC_C(R_1 \| R_2) + 1}$

For $C_C = 0$, $\quad T = \dfrac{2 \times 10^{11} \pi^2}{(s + 200\pi)(s + 20000\pi)} \dfrac{1}{21}$

The graphs above were generated using

$$\text{bode(2e11*pi\textasciicircum2/21,[1 2.02e4*pi 4e6*pi\textasciicircum2])}$$

Blowing up the last decade:

$$\text{w=linspace(1e5,1e6);} \quad \text{bode(2e11*pi\textasciicircum2/21,[1 2.02e4*pi 4e6*pi\textasciicircum2],w)}$$

and the phase margin is approximately 12°

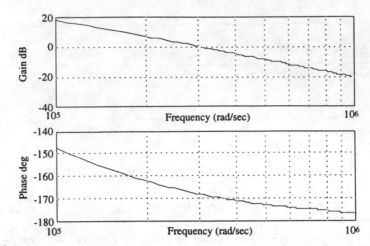

Setting the zero to cancel the second pole,

$$\beta(s) = \frac{R_1}{R_1 + R_2} \frac{sC_C R_2 + 1}{sC_C(R_1 \| R_2) + 1} = \frac{s + \dfrac{1}{C_C R_2}}{s + \dfrac{1}{C_C(R_1 \| R_2)}}$$

$$T = \frac{2 \times 10^{11} \pi^2}{(s + 200\pi)(s + 20000\pi)} \frac{(s + 20000\pi)}{s + 1.319 \times 10^6} = \frac{2 \times 10^{11} \pi^2}{s^2 + 1.320 \times 10^6 s + 8.288 \times 10^6}$$

Using MATLAB:

$$\text{bode(2e11*pi\textasciicircum2,[1 1.320e6 8.288e8])}$$

and then

$$\text{w=linspace(1e6,1e7);} \quad \text{bode(2e11*pi\textasciicircum2,[1 1.320e6 8.288e8],w)}$$

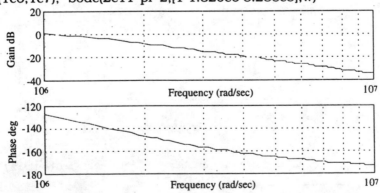

The phase margin is now approximately 50°

18.54

```
num=4e19*pi^3;
p=conv([1 2e5*pi],[1 2e5*pi]);
den=conv([1 2e4*pi],p);
bode(num,den)
```

Results: Frequency $= 6.9 \times 10^5$ rad/s and approximately 66 dB

which agree with the hand calculations in Problem 18.47.

18.55

```
num=2e11*pi^2
den=conv([1 200*pi],[1 20000*pi]);
bode(num/100,den)
```

```
w=logspace(5,6,100);  bode(num/100,den,w)
```

Results: Yes, the amplifier is stable with a phase margin of approximately $26°$.

18.56

$$A_V(s) = \frac{\dfrac{A_o\omega_o}{s+\omega_o}}{1+\dfrac{A_o\omega_o}{s+\omega_o}} = \frac{\omega_T}{s+(1+A_o)\omega_o} \approx \frac{\omega_T}{s+\omega_T} = \frac{2\pi \times 10^6}{s+2\pi \times 10^6}$$

From problem 18.39: $\beta(s) = \dfrac{5 \times 10^4 s}{s^2 + 7 \times 10^4 s + 5 \times 10^8}$

$$T(s) = A_V(s)\beta(s) = \frac{10^{11}\pi s}{\left(s+2\pi \times 10^6\right)\left(s^2 + 7 \times 10^4 s + 5 \times 10^8\right)}$$

Using MATLAB:

```
num=[pi*1e11 0]
den=conv([1 3e5 1e10],[1 5e6])
bode(num,den)
```

It is also instructive to use: nyquist(num,den)

One finds that $|T(j\omega)| < 1$ for all ω, so the phase margin is undefined. The filter is stable. Note that this is a positive feedback system so the point of interest is +1.   The gain of the filter is approximately -3 dB. So the filter has a gain margin of 3 dB.

18.57

$$T(s) = K(s)\beta(s) = \left(\frac{10^7}{s+5 \times 10^6}\right)\left(\frac{10^5 s}{s^2 + 3 \times 10^5 s + 10^{10}}\right) = \frac{10^{12} s}{\left(s+5 \times 10^6\right)\left(s^2 + 3 \times 10^5 s + 10^{10}\right)}$$

Using MATLAB:

```
num=[1e12 0]
den=conv([1 3e5 1e10],[1 5e6])
bode(num,den)
```

It is also instructive to use: nyquist(num,den)

One finds that $|T(j\omega)| < 1$ for all ω, so the phase margin is undefined. The filter is stable. Note that this is a positive feedback system so the point of interest is +1.   The gain of the filter is approximately -3 dB. So the filter has a gain margin of 3 dB.

18.58

$$\beta = \frac{sRC}{sRC+1} = \frac{s}{s+1000} \quad | \quad T = \frac{2\pi \times 10^6 s}{(s+20\pi)(s+1000)}$$

Using MATLAB:

```
num=[2e6*pi 0]; den=conv([1 20*pi],[1 1000]);
w=logspace(0,8,400);
bode(num,den,w)
```

The phase margin is 90° which agrees with Problem 18.51.

18.59

$$\beta = \frac{sRC}{sRC+1} = \frac{s}{s+1000} \quad | \quad A(s) = \frac{10^5}{\left(1+\dfrac{s}{2000\pi}\right)\left(1+\dfrac{s}{200000\pi}\right)} = \frac{4\pi^2 \times 10^{13}}{(s+2000\pi)(s+200000\pi)}$$

$$T = \frac{4\pi^2 \times 10^{13} s}{(s+2000\pi)(s+200000\pi)(s+1000)}$$

Using MATLAB:

```
num=[4e13*pi^2 0];   den=conv([1 1000],conv([1 2000*pi],[1 200000*pi]));
w=logspace(7,8,100);   bode(num,den,w)
```

The phase margin is 1.8° which agrees with Problem 18.52.

18.60

$$\beta(s) = \frac{\dfrac{R_1}{sC_sR_1+1}}{\dfrac{R_1}{sC_sR_1+1}+R_2} = \frac{R_1}{R_1+R_2}\frac{1}{sC_s\left(R_1\|R_2\right)+1} = \frac{1}{9.30\left(1.89\times10^{-6}s+1\right)}$$

$$\beta(s) = \frac{5.69\times10^4}{s+5.29\times10^5} \qquad A_V(s) = \frac{10^7}{s+50} \qquad T(s) = A_V(s)\beta(s)$$

For $\omega \gg 50$, $|T(j\omega)| \approx \dfrac{5.69\times10^{11}}{\omega\sqrt{\omega^2+\left(5.29\times10^5\right)^2}} \rightarrow |T(j\omega)| = 1$ for $\omega = 6.68\times10^5$

$$\Phi_M = 180 - \tan^{-1}\frac{6.68\times10^5}{50} - \tan^{-1}\frac{6.68\times10^5}{5.29\times10^5} = 38.4°$$

18.61

$$A_{V1} = \frac{\mathbf{V_{o1}}}{\mathbf{V_{o2}}} = -\frac{1}{sRC} \qquad \mathbf{V_{o2}} = \left(1+\frac{2R}{2R}\right)\mathbf{V_+} = 2\mathbf{V_+}$$

$$(\mathbf{V_+} - \mathbf{V_{o1}})\frac{G}{2} + sC\mathbf{V_+} + (\mathbf{V_+} - \mathbf{V_{o2}})G_F = 0 \quad \text{Combining these yields}$$

$$A_{V2} = \frac{\mathbf{V_{o2}}}{\mathbf{V_{o1}}} = \frac{G}{sC+\left(\dfrac{G}{2}-G_F\right)} \quad \text{and} \quad T(s) = A_{V1}A_{V2} = \frac{1}{sRC\left(sRC+\dfrac{1}{2}-\dfrac{R}{R_F}\right)}$$

$$\angle T(j\omega_o) = 0 \rightarrow R_F = 2R \text{ and } |T(j\omega_o)| = 1 \rightarrow \omega_o = \frac{1}{RC}$$

18.62

$$\mathbf{V_1} = -\mathbf{V_2}\frac{Z_2}{Z_1} = -\mathbf{V_2}\frac{R}{R+\dfrac{1}{sC}} = -\mathbf{V_2}\frac{sCR}{SCR+1} \quad \bigg| \quad \mathbf{V_2} = \mathbf{V_1}\left(\frac{R}{R+\dfrac{1}{sC}}\right)\left(1+\frac{R_2}{R_1}\right)\left(\frac{R}{R+\dfrac{1}{sC}}\right)\left(1+\frac{R_2}{R_1}\right)$$

$$\mathbf{V_2}\left[1+\left(\frac{sCR}{SCR+1}\right)^3\left(1+\frac{R_2}{R_1}\right)^2\right]=0 \quad \bigg| \quad \left(\frac{j\omega CR}{j\omega CR+1}\right)^3\left(1+\frac{R_2}{R_1}\right)^2=-1$$

$$3\left[90° - \tan^{-1}(\omega CR)\right] = 180° \quad \bigg| \quad \tan^{-1}(\omega CR) = 30° \quad \bigg| \quad \omega CR = \tan(30°) = 0.5774$$

$$\left(1+\frac{R_2}{R_1}\right)^2\left(\frac{\omega CR}{\sqrt{1+(\omega CR)^2}}\right)^3 = \left(1+\frac{R_2}{R_1}\right)^2\left[\frac{\tan(30°)}{\sqrt{1+\tan^2(30°)}}\right]^3 = 1 \rightarrow \frac{R_2}{R_1} = \sqrt{8}-1 = 1.83$$

18.63

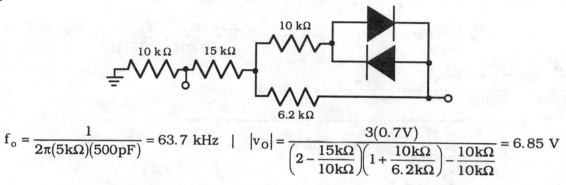

$$f_o = \frac{1}{2\pi(5k\Omega)(500pF)} = 63.7 \text{ kHz} \quad \bigg| \quad |v_O| = \frac{3(0.7V)}{\left(2-\dfrac{15k\Omega}{10k\Omega}\right)\left(1+\dfrac{10k\Omega}{6.2k\Omega}\right)-\dfrac{10k\Omega}{10k\Omega}} = 6.85 \text{ V}$$

18.64

```
*Problem 18.64 - Wien-Bridge Oscillator
C1 1 0 500PF IC=1
RA 1 0 5K
C2 1 2 500PF
RB 2 3 5K
E1 3 0 1 6 1E6
R1 6 0 10K
R2 5 6 15K
R3 3 5 6.2K
R4 4 5 10K
D1 3 4 DMOD
D2 4 3 DMOD
.MODEL DMOD D
.TRAN 10U 10M UIC
.PROBE V(1) V(2) V(3) V(4) V(5) V(6)
.END
```
                   Results: f = 60.0 kHz, amplitude = 6.8 V

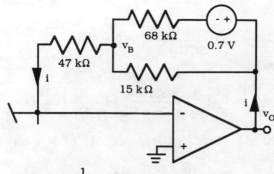

Using Eq. (18.136), $f_o = \dfrac{1}{2\pi\sqrt{3}(5000)(10^{-9})} = 18.4$ kHz

Using Eq. (18.137), the total feedback resistance should be $R_1 = 12R = 60k\Omega$.

The current in R_1 is $I = \dfrac{V_O}{R_1} = \dfrac{V_O}{12R} = \dfrac{V_O}{60k\Omega}$. The voltage at V_B is

$V_B = I(47k\Omega) = \dfrac{47k\Omega}{60k\Omega}V_O$ | In the diode network, $I = \dfrac{V_O}{60k\Omega} = \dfrac{V_O - V_B}{15k\Omega} + \dfrac{V_O - 0.7 - V_B}{68k\Omega}$

$\dfrac{\frac{13}{60}V_O}{15k\Omega} + \dfrac{\frac{13}{60}V_O}{68k\Omega} - \dfrac{V_O}{60k\Omega} = \dfrac{0.7}{68k\Omega} \rightarrow V_O = 10.7$ V

18.66

```
*Problem 18.66 - Phase Shift Oscillator
C1 1 6 1000PF IC=1
RA 1 0 5K
C2 1 2 1000PF
RB 2 0 5K
C3 2 3 1000PF
E1 3 0 0 6 1E6
R2 6 5 47K
R3 5 3 15K
R4 5 4 68K
D1 3 4 DMOD
D2 4 3 DMOD
.MODEL DMOD D
.TRAN 10U 20M UIC
.PROBE V(1) V(2) V(3) V(4) V(5) V(6)
.END
```
        Results: f = 17.5 kHz, amplitude = 11.5 V

18.67 Note that the presence of r_π makes the analysis more complex than the FET case. C_4 is a coupling capacitor, and its impedance is neglected in the analysis. $C_4 = C_1 + C_\pi$. However, the effect of r_π can usually be neglected in the f_o calculation as shown below.

$$\begin{bmatrix} s(C_4 + C_\mu) + g_\pi + \dfrac{1}{sL} & -(sC_4 + g_\pi) \\ -(sC_4 + g_m + g_\pi) & s(C_2 + C_4) + g_m + g_\pi + G_E \end{bmatrix}\begin{bmatrix} V_b \\ V_e \end{bmatrix} = \begin{bmatrix} 0 \\ 0 \end{bmatrix}$$

$$\Delta(s) = s^2\left[C_4 C_2 + C_\mu(C_2 + C_4)\right] + s\left[C_2 g_\pi + C_\mu(g_m + g_\pi + G_E) + C_4 G_E\right]$$

$$+ \dfrac{g_m + g_\pi + G_E}{sL} + g_\pi G_E + \dfrac{(C_2 + C_4)}{L}$$

$$\Delta(j\omega_o) = 0 \quad | \quad \omega_o^2 = \frac{1}{C_{TC}}\left[\frac{1}{L} + \frac{1}{r_\pi R_E(C_2 + C_4)}\right] = \frac{1}{C_{TC}}\left[\frac{1}{L} + \frac{g_m}{\beta_o R_E(C_2 + C_4)}\right] \quad | \quad C_{TC} = C_\mu + \frac{C_2 C_4}{C_2 + C_4}$$

$$\omega_o\left[C_2 g_\pi + C_\mu(g_m + g_\pi + G_E) + C_4 G_E\right] = \frac{g_m + g_\pi + G_E}{\omega_o L}$$

$$\omega_o^2 L\left[C_\mu + \frac{C_2}{\beta_o + 1 + \dfrac{r_\pi}{R_E}} + \frac{C_4}{1 + g_m R_E + \dfrac{R_E}{r_\pi}}\right] = 1 \quad | \quad \omega_o^2 L\left[C_\mu + \frac{C_2}{\beta_o + 1 + \dfrac{\beta_o}{g_m R_E}} + \frac{C_4}{1 + g_m R_E + \dfrac{g_m R_E}{\beta_o}}\right] = 1$$

(a) $C_{TC} = \dfrac{100pF(20pF)}{100pF + 20pF} = 16.7pF \quad | \quad \omega_o^2 = \dfrac{1}{16.7pF}\left[\dfrac{1}{5\mu H} + \dfrac{10mS}{100(1k\Omega)(100pF + 20pF)}\right]$

$$\omega_o^2 = \frac{1}{16.7pF}\left[2 \times 10^5 + 833\right] \rightarrow f_o = 17.5 \text{ MHz}$$

Note that the correction term is negligible: $\omega_o \cong \dfrac{1}{LC_{TC}}$ \qquad (b) $C_{TC} = \dfrac{1}{\dfrac{1}{C_2} + \dfrac{1}{C_4} + \dfrac{1}{C_3}}$

$$C_{TC}^{min} = \frac{1}{\dfrac{1}{100pF} + \dfrac{1}{20pF} + \dfrac{1}{5pF}} = 3.85pF \quad | \quad f_o \cong \frac{1}{2\pi\sqrt{LC_{TC}}} = \frac{1}{2\pi\sqrt{(5\mu H)(3.85pF)}} = 36.3 \text{ MHz}$$

$$C_{TC}^{max} = \frac{1}{\dfrac{1}{100pF} + \dfrac{1}{20pF} + \dfrac{1}{50pF}} = 12.5pF \quad | \quad f_o \cong \frac{1}{2\pi\sqrt{(5\mu H)(12.5pF)}} = 20.1 \text{ MHz}$$

(c) $\omega_o^2 L\left[\dfrac{C_2}{\beta_o + 1 + \dfrac{\beta_o}{g_m R_E}} + \dfrac{C_4}{1 + g_m R_E + \dfrac{g_m R_E}{\beta_o}}\right] \cong \dfrac{1}{C_{TC}}\left[\dfrac{C_2}{\beta_o + 1 + \dfrac{\beta_o}{g_m R_E}} + \dfrac{C_4}{1 + g_m R_E + \dfrac{g_m R_E}{\beta_o}}\right] = 1$

$$\frac{1}{16.7pF}\left[\frac{100pF}{101 + \dfrac{100}{g_m(1k\Omega)}} + \frac{20pF}{1 + g_m(1k\Omega) + \dfrac{g_m(1k\Omega)}{100}}\right] = 1 \quad | \quad \text{MATLAB yields } g_m = 0.211 \text{ mS}$$

$$I_C = (0.211mS)(0.025V) = 5.28 \text{ }\mu A$$

18.68 Assuming the effect of r_π is negligible:

(a) $f_o \cong \dfrac{1}{2\pi}\sqrt{\dfrac{1}{C_{EQ}L}}$ | $C_{EQ} = \dfrac{1}{\dfrac{1}{C_4} + \dfrac{1}{C_\mu + \dfrac{1}{\dfrac{1}{C_1+C_\pi} + \dfrac{1}{C_2}}}}$ | $C_\pi = \dfrac{40(5\text{mA})}{10^9\pi} - 3\text{pF} = 60.7\text{pF}$

$C_{EQ} = \dfrac{1}{\dfrac{1}{0.01\text{uF}} + \dfrac{1}{3\text{pF} + \dfrac{1}{\dfrac{1}{(20+60.7)\text{pF}} + \dfrac{1}{100\text{pF}}}}} = 47.4\text{pF}$ | $f_o \cong \dfrac{1}{2\pi}\sqrt{\dfrac{1}{47.4\text{pF}(20\mu\text{H})}} = 5.17\text{MHz}$

(b) $C_\pi = \dfrac{40(10\text{mA})}{10^9\pi} - 3\text{pF} = 124\text{pF}$ | $C_{EQ} = \dfrac{1}{\dfrac{1}{0.01\text{uF}} + \dfrac{1}{3\text{pF} + \dfrac{1}{\dfrac{1}{20\text{pF}+124\text{pF}} + \dfrac{1}{100\text{pF}}}}} = 61.6\text{pF}$

$f_o \cong \dfrac{1}{2\pi}\sqrt{\dfrac{1}{61.6\text{pF}(20\mu\text{H})}} = 4.53\text{MHz}$

18.69

$C_{TC} = \dfrac{1}{\omega_o^2 L} = \dfrac{1}{\left(4\times10^7\pi\right)^2(3\mu\text{H})} = 21.1\text{pF}$ | $C_{TC} = \dfrac{1}{\dfrac{1}{C_1} + \dfrac{1}{C_2}}$ | $g_m R \geq \dfrac{C_1}{C_2} \to \dfrac{2I_{DS}R}{V_{GS} - V_P} \geq \dfrac{C_1}{C_2}$

$I_{DS} = I_{DSS}\left(1 - \dfrac{V_{GS}}{V_P}\right)^2 = 10\text{mA}\left(1 + \dfrac{V_{GS}}{4}\right)^2$ | $-4 \leq V_{GS} \leq 0$. Suppose we pick V_{GS} in the middle

of this range: $V_{GS} = -2\text{V} \to I_{DS} = 10\text{mA}\left(1 - \dfrac{2}{4}\right)^2 = 2.50\text{mA}$ | $R = \dfrac{2\text{V}}{2.5\text{mA}} = 800\Omega \to 820\ \Omega$

$\dfrac{C_1}{C_2} \leq \dfrac{2I_{DS}R}{V_{GS} - V_P} = \dfrac{2(2)}{-2-(-4)} = 2$ | $C_1 \leq 2C_2$ | Select $C_1 \cong C_2 \cong 42\text{pF}$ | Choosing

$C_1 = 47\text{pF}$ from Appendix C, $C_2 = \dfrac{1}{\dfrac{1}{21.1\text{pF}} - \dfrac{1}{47\text{pF}}} = 38.3\text{pF}$ which is close to 39 pF.

If 47pF and 39pF are used: $f_o = \dfrac{1}{2\pi\sqrt{(21.3\text{pF})(3\mu\text{H})}} = 19.9\ \text{MHz}$

In order to obtain an exact frequency of oscillation, a 33 pF capacitor in parallel with a small variable capacitor could be used. Note that including the FET capacitances would modify the design values.

18.70

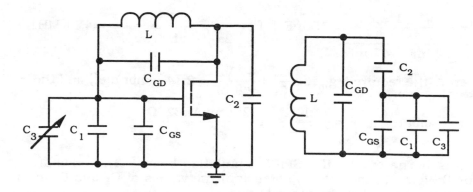

$$C_{TC} = C_{GD} + \cfrac{1}{\cfrac{1}{C_2} + \cfrac{1}{C_1 + C_3 + C_{GS}}} = 4pF + \cfrac{1}{\cfrac{1}{50pF} + \cfrac{1}{50pF + 0 + 10pF}} = 31.27pF$$

$$f_o = \frac{1}{2\pi\sqrt{LC_{TC}}} = \frac{1}{2\pi\sqrt{(10^{-5}H)(31.27 \times 10^{-12}F)}} = 9.00MHz$$

$$g_m r_o \geq \frac{C_1 + C_3 + C_{GS}}{C_2} = \frac{50pF + 0 + 10pF}{50pF} = 1.20 \quad \text{which is easily met.}$$

18.71

(a) $C_{TC} = C_{GD} + \cfrac{1}{\cfrac{1}{C_2} + \cfrac{1}{C_1 + C_3 + C_{GS}}}$ | $C_{TC}^{max} = 4pF + \cfrac{1}{\cfrac{1}{50pF} + \cfrac{1}{50pF + 5pF + 10pF}} = 32.3pF$

$$f_o = \frac{1}{2\pi\sqrt{LC_{TC}}} = \frac{1}{2\pi\sqrt{(10\mu H)(32.3pF)}} = 8.87 \text{ MHz}$$

$$C_{TC}^{min} = 4pF + \cfrac{1}{\cfrac{1}{50pF} + \cfrac{1}{50pF + 50pF + 10pF}} = 38.4pF \mid f_o = \frac{1}{2\pi\sqrt{(10\mu H)(38.4pF)}} = 8.12 \text{ MHz}$$

(b) $g_m r_o \geq \frac{C_1 + C_3 + C_{GS}}{C_2}$ | $g_m r_o \geq \frac{50pF + 5pF + 10pF}{50pF} = 1.30$ and

$$g_m r_o \geq \frac{50pF + 50pF + 10pF}{50pF} = 2.20 \mid \therefore g_m r_o \geq 2.20 \text{ which is easily met.}$$

18.72

(a) $C_D = \cfrac{C_{jo}}{\sqrt{1 + \cfrac{V_{TUNE}}{\phi_j}}}$ | $C_D = \cfrac{20pF}{\sqrt{1 + \cfrac{2V}{0.8V}}} = 10.7pF$ | $C_{TC} = \cfrac{1}{\cfrac{1}{75pF + 10.7pF} + \cfrac{1}{75pF}} = 40.0pF$

$$C_D = \cfrac{20pF}{\sqrt{1 + \cfrac{20V}{0.8V}}} = 3.92pF \mid C_{TC} = \cfrac{1}{\cfrac{1}{75pF + 3.92pF} + \cfrac{1}{75pF}} = 38.5pF$$

$$f_o^{min} = \frac{1}{2\pi\sqrt{(10\mu H)(40.0pF)}} = 7.96 \text{ MHz} \mid f_o^{max} = \frac{1}{2\pi\sqrt{(10\mu H)(38.5pF)}} = 8.11 \text{ MHz}$$

(b) In this circuit, $R = r_o$: $\mu_f = g_m r_o \geq \frac{C_1 + C_D}{C_2}$ | $\mu_f \geq \frac{78.9pF}{75pF} = 1.05$

18.73

$$C_{TC} = \cfrac{1}{\cfrac{1}{220pF} + \cfrac{1}{470pF}} = 150pF \quad | \quad f_o = \cfrac{1}{2\pi\sqrt{(10\mu H)(150pF)}} = 4.11 \text{ MHz}$$

However, the required $g_m R \geq \dfrac{C_2}{C_1} = \dfrac{470pF}{220pF} = 2.14$ is not met, and the circuit

fails to oscillate. $g_m R = \dfrac{2I_{DS}R}{V_{GS} - V_P} \cong \dfrac{2(2.5\text{mA})(820\Omega)}{-2-(-4)} = 1.03!$

This analysis is borne out by the SPICE simulation below. The original circuit does not oscillate, but the circuit oscillates vigorously if the values of C_1 and C_2 are reversed. The values will be interchanged in the second prining.

```
VDD 3 0 DC 10
R 1 0 820
C1 1 0 220PF IC=2
C2 2 1 470PF IC=0
*C1 1 0 470PF IC=2
*C2 2 1 2200PF IC=0
L 2 0 10UH
J1 3 2 1 NFET
.MODEL NFET NJF VTO=-4 BETA=0.625MA
.OP
.TRAN 10N 30U UIC
.PROBE
.END
```

18.74

$$C_{TC} = 3pF + \cfrac{1}{\cfrac{1}{50pF + 10pF} + \cfrac{1}{50pF}} = 30.3pF \quad | \quad f_o = \cfrac{1}{2\pi\sqrt{(10\mu H)(30.3pF)}} = 9.15 \text{ MHz}$$

```
*Problem 18.74 NMOS Colpitts Oscillator
VDD 3 0 DC 12
LRFC 3 2 20MH
C1 1 0 50PF
C2 2 0 50PF
L 2 1 10UH
M1 2 1 0 0 NFET
CGS 1 0 10PF
CGD 1 2 4PF
.MODEL NFET NMOS VTO=1 KP=10MA LAMBDA=0.02
.OP
.TRAN 50N 40U UIC
.PROBE
.END
```

Results: f = 7.5 MHz, amplitude = 80 V peak-peak. There is little to set the amplitude in this circuit, and the frequency of oscillation is significantly in error. Also, μ_f of the transistor greatly exceeds the gain required for oscillation and the waveform at the drain is highly nonlinear. The voltage at the gate is filtered by the LC network and is more sinusoidal in character. A diode from ground to gate could be employed to help limit the amplitude of the oscillation.

18.75

$$f_o = \frac{1}{2\pi\sqrt{(10\mu H + 10\mu H)(20pF)}} = 7.96 \text{ MHz}$$

18.76

$$f_o = \frac{1}{2\pi\sqrt{LC_{TC}}} \mid C_{TC} = \frac{1}{\frac{1}{C} + \frac{1}{C_D}} \mid C = 220pF \mid C_D = \frac{20pF}{\sqrt{1 + \frac{V_{TUNE}}{0.8V}}} \mid L = L_1 + L_2 = 20\mu H$$

(a) $C_D = \dfrac{20pF}{\sqrt{1 + \dfrac{2V}{0.8V}}} = 10.7pF \mid C_{TC} = \dfrac{1}{\dfrac{1}{220pF} + \dfrac{1}{10.7pF}} = 10.2pF$

$$f_o = \frac{1}{2\pi\sqrt{20\mu H(10.2pF)}} = 11.1 \text{ MHz}$$

$C_D = \dfrac{20pF}{\sqrt{1 + \dfrac{20V}{0.8V}}} = 3.92pF \mid C_{TC} = \dfrac{1}{\dfrac{1}{220PF} + \dfrac{1}{3.92pF}} = 3.85pF$

$$f_o = \frac{1}{2\pi\sqrt{20\mu H(3.85pF)}} = 18.1 \text{ MHz} \quad \text{(b)} \quad \mu_f \geq \frac{L_1}{L_2} = 1.00$$

18.77

$$\omega_S = \frac{1}{\sqrt{LC_S}} \mid L = \frac{RQ}{\omega_S}$$

(a) $L - \dfrac{40(25000)}{2x10^7\pi} = 15.915 \text{ mH} \mid C_S = \dfrac{1}{\omega_S^2 L} = \dfrac{1}{\left(2x10^7\pi\right)^2 15.915\text{mH}} = 15.916 \text{ fF}$

(b) $C_P = \dfrac{1}{\dfrac{1}{15.915fF} + \dfrac{1}{10pF}} = 15.890fF \mid f_P = \dfrac{1}{2\pi\sqrt{15.915\text{mH}(15.890\text{fF})}} = 10.008 \text{ MHz}$

(c) $C_P = \dfrac{1}{\dfrac{1}{15.915fF} + \dfrac{1}{32pF}} = 15.907fF \mid f_P = \dfrac{1}{2\pi\sqrt{15.915\text{mH}(15.907\text{fF})}} = 10.003 \text{ MHz}$

18.78

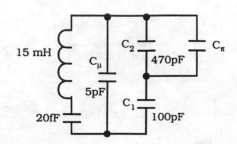

(a) $C_{TC} = \dfrac{1}{\dfrac{1}{20\text{fF}} + \dfrac{1}{470\text{pF}} + \dfrac{1}{100\text{pF}}} = 19.995\text{fF}$ | $f_P = \dfrac{1}{2\pi\sqrt{15\text{mH}(19.995\text{fF})}} = 9.190$ MHz

(b) $I_C = 100\dfrac{5 - 0.7}{100\text{k}\Omega + 101(1\text{k}\Omega)} = 2.14\text{mA}$ | $C_\pi = \dfrac{40(2.14\text{mA})}{2\pi(2.5\text{x}10^8\text{Hz})} - 5\text{pF} = 49.5\text{pF}$

$C_{TC} = \dfrac{1}{\dfrac{1}{20\text{fF}} + \dfrac{1}{5\text{pF} + \dfrac{1}{\dfrac{1}{100\text{pF}} + \dfrac{1}{470\text{pF} + 49.5\text{pF}}}}} = 19.996\text{fF}$

$f_P = \dfrac{1}{2\pi\sqrt{15\text{mH}(19.996\text{fF})}} = 9.190$ MHz

18.79

$C_{TC}^{max} = \dfrac{1}{\dfrac{1}{20\text{fF}} + \dfrac{1}{1\text{pF}} + \dfrac{1}{100\text{pF}} + \dfrac{1}{470\text{pF}}} = 19.60\text{fF}$ | $f_P = \dfrac{1}{2\pi\sqrt{15\text{mH}(19.60\text{fF})}} = 9.28$ MHz

$C_{TC}^{max} = \dfrac{1}{\dfrac{1}{20\text{fF}} + \dfrac{1}{35\text{pF}} + \dfrac{1}{100\text{pF}} + \dfrac{1}{470\text{pF}}} = 19.98\text{fF}$ | $f_P = \dfrac{1}{2\pi\sqrt{15\text{mH}(19.98\text{fF})}} = 9.19$ MHz

18.80

```
*Problem 18.80 BJT Colpitts Crystal Oscillator
VCC 1 0 DC 5
VEE 4 0 DC -5
Q1 1 2 3 NBJT
RE 3 4 1K
RB 2 0 100K
C1 3 0 100PF
C2 2 3 470PF
LC 2 6 15M
CC 6 5 20FF IC=5
RC 5 0 50
.MODEL NBJT NPN BF=100 VA=50 TF=1N CJC=5PF
.OP
.TRAN 2N 20U UIC
.PROBE
.END
```

In the period of time used in the simulation results, node 6 at the interior of the crystal oscillates vigorously, but the oscillation is not coupled well to the other nodes.